W9-ATJ-606

text only

Welcome to
The Monkeyhouse

Go to
Band

$4x + 3y = 9$

$2x + 9y = 2$

$\frac{4}{4} = \frac{2}{1}$

$\begin{bmatrix} a & 3 \\ x & 9 \end{bmatrix}$

$\begin{bmatrix} -4 & 2 \\ 3 & -9 \end{bmatrix}$

ALGEBRA
and Trigonometry
STRUCTURE AND METHOD

Book 2   new edition

572.⁰⁰

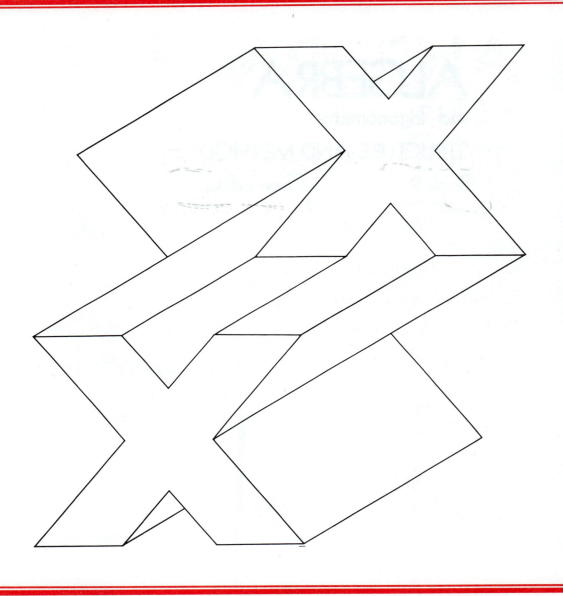

ALGEBRA
and Trigonometry
STRUCTURE AND METHOD
Book 2   new edition

Mary P. Dolciani

Robert H. Sorgenfrey

Richard G. Brown

Robert B. Kane

EDITORIAL ADVISER
William Wooton

TEACHER CONSULTANTS
Karl Randall
Lois B. Whitman

HOUGHTON MIFFLIN COMPANY · BOSTON
Atlanta   Dallas   Geneva, Ill.   Hopewell, N.J.   Palo Alto   Toronto

THE AUTHORS

Mary P. Dolciani, Professor of Mathematical Sciences, Hunter College of the City University of New York.

Robert H. Sorgenfrey, Professor of Mathematics, University of California, Los Angeles.

Richard G. Brown, Mathematics Teacher, The Phillips Exeter Academy, Exeter, New Hampshire.

Robert B. Kane, Director of Teacher Education and Head of the Department of Education, Purdue University.

EDITORIAL ADVISER

William Wooton, former Professor of Mathematics, Los Angeles Pierce College.

TEACHER CONSULTANTS

Karl Randall, Chairman of the Mathematics Department, Hinsdale High School Central, Hinsdale, Illinois.

Lois B. Whitman, Mathematics Teacher, James Monroe High School, Sepulveda, California.

Copyright © 1984, 1982 by Houghton Mifflin Company

All rights reserved. No part of this work may be reproduced or transmitted in any form or by any means, electronic or mechanical, including photocopying and recording, or by any information storage or retrieval system, except as may be expressly permitted by the 1976 Copyright Act or in writing by the publisher. Requests for permission should be addressed in writing to Houghton Mifflin Company, One Beacon Street, Boston, Massachusetts 02108.

Printed in U.S.A.

ISBN: 0-395-34095-0

CONTENTS

4 *Polynomials and Factoring*

5 *Rational Expressions*

6 *Irrational and Complex Numbers*

7 *Quadratic Equations and Functions*

8 *Equations and Numerical Methods*

15 *Matrices and Determinants*

16 *Probability and Statistics*

SYMBOLS

		Page			Page
$=$	equals *or* is equal to	1	$\log_a u$	logarithm of u to the	
$\neq$	does not equal	2		base a	381
a^n	the nth power of a	2	f^{-1}	inverse function of f	387
$\{\ \}$	set	6	Σ	summation sign	418
$>$	is greater than	7	$!$	factorial	434
$<$	is less than	7	$\circ$	degree	441
$-a$	additive inverse of a		$'$	minute	441
	or the opposite of a	15	$''$	second	441
$\therefore$	therefore	20	1^R	1 radian	446
$|a|$	absolute value of a	27	$\overrightarrow{AB}$	vector AB (also	
$\emptyset$	empty set	50		designated $\mathbf{u}$)	508
$\leq$	is less than or		Cos^{-1}	Arc cosine *or*	
	equal to	68		inverse cosine	537
$\geq$	is greater than or		det	determinant	578
	equal to	69	A^{-1}	inverse of matrix A	580
$f(x)$	f of x *or* the value		$_nP_r$	permutations of	
	of f at x	108		n elements taken r at	
$\in$	is an element of	120		a time	606
$\sqrt[n]{b}$	nth root of b	211	$_nC_r$	combinations of n	
$\mathcal{C}$	the set of complex			elements taken r at	
	numbers	234		a time	610
i	imaginary unit		$P(E)$	probability of event E	616
	($i^2 = -1$)	234	$\cap$	intersection	619
$\pm$	plus-or-minus sign	249	$\cup$	union	619
$a^{\frac{p}{q}}$	qth root of pth power		$\bar{E}$	complement of event E	622
	of a	374	σ	standard deviation	627

Greek letters: $\alpha, \beta, \theta, \pi, \phi$ *alpha, beta, theta, pi, phi*

Metric Units of Measure

Length:
- cm   centimeter
- m   meter
- km   kilometer

Time:
- s   second
- min   minute
- h   hour

Mass:
- g   gram
- kg   kilogram

Temperature:
- °C   degrees Celsius
- K   Kelvins

Area:
- cm^2 square centimeter
- m^2 square meter
- km^2 square kilometer
- ha   hectare

Volume:
- cm^3 cubic centimeter
- mL   milliliter
- L   liter

Speed:
- m/s   meters per second
- km/h   kilometers per hour

Force: N   newton

Skyscrapers punctuate the skyline in this night-time view of Chicago. Perhaps the most striking feature of any modern city, the skyscraper is a feat of engineering requiring a wide-ranging knowledge of mathematics.

1

THE REAL
NUMBERS

THE LANGUAGE OF ALGEBRA

1-1 *Simplifying Numerical Expressions*

OBJECTIVE   To simplify numerical expressions.

The chart that begins below and continues on the next page gives a checklist of some of the special words and symbols used in algebra.

DEFINITION	EXAMPLE
Numerical expression, or **numeral:** a group of symbols used to represent numbers	$2 + 8$; $30 \div 3$; 1×10; 10
Value of a numerical expression: the number represented by the expression	Ten is the value of $2 + 8$.
Equation: a sentence formed by placing an **equals sign** $=$ (read "equals" or "is equal to") between two expressions, called the **sides** of the equation. The equation is a true statement if both sides have the same value.	$2 + 8 = 10$; the sides $10 = 1 \times 10$

DEFINITION	EXAMPLE
Does-not-equal sign: the symbol $\neq$ formed by drawing a slash through the equals sign to indicate that an equation is not true. ($\neq$ is read "does not equal" or "is not equal to.")	$2 \times 8 \neq 28$
Sum: the result of adding numbers, called the **terms** of the sum	$7 + 9 = 16$ terms sum
Difference: the result of subtracting one number from another	$8 - 6 = 2$ difference
Product: the result of multiplying numbers, called the **factors** of the product. Multiplication is sometimes shown by a raised dot $\cdot$ instead of a times sign $\times$.	$12 \times 8 = 96$ factors product $4 \cdot 5 = 20$
Quotient: the result of dividing one number by another	$42 \div 6 = 7$ quotient
Power, base, and **exponent:** A power is a product of equal factors. The repeated factor is the base. A positive exponent tells the number of times the base occurs as a factor.	Let the base be 3. First power: $\qquad\qquad\qquad 3 = 3^1$ Second power: $\qquad\qquad 3 \times 3 = 3^2$ 3^2 is also called "three squared." Third power: $\qquad 3 \times 3 \times 3 = 3^3$ 3^3 is also called "three cubed." Fourth power: $\quad 3 \times 3 \times 3 \times 3 = 3^4$
Grouping symbols: pairs of parentheses ( ), brackets [ ], or a bar —— used to group symbols that represent a single number	$3 + (2 \times 6) = 3 + 12$ $8 \times [5 + 1] = 8 \times 6$ $\dfrac{4 + 18}{11} = \dfrac{22}{11}$

Replacing a numerical expression by the simplest or most common symbol having the same value is called **simplifying** the expression. For example,

$$4 \times (3 + 9) = 4 \times 12 = 48$$

and
$$\frac{3 + 33}{12} = \frac{36}{12} = 3.$$

The following principle is used in simplifying expressions.

SUBSTITUTION PRINCIPLE

Changing the numeral by which a number is named in an expression does not change the value of the expression.

Notice how the substitution principle is used to simplify the expression below.

$$(12 + 88) + (2 \times 25) = 100 + 50 = 150$$

When simplifying expressions, we agree to use the following order of operations.

---

1. Simplify the expression within each grouping symbol, proceeding outward from the innermost grouping.
2. Simplify powers.
3. Perform multiplications and divisions in order from left to right.
4. Perform additions and subtractions in order from left to right.

Recall that multiplication symbols are often omitted in expressions with grouping symbols. Thus, $4(3 + 2)$ means $4 \times (3 + 2)$, and $(2^5 - 1)8$ means $(2^5 - 1) \times 8$.

EXAMPLE Simplify: **a.** $2^3 + [4 + (2 - 1)]$

b. $7(6^2 \div 2 \times 3)$

c. $2 \times 6 - 4 \div 2$

SOLUTION **a.** $2^3 + [4 + (2 - 1)] = 2^3 + [4 + 1]$

$$= 2^3 + \quad 5$$
$$= 8 \; + \quad 5$$
$$= 13$$

b. $7(6^2 \div 2 \times 3) = 7(36 \div 2 \times 3)$

$$= 7(18 \times 3)$$
$$= 7(54)$$
$$= 378$$

c. $2 \times 6 - 4 \div 2 = 12 - 4 \div 2$

$$= 12 - 2$$
$$= 10$$

Oral Exercises

Tell whether the two expressions have the same value or different values.

1. 4×4, $4 + 4$

2. $2 + 2$, 2×2

3. $(1 + 1)1$, $1 + 1 \cdot 1$

4. $0 \cdot 1 + 1$, $0(1 + 1)$

5. $\dfrac{8 + 6}{2}$, $8 + \dfrac{6}{2}$

6. $\dfrac{12 - 9}{3}$, $4 - 3$

Tell which operation to perform first. Then simplify each expression.

7. $9 + 1 \cdot 5$

8. $(9 + 1)5$

9. $18 - 3 \div 3$

10. $(18 + 3) \div 3$

11. $3 + 2^3 - 1$

12. $(2 \cdot 3)^2 - 4^2$

13. $\dfrac{9 + 6}{9 \div 3}$

14. $5 \cdot 3^2 - 9 \cdot 2$

15. $[5(3^2 - 9)]2$

Written Exercises

Copy each partial statement. In Exercises 1-4, find the number that makes the statement true. In Exercises 5-14, use one of the symbols $=$ or $\neq$.

A　**1.** $7 \times 8 = \underline{\ ?\ } \times 7$

2. $6 + 3 = 3 + \underline{\ ?\ }$

3. $5 \div \underline{\ ?\ } = 5$

4. $\underline{\ ?\ } \times 10 = 10$

5. $8 \times 1 \underline{\ ?\ } 8 \div 1$

6. $4 \div 2 \underline{\ ?\ } 2 \div 4$

7. $(5 + 4) + 9 \underline{\ ?\ } 5 + (4 + 9)$

8. $6(2 + 7) \underline{\ ?\ } 6 \cdot 2 + 7$

9. $5(4 - 1) \underline{\ ?\ } 5 \cdot 4 - 5 \cdot 1$

10. $(3 + 8) \div 1 \underline{\ ?\ } 3 + 8 \div 1$

11. $\dfrac{10 + 5}{10 - 5} \underline{\ ?\ } \dfrac{2 + 1}{2 - 1}$

12. $\dfrac{9 + 3}{3 + 3} \underline{\ ?\ } \dfrac{9}{3}$

13. $\dfrac{4^2 + 4}{4} \underline{\ ?\ } 16 + 1$

14. $10 - 2^2 \div 2 \underline{\ ?\ } (10 - 2)^2 \div 2$

Simplify.

15. $18 - (6 - 2)$

16. $18 - 6 - 2$

17. $126 \div 6 \div 3$

18. $126 \div (6 \div 3)$

19. $2 - [(7 - 3) - 2]$

20. $[4 - (5 - 2)] - 1$

21. $\dfrac{15 + 7}{15 - 4}$

22. $\dfrac{8 + 20 - 4}{8 - 4}$

23. $3(6 - 2^2)$

24. $3^2(6 - 2)$

25. $5 \cdot 3 - 2 \cdot 7 + 6 \cdot 0$

26. $2[(5^2 + 1) - (4^2 - 1)]$

27. $5[(2^2 - 1) - (2^2 - 2)]$

28. $3(10^2 - 8^2)$

29. $24 \div 12 + 12 \div 4$

30. $4 \cdot 7 - 2^3 \div 2$

31. $[2(7 - 2) - 3^2]3$

32. $8[2(2 + 3) - (3^2 + 1)]$

33. $2 \cdot 4^3 - 3 \cdot 4^2 + 5 \cdot 4 - 7$

34. $5 \cdot 2^3 + 1 \cdot 2^2 - 9 \cdot 2 + 1$

35. $\dfrac{5 + 2 \cdot 5}{2^2 + 1} + 5^2 - 5$

36. $\dfrac{3^2 \cdot 6 \div 3}{2 \cdot 1 + (3 + 1)^2}$

Place grouping symbols in each numerical expression so that it has the given value.

Numerical Expression	Value
B 37. $8 \cdot 3 + 7 - 2$	78
38. $15 \div 5 + 2 \cdot 5 - 1$	11
39. $9 \cdot 7 - 1 + 6 \cdot 8 + 6$	108
40. $7 + 9 \cdot 7 - 2 \div 4 + 2 - 1$	22
41. $2 + 10^2 \div 10 - 6^2$	3^2
42. $3 + 5 \cdot 3 - 1^2$	32

Replace the question marks with operation signs and insert grouping symbols, if necessary, to make each equation a true statement.

43. $2 \underline{\ ?\ } 5^2 - 4 \underline{\ ?\ } 5 = 29$ 44. $7 \underline{\ ?\ } 3^3 \underline{\ ?\ } 2^2 \underline{\ ?\ } 1^5 \underline{\ ?\ } 6 = 10$

In Exercises 45 and 46, you may use any operation signs or grouping symbols.

C 45. Use five 3's to write an expression whose value is 23.

46. Use eight 2's to write an expression whose value is 100.

Calculator Key-In _____

To determine whether your calculator performs arithmetic operations in the same order that is used in simplifying expressions, enter the following example exactly as it appears here:

$$12 + 4 \times 2$$

If your calculator displays 20, it operates algebraically and performs multiplication and division before addition and subtraction. 20 is the correct answer.

If, on the other hand, your calculator displays 32, it performs operations in the order they are entered. To evaluate the expression correctly on your calculator, use the commutative law for addition and rewrite the problem as $4 \times 2 + 12$. Do the multiplication before the addition.

The "$+/-$" key changes the sign on the display. If your calculator performs operations in the order they are entered, you will need the $+/-$ key to evaluate expressions like $12 - 4 \times 2$. First multiply 4×2 on your calculator. Then press the $+/-$ key. Then add 12.

Use a calculator to simplify each expression.

1. $1.7 + 4.6 \times 5.13$ 2. $38 - 6 \times 9$
3. $2 \times 22 - 22 \div 2$ 4. $-3 - 5 \times 13$
5. $.11 \times 30 \div .4 + .5 \times 42.6$ 6. $-7 \times 4 - 28 \div 2 + 6(-3)$

1-2 *Real Numbers and Their Graphs*

OBJECTIVE   To graph real numbers on a line and to compare numbers.

The sets of numbers described in the chart below should be familiar to you from your previous course in algebra. Recall that a *set* is a well-defined collection of objects. *Members* of a set are listed within braces { }, and three dots are used to indicate that a list continues without end.

SET	MEMBERS
the natural numbers	$\{1, 2, 3, \ldots\}$
the whole numbers	$\{0, 1, 2, 3, \ldots\}$
the integers	$\{\ldots, -3, -2, -1, 0, 1, 2, 3, \ldots\}$
the rational numbers	numbers that can be expressed in the form $\frac{a}{b}$ where a is an integer and b is a nonzero integer
the irrational numbers	numbers such as $\sqrt{2}, -\sqrt{5}, \pi$
the real numbers	the rational numbers and the irrational numbers

You have probably worked with number lines like the one in Figure 1-1.

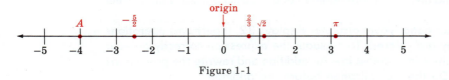

Figure 1-1

In using a number line, we take the following facts for granted.

1. Each point on a number line is paired with exactly one real number, called the **coordinate** of the point.
2. Each real number is paired with exactly one point, called the **graph** of the number on the line.

For example, in Figure 1-1 the coordinate of point A is -4, while the graph of -4 is point A. The graph of zero is the **origin.**

On a horizontal number line, the coordinates of points to the right of the origin usually are positive numbers, while the coordinates of points on the opposite side of the origin are negative numbers.

Notice that a number line shows the order of the numbers. The fact that the graph of -1 is to the left of the graph of 4 in Figure 1-2 is related to the following two equivalent inequalities:

In Words	In Symbols
Negative one is less than four.	$-1 < 4$
Four is greater than negative one.	$4 > -1$

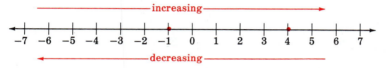

Figure 1-2

On a horizontal number line, such as the one in Figure 1-2, the numbers increase from left to right and decrease from right to left. By looking at the number line, you can see that the following inequalities are true statements.

$$-5 < -2 \qquad -5 < 0 \qquad -5 < 2$$
$$-2 > -5 \qquad 0 > -5 \qquad 2 > -5$$

EXAMPLE **a.** Graph the numbers 4, 1.5, and -3 on a number line;

b. then write inequality statements comparing them.

SOLUTION **a.**

b. $-3 < 4$, $-3 < 1.5$, and $1.5 < 4$;

or

$4 > -3$, $1.5 > -3$, and $4 > 1.5$. *Answer*

A combination of inequalities like $-3 < 1.5$ and $1.5 < 4$ is usually written

$$-3 < 1.5 < 4$$

and read "negative three is less than one and five tenths, which is less than four."

Oral Exercises

State the numbers whose graphs are shown in red.

1.
-6 -5 -4 -3 -2 -1 0 1 2 3 4 5 6

2.
-6 -5 -4 -3 -2 -1 0 1 2 3 4 5 6

3.
-5 -4 -3 -2 -1 0 1 2 3 4 5 6 7

4.
-1 0 1 2 3 4 5 6 7 8 9 10 11

5.
-10 -9 -8 -7 -6 -5 -4 -3 -2 -1 0 1 2

6.
-10 -8 -6 -4 -2 0 2 4 6 8 10 12 14

Tell whether the statement is true or false.

7. $1 > 3$ **8.** $-5 > -6$ **9.** $2 < -4$ **10.** $-3 > -1$

11. $-5 < -5$ **12.** $-1 > -6$ **13.** $0 < -2$ **14.** $0 > -10$

15. $-1 < 0 < 3$ **16.** $-2 > -5 > -10$ **17.** $3 > -1 > 0$ **18.** $-6 < -8 < 0$

Written Exercises

In Exercises 1–10, refer to the number line below, and state the coordinate of the given point.

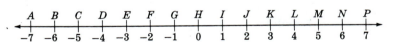

$$A \quad B \quad C \quad D \quad E \quad F \quad G \quad H \quad I \quad J \quad K \quad L \quad M \quad N \quad P$$
-7 -6 -5 -4 -3 -2 -1 0 1 2 3 4 5 6 7

SAMPLE   The point halfway between D and E **SOLUTION** $-3\frac{1}{2}$

A **1.** F **2.** L **3.** H **4.** B **5.** N **6.** C

  7. The point halfway between L and M
  8. The point halfway between F and G
  9. The point one fourth of the way from I to J
  10. The point one third of the way from G to H

Graph the given numbers on a number line. Then write an inequality statement comparing the numbers. Draw a separate line for each exercise.

11. 0, 1, −3   **12.** −2, 0, −4   **13.** 0, $\frac{1}{2}$, −1   **14.** 4, −$\frac{1}{2}$, 1

15. 1.5, −3, −0.5   **16.** −1.5, −2, 4   **17.** −$\frac{3}{4}$, $\frac{1}{4}$, −$\frac{5}{4}$ **18.** $\frac{3}{4}$, −$\frac{1}{4}$, −$\frac{7}{4}$

Use symbols to write each statement.

SAMPLE   Six is greater than negative one.   **SOLUTION** $6 > -1$

19. Negative one is less than two.

20. Negative one is greater than negative two.

21. Zero is greater than negative seven.

22. Negative three is less than negative one.

23. Five is greater than four.

24. One is less than three.

25. Seven is less than ten, which is less than fifty.

26. One is greater than one half, which is greater than negative two.

List the given numbers in order from least to greatest.

B   **27.** −5, −7, 1, −1, 3   **28.** 4, 0, −1, 2, −8

     29. 1, −2$\frac{1}{2}$, −3, 2   **30.** −$\frac{1}{4}$, −$\frac{3}{4}$, $\frac{3}{4}$, −$\frac{7}{4}$

     31. −2, −3.5, −4.5, −1   **32.** −2.4, −2.1, −2, −2.15

On a horizontal number line point R has coordinate −3 and point S has coordinate 1. Write the coordinate of each point described.

33. The point 4 units to the left of S

34. The point 2 units to the right of S

35. The point 3 units to the right of R

36. The point 4 units to the left of R

37. The point halfway between R and S

38. The point one fourth of the way from R to S

C   **39.** The point between R and S that is three times as far from R as it is from S

     40. The point to the left of R that is twice as far from S as it is from R

     41. The point to the right of the origin that is four times as far from R as it is from S

1-3 *Variables*

Consider the equation

$$x + 2 = 2 + x.$$

If you replace x with 5, you obtain the true statement

$$5 + 2 = 2 + 5.$$

In fact, whatever number you use for x in the given equation, you will obtain a true statement. To assert this fact, you may write:

> For all real numbers x, $x + 2 = 2 + x$.

Other forms of this statement are:

> For each real number x, $x + 2 = 2 + x$.
> For every real number x, $x + 2 = 2 + x$.
> For any real number x, $x + 2 = 2 + x$.
> If x is any real number, then $x + 2 = 2 + x$.

In the equation $x + 2 = 2 + x$, the letter x is called a *variable*. A **variable** is a symbol, usually a letter, used to represent any member of a given set. The given set is called the **domain** of the variable. The members of the domain are called the **values** of the variable. *In this book, unless otherwise stated, the domain of all variables is the set of real numbers.*

Now consider the assertion:

> For each real number y, $y + 5 > 9$.

This assertion is surely false, because when you replace y with 1, you obtain the false statement

$$1 + 5 > 9.$$

On the other hand, if you replace y with 6, you convert $y + 5 > 9$ into the true statement

$$6 + 5 > 9.$$

Thus, you can make the following true assertion:

> There is a real number y such that $y + 5 > 9$.

Of course, there are many real numbers for which $y + 5 > 9$ is a true statement. The existence of *just one* is enough to guarantee the truth of the assertion displayed above. Other ways to state this fact are:

> There exists a real number y such that $y + 5 > 9$.
> For at least one real number y, $y + 5 > 9$.
> For some real number y, $y + 5 > 9$.

Such key words as *all, each, every, any, there is, there exists, there are, some,* and *at least one* involve the idea of "how many" or of "quantity." For this reason you call such an expression a **quantifier.**

EXAMPLE 1   State whether the given statement is true or false. Justify each answer.

    a. There is a real number x such that $x^2 = x$.

    b. For all real numbers t, $t^2 = t + 2$.

SOLUTION   **a.** True. In fact, there are two such real numbers, namely 0 and 1, because $0^2 = 0$ and $1^2 = 1$.

    b. False, because $3^2 \neq 3 + 2$. Of course, there are many values for t that change $t^2 = t + 2$ into a false statement, but finding just one is enough to show that the given general statement is false.

The word **unique** is used to mean *one and only one.* Thus, the statement "There exists a unique real number x such that $3x = 48$" is true. The preceding statement is true because the one and only value of x for which "$3x = 48$" is a true statement is 16. On the other hand, the statement "There is a unique real number z such that $z^2 = z$" is false. The preceding statement is false because "$z^2 = z$" is true for two values of z, namely 1 and 0.

Numerical expressions and expressions that contain variables like $2a + 7$ are called **algebraic expressions.** The process of replacing each variable in an expression by a given value of the variable and simplifying the result is known as **evaluating the expression** or **finding its value.**

EXAMPLE 2   If $x = 7$ and $y = 1$, find the value of $\dfrac{5x - 2y}{x + 4y}$.

SOLUTION

1. Replace x with 7 and y with 1, and insert the required multiplication and grouping symbols.

$$\frac{5x - 2y}{x + 4y} = \frac{5(7) - 2(1)}{7 + 4(1)}$$

2. Simplify.

$$= \frac{35 - 2}{7 + 4} = \frac{33}{11} = 3 \quad \textbf{\textit{Answer}}$$

Oral Exercises

Tell which of the following statements are true and which are false.

1. All angles are right angles.
2. Every triangle has three sides.
3. Each real number is greater than zero.
4. Any negative integer is less than zero.
5. There is a positive integer greater than five.

Tell which of the following statements are true and which are false.

6. There is a negative number greater than negative one.

7. For each real number x, $x + x = 2x$.

8. For all real numbers y, $y^2 \neq y$.

9. If a is any real number, then $2a = 2 + a$.

10. For some real number b, $b = 2b$.

11. There is a unique real number t such that $t^4 = 0$.

12. There is a unique real number k such that $k > 4$.

13. There exist real numbers w such that $w^2 > w$.

Written Exercises

Show that each of the following statements is true by finding a value of the variable for which the statement is true.

A **1.** For some integer y, $3y = 21$.

2. There is a real number x such that $4x > 17$.

3. There exists an integer j such that $3j - 1 < 5$.

4. There exists at least one positive number a such that $a^2 - 1 = 0$.

Show that each of the following statements is false by finding a value of the variable for which the statement is false.

5. For all integers z, $z + 1 = 2$.

6. All real numbers r are either positive numbers or negative numbers.

7. Any integer k is less than $2k$.

8. The square of every positive integer p is greater than p.

In Exercises 9–16, evaluate each expression if $x = 2$, $y = 4$, and $z = 3$.

9. $2x^3 + 3x^2 - 4x + 1$

10. $y^3 - y^2 + 5y - 2$

11. $5yz - x + z^3$

12. $z^4 - 2x^2y + 7z$

13. $\dfrac{(z + 1)^2 + x^4}{y^2}$

14. $\dfrac{8 + 5x + 3x^2}{(z + 2)^2}$

15. $\dfrac{3y^2 - 2y + 20}{y^2 - x^2}$

16. $\dfrac{5z^2 - 8z + 14}{y^2 - z^2}$

Evaluate each expression for the given values of the variables.

B **17.** $\dfrac{3(a - 4)^2 + 6(b - 2)}{a - 2 + (b - 4)^2}$; $a = 6$, $b = 7$

18. $\dfrac{2[c + 2(c + d)^2]}{c^2 + 2cd + (d - 2)^2}$; $c = 7$, $d = 3$

19. $\dfrac{5(k - 2l)(k^2 + l^2)}{5k^2 - 2kl + l^2}$; $k = 6$, $l = 3$

20. $\dfrac{(m + 2n)^2(m - n)}{2m^2 + 2m - 3n^2}$; $m = 5$, $n = 3$

Use a quantifier to write a true statement containing the given sentence.

SAMPLE   **a.** $3r - 5 = 28$ **b.** $v \neq v - 1$

SOLUTION   **a.** There exists a real number r such that $3r - 5 = 28$.

b. For all real numbers v, $v \neq v - 1$.

21. $2x + 6 = 2(x + 3)$ **22.** $x^2 - 3x = 0$ **23.** $2y > y + 4$ **24.** $r(6) = 6r$

Self-Test 1

VOCABULARY   See the boldface words in the chart on pages 1 and 2.

simplifying an expression (p. 2)
substitution principle (p. 3)
natural numbers (p. 6)
whole numbers (p. 6)
integers (p. 6)
rational numbers (p. 6)
irrational numbers (p. 6)
real numbers (p. 6)
coordinate (p. 6)
graph (p. 6)

origin (p. 7)
is less than (p. 7)
is greater than (p. 7)
variable (p. 10)
domain (p. 10)
values (p. 10)
quantifier (p. 11)
unique (p. 11)
algebraic expression (p. 11)
evaluating (p. 11)

Simplify.

1. $2[3(4 - 1) + 5^2]$

2. $\dfrac{2 + 3 \cdot 4}{18 \div 9}$

Obj. 1-1, p. 1

3. Graph the following numbers on a number line:

$$2, \ -\frac{2}{3}, \ 0, \ -1\frac{1}{2}, \ -3.$$

Obj. 1-2, p. 6

4. Use symbols to write the following statement:
"Negative two is less than one, which is less than 7."

Tell whether the statement is true or false.

5. $-2 < -5$

6. $3 > -4$

7. There exists a real number y such that $4y - 1 = 23$.

Obj. 1-3, p. 10

8. For all real numbers x, $3x = x + 3$.

Evaluate each expression if $a = 3$, $b = 1$, and $c = 5$.

9. $2a^2 + c^2 - 4b + 1$

10. $a + 5bc - 4$

Check your answers with those at the back of the book.

AXIOMS AND PROOFS

1-4 *Number Properties*

OBJECTIVE   **To identify the axioms for the addition and multiplication of real numbers.**

The following *axioms* about equality of real numbers are used very frequently in algebra. An **axiom,** or **postulate,** is a statement that is assumed to be true.

EQUALITY OF REAL NUMBERS

For all real numbers a, b, and c:

REFLEXIVE PROPERTY	$a = a$.
SYMMETRIC PROPERTY	If $a = b$, then $b = a$.
TRANSITIVE PROPERTY	If $a = b$ and $b = c$, then $a = c$.
ADDITION PROPERTY	If $a = b$, then $a + c = b + c$ and $c + a = c + b$.
MULTIPLICATION PROPERTY	If $a = b$, then $ac = bc$ and $ca = cb$.

EXAMPLE 1   Name the property of equality illustrated in each statement.

   a. If $(n + 3) + (-3) = n + [3 + (-3)]$
   and $n + [3 + (-3)] = n + 0$,
   then $(n + 3) + (-3) = n + 0$.

   b. If $x - 6 = 10$, then $(x - 6) + 6 = 16$.

SOLUTION   **a.** Transitive property   **b.** Addition property

   In algebra we assume that the real numbers obey several other axioms. These axioms, stated on page 15, are formal statements of the following familiar facts about addition and multiplication of real numbers.

1. The sum of two real numbers is a unique real number. The product of two real numbers is a unique real number.

2. You may add or multiply two real numbers in either order:
$$5 + 8 = 8 + 5 \quad \text{and} \quad 5 \times 8 = 8 \times 5.$$

3. In a sum such as $7 + 1 + 9$, you may group any term with an adjacent term:
$$(7 + 1) + 9 = 7 + (1 + 9).$$
Similarly, in a product, you may group any factor with an adjacent factor.

4. When you add the real number 0 to a given real number, the sum is identical to the given number:

$$0 + 6 = 6 + 0 = 6.$$

Similarly, when you multiply the real number 1 by any given real number, the product is identical to the given real number:

$$1 \cdot 6 = 6 \cdot 1 = 6.$$

5. Each real number has an **additive inverse,** or **opposite,** such that the sum of the number and its additive inverse is 0:

$$2 + (-2) = (-2) + 2 = 0.$$

Each nonzero real number has a **reciprocal,** or **multiplicative inverse,** such that the product of the number and its reciprocal is 1:

$$2 \cdot \frac{1}{2} = \frac{1}{2} \cdot 2 = 1.$$

The following axioms are exact statements of these properties.

ADDITION AND MULTIPLICATION OF REAL NUMBERS

Let a, b, and c be real numbers.

CLOSURE AXIOMS

For all a and b, $\boldsymbol{a + b}$ and $\boldsymbol{ab}$ are unique real numbers.

COMMUTATIVE AXIOMS

For all a and b, $\boldsymbol{a + b = b + a}$ and $\boldsymbol{ab = ba}$.

ASSOCIATIVE AXIOMS

For all a, b, and c, $\boldsymbol{(a + b) + c = a + (b + c)}$ and $\boldsymbol{(ab)c = a(bc)}$.

IDENTITY AXIOMS

There exist unique real numbers 0 and 1 such that for every a, $\boldsymbol{0 + a = a}$ and $\boldsymbol{a + 0 = a}$, and $\boldsymbol{1 \cdot a = a}$ and $\boldsymbol{a \cdot 1 = a}$.

INVERSE AXIOMS

For each a, there exists a unique real number $-a$ such that $\boldsymbol{a + (-a) = 0}$ and $\boldsymbol{(-a) + a = 0}$.
(This axiom is also called the *axiom of opposites*.)

For each a except 0, there exists a unique real number $\frac{1}{a}$ having the property that $\boldsymbol{a \cdot \dfrac{1}{a} = 1}$ and $\boldsymbol{\dfrac{1}{a} \cdot a = 1}$.
(This axiom is also called the *axiom of reciprocals*.)

The distributive axiom, shown below, links addition and multiplication.

DISTRIBUTIVE AXIOM OF MULTIPLICATION WITH RESPECT TO ADDITION

For all real numbers a, b, and c,

$$a(b + c) = ab + ac \quad \text{and} \quad (b + c)a = ba + ca.$$

The distributive axiom ensures that

$$9(8 + 5) = (9 \times 8) + (9 \times 5) \quad \text{and} \quad \left(8 \times \tfrac{1}{3}\right) + \left(4 \times \tfrac{1}{3}\right) = (8 + 4)\tfrac{1}{3}.$$

EXAMPLE 2   **SOLUTION**

State the axiom or property that justifies
each step.

1. $\frac{1}{3}(3 + 3x) = \frac{1}{3} \cdot 3 + \frac{1}{3}(3x)$ 1. Distributive axiom

2. $\quad = \frac{1}{3} \cdot 3 + \left(\frac{1}{3} \cdot 3\right)x$ 2. Associative axiom for multiplication

3. $\quad = 1 + 1 \cdot x$ 3. Inverse axiom for multiplication

4. $\quad = 1 + x$ 4. Identity axiom for multiplication

5. $\frac{1}{3}(3 + 3x) = 1 + x$ 5. Transitive property of equality

Note that in Step 3 the inverse axiom for multiplication was used to justify the substitution of 1 for $\frac{1}{3} \cdot 3$. Of course, the substitution principle (p. 3) is also used in this step. In this book we will follow the common practice of omitting many references to the substitution principle.

Oral Exercises

Name the axiom or property that is illustrated in each of the following true statements.

SAMPLE $4 \times (8 \times 5) = (8 \times 5) \times 4$

SOLUTION   Commutative axiom for multiplication

1. $8 + a = a + 8$ **2.** $7(9x) = 63x$

3. $\frac{1}{3}(2 + 7) = (2 + 7)\frac{1}{3}$ **4.** $-6 + 0 = -6$

5. $1 \cdot x = x$ **6.** $2r + 3r = (2 + 3)r$

7. $\left(5 \cdot 9\frac{1}{2}\right) \cdot 2 = 5\left(9\frac{1}{2} \cdot 2\right)$

8. $-\frac{1}{7} + \frac{1}{7} = 0$

9. $-5\left(\frac{1}{-5}\right) = 1$

10. $2 + (m + 1) = 2 + (1 + m)$

11. If $y - 2 = 0$, then $0 = y - 2$.

12. If $s = 4$, then $s + 2 = 6$.

13. If $t = 9$, then $5t = 45$.

14. If $(17 + k) + 12 = 20 + 12$ and $20 + 12 = 32$, then $(17 + k) + 12 = 32$.

15. $(x + y)(a + b) = (x + y)a + (x + y)b$.

16. If $q = p$, then $q + 8 = p + 8$.

17. If $x = y$, then $3x = 3y$.

18. $[2 + (c + d)] + 3(c + d) = 2 + [(c + d) + 3(c + d)]$

19. $7(-3)$ is a real number.

20. If $9z = 36$ and $36 = 9 \cdot 4$, then $9z = 9 \cdot 4$.

Name the property of equality that justifies each of the following informal statements.

21. Numbers equal to the same number are equal.

22. Every number equals itself.

23. If equals are added to equals, the sums are equal.

24. Products of equals are equal.

25. Every equation is reversible.

Written Exercises

State the axiom or property that justifies each lettered step in these chains of equations. A star (*) shows that the step is justified by the substitution principle (p. 3).

A **1.** $79 + (46 + 21) = 79 + (21 + 46)$ **a.** ___?___
$$= (79 + 21) + 46$$ **b.** ___?___
$$= 100 + 46$$ *
$$= 146$$ *

2. $(25 \times 197) \times 4 = (197 \times 25) \times 4$ **a.** ___?___
$$= 197 \times (25 \times 4)$$ **b.** ___?___
$$= 197 \times 100$$ *
$$= 19,700$$ *

3. For all real numbers r:
$$6 + (5r + 14) = (5r + 14) + 6$$ **a.** ___?___
$$= 5r + (14 + 6)$$ **b.** ___?___
$$= 5r + 20$$ *

4. For all real numbers p:

$$9(p \cdot 6) = 9(6p)$$
$$= (9 \cdot 6)p$$
$$= 54p$$

a. ___?___
b. ___?___
    *

5. For each real number x,

$$(3x)(2x) = (3x \cdot 2)x$$
$$= (2 \cdot 3x)x$$
$$= [(2 \cdot 3)x]x$$
$$= (6x)x$$
$$= 6(x \cdot x)$$
$$= 6x^2$$

a. ___?___
b. ___?___
c. ___?___
    *
d. ___?___
    *

6. For all real numbers s and t:

$$(s + 1) + (t + 5) = (s + 1) + (5 + t)$$
$$= [(s + 1) + 5] + t$$
$$= [s + (1 + 5)] + t$$
$$= (s + 6) + t$$
$$= s + (6 + t)$$
$$= s + (t + 6)$$
$$= (s + t) + 6$$

a. ___?___
b. ___?___
c. ___?___
    *
d. ___?___
e. ___?___
f. ___?___

7. For every real number d,

$$8(4d + 1) = 8(4d) + 8 \cdot 1$$
$$= (8 \cdot 4)d + 8 \cdot 1$$
$$= 32d + 8 \cdot 1$$
$$= 32d + 8$$

a. ___?___
b. ___?___
    *
c. ___?___

8. If x and y are any real numbers, then:

$$xy(x + y) = (xy)x + (xy)y$$
$$= x(xy) + (xy)y$$
$$= (x \cdot x)y + x(y \cdot y)$$
$$= x^2y + xy^2$$

a. ___?___
b. ___?___
c. ___?___
    *

9. For each real number n,

$$n + (2 + n) = n + (n + 2)$$
$$= (n + n) + 2$$
$$= (1 \cdot n + 1 \cdot n) + 2$$
$$= (1 + 1)n + 2$$
$$= 2n + 2$$
$$= 2n + 2 \cdot 1$$
$$= 2(n + 1)$$

a. ___?___
b. ___?___
c. ___?___
d. ___?___
    *
e. ___?___
f. ___?___

10. For each real number x:

$$(x^2 + 2x) + (3x^2 + 5x) = [(x^2 + 2x) + 3x^2] + 5x$$
$$= [3x^2 + (x^2 + 2x)] + 5x$$
$$= [(3x^2 + x^2) + 2x] + 5x$$
$$= (3x^2 + x^2) + (2x + 5x)$$
$$= (3x^2 + 1 \cdot x^2) + (2x + 5x)$$
$$= (3 + 1)x^2 + (2 + 5)x$$
$$= 4x^2 + 7x$$

a. ___?___
b. ___?___
c. ___?___
d. ___?___
e. ___?___
f. ___?___
    *

11. For every real number y:

$$3\left(\frac{1}{3}y + 1\right) = 3\left(\frac{1}{3}y\right) + 3 \cdot 1 \qquad \text{a. } \underline{\quad ? \quad}$$

$$= \left(3 \cdot \frac{1}{3}\right)y + 3 \cdot 1 \qquad \text{b. } \underline{\quad ? \quad}$$

$$= 1 \cdot y + 3 \cdot 1 \qquad \text{c. } \underline{\quad ? \quad}$$

$$= y + 3 \qquad \text{d. } \underline{\quad ? \quad}$$

12. For each real number z,

$$\frac{1}{5}[-z + (z + 5)] = \frac{1}{5}[(-z + z) + 5] \qquad \text{a. } \underline{\quad ? \quad}$$

$$= \frac{1}{5}[0 + 5] \qquad \text{b. } \underline{\quad ? \quad}$$

$$= \frac{1}{5} \cdot 5 \qquad \text{c. } \underline{\quad ? \quad}$$

$$= 1 \qquad \text{d. } \underline{\quad ? \quad}$$

Biography Cecilia Payne-Gaposchkin

Cecilia Payne-Gaposchkin was born in Wendover, England, in 1900. She studied astronomy under E. A. Milne at Newnham College, Cambridge, and in 1923 came to the United States on a National Research Fellowship. In 1925 Payne-Gaposchkin earned a doctorate in astronomy at Radcliffe. She joined the staff of the Harvard University Observatory, and in 1938 was named Phillips astronomer there. Payne-Gaposchkin achieved the rank of full professor at Harvard and in 1956 was appointed to chair the astronomy department.

Dr. Payne-Gaposchkin's research focused on variable stars, stellar atmospheres, spectroscopy, and the structure of galaxies. In her study of variable stars with her husband, Harvard astronomer Dr. Sergei Gaposchkin, several million observations were made. The results of this research were published in *Variable Stars* (1938), which soon became a popular sourcebook for astronomers. Payne-Gaposchkin also did a substantial amount of independent research. She studied stars with unusual characteristics, devised new techniques for determining stellar magnitudes from photographic plates, and discovered and photographed the exploding nova of Hercules.

Cecilia Payne-Gaposchkin became a United States citizen in 1931.

1-5 *Theorems and Proofs*

OBJECTIVE   **To derive some properties of real numbers from the axioms and to supply reasons for steps in proofs.**

From the axioms and properties listed in Section 1-4, you can derive many true statements about real numbers. The example below shows how you can reason from the *hypothesis* (that which is given) to the *conclusion*. In the example, each step is justified by a given fact or a previously stated axiom or property.

EXAMPLE   Show that for all real numbers a, b, and c, if $a + c = b + c$, then $a = b$.

SOLUTION

STATEMENTS	REASONS
1. a, b, and c are real numbers; $a + c = b + c$	1. Hypothesis (or Given)
2. $-c$ is a real number.	2. Inverse axiom for addition
3. $(a + c) + (-c) = (b + c) + (-c)$	3. Addition property of equality
4. $a + [c + (-c)] = b + [c + (-c)]$	4. Associative axiom for addition
5. $a + 0 = b + 0$	5. Inverse axiom for addition
6. $\therefore\ a = b$	6. Identity axiom for addition

(Note that $\therefore$ means "therefore.")

   This form of logical reasoning from hypothesis to conclusion is called a **proof.** Assertions to be proved are labeled **theorems.** A theorem that follows easily from another is called a **corollary.** You can use the commutative axiom for addition to prove the following corollary of the last theorem.

COROLLARY: If $c + a = c + b$, then $a = b$.

The last two results make up the *cancellation rule for addition:*

CANCELLATION RULE FOR ADDITION

For all real numbers a, b, and c:

$$\text{If } a + c = b + c, \text{ then } a = b.$$
$$\text{If } c + a = c + b, \text{ then } a = b.$$

   Interchanging the hypothesis and conclusion in an if-then statement gives the **converse** of the statement. For example, the converse of the first part of the theorem above can be stated as follows:

$$\text{If } a = b, \text{ then } a + c = b + c.$$

You should be able to state why the preceding statement is true. Recall that the terms "if and only if" can be used to combine a statement and its converse. For example, the two statements just discussed can be combined as follows:

$$a + c = b + c \text{ if and only if } a = b.$$

The following *cancellation rule for multiplication* can be proved (Exercise 7 on page 24).

CANCELLATION RULE FOR MULTIPLICATION

For all real numbers a and b and nonzero real numbers c:

If $ac = bc$, then $a = b$.
If $ca = cb$, then $a = b$.

After theorems have been proved, they can be used along with axioms and definitions to prove other theorems. For example, you can use the cancellation law for addition to help prove the following theorem:

PROPERTY OF THE OPPOSITE OF A SUM

For all real numbers a and b, $-(\boldsymbol{a} + \boldsymbol{b}) = (-\boldsymbol{a}) + (-\boldsymbol{b})$.
That is, the opposite of a sum of real numbers is the sum of the opposites of the numbers.

Proof

Plan: Show that $(a + b) + [(-a) + (-b)] = 0$ and $(a + b) + [-(a + b)] = 0$, and then use the cancellation rule for addition.

STATEMENTS	REASONS
1. $(a + b) + [(-a) + (-b)]$ $= [(a + b) + (-a)] + (-b)$	1. Associative property for addition
2. $ = [-a + (a + b)] + (-b)$	2. Commutative property for addition
3. $ = [(-a + a) + b] + (-b)$	3. Associative property for addition
4. $ = [0 + b] + (-b)$	4. Inverse axiom for addition
5. $ = b + (-b)$	5. Identity axiom for addition
6. $ = 0$	6. Inverse axiom for addition
7. $0 = (a + b) + [(-a) + (-b)]$	7. Transitive and symmetric properties of equality
8. $(a + b) + [-(a + b)] = 0$	8. Inverse axiom for addition
9. $\therefore (a + b) + [-(a + b)]$ $= (a + b) + [(-a) + (-b)]$	9. Transitive property of equality
10. $\therefore -(a + b) = (-a) + (-b)$	10. Cancellation rule for addition

The property of the opposite of a sum is often used in conjunction with the result that $-(-a) = a$ (Exercise 9 on page 24).

Note that in the preceding proof we did not consider it necessary to state that expressions such as $(a + b)$ and $[(-a) + (-b)]$ are real numbers. The closure axioms for addition and multiplication and the inverse axiom for addition guarantee that expressions involving sums, products, and additive inverses of real numbers, exclusively, are real numbers. Thus, in this book we will not consider it necessary in proofs to state that such expressions are real numbers. When an expression involving a multiplicative inverse is introduced in a proof, however, it is necessary to state and justify the step. The reason is that not all real numbers have multiplicative inverses.

A companion to the last theorem is the *property of the reciprocal of a product*, stated next. (See Exercise 17 on page 25 for a proof.)

PROPERTY OF THE RECIPROCAL OF A PRODUCT

For all nonzero real numbers a and b, the reciprocal of their product is the product of their reciprocals:

$$\frac{1}{ab} = \frac{1}{a} \cdot \frac{1}{b}.$$

Oral Exercises

In each statement, identify the hypothesis and the conclusion.

1. If it snows, then I will wear boots.

2. I will wear boots if it snows.

3. If Wilma is elected mayor, then Roger is a good campaign manager.

4. Smith will succeed if Smith works diligently.

5. If it does not rain and I have the price of a ticket, I will go to the county fair.

6. If I pay my bills, then I am satisfied and my financial reputation is good.

7. If a is a positive integer and a is a factor of 13, then $a = 1$ or $a = 13$.

8. If a triangle is isosceles, then its base angles have the same measure.

9. If the four sides of a rectangle have the same length, the rectangle is a square.

10. If a is a real number, then $-(-a) = a$.

In Exercises 11–16, state the indicated opposite as a sum.

SAMPLE $-[a + (-1)] = -a + [-(-1)] = -a + 1$ *Answer*

11. $-(x + 5)$ **12.** $-[3 + (-b)]$ **13.** $-[-2 + y]$
14. $-[-6 + (-z)]$ **15.** $-[-r + (-s)]$ **16.** $-(-t + v)$

Give the converse of each statement.

17. If an integer is evenly divisible by 2, then it is even.
18. If a triangle has three sides of equal length, then it is an equilateral triangle.
19. If it snows, then I will stay home.

Written Exercises

Give the reasons for the steps in each proof. Recall that the domain of each variable is the set of real numbers unless otherwise stated.

A **1.** $(b + c) + (-c) = b$

Proof:

1. $(b + c) + (-c) = b + [c + (-c)]$
2. $\qquad\qquad\qquad = b + 0$
3. $\qquad\qquad\qquad = b$
4. $\therefore (b + c) + (-c) = b$

2. If $c \neq 0$, $(bc)\dfrac{1}{c} = b$.

Proof:

1. $c \neq 0$

2. $\dfrac{1}{c}$ is a real number.

3. $(bc)\dfrac{1}{c} = b\left(c \cdot \dfrac{1}{c}\right)$

4. $\qquad\quad = b \cdot 1$

5. $\qquad\quad = b$

6. $\therefore (bc)\dfrac{1}{c} = b$

3. If $a = b$ and $c = d$, then $a + c = b + d$.

Proof:

1. $a = b$, and $c = d$
2. $a + c = b + c$
3. $b + c = b + d$
4. $\therefore a + c = b + d$

Give the reasons for the steps in each proof.

4. If $a = b$ and $c = d$, then $ac = bd$.

Proof:

1. $a = b$, and $c = d$
2. $ac = bc$
3. $bc = bd$
4. $\therefore ac = bd$

5. If $r \neq 0$ and $r \cdot r = r$, then $r = 1$.

Proof:

1. $r \neq 0$, and $r \cdot r = r$

2. $\dfrac{1}{r}$ is a real number.

3. $(r \cdot r)\dfrac{1}{r} = r \cdot \dfrac{1}{r}$

4. $(r \cdot r)\dfrac{1}{r} = r\left(r \cdot \dfrac{1}{r}\right)$

5. $\therefore r\left(r \cdot \dfrac{1}{r}\right) = r \cdot \dfrac{1}{r}$

6. $r \cdot 1 = 1$

7. $\therefore \qquad r = 1$

6. If $r + r = r$, then $r = 0$.

Proof:

1. $r + r = r$
2. $(r + r) + (-r) = r + (-r)$
3. $(r + r) + (-r) = r + [r + (-r)]$
4. $\therefore\ r + [r + (-r)] = r + (-r)$
5. $\qquad\qquad r + 0 = 0$
6. $\therefore \qquad\qquad\quad r = 0$

7. a. If $c \neq 0$ and $ac = bc$, then $a = b$.

Proof:

1. $c \neq 0$, and $ac = bc$

2. $\dfrac{1}{c}$ is a real number.

3. $(ac)\dfrac{1}{c} = (bc)\dfrac{1}{c}$

4. $a\left(c \cdot \dfrac{1}{c}\right) = b\left(c \cdot \dfrac{1}{c}\right)$

5. $a \cdot 1 = b \cdot 1$

6. $\therefore \quad a = b$

b. Corollary to the result proved in part (a): If $c \neq 0$ and $ca = cb$, then $a = b$.

Proof:

1. $c \neq 0$, and $ca = cb$
2. $ac = bc$
3. $\therefore\ a = b$

8. If $x + b = a$, then $x = a + (-b)$

Proof:

1. $x + b = a$
2. $(x + b) + (-b) = a + (-b)$
3. $x + [b + (-b)] = a + (-b)$
4. $\qquad\qquad x + 0 = a + (-b)$
5. $\therefore \qquad\qquad\quad x = a + (-b)$

9. $-(-a) = a$

Proof:

1. $a + (-a) = 0$
2. $a = 0 + [-(-a)]$
3. $\therefore\ a = -(-a)$

(*Hint:* Use the result proved in Exercise 8.)

10. If $b \neq 0$ and $xb = a$, then $x = a \cdot \frac{1}{b}$.

Proof:

1. $b \neq 0$, and $xb = a$

2. $\frac{1}{b}$ is a real number.

3. $\qquad (xb)\frac{1}{b} = a \cdot \frac{1}{b}$

4. $x\left(b \cdot \frac{1}{b}\right) = a \cdot \frac{1}{b}$

5. $\qquad x \cdot 1 = a \cdot \frac{1}{b}$

6. $\therefore \qquad x = a \cdot \frac{1}{b}$

B **11.** As a corollary to the theorem in Exercise 8, prove that if $x + b = 0$, then $x = -b$. (Additive inverses are unique.)

12. As a corollary to the theorem in Exercise 10, prove that if $b \neq 0$ and $xb = 1$, then $x = \frac{1}{b}$. (Reciprocals are unique.)

Prove each theorem.

13. If $a \neq 0$, $\dfrac{1}{\frac{1}{a}} = a$.

14. If $ab = b$ and $b \neq 0$, then $a = 1$.

C **15.** If $ax + b = c$ and $a \neq 0$, then $x = \frac{1}{a}[c + (-b)]$.

16. If $\frac{1}{x} = ab$, $a \neq 0$, $b \neq 0$, and $x \neq 0$, then $x = \frac{1}{ab}$.

17. The property of the reciprocal of a product: If $a \neq 0$ and $b \neq 0$, then $\frac{1}{ab} = \frac{1}{a} \cdot \frac{1}{b}$. (*Hint:* Show that $\left(\frac{1}{a} \cdot \frac{1}{b}\right)ab = 1$; then apply the result of Exercise 12.)

Challenge _____

A cube of wood is painted yellow. The cube is to be cut into a number of equal cubes so that at least one of these new, smaller cubes has no painted surfaces. What is the least number of cuts necessary, and how many of the smaller cubes do you get?

Self-Test 2

VOCABULARY
axiom (p. 14)
postulate (p. 14)
additive inverse (p. 15)
opposite (p. 15)
reciprocal (p. 15)
multiplicative inverse (p. 15)

hypothesis (p. 20)
conclusion (p. 20)
proof (p. 20)
theorem (p. 20)
corollary (p. 20)
converse (p. 20)

State the axiom or property that justifies each lettered step in the chain of equations.

1. $\frac{1}{4}[(4 + s) + (-s)] = \frac{1}{4}(4 + [s + (-s)])$ **a.** __?__   Obj. 1-4, p. 14

$= \frac{1}{4}(4 + 0)$ **b.** __?__

$= \frac{1}{4} \cdot 4$ **c.** __?__

$= 1$ **d.** __?__

2. $2(x + y) + 3x = (2x + 2y) + 3x$ **a.** __?__
$= (2y + 2x) + 3x$ **b.** __?__
$= 2y + (2x + 3x)$ **c.** __?__
$= 2y + (2 + 3)x$ **d.** __?__
$= 2y + 5x$ (Substitution principle)

Give the reasons for the steps in each proof.

3. If $a + c = b + d$, and $c = d$, then $a = b$.   Obj. 1-5, p. 20

Proof:
1. $a + c = b + d$, and $c = d$
2. $a + c = b + c$
3. $\therefore \quad a = b$

4. If $a = b$ and $b \neq 0$, then $\frac{1}{b}(a) = 1$.

Proof:
1. $a = b$ and $b \neq 0$

2. $\frac{1}{b}$ is a real number.

3. $\frac{1}{b}(a) = \frac{1}{b}(b)$

4. $\therefore \frac{1}{b}(a) = 1$

Check your answers with those at the back of the book.

OPERATIONS WITH REAL NUMBERS

1-6 *Addition*

OBJECTIVE   To add real numbers.

On the number line, the graphs of additive inverses, like 2 and -2, are on opposite sides of the origin but are equally distant from the origin.

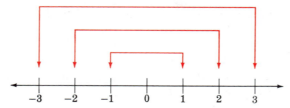

The positive number in any pair of nonzero additive inverses is called the **absolute value** of each of the numbers. The absolute value of a real number a is denoted by $|a|$.

$$|-2| = 2, \quad |2| = 2, \quad |-1.36| = 1.36$$

We define $|0|$ to be 0. Note that you can think of the absolute value of a number as the undirected distance of its graph from the origin on the number line.

EXAMPLE 1   Find the value of $n + |n|$ if **a.** $n = 6$;   **b.** $n = -6$.

SOLUTION   **a.** If $n = 6$, then $n + |n| = 6 + |6| = 6 + 6 = 12$.

  b. If $n = -6$, then $n + |n| = -6 + |-6| = -6 + 6 = 0$.

The inverse axiom for addition tells you that the sum of any real number and its additive inverse is zero. The familiar addition facts for positive numbers together with some of the number properties stated in Sections 1-4 and 1-5 enable you to find the sum of any two real numbers.

EXAMPLE 2   Add: $-5 + (-2)$

SOLUTION $\begin{aligned} -5 + (-2) &= -(5 + 2) \\ &= -7 \end{aligned}$ Property of the opposite of a sum
                                                                Substitution principle

EXAMPLE 3   Add: $-5 + 2$

SOLUTION $\begin{aligned} -5 + 2 &= -(3 + 2) + 2 \\ &= [-3 + (-2)] + 2 \\ &= -3 + [-2 + 2] \\ &= -3 + 0 \\ &= -3 \end{aligned}$ You should be able to name the axioms or properties justifying the steps in this solution.

Using absolute values, you can state rules for adding real numbers in terms of sums and differences of positive numbers and zero.

RULES FOR ADDITION OF POSITIVE AND NEGATIVE NUMBERS

Rule	Example
1. If a and b are both positive, then $a + b = |a| + |b|$.	$5 + 2 = 7$
2. If a and b are both negative, then $a + b = -(|a| + |b|)$.	$-5 + (-2) = -(5 + 2) = -7$
3. If a is positive and b is negative and $|a| > |b|$, then $a + b = |a| - |b|$.	$5 + (-2) = 5 - 2 = 3$
4. If a is positive and b is negative and $|a| < |b|$, then $a + b = -(|b| - |a|)$.	$2 + (-5) = -(5 - 2) = -3$
5. If a and b are additive inverses, then $a + b = 0$.	$-5 + 5 = 0$
6. If a is any real number and b is zero, then $a + b = a$.	$-5 + 0 = -5$

EXAMPLE 4   Simplify: $-13 + 19 + (-16) + 3 + (-7)$

SOLUTION 1   Add the terms in order from left to right.

$$-13 + 19 + (-16) + 3 + (-7) = 6 + (-16) + 3 + (-7)$$
$$= (-10) + 3 + (-7)$$
$$= (-7) + (-7) = -14$$

SOLUTION 2   Use the commutative and associative axioms for addition to group positive and negative terms.

$$-13 + 19 + (-16) + 3 + (-7) = [-13 + (-7) + (-16)] + (19 + 3)$$
$$= -36 + 22$$
$$= -14$$

Oral Exercises

Simplify.

1. $|-8|$ **2.** $|5|$ **3.** $|6 - 6|$ **4.** $|2 + 1|$

5. $|-3| + 3$ **6.** $|4| + (-4)$ **7.** $|-9| + (-9)$ **8.** $-1 + |-1|$

Add.

9. 3 $\underline{2}$ **10.** 6 $\underline{-5}$ **11.** -8 $\underline{4}$ **12.** -7 $\underline{-3}$

13. $-3 + (-8)$ **14.** $18 + (-9)$ **15.** $-12 + 7$ **16.** $-3 + (-10)$

Tell whether the given statement is true or false. Give the reason why.

SAMPLE   If x is any real number, then $|x| > 0$.

SOLUTION   False, because if $x = 0$, then $|x| = 0$. *Answer*

17. If x is any positive number, then $|x| = x$.

18. If x is any negative number, then $|x| = -x$.

19. Some real numbers do not have absolute values.

20. The absolute value of every real number equals the absolute value of the additive inverse of the number.

21. There is a real number that equals the absolute value of its additive inverse.

22. The sum of a positive number and a negative number is always a positive number.

23. The sum of zero and a negative number is never a positive number.

24. The sum of two negative numbers is always less than zero.

Written Exercises

Simplify.

A **1.** $-52 + (-38)$ **2.** $-29 + (-27)$ **3.** $-81 + (-30)$
    4. $-0 + (-68)$ **5.** $17.8 + (-17.8)$ **6.** $-43.5 + 50.5$

    7. $6 + (-9) + (-11) + 10$ **8.** $-14 + 45 + (-16) + (-7)$
    9. $-22 + (-9) + 0 + (-6)$ **10.** $-8 + 23 + (-4) + (-10)$
    11. $-14 + 18 + (-18) + 2 + (-7)$ **12.** $8 + (-11) + (-5) + (-15) + 9$
    13. $21 + 7 + (-8) + (-10) + (-6)$ **14.** $29 + (-7) + (-6) + (-17)$
    15. $37 + (-11) + (-15) + (-18) + 0$ **16.** $-38 + (-17) + 47 + 12 + (-1)$
    17. $48.3 + (-17.2) + (-26.4) + (-4.1)$ **18.** $-39.6 + 28.5 + (-12.7) + (-75.6)$
    19. $|31 + (-26)| + 10 + (-23)$ **20.** $|-15 + 23| + (-8) + 19$
    21. $|-30 + 24| + |-17 + (-24)|$ **22.** $|-41 + (-8)| + |25 + (-36)|$

B **23.** Find the value of $p + 2|p|$:   **a.** if $p = -1$; **b.** if $p = 1$.
    24. Find the value of $q + |q| + (-8)$:   **a.** if $q = -5$; **b.** if $q = -20$.
    25. Evaluate $x + 3|x| + (-10)$:   **a.** if $x = 0$; **b.** if $x = -3$.
    26. Evaluate $y + 7|y| + (-12)$:   **a.** if $y = 0$; **b.** if $y = -2$.

Prove each of the following statements.

C **27.** $r + [-(r + s)] = -s$ **28.** $-t + (t + q) = q$
    29. $-[(-a) + (-b)] + (-b) = a$ **30.** $(a + b) + [-(a + b + c)] = -c$

1-7 *Subtraction*

Subtraction is defined to be the inverse of addition. In general, the **difference** $a - b$ is the number whose sum with b is a. The figure below illustrates this definition on the number line. The red arrow shows the directed distance from b to a.

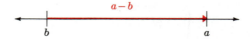

Using the definition of subtraction and the result below you can see that $[a + (-b)]$ and the difference $a - b$ are equal. Notice what happens when you add b and the sum of a and the additive inverse of b.

$$b + [a + (-b)] = b + a + (-b) = a + b + (-b) = a + 0 = a.$$

Thus, the following rule can be stated.

RULE FOR SUBTRACTION

For all real numbers a and b:

$$a - b = a + (-b)$$

EXAMPLE 1   Simplify: **a.** $-3 - 8$ **b.** $9 - (-7)$ **c.** $-2 - (-5)$

SOLUTION   **a.** $-3 - 8 = -3 + (-8) = -11$
b. $9 - (-7) = 9 + [-(-7)] = 9 + 7 = 16$
c. $-2 - (-5) = -2 + [-(-5)] = -2 + 5 = 3$

You can easily see that subtraction is not a commutative operation. For example, $6 - 4 = 2$ but $4 - 6 = -2$. Also, $(6 - 4) - 1 = 2 - 1 = 1$ but $6 - (4 - 1) = 6 - 3 = 3$. Thus, subtraction is not an associative operation.

EXAMPLE 2   Simplify: $15 - 8 - 4 + 1$

SOLUTION 1 $15 - 8 - 4 + 1 = 7 - 4 + 1$
$= 3 + 1$
$= 4$

SOLUTION 2 $15 - 8 - 4 + 1 = 15 + (-8) + (-4) + 1$
$= 15 + 1 + (-8) + (-4)$
$= 16 + (-12)$
$= 4$

Oral Exercises

Simplify.

1. $6 - 10$ **2.** $12 - 15$ **3.** $-10 - 9$

4. $-18 - 2$ **5.** $0 - 6$ **6.** $0 - (-7)$

7. $35 - 35$ **8.** $-3 - (-7)$ **9.** $8 - (-14)$

10. $9 - 5 + 3 - 2$ **11.** $-8 + 9 - 7 + 6$ **12.** $7 - (3 - 5) - (2 - 1)$

In Exercises 13-16, write the indicated opposite as a sum.

SAMPLE $-(a - 2) = -[a + (-2)] = -a + 2$

13. $-(x - 5)$ **14.** $-(3 - b)$ **15.** $-(-2 - y)$ **16.** $-(-t - v)$

Written Exercises

Simplify each expression.

A **1.** $26 - (-18)$ **2.** $-35 - 17$ **3.** $-42 - (-9)$

4. $63 - (-20)$ **5.** $6.4 - (-3.2)$ **6.** $-8.8 - (-7.3)$

7. $12 - 7 + 5 - 8$ **8.** $14 - 2 - 24 + 1$

9. $2.5 + 7 - 8.5 - 9$ **10.** $11 - 4.3 - 6 + 1.3$

11. $7 + (-4) - (-8) - 10$ **12.** $16 - (-18) + (-3) - (-1)$

13. $-19 + 17 - (-6) - (-8) - 1$ **14.** $-12 + 5 - (-9) - (-7)$

15. $2 - (9 - 6) - [8 - (-1)]$ **16.** $-1 - (10 - 8) - [-7 - (-2)]$

17. $0 - [-1 - (-3)] - (-3 - 7)$ **18.** $0 - [-2 - (-6)] - (-1 - 5)$

Find the number that makes the statement true.

B **19.** $\underline{\ ?\ } + 6 = -7$ **20.** $12 + \underline{\ ?\ } = 5$

21. $8 + \underline{\ ?\ } = -8$ **22.** $\underline{\ ?\ } + (-4) = 3$

23. $\frac{4}{7} + \underline{\ ?\ } = -1$ **24.** $\underline{\ ?\ } + \frac{2}{3} = -\frac{1}{3}$

25. $-12.9 + \underline{\ ?\ } = -10$ **26.** $-7.2 + \underline{\ ?\ } = 1.3$

27. Find the change in altitude from 85 m below sea level to 74 m above sea level.

28. Find the difference between a temperature of $-17°C$ and $8°C$.

29. If the voltage across an electric circuit changes from 240 V to -165 V, what is the net change in voltage?

30. At 6:30:15 A.M. (thirty minutes and fifteen seconds after six o'clock) the countdown on a rocket launch stood at -43 seconds. There was a 25 second delay in resuming the count. At what time did the rocket take off?

Supply the reason for each step in the following proofs. Assume that each variable denotes a real number.

31. $-(a - b) = b - a$

    Proof:

    1. $-(a - b) = -[a + (-b)]$
    2. $\qquad\quad = -a + [-(-b)]$
    3. $\qquad\quad = -a + b$
    4. $\qquad\quad = b + (-a)$
    5. $\qquad\quad = b - a$

32. $(a - b) - c = a - (b + c)$

    Proof:

    1. $(a - b) - c = [a + (-b)] + (-c)$
    2. $\qquad\qquad = a + [-b + (-c)]$
    3. $\qquad\qquad = a + [-(b + c)]$
    4. $\qquad\qquad = a - (b + c)$

C **33.** Prove: If $a = b$, then $a - c = b - c$.

    34. Prove: If $a - c = b - c$, then $a = b$.

Career Note   Electrical Engineer

Electrical engineers design, build, and test electronic devices used in industry or sold directly to consumers. Radios, televisions, stereo components, telephone-related products, and computers are among the most familiar. The design of integrated circuits, which are coming into common use in household appliances, automobiles, and industrial machinery, as well as in computers, is an excellent career opportunity for electrical engineers.

Electrical engineers need strong problem-solving skills and must be able to deal with abstract concepts. Their work requires accuracy and careful attention to detail.

Electrical engineers rely on scientists and mathematicians for the theoretical concepts underlying their designs. They also work closely with technicians who are often responsible for constructing a model of the design and monitoring its performance.

Although a bachelor's or a master's degree is sufficient for most engineering careers, electrical engineering demands lifelong education. Electrical engineers must continually keep abreast of the latest technological developments by attending conferences and reading technical magazines and journals. Careers in electrical engineering often lead to high-level positions in management where the ideas for new products originate and the need for them is ascertained.

1-8 *Multiplication*

The theorems stated below express some familiar facts that are useful in finding products of real numbers. (See Exercises 25 and 26 on page 35 for proofs.)

MULTIPLICATIVE PROPERTY OF 0

For every real number a,

$$a \cdot 0 = 0 \quad \text{and} \quad 0 \cdot a = 0.$$

MULTIPLICATIVE PROPERTY OF -1

For every real number a,

$$a(-1) = -a \quad \text{and} \quad (-1)a = -a.$$

The multiplicative property of 0 assures you that

$$-8 \cdot 0 = 0 \quad \text{and} \quad 1 \cdot 0 = 0.$$

By the multiplicative property of -1, the product of any real number and -1 is the additive inverse of the real number. For example,

$$5(-1) = -5, \quad (-1)8 = -8, \quad \text{and} \quad (-1)(-1) = -(-1) = 1.$$

You can use the multiplicative property of -1 along with the multiplication facts of arithmetic to find the product of any two nonzero real numbers. For example:

$$(-6)(-7) = (-1 \cdot 6)(-1 \cdot 7) = (-1)(-1)(6 \cdot 7) = 1(42) = 42$$
$$6(-7) = 6(-1 \cdot 7) = -1(6 \cdot 7) = -1(42) = -42$$

Examples like these suggest the following rules for multiplying nonzero numbers.

---

1. The product of two positive numbers or two negative numbers is a positive number.
2. The product of a positive number and a negative number is a negative number.
3. The absolute value of the product of two or more real numbers is the product of the absolute values of the numbers.

EXAMPLE 1 Simplify: **a.** $(-1)(16)\left(-\frac{1}{4}\right)$ **b.** $(-5)(3x)(-6)(-2y)$

SOLUTION **a.** $(-1)(16)\left(-\frac{1}{4}\right) = (-1)(-1)(16)\left(\frac{1}{4}\right) = 1 \cdot 4 = 4$

b. $(-5)(3x)(-6)(-2y) = (-5)(-6)(3)(-2)xy = 30(-6)xy = -180xy$

EXAMPLE 2 Multiply: $-2(5x + 9)$

SOLUTION $\begin{aligned} -2(5x + 9) &= (-2)5x + (-2)9 \\ &= -10x + (-18) \\ &= -10x - 18 \quad \textbf{\textit{Answer}} \quad \text{(written as a difference)} \end{aligned}$

You can show that multiplication is distributive with respect to subtraction (Exercise 28 on page 35). That is, for all real numbers a, b, and c,

$$a(b - c) = ab - ac.$$

EXAMPLE 3 Multiply: $-2(5x - 9)$

SOLUTION $\begin{aligned} -2(5x - 9) &= (-2)5x - (-2)9 \\ &= -10x - (-18) \\ &= -10x + 18 \quad \textbf{\textit{Answer}} \end{aligned}$

Oral Exercises

Simplify.

1. $5(-7)$ **2.** $(-2)(-8)$ **3.** $(-4)(-1)$ **4.** $(-9)5$

5. $\left(-\frac{1}{2}\right)14$ **6.** $-24\left(-\frac{1}{3}\right)$ **7.** $-1 \cdot -2 \cdot -3$ **8.** $-2 \cdot -4 \cdot -1$

9. $-6 \cdot 0 \cdot 8$ **10.** $(-1)(-5x)$ **11.** $-3(8y)$ **12.** $(-x)(-4t)$

Without doing the computation, tell whether each expression represents a positive number, a negative number, or zero.

13. $-7(-3)(-1)4(-8)$ **14.** $17(15 - 15)(-2)(-8)$

15. $-12(-42)8(-3)(-0)$ **16.** $-[-1(-3)(-8)(-9)(-7)]$

17. $(-2)^3(-5)(-7)$ **18.** $13(-3)^4(-11)$

Written Exercises

Simplify.

A **1.** $-8 \cdot 0 \cdot -7 \cdot 8$ **2.** $-7 \cdot -3 \cdot -1 \cdot 5$

     3. $(-10)(-12)(-11)$ **4.** $(-15)4(-9)$

     5. $39(-3) + 39(-7)$ **6.** $41 \cdot 14 - 41 \cdot 4$

     7. $29(-8) - 29(12)$ **8.** $-17 \cdot 14 + (-17)6$

9. $12(-4)(-15)(-9)$

10. $64(-8)(-0)(-5)$

11. $10 - 5(17 - 7)$

12. $-8 - 6(-9 + 3) + 8$

13. $[64 - 5(1 + 4)](-8 - 5)$

14. $[36 - 4(3 + 1)](4 - 6)$

Evaluate each expression for the given value of the variable.

15. $x^3 - 3x^2 + 7x - 8; \quad x = -1$

16. $2y^3 + y^2 - 8y - 10; \quad y = -2$

17. $z^4 + z^3 + 2z^2 - z - 3; \quad z = -1$

18. $w^5 - 5w^4 + w^3 - 8w^2 + 4w; \quad w = 0$

Multiply.

19. $-8(-3x + 2)$

20. $5(8y - 1)$

21. $7(-7n - 11)$

22. $-4(-1 - 6k)$

23. $-2(x^2 - 3x - 1)$

24. $-3(y^3 - 2y^2 - 1)$

Supply the reasons for the steps in the following proofs. Assume the domain of each variable is the set of real numbers.

B **25.** $a \cdot 0 = 0$ and $0 \cdot a = 0$

Proof:

1. $\qquad 0 + 0 = 0$
2. $\qquad a(0 + 0) = a \cdot 0$
3. $\qquad a(0 + 0) = a \cdot 0 + a \cdot 0$
4. $a \cdot 0 + a \cdot 0 = a \cdot 0$
   (*Hint:* See Exercise 6 on page 24.)
5. $\therefore \qquad a \cdot 0 = 0$
6. $\qquad 0 \cdot a = 0$

26. $a(-1) = -a$ and $(-1)a = -a$

Proof:

1. $\qquad\qquad a = 1 \cdot a$
2. $(-1)a + a = (-1)a + 1 \cdot a$
3. $\qquad\qquad = [-1 + 1]a$
4. $\qquad\qquad = 0 \cdot a$
5. $\qquad\qquad = 0$
6. $(-1)a + a = 0$
7. $\quad -a + a = 0$
8. $(-1)a + a = -a + a$
9. $\therefore \quad (-1)a = -a$
10. $\qquad a(-1) = -a$

27. Use the multiplicative property of 0 to explain why 0 has no reciprocal.

C **28.** **a.** Prove that multiplication is distributive with respect to subtraction:

$$a(b - c) = ab - ac.$$

The first three steps of the proof are given below. Supply reasons for these steps and complete the proof.

Proof:

1. $a(b - c) = a[b + (-c)]$ 1. $\underline{\ \ ?\ \ }$
2. $\qquad\qquad = ab + a(-c)$ 2. $\underline{\ \ ?\ \ }$
3. $\qquad\qquad = ab + a[(-1)c]$ 3. $\underline{\ \ ?\ \ }$

b. Prove: $(b - c)a = ba - ca$.

Computer Key-In

People have always been looking for short cuts in doing arithmetic calculations and for mechanical aids to take the drudgery out of tedious tasks. Calculators and computers have been developed to do both of these things.

An early mechanical calculator was the *abacus.* Several forms were developed, but each consisted of a frame and wires with beads strung on them. Abacuses are still used in some parts of the world, and skilled operators can use them with great speed and accuracy.

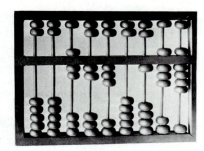

Later mechanical digital calculators were built with geared wheels and were operated by cranks or push buttons.

Vacuum tubes were used in early radios and in early electronic computers. The invention of the transistor in 1947 to replace the vacuum tube made it possible to reduce the size of radios and computers. More recently, printed circuits have been developed so that computers can be made even smaller. The working parts of a computer can be put on a "chip" as shown below.

An electronic computer consists of a central processing unit connected to input devices, output devices, and various storage facilities. It is operated by means of *programs* which can be stored in it.

Sometimes a computer is connected to several *terminals* so that several people can work with the computer at the same time. This is called *time-sharing.* In this case, there must be a program in the computer to keep track of all these operators and their work. As computers get smaller, more people will have their own computers, called *microcomputers* or *personal computers.*

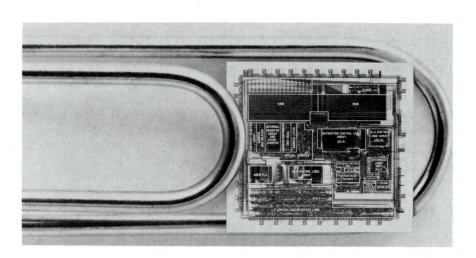

1-9 *Division*

OBJECTIVE **To divide real numbers.**

Division is defined to be the inverse of multiplication. In general, if b is not zero, the **quotient** $a \div b$ is the number whose product with b is a. The following rule is a consequence of this definition.

RULE FOR DIVISION

For every real number a and nonzero real number b,

$$a \div b = a \cdot \frac{1}{b}, \quad \text{or} \quad \frac{a}{b} = a \cdot \frac{1}{b}.$$

For example,

$$18 \div 3 = 18 \times \frac{1}{3} = 6 \quad \text{and} \quad 9 \div \left(-\frac{1}{5}\right) = 9(-5) = -45.$$

Examples like the ones above suggest the following rules for dividing positive and negative numbers.

---

1. The quotient of two positive numbers or two negative numbers is a positive number.
2. A quotient of two numbers, one of which is positive and the other negative, is a negative number.
3. The absolute value of a quotient of two numbers is equal to the quotient of the absolute values.

EXAMPLE Simplify **a.** $-72 \div 12 \div (-2)$

  b. $-200 \div \left(-\frac{1}{3}\right) \div (-10)(-6)$

SOLUTION **a.** $-72 \div 12 \div (-2) = (-72 \div 12) \div (-2) = -6 \div (-2) = -6\left(-\frac{1}{2}\right) = 3$

  b. $-200 \div \left(-\frac{1}{3}\right) \div (-10)(-6) = \left[-200 \div \left(-\frac{1}{3}\right)\right] \div (-10)(-6)$

  $= [-200(-3)] \div (-10)(-6)$

  $= [600 \div (-10)](-6)$

  $= -60(-6) = 360$

Division is neither commutative nor associative (Exercises 17 and 18 on page 39). Division is distributive with respect to addition and subtraction (Exercises 23 and 24 on page 39).

Oral Exercises

Simplify.

1. $36 \div (-9)$

2. $-18 \div (-3)$

3. $-49 \div 7$

4. $-51 \div 1$

5. $\dfrac{-28}{-4}$

6. $\dfrac{48}{-16}$

7. $\dfrac{-64}{-8}$

8. $\dfrac{12}{-1}$

Without doing the computation, tell whether each quotient represents a positive number, a negative number, or zero.

9. $\dfrac{17(-58)(-4)}{-81(-30)(-6)}$

10. $-\dfrac{-1 \cdot 24 \cdot 7}{72(-3)(-5)}$

11. $\dfrac{(-3)(0)(-55)(-1)}{(1)(2)(-5)(-7)}$

12. $\dfrac{-2(-7 + 7)(-6)(-2)}{-12 \cdot 7(-2)}$

Complete each sentence by replacing the symbol __?__ with one of the words "positive" or "negative" to produce a true statement.

13. The quotient of a negative number divided by a positive number is a __?__ number.

14. The quotient of a negative number divided by a negative number is a __?__ number.

15. The quotient of a positive number divided by a negative number is a __?__ number.

16. The reciprocal of a negative number is a __?__ number.

Written Exercises

Simplify each expression. Express all fractions in simplest form.

A **1.** $24 \div 6 \div (-2)$

2. $16 \div (-2) \div (-1)$

3. $-81 \div (-9) \div (-3)$

4. $0 \div (-36) \div 6$

5. $-0 \div (-52) \div 13$

6. $-500 \div (-25) \div (-10)$

7. $\dfrac{-144 + 2(-180)}{14(-3)(-6)}$

8. $\dfrac{6[-8 + 2(3 - 1)]}{-2(7 + 5)}$

9. $\dfrac{-5[3 - (7 + 2)]}{-(9 - 10)}$

10. $\dfrac{-14 \div 2 \cdot 3}{-15 - 2(-4)}$

11. $\dfrac{4[5 \cdot 8 \div 10]}{[17 + 3(-5)]^2}$

12. $\dfrac{[-5(-4) + 36 \div (-2)]^3}{(7 - 15)2^3}$

13. $[3 \cdot 6 - (-9) \cdot 2 \div (-1)] \div 3 + (-1)$

14. $4(-12) \div [2(-3) + 24 \div 2]$

15. $36 + [(-9 \div 3)(-4)] \div \left(-\dfrac{1}{3}\right)$

16. $16 + [(-6 \div 2)2] + 5 \div \left(-\dfrac{1}{2}\right)$

B 17. Write an example to show that division is not commutative.

18. Write an example to show that division is not associative.

Supply the reasons for the steps in the following proofs. Assume that the domain of each variable is the set of real numbers.

19. If $a \neq 0, \frac{a}{a} = 1$.

Proof:

1. $\quad \frac{a}{a} = a\left(\frac{1}{a}\right)$

2. $\quad\quad = 1$

3. $\therefore \frac{a}{a} = 1$

20. If $b \neq 0, \frac{0}{b} = 0$.

Proof:

1. $\quad \frac{0}{b} = 0\left(\frac{1}{b}\right)$

2. $\quad\quad = 0$

3. $\therefore \frac{0}{b} = 0$

21. $\frac{1}{-1} = -1$

Proof:

1. $\quad (-1)(-1) = -(-1)$

2. $\quad\quad -(-1) = 1$

3. $\therefore (-1)(-1) = 1$

4. $\therefore \quad\quad -1 = \frac{1}{-1}$

(*Hint:* See Exercise 9 on page 24.)

22. If $a \neq 0, \frac{1}{-a} = -\frac{1}{a}$.

Proof:

1. $\quad \frac{1}{-a} = \frac{1}{-1 \cdot a}$

2. $\quad\quad = \frac{1}{-1} \cdot \frac{1}{a}$

3. $\quad\quad = -1 \cdot \frac{1}{a}$

4. $\quad\quad = -\frac{1}{a}$

5. $\therefore \frac{1}{-a} = -\frac{1}{a}$

Prove each of the following theorems.

C 23. If $c \neq 0, \frac{a+b}{c} = \frac{a}{c} + \frac{b}{c}$. (Division is distributive with respect to addition.)

24. If $c \neq 0, \frac{a-b}{c} = \frac{a}{c} - \frac{b}{c}$. (Division is distributive with respect to subtraction.)

25. $(ab) \div b = a \quad (b \neq 0)$

26. $a + \frac{c}{b} = \frac{ab+c}{b} \quad (b \neq 0)$

(*Hint:* See Exercises 23 and 25.)

Self-Test 3

VOCABULARY   absolute value (p. 27)

Simplify.

1. $-54 + (-7) + 76$

2. $|8 + (-14)| + (-13)$ Obj. 1-6, p. 27

3. $-42 - (-20) - 39$

4. $7.5 - (8.3 - 9)$ Obj. 1-7, p. 30

5. $-3(-15 + 2) + 12(-7)$

6. $-9(-2 + 4z - 3z^2)$ Obj. 1-8, p. 33

7. Evaluate the expression $2b^2 - 3b - 28$ if $b = -3$.

Simplify.

8. $\dfrac{-9(-2 + 6) - 4}{(-2)^3}$

9. $\dfrac{-156 \div 12 \div \left(-\frac{1}{4}\right)}{-(8 - 10)^2}$ Obj. 1-9, p. 37

Check your answers with those at the back of the book.

EXTRA

Logical Symbols: Quantifiers

In mathematical logic, quantifiers such as those you studied in Section 1-3 are represented by symbols. The table at the right shows these symbols, together with their meanings.

Symbol	Meaning
$\forall_x$	"For all x." "For every x." "For each x," etc.
$\exists_x$	"There exists an x." "There is an x." "For some x," etc.

For examples of the use of symbolic quantifiers, study the following sentences, in which each variable is understood to represent a real number.

Words	Symbols
For every x, x + 2x = 3x.	$\forall_x x + 2x = 3x$
For all x, x + 7 = 7 + x.	$\forall_x x + 7 = 7 + x$
For some x, x + 5 = 10.	$\exists_x x + 5 = 10$
For all a and b, (a + b) + 2 = a + (b + 2).	$\forall_a \forall_b (a + b) + 2 = a + (b + 2)$
For every a, there is a b for which b = 2a.	$\forall_a \exists_b b = 2a$

You can also read the quantifier $\exists_x$ in this way: "There is at least one x." A symbol used in place of the words "There is exactly one x," or "There is a unique x," is $\exists!_x$. For example, the statement $\forall_x \exists!_y x + y = 0$ is read:

For every x, there is a unique y such that $x + y = 0$.

Exercises

Express each of the following statements using a symbol for the quantifier. Assume that all variables represent real numbers.

1. For all x, $2x = x + x$.

2. For some y, $y^2 = 17$.

3. There is a unique real number x such that $4x + 3 = 17$.

4. For every y, there exists a unique x such that $x = 2y$.

5. For all real numbers x and all real numbers y, $x + y = y + x$.

6. For all real numbers r, there exists a unique real number x such that $r + x = 0$.

Chapter Summary

1. The words and symbols used in algebra have specific mathematical definitions (see pages 1–2).

2. Every real number can be graphed as a point on a number line. The real number is the *coordinate* of the point. If point A is to the right of point B on the number line, then the coordinate of A is greater than the coordinate of B.

3. The members of the domain of a variable are the *values* of the variable. *Quantifiers* state how many members of the domain of a variable should be considered in a particular statement.

4. *Axioms* and *postulates* are assumptions made about real numbers (see pages 15–16). From these you can derive other properties called *theorems*. Every step in the proof of a theorem can be justified by an axiom, a definition, a given fact, or a theorem previously proved.

5. The definitions of addition, subtraction, multiplication, and division are used in *simplifying expressions* and proving theorems.

Chapter Review

Give the letter of the correct answer.

1. Simplify $5(28 - 3 \cdot 2^3)$.   **1-1**

    a. 1000   **b.** 116   **c.** 20   **d.** -940

2. Simplify $\dfrac{1 + 7(8 + 3)}{3^2 + 2^2}$.

   a. $\dfrac{78}{25}$ **b.** 6   **c.** $\dfrac{88}{13}$ **d.** 5

3. Arrange $3, \dfrac{1}{2}, -\dfrac{2}{3}, 0, -1, -\dfrac{1}{2}$ from least to greatest.   1-2

   a. $0, -\dfrac{1}{2}, \dfrac{1}{2}, -\dfrac{2}{3}, -1, 3$ **b.** $-\dfrac{1}{2}, -\dfrac{2}{3}, -1, 0, \dfrac{1}{2}, 3$

   c. $-1, -\dfrac{1}{2}, -\dfrac{2}{3}, 0, \dfrac{1}{2}, 3$ **d.** $-1, -\dfrac{2}{3}, -\dfrac{1}{2}, 0, \dfrac{1}{2}, 3$

4. Evaluate $\dfrac{5bc + a^2 - 1}{9 \div c}$ if $a = 4$, $b = 2$, and $c = 3$.   1-3

   a. 15   **b.** 135   **c.** $\dfrac{5}{3}$ **d.** 13

5. State the axiom or property that is illustrated by the statement   1-4
$$(m + 8)n = mn + 8n.$$
   a. Distributive axiom   **b.** Multiplication property

   c. Identity axiom of   **d.** Symmetric property
      multiplication

6. A theorem which follows easily from another theorem is a _?_ .   1-5

   a. axiom   **b.** corollary   **c.** property   **d.** theorem

7. Simplify $-18 + |-16| + 12$.   1-6

   a. -22 **b.** 10   **c.** 46   **d.** -10

8. Simplify $|-9 + 20| + (-13.7)$.

   a. 24.7   **b.** -42.7 **c.** 15.3   **d.** -2.7

9. Simplify $-56 - (-48)$.   1-7

   a. 104   **b.** 8   **c.** 16   **d.** -8

10. Simplify $0.4 - 3.9 - 6$.

   a. -9.5 **b.** 2.5   **c.** 4.1   **d.** -10.3

11. Simplify $6(-7) - (-9)(-5)$.   1-8

   a. 87   **b.** 3   **c.** -3 **d.** -87

12. Simplify $-3(-4x^3 + 2x - 1)$.

   a. $12x^3 + 6x - 3$ **b.** $12x^3 - 6x + 3$

   c. $-12x^3 - 6x + 3$ **d.** $-12x^3 - 6x - 3$

13. Simplify $\dfrac{[(-9)(8) - (-6)^2] \div 4}{(2 - 11)(4 - 5)}$.   1-9

   a. 1   **b.** -3 **c.** 3   **d.** -1

Chapter Test

Simplify.

1-1

1. $\frac{9 + 12}{9 - 2} + 23 - 4^2 \div 8$ **2.** $(6 + 5)4 - 3 \cdot (2^3 - 1)$

1-2

3. Graph $-\frac{1}{2}, \frac{1}{2}, 2$, and $-\frac{3}{4}$ on a number line. Then list the numbers in order from least to greatest.

4. On a number line point C has coordinate $4\frac{1}{2}$, and point D is $5\frac{3}{4}$ units to the left of C. Find the coordinate of D.

1-3

5. Tell whether the following statement is true or false: There is a unique integer n such that $n^2 = 2n$.

6. If $r = 3$ and $s = 5$, evaluate the expression

$$\frac{2[(s^2 - r^2) + (s - r)^2]}{r^2 - s}.$$

Name the axiom or property that is illustrated in each of the following statements.

1-4

7. $7a(5 + 2c) = 7a(2c + 5)$

8. If $a^2(b^3c) = (a^2b^3)c$, then $(a^2b^3)c = a^2(b^3c)$.

1-5

9. Give the reasons for the steps in the following proof.
$a + [-(a + b)] = -b$

Proof:
1. $a + [-(a + b)] = a + [-a + (-b)]$
2. $\qquad\qquad\quad = [a + (-a)] + (-b)$
3. $\qquad\qquad\quad = 0 + (-b)$
4. $\qquad\qquad\quad = -b$

1-6

10. Evaluate $a + |8 + a|$ if $a = -17$.

Simplify.

1-7

11. $36 + (-48) + |-18 + (-38)|$ **12.** $-3.6 - (-8.4) + (-5.9)$

1-8

13. $3 - (4 - 9) - (-6 - 5)$ **14.** $(-2)^3[-8 - (-3)]$

15. $-5x^2(8 - 6x)$

16. $(3^4 - 5)(12 - 2^3)(0)(71 + 3^3)$

17. Evaluate $m^4 - 3m^3 - 2m^2 + m - 1$ if $m = -2$.

Simplify.

18. $-180 \div (-15) \div (-3)$ **19.** $\frac{-4[-5 \cdot 2 - (-3) \cdot 2]}{-18 - 2(-4)}$

1-9

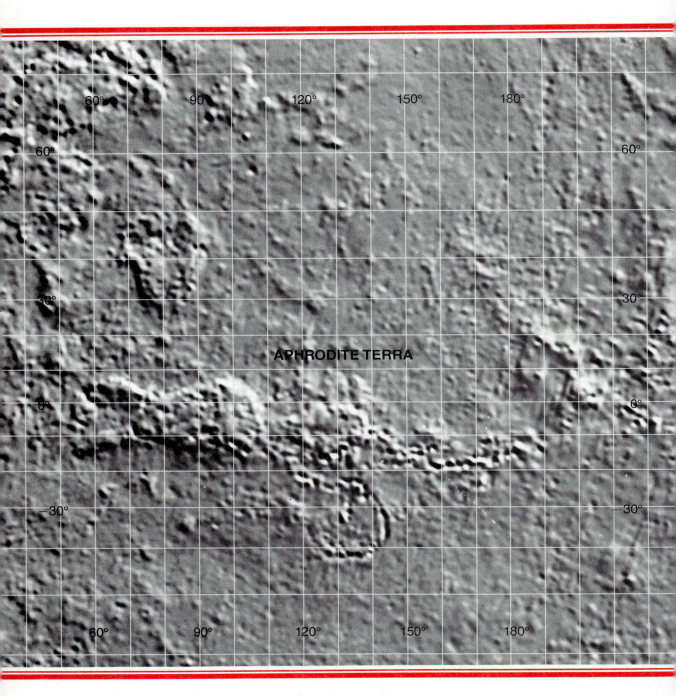

APHRODITE TERRA

A relief map of Venus was produced from data collected with the use of radar by the Pioneer Venus Orbiter. The portion above shows most of the Aphrodite Terra, a highland region. A part of the other major highland area on Venus, Ishtar Terra, is visible at the upper left.

2

EQUATIONS AND INEQUALITIES

EQUATIONS

2-1 Polynomials

OBJECTIVE   **To simplify, add, and subtract polynomials.**

A numeral, a variable, or an indicated product of a numeral and one or more variables is called a **monomial.** Here are some monomials:

$$-2, \quad 7z^4, \quad y, \quad -8a^3b^2, \quad \tfrac{1}{3}n^2m$$

The quotient $-\dfrac{8}{x}$ is not a monomial since the variable is in the denominator. A monomial that contains no variable is called a **constant monomial,** or **constant.** For example, -2 is a constant.

The numerical factor in a monomial is called the **coefficient,** or **numerical coefficient.**

The number of times a variable occurs as a factor in a monomial is called the **degree of the variable.** For example, in the monomial

$$4xy^5 \quad \begin{cases} x & \text{has degree 1, and} \\ y & \text{has degree 5.} \end{cases}$$

The **degree of a monomial** is the total number of times its variables occur as factors. Clearly, the degree of a monomial equals the sum of the degrees of its variables. Thus, the degree of $4xy^5$ is $1 + 5$, or 6. The degree of any nonzero constant monomial is 0. The monomial 0 has *no* degree.

Monomials that are identical or that differ only in their numerical coefficients are called **similar,** or **like.** For example,

$$8x^3yz^2 \text{ and } -x^3yz^2 \text{ are similar,}$$

but

$$ab^3 \text{ and } 5a^3b \text{ are not similar.}$$

A monomial or a sum of monomials is called a **polynomial.** A polynomial such as $2x^2 + (-3x) + (-8)$ is usually written as $2x^2 - 3x - 8$. A polynomial consisting of two terms is called a **binomial,** and a polynomial of three terms is called a **trinomial.** For example, $3y^5 - 8$ is a **binomial,** and $5n^2 + 7n + 8$ is a **trinomial.**

A polynomial is simplified, or in **simplest form,** when no two of its terms are similar. The terms of a simplified polynomial are usually arranged in order of decreasing degree in one of the variables. The **degree of a polynomial** is the greatest of the degrees of its terms after it has been simplified.

EXAMPLE 1 Simplify, arranging terms in order of decreasing degree in x, and give the degree of the polynomial.

$$z^5 - 5x^2z^3 + 2 + 3x^3z - z^5 + 9 + x^2z^3$$

SOLUTION
$$
\begin{aligned}
z^5 - 5x^2z^3 &+ 2 + 3x^3z - z^5 + 9 + x^2z^3 \\
&= (z^5 - z^5) + (-5x^2z^3 + x^2z^3) + 3x^3z + (2 + 9) \\
&= (1 - 1)z^5 + (-5 + 1)x^2z^3 + 3x^3z + 11 \\
&= 0z^5 + (-4)x^2z^3 + 3x^3z + 11 \\
&= 3x^3z - 4x^2z^3 + 11.
\end{aligned}
$$

The degrees of the terms are in order 4, 5, and 0.
∴ the degree of the polynomial is 5. ***Answer***

Be sure that you see how the properties of real numbers justify the steps in the solution of Example 1.

To add two or more polynomials, you write the sum and simplify by adding similar terms. To subtract a polynomial, you add its opposite and simplify.

EXAMPLE 2 Add $5y^2 + 3y$ and $y^2 - 4y + 6$.

SOLUTION 1 $(5y^2 + 3y) + (y^2 - 4y + 6) = (5y^2 + y^2) + [3y + (-4y)] + 6$
$$= 6y^2 - y + 6 \quad \textbf{\textit{Answer}}$$

SOLUTION 2 You can also add vertically.

$$
\begin{array}{r}
5y^2 + 3y \\
y^2 - 4y + 6 \\
\hline
6y^2 - y + 6 \quad
\end{array}
$$ ***Answer***

EXAMPLE 3   Subtract $y^2 - 4y + 6$ from $5y^2 + 3y$.

SOLUTION
$$5y^2 + 3y - (y^2 - 4y + 6) = 5y^2 + 3y + (-y^2) + 4y + (-6)$$
$$= (5y^2 - y^2) + (3y + 4y) - 6$$
$$= 4y^2 + 7y - 6 \quad \textbf{\textit{Answer}}$$

Expressions that are equal for every value of the variable for which each expression makes sense are called **equivalent expressions.** An equation whose sides are equivalent expressions is called an **identity.** Example 2 above shows that $(5y^2 + 3y) + (y^2 - 4y + 6)$ and $6y^2 - y + 6$ are equivalent expressions. Consequently, the following equation is an identity:

$$(5y^2 + 3y) + (y^2 - 4y + 6) = 6y^2 - y + 6$$

Notice how the distributive property is used in Example 4.

EXAMPLE 4   Simplify $6t + 5s - (2t - 4s) + 3(t - 3s)$ and express the result as an identity.

SOLUTION
$$6t + 5s - (2t - 4s) + 3(t - 3s)$$

$$6t + 5s - 2t + 4s + 3t - 9s$$

$$6t - 2t + 3t + 5s + 4s - 9s$$

$$7t + 0s$$

$$7t$$

$$\therefore 6t + 5s - (2t - 4s) + 3(t - 3s) = 7t \quad \textbf{\textit{Answer}}$$

Oral Exercises

Identify each of the following polynomials as a monomial, binomial, or trinomial, give its degree, and state the coefficients.

1. z

2. -5

3. x^2yz

4. $a^6 - 2$

5. $4^2 - 16$

6. $2x^2y - xy^4 + 3$

7. $6r - 7r^3$

8. $1 + 2x^2 - 3x$

Read each polynomial in simplest form with terms in order of decreasing degree in x, and state the degree of the polynomial.

9. $5x + x^2 - 4$

10. $x^3 + 2x - x^2$

11. $xy^2 - 3x^2 + y$

12. $x^4 + 7x^3y - x^4 - y^3$

13. $x^2y - xy^2 + 5 + xy^2$

14. $x^4 - x + 6 - x^3 + x^5$

For each pair of polynomials, give
a. the sum when the second is added to the first, and
b. the difference when the second is subtracted from the first.

15. $4x + 8, 2x + 1$

16. $5y - 9, y + 9$

17. $a^2 + 3a + 8, 2a - 1$

18. $-2x^2 + 4x - 1, x^2 + 3$

19. $6 - z^2, 4 - z + z^2$

20. $-7 + 3s + 5s^2, -s + 4s^2$

Written Exercises

Simplify and express the result as an identity.

A　**1.** $(5x + 8) - (3x - 7) + 4x$

3. $3(a + 4) + (a - 7)$

5. $8\left(q - \dfrac{1}{2}\right) - (q - 4)$

7. $m^2 + 4(m^2 - 1) + 3$

9. $a + 6(a + b) - 7(a - b) + b$

11. $5(x - y) - 2(x + y) + 10xy$

13. $(6a^2 - 6a - 4) + (a^2 - a)$

15. $(1 - 4y + y^2) - (y + y^2 - 1)$

2. $7c - (4c + 2) + (6c - 7)$

4. $2(x - 2) - (x + 5)$

6. $3(v^2 - 2) - 15\left(\dfrac{1}{3} - v^2\right)$

8. $b^2 + 8(1 - b^2) + 7$

10. $-2(h - p) - h + 3(h + p) - p$

12. $7(n + k) - 6(n - k) + nk$

14. $(5c^2 - c + 2) + (1 - 2c + c^2)$

16. $(2x^2 - x + 3) - (4 - 3x + x^2)$

B　**17.** $(6x^3 - 5x + 2x^2 - 1) + (3 - 7x - x^2 - x^3)$

18. $(5y^2 - y^3 + 6 - y) + (3y^3 - 1 + y - y^2)$

19. $(w^3 - 7w^2 - w + 4) - (w^3 - 8w^2 + 2w + 3)$

20. $(2t^3 + 8t^2 - 9) - (4t^3 - 8t - 9)$

21. $(12x^2 - 5xy - y^2) + (-2y^2 + 4xy - x^2)$

22. $(a^3 + 3a^2b + b^3) + (a^3 - 3ab^2 - b^3)$

Find values for a, b, and c so that the given equation is an identity.

C　**23.** $(2x^3 + 3ax^2 + 6x - 4) - (x^3 + x^2 - 7x + b) = x^3 + 8x^2 + cx - 5$

24. $(5ay^3 - y^2 + 2y + b) - (6 + 4y - 2y^2 - y^3) = 16y^3 + y^2 + cy + 13$

Calculator Key-In _____

To square a number on your calculator, you can, of course, just multiply it by itself. If your calculator has a key marked "x^2," pressing it will square the displayed number. Experiment by entering the number 9 and then pressing the x^2 key.

　Use the x^2 key to evaluate $2x^2$ when $x = 3$. The correct answer is 18. If your display shows 36, you will have to square 3 before multiplying by 2.

Find the value of each polynomial using the given value of the variable.

1. $x^2 - 3x + 4$; $x = 5$ 　　　　　**2.** $4x^2 + 2x - 1$; $x = -3$

3. a. Enter 1.01 on your calculator. Then press the x^2 key. Which is larger, 1.01^2 or 1.01? Press the x^2 key five more times. Are the numbers increasing or decreasing in size?

　　b. Enter 0.99 and repeat part (a) making the same comparisons.

　　c. What conclusion can be drawn from parts (a) and (b)?

2-2 Solving Equations in One Variable

OBJECTIVE To solve certain equations in one variable.

An equation or inequality that contains a variable, such as

$$4a - 1 = 0 \quad \text{or} \quad y + 5 > 9,$$

is called an **open sentence.** Any value of the variable that makes the open sentence true is a **solution,** or **root,** of the open sentence and is said to satisfy it. Thus, $\frac{1}{4}$ is a solution of

$$4a - 1 = 0,$$

because $4 \times \frac{1}{4} - 1 = 0$ is true; 5 is not a solution of $4a - 1 = 0$, because $4 \times 5 - 1 = 0$ is false.

Finding all of the solutions of an open sentence is called **solving** the sentence. The set of all solutions of a sentence over a given domain of the variable is called the **solution set** of the sentence *over* that domain. *Unless otherwise stated, open sentences in this book are to be solved over the set of real numbers.*

Study the following two sequences of equations.

$$\begin{array}{ll}
4x + 15 = 43 & x = 7 \\
4x + 15 - 15 = 43 - 15 & 4(x) = 4(7) \\
4x = 28 & 4x = 28 \\
\dfrac{4x}{4} = \dfrac{28}{4} & 4x + 15 = 28 + 15 \\
x = 7 & 4x + 15 = 43
\end{array}$$

Do you see that if the first statement in either sequence is true for some value of x, then the last statement in the sequence is also true for that value of x? Thus, $4x + 15 = 43$ and $x = 7$ have the same solution set, namely $\{7\}$. Equations having the same solution set over a given domain are called **equivalent equations** over that domain. To solve an equation, you usually transform it into a simple equivalent equation whose solution set is apparent.

TRANSFORMATIONS THAT PRODUCE EQUIVALENT EQUATIONS

1. Substitute for any expression in a given equation an equivalent expression.
2. Add to or subtract from each side of a given equation the same number or the same polynomial in any variable appearing in the equation.
3. Multiply or divide each side of a given equation by the same nonzero number.

Transformation 1 on the preceding page enables you to simplify one side or both sides of an equation.

EXAMPLE 1 Solve $3(5n - 9) + 1 = 7n - 50$.

SOLUTION

1. Copy the equation.

$$3(5n - 9) + 1 = 7n - 50$$

2. Simplify the left side.

$$15n - 27 + 1 = 7n - 50$$
$$15n - 26 = 7n - 50$$

3. Add 26 to each side.

$$15n - 26 + 26 = 7n - 50 + 26$$
$$15n = 7n - 24$$

4. Subtract $7n$ from each side. This transformation produces an equivalent equation with a variable on just one side.

$$15n - 7n = 7n - 24 - 7n$$
$$8n = -24$$

5. Divide each side by 8.

$$\frac{8n}{8} = \frac{-24}{8}$$
$$n = -3$$

Check:

$$3(5n - 9) + 1 = 7n - 50$$
$$3[5(-3) - 9] + 1 \overset{?}{=} 7(-3) - 50$$
$$3[-15 - 9] + 1 \overset{?}{=} -21 - 50$$
$$3[-24] + 1 \overset{?}{=} -71$$
$$-72 + 1 \overset{?}{=} -71$$
$$-71 = -71 \quad \checkmark$$

∴ the solution is -3. **Answer**

Example 1 illustrates how to check your work against error by showing that the number found to be the solution actually satisfies the *given* equation.

Addition and subtraction are called **inverse operations** because each "undoes" the other. Thus, in Step 3 of Example 1, you add 26 to both sides to "undo" the subtraction. Multiplication and division are inverse operations as well. In Step 5 you divide each side by 8 to "undo" the multiplication.

When solving equations, you cannot assume that an equation has exactly one root. Recall from Section 2-1 that an equation that is true for all values of the variable is an *identity*. It is also possible that an equation can be true for *no* values of the variable. In such a case the solution set has no members. The set with no members, denoted ∅, is called the **empty set,** or the **null set.**

EXAMPLE 2 Solve $4(x - 1) = 2(2x - 1)$. (The solution is given at the top of the next page.)

SOLUTION

$$4(x - 1) = 2(2x - 1)$$
$$4x - 4 = 4x - 2$$
$$4x - 4x = 4 - 2$$
$$0 = 2$$

Since the equation is equivalent to the false statement $0 = 2$, the equation has no roots. Its solution set is $\emptyset$. **Answer.**

A **formula** is an equation that states a relationship among quantities represented by variables. Table 7 (page 659) lists some formulas from geometry. For example, the perimeter P of a rectangle is given by the formula

$$P = 2l + 2w.$$

The variables l and w represent the length and width of the rectangle. Given values for all but one of the quantities, you can solve for the remaining quantity.

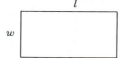

EXAMPLE 3 If the perimeter of a rectangle is 56 cm and the length is 18 cm, find the width.

SOLUTION

$$P = 2l + 2w$$
$$56 = 2(18) + 2w$$
$$56 = 36 + 2w$$
$$20 = 2w$$
$$10 = w$$

Check: $P = 2l + 2w$
$$56 \overset{?}{=} 2(18) + 2(10)$$
$$56 \overset{?}{=} 36 + 20$$
$$56 = 56 \ \checkmark$$

$\therefore$ the width of the rectangle is 10 cm. **Answer**

When you solve a formula or other equation for a certain variable, you regard all other variables in the equation as constants. Then use the transformations that produce equivalent equations.

EXAMPLE 4 Solve the formula $V = \frac{1}{3} s^2 h$ for h.

SOLUTION

$$V = \frac{1}{3} s^2 h$$

$$3(V) = 3\left(\frac{1}{3} s^2 h\right)$$

$$3V = s^2 h$$

$$\frac{3V}{s^2} = \frac{s^2 h}{s^2} \quad (\text{Assume } s \neq 0)$$

$$h = \frac{3V}{s^2} \quad \textbf{Answer}$$

Oral Exercises

State the transformation needed to change the first equation into the second equation.

SAMPLE $14y + 3 - 8y = 15$; $6y + 3 = 15$

SOLUTION   Simplify the left side of the equation.

1. $4x - 5 = 19$; $4x = 24$
2. $6 + y - 1 = 2y - 3$; $y + 5 = 2y - 3$
3. $4x = 24$; $x = 6$
4. $3r = -18$; $r = -6$
5. $2w = 9w - 8 - 5w$; $2w = 4w - 8$
6. $7k = 6k - 5$; $k = -5$
7. $\frac{1}{5}(y - 6) = 11$; $y - 6 = 55$
8. $x + 4 = 7x - 14$; $4 = 6x - 14$

Written Exercises

Solve. If the equation has no solution, so state.

A
1. $3x - 2 = 1$
2. $\frac{1}{2}y - 1 = 0$
3. $4t - 2 = 2t$

4. $2m - 5 = 3$
5. $2p + 9 = p + 9$
6. $2m - 4 = 3m - 4$

7. $5n - 1 = 29$
8. $7z + 2 = 58$
9. $\frac{3}{4}y = 36$

10. $\frac{1}{5}q - 12 = 0$
11. $3v - 15 - v = 5$
12. $9p = p - 40$

13. $v = 54 - 2v - 3v$
14. $m + 2m + 3m + 42 = 0$
15. $3(t - 4) + 1 = t + 9$

16. $2(u + 3) - 1 = 11 + 2u$
17. $3(2 + s) = 2(s - 6)$
18. $4(x - 2) = 7(x - 2)$

19. $\frac{1}{2}(m - 2) = 4$
20. $\frac{1}{3}(x + 1) = 7$
21. $2(2d - 1) + 5 = 27$

22. $3(c + 8) + c = 32$
23. $3(n - 5) - n = n - 1$
24. $3z - (8 - z) = z + 7$

25. $17x - 6(x + 3) = 17x - 3x$
26. $3x + 20 = 4 - 3(8 - 3x)$

Solve the equation for the given variable.

27. $F = \frac{9}{5}C + 32$ for C
28. $A = \frac{1 + b}{2}$ for b
29. $z - b = 2z - b$ for z

30. $v - a = a - v$ for v
31. $ay + a = 1 + a$ for y
32. $m - mx = m - 1$ for x

In each formula, substitute the given values of the variables; then solve for the remaining variable, which is printed in red.

SAMPLE $S = -4.9t^2 + vt$; $S = 6$, $t = 2$ (height of a projectile)

SOLUTION $6 = -4.9(2)^2 + v(2)$
$6 = -19.6 + 2v$
$25.6 = 2v$
$v = 12.8$ **Answer**

B 33. $A = \dfrac{x + y + z}{3}$; $A = 14$, $x = -8$, $y = 3$ (average of three numbers)

    34. $d = rt$; $d = 440$, $r = 55$ (distance traveled at uniform speed)

    35. $A = P(1 + rt)$; $A = 115$, $P = 100$, $t = 2$ (amount at simple interest)

    36. $K = \dfrac{mv^2}{2}$; $K = 1250$, $v = 10$ (kinetic energy)

    37. $S = \dfrac{n}{2}[2a + (n - 1)d]$; $S = 65$, $n = 5$, $a = 7$ (sum of arithmetic series)

    38. $E = al(T - t)$; $E = 0.06$, $a = 0.00001$, $l = 100$, $t = 20$ (expansion of a heated rod)

    39. $m = \dfrac{y_2 - y_1}{x_2 - x_1}$; $m = 1$, $x_1 = 2$, $y_2 = 7$, $x_2 = 6$ (slope of a line)

    40. $d = \dfrac{a}{2}(2t - v)$; $d = 50.2$, $a = 9.8$, $t = 2$ (distance traveled under constant acceleration)

C 41–48. In Exercises 33–40, solve each formula for the variable printed in red in terms of the other variables. (Ignore the given values.)

Biography Granville T. Woods

Granville Woods (1856–1910) was born in Columbus, Ohio. Although he never finished elementary school, he developed a strong interest in electricity as a result of jobs in a machine shop and on railroads. He spent his free time studying books borrowed from friends, employers, and libraries. With the knowledge he had obtained, he was able to get a job as an engineer on the British steamer *Ironsides*.

In 1881 Woods opened his own factory in Cincinnati for the manufacture of telephone, telegraph, and electrical equipment. Thermal power and steam engines also attracted his attention. His first patent was granted in 1884 for an improved steam-boiler furnace.

Woods was one of the most prolific inventors of his time. In all, he patented well over 50 inventions. He is best known for those inventions that promoted safety and efficiency in electric railway travel.

2-3 *Words into Symbols*

To apply algebra, you often must translate word phrases into numerical or variable expressions. In certain applications facts from geometry and science are also needed. Besides knowing the formulas in Table 7 (page 659), you should be familiar with the information in this chart.

KNOW ↓

Angle: a figure formed by two rays that have the same endpoint. To indicate that the measure of $\angle A$ is 35°, we simply write $\angle A = 35°$.

35°
A $\angle A = 35°$

Complementary angles: two angles whose measures have the sum 90°.

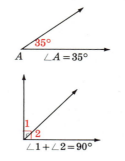

$\angle 1 + \angle 2 = 90°$

Supplementary angles: two angles whose measures have the sum 180°.

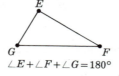

$\angle BCE + \angle ECD = 180°$

The sum of the measures of the angles of a triangle is 180°.

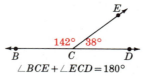

$\angle E + \angle F + \angle G = 180°$

Isosceles triangle: a triangle having at least two equal sides and two equal angles. The two equal sides are called *legs* and the included angle is called the *vertex angle.*

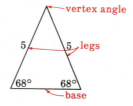

Equilateral triangle: a triangle having three equal sides. Each angle measures 60°.

Perimeter (P) of a polygon: the sum of the lengths of the sides.

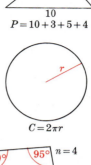

$$P = 10 + 3 + 5 + 4$$

Circumference (C) of a circle: the distance around the circle.

$$C = 2\pi r$$

The sum (S) of the measures of the angles of a polygon with n sides is given by the formula $S = 180(n - 2)^\circ$.

$$S = 80^\circ + 95^\circ + 110^\circ + 75^\circ = 360^\circ$$
$$= 180(4 - 2)^\circ$$

EXAMPLE 1 In an isosceles triangle, the vertex angle measures x°.

    a. What is the measure of each of the other angles?

    b. If the perimeter is 300 cm and the length of each of the legs is y cm, what is the length of the base?

SOLUTION **a.** The sum of the measures of the other angles is $(180 - x)^\circ$; $\therefore$ the measure of each is $\frac{1}{2}(180 - x)^\circ$. ***Answer***

    b. The sum of the lengths of the two equal sides is $2y$ cm; $\therefore$ the length of the base is $(300 - 2y)$ cm. ***Answer***

In describing uniform motion, that is, motion in a single direction at a constant speed, you use the formula

$$\text{distance} = \text{rate} \times \text{time, or } d = rt.$$

EXAMPLE 2 Two planes leave an airport at noon, one flying north at a certain speed, and the other flying south at twice that speed. Use any convenient variable to express the distance between the planes three hours later.

$D = rt$

SOLUTION

	Rate (km/h)	Time (h)	Distance (km)
Northbound Plane	r	3	$3r$
Southbound Plane	$2r$	3	$6r$

Let r = the speed in km/h (kilometers per hour) of the northbound plane. The table then shows the given information.

In three hours, the distance between the planes is $3r + 6r$, or $9r$ km. ***Answer***

Use the chart below to review your knowledge of consecutive numbers.

CONSECUTIVE NUMBERS

Integers	$\dots, -3, -2, -1, 0, 1, 2, 3, \dots$	$n - 1, n, n + 1, n + 2$ are four consecutive integers if n is an integer.
Even Integers (multiples of 2)	$\dots, -6, -4, -2, 0, 2, 4, 6, \dots$	$n - 2, n, n + 2, n + 4$ are four consecutive even integers if n is even,
Odd Integers	$\dots, -5, -3, -1, 1, 3, 5, \dots$	and four consecutive odd integers if n is odd.

EXAMPLE 3 What is the sum of three consecutive even integers:
a. if the greatest is k?
b. if the middle one is m?

SOLUTION **a.** $k + (k - 2) + (k - 4)$, or $3k - 6$;
b. $(m - 2) + m + (m + 2)$, or $3m$ *Answer*

Oral Exercises

Express the number described in terms of x.

SAMPLE Five more than x **SOLUTION** $x + 5$

1. Six less than x
2. Eight decreased by x
3. Ten more than twice x
4. Five less than half of x
5. Five times x, decreased by 2
6. Five times the quantity x decreased by 2

In Exercises 7–22, express your answer in terms of the variable given.

7. If m is an integer, what is the next greater integer? the next smaller integer?
8. If e is an even integer, what is the next greater even integer? the next smaller even integer?
9. If one taco costs 65¢, how much do y tacos cost?
10. How far will a car traveling at 85 km/h go in t hours?
11. How far will a car traveling at s km/h go in 3 hours?
12. How long will it take a car traveling at 88 km/h to go z km?

13. What is the degree measure of an angle whose complement measures $x°$?

14. What is the degree measure of an angle whose supplement measures $y°$?

15. What is the perimeter of a square, if each side is $2a$ cm long?

16. What is the perimeter of an equilateral triangle if each side is $(a - 2)$ m long?

17. Pat is t cm tall. If Ron is 5 cm taller than Pat, how tall is Ron?

18. Margo is x years old. How old was she 3 years ago?

19. Bill has saved m dollars toward the price of a $150 bicycle. How much more must he save to buy the bicycle?

20. What is the value in cents of x dimes and $2x$ quarters?

21. What is the perimeter of an isosceles triangle if the base has length b cm and the other sides are each 1 cm shorter?

22. The ages of the three Brown children are consecutive odd integers, and the eldest is y years old. How old is the youngest?

Written Exercises

Express your answers in simplest form.

A 1. How many persons are at a meeting where there are x men, eight more women than men, and three children?

2. If you have read $(t - 5)$ pages of a 100-page book, how many pages are left to be read? $105 - t$

3. One angle of a triangle measures $r°$ and a second angle is three times as large. What is the measure of the third angle?

4. The lengths in meters of the sides of a triangle are consecutive integers. The shortest side is y m long. What is the perimeter?

5. The perimeter of an isosceles triangle is 300 cm and the length of its base is z cm. How long is each leg?

6. Each of the equal angles of an isosceles triangle measures $a°$. What is the measure of the third angle?

7. Measured from hip to shoulder, the length of a tiger is 20 cm longer than twice the length of a dachshund, h cm long. An elephant is 63 cm longer than the tiger. How long is the elephant?

8. Amy is 5 years younger than her brother Ted, who is n years old. Mack is 2 years older than Amy. How old is Mack?

9. A woman is now twice as old as her daughter, who is d years old. How old was each of them twenty years ago?

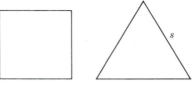

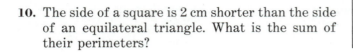

10. The side of a square is 2 cm shorter than the side of an equilateral triangle. What is the sum of their perimeters?

11. The width of a rectangular field is 12 m shorter than the length. How much fencing is needed to enclose it and divide it into two parts as shown?

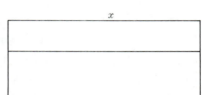

12. Four years from now Barbara will be three times as old as her sister Frieda is now. Complete the following chart.

	Age now	Age four years from now
Frieda	z	?
Barbara	?	?

13. A car traveled for 2 h at r km/h, then decreased the speed by 9 km/h and traveled for 3 more hours. How far did the car go?

14. Two jets leave an airport at noon, one flying east at s km/h, and the other flying west at a rate 100 km/h faster. How many kilometers apart are they at 4 P.M.?

In Exercises 15–20, express your answer in terms of any convenient variable.

B 15. A car traveling on an expressway makes a trip of 150 km at an average speed of 75 km/h. Returning via a local route, the trip is lengthened by a certain distance, and the average speed is 25 km/h slower. What is the total traveling time?

16. Jack and Jill set out at the same time, travel toward each other, and meet after 3 hours. If the rate of one exceeds the rate of the other by 12 km/h, how far apart are their starting points?

17. A purse contains dimes, quarters, and nickels. There are twice as many quarters as dimes and half as many nickels as dimes. What is the total value in cents of the coins?

18. A grocer had 50 kg of coffee, part of which was sold at $7.99/kg and the rest at $8.99/kg. How much did the grocer receive for all of the coffee?

19. In trapezoid $ABCD$, $\angle A$ measures 15° more than $\angle B$. Also, the measure of $\angle A$ is four times the measure of $\angle D$. What is the measure of $\angle C$?

2-4 Solving Problems with Equations

OBJECTIVE: To solve word problems by using an equation in one variable.

A "word problem" can often be solved by translating the information given about numbers and their relationships into an open sentence—usually an equation or inequality. Then the solution of the open sentence gives you the solution of the problem. The following general method will help you to solve word problems. Study the examples that follow it.

PLAN FOR SOLVING A WORD PROBLEM

Step 1 Read the problem carefully and decide what numbers are asked for.

Step 2 Choose a variable and use it with the given facts to represent the number(s) described in the problem. Making a chart or drawing a sketch may be helpful.

Step 3 Write an open sentence based on the given facts.

Step 4 Solve the open sentence and find the required numbers.

Step 5 Check your results with the words of the problem. Give the answer.

EXAMPLE 1 Tickets to the Little Theater were $3 each for balcony seats and $5 each for orchestra seats. For a certain performance, there were 60 more orchestra tickets sold than balcony tickets. The ticket sales totaled $1324. How many balcony tickets were sold? How many orchestra tickets were sold?

SOLUTION

Step 1 The problem asks for the number of balcony tickets sold and for the number of orchestra tickets sold.

Step 2 Let x = the number of balcony tickets.
Then $x + 60$ = the number of orchestra tickets.

	Price	× Number =	Sales
Balcony	3	x	$3x$
Orchestra	5	$x + 60$	$5(x + 60)$
Total Ticket Sales			1324

(*Solution continued on page 60.*)

Step 3

Balcony Ticket Sales	+	Orchestra Ticket Sales	=	Total Ticket Sales
$3x$	+	$5(x + 60)$	=	1324

Step 4

$$3x + 5x + 300 = 1324$$
$$8x + 300 = 1324$$
$$8x = 1024$$
$$x = 128 \text{ (Balcony)}$$
$$x + 60 = 188 \text{ (Orchestra)}$$

Step 5 Is the number of orchestra tickets 60 more than the number of balcony tickets?

$$188 \stackrel{?}{=} 128 + 60$$
$$188 = 188 \quad \checkmark$$

Is the sum of the ticket sales of orchestra and balcony tickets $1324?

$$188(5) + 128(3) \stackrel{?}{=} 1324$$
$$940 + 384 \stackrel{?}{=} 1324$$
$$1324 = 1324 \quad \checkmark$$

$\therefore$ 128 balcony tickets were sold, and 188 orchestra tickets were sold. ***Answer***

EXAMPLE 2 The lengths of two opposite sides of a square are increased by 4 m, and the lengths of the other two sides are decreased by 2 m. The perimeter of the rectangle formed is 28 m. Find the dimensions of the rectangle.

SOLUTION

Step 1 The problem asks for the dimensions of the rectangle. Therefore, you need to find the length and width of the rectangle.

Step 2 Let s = length, in meters, of one side of the square. (The variable need not represent a number that is asked for.)

Then $s + 4$ = length of the rectangle, and $s - 2$ = width of the rectangle.

Perimeter of rectangle = $2(s + 4) + 2(s - 2)$

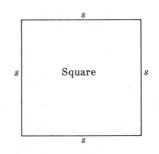

Step 3 Perimeter of rectangle is 28 m.

$$2(s + 4) + 2(s - 2) = 28$$

Step 4
$$2s + 8 + 2s - 4 = 28$$
$$4s + 4 = 28$$
$$4s = 24$$
$$s = 6$$
$$\therefore s + 4 = 10 \text{ (length)}; \quad s - 2 = 4 \text{ (width)}$$

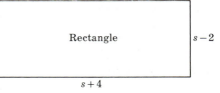

Step 5 The check is left for you.

$\therefore$ the dimensions of the rectangle are 10 m by 4 m. ***Answer***

Tables are often helpful in organizing the data in a uniform motion problem.

EXAMPLE 3   Lorna leaves State U on a moped trip at the rate of 24 km/h. One hour later, her roommate, Sally, realizing that Lorna has forgotten some camping gear, sets out by car. How fast must Sally drive to overtake Lorna in half an hour?

SOLUTION

Step 1   The problem asks for Sally's speed in kilometers per hour.

Step 2   Let r = Sally's speed in kilometers per hour. Use the formula

$$d = rt$$

and arrange the given facts in a table.

	Rate (km/h) $\times$	Time (h) $=$	Distance (km)
Sally (in car)	r	$\frac{1}{2}$	$\frac{1}{2}r$
Lorna (on moped)	24	$\frac{3}{2}$	36

The following diagram pictures the situation after Sally has driven for one half hour, and Lorna for one and one half hours.

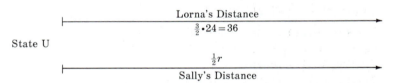

Step 3   Sally overtakes Lorna when each has traveled the same distance.

$$\underbrace{\text{Distance traveled by Sally}}_{\frac{1}{2}r} \quad \underbrace{\text{is the same as}}_{=} \quad \underbrace{\text{distance traveled by Lorna.}}_{36}$$

Step 4 $\frac{1}{2}r = 36$

$r = 72$

Step 5   The check is left for you to do.

$\therefore$ to overtake Lorna in half an hour, Sally must drive at 72 km/h.   **Answer**

Problems

Solve.

A 1. Together Al and Mary have $99. Mary has $3 more than seven times as much money as Al. How much money does each have?

2. A laboratory used 120 fence posts in an experiment comparing two types of paint. Six fewer than twice as many fence posts were painted with paint A as were painted with paint B. How many fence posts were painted with paint A? paint B?

3. One number is three times another number. The sum of the numbers is 84. Find the numbers.

4. One number is 8 less than another number. The sum of the numbers is 96. Find the numbers.

5. In an isosceles triangle, the length of each leg exceeds twice the base by 4 cm, and the perimeter is 98 cm. How long is each side?

6. If each of the base angles of an isosceles triangle measures 10° less than twice the vertex angle, find the measure of each angle.

7. The basic charge to rent a U-Drive truck from Gloster to Fenwick is $120, which includes a travel allowance of 330 km. For each kilometer above the basic allowance, there is an additional charge of 20 cents. The Masseys paid U-Drive $134 to move from Gloster to Fenwick. How far did they drive the truck?

8. In one year twice as many trees in a certain forest of 5000 trees were destroyed by fire as were felled by disease. At the end of the year only 3200 healthy trees remained. How many trees were destroyed by fire?

9. Find three consecutive even integers whose sum is 162.

10. Find three consecutive odd integers whose sum is 183.

11. The lengths of the sides of a four-sided field are given by consecutive integers, each indicating a number of meters. If the perimeter of the field is 66 m, find the lengths of the sides.

12. The degree measures of an angle and its complement are consecutive even integers. Find the measure of each angle.

13. At 7:00 A.M. two planes leave an airport, one flying south at 475 km/h, the other flying north at 650 km/h. At what time will they be 4500 km apart?

14. At 5:00 P.M. a plane leaves an airport and flies due north at 588 km/h. At 6:00 P.M. a second plane leaves the airport, also flying north but at 732 km/h. When does the second plane overtake the first?

B 15. A number is 5 more than 4 times another. The greater number decreased by $\frac{2}{3}$ the smaller equals 20. Find the numbers.

16. Five times the measure of the complement of an angle is equal to $\frac{5}{7}$ of the measure of the supplement of the angle. Find the measure of the angle, its complement, and its supplement.

17. A pollution control device on a car reduces the amount of an air pollutant by 55 ppm (parts per million) per hour. When the device is installed, it will take a car 7 h to emit the same amount of the pollutant that it formerly did in 2 h. How much of the pollutant did the car originally emit per hour?

18. At noon a train leaves Della for Midtown, 800 km south. At 2 P.M., a train on a parallel track leaves Midtown for Della. If each train travels 75 km/h, at what time will they pass each other?

C 19. In an election, 2500 votes were cast. If 40 voters had switched from the winner to the loser, the loser would have won by 20 votes. How many votes did each candidate actually receive?

20. At the end of the first half of a basketball game the Jays and the Lions were tied. During the second half the Jays scored 48 points, and the Lions scored twice as many points as they had in the first half. What was the final score if the Jays won by 2 points?

when multiplying or dividing by a negative number, change the sign

Self-Test 1

VOCABULARY

monomial (p. 45)
constant (p. 45)
coefficient (p. 45)
degree of a variable (p. 45)
degree of a monomial (p. 45)
similar (p. 46)
polynomial (p. 46)
simplest form (p. 46)
degree of a polynomial (p. 46)
equivalent expressions (p. 47)

identity (p. 47)
open sentence (p. 49)
solution (p. 49)
root (p. 49)
solving (p. 49)
solution set (p. 49)
equivalent equations (p. 49)
inverse operations (p. 50)
empty set (p. 50)
formula (p. 51)

Express in simplest form.

1. $(6x - 3) + (2x + 5) - (3x - 4)$ **2.** $3ab - 2a(5 - 3b) + b(6a - 4)$ **Obj. 2-1, p. 45**

Solve.

3. $5y - 2y = 27$ **4.** $3z + 11 = z - 9$ **Obj. 2-2, p. 49**

5. Translate into a mathematical expression in simplest form: the sum of three consecutive integers.   **Obj. 2-3, p. 54**

6. The measure of the complement of an angle is 20° more than the measure of the angle. What is the measure of the angle?   **Obj. 2-4, p. 59**

Check your answers with those at the back of the book.

INEQUALITIES AND APPLICATIONS

2-5 *Solving Inequalities in One Variable*

OBJECTIVE **To solve certain inequalities in one variable**

The inequality

$$x < 3$$

is satisfied by every real number less than 3. The graph of this inequality is shown in red on the number line below. Note the use of the open circle to show that 3 is not a solution.

To find solutions of inequalities like

a. $2x - 1 > 7$ or   **b.** $1 + 3(4 - y) > 19$

you use methods similar to those used to solve equations. These methods are based on the following axioms of order for real numbers, which are taken for granted.

Let a, b, and c be any real numbers.

AXIOM OF COMPARISON

Exactly one of the following statements is true:

$$a < b, \ a = b, \ \text{or} \ a > b.$$

TRANSITIVE AXIOM OF ORDER

If $a < b$ and $b < c$, then $a < c$.

ADDITION AXIOM OF ORDER

If $a < b$, then $a + c < b + c$.

MULTIPLICATION AXIOM OF ORDER

1. If $a < b$ and $c > 0$, then $ac < bc$.
2. If $a < b$ and $c < 0$, then $ac > bc$.

Since subtraction can be expressed in terms of addition, and division can be expressed in terms of multiplication, the order axioms apply to all four operations.

The transformations that produce equivalent inequalities, listed below, are based on the preceding axioms.

TRANSFORMATIONS THAT PRODUCE EQUIVALENT INEQUALITIES

1. Substituting for either side of the inequality an expression equivalent to that side.
2. Adding to (or subtracting from) each side of an equality the same number or the same polynomial in any variable appearing in the inequality.
3. Multiplying (or dividing) each side by the same positive number.
4. Multiplying (or dividing) each side by the same negative number and reversing the inequality sign.

EXAMPLE   Solve each inequality and draw its graph.

$$\textbf{a. } 2x - 1 > 7 \qquad \textbf{b. } 1 + 3(4 - y) > 19$$

SOLUTION

a. $2x - 1 > 7$

$$2x > 8$$

$$\frac{2x}{2} > \frac{8}{2}$$

$$x > 4$$

∴ the solution set consists of the real numbers greater than 4, and its graph is shown below.   *Answer*

b. $1 + 3(4 - y) > 19$

$$1 + 12 - 3y > 19$$

$$13 - 3y > 19$$

$$-3y > 6$$

$$\frac{-3y}{-3} < \frac{6}{-3} \quad \longleftarrow \text{Note direction change}$$

$$y < -2$$

∴ the solution set consists of the real numbers less than -2; its graph is shown below.   *Answer*

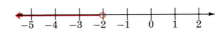

The solution set to part (b) of the previous example can be written as $\{y : y < -2\}$, which is read, "the set of all y such that y is less than -2." This notation will be used throughout the rest of this chapter.

Certain inequalities are true for all real numbers, and others have no solution. For example, $2x > 2(x + 1)$ has no solution, and $3x < 3(x + 2)$ is true for all real numbers.

Oral Exercises

State the transformation needed to change the first inequality into the second inequality.

SAMPLE $-5x < 20;\ \ x > -4$

SOLUTION   Divide each side by negative five and reverse the inequality sign.

1. $y - 2 > 9;\ y > 11$

2. $z + 4 < 3;\ z < -1$

3. $6t < 18;\ t < 3$

4. $\frac{1}{3}t > 5;\ t > 15$

5. $x + 4 + x < 9;\ 2x + 4 < 9$

6. $2s < s - 7;\ s < -7$

7. $-\frac{1}{2}v > 2;\ v < -4$

8. $5 > 2(1 - a);\ 5 > 2 - 2a$

9. $5z < 20 + z;\ 4z < 20$

10. $-3y < 21;\ y > -7$

Written Exercises

Solve and graph each inequality.

SAMPLE $x - 5 < 1$

SOLUTION $\{x: x < 6\}$

A   **1.** $x + 4 < 7$

2. $4y > 12$

3. $\frac{1}{2}z > -7$

4. $b - 5 < -4$

5. $-2k < 14$

6. $-2m > -10$

7. $2y + 3 > -3$

8. $3x + 7 < 10$

9. $5n + 17 > 12$

10. $-2t + 1 > -5$

11. $4d - 7 < 3d$

12. $3p + 1 < 2p - 1$

13. $9h - 6 > 7h - 6$

14. $4g + 7 > 3(g + 2)$

15. $2(3x - 1) > 3(x - 1)$

16. $2(v + 3) - 5 > 5(v - 1)$

17. $8(1 - z) < 1 - (2z + 5)$

18. $4 - (3 - n) < 3n - (3 - 2n)$

19. $5(1 + y) > 3y - (1 - y)$

20. $2(1 - 2x) + x < 3(1 + x) - 7$

Solve. If the inequality has no solution, so state.

B   **21.** $3[2x - (x + 1)] < 5(x + 3)$

22. $3x - 2(x + 1) > x + 2$

23. $2[3(1 - s) - 2(2 - s)] > s + 7$

24. $7y - 3(2y + 1) < 2(y + 2) - (y - 1)$

25. Show by a numerical example that even though $a > b$, it need not be true that $a^2 > b^2$.

26. Show by a numerical example that even though $a > b$ and $c > d$, it need not be true that $a - c > b - d$.

In Exercises 27–30, prove the given statement given that a, b, c, and d represent real numbers.

C **27.** If $a < b$ and $c < d$, then $a + c < b + d$.
(*Hint:* Show that $a + c < b + c$ and that $b + c < b + d$.)

28. If $a > b > 0$ and $c > d > 0$, then $ac > bd$. (*Hint:* Show that $ac > bc$ and that $bc > bd$.)

29. If $0 < a < b$, then $a^2 < b^2$.   **30.** If $a < b < 0$, then $a^2 > b^2$.

Computer Key-In

Programs for computers are written in specially designed computer languages that make it easy for people to tell a computer what to do. A program, called a *compiler*, is stored in the computer to translate the languge into direct instructions to the computer.

Several languages are available. Among them, FORTRAN is a scientific language, COBOL is a business-oriented language, and BASIC (which is used in this book) is a general language designed for easy interaction with the computer. BASIC was designed at Dartmouth College by John G. Kemeny and Thomas E. Kurtz and introduced in 1964. Many features have been added to the original BASIC, and it is now an extremely useful and effective language.

Computers are especially useful in processing large amounts of data very rapidly. This involves inputting and storing the data (called *data banks*) and then writing a program that will search and find (retrieve) the information desired. The people using these programs at terminals do not need to be computer programmers. They only need to know how to use the program stored in the computer. Examples of these programs are:

Theater ticket reservations and sales
Airline ticket reservations and sales
Hotel reservations
Manufacturing inventories and sales
Medical records and diagnostic clues
General library indexing

2-6 *Solving Combined Inequalities*

OBJECTIVE   To solve certain combined inequalities.

A sentence formed by joining two sentences with the word *and* is called a **conjunction.** A conjunction is true when both sentences are true. A sentence formed by joining two sentences with the word *or* is called a **disjunction.** A disjunction is true when at least one of the sentences is true. Conjunctions and disjunctions involving inequalities are frequently used.

Recall from Section 1-2 that the conjunction

$$-4 < y \text{ and } y < 2$$

is usually written as "$-4 < y < 2$." Note that "$x \leq 4$" stands for the disjunction

$$x < 4 \text{ or } x = 4$$

and is usually read "x is less than or equal to 4." In the graph of this disjunction, which is shown below, a solid red dot has been used to show that 4 is in the graph.

To solve a conjunction, you find the values of the variable for which *both* sentences are true. To solve a disjunction, you find the values of the variable for which at least one of the sentences is true.

EXAMPLE   Find the solution set of $-5 < \frac{1}{2}t + 1 \leq 1$, and draw its graph.

SOLUTION   To solve the inequality $-5 < \frac{1}{2}t + 1 \leq 1$, you solve the conjunction:

$$-5 < \tfrac{1}{2}t + 1 \qquad \text{and} \qquad \tfrac{1}{2}t + 1 \leq 1$$

$$-6 < \tfrac{1}{2}t \qquad\qquad\qquad \tfrac{1}{2}t \leq 0$$

$$-12 < t \qquad\qquad\qquad\qquad t \leq 0$$

$$-12 < t \leq 0$$

∴ the solution set is $\{t: -12 < t \leq 0\}$, and its graph is shown below.   ***Answer***

Oral Exercises

Tell whether the given sentence is true or false.

1. $-5 < -1$ and $1 < 5$ **2.** $2 > 0$ and $-2 > -1$ **3.** $-3 < 0$ and $3 > 0$

4. $1 > -2$ and $0 < -4$ **5.** $-3 < -1$ or $0 < 4$ **6.** $2 > 5$ or $-3 > -2$

Match each graph with one of the open sentences given in a–h.

7.

8.

9.

10.

11.

12.

a. $-1 \le x \le 2$

b. $x \le 0$ or $x \ge 1$

c. $x > -3$

d. $x > 2$

e. $x \le 3$

f. $-2 < x \le 2$

g. $x \le -1$ or $x > 2$

h. $-1 \le x < 2$

Written Exercises

Solve each open sentence and graph each solution set that is not empty.

A **1.** $x + 4 \le 7$ **2.** $y - 3 \ge 1$ **3.** $-6 \le z - 4 < 0$

4. $2 \le x + 5 < 7$ **5.** $1 < 2y - 7 \le 3$ **6.** $-1 < 3t - 2 < 11$

7. $-3 > 1 - w > 2$ **8.** $4 \ge 3 - s \ge 0$ **9.** $3 \ge \frac{n}{2} - 1 > -2$

10. $-1 > \frac{c}{3} - 2 > -5$ **11.** $-5 < 1 - 2k < 3$ **12.** $-6 \le 2 - 3m \le 6$

B **13.** $2a - 4 < a - 1 \le 2a + 1$ **14.** $z - 2 \le 2z \le 3z - 1$

15. $1 - p > 2$ or $1 - p < -2$ **16.** $2t - 5 > 3$ or $2t - 5 < -3$

17. $3x - 1 \le 2x$ or $3x - 1 \ge -2x$ **18.** $2y < y + 1$ or $2y < -(y + 1)$

C **19.** $3z + 5 < z + 7$ and $3 - z < 1$ **20.** $7 - 2m \ge 5$ and $11 + 2m > 5 - m$

21. $3r - 2 > 3 - 2r$ or $r - 2 > 3 - r$ **22.** $3q + 2 < 5q - 1$ or $2q + 1 > -q$

23. $-5 \le 3 + 2k \le 1$ or $0 \le 3(k - 1) \le 9$

24. $-6 < 2(g - 3) < 2$ or $4 < 3 - g < 9$

25. $-7 < 2k + 1 < 9$ and $[k - 1 \ge 2$ or $2 - k \ge 5]$

26. $[3p - 1 < 8$ or $2(p - 1) < -6]$ and $-1 \le 2p \le 3$

2-7 Absolute Value in Open Sentences

OBJECTIVE   To solve equations and inequalities involving absolute values.

The figure below suggests a useful way of thinking about absolute value.

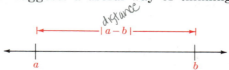

On the number line, the distance between the graphs of the numbers a and b is the absolute value of the difference of a and b. For simplicity, we usually speak of "the distance between a and b" instead of "the distance between the graphs of a and b."

EXAMPLE 1   Find the distance between: **a.** 4 and 9; **b.** -6 and 1; **c.** -3 and -5.

SOLUTION   **a.** $|4 - 9| = |-5| = 5$ *Answer*

b. $|-6 - 1| = |-7| = 7$ *Answer*

c. $|-3 - (-5)| = |-3 + 5| = |2| = 2$ *Answer*

Thinking in terms of distance on the number line can help you to solve open sentences involving absolute value.

EXAMPLE 2   Solve $|z - 4| = 3$.

SOLUTION 1   To satisfy the equation

$$|z - 4| = 3,$$

z must be a number whose distance from 4 is 3. Thus, you can think of starting at 4 and moving 3 units in either direction on the number line.

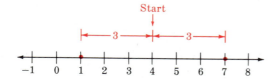

You arrive at 7 and 1 as the solutions. ∴ the solution set is $\{1, 7\}$.   *Answer*

SOLUTION 2   Another way to solve Example 2 is to note that

$$|z - 4| = 3$$

is equivalent to

$$z - 4 = -3 \quad \text{or} \quad z - 4 = 3$$
$$z = 1 \qquad\qquad z = 7$$

∴ the solution set is $\{1, 7\}$.   *Answer*

EXAMPLE 3 Solve and graph $|x - 2| \leq 5$.

SOLUTION 1 To satisfy the inequality $|x - 2| \leq 5$, x must be a number whose distance from 2 is no more than 5. So, starting at 2, the numbers up to and including 7 will satisfy the given inequality, along with the numbers down to and including -3. Thus, the solution set consists of the numbers between -3 and 7, inclusive.

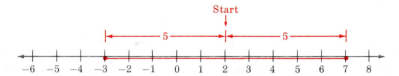

Therefore, the given inequality is equivalent to the sentence

$$-3 \leq x \leq 7.$$

∴ the solution set is $\{x: -3 \leq x \leq 7\}$, and the graph is shown above. ***Answer***

SOLUTION 2 This solution is based on the fact that when b is a positive integer, the inequality $|x - a| < b$ is equivalent to $-b < x - a < b$.

Note that $|x - 2| \leq 5$ is equivalent to the combined inequality

$$-5 \leq x - 2 \leq 5.$$

$$\begin{array}{ccc} -5 \leq x - 2 & \text{and} & x - 2 \leq 5 \\ -3 \leq x & & x \leq 7 \end{array}$$

$$-3 \leq x \leq 7$$

∴ the solution set is $\{x: -3 \leq x \leq 7\}$, and the graph is shown above. ***Answer***

EXAMPLE 4 Solve and graph $|2u - 3| < 7$.

SOLUTION $|2u - 3| < 7$ is equivalent to

$$-7 < 2u - 3 < 7$$

$$\begin{array}{ccc} -7 < 2u - 3 & \text{and} & 2u - 3 < 7 \\ -4 < 2u & & 2u < 10 \\ -2 < u & & u < 5 \end{array}$$

$$\therefore -2 < u < 5$$

∴ the solution set is $\{u: -2 < u < 5\}$, and the graph is shown above. ***Answer***

EXAMPLE 5 Solve and graph $|t + 5| > 4$

SOLUTION 1 Because $t + 5 = t - (-5)$, $|t + 5| > 4$ is equivalent to

$$|t - (-5)| > 4.$$

Hence, the distance between t and -5 must be greater than 4, as shown in the graph below.

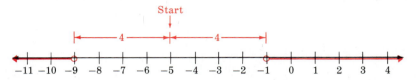

Therefore, the given inequality is equivalent to the open sentence

$$t < -9 \qquad \text{or} \qquad -1 < t.$$

∴ the solution set is $\{t: t < -9 \text{ or } -1 < t\}$, and the graph is shown above. *Answer*

SOLUTION 2 Note that $|t + 5| > 4$ is equivalent to the open sentence

$$
\begin{array}{ccc}
-(t + 5) > 4 & \text{or} & t + 5 > 4 \\
t + 5 < -4 & & (t) + 5 - 5 > 4 - 5 \\
t < -9 & & t > -1
\end{array}
$$

$$t < -9 \qquad \text{or} \qquad t > -1$$

∴ the solution set is $\{t: t < -9 \text{ or } t > -1\}$, and the graph is shown above. *Answer*

Oral Exercises

In Exercises 1–6:
a. translate the sentence into a statement involving the distance between numbers;
b. write an equivalent open sentence without absolute values.

SAMPLE $|x + 1| > 5$

SOLUTION **a.** The distance from x to -1 in either direction is greater than 5.

b. $x + 1 > 5 \qquad \text{or} \qquad x + 1 < -5$

1. $|y| \geq 3$ **2.** $|s| \leq 4$ **3.** $|y + 9| \leq 2$

4. $|t - 1| > 0$ **5.** $|z - 6| < 1$ **6.** $|r - \frac{3}{2}| > \frac{5}{2}$

Use absolute values to state an inequality equivalent to each of the following open sentences.

SAMPLE $-7 \leq x - 4 \leq 7$ **SOLUTION** $|x - 4| \leq 7$

7. $-2 < w + 8 < 2$ **8.** $-5 \leq 4 - k \leq 5$

9. $2p > 8$ or $2p < -8$ **10.** $q + 11 \geq 2$ or $q + 11 \leq -2$

11. $z + 4 \leq 5$ and $z + 4 \geq -5$ **12.** $-10 \leq 3t + 2 \leq 10$

Written Exercises

A **1–12.** Graph the solution set of each of the open sentences in Oral Exercises 1–12 on a separate number line.

Solve. Graph each solution set that is not empty.

13. $|3x - 10| = 1$ **14.** $|1 - 2y| = 7$

15. $|5k - 20| \leq 0$ **16.** $|7t + 21| \geq 0$

17. $\left| \dfrac{r}{2} - 3 \right| > 2$ **18.** $\left| \dfrac{s}{3} + 1 \right| \leq 4$

19. $|4 - 3n| \leq 1$ **20.** $|3 - 4p| > 11$

B **21.** $|r - 2| + 3 = 4$ **22.** $|z + 4| - 1 = 6$

23. $|x + 7| - 4 \geq -1$ **24.** $|y - 3| + 3 < 5$

25. $2 - |1 - h| > 1$ **26.** $5 - |2 - a| \leq 3$

27. $2|3t - 7| + 9 = 17$ **28.** $11 + 3|4t + 1| = 7$

29. $6 - 5|3 - 2z| > 21$ **30.** $19 - 4|2 - 5x| > 11$

C **31.** Show that if x, a, and b are real numbers such that $|x + b| < a$, then $-a - b < x < a - b$.

32. Show that if x, a, and b are real numbers such that $|x - b| > a$, then $x > a + b$ or $x < -a + b$.

CHALLENGE

One day a visitor to a distant land stood at a fork in the road. The visitor knew that each path led to a different village. The inhabitants of one village always told the truth. The inhabitants of the other village always lied. Luckily, a local citizen happened along and agreed to answer one and only one question. The visitor thought for awhile and finally asked a simple question that was guaranteed to indicate the right path to the village of truth tellers, no matter which village the person was from.

What was the question, and why did the visitor ask that particular question?

2-8 *Solving Problems with Inequalities*

OBJECTIVE   To solve word problems by using inequalities in one variable.

Sometimes the solution of a word problem involves an inequality.

EXAMPLE 1   To qualify in a fishing contest, each contestant had to land three trout, averaging at least 36.0 cm in length. The first trout Pat Greene caught measured 31.4 cm, the second, 38.2 cm. At least how long must her third catch be for Pat to qualify?

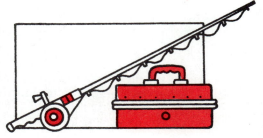

SOLUTION

Step 1   The problem asks for the shortest length possible for Pat's third trout, if her three trout have an average length of at least 36.0 cm.

Step 2   Let x = the length in centimeters of the third trout.

Then $\dfrac{31.4 + 38.2 + x}{3}$ = the average length.

Step 3   The average length   is at least   36.0

$$\dfrac{31.4 + 38.2 + x}{3} \qquad \geq \qquad 36.0$$

Step 4

$$\dfrac{69.6 + x}{3} \qquad \geq \qquad 36.0$$

$$3\left(\dfrac{69.6 + x}{3}\right) \qquad \geq \qquad 3(36.0)$$

$$69.6 + x \qquad \geq \qquad 108.0$$

$$x \qquad \geq \qquad 38.4$$

Step 5   If $x \geq 38.4$, is the average length at least 36.0?

$$\dfrac{31.4 + 38.2 + 38.4}{3} \geq 36.0$$

$$\dfrac{108.0}{3} \geq 36.0 \quad \checkmark$$

∴ the third trout should be at least 38.4 cm long.   ***Answer***

EXAMPLE 2   Find all sets of four positive consecutive odd integers such that the sum of the first three is less than twice the greatest.

SOLUTION

Step 1   The problem asks for four consecutive odd integers that are positive; the sum of the first three must be less than twice the greatest.

Step 2   Let the first of these integers be n.
Then the other three are $n + 2$, $n + 4$, and $n + 6$.

Step 3   The sum of the first three is less than twice the greatest.

$$n + (n + 2) + (n + 4) \qquad < \qquad 2(n + 6)$$

Step 4
$$3n + 6 < 2n + 12$$
$$n + 6 < 12$$
$$n < 6$$

Since the least number in the set must be positive, odd, and less than 6, there are only three choices: 1, 3, and 5.

∴ the three sets are $\{1, 3, 5, 7\}$, $\{3, 5, 7, 9\}$, and $\{5, 7, 9, 11\}$. ***Answer***

Step 5   Is the sum of the first three consecutive odd integers less than twice the greatest?

Check for $\{1, 3, 5, 7\}$: $1 + 3 + 5 \overset{?}{<} 2(7)$
$$9 < 14 \quad \checkmark$$

Checking that $\{3, 5, 7, 9\}$ and $\{5, 7, 9, 11\}$ meet this condition is left for you. To determine whether these three sets of numbers are *all* the solutions, check the next possible set of four consecutive odd integers, $\{7, 9, 11, 13\}$, to see whether the requirement is satisfied.

$$7 + 9 + 11 \overset{?}{<} 2(13)$$
$$27 \not< 26$$

∴ the required sets are $\{1, 3, 5, 7\}$, $\{3, 5, 7, 9\}$, and $\{5, 7, 9, 11\}$.
  Answer

Problems

Solve.

A **1.** Find all the sets of three consecutive, positive, even integers whose sum is less than 20.

    2. The average of two integers is less than or equal to 42. One of the integers is 12 more than the other. What is the greatest possible value for the greater integer?

    3. The length of each of the legs of an isosceles triangle is 10 cm greater than 3 times the length of the base. If the perimeter of the triangle is to be at least 90 cm, what is the minimum value for the length of the base?

4. Eduardo has a group of quarters and dimes whose values is at most $4.05. He has five times as many quarters as dimes. At most how many quarters does he have?

5. Lucy has 63 m of fencing with which she plans to fence in a garden and partition it as shown in the diagram. If the garden is to be a rectangle, at most 21 m in length, what is the minimum width of the garden?

6. Beth has quiz grades of 91, 83, 69, and 74. What is the lowest grade she can receive on a fifth quiz that will enable her to maintain an average of at least 81?

7. When Elwood took a rectangular scarf out of the dryer, he found that its length had shrunk by 5 cm although its width was unchanged. If the scarf had originally been six times as long as it was wide, find the maximum values of the original dimensions of the scarf given that the scarf lost at most 95 cm^2 in area.

8. A furniture factory can manufacture a chair in 20 min and a sofa in 30 min. If the factory plans to produce 3 chairs for every sofa, what is the maximum number of each that can be produced in 9 h?

B 9. A hydrofoil stops for equal amounts of time at 5 ports between Jonesport and Marlintown, which are 30 km apart. The hydrofoil is actually under way for 15 min of the trip. At most, how long can the hydrofoil remain at each port if the average speed for the trip, including stops, is to be at least 60 km/h?

10. During the first 20 km of a 50 km bicycle race, Rosa's average speed was 30 km/h. What must her average speed be during the remainder of the race if she is to finish the race in less than 1.5 h?

C 11. The length a of the top base of a trapezoid is equal to the height h. The bottom base b is 6 cm longer than the top base. What are the maximum integral values for a, b, and h if the area of the trapezoid is not to exceed 84 cm^2?

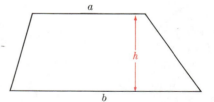

Self-Test 2

VOCABULARY   equivalent inequalities (p. 65)   disjunction (p. 68)
                   conjunction (p. 68)

Solve and graph each inequality.

1. $5d - 10 < 15$

2. $2(m - 3) \geq 3(m + 1)$ Obj. 2-5, p. 64

3. $2 < x + 3 \leq 5$

4. $-4 \leq \dfrac{n}{2} - 6 \leq 1$ Obj. 2-6, p. 68

Solve and graph each open sentence.

5. $|x - 2| \leq 0$ **6.** $|r + 3| \leq 6$ Obj. 2-7, p. 70

7. Bill and June live no more than 50 km apart. They both leave   Obj. 2-8, p. 74
their houses at 11:00 A.M., heading toward each other. Bill trav-
els at 15 km/h and June at 10 km/h. What is the latest time
that they will meet?

Check your answers with those at the back of the book.

Chapter Summary

1. A *monomial* is a numeral, a variable, or an indicated product of a
numeral and one or more variables. The *degree* of a monomial is the
total number of times its variables occur as factors.

2. A *polynomial* is a sum of monomials. Polynomials may be added (or
subtracted) by adding (or subtracting) similar terms.

3. Any value of the variable that makes an open sentence true is a
solution, or *root*, of the open sentence. Finding all the solutions of an
open sentence is called *solving the open sentence*.

4. Equations can be solved using the transformations on page 49. Inequalities can be solved using the transformations on page 65.

5. Word problems can be solved by translating the information given
into an equation or inequality. See the five-step problem-solving
method presented on page 59.

Chapter Review

1. Express $(4x - 3) + (3x + 4) - (2x - 8)$ in simplest form. 2-1
   a. $9x + 15$ **b.** $5x + 9$ **c.** $5x - 7$ **d.** $9x - 1$

2. Express $(5a - 2b) - (3a + 4b) + (a + 9b)$ in simplest form.
   a. $9a + 15b$ **b.** $3a + 11b$ **c.** $9a - 15b$ **d.** $3a + 3b$

3. Solve $3c - 5c = -4c + 36$. 2-2
   a. 6 **b.** -6 **c.** 18 **d.** 9

4. Solve $2(a - 3) + a = 27 - 2a + 7$.
   a. 37 **b.** 8 **c.** 40 **d.** 28

5. Sol is twice as old as Leroy, who is r years old. Lucille is 4 years 2-3
older than Sol. How old is Lucille?
   a. $2r - 4$ **b.** $r + 6$ **c.** $2r + 4$ **d.** $r - 6$

6. The measure of each of the base angles of an isosceles triangle is 24° less than the measure of the vertex angle. Find the measure of the vertex angle.

2-4

    a. 76°   **b.** 52°   **c.** 68°   **d.** 44°

7. Solve $6h - 4 > 2h - 17$.

2-5

    a. $h < 3\frac{1}{4}$ **b.** $h > 3\frac{1}{4}$ **c.** $h < -3\frac{1}{4}$ **d.** $h > -3\frac{1}{4}$

8. Solve $3(y + 2) \le 5y + 14$.

    a. $y \le 4$ **b.** $y \ge -4$ **c.** $y \le -4$ **d.** $y \ge 4$

9. Solve $-4 < \frac{m}{2} + 2 \le 6$.

    a. $-12 < m \le 16$ **b.** $-12 < m \le 8$ **c.** $-4 < m < 8$ **d.** $-20 < m \le 28$

10. Solve $|2x + 6| = 10$.

2-7

    a. $\{2, -8\}$ **b.** $\{-2, -8\}$ **c.** $\{2, 8\}$ **d.** $\{-2, 8\}$

11. Solve $\left|\frac{z}{3} - 9\right| < 6$.

    a. $z < 45$ **b.** $1 < z < 5$ **c.** $9 < z < 45$ **d.** $-9 < z < -45$

12. Suellen's father is 9 times as old as she is now. In 12 years he will be at most 3 times as old as Suellen. At most, how old is Suellen?

2-8

    a. 3   **b.** 5   **c.** 4   **d.** 6

Chapter Test

Express as a polynomial in simplest form.

    1. $6a + 5 - (2a - 3) + a - 2$ **2.** $2x - 4 + 3x + 1 - (7x + 8)$

2-1

Solve.

    3. $5y + 72 + 4y = 0$ **4.** $3a + 16 = 5a + 32$

2-2

    5. One number is six less than four times a second number. If the second number is n, what is the sum of the two numbers?

2-3

    6. At 9 P.M. two planes leave an airport. One heads south at 520 km/h and the other heads north at 600 km/h. At what time will they be 2800 km apart?

2-4

Solve and graph each open sentence.

    7. $3 + 5c \ge c - 9$ **8.** $3(a + 3) + 4 \le a - 1$

2-5

    9. $0 \le 8 + 4x < 24$ **10.** $|10 + 5m| \ge 25$

2-6, 2-7

    11. Find the smallest possible values for a set of three consecutive odd integers whose sum is greater than 81.

2-8

Symbolic Logic: Boolean Algebra

Most people think of algebra as the study of operations with numbers and variables. Another kind of algebra that is used in the design of electronic digital computers involves operations with logical statements. In fact, complex electrical circuits can be analyzed using logical statements similar to those you will work with in Exercises 1–18. This "algebra of logic" is called **Boolean algebra** in honor of its originator, George Boole (British, 1815–1864).

In Boolean algebra you use letters such as *p*, *q*, *r*, *s*, and so on, to stand for statements. For example, you might let *p* represent the statement "3 is an odd integer," and *q*, the statement "5 is less than 3." In this case, the statement *p* has the truth value T (the statement is true), whereas *q* has the truth value F (the statement is false).

The table below shows the operations that are used in Boolean algebra to produce compound statements from any given statements *p* and *q*.

Operation	How Read	Symbols
Conjunction	*p* and *q*	$p \wedge q$
Disjunction	*p* or *q*	$p \vee q$
Conditional	If *p*, then *q*	$p \rightarrow q$
Equivalence	*p* if and only if *q*	$p \leftrightarrow q$
Negation	not *p*	$\sim p$

The rules for assigning truth values to compound statements are shown in the five *truth tables* appearing below and on page 80.

Conjunction

p	*q*	$p \wedge q$
T	T	T
T	F	F
F	T	F
F	F	F

Disjunction

p	*q*	$p \vee q$
T	T	T
T	F	T
F	T	T
F	F	F

Notice that the conjunction $p \wedge q$ is true when *both* *p* and *q* are true; otherwise, $p \wedge q$ is false. On the other hand, the disjunction $p \vee q$ has the value T provided **at least one** of the statements *p*, *q* is true.

When is the conditional $p \to q$ false? Only when p is true and q is false.

The equivalence $p \leftrightarrow q$ is a brief way of stating the conjunction

$$(p \to q) \wedge (q \to p).$$

The equivalence is true when p and q are both true or both false.

Conditional

p	q	$p \to q$
T	T	T
T	F	F
F	T	T
F	F	T

Equivalence

p	q	$p \leftrightarrow q$
T	T	T
T	F	F
F	T	F
F	F	T

Negation

p	$\sim p$
T	F
F	T

The negation $\sim p$ is the denial of p. Therefore, it is reasonable to agree that $\sim p$ is false when p is true, and true when p is false.

EXAMPLE 1 Let r stand for "$1 > 2$," and s, for "$2 < 4$." Read each of the following statements. Then by referring to the truth tables above and on page 79, give the truth value of the statement and a reason for your answer.

  a. $r \wedge s$ **b.** $r \vee s$ **c.** $r \to s$ **d.** $r \leftrightarrow s$ **e.** $\sim r$

SOLUTION **a.** $r \wedge s$: $1 > 2$ and $2 < 4$. F; the truth value of r is F.
  b. $r \vee s$: $1 > 2$ or $2 < 4$. T; the truth value of s is T.
  c. $r \to s$: If $1 > 2$, then $2 < 4$. T; the truth value of r is F, and that of s is T.
  d. $r \leftrightarrow s$: $1 > 2$ if and only if $2 < 4$. F; r and s have different truth values.
  e. $\sim r$: not $(1 > 2)$, that is $1 \leq 2$. T; the truth value of r is F.

EXAMPLE 2 Show that for all truth values of r, p, and q, the truth value of

$$r \vee (p \wedge q) \leftrightarrow (r \vee p) \wedge (r \vee q)$$

is T.

SOLUTION Plan: Construct a truth table containing the *eight* combinations of truth values for r, p, and q.

Can you tell how the table on page 81 was constructed? Entries in column 4 were obtained by "*and*-ing" the entries in columns 2 and 3. The entries in column 5 result from "*or*-ing" the entries in columns 1 and 4. The rest of the table is obtained similarly.

r	p	q	$p \wedge q$	$r \vee (p \wedge q)$	$r \vee p$	$r \vee q$	$(r \vee p) \wedge (r \vee q)$
T	T	T	T	T	T	T	T
T	T	F	F	T	T	T	T
T	F	T	F	T	T	T	T
T	F	F	F	T	T	T	T
F	T	T	T	T	T	T	T
F	T	F	F	F	T	F	F
F	F	T	F	F	F	T	F
F	F	F	F	F	F	F	F

When you compare the fifth and last columns, you can see that $r \vee (p \wedge q)$ and $(r \vee p) \wedge (r \vee q)$ have the same array of truth values. Therefore,

$$r \vee (p \wedge q) \leftrightarrow (r \vee p) \wedge (r \vee q)$$

is a true statement no matter what truth values are assigned to r, p, and q.

A compound statement that is true for all truth values of its component statements is called a **tautology**. For example,

$$p \leftrightarrow p$$

is a tautology.

Exercises

In Exercises 1–9 assume that r and p are true statements and that q is a false statement. Determine the truth value of each statement.

1. $q \rightarrow r$
2. $\sim r \wedge p$
3. $p \vee \sim q$
4. $r \wedge (p \vee q)$
5. $p \vee (q \wedge r)$
6. $(p \vee r) \rightarrow q$
7. $\sim p \rightarrow (q \vee \sim r)$
8. $r \rightarrow (q \rightarrow r)$
9. $(p \rightarrow q) \leftrightarrow (\sim p \vee q)$

Given that $p \rightarrow q$ is false, show that each statement in Exercises 10–12 is true.

10. $q \rightarrow p$
11. $p \wedge \sim q$
12. $(p \vee q) \wedge p$

Construct a truth table for each of the following statements. Is the statement a tautology?

13. $(p \vee q) \rightarrow p$
14. $(q \wedge \sim q) \rightarrow p$
15. $(p \vee q) \leftrightarrow (q \vee p)$
16. $(p \rightarrow q) \leftrightarrow (\sim p \vee q)$
17. $r \wedge (p \vee q) \leftrightarrow (r \wedge p) \vee (r \wedge q)$
18. $[(p \rightarrow q) \wedge (q \rightarrow r)] \rightarrow (p \rightarrow r)$

The five-lined skink is a reptile that gets its name from the five lines of color which can be traced from its head to its tail. See Example 2 on page 112 for an application of the function concept to the study of reptiles.

3

GRAPHS AND FUNCTIONS

POINTS AND LINES IN THE PLANE

3-1 *The Coordinate Plane*

(x, y)

OBJECTIVE To graph ordered pairs of numbers in a coordinate plane and to find the coordinates of any point in the plane.

To set up a **coordinate plane,** take these steps:

1. In the plane choose two reference lines or **axes,** intersecting at right angles at a point O, the **origin.** As shown in Figure 3-1, one axis is usually horizontal, and the other, vertical.

2. Using convenient units of length (not necessarily the same on both axes), make each axis a number line whose zero point is O. In Figure 3-1, the positive direction on each axis is shown by an arrowhead.

Figure 3-1 also shows the numbering of the four **quadrants** into which the axes separate the plane.

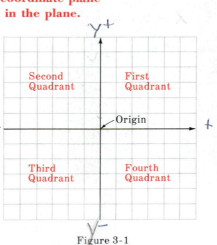

Second Quadrant

First Quadrant

Origin

Third Quadrant

Fourth Quadrant

Figure 3-1

83

Each point in the coordinate plane is assigned a unique pair of real numbers, or **coordinates.** To find the coordinates of a point P, draw (or imagine) a vertical line, v, and a horizontal line, h, through P (Figure 3-2). The *first coordinate*, or **abscissa**, of P is the number paired with the point of intersection of v and the horizontal axis. The *second coordinate*, or **ordinate**, of P is the number paired with the point of intersection of h and the vertical axis. The abscissa and ordinate of the point P are -5 and 3, respectively. You write these coordinates as the **ordered pair** $(-5, 3)$. You refer to P as the point $(-5, 3)$ and write $P(-5, 3)$. The coordinates of several other points are also shown in Figure 3-2.

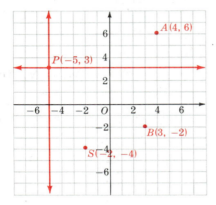

Figure 3-2

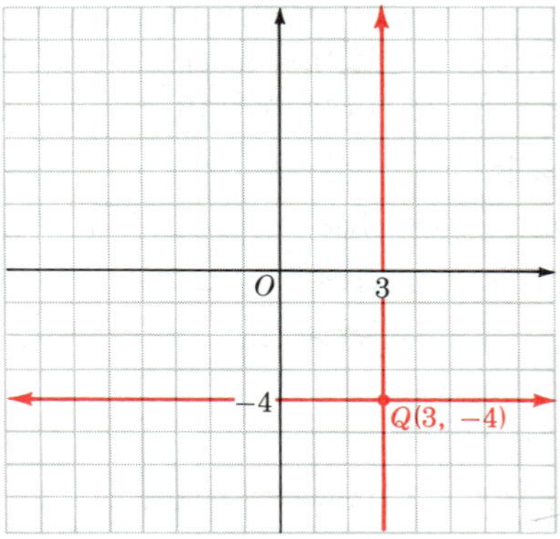

Figure 3-3

On the other hand, given an ordered pair of real numbers such as $(3, -4)$, you can assign a point, or **graph,** to it by reversing the process described above. Thus (Figure 3-3), you draw a vertical line through the point paired with 3 on the horizontal axis and a horizontal line through the point paired with -4 on the vertical axis. Q, the point of intersection of these lines, is the graph of $(3, -4)$. Locating a point this way is called **graphing the ordered pair of numbers** or **plotting the point.**

In working with a coordinate plane, you take the following facts for granted.

1. There is exactly one ordered pair of real numbers paired with each point in the coordinate plane.
2. There is exactly one point in the coordinate plane paired with each ordered pair of real numbers.

This one-to-one pairing of all points of a plane with all ordered pairs of real numbers is called a **plane rectangular coordinate system.** It is also called a **Cartesian coordinate plane** in honor of its inventor, René Descartes, the eminent French mathematician and philosopher (1596–1650).

Note that two ordered pairs are equal when their first coordinates are equal and their second coordinates are equal. Thus,

$$(-4, 9) = (2 - 6, 3^2),$$

but

$$(-4, 9) \neq (9, -4).$$

Oral Exercises

1–12. State the coordinates of each point denoted by a letter (*A*–*L*).

In each of Exercises 13–22, name the quadrants or axes containing the indicated points.

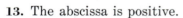

13. The abscissa is positive.

14. The abscissa is negative.

15. The ordinate is negative.

16. The ordinate is positive.

17. The abscissa is zero.

18. The ordinate is zero.

19. The abscissa and ordinate are both negative.

20. The abscissa is positive, but the ordinate is negative.

21. The abscissa equals the ordinate.

22. The abscissa equals the negative of the ordinate.

State whether or not the ordered pairs are equal.

23. $(7, 3)$, $(3, 7)$ **24.** $(5, 5)$, $(5, -5)$

25. $(2 \times 4, 0)$, $(8, 1 - 1)$ **26.** $(7 \times 6, 3^4)$, $(6 \times 7, 9^2)$ (x, y)

Written Exercises 1–31 odd

Graph each ordered pair of numbers.

A **1.** $(5, 3)$ **2.** $(7, -4)$ **3.** $(-6, -5)$ **4.** $(-6, 5)$

     5. $(-4, 0)$ **6.** $(0, 1)$ **7.** $(-1, 4)$ **8.** $(-1, -1)$

     9. $(-2.5, 3)$ **10.** $(1.5, 4)$ **11.** $(0, -7)$ **12.** $(-8, 0)$

Plot each pair of points *P* and *T*, and find the length of the segment joining them.

13. $P(3, 0)$, $T(8, 0)$ -5 **14.** $P(1, 0)$, $T(-6, 0)$ **15.** $P(-1, 1)$, $T(8, 1)$

16. $P(2, 4)$, $T(2, -6)$ **17.** $P(-3, -2)$, $T(-3, 5)$ **18.** $P(0, -1)$, $T(0, 5)$

Find all real values of x and y for which the ordered pairs are equal.

19. $(x, 5) = (-3, y + 1)$

20. $(x - 2, 7), (4, y)$

B **21.** $(x, y) = (8 - x, 2y)$

22. $(x, y) = (-x, 18 - 2y)$

23. $(7 - 2x, -6 + y) = (-x, 6 + 5y)$

24. $(x - 3, 2y + 1) = (3x + 5, 16 + 7y)$

25. $(|x|, |y|) = (2, 3|y| - 10)$

26. $(|x|, |y|) = (8 - |x|, 1)$

Each of Exercises 27–32 lists three vertices of a rectangle. Graph these vertices, sketch the rectangle, and determine the coordinates of the fourth vertex.

27. $(-2, -6), (5, 0), (-2, 0)$

28. $(-3, 5), (-6, 5), (-6, -6)$

29. $(-1.5, -2), (-6, -8), (-6, -2)$

30. $(2, -1.5), (-2, -2), (2, -2)$

31. $(-5, -5), (-3, 3), (0, 0)$

32. $(0, 0), (3, 6), (2, -1)$

For any three given points not all on one line, there are three possible ways of choosing a fourth point so that the four points are the vertices of a parallelogram. In each of Exercises 33 and 34, three vertices of a parallelogram are given. What are the coordinates of the three possible fourth vertices of the parallelogram?

C **33.** $(1, -2), (-3, -3), (1, 2)$

34. $(0, -6), (-4, -4), (5, 0)$

35. What is the length of the segment joining $P(a, b)$ and $T(a, c)$?

36. What is the length of the segment joining $P(a, b)$ and $T(d, b)$?

Biography Gertrude Rand Ferree

Dr. Gertrude Rand Ferree was trained as a psychologist at Bryn Mawr College, receiving her Ph.D. there in 1911. Most of her professional career was devoted to the study of human vision. She played a major role in the development of the plates used to identify color blindness. These plates are covered with shaded, colored dots outlining numerals in different colors from the background; you may have been tested with them yourself.

In addition to her work with color vision, she studied light sensitivity, peripheral light and color sensitivity, and spatial orientation. Dr. Ferree is co-holder of many patents for optical devices and instruments.

3-2 *Open Sentences in Two Variables*

OBJECTIVE To solve certain open sentences in two variables.

Equations and inequalities such as

$$3x + 2y = 14, \quad y = x^2 - 7, \quad \text{and} \quad x - 5y \leq 8$$

are called **open sentences** in two variables. A **solution** of an open sentence in the two variables, x and y, is an ordered pair of numbers—the first, a value of x, and the second, a value of y—that together make the sentence a true statement. For example, $(4, 1)$ is a solution of

$$3x + 2y = 14$$

because

$$3 \times 4 + 2 \times 1 = 12 + 2 = 14;$$

but $(5, 1)$ is not a solution of the given equation, because

$$3 \times 5 + 2 \times 1 = 15 + 2 \neq 14.$$

A solution is said to **satisfy** an open sentence. The set of all solutions is called the **solution set** of the open sentence. Finding the solution set is called **solving** the open sentence.

EXAMPLE 1 Solve $3x + 2y = 14$ if the values of x and y are whole numbers; that is, members of the set $\{0, 1, 2, 3, \ldots\}$. Plot all solutions.

SOLUTION

1. Solve the equation for y.
$$3x + 2y = 14$$
$$2y = 14 - 3x$$
$$y = 7 - \tfrac{3}{2}x$$

2. Replace x with its values in turn and find the corresponding values of y.

3. If a value of y found in Step 2 is a whole number, then the pair of corresponding values is a solution of the sentence.

x	$7 - \tfrac{3}{2}x$	y	Solution
0	$7 - \tfrac{3}{2}(0)$	7	$(0, 7)$
1	$7 - \tfrac{3}{2}(1)$	$\tfrac{11}{2}$	Not a solution
2	$7 - \tfrac{3}{2}(2)$	4	$(2, 4)$
3	$7 - \tfrac{3}{2}(3)$	$\tfrac{5}{2}$	Not a solution
4	$7 - \tfrac{3}{2}(4)$	1	$(4, 1)$
5	$7 - \tfrac{3}{2}(5)$	$-\tfrac{1}{2}$	Not a solution
If $x \geq 5$, then $y \leq 0$.			

$\therefore$ the solution set is $\{(0, 7), (2, 4), (4, 1)\}$. The solutions are plotted in Figure 3-4 on the next page. ***Answer***

In Figure 3-4 note that the horizontal axis has been labeled as the **x-axis** and the vertical axis as the **y-axis.** Thus, you may call the abscissa of a point the **x-coordinate** and the ordinate the **y-coordinate.**

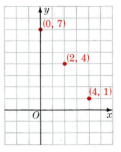

Figure 3-4

Open sentences in two variables are used in solving certain word problems. Frequently, it is convenient to use letters other than x and y. In such cases, the letter first in alphabetic order corresponds to the first number in the ordered pair. Thus, $(2, -3)$ is a solution to the equation $5m + n = 7$.

EXAMPLE 2 In a two-digit integer, the tens' digit is greater than four more than three times the units' digit. Find all such positive integers.

SOLUTION Recall that every positive integer can be expressed in expanded form. For example:

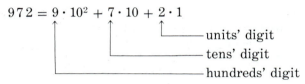

$$972 = 9 \cdot 10^2 + 7 \cdot 10 + 2 \cdot 1$$

units' digit
tens' digit
hundreds' digit

Step 1 The problem asks for every positive integer with (a) two digits in its decimal numeral and (b) the tens' digit greater than 4 more than three times the units' digit.

Step 2 Let u = units' digit and t = tens' digit.
∴ the integer $= 10t + u$.
The possible values of u are 0, 1, 2, 3, 4, 5, 6, 7, 8, 9.
The possible values of t are 1, 2, 3, 4, 5, 6, 7, 8, 9.

Step 3 Tens' digit is greater than 4 more than three times units' digit
t $>$ 4 $+$ $3u$

Step 4 Replace u with its successive values and find the corresponding values of t.

u	$4 + 3u$	$t > 4 + 3u$	Solutions (u, t)
0	$4 + 3 \cdot 0 = 4$	$t > 4$	$(0, 5), (0, 6), (0, 7), (0, 8), (0, 9)$
1	$4 + 3 \cdot 1 = 7$	$t > 7$	$(1, 8), (1, 9)$
2	$4 + 3 \cdot 2 = 10$	$t > 10$	None
Greater values of u yield values of t that exceed 10.			

Step 5 The check is left to you.
∴ the integers represented by $10t + u$ are 50, 60, 70, 80, 90, 81, and 91. ***Answer***

34.

x	y
1	2
2	1
3	0
4	-1

35.

x	y
1	3
2	5
4	9
8	13

36.

x	y
6	4
3	-1
0	-6
-6	-16

B 37. Give a reason for each step in the following proof of part 2 of the theorem on page 98. Let $Ax + By = C$ be an equation of L and use the assumptions given in the theorem.

1. $m = -\dfrac{A}{B}$

2. $\dfrac{y_2 - y_1}{x_2 - x_1} = -\dfrac{A}{B}$

3. $B(y_2 - y_1) = -A(x_2 - x_1)$
4. $By_2 - By_1 = -Ax_2 + Ax_1$
5. $Ax_2 + By_2 = Ax_1 + By_1$

6. But $Ax_1 + By_1 = C.$

7. Hence, $Ax_2 + By_2 = C.$
8. $\therefore (x_2, y_2)$ is on L.

38. a. Find the slope of the line containing the points $(5, 3)$ and $(3, 2)$.
b. If the point $(-3, a + 1)$ is on the line, find the value of a.
39. a. Find the slope of the line containing the points $(-2, 4)$ and $(0, 2)$.
b. If the point $(3, a - 1)$ is on the line, find the value of a.

Determine c so that the slope of the graph of each equation has the given value.

40. $4cx - 3y = 15; m = 8$ **41.** $2x + 5cy = 7; m = \frac{1}{15}$
42. $(c + 8)x - 3y + 7 = 0; m = c$ **43.** $cx + 2y + 1 = 0; m = c + 3$

Determine k so that the slope of the line through each pair of points has the given value.

44. $(1, 7k), (-3, 5k); m = -\frac{1}{2}$ **45.** $(1, k), (4, -k); m = \frac{8}{3}$

C 46. $(k, -1), (-3k, -5); m = 3$ **47.** $(2k, -1), (k + 1, -5); m = \frac{1}{2}$
48. $(3, |k|), (4, k); m = -2$ **49.** $(3, k), (4, |k|); m = 1$

3-5 *Finding an Equation of a Line*

OBJECTIVE   To find an equation of a line, given
         (1) its slope and the coordinates of a point on the line; or
         (2) the coordinates of two points on the line; or
         (3) its slope and *y*-intercept.

Study the following example.

EXAMPLE 1   Find an equation of the line having slope $-\frac{4}{3}$ and passing through the point $(-5, 2)$.

SOLUTION   Let (x, y) be any point on the line other than $(-5, 2)$. Using the slope formula, you find:

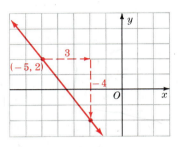

Figure 3-16

$$\frac{y - 2}{x - (-5)} = -\frac{4}{3}$$

So, $\dfrac{y - 2}{x + 5} = \dfrac{-4}{3}$

$$3(y - 2) = -4(x + 5)$$
$$3y - 6 = -4x - 20$$
$$4x + 3y = -14$$

3y = −4x −14

Check: Does $(-5, 2)$ satisfy the equation? $4(-5) + 3(2) \overset{?}{=} -14$
$$-20 + 6 = -14 \quad \checkmark$$

Is the slope $-\frac{4}{3}$? $4x + 3y = -14; \dfrac{-A}{B} = -\dfrac{4}{3} \quad \checkmark$

$\therefore$ an equation of the line is $4x + 3y = -14$. ***Answer***

The equation "$4x + 3y = -14$" is not the *only* equation of the line in Example 1. For example, "$-4x - 3y = 14$," "$8x + 6y = -28$," and "$y = -\frac{4}{3}x - \frac{14}{3}$" are also equations of the line.

You can use the method of Example 1 to find an equation of a line having any given slope m and passing through any given point (x_1, y_1). For any other point (x, y) lies on the line if and only if

$$\frac{y - y_1}{x - x_1} = m.$$

Since $x \neq x_1$, the multiplication property of equality implies

$$y - y_1 = m(x - x_1).$$

The equation $y - y_1 = m(x - x_1)$ is called the **point-slope form** of the equation of a line. Although the derivation of this equation applied only to points other than (x_1, y_1), it should be obvious that this point satisfies the equation.

102   *CHAPTER 3*

EXAMPLE 2 Find an equation of the form "$Ax + By = C$" of the line passing through the points $(7, 4)$ and $(-2, -3)$.

SOLUTION $m = \dfrac{-3-4}{-2-7} = \dfrac{-7}{-9} = \dfrac{7}{9}$

Choose one of the points, say $(7, 4)$, to be (x_1, y_1) and use the point-slope form.

$$y - y_1 = m(x - x_1)$$
$$y - 4 = \tfrac{7}{9}(x - 7)$$
$$9(y - 4) = 7(x - 7)$$
$$9y - 36 = 7x - 49$$
$$7x - 9y = 13 \quad \textbf{\textit{Answer}}$$

Checking that $(-2, -3)$ satisfies this equation is left to you.

In the next example, you are given the slope of a line and the point where the line crosses the y-axis.

EXAMPLE 3 Find an equation of the line having slope 2 and passing through $(0, -6)$.

SOLUTION $y - y_1 = m(x - x_1)$
$$y - (-6) = 2(x - 0)$$
$$y + 6 = 2x$$
$$y = 2x - 6 \quad \textbf{\textit{Answer}}$$

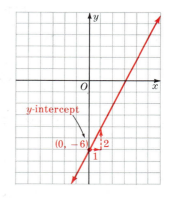

Figure 3-17

Notice in Figure 3-17 that -6 is called the *y-intercept* of the line. In general, the y-coordinate of the point where a line crosses the y-axis is called the **y-intercept** of the line. To find an equation of a line having slope m and y-intercept b, you can use the point-slope form with $(0, b)$ as the point (x_1, y_1).

$$y - y_1 = m(x - x_1)$$
$$y - b = m(x - 0)$$
$$y - b = mx$$
$$y = mx + b$$

The equation $y = mx + b$ is called the **slope-intercept form** of the equation of a line.

EXAMPLE 4 Find an equation of the line with slope -0.7 and y-intercept 3.

SOLUTION $y = mx + b$
$$\therefore y = -0.7x + 3 \quad \textbf{\textit{Answer}}$$

In a plane, different lines having the same slope, or different lines having no slope, are called **parallel lines.**

EXAMPLE 5 Find the y-intercept of the line L that crosses the x-axis at $(2, 0)$ and is parallel to the graph of $3x - 4y = -8$, and write an equation for L in standard form.

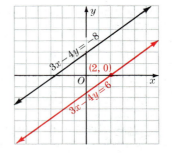

Figure 3-18

SOLUTION The slope of the line $3x - 4y = 8$ is $\dfrac{3}{4}$. (Why?) Thus, the slope-intercept form of the equation for L is

$$y = \frac{3}{4}x + b.$$

Because the graph of $(2, 0)$ is on the line, it must satisfy this equation. This fact enables you to substitute 2 for x and 0 for y, and solve for b.

$$0 = \frac{3}{4}(2) + b$$

$$0 = \frac{3}{2} + b$$

$$b = -\frac{3}{2}$$

The slope-intercept equation of L is

$$y = \frac{3}{4}x - \frac{3}{2}.$$

$\therefore$ an equation of L in standard form is $3x - 4y = 6$. **Answer**

The x-coordinate of the point where a line crosses the x-axis is called the **x-intercept** of the line. For example, the x-intercept of the line $3x - 4y = 6$ is 2 (see Figure 3-18).

Oral Exercises

State the point-slope form of the equation of the line containing the given point and having the given slope m.

1. $(0, 2); m = 1$ **2.** $(3, 0); m = 2$ **3.** $(-1, 4); m = -1$

4. $(5, -1); m = -\frac{1}{2}$ **5.** $(2, 7); m = 0$ **6.** $(-2, -8); m = 0$

State the slope-intercept form of the equation of the line having the given slope m and y-intercept b.

7. $m = 3; b = 2$ **8.** $m = -5; b = 6$ **9.** $m = -4; b = -1$

10. $m = -\frac{1}{3}; b = 0$ **11.** $m = 0; b = -2$ **12.** $m = 0; b = 0$

State the slope and y-intercept of the graph of each equation.

13. $-2x + y = 5$ **14.** $3y - x = 12$ **15.** $0 = 4 - x - y$ **16.** $8x - 2y = 1$

State whether or not the lines whose equations are given are parallel.

17. $y = 7x + 4$
    $y = 7x - 9$

18. $x = -2$
    $x = 1$

19. $x - y = 2$
    $y - x = -2$

Written Exercises

Find an equation in standard form for the line containing the given point and having the given slope.

A 1. $(0, 8); m = 3$ 2. $(3, 7); m = 2$ 3. $(-2, -3); m = -1$

4. $(0, -2); m = -5$ 5. $(0, 0); m = \frac{1}{2}$ 6. $(0, 0); m = -\frac{1}{3}$

7. $(3, -3); m = 0$ 8. $(-4, -3); m = 0$ 9. $(4, 0); m = -\frac{3}{5}$

10. $(-2, 0); m = \frac{8}{9}$ 11. $(9, -2);$ no slope 12. $(3, -1);$ no slope

Find an equation in standard form for the line having the given slope m and y-intercept b.

13. $m = -1, b = 3$ 14. $m = 3, b = -1$ 15. $m = \frac{3}{5}, b = -2$

16. $m = -\frac{4}{7}, b = 8$ 17. $m = -\frac{1}{5}, b = \frac{7}{10}$ 18. $m = \frac{2}{5}, b = -\frac{3}{10}$

19. $m = 0, b = 9$ 20. $m = 0, b = -\frac{5}{2}$ 21. $m = -3, b = 0$

22. $m = \frac{2}{7}, b = -10$ 23. $m = 0.2, b = 1.6$ 24. $m = -1.4, b = -0.7$

Find an equation in standard form for the line passing through the given points.

25. $(3, 2), (6, 7)$ 26. $(2, 5), (4, 6)$ 27. $(-4, 1), (0, 2)$ 28. $(-1, 0), (2, 3)$
29. $(0, 0), (3, -1)$ 30. $(14, -7), (0, 0)$ 31. $(-1, -1), (3, 0)$ 32. $(1, -2), (0, -3)$
33. $(-6, 0), (-6, -5)$ 34. $(0, 0), (0, -9)$ 35. $(-2, 7), (7, 7)$ 36. $(3, 8), (-1, 8)$

Find an equation in standard form for the line described.

B 37. With y-intercept 6 and parallel to the graph of $y = x - 15$
38. With y-intercept -4 and parallel to the graph of $x + y = 11$
39. Passing through $(0, 1)$ and parallel to the graph of $10x - 2y = 3$
40. Passing through $(2, -5)$ and parallel to the graph of $x + 3 = 0$
41. With x-intercept -2 and parallel to the graph of $3x + 2y = 12$
42. With x-intercept 3 and parallel to the graph of $2x - 7y - 4 = 0$
43. With x-intercept 4 and y-intercept 3

Find an equation in standard form for the line described.

44. With x-intercept -6 and y-intercept 1

45. With x-intercept 2 and having no slope

46. With x-intercept -5 and having no slope

47. Passing through $(3, -2)$ and parallel to the line joining $(0, 6)$ and $(2, -1)$

48. Passing through $(4, -5)$ and parallel to the line joining $(-2, 0)$ and $(-1, 1)$

C 49. Show that the quadrilateral whose consecutive vertices have coordinates $A(4, 1)$, $B(6, 2)$, $C(9, 3)$, and $D(7, 2)$ is a parallelogram.

50. Repeat Exercise 49 for vertices $A(4, 2)$, $B(3, 0)$, $C(0, 3)$, and $D(1, 5)$.

51. Show that an equation of the line containing points (x_1, y_1) and (x_2, y_2) such that $x_1 \neq x_2$ is $y - y_1 = \dfrac{y_2 - y_1}{x_2 - x_1}(x - x_1)$. (Two-point form)

52. Show that an equation of the line having x-intercept a and y-intercept b such that $a \neq b$ is $\dfrac{x}{a} + \dfrac{y}{b} = 1$. (Intercept form)

Self-Test 2

VOCABULARY	slope (p. 96)	slope-intercept form of the
	point-slope form of the equa-	equation of a line (p. 103)
	tion of a line (p. 102)	x-intercept (p. 104)
	y-intercept (p. 103)	parallel lines (p. 104)

1. Find the slope of the line through the points: **Obj. 3-4, p. 96**
  a. $(3, 8), (1, 4)$ **b.** $(0, -6), (4, -5)$

2. Find the slope of the line with equation $5x - 3y = 18$.

3. Draw the graph of the line through the point $(5, -1)$ with slope $= \frac{3}{4}$.

4. Determine the y-intercept of the line $5x - 3y = 18$.   **Obj. 3-5, p. 102**

5. Find an equation in standard form for the line with slope $\frac{2}{3}$ and y-intercept 5.

6. Find an equation in standard form for the line passing through the points $(5, 2)$ and $(1, -6)$.

7. Find an equation in standard form for a line with no slope passing through the point $(3, -4)$.

8. Find an equation in standard form for the line passing through $(-2, 4)$ and parallel to the graph of $x + y = 6$.

Check your answers with those at the back of the book.

FUNCTIONS AND VARIATION

3-6 *Functions*

OBJECTIVE To find the values of a function and to draw its graph.

Figure 3-19 pictures a **mapping** of the members of a set D onto the members of the set R. Each member of D is mapped (by an arrow) onto exactly one member of R. This mapping or pairing is called a *function* with *domain D* and *range R*. In general, a **function** consists of two sets, the domain and the range, together with a pairing that assigns to each member of the **domain** exactly one member of the **range.** Each member of the range must be paired with at least one member of the domain.

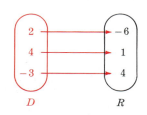

Figure 3-19

The ordered pairs of numbers that form the function pictured in Figure 3-19 are

$$(2, -6), (4, 1), (-3, 4),$$

whose graphs are shown in Figure 3-20. These three points form the graph of the function. Note that numbers in the domain are associated with the horizontal axis, while numbers in the range are associated with the vertical axis.

Letters such as f, g, F, and t often name functions. The arrow notation is used to show how numbers in the domain and the range of a function are paired. For example,

$$f: x \to x^2 - 6x + 10$$

is read, "The function f that pairs x in the domain with $x^2 - 6x + 10$ in the range." Such an expression is called the **rule** for the function. To define the function completely, you must also tell what its domain is, of course. The numbers assigned by the rule form its range.

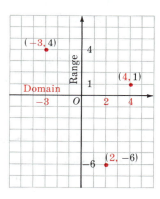

Figure 3-20

EXAMPLE 1 Find the members of the range of $f: x \to x^2 - 6x + 10$, if the domain $D = \{1, 2, 3, 4\}$. Draw the graph of f.

SOLUTION In $x^2 - 6x + 10$, replace x by each member of D to find the members of the range R as shown in the table at the right.

$\therefore R = \{1, 2, 5\};$ the graph is shown in Figure 3-21 on page 108. ***Answer***

x	$x^2 - 6x + 10$
1	$1^2 - 6(1) + 10 = 5$
2	$2^2 - 6(2) + 10 = 2$
3	$3^2 - 6(3) + 10 = 1$
4	$4^2 - 6(4) + 10 = 2$

Note that f assigns to both 2 and 4 the number 2 in the range. Each number in $D = \{1, 2, 3, 4\}$, however, has just one partner in $R = \{1, 2, 5\}$.

Members of the range are called the **values** of a function. Thus, in Example 1, the values of f are 1, 2, and 5. To show that f assigns to the number 3 the value 1, you write

$$f(3) = 1$$

which is read "f at three equals one" or "f of three equals one" or "the value of f at three equals one." CAUTION! $f(3)$ is not the product of f and 3; instead, it represents the number that f assigns to 3.

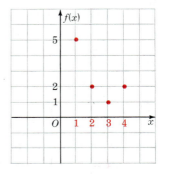

Figure 3-21

For any function f, $f(x)$ denotes **the value of f at x.** Very often a function f is defined simply by giving a **formula,** or equation, for $f(x)$ and stating the domain, as in Example 2.

EXAMPLE 2   Draw the graph of f if $f(x) = |x| - 2$ and $D = \{-2, -1, 0, 1, 2\}$.
SOLUTION   The table of values of f is shown at the left below, and the graph is at the right. Note that the vertical axis is labeled "$f(x)$."

x	$|x| - 2 = f(x)$
-2	$|-2| - 2 = 0$
-1	$|-1| - 2 = -1$
0	$|0| - 2 = -2$
1	$|1| - 2 = -1$
2	$|2| - 2 = 0$

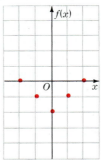

Figure 3-22

When defining a function, the formula is often stated without giving the domain. For such functions, *unless otherwise stated, take as the domain the set of those real numbers for which the formula produces real numbers.* Here are some examples.

Formula	Domain
$f(x) = x^3 + 8$	{the real numbers}
$g(x) = \dfrac{1}{x - 2}$	{all real numbers except 2}
$h(x) = \sqrt{x + 5}$	{all the real numbers greater than or equal to -5}

EXAMPLE 3   If $f(x) = 2x - 1$ and $g(x) = x^2 - 2x + 1$, find the requested values.

a. $g(f(2))$ **b.** $f(g(2))$

SOLUTION **a.** $f(2) = 2 \cdot 2 - 1 = 3$; $g(f(2)) = 3^2 - 2 \cdot 3 + 1 = 4$ *Answer*

b. $g(2) = 2^2 - 2 \cdot 2 + 1 = 1$; $f(g(2)) = 2 \cdot 1 - 1 = 1$ *Answer*

Oral Exercises

State the domain and range of the function pictured in each mapping.

1. 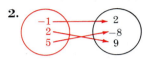 **2.** **3.** 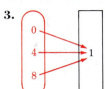 **4.**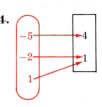

State $f(-2)$ for each of the following functions.

5. $f: x \to -x$ **6.** $f: x \to x + 2$ **7.** $f: x \to 2x - 3$

8. $f: x \to -x - 2$ **9.** $f: x \to \frac{1}{2}x + 1$ **10.** $f: x \to x^2 + 6$

For the given rule, find the missing coordinate of each ordered pair, and state the domain of each function.

11. $g(x) = x^3 + 1$; $(3, \underline{\ ?\ })$; $(-2, \underline{\ ?\ })$; $(\underline{\ ?\ }, 1)$

12. $r(x) = \frac{1}{4}x + 5$; $(0, \underline{\ ?\ })$; $(-8, \underline{\ ?\ })$; $(\underline{\ ?\ }, 2)$

13. $s(x) = 2|x| + 1$; $(-1, \underline{\ ?\ })$; $(\frac{1}{2}, \underline{\ ?\ })$; $(\underline{\ ?\ }, 7)$ with $x < 0$

14. $t(x) = \dfrac{1}{x - 1}$; $(0, \underline{\ ?\ })$; $\left(\dfrac{3}{2}, \underline{\ ?\ }\right)$; $(\underline{\ ?\ }, 1)$

Written Exercises

List the members of the range of each function with the given domain.

A **1.** $f: x \to 3x - 2$, $D = \{-2, 0, 1\}$ **2.** $t: x \to 4 - 5x$, $D = \{-1, 0, 2\}$

3. $n: x \to x^2 - 2$, $D = \{-2, -1, 1, 2\}$ **4.** $h: x \to x^3 - 1$, $D = \{-2, -1, 1, 2\}$

5. $k: a \to a^2 - 2a + 1$, $D = \{-1, 0, 1, 2, 3\}$

6. $g: b \to b^2 + 2b + 5$, $D = \{-3, -2, -1, 0, 1\}$

7. $m(x) = 1 - |x|$, $D = \{-2, -1, 0, 1, 2\}$

8. $s(x) = |-x|$, $D = \{-3, -1, 1, 3\}$

9–16. Draw the graph of each function in Exercises 1–8.

In Exercises 17–20, determine whether or not the given functions are equal (have the same set of ordered pairs).

B **17.** $F: x \to x^2 - 1$, $D = \{-1, 0, 1\}$; $G: x \to 1 - x^2$, $D = \{-1, 0, 1\}$

18. $H: x \to \dfrac{1 - 2x}{3}$, $D = \{-1, 2, 5\}$; $K: x \to \dfrac{1 - 2x}{3}$, $D = \{-4, -1, 2\}$

In Exercises 19-20, determine whether or not the given functions are equal.

19. $P: x \to (x-1)^4$, $D = \{-2, 1, 3\}$; $\quad f: a \to (a-1)^4$, $D = \{1, 3, -2\}$

20. $g: l \to (3-l)^2$, $D = \{-1, 1, 4\}$; $\quad S: c \to (c-2)^2$, $D = \{4, 1, -1\}$

If $f(x) = 4x - 1$ and $g(x) = 1 + x^2$, find each of the following.

21. $g(f(2))$ **22.** $f(g(-1))$ **23.** $g(f(-1))$

24. $g(f(0))$ **25.** $f(g(0))$ **26.** $g(f(-3))$

C **27.** $f(g(a))$ **28.** $g(f(a))$ **29.** $g(f(a-1))$

30. If f is a function such that $f(1+x) = f(x) + f(1)$ for all real numbers x, show that:

    a. $f(0) = 0$;   **b.** $f(-1) = -f(1)$.

31. If g is a function such that $g(3x) = g(3) + g(x)$ for all real numbers x, show that

    a. $g(3) = 0$;   **b.** $g(1) = 0$.

32. If L is a function such that for all positive real numbers a and b,
$$L(ab) = L(a) + L(b),$$
show that:

    a. $L(b^2) = 2L(b)$;   **b.** $L(1) = 0$.

33. Let E be a function such that $E(x)$ is never 0 and for all real numbers a and b,
$$E(a+b) = E(a) \cdot E(b).$$

    a. By setting $a = 0$, show that $E(0) = 1$.

    b. Then show that $E(-b) = \dfrac{1}{E(b)}$.

Application   Restaurant Franchises

The holder of a franchise pays the parent chain of restaurants a percentage of its sales in exchange for a variety of services. These include the use of the company name, menu planning, purchasing services, the use of recipes that the chain owns, and advertising.

The Salad Stop Restaurants charge a fee of 2% of sales up to $300,000; 4% of sales from $300,000 to $500,000; and 6% of sales over $500,000. Answer the following questions concerning the chain.

1. The Salad Stop in Deauville has sales of $350,000 one year. What is the franchise fee?

2. The Salad Stop in the Pepper Valley Mall has sales of $580,000. What is the franchise fee?

3-7 *Linear Functions*

To find an equation defining a linear function given either the slope and a point on the graph of the function or two points on the graph.

Let g be the function

$$g: x \rightarrow -3x + 2.$$

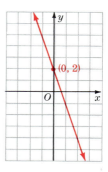

Then the equation $y = g(x)$ is the same as $y = -3x + 2$, and its graph is a straight line whose slope is -3 and whose y-intercept is 2 (Figure 3-23). Thus, g is called a *linear function*. In general, for any real numbers b and m, the function g defined by

$$g(x) = mx + b$$

is a **linear function** whose graph is the straight line with slope m and y-intercept b. The graph of the function g is the same as the graph of

Figure 3-23

$$y = g(x) \quad \text{or} \quad y = mx + b.$$

If $m = 0$, then $g(x) = b$ for every value of x, and g is a constant function. Its graph is a horizontal line (Figure 3-24).

Figure 3-24

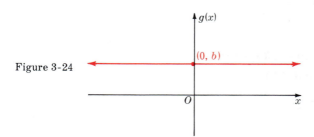

EXAMPLE 1 The slope of the graph of a linear function f is $\frac{3}{2}$ and $f(-4) = 0$.

    a. Find a formula for $f(x)$.

    b. Which, if either, of the points $(-2, 9)$ and $(2, 9)$ is on the graph of f?

SOLUTION **a.** You need to find numbers m and b such that

$$f(x) = mx + b.$$

Since m is the slope of the graph of f, $m = \frac{3}{2}$ and

$$f(x) = \frac{3}{2}x + b.$$

Since $f(-4) = 0$, proceed as follows:

$$\frac{3}{2}(-4) + b = 0$$
$$-6 + b = 0$$
$$b = 6$$

$\therefore f(x) = \frac{3}{2}x + 6$ ***Answer***

(*Solution continued on p. 112.*)

b. A point (x, y) is on the graph of f if and only if $f(x) = y$.

Since $f(-2) = \frac{3}{2}(-2) + 6 = 3 \neq 9$, the point $(-2, 9)$ is *not* on the graph of f.

Since $f(2) = \frac{3}{2}(2) + 6 = 9$, the point $(2, 9)$ *is* on the graph of f. **Answer**

EXAMPLE 2 A biologist reported that the total length of a certain kind of reptile is a linear function of the length of the tail for tail lengths between 30 mm and 200 mm. The following measurements were given:

Tail Length	Total Length
60 mm	429 mm
125 mm	884 mm

What is the total length of a reptile whose tail is 150 mm long?

SOLUTION Let $F(x)$ be the total length in millimeters of a reptile whose tail length is x mm. Then

$$F(60) = 429 \quad \text{and} \quad F(125) = 884.$$

To find the slope m of the graph of F, note that

$$m = \frac{F(125) - F(60)}{125 - 60} = \frac{884 - 429}{125 - 60} = \frac{455}{65} = 7$$

$\therefore F(x) = 7x + b$.

Since $F(60) = 429$, you find:

$$429 = 7(60) + b$$
$$429 = 420 + b, \text{ so } b = 9$$

$\therefore F(x) = 7x + 9$.

$$F(150) = 7(150) + 9 = 1059$$

$\therefore$ the total length of a reptile whose tail is 150 mm long is 1059 mm.

Answer

Oral Exercises

Is there a linear function containing the ordered pairs in each table? If there is, state the slope of its graph.

SAMPLE 1

x	y
-1	1
0	4
1	7
2	10

SOLUTION The ordered pairs belong to a linear function because for each pair of ordered pairs, (x_1, y_1) and (x_2, y_2), in the table,

$$\frac{y_2 - y_1}{x_2 - x_1} = 3$$

$\therefore$ the slope of the graph is 3. **Answer**

1. x	y
1	4
2	5
3	6
4	7

2. x	y
3	0
4	4
5	8
6	12

3. x	y
−2	6
−1	3
0	0
1	−3

4. x	y
8	4
9	1
10	−2
11	−4

Written Exercises

In each of Exercises 1–8, the slope of the graph of a linear function is given together with a function value. Find a formula for the function.

A **1.** $3; f(0) = -7$ **2.** $2; g(1) = 4$ **3.** $-5; k(3) = 6$ **4.** $-1; r(12) = -9$

5. $\frac{4}{3}; t(3) = -1$ **6.** $\frac{1}{4}; f(-16) = -2$ **7.** $0; h(-5) = \frac{1}{2}$ **8.** $-12; s\left(\frac{1}{2}\right) = 30$

In each of Exercises 9–16, two values of a linear function are given. Find the indicated third value. (*Hint:* Find a formula for $f(x)$, as in Example 2 on page 112, and then find the requested function value.)

9. $f(-2) = -3; f(3) = 7; f(10) = \underline{\ ?\ }$ **10.** $f(2) = 8; f(4) = 4; f(0) = \underline{\ ?\ }$

11. $f(-3) = -2; f(0) = -8; f(-4) = \underline{\ ?\ }$ **12.** $f(-1) = 3; f(7) = 7; f(1) = \underline{\ ?\ }$

13. $g(-5) = 7; g(-1) = 5; g(3) = \underline{\ ?\ }$ **14.** $g(-5) = 5; g(-3) = 0; g(2) = \underline{\ ?\ }$

15. $h(2) = 0; h(-4) = 4; h(5) = \underline{\ ?\ }$

16. $h(-2) = -6; h(-12) = 4; h(-5) = \underline{\ ?\ }$

B **17.** A linear function L maps 18 onto 1, and -12 onto -4. What is $L(0)$?

18. A linear function N maps -24 onto 0, and 8 onto 14. What is $N(-16)$?

19. If $T(x) = k(2x - 1)$ and $T(3) = 30$, find a value of x such that $T(x) = 24$.

20. If $s(x) = k(3x + 1)$ and $s(8) = 5$, find a value of x such that $s(x) = -7$.

C **21.** If $f(x) = mx + b$, and a and c are different real numbers, find the value of

$$\frac{f(c) - f(a)}{c - a}.$$

22. If $f(x) = mx + b$ and $f(2) = 2f(1)$, show that $b = 0$.

Problems

Solve, assuming that each relationship described is linear.

A **1.** At $15°$C the length of a metal rod is 72.6 cm. At $95°$C, its length is 72.8 cm. How long is the rod when its temperature is $75°$C?

TEST: FRIDAY
CH-2

2. A mass of 40 g causes a wire spring to stretch to a length of 6.2 cm, and a mass of 60 g stretches the spring to a length of 6.7 cm. What will be the length of the spring if a 90 g mass is attached?

3. A painter receives $77 for a job requiring 8 hours of work and $116 for a 14-hour job. How much does the painter receive for a job that takes 26 hours?

4. The toll for a telephone call of 2 minutes between two particular cities is $.79, and the toll for a 5-minute call is $1.60. What is the toll for a call of 9 minutes?

5. The taxi fare for a 1 km trip within the limits of New Troy City is $1.70. A trip of 3 km costs $3.30. What is the fare for a 2 km trip?

6. A diamond ring of 40 points costs $405. A 100-point diamond ring costs $825. How much does a 75-point diamond ring cost?

7. A company's total cost of operations is $525,000 when its sales are $600,000, and $760,000 when sales are $900,000. What is the total cost of operations if sales are $1,000,000?

8. The tax on a net income of $16,000 is $3320, and on $16,400 is $3408. At this rate what is the tax on a net income of $16,750?

B 9. In a circuit of 54 V a voltmeter registers 72 on its scale of 0–100. What is the maximum number of volts the meter can measure?

10. In a psychological test a subject scored 136 on a scale of 0–170. Convert that score to a scale of 0–100.

C 11. For a certain class of electric service, Upper-East Utilities charges the following monthly rate:

$$\text{Customer Service Charge} \quad \$5.25$$
Energy Charge:
First 900 kW · h: 4.756¢ per kW · h
All over 900 kW · h: 4.150¢ per kW · h

If E is the total monthly charge in cents for N kW · h, express E in terms of N, if

a. $N \le 900$;
b. $N > 900$.

Then draw a graph of E for $0 < N \le 1000$.

12. The monthly rate for residential gas service charged by Upper-East Utilities includes:

Customer Service Charge $3.30
First 3 m³: 16.70¢/m³ (cents per cubic meter)
All over 3 m³: 14.03¢/m³

If G is the total monthly charge in cents for M m³, express G in terms of M if

a. $M \le 3$;
b. $M > 3$.

Then draw a graph of G for $0 < M \le 6$.

3-8 *Direct Variation and Proportion*

OBJECTIVE   To solve problems involving direct variation.

The table in Figure 3-25 shows the approximate time x in seconds it takes for the sound of a thunderbolt to travel the distance y kilometers from the source of the sound.

x s	y km	$\frac{y}{x}$ km/s
6	2	$\frac{1}{3}$
9	3	$\frac{1}{3}$
12	4	$\frac{1}{3}$

Figure 3-25

The ratio $\frac{y}{x}$ is the same for each ordered pair (x, y); in fact,

$$\frac{y}{x} = \frac{1}{3}, \quad \text{or} \quad y = \frac{1}{3}x.$$

You can say that y varies directly as x.

In general, a linear function defined by an equation of the form

$$y = mx$$

where m is a nonzero constant is called a **linear direct variation** (or simply a **direct variation**). You say that

> *y varies directly as x*

or

> *y varies with x.*

The constant m is called the **constant of variation.**

EXAMPLE 1   If a fixed mass of a given gas is under constant pressure, then its volume varies directly as the absolute temperature of the gas. Absolute temperature is measured in kelvins (K). Zero on the Kelvin scale is called absolute zero and is equal to $-273.15°$C. If a gas occupies 7.5 L at 300 K, and if the pressure remains constant, find:

a. the constant of variation;
b. the temperature at which the volume would be 8.2 L.

SOLUTION   Let $x =$ the temperature in kelvins, and
$y =$ the volume of the gas in liters.
Then $y = mx$.

a. $y = 7.5$ when $x = 300$

$$7.5 = m(300)$$

$$m = \frac{7.5}{300} = \frac{1}{40} \quad \textbf{\textit{Answer}}$$

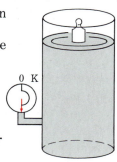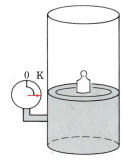

(Solution continued on p. 116.)

b. $y = \frac{1}{40}x$

Substitute 8.2 for y in the equation.

$8.2 = \frac{1}{40}x$, $x = 328\,\text{K}$ **Answer**

The graph of every direct variation, $y = mx$, whose domain is the set of real numbers is a line that passes through the origin and has slope m (Figure 3-26). Also, if one ordered pair of the direct variation is (x_1, y_1) and another is (x_2, y_2) and neither is $(0, 0)$, then

$$y_1 = mx_1 \quad \text{and} \quad y_2 = mx_2.$$

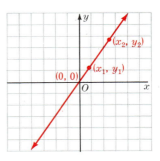

Figure 3-26

Therefore, you can find the ratios

$$\frac{y_1}{x_1} = m \quad \text{and} \quad \frac{y_2}{x_2} = m.$$

Since each ratio equals m, the ratios are equal. Thus

If (x_1, y_1) and (x_2, y_2) are ordered pairs of a direct variation and neither is $(0, 0)$, then

$$\frac{y_1}{x_1} = \frac{y_2}{x_2}.$$

This equality of ratios is called a proportion. For this reason, m is often called the **constant of proportionality,** and y is said to be **directly proportional to x.** The proportion is sometimes written

$$y_1 : x_1 = y_2 : x_2$$

and read "y_1 is to x_1 as y_2 is to x_2." You call x_1 and y_2 the **means** and y_1 and x_2 the **extremes** of the proportion.

$$\underset{\text{extremes}}{\overset{\text{means}}{y_1 : x_1 = y_2 : x_2}}$$

Multiplying both members of the proportion

$$\frac{y_1}{x_1} = \frac{y_2}{x_2}$$

by $x_1 x_2$, you find

$$y_1 x_2 = y_2 x_1.$$

Thus, in any proportion the product of the extremes equals the product of the means.

EXAMPLE 2   Which is the better value: an 800 mL bottle of cranberry juice at $1.36 or a 650 mL bottle of the same juice at $.85?

SOLUTION   Let x = the cost in cents of the 650 mL bottle if it were priced at the same rate as the 800 mL bottle. Then you can write and solve the following proportion.

$$\frac{x}{650} = \frac{136}{800}$$

$$x = \frac{136(650)}{800} = \frac{136(13)}{16} = \frac{17(13)}{2} = \frac{221}{2} = 110.5$$

$\therefore$ at the same rate charged for the 800 mL bottle, you would pay more than $1.10 for the 650 mL bottle. Since the 650 mL bottle costs only $.85, it is the better buy.   *Answer*

(When shopping at a store that displays unit prices, you can compare them to find the better buy.)

Oral Exercises

In each of Exercises 1–8, an ordered pair of a direct variation is given. State the constant of proportionality. Assume no variable is zero.

SAMPLE $(4, -36)$ **SOLUTION** $\dfrac{y}{x} = \dfrac{-36}{4} = -9$

1. $(5, 40)$ **2.** $(18, 3)$ **3.** $(7, 2)$ **4.** $(24, -30)$

5. $\left(1, -\frac{1}{6}\right)$ **6.** $\left(\frac{1}{4}, 1\right)$ **7.** $(a, 3a)$ **8.** $(2c, c)$

State a formula in terms of the indicated variables for the values of the given direct variation.

9. The distance (d) that an automobile travels at a uniform speed of 88 km/h is directly proportional to the number (t) of hours traveled.

10. The circumference (C) of a circle is directly proportional to its radius (r).

11. The annual simple interest (i) on a loan at 12% varies directly as the amount (P) borrowed.

12. If an appliance manufacturer offers a 30% rebate (R), the rebate varies directly as the list price (P).

13. The scaled distance (S) on a topographic map is directly proportional to the actual distance (D). (Constant of proportionality = 4×10^{-5})

14. In an electrical circuit with a resistance of 2 ohms, the current (I) in amperes varies directly as the voltage (E). (Constant of variation = 0.5)

Written Exercises

A 1. If y varies directly as x, and $y = 42$ when $x = 14$, find y when $x = 8$.

2. If y varies directly as x, and $y = 8$ when $x = 56$, find y when $x = 84$.

3. If r is directly proportional to s, and $s = 8$ when $r = 34$, find s when $r = 221$.

4. If w is directly proportional to z, and $z = 81$ when $w = 45$, find z when $w = 120$.

5. If A varies directly as $|B|$, and $A = 126$ when $B = 6$, find A when $B = -\frac{1}{7}$.

6. If R varies directly as $|V|$, and $(R_1, V_1) = (72, 10)$, find R_2, if $V_2 = -45$.

7. If y is directly proportional to $x + 3$, and $y = 21$ when $x = 11$, find the constant of proportionality.

8. If y varies directly as $x - 8$, and $y = 42$ when $x = 26$, find the constant of variation.

If none of x_1, x_2, y_1, or y_2 is zero, prove each of the following properties of the proportion $\dfrac{y_1}{x_1} = \dfrac{y_2}{x_2}$.

B 9. $x_1 y_2 = x_2 y_1$

10. $\dfrac{x_1}{y_1} = \dfrac{x_2}{y_2}$

11. $\dfrac{y_1}{y_2} = \dfrac{x_1}{x_2}$

12. $\dfrac{x_2}{x_1} = \dfrac{y_2}{y_1}$

13. $\dfrac{x_1 + x_2}{x_2} = \dfrac{y_1 + y_2}{y_2}$ $\left(\textit{Hint: } \text{Add 1 to each side of } \dfrac{x_1}{x_2} = \dfrac{y_1}{y_2}.\right)$

14. $\dfrac{x_1 - x_2}{x_2} = \dfrac{y_1 - y_2}{y_2}$ $\left(\textit{Hint: } \text{Add } -1 \text{ to each side of } \dfrac{x_1}{x_2} = \dfrac{y_1}{y_2}.\right)$

15. If $y_1 \neq y_2$, $\dfrac{x_1 - x_2}{y_1 - y_2} = \dfrac{x_1}{y_1}$. (*Hint:* Use the result of Exercise 14.)

16. If $x_1 \neq x_2$ and $y_1 \neq y_2$, $\dfrac{x_1 + x_2}{x_1 - x_2} = \dfrac{y_1 + y_2}{y_1 - y_2}$. (*Hint:* Use the results of Exercises 13 and 14.)

C 17. Prove that if g is a direct variation over the set of real numbers, then for every pair of real numbers a and c,

$$g(a + c) = g(a) + g(c).$$

18. Prove that if g is a linear function other than a direct variation or the function $g(x) = 0$, then for every pair of real numbers a and c,

$$g(a + c) \neq g(a) + g(c).$$

Problems

Solve.

A
1. A realtor makes a commission of $5100 on a sale of $85,000. At the same rate, what would be the commission on a sale of $115,000?

2. If 26 L of diesel fuel costs $10.92, how much does 40 L of this fuel cost?

3. The average gain in mass of rats fed an experimental diet was directly proportional to the number of weeks that the experiment ran. If the average mass gained after 3 weeks on the diet was 45 g, what was the average gain in mass after 5 weeks?

4. The number of mutations produced by irradiating fruit flies with x-rays varied directly with the intensity of the x-ray dosage. If 15 x-ray units produced 35 mutations, how many mutations were produced by 48 x-ray units?

5. If 100 cm³ of normal human blood contains 12 g of hemoglobin, how much hemoglobin would 75 cm³ of the same blood contain?

6. In ammonia, 14 parts by mass of nitrogen are combined with 3 parts of hydrogen. How much hydrogen must be combined with 378 g of nitrogen to produce ammonia?

7. On a blueprint, a square 10 m on a side was shown as a square 6 cm on a side. How long would a girder appear on the blueprint if the girder was actually 15 m long?

8. Which is the better value: a 360 g jar of peanut butter at $.96 or a 510 g jar at $1.44?

9. The speed of a body falling freely from rest in a vacuum varies directly with the length of time that it falls. If, after 6 seconds, a body was falling at 58.8 m/s, how fast was it falling 4 seconds later?

10. When water freezes, it expands 9% of its volume. How much water must freeze to form 654 m³ (cubic meters) of ice?

B
11. At Daniel's Diner, a 5 kg ham yields 22 portions. At Scudder's Restaurant, an 8 kg ham serves 34 people. Which restaurant serves larger portions of ham?

12. Japan is reported to have a population density of 300 persons per square kilometer. If the population were uniformly distributed across the country, how many people would live in a district shaped like a square, 25 kilometers on a side?

13. The average number of red cells in a cubic millimeter (mm³) of a man's blood is 5,000,000. In order to perform a test on a sample of Roger Hall's blood, a laboratory technician dilutes 1 part of blood with 199 parts of salt solution. How many red blood cells would the technician expect to find in 3.5 mm³ of the diluted solution?

3-9 Relations

OBJECTIVE   **To identify the domain and range and to draw the graph of a relation.**

The diagram at the left in Figure 3-27 shows how each number in the set

$$D = \{0, 1, 4, 9\}$$

is paired with *one or more* numbers in the set

$$R = \{-4, -2, 0, 2, 4, 6\}.$$

   The same pairing is shown in the adjoining table, in the graph, and in the listing of the set of ordered pairs of numbers.

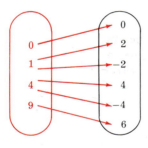

0	0
1	2
1	−2
4	4
4	−4
9	6

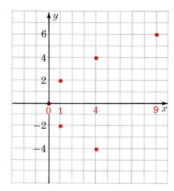

$\{(0, 0), (1, 2), (1, -2), (4, 4), (4, -4), (9, 6)\}$

Figure 3-27

   Is this pairing a function with domain D and range R? No! In a function, each member of the domain is assigned *exactly one* partner in the range. The given pairing, however, assigns *two* range numbers, 2 and −2, to the domain number 1. This pairing is an example of a *relation*. A **relation** is any set of ordered pairs. The set of first coordinates in the ordered pairs is the **domain** of the relation, and the set of second coordinates is the **range.**

   A function is a special kind of relation. A function is a relation in which different ordered pairs have different first coordinates. Thus, no vertical line intersects the graph of a function in more than one point.

   The solution set of any open sentence in two variables defines a relation.

EXAMPLE   Graph the relation

$$\{(x, y) : x \in \{-2, -1, 0, 1, 2\} \text{ and } y = x^2 - 1\}$$

(read "the set of ordered pairs (x, y) such that x belongs to the set whose members are $-2, -1, 0, 1, 2$ and $y = x^2 - 1$.") Is this relation a function?

SOLUTION   The table of ordered pairs is shown at the left below. The graph is shown in Figure 3-28.

x	$x^2 - 1 = y$
-2	$(-2)^2 - 1 = 3$
-1	$(-1)^2 - 1 = 0$
0	$(0)^2 - 1 = -1$
1	$(1)^2 - 1 = 0$
2	$(2)^2 - 1 = 3$

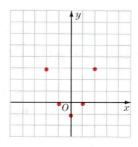

Figure 3-28

The relation is a function because different ordered pairs all have different first coordinates.   ***Answer***

When a relation is given as the solution set of an open sentence in two variables and the domain and range are not specified, *include in the domain and the range those real numbers and only those real numbers for which the open sentence is true.* For example,

$$\left\{(x, y) : y \geq \frac{1}{x(x - 2)}\right\}$$

is a relation whose domain is

{all real numbers except 0 and 2}.

Oral Exercises

State the domain and range of each relation. Is the relation a function?

1. $\{(2, 2), (1, -5), (-1, 4)\}$

2. $\{(0, 6), (5, 7), (1, 6)\}$

3. $\{(1, 3), (1, -3), (-2, 5)\}$

4. $\{(5, 8), (7, 2), (5, 10)\}$

5. $\{(0, 0), (0, 9), (1, 6), (-1, 6)\}$

6. $\{(0, -5), (-1, 3), (1, 2), (2, 2)\}$

In Exercises 7-14, state the ordered pairs in the relation pictured by the mapping diagram or graph. Is the relation a function?

7.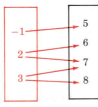

8.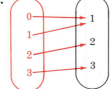

9.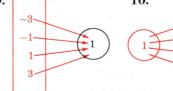

10.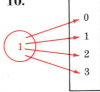

11.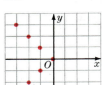

12.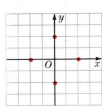

13.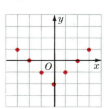

14.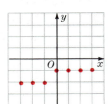

State the domain and range of each relation. Is the relation a function?

SAMPLE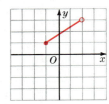

SOLUTION $D = \{x: -1 \le x < 2\}$
$R = \{y: \quad 1 \le y < 3\}$

The relation is a function.

15.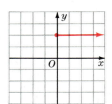

16.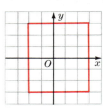

17.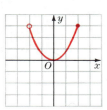

18.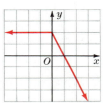

State the domain of each relation.

19. $\left\{(x, y): y = \dfrac{3}{x - 5}\right\}$

20. $\left\{(x, y): y < \dfrac{1}{x^2 - 4}\right\}$

21. $f: f(x) = \dfrac{1}{|x|}$

22. $g: g(x) = \dfrac{x}{|x - 7|}$

23. $\{(a, b): |a| + |b| = 1\}$

24. $\left\{(x, y): y^2 = \dfrac{1}{x + 2}\right\}$

Written Exercises

In Exercises 1–6, graph each relation and determine whether or not it is a function. If the relation is not a function, draw a vertical line that intersects the graph in more than one point.

A **1.** $\{(0, -1), (1, -2), (2, -3)\}$

2. $\{(1, 2), (0, 3), (-1, 0)\}$

3. $\{(-2, 0), (-1, 0), (-2, 1)\}$

4. $\{(4, 3), (-4, 3), (1, 6), (-1, 6)\}$

5. $\{(0, 1), (1, 1), (2, 1), (3, 1)\}$

6. $\{(1, -1), (1, 1), (4, 2), (4, -2)\}$

State the range, and graph each of the following relations over the domain $\{-3, -2, -1, 0, 1, 2, 3\}$. Is the relation a function?

7. $\{(x, y): y = 2x - 1\}$

8. $\{(x, y): x + y = 1\}$

9. $\{(x, y): y = x^2 - 1\}$

10. $\left\{(x, y): y = \dfrac{x^2}{2}\right\}$

B **11.** $\{(x, y): |y| = x + 3\}$

12. $\{(x, y): |y| = 3 - x\}$

13. $\{(x, y): |y| = |x| - 1\}$

14. $\{(x, y): |y| = |x| + 1\}$

15. $\{(x, y): y = x^2 + 2x - 5\}$

16. $\{(x, y): y = x^2 - x - 1\}$

State the range, and graph each of the following relations over the domain $\{-3, -2, -1, 0, 1, 2, 3\}$. Is the relation a function?

SAMPLE $\{(x, y): y \geq |x| - 1\}$

SOLUTION

1. Replace x with each of its values in turn, and determine all corresponding real values of y.
2. Since the least value of y is -1, the range is $\{y: y \geq -1\}$.
3. The graph is shown in the figure at the right.

The relation is not a function.   *Answer*

x	$|x|$	$y \geq |x| - 1$
-3	3	$y \geq 3 - 1; y \geq 2$
-2	2	$y \geq 2 - 1; y \geq 1$
-1	1	$y \geq 1 - 1; y \geq 0$
0	0	$y \geq 0 - 1; y \geq -1$
1	1	$y \geq 1 - 1; y \geq 0$
2	2	$y \geq 2 - 1; y \geq 1$
3	3	$y \geq 3 - 1; y \geq 2$

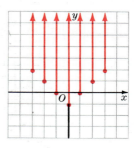

17. $\{(x, y): y < 2x - 1\}$

18. $\{(x, y): y \geq 1 - x\}$

C **19.** $\{(x, y): y > |x|\}$

20. $\{(x, y): y < -|x|\}$

21. $\{(x, y): y \leq |1 - x|\}$

22. $\{(x, y): y \geq |x + 2|\}$

Self-Test 3

VOCABULARY

mapping (p. 107)
function (p. 107)
domain (p. 107)
range (p. 107)
rule (p. 107)
value of f at x (p. 108)
linear function (p. 111)
linear direct variation (p. 115)
y varies directly as x (p. 115)

constant of variation (p. 115)
y is directly proportional to x (p. 116)
constant of proportionality (p. 116)
means (p. 116)
extremes (p. 116)
relation (p. 120)

1. State the domain and range of the function pictured in the mapping.
2. List the members of the range of the function $f: x \rightarrow 4x - 5$ with domain $D = \{3, 1, -2\}$.
3. Find a formula for the linear function f with slope 2 if $f(1) = 3$.

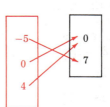

Obj. 3-6, p. 107

Obj. 3-7, p. 111

4. If y varies directly with x, and $y = 27$ when $x = 18$,

    a. find y when $x = 10$;

    b. find the constant of variation.

Obj. 3-8, p. 115

5. Graph the relation $\{(3, -2), (4, 1), (6, -2), (-1, 1)\}$ and determine whether or not it is a function. If the relation is not a function, draw a vertical line that intersects the graph in more than one point.

Obj. 3-9, p. 120

Check your answers with those at the back of the book.

Computer Key-In

From time to time, special sections which can be used with a computer will be presented. If you have access to a computer that will accept programs written in BASIC, you may wish to try these sections.

In this chapter, you have learned to find equations of straight lines under certain given conditions. It is possible to write programs that will tell the computer how to do this. First, it is necessary to describe a problem. Consider this:

> To write a program to print out an equation of a straight line in slope-intercept form, given the coordinates of two points on it.

First, you must find algebraic expressions for the slope and the intercept that the computer can evaluate.

The slope of a straight line through points (x_1, y_1) and (x_2, y_2) is

$$\frac{y_2 - y_1}{x_2 - x_1}.$$

The slope of a straight line is constant, and so in general:

$$\frac{y - y_1}{x - x_1} = \frac{y_2 - y_1}{x_2 - x_1}$$

or:

$$y = \left(\frac{y_2 - y_1}{x_2 - x_1}\right)x - \left(\frac{y_2 - y_1}{x_2 - x_1}\right)x_1 + y_1$$

$$= \left(\frac{y_2 - y_1}{x_2 - x_1}\right)x + \left(\frac{x_2 y_1 - x_1 y_2}{x_2 - x_1}\right)$$

This is in the form

$$y = mx + b,$$

where

$$m = \frac{y_2 - y_1}{x_2 - x_1} \quad \text{and} \quad b = \frac{x_2 y_1 - x_1 y_2}{x_2 - x_1}.$$

BASIC allows a variable to be represented by a letter followed by a digit. Thus, it is convenient to represent

$$x_1 \text{ as X1}, \quad x_2 \text{ as X2}, \quad y_1 \text{ as Y1}, \quad y_2 \text{ as Y2}.$$

The following program can be used to find an equation of a straight line through two given points. Notice that each INPUT statement will print only one question mark, but the computer will expect *two* values (with a comma between) to be typed in.

```
10   PRINT "TO FIND AN EQUATION OF A STRAIGHT"
20   PRINT "LINE IN SLOPE-INTERCEPT FORM,"
30   PRINT "GIVEN THE COORDINATES OF TWO"
40   PRINT "POINTS ON IT:"
50   PRINT
60   PRINT "INPUT X1, Y1";
70   INPUT X1, Y1
80   PRINT "INPUT X2, Y2";
90   INPUT X2, Y2
100  LET M=(Y2-Y1)/(X2-X1)
110  LET B=(X2*Y1-X1*Y2)/(X2-X1)
120  PRINT
130  PRINT "Y = (";M;")X + (";B;")"
140  END
```

Exercises

1. Verify that an equation of a straight line through points (x_1, y_1) and (x_2, y_2) can be written in the form

$$(y_2 - y_1)x + (x_1 - x_2)y = x_1 y_2 - x_2 y_1,$$

and write a program that will print out an equation in this form.

2. Combine the program of Exercise 1 and the program in the text to print out both forms.

Chapter Summary ━━━━━━━━━━

1. The *graph*, in the *Cartesian* or *coordinate plane*, of a *linear equation in two variables* is a line. *Standard form* for such an equation is $Ax + By = C$. If $A = 0$, the line is horizontal. If $B = 0$, the line is vertical.

2. The *slope m* of the line joining (x_1, y_1) and (x_2, y_2) is given by the formula:

$$m = \frac{y_2 - y_1}{x_2 - x_1} \, (x_2 \neq x_1)$$

3. You can determine the equation of a line given any two points on the line, the slope of the line and one point, or the slope and the y-intercept. The *slope-intercept* form of a line is $y = mx + b$, where m is the slope and b is the y-intercept.

4. *Functions* map elements of the *domain* onto elements of the *range*. The graph of the ordered pairs formed by this pairing is the graph of the function.

5. The *rule* of the function determines which element of the domain is mapped onto which element of the range. The rule may be expressed in a *formula*.

6. A *linear function* is a function that can be written in the form $f(x) = mx + b$.

7. If $y = mx$ for some nonzero constant x, then y is said to *vary directly* with x; m is the *constant of variation*, or *constant of proportionality*. The graph of the direct variation $y = mx$ is a line through the origin with slope m.

8. Word problems can be stated and solved using direct variation, proportions, and linear functions.

Chapter Review

1. For what value of y does $(4, 1 - y) = (4, y - 3)$?   **3-1**

    a. 2   **b.** 4   **c.** 3   **d.** -2

2. Which equation is equivalent to $-4x + 3y = 12$?   **3-2**

    a. $y = \frac{3}{4}x + 4$ **b.** $y = \frac{4}{3}x - 4$ **c.** $y = \frac{4}{3}x + 4$

3. For what value of y is the ordered pair $(3, y)$ a solution of $2x - y = 2$?

    a. 3   **b.** -4 **c.** 4   **d.** -4

4. Which is the best description of the graph of $5x - 4y = 0$?   **3-3**

    a. a horizontal line
    b. a vertical line
    c. a line that contains the origin
    d. a line that makes a 45° angle with the x-axis

5. Determine the value of k for which $(-3, -1)$ lies on the graph of $4x + 3ky = -6$.

    a. 2   **b.** $\frac{2}{9}$ **c.** -2 **d.** $-\frac{2}{9}$

6. Find the slope of the line passing through the points $(2, 4)$ and $(4, 0)$.   **3-4**

    a. 0   **b.** 2   **c.** $-\frac{1}{2}$ **d.** -2

7. Which of the following lines does *not* have a slope equal to $\frac{2}{3}$?

    a. $2x + 3y = 6$ **c.** $3y = 4 + 2x$ **c.** $\frac{x}{6} - \frac{y}{4} = 1$

8. Write an equation of the line containing $(5, -2)$ and $(8, 4)$.   **3-5**

    a. $2x - y = 12$ **b.** $x - 2y = 9$ **c.** $2x + y = 20$

9. Find an equation in standard form of the line with slope $\frac{1}{2}$ and passing through $(-1, 0)$.

 a. $x - 2y = 2$ **b.** $x - 2y = 1$ **c.** $x - 2y = -1$

10. Which of the following is *not* an ordered pair of the function whose formula is $h(x) = \dfrac{2x}{x + 3}$?   3-6

 a. $(3, 1)$ **b.** $(0, 0)$ **c.** $\left(a, \dfrac{2a}{a + 3}\right)$ **d.** $(-3, 0)$

11. If $f(x) = x^2 - 5$ and $g(x) = 1 - x$, find $g(f(-2))$.

 a. 4   **b.** 0   **c.** 10   **d.** 2

12. $f(x)$ is a linear function with slope 3 and $f(2) = 2$. Find $f(4)$.   3-7

 a. 8   **b.** 4   **c.** -4 **d.** -3

13. If p is a linear function such that $p(9) = 4$ and $p(0) = -8$, find $p(3)$.

 a. 0   **b.** 4   **c.** -4 **d.** -12

14. If y varies directly as x, and $y = 51$ when $x = 17$, find y when $x = 2$.   3-8

 a. 6   **b.** 34   **c.** 102   **d.** 51

15. If 240 L of fuel costs \$91.20, how much does 300 L of this fuel cost?

 a. \$240   **b.** \$114   **c.** \$72.96   **d.** \$101.42

16. State the range of the relation $\{(x, y): y = 2x + 2\}$ over the domain $\{-2, -1, 0, 1, 2\}$.   3-9

 a. $\{-2, 0, 2, 4, 6\}$ **b.** $\{-2, -1, 0, 1, 2\}$ **c.** $\{-4, -2, 0, 1, 2\}$

17. Is the relation in Review Item 16 a function?

 a. Yes   **b.** No

Chapter Test

1. The points $(4, -2)$ $(4, 3)$ and $(-5, -2)$ are three vertices of a rectangle. Graph these three points, sketch the rectangle, and determine the coordinates of the fourth vertex.   3-1

2. Find the solution set of the open sentence $2x - y \geq -3$ for the given replacement set of x if the set of positive integers is the replacement set of y.   3-2

 a. $\{-1, 0\}$ **b.** $\{-2\}$

3. Draw the graphs of the following equations: 3-3

 a. $5x - 2y = 10$ **b.** $3x = 6$

4. Determine the value of k for which the point $(-1, 2)$ lies on the line whose equation is $9x + 2ky = 15$.

5. Draw the graph of the line passing through the point $(1, -2)$ and having the slope described.   3-4

 a. With slope $-\frac{3}{2}$ **b.** With no slope

6. Find the slope of the line through the points $(-6, -2)$ and $(-4, 7)$.

7. Find the slope of the line whose equation is $x - 4y = 3$.

8. Find the equation in standard form of the line with slope $\frac{2}{3}$ and y-intercept $-\frac{5}{2}$.

9. Find an equation in slope-intercept form of the line passing through $(-2, 2)$ with x-intercept equal to 3.   3-5

10. Find an equation in standard form of the line passing through $(-2, 5)$ with slope -1.

11. List the members of the range of the function $g: x \rightarrow 3 - x^2$ with domain $D = \{-1, 0, 1, 2\}$.   3-6

12. Consider the function $f: x \rightarrow 2x + 5$.
  a. Draw the graph of f for the domain $D = \{-3, 0, 2\}$.
  b. Supply the missing coordinate in each ordered pair: $(-\frac{3}{2}, ?)$; $(?, 3)$.
  c. Find $f(f(1))$.

13. Let f be a linear function, $f(6) = 2$, and $f(-3) = -4$.   3-7
  a. Find $f(0)$.   **b.** Find x such that $f(x) = 12$.

14. The area of a triangle with a constant height varies directly with the length of the base. If the area is 42 cm² when the base is 8 cm, find the area when the base is 6 cm.   3-8

15. State the range and graph the relation $\{(x, y): y \leq x + 1\}$ over the domain $\{-2, -1, 0, \frac{3}{2}\}$. Is the relation a function?   3-9

Calculator Key-In _____

You can use a calculator to solve a proportion.

EXAMPLE Solve the following proportion for x correct to the nearest thousandth:

$$\frac{x}{141} = \frac{1.5627}{233}$$

SOLUTION $\frac{x}{141} = \frac{1.5627}{233}$

$$x = \frac{1.5627 \times 141}{233}$$

$$x \approx 0.9456682 \approx 0.946 \quad \textit{Answer}$$

Use a calculator to solve these proportions. Round the answer to the nearest thousandth.

1. $\frac{a}{173} = \frac{9.72}{191}$ **2.** $\frac{0.52}{23} = \frac{b}{61}$ **3.** $\frac{0.094}{111} = \frac{c}{97}$

4. $\frac{1295}{d} = \frac{58}{13}$ **5.** $\frac{4.38}{0.05} = \frac{2.34}{e}$ **6.** $\frac{0.89}{f} = \frac{5.2}{1.71}$

Cumulative Review (Chapters 1-3)

Simplify.

1. $7(3^2 - 1) \div 4 + 3$ **2.** $-19 + |-14| + 7$ **3.** $-8 - (2 - 9) - 4$

4. $(-3 - 5)(-3 + 5)$ **5.** $\dfrac{27 \div (-3) - 11}{[-3 - (-1)]^2}$ **6.** $2x(x - 6) - 3(2x + 1)$

Evaluate if $r = 3$, $s = 7$, $t = 4$, and $w = -2$.

7. $(s^2 - 2rt) \div (r^2 + t^2)$ **8.** $w^4 + w^3 - 3w^2 - 5w$

Is the statement true or false? Explain.

9. $|-9| < -4.5$ **10.** For every real number x, $x \cdot \dfrac{1}{x} = 1$.

Give the reasons for the steps. Assume that x is a real number.

11. a. $3(x + 4) + (-12) = (3x + 12) + (-12)$ **12. a.** $4(\frac{1}{4 \cdot 3})x = 4(\frac{1}{4} \cdot \frac{1}{3})x$

     b. $= 3x + [12 + (-12)]$ **b.** $= (4 \cdot \frac{1}{4})\frac{1}{3}x$

     c. $= 3x + 0$ **c.** $= 1 \cdot \frac{1}{3}x$

     d. $= 3x$ **d.** $= \frac{1}{3}x$

Solve and graph each equation or inequality.

13. $4(7 - 3a) = -7a + 3$ **14.** $\frac{1}{6}(2b + 4) = -3$ **15.** $5 - (9 - 4z) < -8z$

16. $-1 \geq 4t - 3 > -7$ **17.** $|k - 5| = 2$ **18.** $|4r + 3| > 13$

19. Solve $A = \frac{1}{2}(a + b)h$ for h.

20. Solve $4r + 3s = 24$ if the set of whole numbers is the replacement set for r and s.

21. Find the slope-intercept form of the equation $7x - 4y = 8$. Graph the equation.

22. Find an equation of the form $Ax + By = C$ for the line:
a. with slope $\frac{1}{2}$ and y-intercept $\frac{3}{2}$.
b. with slope -3 and containing point $(-2, -1)$.
c. containing points $(2, -2)$ and $(6, 1)$.

23. The slope of the graph of a linear function f is -2, and $f(3) = -1$.
a. Find a formula for the function.
b. If the function has domain $\{-1, 0, 1, 2, 3\}$, draw the graph of f.

24. If g is a linear function, $g(-1) = 2$ and $g(3) = 4$, find $g(0)$.

25. If y varies directly as x, and $y = 12$ when $x = 100$, find y when $x = 175$.

26. Graph the relation $\{(-6, -1), (-3, -2), (-2, -3), (-1, -6)\}$. Is the relation a function?

*To the driver of a racing car, velocity and acceleration are just
two of many critical factors that must be considered in the course
of a race. Polynomial equations are used in the study of velocity
and acceleration.*

4

POLYNOMIALS AND FACTORING

PRODUCTS

4-1 *Multiplying by a Monomial*

OBJECTIVE To review certain laws of exponents and apply them to multiplication by a monomial.

In working with polynomials you will need to use the laws of exponents illustrated and then stated formally below.

1. $5^3 \cdot 5^4 = 5^{3+4} = 5^7$

2. $(3a)^2 = 3^2 \cdot a^2 = 9a^2$

3. $(3^2)^3 = 3^{2 \cdot 3} = 3^6$

4. $\dfrac{4^5}{4^2} = 4^{5-2} = 4^3$

LAWS OF EXPONENTS

If a and b are real numbers and m and n are positive integers:

1. $b^m \cdot b^n = b^{m+n}$

2. $(ab)^m = a^m \cdot b^m$

3. $(b^m)^n = b^{mn}$

4. If $m > n$ and $b \neq 0$: $\dfrac{b^m}{b^n} = b^{m-n}$

Note that in laws 1 and 4 the *bases* are the same; in law 2 the *exponents* are the same.

Proof of law 1

STATEMENTS	REASONS

$\overbrace{}^{m\ factors}\ \overbrace{}^{n\ factors}$

1. $\quad b^m b^n = (b \cdot b \dots b)(b \cdot b \dots b)$ — Definition of a power

2. $\qquad\quad = \underbrace{(b \cdot b \dots\dots\dots\dots b)}_{m\ +\ n\ factors}$ — Associative axiom for multiplication

3. $\qquad\quad = b^{m+n}$ — Definition of a power

4. $\therefore\ b^m b^n = b^{m+n}$ — Transitive property of equality

Proofs of laws 2–4 are called for in Exercises 39–41.

You can use laws 1–3 together with the commutative and associative axioms for multiplication to simplify products of monomials such as the following.

EXAMPLE 1 Simplify: **a.** $(3xy^2)(-2x^3y^4)$ **b.** $(2n)^4$ **c.** $(-3x^2y^3)^3$

SOLUTION **a.** $(3xy^2)(-2x^3y^4) = 3(-2)(x \cdot x^3)(y^2 \cdot y^4) = -6x^4y^6$

b. $(2n)^4 = 2^4 \cdot n^4 = 16n^4$

c. $(-3x^2y^3)^3 = (-3)^3(x^2)^3(y^3)^3 = -27x^6y^9$

EXAMPLE 2 Simplify $\dfrac{4a^3b^2}{2a^2b}$ assuming $a \neq 0$ and $b \neq 0$.

SOLUTION $\dfrac{4a^3b^2}{2a^2b} = \dfrac{4}{2} \cdot \dfrac{a^3}{a^2} \cdot \dfrac{b^2}{b} = 2ab$

To multiply a polynomial by a monomial, you use law 1 together with the distributive axiom.

EXAMPLE 3 Write $2x^2(x^3 - 3x^2 + x)$ as a polynomial in simplest form.

SOLUTION $2x^2(x^3 - 3x^2 + x) = (2x^2)x^3 + (2x^2)(-3x^2) + (2x^2)(x)$
$$= 2x^5 - 6x^4 + 2x^3$$

Oral Exercises

Simplify each expression. Assume that variable expressions in exponents or in denominators represent positive integers.

1. $x^2 \cdot x^4$ **2.** $a^3 \cdot a^4$ **3.** $2^2 \cdot 2^3$ **4.** $8^n \cdot 8$

5. $5^x \cdot 5^y$ **6.** $(xy)^2$ **7.** $(-4a)^2$ **8.** $(x^4)^2$

9. $(x^2)^3$ **10.** $(b^a)^2$ **11.** $(-3x)^3$ **12.** $2^2 \cdot 2 \cdot 2^3$

13. $\dfrac{a^5}{a^2}$ **14.** $\dfrac{3^8}{3^5}$ **15.** $\dfrac{2^{3n}}{2^n}$ **16.** $\dfrac{(x^2)^3}{x^4}$

State the product as a polynomial.

17. $a(a^2 - b^2)$ **18.** $x^2(4x + 9)$ **19.** $-5y(4y^2 - z)$

20. $5k(k + k^2)$ **21.** $3a(a^2 - 2ab + b^2)$ **22.** $-2x^2(x^3 + y^3)$

Written Exercises

Simplify each expression. Assume that variable expressions in exponents or in denominators represent positive integers.

A   **1.** $4a^2 \cdot 2a^3$ **2.** $10y^3 \cdot y^{10}$ **3.** $(y^4)^4$

     4. $(-x^2)^3$ **5.** $(-4a)^2$ **6.** $(2mn)^3$

     7. $\dfrac{16c^7}{6c^3}$ **8.** $\dfrac{-27a^{14}}{33a^7}$ **9.** $-4x(x^2y + xy^2)$

     10. $-5a(a^2 - 5a + 4)$ **11.** $a^4 \cdot a^3 \cdot a^2$ **12.** $-5m^7 \cdot 3m^2 \cdot 4m^{72}$

     13. $4xy(3x^2y^2)(-8x^3y^3)$ **14.** $-(-a^2b^3)^3$ **15.** $2xy(x^2 - 4xy + 4)$

     16. $15a^2(15a^2 - ab + 12)$ **17.** $\dfrac{25x^8y^7}{35x^4y^3}$ **18.** $\dfrac{-32m^5n^{23}p^3}{18m^2n^{17}}$

     19. $(-a)(-4a^3)^2$ **20.** $6xy(-4x^2y^2)^3$ **21.** $b^6 \cdot 4b^a$

     22. $c^x \cdot c^5 \cdot c^{2x}$ **23.** $5x^{t+1} \cdot x^{t-1}$ **24.** $-6y^{a+x} \cdot y^{a-x}$

SAMPLE $x^n(x^{n+1} - 3x^n + 5)$

SOLUTION $x^n(x^{n+1} - 3x^n + 5) = x^{n+n+1} - 3x^{n+n} + 5x^n$
$$= x^{2n+1} - 3x^{2n} + 5x^n$$

B   **25.** $y^{3n}(y^n + 2y^{2n} + 4)$ **26.** $x^a(x^{c-a} + x^{c+a})$

     27. $3m^n(-2m^{2n} + 4m^n - 1)$ **28.** $-3x^m(-7x^m - 3x^{2m} + 5x^{3m})$

     29. $x^2y(x^m + x^my^m + y^m)$ **30.** $-10a^nb^n(a^nb^n - 7ab + 8)$

Simplify each expression. Assume that variables in exponents represent positive integers and that no denominator is zero.

     31. $(3m^3)(2n^2)^2 + 5m^3n^4$ **32.** $2x^2(x^3 + y^3) - x^5 - y^6$

     33. $(-6a^2)(-12b^2) - (10ab)^2$ **34.** $(4d^2)(-4cd) + (3cd)(-3d^2) - cd^3$

     35. $\dfrac{12y^{3a+4c}}{28y^a}$ **36.** $\dfrac{-2x^{p+q}}{-26x^{p-q}}$

     37. $\dfrac{18m^{x-y}}{-30m^{x-2y}}$ **38.** $\dfrac{35z^{2m-n}}{14z^{m-2n}}$

C   **39.** Prove law 2 of exponents (page 131).

     40. Prove law 3 of exponents (page 131).

     41. Prove law 4 of exponents (page 131).

4-2 *Multiplying Polynomials*

OBJECTIVE   **To multiply any two polynomials.**

The product of any two polynomials, no matter the number of terms, can be found by applying the distributive axiom. Multiply each term of one of the polynomials by each term of the other and add the monomial products.

EXAMPLE   Multiply: $(2x + 1)(3x^2 + 2x + 1)$

SOLUTION $(2x + 1)(3x^2 + 2x + 1) = 2x(3x^2 + 2x + 1) + 1(3x^2 + 2x + 1)$
$$= 6x^3 + 4x^2 + 2x + 3x^2 + 2x + 1$$
$$= 6x^3 + 7x^2 + 4x + 1$$

If you wish, you may arrange the work vertically, as at the right. It is a good idea, however, to accustom yourself to using the horizontal form.

$$3x^2 + 2x + 1$$
$$\underline{2x \ + 1}$$
$$6x^3 + 4x^2 + 2x$$
$$\underline{\quad\quad 3x^2 + 2x + 1}$$
$$6x^3 + 7x^2 + 4x + 1$$

When both polynomials are binomials you can save time if you learn to state the product at sight. Study the technique demonstrated below.

$$(2x - 3)(3x - 2) = 6x^2 - 13x + 6$$

The diagram shows how the terms in the product are obtained.

1. Multiply the *first terms* of the binomials.
2. Multiply the *first term* of each binomial by the *second term* of the other binomial; combine like terms, if possible.
3. Multiply the *second terms* of the binomials.

Certain pairs of factors have special multiplication patterns. If you recognize these special cases, you can shorten your work in writing products.

1. $(a + b)^2 = a^2 + 2ab + b^2$

   Example: $(3x + 2y)^2 = (3x)^2 + 2(3x)(2y) + (2y)^2$
   $$= 9x^2 + 12xy + 4y^2$$

2. $(a - b)^2 = a^2 - 2ab + b^2$

   Example: $(4n - y)^2 = (4n)^2 - 2(4n)(y) + (y)^2$
   $$= 16n^2 - 8ny + y^2$$

3. $(a + b)(a - b) = a^2 - b^2$

   $Example:$ $(5x + 2y)(5x - 2y) = (5x)^2 - (2y)^2$
   $$= 25x^2 - 4y^2$$

Oral Exercises

Express each product as a polynomial in simplest form.

1. $(x + 1)(x + 2)$ **2.** $(x - 1)(x - 2)$ **3.** $(x - 1)(x + 2)$

4. $(y + 3)(y + 4)$ **5.** $(y + 3)(y - 4)$ **6.** $(y - 4)(y - 4)$

7. $(z + 3)(z + 3)$ **8.** $(t + 5)(t - 5)$ **9.** $(b - 4)(b + 4)$

10. $(2x + 3)(2x - 3)$ **11.** $(2a + 3)^2$ **12.** $(5x - 1)(2x + 3)$

Express the square of each expression as a polynomial in simplest form.

13. $-5x$ **14.** $x^2 y$ **15.** $x + y$

16. $y + 1$ **17.** $3x - 1$ **18.** $2a + b$

Written Exercises

Express as a polynomial in simplest form.

A   **1.** $(4x - 1)(2x + 3)$ **2.** $(9m - 4)(2m - 3)$ **3.** $(7c + 3)(7c - 3)$

     4. $(3b + 8)(3b - 8)$ **5.** $(2r - 5)^2 (2r-5)$ **6.** $(a + 4b)^2$

     7. $(x + 7)(2x - 3)$ **8.** $(4y - 1)(2y - 7)$ **9.** $(6m + 5)(5m + 6)$

     10. $(11a + 4)(a + 3)$ **11.** $(8x - 5)(3x + 2)$ **12.** $(r - s)(r + 5s)$

     13. $(5a - 2b)(5a + 2b)$ **14.** $(b - 2a)(2a + b)$ **15.** $(5x + 2)(x - 14)$

     16. $(13a + 1)(a + 13)$ **17.** $(11 - 5z)(5z + 11)$ **18.** $(7m + 6n)(7m - 6n)$

     19. $(4n^2 + 5)(3n^2 - 1)$ **20.** $(m + n^2)(n + m^2)$ **21.** $(x^3 + 2)^2$

     22. $(9 - 2x^2)^2$ **23.** $(a + 2)(a + b + 1)$ **24.** $s(s + 1)(s + 2)$

Express as a polynomial in simplest form. Assume that variable expressions as exponents represent positive integers.

B   **25.** $(2a + 7)(3c - 2)$ **26.** $(7xy - 2z)(4xy + 5z)$

     27. $(6m + 1)(3m^2 - 9m + 5)$ **28.** $(25c - 2)(8c + 11)$

     29. $(4a^2 c - 5b)(4a^2 c + 5b)$ **30.** $(a^n - 5)^2$

     31. $(x^n - y^n)^2$ **32.** $(a + b - c)(a - b)$

     33. $(a + b + c)^2$ **34.** $(2n - 3)(n + 2)(n - 2)$

     35. $[a^3(2a - 1)]^2$ **36.** $3x(5x - y)(5x + y)$

     37. $x^2 y^2 (x - 3y)(x + 2y)$ **38.** $5x(x - 2y)^2$

     39. $-3x(x - 3y)^2$ **40.** $[a + (b + 1)][a - (b + 1)]$

     41. $(x^2 + y^2)(x^2 - y^2)$ **42.** $(a^2 + b^2)(a + b)$

Express as a polynomial in simplest form.

43. $(a + b)^3$

44. $(m^2 + n^2)(m + n)(m - n)$

C 45. $(a + b)(a^2 - ab + b^2)$

46. $(a - b)(a^2 + ab + b^2)$

Find the value of k that will make the statement an identity.

47. $(kn - 4)(kn - 1) = k^2n^2 - 20n + 4$ **48.** $(6r - k)(3r + k) = 18r^2 + 15r - k^2$

49. $(kx + 4)^2 = k^2x^2 - 40x + 16$ **50.** $(3x + k)(9x^2 + 21x + k^2) = 27x^3 + k^3$

Self-Test 1

Simplify.

1. $3y^3(-7y^2)$ **2.** $3c^2(2c^3 - 5c - 4)$ Obj. 4-1, p. 131

3. $(3x + y)(3x - y)$ Obj. 4-2, p. 134

4. $(5m - 7)(3m + 4)$

5. $(4n + 1)(3n^2 + 5n + 2)$

Check your answers with those at the back of the book.

Biography Manuel Vallarta

Manuel Sandoval Vallarta (1899–1977) developed a strong interest in mathematics and physics during his school days in Mexico City. He pursued those topics further at the Massachusetts Institute of Technology. In Germany, on a Guggenheim Fellowship, he had the good fortune to study relativity with Albert Einstein and electromagnetic theory with Max Planck. Later, at M.I.T., he did research on cosmic rays.

In 1946 Vallarta returned to Mexico. During the rest of his life, he actively participated in the development of modern science there. He founded and directed the Instituto Nacional de Energiá Nuclear. There, young scientists could present the results of their research and exchange ideas with visiting scientists from all over the world.

Vallarta served as a member of several international scientific groups including the United Nations Atomic Energy Commission, of which he was president, UNESCO, and the International Commission on Weights and Measures.

FACTORING

4-3 *Factoring a Monomial*

OBJECTIVE To factor monomials; to find their GCF and LCM.

In earlier work you wrote equations like $4 \times 6 = 24$ and used the terms *factor* and *product* as indicated.

$$\underset{\text{factors}}{4 \times 6} = \underset{\text{product}}{24}$$

In algebra you say that 4 and 6 are **positive integral factors** of 24. The product 24 is a **multiple** of 4 and of 6.

When you factor a number, you need to specify the set from which the factors may be chosen, that is, the **factor set.** The integer 21, factored over the set of integers, can be expressed as $21 \cdot 1$, $(-21)(-1)$, $3 \cdot 7$, or $(-3)(-7)$. In this book integers will be factored over the set of integers unless some other set is specified.

A set of numbers useful in factoring is the set of *prime numbers*, or *primes*. An integer greater than 1 whose only positive integral factors are itself and 1 is called a **prime number,** or **prime.** Over the set of primes, the only factors of 21 are 3 and 7. You can say that the **prime factors** of 21 are 3 and 7 and that $3 \cdot 7$ is the *prime factorization of* 21. To find the **prime factorization** of a positive integer, express it as the product of primes.

GCF — the lowest power of each common prime factor
LCM — the greatest power of every prime number

EXAMPLE 1 What is the prime factorization of 396?

SOLUTION Notice the systematic way of finding the prime factorization of a large number.

$$\begin{aligned}
396 &= 2 \cdot 198 \\
&= 2 \cdot 2 \cdot 99 \\
&= 2 \cdot 2 \cdot 3 \cdot 33 \\
&= 2 \cdot 2 \cdot 3 \cdot 3 \cdot 11 \\
&= 2^2 \cdot 3^2 \cdot 11
\end{aligned}$$

The prime factorization of 396 is $2^2 \cdot 3^2 \cdot 11$. *Answer*

The use of prime factorization is helpful in finding the *greatest common factor* (GCF) and the *least common multiple* (LCM) of two or more integers. The greatest integer that is a factor of each of the given integers is called their **greatest common factor.** The smallest positive integer that is a multiple of each of the given integers is called their **least common multiple.** Study Example 2 on the next page to see an easy way of finding the GCF and LCM.

EXAMPLE 2   Find **(a)** the GCF and **(b)** the LCM of 180 and 168.

SOLUTION   Write the prime factorizations.

$$180 = 2^2 \cdot 3^2 \cdot 5 \qquad 168 = 2^3 \cdot 3 \cdot 7$$

a. Take the *lower* power of each common prime factor.

$$\text{GCF} = 2^2 \cdot 3 = 12$$

The GCF of 180 and 168 is 12.   *Answer*

b. Take the *greater* power of every prime in the factorizations of the numbers.

$$\text{LCM} = 2^3 \cdot 3^2 \cdot 5 \cdot 7 = 2520$$

The LCM of 180 and 168 is 2520.   *Answer*

Factoring monomials is very similar to factoring integers. For example, $8xy$ is a factor of $24x^2y$ because $24x^2y = 8xy \cdot 3x$. Further, $24x^2y$ is a multiple of $3x$ and of $8xy$. In this book *monomials with integral coefficients will be factored over the set of monomials with integral coefficients unless another set is specified.*

The monomial with the greatest numerical coefficient and the greatest degree that is a factor of each of several monomials is called the **greatest common monomial factor (GCF)** of the monomials. The monomial with least positive coefficient and least degree that is a multiple of each of several monomials is called the **least common multiple (LCM)** of the monomials. If a coefficient is negative, first write it as -1 times the opposite of the original coefficient, and use the resulting positive number in finding the GCF and LCM.

EXAMPLE 3   Find **(a)** the GCF and **(b)** the LCM of $27x^2y^2$ and $-18x^3yz$.

SOLUTION   Write the prime factorizations of the coefficients.

$$27 = 3^3 \qquad -18 = (-1)(2)(3^2)$$

a. 1. GCF of the coefficients is 3^2, or 9.

2. Compare the powers of each variable occurring in *both* monomials, x^2y^2 and x^3yz. Use the power with the *lower* exponent.

   Compare x^2 and x^3; use x^2.   Compare y^2 and y; use y.
   Do not use z.   (Why?)

3. GCF $= 9x^2y$

   The GCF of $27x^2y^2$ and $-18x^3yz$ is $9x^2y$.   *Answer*

b. 1. The LCM of the coefficients is $2 \cdot 3^3$, or 54.

2. Compare the powers of each variable occurring in *either* monomial. Use the power with the *greater* exponent.

   Compare x^2 and x^3; use x^3.   Compare y^2 and y; use y^2.   Use z.

3. LCM $= 54x^3y^2z$

   The LCM of $27x^2y^2$ and $-18x^3yz$ is $54x^3y^2z$.   *Answer*

Oral Exercises

Give the prime factorization of each integer.

1. 8   **2.** 18   **3.** 21   **4.** 30

Find the GCF and LCM of the given integers.

5. 8 and 18   **6.** 18 and 21   **7.** 21 and 30   **8.** 18 and 30

Written Exercises

Factor each integer over the set of primes.

A **1.** 162   **2.** 430   **3.** 41   **4.** 330
     5. 441   **6.** 125   **7.** 315   **8.** 2000

Find **(a)** the GCF and **(b)** the LCM of the following monomials.

9. $26, 39$ **10.** $45, 60$ **11.** $24, -108$

12. $3x^2, 15xy$ **13.** $-21m^2n, 28mn^2$ **14.** $42r^2s^2, 63rs^3$

15. $18x^2y^3z^2, 72xy^2z^5$ **16.** $-3bc^3, 14a^2b^2$ **17.** $57m^3nr^2, 38m^2n^2r^4$

18. $36a, 12b, 20a^2b^2$ **19.** $104x^3, 16y^3$ **20.** $-42m^3n^2p, 147m^2p^3, -84m^2n^2p$

B **21.** If p and q are both prime, what are their GCF and LCM?

22. List all the positive integral factors of 28, other than 28 itself, and show that the sum of the numbers in the list equals 28.

23. List all the positive integral factors of 496, other than 496 itself, and show that the sum of the numbers in the list equals 496.

24. Let p be an *odd prime* number. List the positive integral factors of $2p$, and show that their sum is $3(1 + p)$.

25. The GCF of two monomials is $3v^3w^4$, and their LCM is $18v^7w^6$. If one of the monomials is $6v^3w^6$, find the other monomial.

Calculator Key-In _____

Many calculators have a key that enables you to find powers of a number. Such keys are frequently designated y^x.

Evaluate the following using a calculator.

1. 9^5 **2.** 1.3^5 **3.** 0.27^5 **4.** 0.14^3 **5.** 1.7^7

6. 2.04^3 **7.** 40.2^2 **8.** 7.31^4 **9.** 1.05^{12} **10.** 1.11^4

4-4 *Factoring a Polynomial*

OBJECTIVE   **To factor polynomials using greatest monomial factors and special factoring patterns.**

The first step in factoring a polynomial in simple form is to see whether the terms contain a common monomial factor other than 1. The **greatest monomial factor** of a polynomial is the greatest common monomial factor of its terms. If there is a greatest monomial factor besides 1, then rewrite the given polynomial as the product of its greatest monomial factor and a polynomial whose greatest monomial factor is 1. For example,

$$16x^2 + 20x = 4x(4x + 5)$$

The process of expressing a polynomial as a product of other polynomials belonging to a given set is called **polynomial factoring.** *Unless otherwise stated, the factor set for a polynomial whose terms have integral coefficients will be the set of all polynomials whose terms have integral coefficients.*

Study the following polynomials, which are factored using greatest monomial factors.

$$4y^4 - 12y^3 + 4y^2 = 4y^2(y^2 - 3y + 1)$$
$$8ax^3 - 4ax^2 - ax = ax(8x^2 - 4x - 1)$$

The special product patterns in Section 4–2 are also useful in factoring. Use the symmetric property to restate the patterns as follows:

        Trinomial Squares: $a^2 + 2ab + b^2 = (a + b)^2$

EXAMPLE 1   Factor: **a.** $x^2 + 10x + 25$ **b.** $16x^2 + 8xy + y^2$

SOLUTION   **a.** $a = x, b = 5, 2ab = 2 \cdot x \cdot 5 = 10x$

             $\therefore x^2 + 10x + 25 = (x + 5)^2$

         b. $a = 4x, b = y, 2ab = 2 \cdot 4x \cdot y = 8xy$

             $\therefore 16x^2 + 8xy + y^2 = (4x + y)^2$

        Trinomial Squares: $a^2 - 2ab + b^2 = (a - b)^2$

EXAMPLE 2   Factor: **a.** $r^2 - 16rs + 64s^2$ **b.** $9x^2 - 30x + 25$

SOLUTION   **a.** $a = r, b = 8s, 2ab = 2 \cdot r \cdot 8s = 16rs$

             $\therefore r^2 - 16rs + 64s^2 = (r - 8s)^2$

         b. $a = 3x, b = 5, 2ab = 2 \cdot 3x \cdot 5 = 30x$

             $\therefore 9x^2 - 30x + 25 = (3x - 5)^2$

The thought process indicated by the parts of the examples printed in red, above, shows how to recognize that the polynomial to be factored is actually a trinomial square.

Difference of Squares: $a^2 - b^2 = (a + b)(a - b)$

EXAMPLE 3   Factor: **a.** $25x^2 - 1$ **b.** $2n^4 - 162$

SOLUTION   **a.** $a = 5x, b = 1$

$\therefore 25x^2 - 1 = (5x + 1)(5x - 1)$

b. $2n^4 - 162 = 2(n^4 - 81)$
$= 2(n^2 + 9)(n^2 - 9)$
$= 2(n^2 + 9)(n + 3)(n - 3)$
$\therefore 2n^4 - 162 = 2(n^2 + 9)(n + 3)(n - 3)$

Two other patterns you may find useful are those for factoring the **sum or difference of two cubes.**

$$a^3 + b^3 = (a + b)(a^2 - ab + b^2)$$
$$a^3 - b^3 = (a - b)(a^2 + ab + b^2)$$

EXAMPLE 4   Factor: **a.** $x^3 + 1$ **b.** $8x^3 - 27$

SOLUTION   **a.** $x^3 + 1 = (x + 1)(x^2 - x + 1)$

b. $8x^3 - 27 = (2x - 3)[(2x)^2 + (2x)(3) + 3^2]$
$= (2x - 3)(4x^2 + 6x + 9)$

Sometimes factoring a polynomial requires more than one method of factoring. Example 3(b) above first used a greatest monomial factor and then the difference of squares twice in succession.

You may also find it helpful to rearrange terms in a polynomial before trying to factor it. In the following example the arrows indicate an appropriate grouping of the terms of the polynomial.

EXAMPLE 5   Factor $3ab - 20cd - 15ac + 4bd$.

SOLUTION $3ab - 20cd - 15ac + 4bd = (3ab - 15ac) + (4bd - 20cd)$
$= 3a(b - 5c) + 4d(b - 5c)$
$= (3a + 4d)(b - 5c)$

In the next example notice that the first three terms of the polynomial form the square of a binomial. When you group these terms, you see that the polynomial itself can be expressed as a difference of squares.

EXAMPLE 6   Factor $y^2 - 6y + 9 - z^2$.

SOLUTION $y^2 - 6y + 9 - z^2 = (y^2 - 6y + 9) - z^2$
$= (y - 3)^2 - z^2$
$= [(y - 3) + z][(y - 3) - z]$
$= (y + z - 3)(y - z - 3)$

Oral Exercises

State the greatest monomial factor of each polynomial.

1. $3ab - 6ac$ **2.** $15x^2y^2 - 12xy$ **3.** $16x^6 - 56x^4 + 24x^2$

Which of these polynomials are trinomial squares? Give a reason for your answer.

4. $a^2 + 2a + 1$ **5.** $x^2 - x + 1$ **6.** $4x^2 - 4x - 1$

7. $9y^2 - 6y + 1$ **8.** $16m^2 - 12m + 9$ **9.** $c^4 + 18c^2 + 81$

Written Exercises

Factor each polynomial.

A
1. $32x^3 - 48x^2$ **2.** $2a^2 - 5a^3b$

3. $x^2 - 81$ **4.** $y^2 - 144$

5. $x^3y^2z^3 - 2x^3y^2z^2 + 4x^2y^2z^4$ **6.** $27c^3d^2 - 18c^2d + 9bc^2d$

7. $m^2 - 8m + 16$ **8.** $9p^2 + 6p + 1$

9. $x^2 + 6x + 9$ **10.** $y^2 - 10y + 25$

11. $3x^2 - 27$ **12.** $75y^2 - 3$

13. $-9 - 6x - x^2$ **14.** $48 - 24d + 3d^2$

15. $b(a - 4) + 5(a - 4)$ **16.** $r(r - s) + s(s - r)$

17. $4x^3 + 32$ **18.** $5y^3 - 135z^3$

19. $-n^2 - 4n - 4$ **20.** $n^3 - 16n^2 + 64n$

21. $ax - bx + ay - by$ **22.** $3n^2 + 2r - 2nr - 3n$

23. $3x^2 - 24x + 48$ **24.** $50x^3 - 20x^2y + 2xy^2$

25. $-x^2 + 50x - 625$ **26.** $-14x + x^2 + 49$

27. $125 - y^3$ **28.** $1728 - n^3$

29. $36x^2y^2 - 4x^2$ **30.** $24x^2 - 54y^2$

B
31. $y^6 + 27$ **32.** $y^6 - 729$

33. $(n - 1)^2 - 4y^2$ **34.** $x^2 + 6x + 9 - 36y^2$

35. $1 - 27y^3$ **36.** $1 + 8x^3$

37. $x^2 - y^2 + 7y - 7x$ **38.** $x^4 - 16$

39. $(n + 3)^2 - 8(n + 3) + 16$ **40.** $(x + 2)^2 - 81$

41. $27 - r^3$ **42.** $64 + s^3$

43. $1 - x^2 - 2xy - y^2$ **44.** $36 - 4a^2 + 4ab - b^2$

Factor. Variables used in exponents represent positive integers.

C
45. $(c - 2)^3 - (c - 2)^5$ **46.** $a^{2n} - 4$ **47.** $x^{3n} - y^{3n}$

48. $x^{2n} + 24x^n + 144$ **49.** $25y^{2n} - 80y^n + 64$ **50.** $(r - 1)^6 + (1 - r)^3$

51. $27s^3 - (r - 1)^3$ **52.** $(x - 1)^4 - (y + 1)^2$ **53.** $25 - x^{2n}$

4-5 *Factoring a Quadratic Polynomial*

OBJECTIVE   **To factor quadratic polynomials.**

A polynomial of the form

$$ax^2 + bx + c, a \neq 0$$

is called a **quadratic polynomial** in x. In a polynomial in x that is expressed in simplest form a term of *second* degree such as ax^2 is called the **quadratic term,** a term of *first* degree such as bx is the **linear term,** and c is the **constant term.**

A quadratic polynomial in which neither $b = 0$ nor $c = 0$ is called a **quadratic trinomial.** In Section 4-4 you have factored a special type of quadratic trinomial, the *trinomial square.* Now consider a quadratic trinomial that is not necessarily a trinomial square.

If a quadratic trinomial can be factored, its factors will have the form $px + r$ and $qx + s$. That is,

$$ax^2 + bx + c = (px + r)(qx + s) = pqx^2 + (rq + ps)x + rs.$$

You see that the following relationships must be true.

$$a = pq$$
$$b = rq + ps$$
$$c = rs$$

Use these relationships to help find the factors of a trinomial. Follow the examples step by step to understand the thought process.

EXAMPLE 1   Factor $x^2 - 5x + 6$.

SOLUTION   *Clue 1:* $1 = pq$; use $p = 1$ and $q = 1$.
Write the first terms: $(x \quad)(x \quad)$

Clue 2: $6 = rs$
Since the product rs is *positive* and the sum $r \cdot 1 + 1 \cdot s$, or $r + s$, is *negative*, both r and s must be negative: $(x - \quad)(x - \quad)$
Because $rs = 6$, the only integral choices for r and s are -6 and -1 or -2 and -3. That is, the only possible factors are

$$(x - 6)(x - 1) \text{ and } (x - 2)(x - 3).$$

Clue 3: $-5 = r \cdot 1 + 1 \cdot s = r + s$
Since you also require that $r + s = -5$, the second of these possibilities is the correct one. That is,

$$x^2 - 5x + 6 = (x - 2)(x - 3). \quad \textbf{\textit{Answer}}$$

Except for trivial changes in the factors, such as writing them as $(2 - x)(3 - x)$ or $(-x + 2)(-x + 3)$ or interchanging them, as $(x - 3)(x - 2)$, this factoring is *unique.* It is the only possible factoring in the given factor set.

EXAMPLE 2 Factor $15x^2 + x - 2$

SOLUTION *Clue 1:* $15 = pq$

Possible Values of p and q	Corresponding Factors
$p = 1, q = 15$	$(x \quad)(15x \quad)$
$p = 3, q = 5$	$(3x \quad)(5x \quad)$

Clue 2: $-2 = rs$

Since the product rs is *negative*, one of its factors must be *positive* and the other *negative*. The possibilities are

$$(1)(-2) \text{ and } (-1)(2).$$

Clue 3: $1 = rq + ps$

Trial Factors	Corresponding Linear Term
$(x + 1)(15x - 2)$	$15x - 2x = 13x$
$(x - 1)(15x + 2)$	$-15x + 2x = -13x$
$(3x + 1)(5x - 2)$	$5x - 6x = -x$
$(3x - 1)(5x + 2)$	$-5x + 6x = x$

Only the last trial gives the correct linear term, x.

$\therefore 15x^2 + x - 2 = (3x - 1)(5x + 2)$ ***Answer***

Sometimes there are many combinations of trial factors to consider. With practice you will be able to select the correct one more readily.

A polynomial that cannot be expressed as a product of polynomials of lower degree belonging to a given factor set is said to be **irreducible** over that set.

EXAMPLE 3 Factor $y^2 + 2y + 4$.

SOLUTION The only possible factorings are $(y + 1)(y + 4)$ and $(y + 2)(y + 2)$. When you expand these products, however, you find that neither of the resulting trinomials has $2y$ as its linear term. Hence, $y^2 + 2y + 4$ cannot be factored and is *irreducible*. ***Answer***

An irreducible polynomial whose greatest monomial factor is 1 is called a **prime polynomial** over the set. Thus, $y^2 + 2y + 4$ is a prime polynomial. The polynomial $2y^2 + 2y + 4$, however, is irreducible but not prime, since $2y^2 + 2y + 4 = 2(y^2 + y + 2)$.

The factoring of a polynomial over a set is *complete* when each factor is either a monomial, a prime polynomial, or a power of a prime polynomial. To factor $3x^6 - 48x^2$ completely, you write

$$3x^6 - 48x^2 = 3x^2(x^4 - 16) = 3x^2(x^2 + 4)(x^2 - 4)$$
$$= 3x^2(x^2 + 4)(x + 2)(x - 2).$$

At times you may need to find the *GCF* or *LCM* of a set of polynomials. The common factor having greatest degree and greatest constant factor is called the **greatest common factor (GCF)** of the given polynomials. The **least common multiple (LCM)** is the common multiple having least degree and least possible constant factor.

EXAMPLE 4   Find the GCF and LCM of $2x^3 - 2x$ and $4x^3 - 12x^2 - 16x$.

SOLUTION   Factor the polynomials completely.

$2x^3 - 2x = 2x(x^2 - 1) = 2x(x + 1)(x - 1)$

$4x^3 - 12x^2 - 16x = 4x(x^2 - 3x - 4) = 4x(x - 4)(x + 1)$

GCF $= 2x(x + 1)$ ***Answer***

LCM $= 4x(x - 4)(x + 1)(x - 1)$ ***Answer***

Oral Exercises

For each polynomial, find a pair of numbers whose sum is the coefficient of the linear term and whose product is the constant term.

1. $x^2 + 5x + 4$ **2.** $y^2 + 5y + 6$ **3.** $s^2 - 6s + 9$

4. $t^2 + 8t + 12$ **5.** $x^2 - 7x + 12$ **6.** $z^2 - 2z - 8$

7. $m^2 + 7m - 8$ **8.** $p^2 - 19p + 48$ **9.** $x^2 + 2x - 48$

Which of the following are prime polynomials?

10. $x^2 - 5x$ **11.** $x^2 + 4$ **12.** $y^2 - 9$

13. $z^2 + z + 1$ **14.** $2x + 3$ **15.** $x^2 - 2x + 1$

Written Exercises

Factor completely.

A   **1.** $x^2 + 10x + 9$ **2.** $y^2 + 6y + 8$ **3.** $n^2 + 10n + 21$

    4. $r^2 + 8r + 15$ **5.** $x^2 - 7x + 10$ **6.** $n^2 - 9n + 18$

    7. $n^2 + 2n - 3$ **8.** $n^2 + n - 20$ **9.** $x^2 - 2x - 3$

    10. $n^2 + 6n - 7$ **11.** $12 - t - t^2$ **12.** $12 + 4n - n^2$

    13. $2n^2 - n - 3$ **14.** $12x^2 - 16x + 5$ **15.** $x^2 - 9x + 12$

    16. $6n^2 - 19n + 15$ **17.** $29y - 21 + 10y^2$ **18.** $-43n - 20 + 12n^2$

    19. $10n^2 - n - 3$ **20.** $16y^2 + 17y - 14$ **21.** $14n^2 + 25n + 6$

    22. $6x^2 - 31x + 5$ **23.** $2t^2 - 3t - 5$ **24.** $6s^2 - 7s - 20$

B   **25.** $6n^2 - 3n - 9$ **26.** $4n^2 + 2n - 6$ **27.** $4x^3 - 11x^2 - 3x$

    28. $6n^3 - 7n^2 - 5n$ **29.** $5t^4 - 7t^2 + 2$ **30.** $4r^4 + 3r^2 - 1$

    31. $2x - 16x^4$ **32.** $3x + 81x^4$ **33.** $2t^4 - 9t^2 + 9$

    34. $5t^4 - 25t^2 + 20$ **35.** $5n^3 + 20n^2 + 15n$ **36.** $49x^2 - 14x + 1 - 4y^2$

$a = 7x - 1$

$b = 2y$

$(7x - 1 - 2y)(7x - 1 - 2y)$

Find the (a) GCF and (b) LCM of each set of polynomials.

37. $x^2 - 9$, $x^2 + 6x + 9$ 　　　　　　　**38.** $x^2 + 4x + 3$, $x^2 - 2x - 3$

39. $6x^2 + 7x - 3$, $3x^2 + 26x - 9$ 　　　**40.** $x^3 - y^3$, $x^2 - y^2$, $x - y$

41. $rs^2 - 2rsv + rv^2$, $rs - rv$ 　　　　　**42.** $x^2 - y^2$, $2x - 2y$, $y^2 - xy$

Factor completely. Assume that variables in exponents denote positive integers.

C **43.** $x^{6n} - 5x^{3n} + 4$ 　　　　　　　　　**44.** $x^{4n} + 5x^{2n} - 6$

45. $2(n - 1)^2 - 4(n - 1) + 2$ 　　　　　**46.** $(y^2 + y - 6)^2 - (y^2 - y - 2)^2$

47. $2x^{4n} - 13x^{2n} + 15$ 　　　　　　　　**48.** $x^{8n} - 2x^{4n} + 1$

49. $x(x - 2)^2 - 4x(x - 2) + 4x$ 　　　　**50.** $(y^2 + 3y - 40)^2 - (y^2 + 7y - 8)^2$

Self-Test 2

VOCABULARY　　positive integral factor (p. 137)　　polynomial factoring (p. 140)
multiple (p. 137)　　trinomial square (p. 140)
factor set (p. 137)　　difference of squares (p. 141)
prime factor (p. 137)　　quadratic polynomial (p. 143)
prime factorization (p. 137)　　quadratic term (p. 143)
greatest common factor (GCF)　　linear term (p. 143)
　(p. 137)　　constant term (p. 143)
least common multiple (LCM)　　quadratic trinomial (p. 143)
　(p. 137)　　irreducible (p. 144)
greatest common monomial　　prime polynomial (p. 144)
　factor (GCF) (p. 138)　　greatest common factor (GCF)
least common multiple (LCM)　　　of polynomials (p. 145)
　of monomials (p. 138)　　least common multiple (LCM)
greatest monomial factor　　　of polynomials (p. 145)
　(p. 140)

Factor over the set of primes.

1. 260 　　　　　　　　**2.** 300 　　　　　　　　Obj. 4-3, p. 137

Find (a) the GCF and (b) the LCM.

3. $9m^3$, $3m^2n$ 　　　　　**4.** $-18x^2y^2$, $12xy^3$

Factor completely.

5. $4x^2 - 1$ 　　　　　　**6.** $a^2 - 4a + 4$ 　　　　　Obj. 4-4, p. 140

7. $4x^2 + 24x$ 　　　　　**8.** $y^3 - 8$

9. $m^2 - 9m + 20$ 　　　**10.** $6x^2 - x - 12$ 　　　　Obj. 4-5, p. 143

Check your answers with those at the back of the book.

APPLICATIONS OF FACTORING

4-6 *Solving Polynomial Equations by Factoring*

OBJECTIVE To solve equations by factoring.

Equations that can be written with 0 as one side and a polynomial as the other side are called **polynomial equations.** When the polynomial can be written as the product of factors of degree 1 you have an additional method for solving equations. The basis for the solution is the *zero-product property*, developed below.

The *multiplicative property of zero* (Section 1-8) guarantees the following theorem for real numbers a and b:

If $a = 0$ or $b = 0$, then $ab = 0$.

The converse of this theorem is the theorem:

If $ab = 0$, then $a = 0$ or $b = 0$.

Although the converse of a theorem need not be true, this one can be proved.

Proof:

If $a = 0$, the conclusion is true. Therefore, consider the case $a \neq 0$. Then:

STATEMENTS	REASONS
1. $\frac{1}{a}$ is a real number.	Inverse axiom for multiplication
2. $ab = 0$	Given
3. $\frac{1}{a}(ab) = \frac{1}{a} \cdot 0$	Multiplication property of equality
4. Left side: $\frac{1}{a}(ab) = \left(\frac{1}{a} \cdot a\right)b = 1 \cdot b = b$	Associative axiom for multiplication, inverse axiom for multiplication, identity axiom for multiplication
5. Right side: $\frac{1}{a} \cdot 0 = 0$	Multiplicative property of 0
6. $\therefore b = 0$	Substitution principle, using steps 3, 4, and 5

$\therefore$ given $ab = 0$, it follows that $a = 0$ or $b = 0$.

The zero-product property, given on the next page, combines the theorem stated above and its converse, which has just been proved.

ZERO-PRODUCT PROPERTY

For all real numbers a and b,

$$ab = 0 \text{ if and only if } a = 0 \text{ or } b = 0.$$

The zero-product property can be extended to more than two factors. In general, a product is zero if and only if at least one of its factors is zero.

EXAMPLE 1 Solve $(x - 2)(3x - 9) = 0$.

SOLUTION Using the zero-product property, write the equivalent compound sentence.

$$x - 2 = 0 \quad \text{or} \quad 3x - 9 = 0$$
$$x = 2 \quad \quad \quad x = 3$$

The check is left for you.

$\therefore$ The solution set is $\{2, 3\}$. **Answer**

EXAMPLE 2 Solve $2x^3 + 9x^2 = -4x$

SOLUTION
1. Transform to an equivalent equation with 0 as one side.
   $$2x^3 + 9x^2 + 4x = 0$$

2. Factor the polynomial.
   $$x(2x^2 + 9x + 4) = 0$$
   $$x(2x + 1)(x + 4) = 0$$

3. Solve the equivalent compound sentence.

$$x = 0 \quad \text{or} \quad 2x + 1 = 0 \quad \text{or} \quad x + 4 = 0$$
$$x = 0 \quad \quad 2x = -1 \quad \quad x = -4$$
$$x = -\tfrac{1}{2}$$

4. The check is left for you.
5. The solution set is $\{0, -\tfrac{1}{2}, -4\}$. **Answer**

A number r is called a **zero** of a function f if $f(r) = 0$. For example,

$$3 \text{ is a zero of the function } g \colon x \to x^2 - 9$$

because $g(3) = 3^2 - 9 = 0$. Note that -3 is also a zero of g.

EXAMPLE 3 Find the zeros of the function $m \colon x \to (x - 1)^2 - 8x + 24$.

SOLUTION
1. Solve the equation $m(x) = 0$, or $(x - 1)^2 - 8x + 24 = 0$.

2. Simplify.
$$x^2 - 2x + 1 - 8x + 24 = 0$$
$$x^2 - 10x + 25 = 0$$

3. Factor.
$$(x - 5)^2 = 0$$

4. Solve the equivalent compound sentence.

$$x - 5 = 0 \quad \text{or} \quad x - 5 = 0$$
$$x = 5 \quad | \quad x = 5$$

5. Check: $(5 - 1)^2 - 8(5) + 24 = 16 - 40 + 24 = -24 + 24 = 0$

6. The only zero of m is 5. (As you will see, 5 is a *double zero* of m.)

Answer

In Example 3, the polynomial defining the function m has two identical factors, and so the corresponding zero of the function is called a **double zero.** Similarly, the equation $m(x) = 0$ is said to have a **double root.**

In general, the zeros and roots arising from multiple identical factors are called **multiple zeros** of functions and **multiple roots** of equations, respectively.

Oral Exercises

Solve each equation.

1. $3(x - 4) = 0$ **2.** $y(y + 4) = 0$ **3.** $2x(x + 3) = 0$

4. $\frac{1}{2}k(k + 8) = 0$ **5.** $(2r - 1)(2r + 1) = 0$ **6.** $9m(m - 1)(m + 5) = 0$

State all zeros of the function. Identify all double zeros.

7. $f(y) = 3y + 9$ **8.** $g(x) = x^2 - 16$ **9.** $h(m) = (m + 2)(3m - 1)$

10. $f(x) = 4x^2(x + 3)$ **11.** $g(b) = (b - 4)^2$ **12.** $h(l) = (l - 1)^2(l + 10)$

Written Exercises

Solve. Identify all double roots.

A   **1.** $(x - 4)(x + 4) = 0$ **2.** $x(x + 8) = 0$ **3.** $(5y - 2)(2y + 1) = 0$

    4. $(3y - 1)(y - 7) = 0$ **5.** $n^2 - 4n + 3 = 0$ **6.** $t^2 - 5t + 6 = 0$

    7. $x^2 - 5x = 0$ **8.** $y^2 + 8y = 0$ **9.** $5y = 10y^2$

  10. $y^2 - 8y + 16 = 0$ **11.** $n^2 + 14n + 49 = 0$ **12.** $12y = 6y^2$

  13. $m^2 + 10 = -7m$ **14.** $4 + 3x = x^2$ **15.** $2m^2 - 5m + 2 = 0$

  16. $3m^2 + 8m - 3 = 0$ **17.** $x^4 = 9x^2$ **18.** $6x^2 = 13x + 8$

  19. $(x + 3)(x - 3) = 7$ **20.** $(x + 3)(x - 3) = -5$ **21.** $6y^2 + 2y - 4 = 0$

  22. $18m^2 - 3m - 36 = 0$ **23.** $(2 - y)^2 + y^2 = 2$ **24.** $2z^3 - 4z^2 - 16z = 0$

Solve. Identify all double roots.

B **25.** $4x^2 - 25 = 0$

26. $(x - 4)(x + 3)(x + 4) = 0$

27. $(x^2 - 1)(x - 3) = 0$

28. $x^4 + 5x^2 + 6 = 0$

29. $x^4 - 8x^2 + 16 = 0$

30. $2x^3 - 8x = 0$

31. $x^4 + 3x^2 = 4$

32. $x^4 - 13x^2 + 36 = 0$

33. $x^3 - 10x^2 + 25x = 0$

34. $x^5 + 4x = 5x^3$

Find all the zeros of the function.

35. $f(x) = (x + 5)^2 + 4x - 57$

36. $f(h) = (h + 1)^2 + 2(h + 1)$

37. $f(k) = (k - 1)^2 - 4k + 8$

38. $f(n) = (n + 1)^2 + 6(n + 1) + 9$

For each statement in Exercises 39–44:
a. Indicate whether the statement is true or false.
b. Write the converse of the statement and indicate whether it is true or false.
c. If a statement and its converse are both true, rewrite them as a single "if and only if" statement.

C **39.** If $a = b$, then $ac = bc$.

40. If $ab > 0$, then $a > 0$ and $b > 0$.

41. If $m = n$, then $m^2 = n^2$.

42. If $2x + 3y = 9$, then $y = 3 - \frac{2}{3}x$.

43. If $p < 2$, then $p^2 < 4$.

44. If $a > b > 0$, then $0 < \frac{1}{a} < \frac{1}{b}$.

ḟistorical ṅote Prime Numbers

In addition to their work in geometry, early Greek mathematicians made significant advances in the field of number theory. In Book IX of *Elements* (about 300 B.C.) Euclid showed that there is an infinite number of primes.

Although no formula for generating primes exists, another Greek, Eratosthenes (about 240 B.C.), devised an efficient method for listing primes. Since no primes except 2 are even, Eratosthenes began by listing positive odd integers beginning with 3. He then crossed out all multiples of 3. Since 5, the next number in the list, had not been crossed out, it had to be prime. Eratosthenes then crossed out all multiples of 5, then 7, then 11, and so on (9 had already been crossed out as a multiple of 3). Using / for a multiple of 3, / for a multiple of 5, and \ for a multiple of 7, this method (known as "Eratosthenes' sieve") is illustrated below.

3	5	7	9̸	11	13	1̸5̸	17	19	2̸1̸	23	2̸5̸
2̸7̸	29	31	3̸3̸	3̸5̸	37	3̸9̸	41	43	4̸5̸	47	4̸9̸
5̸1̸	53	5̸5̸	5̸7̸	59	61	6̸3̸	6̸5̸	67	6̸9̸	71	73
7̸5̸	7̸7̸	79	8̸1̸	83	8̸5̸	8̸7̸	89	9̸1̸	9̸3̸	9̸5̸	97	9̸9̸

4-7 *Solving Problems with Polynomial Equations*

OBJECTIVE   **To solve word problems using polynomial equations.**

The zero-product property can also be used to solve problems that can be expressed as polynomial equations. The plan for solving a word problem (Section 2-4) is useful here. It is especially important to check results since, as you will see in the following example, a solution of the equation is not always a solution of the problem.

EXAMPLE   The Smiths' living room is square. The Chases' living room is rectangular but not square. It measures 3 m less on one side than the Smiths' but 2 m more on an adjacent side; it contains 300 m² of floor space. Which room has the greater floor space and how much greater is it?

SOLUTION

Step 1 The problem asks which room has the greater floor space and by how many square meters it is greater.

Step 2 If you know the dimensions of the rooms you can calculate the areas. Drawing a diagram to show the information you know will be helpful.

Let s = the length of the Smiths' room in meters.
Then $s + 2$ = the length of the Chases' room in meters, and
$s - 3$ = the width of the Chases' room in meters.

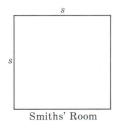

Smiths' Room

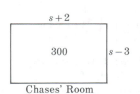

Chases' Room

Step 3 Write an equation for the area of the Chases' room.
$$(s + 2)(s - 3) = 300$$

Step 4
$$s^2 - s - 6 = 300$$
$$s^2 - s - 306 = 0$$
$$(s - 18)(s + 17) = 0$$
$$s = 18 \text{ or } s = -17$$

Step 5 Since it is not meaningful to use -17 as a length, reject it as a solution of the problem. Check 18 in the original problem.
$$(18 + 2)(18 - 3) \overset{?}{=} 300$$
$$20 \cdot 15 = 300 \quad \sqrt{}$$

∴ The area of the Smiths' room is 18^2, or 324 m². Its floor space is greater by $324 - 300$, or 24 m². **Answer**

Problems

A **1.** The sum of a number and its square is 30. Find the number.

   2. The square of a number is 195 more than twice the number. What is the number?

   3. Find three consecutive positive integers such that the sum of the squares of the largest two is 181.

   4. Find four consecutive integers such that the sum of the squares of the first two is 11 less than the square of the fourth.

   5. A narrow rectangular strip of land has an area of 40 m². The sum of the lengths of two adjacent sides is 22 m. How long and how wide is the strip?

   6. A rectangular house lot has an area of 1050 m². Its length exceeds its width by 5 m. What are the dimensions of the lot?

   7. A city park is shaped like a right triangle with length of one leg twice the length of the other leg. The area is 2500 m². What are the lengths of its legs?

B **8.** A pennant has the shape of an isosceles triangle. Its height is 5 cm longer than three times its base. Its area is 650 cm². Find the length of its base and its height.

   9. Find three consecutive even integers such that the sum of the product of the first two and the product of the last two is 648.

  10. The sum of a number and its cube is the same as twice the square of the number. Find the number.

  11. Archie, Belinda, and Claire leave from the same point at the same time. Archie cycles north at a speed 3 km/h less than Claire's speed, and Belinda cycles east at a speed 4 km/h more than Claire's speed. After one hour, Archie and Belinda are 17 km apart. Find the speed of each of the three cyclists.

  12. A farmer plans to build a fence to enclose a rectangular field. One side of the field is along a river, and no fence is needed there. The farmer has 110 m of fence available, and the field must have an area of 1200 m². What should the dimensions of the field be?

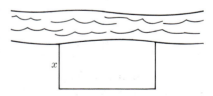

  13. Since the solution is not correct, there is an error in the following argument. Which statement does not follow logically from the preceding one?

$$x^2 - 3x + 2 = 6$$
$$\therefore (x - 1)(x - 2) = 2 \cdot 3$$
$$\therefore x - 1 = 2 \text{ or } x - 2 = 3$$
$$x = 3 \qquad x = 5 \qquad \therefore \text{ the solution set is } \{3, 5\}.$$

C 14. An open rectangular box is to be made by cutting out squares from the corners of a piece of cardboard measuring 80 cm by 100 cm and folding along the dotted lines. If the original length of a side of the cutout is doubled, it is found that the volume of the box remains the same. What is the original length x?

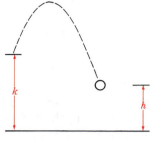

In the following problems, use the formula $h = k + rt - 4.9t^2$. It gives the approximate height h in meters of an object, t seconds after it is propelled upward from a height of k meters at an initial speed of r meters per second. (*Hint:* You will probably find it helpful to transform your equations into equivalent ones that do not contain decimals.)

15. A ball is thrown vertically upward with a speed of 14.7 m/s from a tower 58 m high. After how many seconds will the ball be 9 m above the ground?

16. A projectile is fired from the ground with an upward speed of 245 m/s. After how many seconds will it return to the ground?

17. A rocket is moving vertically at a speed of 17.15 m/s at an altitude of 90 m when its propellant is exhausted. How much time will elapse before the rocket is again at 90 m altitude?

18. From the top of a cliff 102 m high, an arrow is shot vertically into the air at an initial speed of 44.1 m/s. After how many seconds will the arrow be 200 m above the base of the cliff? Explain why you expect two solutions.

CHALLENGE ─────────────

In the following division problem involving letters, each letter represents a different number from 0 to 9. The vowels a, e, i, o, and u represent even numbers. The consonants represent odd numbers. Change the letters into the numbers that they represent.

```
            xxzst
      tz)uizotz
         tz
         xxz
         tz
         eao
         stz
          ott
          ooz
           zoz
           zoz
             a
```

4-8 *Solving Inequalities*

OBJECTIVE   To use factoring in solving inequalities.

Some inequalities can be expressed with a polynomial as one side and 0 as the other. If you can factor the polynomial into factors of degree less than two, you can solve the given inequality. To solve the inequality, use the fact that a product of nonzero factors is *negative* if the number of negative factors is *odd*, and the product is *positive* if the number of negative factors is *even*.

EXAMPLE 1   Find and graph the solution set of $x^2 + x > 12$.

SOLUTION
$$x^2 + x > 12$$
$$x^2 + x - 12 > 0$$
$$(x + 4)(x - 3) > 0$$

Since the product is positive, the two factors are either both positive or both negative.

Both Positive	or	Both Negative

$x + 4 > \quad 0$ and $x - 3 > 0$ | $x + 4 < \quad 0$ and $x - 3 < 0$
$\quad x > -4$ | $\quad x > 3$ | $\quad x < -4$ | $\quad x < 3$

This conjunction is equivalent to $x > 3$.   This conjunction is equivalent to $x < -4$.

The solution set of the original inequality is the solution set of disjunction $x > 3$ or $x < -4$.

$\therefore$ the solution set is $\{x: x > 3$ or $x < -4\}$, which is graphed below.

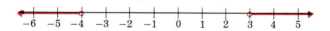

Answer

Notice the relationship between the graph of Example 1 and the graph of Example 2.

EXAMPLE 2   Find and graph the solution set of $x^2 + x < 12$.

SOLUTION
$$x^2 + x < 12$$
$$x^2 + x - 12 < 0$$
$$(x + 4)(x - 3) < 0$$

Since the product is negative, one factor must be positive and the other negative.

$x + 4 > \quad 0$ and $x - 3 < 0$ or $x + 4 < \quad 0$ and $x - 3 > 0$
$\quad x > -4$ | $\quad x < 3$ $\quad x < -4$ | $\quad x > 3$

This conjunction is equivalent to $-4 < x < 3$.   This conjunction has no solution.

The solution set of the original inequality is the solution set of $-4 < x < 3$.

$\therefore$ the solution set is $\{x: -4 < x < 3\}$, which is graphed below.

Answer

A visual method of solving inequalities is the use of a **sign graph,** shown in Example 3. This method uses the fact that a product of n nonzero factors will be negative when and only when there is an odd number of negative factors.

EXAMPLE 3 Find and graph the solution set of $4x^3 \le 16x$.

SOLUTION 1.
$$4x^3 \le 16x$$
$$4x^3 - 16x \le 0$$
$$4x(x^2 - 4) \le 0$$
$$4x(x + 2)(x - 2) \le 0$$

Since 4 is a positive number, you can remove it from consideration. Only the signs of the remaining factors determine the sign of the product.

2. To draw the sign graph, first draw four number lines, one for each factor and one for the product. Then label the part where the indicated factor is positive and where it is negative.

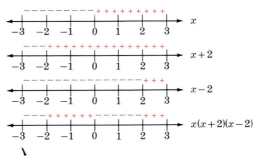

3. The product $x(x + 2)(x - 2)$ is negative when either exactly one factor is negative or when exactly three factors are negative. The product is positive when either exactly two factors are negative or no factor is negative. Label the final product number line accordingly.

$\therefore$ the solution set is $\{x: x \le -2 \text{ or } 0 \le x \le 2\}$, graphed below.

Answer

Oral Exercises

For each inequality, state the letter of the graph of its solution set.

1. $(x + 3)(x - 1) > 0$

2. $(x - 3)(x + 1) \leq 0$

3. $(x + 3)(x - 1) \geq 0$

4. $(x - 3)(x + 1) > 0$

5. $(x + 3)(x - 1) < 0$

6. $(x - 3)(x + 1) < 0$

a.

b.

c.

d.

e.

f.

Written Exercises

Find and graph the solution set of each inequality.

A 1. $x^2 - 3x < 0$ 2. $t^2 - 2t > 0$ 3. $y^2 + 4y + 4 > 0$

4. $t^2 - 6t + 9 \leq 0$ 5. $4m^2 \leq 16$ 6. $81 - v^2 \geq 0$

7. $n^2 - 6n > -5$ 8. $x^2 + 18 < 9x$ 9. $y^2 + 3y < 4$

10. $9n^2 \geq 25$ 11. $18 + y^2 < 10y - 7$ 12. $m(m + 2) > 8$

B 13. $2x^2 + 3x < 20$ 14. $3x^2 - 10x \leq -3$ 15. $y^2 + 1 < 0$

16. $3y^2 - 17y \geq 6$ 17. $10x^2 + 7x \leq 12$ 18. $4x^3 - 25x > 0$

C 19. $x^4 \geq 10x^2 - 9$ 20. $(x + 1)(x^2 - x - 2)(x^2 - 4x + 4) < 0$

Self-Test 3

VOCABULARY polynomial equation (p. 147)   multiple zeros (p. 149)
zero of a function (p. 148)   multiple roots (p. 149)
double zero (p. 149)   sign graph (p. 155)
double root (p. 149)

Solve each equation.

1. $(x - 2)(x + 4) = 0$ 2. $3x^2 = x + 10$ **Obj. 4-6, p. 147**

3. A rectangular picture is mounted on a rectangular mat with an even Obj. 4-7, p. 151 border of mat visible on all four sides. The mat measures 60 cm by 40 cm. The picture covers one third of the mat. How wide is the border?

Find and graph the solution set of each inequality.

4. $y^2 - 5y + 6 > 0$ **5.** $x^2 + 3x < 10$ Obj. 4-8, p. 154

Check your answers with those at the back of the book.

Chapter Summary

1. If a and b are real numbers and m and n are positive integers, the following *laws of exponents* are true.

   Law 1. $b^m b^n = b^{m+n}$ Law 2. $(ab)^m = a^m b^m$ Law 3. $(b^m)^n = b^{mn}$

   Law 4. If $m > n$ and $b \neq 0$: $\dfrac{b^m}{b^n} = b^{m-n}$

2. To find the product of two polynomials, multiply each term of one polynomial by each term of the other using the laws of exponents and simplify the result.

3. To find the *prime factorization* of an integer, write it as the product of *primes*. Use prime factorization to find the *greatest common factor* (*GCF*) and *least common multiple* (*LCM*) of two or more integers.

4. The monomial having greatest degree and greatest coefficient that is a factor of each of several monomials is their *greatest common monomial factor* (*GCF*).

5. The monomial with lowest degree and lowest positive coefficient that is a multiple of each of several monomials is their *least common multiple* (*LCM*).

6. To factor a polynomial, first look for a greatest monomial factor. After factoring the greatest monomial factor, look for special factoring patterns such as *trinomial squares* and *differences of squares*. If no special factoring pattern presents itself, look for a pair of binomial factors.

7. Many *polynomial equations* can be solved by the use of factoring and the *zero-product property*. Many *inequalities* can be solved by factoring and analyzing sign patterns among the factors.

Chapter Review

Give the letter of the correct answer.

1. Express $(-x^2)^3(x^2)$ in simplest form.

    a. x^8 **b.** $-x^8$ **c.** x^7 **d.** $-x^7$

4-1

2. Express $4a(a^2 - 2ab + b^2)$ in simplest form.

    a. $4a^3 - 8ab + ab^2$ **b.** $4a^3 + 4ab + ab^2$ **c.** $4a^3 - 8a^2b + 4ab^2$

3. Express $(x + 1)(x^2 - 4x + 4)$ as a polynomial in simplest form.

    a. $x^3 - 3x^2 + 4$ **b.** $x^3 - 4x^2 + 4x + 1$ **c.** $x^3 - 3x^2 - 8x + 4$

4-2

4. Express $(2x - y)(2x + y)$ as a polynomial in simplest form.

    a. $4x^2 - xy + y^2$ **b.** $4x^2 - 4xy - y^2$ **c.** $4x^2 - y^2$

5. Find the GCF of $12x^2y^3$, $18xy^2$, and $24x^3y^3$.

    a. $12x^2y^2$ **b.** $72x^3y^3$ **c.** $6x^2y^3$ **d.** $6xy^2$

4-3

6. Find the LCM of $8x^3$, $4x^2y^2$, $10y^3$.

    a. $40x^3y^3$ **b.** $80x^3y^3$ **c.** $320x^2y^2$ **d.** $40x^5y^5$

7. Factor $3n^2 - 27$ completely.

    a. $3(n - 3)^2$ **b.** $3(n^2 - 9)$ **c.** $3(n + 3)(n - 3)$

4-4

8. Factor $25x^2 - 10x + 1$ completely.

    a. $(5x + 1)(5x - 1)$ **b.** $(5x - 1)^2$ **c.** $(x - 5)^2$

9. Factor $y + 2y^2 - 3$ completely.

    a. $(y + 3)(y - 1)$ **b.** $(2y + 3)(y - 1)$ **c.** $(y - 3)^2$

4-5

10. Factor $12t^2 + 5t - 2$ completely.

    a. $(4t - 1)(3t + 2)$ **b.** $(6t - 2)(2t + 1)$ **c.** $(4t + 1)(3t - 2)$

11. Solve the equation $x(x - 3) = 0$.

    a. $\{3\}$ **b.** $\{0, -3\}$ **c.** $\{1, 3\}$ **d.** $\{0, 3\}$

4-6

12. Solve the equation $5x^2 + 13x - 6 = 0$.

    a. $\{\frac{2}{5}, -3\}$ **b.** $\{-\frac{2}{5}, 3\}$ **c.** $\{2, -\frac{3}{5}\}$ **d.** $\{2, -3\}$

13. A convention hall is built in a square shape. Strips 3 m wide are reserved along two opposite sides for walkways, leaving 720 m² for the exhibit area. How wide is the hall?

    a. 24 m   **b.** 36 m   **c.** 30 m   **d.** -24 m

4-7

14. Graph the solution set of $x^2 > -5x - 6$.

    a.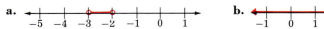

    b.

    c.

    d.

4-8

Chapter Test

1. Multiply $4xy^2$ by $-5x^2y$. 4-1

2. Simplify $(-4m^2n)^3$.

Express the product as a polynomial in simplest form.

3. $2x^2(x^2 + 9x + 18)$

4. $(3a - b)(3a + b)$ 4-2

5. $(3a - b)^2$

6. $(x - 3)(x + 5)$

7. Find the prime factorization of 210. 4-3

8. What is the GCF of $9a^2b^2$ and $-12ab^2c^3$?

9. Is $x^2 - 4x + 4$ a trinomial square? State a reason for your answer. 4-4

Factor completely.

10. $4x^2 - 9$ **11.** $9x^2 + 12xy + 4y^2$

12. $3x^2 + 14x - 5$ **13.** $7a^2 + 11ab - 6b^2$ 4-5

Solve.

14. $x^2 + 3x = 28$ **15.** $2x^2 + 9x - 5 = 0$ 4-6

16. One section of a hip roof is in the form of an isosceles triangle. The width of the house, which is the base of the triangle, is 9 m more than the height of the triangle. If there is 68 m² of roofing material available for this section, how wide can the house be for the amount of roofing to be adequate? 4-7

17. Find and graph the solution set of $n^2 - n - 20 \leq 0$. 4-8

Computer Key-In

Computers are very effective in doing repetitive operations such as testing for factors of numbers. To do this, it is convenient to use the *greatest integer function*, INT(X), which will find the greatest integer less than or equal to X. Thus:

$$\text{INT}(4) = 4, \quad \text{INT}(4.35) = 4, \quad \text{INT}(4.99) = 4$$
$$\text{INT}(-4.35) = -5, \quad \text{INT}(-4.99) = -5$$

This function can be used to test whether or not a division is exact, that is, whether or not the divisor is a factor:

$$12/3 = 4; \quad 12/3 = \text{INT}(12/3), \text{ and so 3 is a factor of 12.}$$
$$12/5 = 2.4; \quad 12/5 \neq \text{INT}(12/5), \text{ and so 5 is not a factor.}$$

The factors are found by testing numbers in succession. This is done in the following program by using a FOR-NEXT loop. This program will find factors of a given whole number.

```
10  PRINT "WHAT IS YOUR WHOLE NUMBER";
20  INPUT W
30  PRINT "FACTORS OF";W;" ARE:"
40  FOR F=1 TO W
50  LET Q=W/F
60  IF Q <> INT(Q) THEN 80
70  PRINT F;" AND";Q
80  NEXT F
90  END
RUN
```

```
WHAT IS YOUR WHOLE NUMBER?576
FACTORS OF 576 ARE:
  1  AND  576
  2  AND  288
  3  AND  192
  4  AND  144
  6  AND  96
  8  AND  72
  9  AND  64
 12  AND  48
 16  AND  36
 18  AND  32
 24  AND  24
 32  AND  18
 36  AND  16
 48  AND  12
 64  AND  9
 72  AND  8
 96  AND  6
144  AND  4
192  AND  3
288  AND  2
576  AND  1
```

Notice that after the factors 24 and 24 are found (the *square root* of 576 is 24), the pairs of factors repeat in reverse order. Therefore, you can find all the factors by considering numbers less than or equal to the square root. In BASIC, square root is found from SQR(X). Thus, you can shorten the work by changing line 40 to:

```
40 FOR F=1 TO SQR(W)
```

Exercises

Using the program given in the text, find the factors of:

1. a. 111	b. 1111	c. 11,111	d. 111,111
2. a. 123	b. 1234	c. 12,345	d. 123,456
3. a. 987	b. 9876	c. 98,765	d. 987,654
4. a. 321	b. 4321	c. 54,321	d. 654,321

5. Type in the following program and RUN it for the numbers given in Exercises 1–4. The REM statements show the parts of the program.

```
10   PRINT "TO LIST THE PRIME FACTORS OF A WHOLE NUMBER,"
20   PRINT "INPUT THE NUMBER:";
30   INPUT W
40   REM***INTRODUCE Z TO COUNT THE FACTORS.
50   LET Z=0
60   REM***DIVIDE BY 2 UNTIL DIVISION IS NOT EXACT OR QUOTIENT IS 1.
70   LET M=W
80   LET F=2
90   LET Q=M/F
100  IF Q <> INT(Q) THEN 180
110  LET Z=Z+1
120  PRINT F;
130  IF Q=1 THEN 290
140  REM***LET QUOTIENT BE NEW DIVIDEND.
150  LET M=Q
160  GOTO 90
170  REM***DIVIDE BY ODD NUMBERS IN SUCCESSION.
180  FOR F=3 TO M STEP 2
190  LET Q=M/F
200  IF Q <> INT(Q) THEN 270
210  LET Z=Z+1
220  PRINT F;
230  IF Q=1 THEN 290
240  REM***LET QUOTIENT BE NEW DIVIDEND.
250  LET M=Q
260  GOTO 190
270  NEXT F
280  REM***PRINT OUTPUT.
290  IF Z>1 THEN 320
300  PRINT " IS PRIME."
310  STOP
320  PRINT " ARE THE PRIME FACTORS OF"W;"."
330  END
```

Seawater contains many dissolved substances in various amounts. For example, a 10^5 kg sample of seawater contains on the average more than 2.6×10^3 kg of common salt (sodium chloride). It also contains about 1.4×10^{-4} kg of gold, from dissolved gold salts.

5

RATIONAL EXPRESSIONS

EXPONENTS

5-1 *Quotient Rules*

OBJECTIVE To simplify quotients using the laws of exponents.

When you multiply two fractions, for example,

$$\frac{2}{3} \cdot \frac{5}{7} = \frac{2 \cdot 5}{3 \cdot 7} = \frac{10}{21},$$

you use the multiplication rule for fractions:

MULTIPLICATION RULE FOR FRACTIONS

If p, q, r, and s are any real numbers, $q \neq 0$ and $s \neq 0$, then

$$\frac{p}{q} \cdot \frac{r}{s} = \frac{pr}{qs}.$$

A proof of this rule is given in Exercise 35 on page 167. Because equality is symmetric, you also have the property of quotients:

PROPERTY OF QUOTIENTS

If p, q, r, and s are any real numbers, $q \neq 0$ and $s \neq 0$, then

$$\frac{pr}{qs} = \frac{p}{q} \cdot \frac{r}{s}.$$

Examples of the property of quotients are

$$\frac{28 \cdot 15}{7 \cdot 3} = \frac{28}{7} \cdot \frac{15}{3} = 4 \cdot 5 = 20$$

and

$$\frac{36b^5}{9b^3} = \frac{36}{9} \cdot \frac{b^5}{b^3} = 4b^2.$$

If $r \neq 0$, then you can replace s by r in the property of quotients to obtain $\frac{pr}{qr} = \frac{p}{q} \cdot \frac{r}{r}$. Since $\frac{r}{r} = 1$ for any nonzero r, you obtain the cancellation rule for fractions:

CANCELLATION RULE FOR FRACTIONS

If p, q, and r are any real numbers and $r \neq 0$, then

$$\frac{pr}{qr} = \frac{p}{q}.$$

Examples are

$$\frac{30}{18} = \frac{5 \cdot 6}{3 \cdot 6} = \frac{5}{3} \quad \text{and} \quad \frac{2ab}{4bc} = \frac{a \cdot 2b}{2c \cdot 2b} = \frac{a}{2c}.$$

In Section 4-1 you learned laws of exponents 1, 2, 3, and 4 (see box on page 165). Law 1 enables you to multiply powers of the same base by *adding* exponents; for example,

$$6^3 \cdot 6^5 = 6^{3+5} = 6^8, \quad \text{and} \quad x^4 \cdot x^3 = x^{4+3} = x^7.$$

Law 4 enables you to divide powers of the same base by subtracting exponents; for example

$$\frac{6^8}{6^5} = 6^{8-5} = 6^3.$$

Law 4 was limited to quotients in which the exponent in the numerator was greater than the exponent in the denominator. With the help of the cancellation rule for fractions, you can now divide powers of the same base when the greater exponent is in the denominator.

$$\frac{x^3}{x^7} = \frac{1 \cdot x^3}{x^4 \cdot x^3} = \frac{1}{x^4}$$

Notice that you are now *subtracting* exponents:

$$\frac{6^8}{6^5} = 6^{8-5}, \quad \text{and} \quad \frac{x^3}{x^7} = \frac{1}{x^{7-3}}$$

These examples illustrate laws 4 and 5 on the next page.

Assume that m and n are positive integers and that a and
real numbers. In laws 4, 5, and 6, assume $a \neq 0$. In law 7 ass
$b \neq 0$.

1. $a^m \cdot a^n = a^{m+n}$ 2. $(ab)^n = a^n b^n$ 3. $(a^m)^n = $

4. If $m > n$: $\dfrac{a^m}{a^n} = a^{m-n}$ 5. If $n > m$: $\dfrac{a^m}{a^n} = \dfrac{1}{a^{n-m}}$

6. If $m = n$: $\dfrac{a^m}{a^n} = 1$ 7. $\left(\dfrac{a}{b}\right)^n = \dfrac{a^n}{b^n}$

A shortened proof of law 5 is given below. Only the most important
steps are stated and justified.

STATEMENTS	REASONS
1. $a^n = a^{(n-m)+m} = a^{n-m} \cdot a^m$	Law 1
2. $\dfrac{a^m}{a^n} = \dfrac{1 \cdot a^m}{a^{n-m} \cdot a^m}$	Substitution
3. $\therefore \dfrac{a^m}{a^n} = \dfrac{1}{a^{n-m}}$	Cancellation rule for fractions

The laws of exponents are useful in simplifying expressions involving powers. An expression involving powers is said to be **simplified**
when each base appears only once and there are no "powers of powers."
Fractions should be in simplest form.

EXAMPLE   Simplify: **a.** $\dfrac{6ac^5}{8a^3c^3}$ **b.** $\dfrac{x}{z^2} \cdot \left(\dfrac{z}{x^2}\right)^3$

SOLUTION   **a.** Two methods are shown.

Method 1: Think of each variable separately and use law 4 or 5.

$$\frac{6ac^5}{8a^3c^3} = \frac{6}{8} \cdot \frac{a}{a^3} \cdot \frac{c^5}{c^3} = \frac{3}{4} \cdot \frac{1}{a^2} \cdot \frac{c^2}{1} = \frac{3c^2}{4a^2}$$

Method 2: Find the GCF of the numerator and the denominator and
use the cancellation rule for fractions.

$$\frac{6ac^5}{8a^3c^3} = \frac{3c^2 \cdot 2ac^3}{4a^2 \cdot 2ac^3} = \frac{3c^2}{4a^2}$$

b. $\dfrac{x}{z^2}\left(\dfrac{z}{x^2}\right)^3 = \dfrac{x}{z^2} \cdot \dfrac{z^3}{(x^2)^3} = \dfrac{x}{z^2} \cdot \dfrac{z^3}{x^6} = \dfrac{xz^3}{x^6z^2} = \dfrac{z}{x^5}$

(This solution was obtained by the use of Method 1.)

...each expression. Assume that no denominator is 0 and that
...les appearing in exponents denote positive integers.

1. $x^5 \cdot x^2$ x^7

2. $(x^5)^2$ x^{10}

3. $\dfrac{x^5}{x^2}$ x^3

4. $\dfrac{x^2}{x^5}$ $\dfrac{1}{x^3}$

5. $\left(\dfrac{a}{3}\right)^2$ $\dfrac{a^2}{9}$

6. $\dfrac{t^2 \cdot t^3}{t^4}$ $\dfrac{t^5}{t^4} = t$

7. $\dfrac{a^{3m}}{a^m}$ a^{2m}

8. $\dfrac{x^6}{(x^2)^3}$ $\dfrac{x^6}{x^6} = 1$

9. $\left(\dfrac{-x^3}{3}\right)^2$ $\dfrac{x^6}{9}$

10. $\left(\dfrac{-2}{a^2}\right)^3$ $\dfrac{8}{a^6}$

11. $\dfrac{ct^2}{c^2t}$ $\dfrac{t}{c}$

12. $\dfrac{6pq^2}{2pq}$ $= 3q$

Written Exercises

Simplify each expression. Assume that no denominator is 0 and that all
exponents are positive integers.

A

1. $\dfrac{8c^5}{12c^2}$

2. $\dfrac{25n^3}{15n^7}$

3. $\dfrac{b^{n+2}}{b^n}$

4. $\dfrac{2m^3n}{8mn^3}$

5. $\dfrac{-36a^3x^3}{30a^4x^2}$

6. $\dfrac{-51c^3t^4}{17c^2t}$

7. $\dfrac{-8p^2q^3}{-32p^3q^3}$

8. $\dfrac{-15x^3y}{-10xy^3}$

9. $\dfrac{3a^3}{b^2} \cdot \dfrac{b^3}{6a}$

10. $\dfrac{2c}{d^3} \cdot \dfrac{5d^2}{4c^2}$

11. $\dfrac{(-2a^2)^2}{a^3}$

12. $\dfrac{(-b^2)^3}{(-b^3)^2}$

13. $\left(\dfrac{x^2y^3}{x^3y}\right)^2$

14. $\left(\dfrac{2s^3}{s^2t}\right)^3$

15. $\left(\dfrac{8c}{12c^2}\right)^2$

16. $\dfrac{(2a^2c)^3}{a^3c^2}$

17. $\dfrac{3h^3k^2}{(2hk^2)^3}$

18. $\dfrac{(-m^3n)^3}{(2m^4n)^2}$

19. $\dfrac{(-2x^4y^2)^3}{(-3x^2y^3)^2}$

20. $\dfrac{(ab^2c^3)^3}{(abc^3)^2}$

21. $\dfrac{(x^2y^3)^5}{(xy^2z)^3}$

22. $\dfrac{-4(x^2y)^2}{(-4x^2y)^2}$

23. $\dfrac{(b^3)^n}{(b^n)^2}$

24. $\dfrac{(a^3)^n}{a \cdot a^n}$

B

25. $\left(\dfrac{2a^2}{3}\right)^2 \cdot \dfrac{3b}{a^4}$

26. $\dfrac{4x^2}{yz^2}\left(\dfrac{z}{2x}\right)^3$

27. $\left(\dfrac{-4x^2}{3y}\right)^2\left(\dfrac{-y}{2x}\right)^3$

28. $\left(\dfrac{t^3}{u^4}\right)^2\left(\dfrac{-tu}{v}\right)^3$

29. $\dfrac{a^nb^{n-1}}{(ab)^{n-1}}$

30. $\dfrac{c^{2n}d^{n+1}}{(c^2d)^n}$

31. $\dfrac{x^{k-2}y^{2k}}{x^{k+1}(y^{k-1})^2}$

32. $\left(\dfrac{u}{v^2}\right)^n\left(\dfrac{uv}{w}\right)^{2n}\left(\dfrac{w}{u}\right)^{3n}$

33. The multiplication rule for fractions can be written in the form
$(p \div q) \cdot (r \div s) = (p \cdot r) \div (q \cdot s)$. Replace $\div$ by $-$ and $\cdot$ by $+$. Is
the resulting equation true?

34. Repeat Exercise 33 for the cancellation rule for fractions.

35. Supply the reason(s) for each step of the following proof of the multiplication rule for fractions.

1. $\dfrac{p}{q} \cdot \dfrac{r}{s} = \left(p \cdot \dfrac{1}{q}\right)\left(r \cdot \dfrac{1}{s}\right)$ _____?_____

2. $= pr\left(\dfrac{1}{q} \cdot \dfrac{1}{s}\right)$ _____?_____ and _____?_____

3. $= pr \cdot \dfrac{1}{qs}$ _____?_____

4. $= \dfrac{pr}{qs}$ _____?_____

5. $\dfrac{p}{q} \cdot \dfrac{r}{s} = \dfrac{pr}{qs}$ _____?_____

$$\frac{\dfrac{a}{b} + \dfrac{c}{1}}{}$$

$$\frac{ab^{-1} + c}{a^{-1}b + a}$$

Career Note Auto Mechanic

Auto mechanics involves the diagnosis and repair of mechanical malfunctions. When an automobile is brought in for repair, the mechanic must first analyze the problem. Sometimes the problem is obvious, but often only clues to the real source of trouble are present.

Once the diagnosis has been made, the mechanic must advise the customer what repairs are needed. Consideration must be given to the severity of the damage, the cost of the repair, the overall condition of the car, and the likelihood of further damage if no repair is made.

In repairing cars, auto mechanics use a variety of custom tools and parts. Diagrams, charts, and reference manuals help them analyze the structure and function of the part or parts needing repair. Auto mechanics work alone but must be able to communicate effectively with supervisors and, in small repair shops, directly with customers.

Increasingly strict anti-pollution and fuel conservation requirements ensure that technological changes will continue to occur in the automobile industry. Auto mechanics must familiarize themselves annually with new models and new tools.

An auto mechanic should enjoy using tools, tinkering with mechanical devices, and discovering how things work. Completion of automotive school is the usual preparation for a career in auto mechanics.

5-2 *Zero and Negative Exponents*

To simplify expressions involving zero and negative exponents.

In this section you will see that the definitions of powers can be extended to permit all integers to be exponents, not just positive integers. Moreover, you will see that the meanings given to such expressions as 2^0, 10^{-3}, c^0, and x^{-2} are chosen so that the laws of exponents stated on page 165 continue to hold.

If law 1,

$$a^m \cdot a^n = a^{m+n},$$

is to hold when $m = 0$, this statement must be true:

$$a^0 a^n = a^{0+n} = a^n$$

If $a \neq 0$, you can divide by a^n and obtain

$$a^0 = \frac{a^n}{a^n} = 1.$$

Secondly, if law 1 is to hold for negative exponents, the following statement must be true: If n is a positive integer and $a \neq 0$,

$$a^{-n} a^n = a^{-n+n} = a^0 = 1.$$

Since $a^{-n} a^n = 1$, a^{-n} must be the reciprocal of a^n. Thus,

$$a^{-n} = \frac{1}{a^n}.$$

Therefore, zero and negative exponents are defined as follows:

If n is a positive integer and $a \neq 0$:

$$a^0 = 1 \qquad a^{-n} = \frac{1}{a^n}$$

For example, if the variables are not zero:

$$10^{-3} = \frac{1}{10^3} = \frac{1}{1000}$$

$$5c^0 = 5 \cdot 1 = 5$$

$$2x^{-3} = 2 \cdot \frac{1}{x^3} = \frac{2}{x^3}$$

$$(3a^2)^{-1} = \frac{1}{3a^2}$$

Because $a^{-n} = \dfrac{1}{a^n}$, and division by zero is not defined, the base of a power with a negative exponent must be nonzero. To simplify matters we make the following agreement, to hold for the rest of the book. *In any algebraic expression, the domains of all variables are restricted so that denominators of fractions and bases of powers with negative or zero exponents shall not be zero.* For example, in the expression

$$\frac{x^{-2}y^{-1}}{x-1},$$

you can assume that $x \neq 0$, $x \neq 1$ and $y \neq 0$ even though these restrictions are not stated.

It can be shown that all the laws of exponents hold even when some of the exponents are negative or zero. For example, law 3 now implies that

$$(a^3)^{-2} = a^{3(-2)} = a^{-6}.$$

This statement can be justified with the help of law 3 for *positive* exponents:

$$(a^3)^{-2} = \frac{1}{(a^3)^2} = \frac{1}{a^{3 \cdot 2}} = \frac{1}{a^6} = a^{-6}$$

You can now see that laws 4 and 5 are closely related since they give the same results. For example,

By law 4: $\quad \dfrac{a^2}{a^7} = a^{2-7} = a^{-5} = \dfrac{1}{a^5}$

By law 5: $\quad \dfrac{a^2}{a^7} = \dfrac{1}{a^{7-2}} = \dfrac{1}{a^5}$

EXAMPLE 1 Express in simplest form without negative exponents:

a. 43×10^{-4} 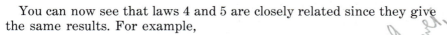 **b.** $\dfrac{3^0 a^{-3} x}{2^{-1} a^{-1} x^{-2}}$

SOLUTION **a.** $43 \times 10^{-4} = 43 \times \dfrac{1}{10^4} = \dfrac{43}{10000} = 0.0043$

b. 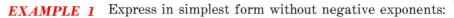 $\dfrac{3^0 a^{-3} x}{2^{-1} a^{-1} x^{-2}} = 2a^{-3-(-1)}x^{1-(-2)} = 2a^{-2}x^3 = \dfrac{2x^3}{a^2}$

The fact that

$$\left(\frac{a}{b}\right)^{-n} = \left(\frac{b}{a}\right)^n$$

often is useful. For example,

$$\left(-\frac{p^2}{q}\right)^{-3} = \left(-\frac{q}{p^2}\right)^3 = (-1)^3 \frac{q^3}{p^6} = -\frac{q^3}{p^6}.$$

Sometimes negative exponents are introduced in order to write expressions without using fractions, as in Example 2.

EXAMPLE 2 Express without using fractions:

  a. $\dfrac{9}{100,000}$ **b.** $\dfrac{5a}{xy^2}$

SOLUTION   **a.** $\dfrac{9}{100,000} = \dfrac{9}{10^5} = 9 \times 10^{-5}$ **b.** $\dfrac{5a}{xy^2} = 5ax^{-1}y^{-2}$

Oral Exercises

Express each of the following as a numeral or a positive power of a variable.

1. $\dfrac{1}{5^{-2}}$ **2.** $3^{-3} \cdot 3^5$ **3.** $\dfrac{2^2}{2^{-2}}$ **4.** $(3^{-1})^{-2}$

5. $x^3 \cdot x^{-5}$ **6.** $t^{-2} \cdot t^{-1}$ **7.** $a^4 \cdot a^{-4}$ **8.** $3c^0$

9. $(3c)^0$ **10.** $\dfrac{1}{x^{-3}}$ **11.** $\dfrac{u}{u^{-2}}$ **12.** $\left(\dfrac{a}{a^4}\right)^{-1}$

13. a^{-3} **14.** $2x^{-1}$ **15.** $\dfrac{3}{x^{-2}}$ **16.** $\dfrac{1}{2t^{-1}}$

Written Exercises

Express each of the following as an integer or a quotient of integers.

A **1.** $2 \cdot 3^{-2}$ **2.** $(2 \cdot 3)^{-2}$ **3.** $(-3^{-1})^{-2}$ **4.** $(-5^{-2})^{-1}$

  5. $(3^2 \cdot 5^0)^{-1}$ **6.** $(3^2 \cdot 5^{-1})^0$ **7.** $2\left(\dfrac{2}{5}\right)^{-2}$ **8.** $\left(\dfrac{3}{4}\right)^{-1}\left(\dfrac{4}{3}\right)^{-2}$

Express each of the following as a decimal numeral.

SAMPLE $\left(-\dfrac{5}{3}\right)^{-2} = \left(-\dfrac{3}{5}\right)^{2} = \dfrac{9}{25} = 0.36$

9. 27×10^{-2} **10.** 345×10^{-2} **11.** 4.9×10^{-4} **12.** 9.27×10^{-3}

13. $\left(\dfrac{5}{2}\right)^{-2}$ **14.** $\left(-\dfrac{2}{3}\right)^{-3}$ **15.** $(-5 \cdot 3^{-2})^{-1}$ **16.** $(5 \cdot 2^{-3})^{-2}$

Express each of the following in simplest form, without negative or zero exponents.

17. $\dfrac{3x^{-2}}{y}$ **18.** $\dfrac{2ab^{-1}}{bc^{-2}}$ **19.** $\dfrac{ax^2}{y^{-2}z^{-1}}$ **20.** $\dfrac{2u^{-2}}{vw^{-1}}$

21. $\left(\dfrac{1}{x^{-3}}\right)^{2}$ **22.** $\left(\dfrac{1}{x^{-2}}\right)^{-3}$ **23.** $(a^{-1}b^2)^{-1}$ **24.** $(r^{-2}s)^{-2}$

25. $\left(\dfrac{t^2}{t^{-1}}\right)^{-1}$ **26.** $\left(\dfrac{a^{-2}}{a^2}\right)^{-2}$ **27.** $\dfrac{uv^{-2}}{3u^{-1}v^3}$ **28.** $\dfrac{2s^{-1}t}{s^2t^{-2}}$

29. $\dfrac{5a^{-1}c^{-3}}{ab^{-1}c^{-2}}$ **30.** $\dfrac{4uv^{-2}}{3u^{-2}v^{-1}w^{-1}}$ **31.** $\dfrac{(xy^2)^{-2}}{x^2y^{-4}}$ **32.** $\dfrac{(a^2t)^{-1}}{at^{-2}}$

33. $\dfrac{2x^{-1}}{y^2}\left(\dfrac{x^2}{y}\right)^{-2}$

34. $\dfrac{u^2}{v^{-1}}\left(\dfrac{2v^2}{u^{-1}}\right)^{-2}$

35. $\left(\dfrac{r^{-1}}{s^2}\right)^{-1}\left(\dfrac{3r}{2s^{-2}}\right)^{-2}$

36. $\dfrac{(mn)^{-2}}{m^3}\left(\dfrac{1}{m^2n^{-3}}\right)^{-3}$

37. $\dfrac{3a^4}{b^{-2}}+\left(\dfrac{b^{-1}}{a^2}\right)^{-2}$

38. $\dfrac{5x^3}{y^6}+\left(-\dfrac{y^2}{x}\right)^{-3}$

In Exercises 39–42, when the ? in the given statement is replaced by $=$, the resulting equation is not an identity. Show this fact by assigning the indicated values to the variables.

39. $(x+y)^{-1}\,?\,x^{-1}+y^{-1};\ x=2,\ y=2.$

40. $(x+y)^{-2}\,?\,x^{-2}+y^{-2};\ x=1,\ y=1.$

41. $(ax)^{-2}\,?\,ax^{-2};\ a=2,\ x=1.$

42. $ax^{-1}\,?\,\dfrac{1}{ax};\ a=2,\ x=1.$

In each of the following, replace the ? by a polynomial to make a true statement.

SAMPLE $2x^{-3}-5x^{-1}+3=x^{-3}(?)$

SOLUTION $2x^{-3}-5x^{-1}+3=x^{-3}(2-5x^2+3x^3)$

B **43.** $x^{-2}+2x^{-1}+1=x^{-2}(?)$

44. $3t^{-3}-2t^{-2}+1=t^{-3}(?)$

45. $z^{-4}+2z^{-3}+5z^{-2}+z^{-1}+2=z^{-4}(?)$

46. $3x^{-4}+x^{-2}+1=x^{-4}(?)$

47. $\dfrac{2}{t^3}+\dfrac{1}{t^2}-\dfrac{4}{t}+3=\dfrac{1}{t^3}(?)$

48. $-\dfrac{1}{x^3}+\dfrac{2}{x}-3=-\dfrac{1}{x^3}(?)$

49. $2x(x+1)^{-2}+(x+1)^{-1}=(x+1)^{-2}(?)$

50. $2t^2(t^2+4)^{-2}-(t^2+4)^{-1}=(t^2+4)^{-2}(?)$

51. $(x+2)^{-1}-4(x+2)^{-3}=(x+2)^{-3}(?)$

52. $1+2(u-1)^{-1}-3(u-1)^{-2}=(u-1)^{-2}(?)$

53. Give reasons for the steps in the following proof that exponent law 1 is valid when both exponents are negative: Let m and n be positive integers. Then

1. $a^{-m}a^{-n}=\dfrac{1}{a^m}\cdot\dfrac{1}{a^n}$ _____?_____

2. $\phantom{a^{-m}a^{-n}}=\dfrac{1}{a^m\cdot a^n}$ _____?_____

3. $\phantom{a^{-m}a^{-n}}=\dfrac{1}{a^{m+n}}$ _____?_____

4. $a^{-m}a^{-n}=a^{-(m+n)}$ _____?_____

5. $\phantom{a^{-m}a^{-n}}=a^{-m+(-n)}$ _____?_____

In Exercises 54–59, prove the stated forms of laws of exponents, given that m and n are positive integers (recall Exercise 53) and that $m>n$. Use the laws of exponents for positive exponents.

C **54.** $a^m a^{-n}=a^{m+(-n)}$

55. $(a^m)^{-n}=a^{m(-n)}$

56. $(a^{-m})^n=a^{(-m)n}$

57. $\dfrac{a^{-m}}{a^n}=a^{(-m)+(-n)}$

58. $\dfrac{a^m}{a^{-n}}=a^{m-(-n)}$

59. $\dfrac{a^{-m}}{a^{-n}}=a^{(-m)-(-n)}$

5-3 Scientific Notation

Scientific notation provides an efficient way of dealing with very large and very small numbers. The list below shows several numbers expressed in scientific notation.

$$2,870,000 = 2.87 \times 10^6$$
$$28,700 = 2.87 \times 10^4$$
$$287 = 2.87 \times 10^2$$
$$2.87 = 2.87 \times 10^0$$
$$0.0287 = 2.87 \times 10^{-2}$$
$$0.000287 = 2.87 \times 10^{-4}$$
$$0.00000287 = 2.87 \times 10^{-6}$$

In general:

To express a number in **scientific notation,** express it in the form

$$m \times 10^n,$$

where m is a number such that $1 \le |m| < 10$; and n is an integer.

The digits in the factor m should all be *significant*. A **significant digit** of a decimal numeral is any nonzero digit or any zero whose purpose is not just to place the decimal point. In the following examples the significant digits are shown in red.

4005   0.2030   340.0   0.00503

A numeral such as 4800 does not indicate clearly which, if any, of the zeros is significant. Scientific notation eliminates this problem. Expressing 4800 as

$$4.8 \times 10^3,\ 4.80 \times 10^3,\quad \text{or}\quad 4.800 \times 10^3$$

indicates, respectively, that none, one, or both of the zeros are significant.

Numbers expressed in scientific notation can be compared easily:

$$3.02 \times 10^5 < 5.70 \times 10^5 \quad \text{because } 3.02 < 5.70$$
$$6.9 \times 10^{-3} < 9.1 \times 10^{-3} \quad \text{because } 6.9 < 9.1$$
$$9.681 \times 10^3 < 2.012 \times 10^4 \quad \text{because } 3 < 4$$
$$8.7 \times 10^{-4} < 3.5 \times 10^{-3} \quad \text{because } -4 < -3$$

Scientific notation helps you make quick "order-of-magnitude" estimates of products and quotients.

EXAMPLE   Find a one-significant-digit estimate of x when

$$x = \frac{4176 \times 762.0 \times 0.008708}{0.5312}.$$

SOLUTION $x = \dfrac{4176 \times 762.0 \times 0.008708}{0.5312}$

$\approx \dfrac{4000 \times 800 \times 0.009}{0.5}$ ⎰ Round each number to one
⎱ significant digit.

$= \dfrac{4 \times 10^3 \times 8 \times 10^2 \times 9 \times 10^{-3}}{5 \times 10^{-1}}$ ⎰ Express each approximation
⎱ in scientific notation.

$= \dfrac{4 \times 8 \times 9}{5} \times 10^{3+2-3-(-1)}$

$= \dfrac{288}{5} \times 10^3 = 57.6 \times 10^3 \approx 6 \times 10^4$ ⎰ Compute, and give the result
⎱ to one significant digit.

$\therefore x \approx 6 \times 10^4$, or 60,000.   **Answer**

Note that the digit obtained in the process illustrated above may not always be correct because of rounding errors. (In the example, $x = 52{,}160$ to four significant digits.) Nevertheless, such estimates do guard against gross order-of-magnitude mistakes.

Oral Exercises

State the number of significant digits in each numeral.

1. 3047   **2.** 90,082   **3.** 14.0   **4.** 1.600
5. 0.013   **6.** 0.002   **7.** 0.020   **8.** 0.200
9. 2.46×10^5 **10.** 3.010×10^3 **11.** 1.0200×10^{-3} **12.** 1.6×10^{-16}

Which is greater, x or y?

13. $x = 6.4 \times 10^3$, $y = 4.6 \times 10^3$ **14.** $x = 2.10 \times 10^{-5}$, $y = 1.82 \times 10^{-5}$
15. $x = 6.2 \times 10^4$; $y = 4.1 \times 10^5$ **16.** $x = 9.1 \times 10^{-4}$, $y = 1.2 \times 10^{-5}$
17. $x = 4370$; $y = 3.41 \times 10^4$ **18.** $x = 6.920 \times 10^5$, $y = 96230$
19. $x = 0.0041$, $y = 3.2 \times 10^{-2}$ **20.** $x = 3.69 \times 10^{-4}$, $y = 0.0000623$

Written Exercises

Express each of the following in scientific notation.

A   **1.** 47.1   **2.** 60.5   **3.** 4906   **4.** 501.0
  5. 69.20   **6.** 42.00   **7.** 0.025   **8.** 0.643
  9. 0.00040   **10.** 0.00510   **11.** $\dfrac{83}{100}$ **12.** $\dfrac{4063}{10}$
  13. 3,050,700   **14.** 0.0000001320

Express each of the following in decimal form.

15. 10^5 **16.** 10^6 **17.** 10^{-3} **18.** 10^{-5}

19. 2.04×10^2 **20.** 2.6×10^4 **21.** 9.18×10^{-4} **22.** 7.21×10^{-3}

Simplify each expression. Give answers in both scientific notation and decimal form.

23. $\dfrac{(2 \times 10^6)(8 \times 10^{-2})}{4 \times 10^2}$

24. $\dfrac{(5.0 \times 10^6)(7.5 \times 10^{-1})}{1.5 \times 10^7}$

25. $\dfrac{(2.4 \times 10^{-3})(1.5 \times 10^{-2})}{(1.6 \times 10^{-6})(5.0 \times 10^0)}$

26. $\dfrac{(4.8 \times 10^{17})(1.5 \times 10^{-5})}{(6.0 \times 10^7)(1.2 \times 10^5)}$

Find a one-significant-digit estimate of each of the following.

B 27. $\dfrac{392 \times 51.6}{0.0802 \times 4920}$ *1100 × 50*
0.08 × 5000

28. $\dfrac{0.00203 \times 48.2}{0.0264 \times 0.185}$

29. $\dfrac{697 \times (8.16)^2}{0.0211 \times 43.7}$ *4 × 10² × 5×10¹*

30. $\dfrac{5.26 \times (0.421)^3}{(4.69)^2 \times 0.0701}$

4·5 / 8·5 = 1/2 = 0.58 × 10⁻² × 5×10³
(10²)(10¹) / (10⁻²)(10³) = 10³/10¹ = 10²
0.5·×10²+10⁻¹ / 5×10¹
50

Problems

Solve. In these problems the numbers to be multiplied or divided are approximations. Therefore, answers should contain the same number of significant digits as in the given data. Express your answers in scientific notation and in decimal form.

A 1. The diameters of the sun and moon are 1.39×10^6 km and 3.48×10^3 km, respectively. Find the ratio of the diameter of the sun to that of the moon.

2. The masses of a proton and an electron are 1.67×10^{-24} g and 9.11×10^{-28} g, respectively. Find the ratio of the mass of a proton to that of an electron.

3. The astronomical unit (AU), used in planetary astronomy, is the mean distance from the sun to the earth, 1.50×10^{11} m. The light year (ly), used in stellar astronomy, is the distance light will travel in a year, 9.46×10^{15} m. How many astronomical units are there in a light year?

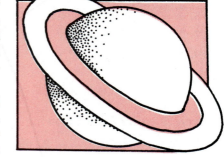

4. The mean distances from the sun to Mercury and Saturn are 5.791×10^7 km and 1.427×10^9 km, respectively. Express these distances in astronomical units. (See Problem 3 for the definition of an astronomical unit.)

5. A steady current of 1 A flowing through a solution of silver nitrate will deposit 1.118×10^{-3} g of silver in 1.000 s. How much silver will be deposited by a current of 15 A in 1.000 h?

6. How long does it take a computer signal to travel 60 cm at 2.4×10^{10} cm/s? Express your answer in nanoseconds (ns); 1 ns $= 10^{-9}$ s.

7. The designers of a computer wish to limit to 5 ns the time it takes signals to travel from one component to another. (See Problem 6 for the definition of nanosecond.) If signals travel at 2.4×10^{10} cm/s, what restriction does this put on the distance between components?

B 8. If in the Einstein equation $E = mc^2$, m denotes mass in kilograms and c denotes the speed of light, 2.99×10^8 m/s, then E denotes energy in joules (J). Find how many kilowatt-hours (kW · h) of energy would be released by converting 100 g of matter. (1 kW · h $= 3.6 \times 10^6$ J.)

C 9. The masses of the sun and the earth are 1.99×10^{30} kg and 5.97×10^{24} kg, respectively, and their radii are 6.96×10^8 m and 6.38×10^6 m. Use these data to show that the overall density of the earth is about four times that of the sun. (Density is mass divided by volume.)

Self-Test 1

VOCABULARY   scientific notation (p. 172)
significant digit (p. 172)

Express in simplest form without negative exponents.

1. $\dfrac{20ax^6}{15ax^3}$

2. $\left(-\dfrac{ab^2}{3c}\right)^2\left(\dfrac{6ac}{b^2}\right)$ Obj. 5-1, p. 163

3. $(-2a^0)^{-3}$

4. $\dfrac{x^2}{2y^{-1}}\left(\dfrac{x}{y^2}\right)^{-2}$ Obj. 5-2, p. 168

5. Replace the ? with a polynomial in simplest form.
$$x^{-2} + 2x^{-1} + 3 = x^{-2}(?)$$

Express in scientific notation.

6. 47,275

7. 0.0000254   Obj. 5-3, p. 172

Express in decimal form.

8. 8.763×10^5

9. 4.415×10^{-3}

10. Give a one-significant-digit estimate of $\dfrac{31,200 \times 0.00292}{0.8105}$.

Check your answers with those at the back of the book.

RATIONAL EXPRESSIONS   **175**

Application   Precision and Accuracy

When working with measurements of physical things, it is often necessary to specify the *precision* and the *accuracy* of the data involved. The **precision** of a measurement is given by the unit used in making it.

For example, a biochemist might determine the length of a chain molecule to be 0.086 mm, precise to the nearest thousandth of a millimeter. This means that the digit 6 is trustworthy and hence that the error in the measurement does not exceed 0.0005 mm.

In another situation, a prospector might pace off the distance from a stream to a mineshaft and find it to be 358 m (precise) to the nearest meter. In this case the maximum possible error is 0.5 m.

The precision of a measurement says little about its accuracy. The measurement of a length precise to the nearest centimeter may not be very accurate if the length is that of a pencil. But the accuracy would be extremely great if the length is that of a highway. **Accuracy** is defined to be the *relative error,* that is, the ratio of the maximum possible error in the measurement to the measurement itself.

Thus, the accuracy of the biochemist's measurement can be found as follows:

$$\frac{\text{maximum possible error}}{\text{measurement}} = \frac{0.0005}{0.086}$$
$$\approx 0.0058 = 0.58\%$$

The accuracy of the prospector's measurement can be found as follows:

$$\frac{0.5}{358} \approx 0.0014 = 0.14\%$$

The prospector has made the more accurate measurement because the relative error is smaller.

5-4 *Rational Algebraic Expressions*

OBJECTIVE **To write rational expressions in simplest form.**

A quotient of polynomials is called a **rational algebraic expression,** or **rational expression.** Here are three examples:

$$\frac{3ax^2}{z} \qquad \frac{t^2 - 2t - 3}{t^2 + 4} \qquad (x + 3)(x - 3)^{-2}$$

It should be apparent that the third expression is equivalent to $\frac{x + 3}{(x - 3)^2}$.

A rational expression is said to be in simplest form when it is written as a quotient of polynomials whose greatest common factor is 1 (recall Section 4-3). To simplify a rational expression you can divide its numerator and denominator by their greatest common factor. This process is justified by the cancellation rule for fractions (page 164).

As Examples 1 and 2 will show, the most efficient way to simplify a rational expression is to factor the numerator and denominator and then eliminate their common factors. This process is equivalent to dividing by the GCF of the numerator and denominator.

EXAMPLE 1 Simplify $(2x^2 - 3x - 2)(2x^2 - 2x - 4)^{-1}$.

SOLUTION

$$(2x^2 - 3x - 2)(2x^2 - 2x - 4)^{-1} = \frac{2x^2 - 3x - 2}{2x^2 - 2x - 4} \qquad \text{Express as a fraction.}$$

$$= \frac{(x - 2)(2x + 1)}{2(x + 1)(x - 2)} \qquad \text{Factor the numerator and denominator.}$$

$$= \frac{(x - 2)(2x + 1)}{2(x + 1)(x - 2)} \qquad \text{Cancel common factors.}$$

$$= \frac{2x + 1}{2(x + 1)} \qquad \textit{Answer}$$

Factors of the numerator and denominator may be negatives of each other, as in Example 2.

EXAMPLE 2 Simplify $\frac{4t^2 - t^4}{t^3 - 3t^2 + 2t}$.

SOLUTION

$$\frac{4t^2 - t^4}{t^3 - 3t^2 + 2t} = \frac{t^2(2 - t)(2 + t)}{t(t - 2)(t - 1)}$$

$$= \frac{t^2(-1)(t - 2)(2 + t)}{t(t - 2)(t - 1)} \quad \begin{cases} \text{Write } (2 - t) \\ \text{as } (-1)(t - 2). \end{cases}$$

$$= \frac{-t(2 + t)}{t - 1}, \text{ or } -\frac{t(t + 2)}{t - 1} \quad \textit{Answer}$$

Every simplified rational expression in one variable defines a *rational function*. A function that is defined by a quotient (in simplest form) of two polynomials is called a **rational function.**

EXAMPLE 3 A rational function of f is defined by the following:

$$f(x) = (x^2 - 4)(x^3 - x)^{-1}$$

a. Determine the domain of f.

b. Find the zeros (page 148) of f.

SOLUTION
$$f(x) = \frac{x^2 - 4}{x^3 - x} = \frac{(x - 2)(x + 2)}{x(x - 1)(x + 1)}$$

a. Because division by zero is not defined, f is not defined at any zero of the denominator. Hence the domain of f is all real numbers except 0, 1, and -1. *Answer*

b. $f(x) = 0$ if and only if $(x - 2)(x + 2) = 0$. Therefore, the zeros of f are 2 and -2. *Answer*

Oral Exercises

In Exercises 1–12:
a. State the domain of f.
b. State the zeros of f, if any.

1. $f(x) = \frac{x - 1}{x - 2}$

2. $f(x) = \frac{x - 2}{x}$

3. $f(t) = \frac{t}{t + 1}$

4. $f(u) = \frac{u^2}{u + 3}$

5. $f(r) = \frac{1}{r - 5}$

6. $f(x) = \frac{x + 3}{2}$

7. $f(t) = \frac{t^2 + 1}{t^2 + 9}$

8. $f(x) = \frac{x^2 + 4}{x - 2}$

9. $f(x) = \frac{x(x - 2)}{x - 1}$

10. $f(t) = \frac{(t - 1)(t + 1)}{t(t - 3)}$

11. $f(u) = (u - 3)(u + 3)^{-1}$ 12. $f(x) = x^{-2}(x + 2)$

Written Exercises

Simplify each rational expression.

A 1. $\frac{4x^2 - 6x}{2x^2}$

2. $\frac{12m^3 - 6m}{3m^2}$

3. $\frac{at^3 + a^2t^2 - 2a^3t}{at}$

4. $\frac{6u^2v^3 - 8u^4v}{12u^2v^2}$

5. $(1 - x)(x - 1)^{-1}$

6. $t(2 - t)(t - 2)^{-1}$

7. $\frac{(t - 1)^2}{t^2 - 1}$

8. $\frac{x^2 - 4}{(x - 2)^2}$

9. $(x^2 - 9)(x^2 - 6x + 9)^{-1}$

10. $(4 + 4t + t^2)(4 - t^2)^{-1}$ 11. $\frac{z^3 - z}{z^2 - 2z + 1}$

12. $\frac{(x + 1)(x^2 - 1)}{(x - 1)(x + 1)^2}$

13. $(u^2 - u - 2)(u^2 - 4)^{-1}$

14. $(t^2 - 4t + 4)(t^2 - 3t + 2)^{-1}$

15. $\dfrac{2x^2 + 3x - 2}{x - 4x^3}$

16. $\dfrac{x^2 - x^4}{x^3 + x^2 - 2x}$

17. $(t^3 + 4t^2 + 4t)(t^3 + 8)^{-1}$

18. $(u^4 - 1)(u^4 - u^2)^{-1}$

19. $\dfrac{3x^2 - 10x + 3}{2x^2 - 5x - 3}$

20. $\dfrac{3s^2 - 13s + 12}{s^2 + s - 12}$

In each of Exercises 21-28 a rational function is defined.
a. Determine the domain of the function.
b. Find the zeros of the function.

21. $f(x) = \dfrac{x^2 - 4}{x^2 + 4}$

22. $g(x) = \dfrac{x^2 + 4}{x^2 - 4x}$

23. $h(t) = \dfrac{t^4 - 1}{t^3 - 8}$

24. $F(t) = \dfrac{t^3 + 8}{t^2 + 2t - 8}$

25. $g(x) = \dfrac{x - 4x^3}{x^2 - 4}$

26. $f(x) = \dfrac{x^2 - 6x + 9}{2x^2 - 5x + 3}$

B **27.** $h(x) = \dfrac{x^3 + 2x^2 - x - 2}{x^3 - 2x^2 + x - 2}$

28. $g(t) = \dfrac{t^4 + t^2 - 2}{t^3 + 2t^2 + t + 2}$

Simplify.

29. $\dfrac{x^4 - y^4}{(x^2 - y^2)^2}$

30. $\dfrac{x^4 - y^4}{x^4 + 2x^2y^2 + y^4}$

31. $\dfrac{u^4 - v^4}{u^3 + v^3}$

32. $\dfrac{(u - v)[w^2 - (u + v)w + uv]}{(u - w)[v^2 - (u + w)v + uw]}$

33. $\dfrac{x^2 - 2ax + a^2 + x - a}{x^2 - a^2}$

34. $\dfrac{r^3 - r^2 + s^2 + s^3}{r^2 + 2rs + s^2}$

35. $\dfrac{t^4 - 1}{t^3 - t^2 - t + 1}$

36. $\dfrac{x^3 - x^2 + x - 1}{x^3 + x^2 - x - 1}$

37. $\dfrac{18 + 9x - 2x^2 - x^3}{x^3 - 3x^2 - 4x + 12}$

38. $\dfrac{x^6 - 2x^3y^3 + y^6}{x^3 - x^2y - xy^2 + y^3}$

C **39.** $\dfrac{(x^2 - 4)^2(x + 2) - 2(x^2 - 4)(x + 2)^2}{(x - 4)^2}$

40. $\dfrac{(x^2 - 3)^2(x - 3) - x(x^2 - 3)(x - 3)^2}{x^2 - 4x + 3}$

41. $\dfrac{3(t^2 - 2)^2(t^2 + 5) - 2(t^2 - 2)(t^2 + 5)^2}{(t^2 - 2)(t - 4)^2}$

42. $\dfrac{(t^3 + 1)^2(t^2 + 1) - t(t^3 + 1)(t^2 + 1)^2}{t^2 - 1}$

43. $\dfrac{(r^3 - 1)(r^3 + 1)^2 + (r^3 - 1)^2(r^3 + 1)}{3r^5 - 3r^4}$

5-5 *Dividing Polynomials*

OBJECTIVE **To divide one polynomial by another of lower or equal degree.**

When you write a fraction as a mixed number, you are performing a simple division of integers. For example:

$$\frac{17}{5} = 3 + \frac{2}{5} = 3\frac{2}{5}$$

Sometimes rational algebraic expressions are written in a similar fashion as *mixed expressions*. A sum or difference of a polynomial and a fraction is called a **mixed expression.** Polynomial division can be used to write rational expressions as mixed expressions. For example,

$$\frac{x^2 + 3x + 2}{x} = \frac{x^2}{x} + \frac{3x}{x} + \frac{2}{x} = (x + 3) + \frac{2}{x}$$

The two equations displayed above illustrate the equation appearing in the following division algorithm:

$$\frac{\text{Dividend}}{\text{Divisor}} = \text{Quotient} + \frac{\text{Remainder}}{\text{Divisor}}$$

This statement is equivalent to

$$\text{Dividend} = \text{Divisor} \times \text{Quotient} + \text{Remainder},$$

a form that is useful for checking the results of divisions.

When you cannot perform a division at sight, you can use the long-division process illustrated below for the quotient $859 \div 23$.

$$
\begin{array}{r}
37 \\
23\overline{)859} \\
690 \\
\hline
169 \\
161 \\
\hline
8
\end{array}
$$

690 ← subtract 30×23

161 ← subtract 7×23

$859 - (30 \times 23) - (7 \times 23) = 8$

$859 = (30 \times 23) + (7 \times 23) + 8$

$859 = 37 \times 23 + 8$

$\therefore \ \frac{859}{23} = 37 + \frac{8}{23}.$

Note that the process ends when the remainder is less than the divisor.

You can use a similar process to find the quotient of two polynomials, for example, $(x^3 + 5x^2 + 3x + 2) \div (x + 3)$.

$$
\begin{array}{r}
x^2 + 2x \ - 3 \longleftarrow \text{quotient} \\
\text{divisor} \rightarrow x + 3\overline{)x^3 + 5x^2 + 3x + \ 2} \leftarrow \text{dividend} \\
x^3 + 3x^2 \longleftarrow \text{subtract } x^2(x + 3) \\
\hline
2x^2 + 3x \\
2x^2 + 6x \longleftarrow \text{subtract } 2x(x + 3) \\
\hline
- 3x + \ 2 \\
- 3x - \ 9 \longleftarrow \text{subtract } -3(x + 3) \\
\hline
11
\end{array}
$$

$$\therefore \underbrace{\frac{x^3 + 5x^2 + 3x + 2}{x + 3}}_{\substack{\text{Dividend} \\ \text{Divisor}}} = \underbrace{x^2 + 2x - 3}_{\text{Quotient}} + \underbrace{\frac{11}{x + 3}}_{\substack{\text{Remainder} \\ \text{Divisor}}}$$

The process now ends when the remainder is 0 or of lower degree than the divisor. To check the results, use the form

$$\text{Dividend} \quad = \quad \text{Divisor} \times \text{Quotient} \quad + \text{Remainder}.$$
$$x^3 + 5x^2 + 3x + 2 \overset{?}{=} (x + 3)(x^2 + 2x - 3) \qquad + \qquad 11$$
$$x^3 + 5x^2 + 3x + 2 \overset{?}{=} x^3 + 2x^2 - 3x + 3x^2 + 6x - 9 + \qquad 11$$
$$x^3 + 5x^2 + 3x + 2 = x^3 + 5x^2 + 3x + 2 \quad \checkmark$$

Before dividing, arrange the terms of both dividend and divisor in order of decreasing degree of the same variable. The next example shows how to insert missing terms using 0 as a coefficient.

EXAMPLE   Divide $2t^3 + 4u^3 - 5t^2u$ by $2t^2 - 2u^2 - tu$.

SOLUTION

$$
\begin{array}{r}
t - 2u \\
2t^2 - tu - 2u^2 \overline{\smash{\big)}\ 2t^3 - 5t^2u + 0tu^2 + 4u^3} \\
\underline{2t^3 - \ \ t^2u - 2tu^2} \\
-4t^2u + 2tu^2 + 4u^3 \\
\underline{-4t^2u + 2tu^2 + 4u^3} \\
0
\end{array}
$$

add a 0 for descending order

$$\therefore \frac{2t^3 + 4u^3 - 5t^2u}{2t^2 - 2u^2 - tu} = t - 2u \quad \textbf{\textit{Answer}}$$

Check: $2t^3 + 4u^3 - 5t^2u \overset{?}{=} (t - 2u)(2t^2 - 2u^2 - tu)$
$$2t^3 + 4u^3 - 5t^2u \overset{?}{=} (2t^3 - 2tu^2 - t^2u) - (4t^2u - 4u^3 - 2tu^2)$$
$$2t^3 + 4u^3 - 5t^2u = 2t^3 + 4u^3 - 5t^2u \quad \checkmark$$

M T W Th Fr
$\frac{5}{6}$ $\frac{5}{6}$

Oral Exercises

State the quotient and the remainder in each of the following divisions.

1. $\dfrac{x + 2}{x}$ 2. $\dfrac{3t - 1}{t}$ 3. $\dfrac{x^2 - 1}{x^2}$ 4. $\dfrac{2u^2 + 4}{u^2}$

5. $\dfrac{z^2 + 4}{z}$ 6. $\dfrac{x^2 - 1}{x}$ 7. $\dfrac{6t^2 + t + 2}{t}$ 8. $\dfrac{x^2 - 2x + 1}{x}$

SAMPLE $\dfrac{x + 5}{x + 2} = \dfrac{(x + 2) + 3}{x + 2} = \dfrac{x + 2}{x + 2} + \dfrac{3}{x + 2} = 1 + \dfrac{3}{x + 2}$

       $\therefore$ the quotient is 1; the remainder is 3.   *Answer*

9. $\dfrac{x + 3}{x + 1}$ 10. $\dfrac{x + 7}{x + 3}$ 11. $\dfrac{t + 2}{t + 5}$ 12. $\dfrac{s}{s - 3}$

13. $\dfrac{x^2 + 2x + 5}{x + 2}$ 14. $\dfrac{x^2 - 3x + 2}{x - 3}$

Written Exercises

Perform the indicated divisions.

A **1.** $\dfrac{x^2 + 3x + 4}{x - 2}$ **2.** $\dfrac{t^2 - 2t + 5}{t + 1}$ **3.** $\dfrac{2 + 5u + u^2}{3 + u}$

4. $\dfrac{x^2 + 2x}{x + 3}$ **5.** $\dfrac{6u^2 - u - 4}{3u - 2}$ **6.** $\dfrac{2 - 5r + 2r^2}{1 + 2r}$

7. $\dfrac{4x^2 - 15}{2x - 5}$ **8.** $\dfrac{15t^2 - t - 1}{5t + 3}$ **9.** $\dfrac{x^3 + 5x^2 + 4x + 2}{x + 2}$

10. $\dfrac{z^3 - z^2 + 12}{z + 2}$ **11.** $\dfrac{2 - 3x + 4x^2 - 6x^3}{2 - 3x}$ **12.** $\dfrac{1 + x + 12x^3}{1 + 2x}$

13. $\dfrac{6x^3 - 8x^2 - 5x + 2}{2x^2 - 4x + 1}$ **14.** $\dfrac{t^3 - t^2 - 7t + 17}{t^2 - 4t + 5}$

15. $\dfrac{x^4 + 2x^3 + 6x - 6}{x + 3}$ **16.** $\dfrac{t^4 - 3t^3 + 6t - 18}{t^2 + 2}$

17. $\dfrac{18c^4 - 8c^2 - 3c + 6}{3c - 2}$ **18.** $\dfrac{2d^4 + 13d^3 - 5d - 4}{2d + 1}$

19. $\dfrac{8p^2 - 2pq - 5q^2}{2p + q}$ **20.** $\dfrac{6x^2 - 7ax - 6a^2}{2x - 3a}$

21. $\dfrac{4u^2 + 5uv - 6v^2}{4u - 3v}$ **22.** $\dfrac{2x^3 - 3x^2y + y^3}{x - y}$

B **23.** $\dfrac{6p^3 + 11p^2q - q^3}{2p^2 + 3pq - q^2}$ **24.** $\dfrac{2m^3 - 7mn^2}{2m^2 + 4mn + n^2}$

25. $\dfrac{x^4 + 4}{x^2 + 2x + 2}$ **26.** $\dfrac{x^8 + 4}{x^4 - 2x^2 + 2}$

27. $\dfrac{x^3 + a^3}{x + a}$ **28.** $\dfrac{x^4 + a^4}{x + a}$

29. $\dfrac{x^6 + a^6}{x + a}$ **30.** $\dfrac{x^5 + a^5}{x + a}$

C **31.** When the polynomial $f(x)$ is divided by $x - 2$, the quotient is $2x + 1$ and the remainder is 5. Find $f(x)$.

32. When $x^3 - x + 9$ is divided by the polynomial $g(x)$, the quotient is $x + 2$ and the remainder is 3. Find $g(x)$.

33. When $x^2 + 3x + b$ is divided by $x + a$, the quotient is $x - 2$ and the remainder is 7. Find a and b.

34. Find the value of c so that when $x^3 - cx^2 + 2x + (c - 3)$ is divided by $x - 2$, the remainder is 0.

35. Find the value of k so that when $k^2x^2 + (3k - 1)x - 17$ is divided by $x + 2$, the remainder is 3.

5-6 *Products and Quotients*

OBJECTIVE   **To multiply and divide rational expressions.**

The multiplication rule for fractions, $\frac{p}{q} \cdot \frac{r}{s} = \frac{pr}{qs}$, can be extended to more than two factors:

> The product of two or more fractions is the fraction whose numerator is the product of the numerators and whose denominator is the product of the denominators of the given fractions.

For example,

$$6 \cdot \frac{2x}{3y} \cdot \frac{y^2}{x+y} = \frac{6 \cdot 2x \cdot y^2}{1 \cdot 3y \cdot (x+y)} = \frac{4xy \cdot 3y}{(x+y) \cdot 3y} = \frac{4xy}{x+y}.$$

Products of rational expressions should be written in simplest form. The cancellation rule for fractions enables you to divide the numerator and denominator by their common factors.

EXAMPLE 1   Simplify the product

$$\frac{2t^2 + 4t}{4t^2 - 4t + 1} \cdot \frac{2t^2 - 5t + 2}{t^2 - 4}.$$

SOLUTION $\dfrac{2t^2 + 4t}{4t^2 - 4t + 1} \cdot \dfrac{2t^2 - 5t + 2}{t^2 - 4} = \dfrac{2t(t+2)}{(2t-1)^2} \cdot \dfrac{(2t-1)(t-2)}{(t+2)(t-2)}$

$$= \frac{2t \cdot (t+2)(2t-1)}{(2t-1) \cdot (t+2)(2t-1)}$$

$$= \frac{2t}{2t-1} \quad \textbf{\textit{Answer}}$$

Recall that a quotient equals the product of the dividend and the reciprocal of the divisor (the rule for division on page 37). Also, the reciprocal of $\frac{r}{s}$ is $\frac{s}{r}$ because $\frac{r}{s} \cdot \frac{s}{r} = 1$. Combining these facts gives the division rule for fractions.

> DIVISION RULE FOR FRACTIONS
>
> If p is a real number, and q, r, and s are nonzero real numbers:
>
> $$\frac{p}{q} \div \frac{r}{s} = \frac{p}{q} \cdot \frac{s}{r}$$

Examples of the division rule for fractions are

$$\frac{25}{12} \div \frac{5}{8} = \frac{25}{12} \cdot \frac{8}{5} = \frac{2^3 \cdot 5^2}{2^2 \cdot 3 \cdot 5} = \frac{2 \cdot 5}{3} = \frac{10}{3}$$

and

$$\left(\frac{4a^2 b}{3c}\right) \div \left(-\frac{4a^2}{9bc^2}\right) = -\frac{4a^2 b}{3c} \cdot \frac{9bc^2}{4a^2} = -3b^2 c.$$

It is sometimes helpful to rewrite a quotient using the $\div$ sign, as in Example 2.

EXAMPLE 2 Simplify the quotient $\dfrac{\dfrac{x^2 - 4ax + 3a^2}{x + a}}{x^2 - 2ax - 3a^2}$.

SOLUTION

$$\frac{\dfrac{x^2 - 4ax + 3a^2}{x + a}}{x^2 - 2ax - 3a^2} = \frac{x^2 - 4ax + 3a^2}{x + a} \div (x^2 - 2ax - 3a^2)$$

$$= \frac{x^2 - 4ax + 3a^2}{x + a} \cdot \frac{1}{x^2 - 2ax - 3a^2}$$

$$= \frac{(x - a)(x - 3a)}{x + a} \cdot \frac{1}{(x + a)(x - 3a)}$$

$$= \frac{x - a}{(x + a)^2} \quad \textbf{\textit{Answer}}$$

EXAMPLE 3 Simplify $\dfrac{y^2 - 16}{y^4} \div \dfrac{y^2 + y - 12}{6} \cdot \dfrac{y^4 + 3y^3}{2y - 8}$

SOLUTION

$$\frac{y^2 - 16}{y^4} \div \frac{y^2 + y - 12}{6} \cdot \frac{y^4 + 3y^3}{2y - 8} = \frac{y^2 - 16}{y^4} \cdot \frac{6}{y^2 + y - 12} \cdot \frac{y^4 + 3y^3}{2y - 8}$$

$$= \frac{(y + 4)(y - 4)}{y^4} \cdot \frac{6}{(y + 4)(y - 3)} \cdot \frac{y^3(y + 3)}{2(y - 4)}$$

$$= \frac{3(y + 3)}{y(y - 3)}$$

Oral Exercises

Find the indicated product or quotient.

1. $\dfrac{2}{5} \cdot \dfrac{1}{2}$ **2.** $\dfrac{4}{5} \cdot \dfrac{1}{2}$ **3.** $\dfrac{4}{5} \div 2$ **4.** $\dfrac{4}{5} \div \dfrac{1}{2}$

5. $\dfrac{2}{a} \cdot \dfrac{1}{a^2}$ **6.** $\dfrac{2}{a} \div \dfrac{1}{a^2}$ **7.** $\dfrac{a}{b} \div \dfrac{a}{b^2}$ **8.** $\dfrac{2}{x} \div \dfrac{4}{x^2}$

9. $\dfrac{2a^2}{3} \cdot \dfrac{9}{4a}$ **10.** $\dfrac{5a}{8b} \cdot \dfrac{2b^3}{5a}$ **11.** $\dfrac{1}{2x} \div \dfrac{2}{3x^2}$ **12.** $\dfrac{2z^2}{5k} \div \dfrac{5k}{2z^2}$

Written Exercises

Find the indicated product or quotient. Write answers in simplest form with no zero or negative exponents.

A

1. $\dfrac{9}{42}\left(-\dfrac{5}{2}\right)\left(\dfrac{15}{28}\right)^{-1}$

2. $\dfrac{36}{55}\left(-\dfrac{44}{21}\right)\left(-\dfrac{8}{35}\right)^{-1}$

3. $\dfrac{12a^2}{5}\cdot\dfrac{10}{3a}$

4. $\dfrac{-2x}{15}\cdot\dfrac{5}{x^3}$

5. $\dfrac{3t^2}{10}\div\dfrac{6t}{5}$ $\dfrac{3t^2}{10}\cdot\dfrac{5^1}{6t}=\dfrac{3t^2}{12t}$

6. $\dfrac{c^3}{12}\div\dfrac{1}{6c}$

7. $\dfrac{4a^2b}{5}\cdot\dfrac{b^3}{6a^3}\cdot\left(\dfrac{b^2}{5}\right)^{-1}$

8. $\dfrac{2a^3x^4}{3c}\cdot\dfrac{9c^2}{ax^2}\cdot\left(\dfrac{3ax}{c}\right)^{-1}$ $\dfrac{c^2}{4t}$

9. $\dfrac{10u^3v}{w^2}\div\dfrac{2u^2v^2}{w}$

10. $\dfrac{4xy}{-5z}\div\dfrac{2x^2}{yz}$

11. $\dfrac{x-1}{x^2-4}\cdot\dfrac{x^2+x-6}{x^2-1}$ $\dfrac{t}{4}$

12. $\dfrac{2x^2+3x-2}{2x^2-3x-2}\cdot\dfrac{x-2}{x+2}$

13. $\dfrac{t^2+t-6}{t^2+3t+2}\div\dfrac{t^2-4}{t^2-1}$

14. $\dfrac{u^4+4u+4}{2-u}\div\dfrac{u^2+u-2}{u^2-4u+4}$

B **15.** If $f(x)=\dfrac{x^2-2x-3}{x^2-2x+1}$ and $g(x)=\dfrac{x+1}{x-3}$, find $f(x)\cdot g(x)$.

16. If $f(x)=\dfrac{x^2+2x-3}{x^2-2x-8}$ and $g(x)=\dfrac{x^2-5x+4}{x^2+5x+6}$, find $f(x)\cdot g(x)$.

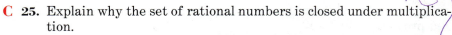

Write the given expression as a single fraction in lowest terms.

17. $\dfrac{x^2+a^2}{x+a}\div\dfrac{x^4-a^4}{(x-a)^2}$

18. $\dfrac{x^4-a^4}{(x+a)^2}\cdot\left(\dfrac{x^3-a^3}{x+a}\right)^{-1}$

19. $\dfrac{6u+3v}{v}\cdot\dfrac{2uv^3}{4u^2-v^2}\cdot\left(\dfrac{6u^2v}{2u-v}\right)^{-1}$

20. $\dfrac{s^2-2st}{s+2t}\cdot\dfrac{s^2+3st+2t^2}{s^2-t^2}\div\dfrac{2t-s}{t-s}$

21. $\dfrac{2x^2-x-3}{2x^2+x-3}\cdot\left(\dfrac{6x^2-7x-3}{x^2+2x-3}\right)^{-1}\div\left(\dfrac{2x+3}{x+3}\right)^{-1}$

22. $\dfrac{x^2+x-12}{x^3+27}\cdot\left(\dfrac{3x-9}{x^2+x-6}\cdot\dfrac{x^2+2x-8}{x^2-3x+9}\right)^{-1}$

23. $\dfrac{u^2-2uv-15v^2}{u^2-9v^2}\cdot\left(\dfrac{9uv^2-6u^2v+u^3}{30v^2+11uv+u^2}\cdot\dfrac{25v^2-u^2}{u^2-3uv}\right)^{-1}$

24. $\dfrac{t^2+4at+4a^2}{(2t-3a)^2}\cdot\left(\dfrac{4t^2-4a^2}{4t^2-9a^2}\right)^{-1}\div\left(\dfrac{3at-3a^2}{2t^2+4at}\right)^{-1}$

C **25.** Explain why the set of rational numbers is closed under multiplication.

26. Explain why the set of rational numbers is closed under division, excluding division by zero.

27. Explain why the set of rational functions is closed under multiplication.

28. Explain why the set of rational functions is closed under division, excluding division by zero.

5-7 *Sums and Differences*

Objective   **To add and subtract rational expressions.**

The rule for division and the distributive law provide a means of writing the sum of fractions with equal denominators as a simple fraction:

$$\frac{a}{c} + \frac{b}{c} = a \cdot \frac{1}{c} + b \cdot \frac{1}{c} = (a + b) \cdot \frac{1}{c} = \frac{a + b}{c}$$

This result can be extended to more than two terms and to subtraction. Here are some examples:

$$\frac{7}{15} + \frac{4}{15} - \frac{1}{15} = \frac{7 + 4 - 1}{15} = \frac{10}{15} = \frac{2}{3}$$

$$\frac{3x}{2x + 1} - \frac{3}{2x + 1} + \frac{x + 5}{2x + 1} = \frac{3x - 3 + x + 5}{2x + 1} = \frac{4x + 2}{2x + 1} = \frac{2(2x + 1)}{2x + 1} = 2$$

To add or subtract fractions with different denominators, first find the **least common denominator (LCD)** of the fractions, which is the least common multiple (LCM) of their denominators. Then express each fraction as an equivalent fraction having the LCD as denominator, and combine the resulting fractions, and simplify.

EXAMPLE 1   Simplify $\frac{5}{12} + \frac{7}{30} - 2$.

SOLUTION
1. Because $12 = 2^2 \cdot 3$ and $30 = 2 \cdot 3 \cdot 5$, their LCM is $2^2 \cdot 3 \cdot 5$.
   Thus, the LCD is 60.

2. $\frac{5}{12} = \frac{5 \cdot 5}{12 \cdot 5} = \frac{25}{60}; \frac{7}{30} = \frac{7 \cdot 2}{30 \cdot 2} = \frac{14}{60}; 2 = \frac{120}{60}$

3. $\frac{5}{12} + \frac{7}{30} - 2 = \frac{25}{60} + \frac{14}{60} - \frac{120}{60} = \frac{25 + 14 - 120}{60}$

   $$= \frac{-81}{60} = -\frac{27}{20} \quad \textit{Answer}$$

EXAMPLE 2   Simplify $\frac{1}{2c^2} + \frac{1}{2d^2} - \frac{1}{cd}$.

SOLUTION
1. The LCM of $2c^2$, $2d^2$, and cd is $2c^2d^2$.

2. $\frac{1}{2c^2} = \frac{d^2}{2c^2d^2}; \frac{1}{2d^2} = \frac{c^2}{2c^2d^2}; \frac{1}{cd} = \frac{2cd}{2c^2d^2}$

3. $\frac{1}{2c^2} + \frac{1}{2d^2} - \frac{1}{cd} = \frac{d^2}{2c^2d^2} + \frac{c^2}{2c^2d^2} - \frac{2cd}{2c^2d^2}$

   $$= \frac{d^2 + c^2 - 2cd}{2c^2d^2} = \frac{(d - c)^2}{2c^2d^2} \quad \textit{Answer}$$

When you add fractions, factoring the denominators in place will often shorten the work, as shown in Example 3.

EXAMPLE 3 Simplify $\dfrac{3}{x^2 + x - 6} - \dfrac{2}{x^2 - 3x + 2}$.

SOLUTION

$$\frac{3}{x^2 + x - 6} - \frac{2}{x^2 - 3x + 2} = \frac{3}{(x - 2)(x + 3)} - \frac{2}{(x - 1)(x - 2)}$$

$$= \frac{3(x - 1)}{(x - 1)(x - 2)(x + 3)} - \frac{2(x + 3)}{(x - 1)(x - 2)(x + 3)}$$

$$= \frac{3x - 3 - 2x - 6}{(x - 1)(x - 2)(x + 3)}$$

$$= \frac{x - 9}{(x - 1)(x - 2)(x + 3)} \quad \textbf{\textit{Answer}}$$

Oral Exercises

Express in simplest form.

1. $\dfrac{1}{5} + \dfrac{3}{5}$

2. $\dfrac{5}{7} - \dfrac{2}{7}$

3. $\dfrac{7}{10} - \dfrac{3}{10}$

4. $\dfrac{5}{9} + \dfrac{4}{9}$

5. $\dfrac{5}{12} - \dfrac{11}{12}$

6. $\dfrac{7}{10} + \dfrac{1}{10} - \dfrac{5}{10}$

7. $\dfrac{3m}{5n} - \dfrac{m}{5n}$

8. $\dfrac{2}{3a} - \dfrac{1}{3a}$

9. $\dfrac{x}{8} + \dfrac{3x}{8}$

10. $\dfrac{m}{8n} + \dfrac{3m}{8n}$

11. $\dfrac{3}{x + y} - \dfrac{2}{x + y}$

12. $\dfrac{a}{a + b} + \dfrac{b}{a + b}$

Written Exercises

Simplify.

A

1. $\dfrac{3}{4} + \dfrac{3}{8} - \dfrac{1}{2}$

2. $\dfrac{1}{12} - \dfrac{1}{6} + \dfrac{1}{3}$

3. $\dfrac{7}{20} + \dfrac{1}{15} - 1$

4. $\dfrac{8}{21} + \dfrac{4}{35} - \dfrac{3}{7}$

5. $\dfrac{a + 1}{2} + \dfrac{a - 2}{4}$

6. $\dfrac{x + 1}{3} - \dfrac{x + 1}{6}$

7. $\dfrac{5}{3c} - \dfrac{1}{6c}$

8. $\dfrac{b}{2a} + \dfrac{b}{3a}$

9. $\dfrac{x + 1}{x^2} - \dfrac{1}{2x}$

10. $\dfrac{b}{2a} + \dfrac{a}{3b}$

11. $\dfrac{3x - 2}{2x} + \dfrac{2x + 3}{3x}$

12. $\dfrac{3}{2c^2} + \dfrac{3}{5c}$

13. $\dfrac{3}{2xy^2} + \dfrac{2}{x^2y}$

14. $\dfrac{1}{2ab^2} - \dfrac{1}{3a^2b}$

15. $x^{-2} + 2x^{-3}$

16. $t^2 - t^{-2}$

17. $\dfrac{u}{vw} + \dfrac{v}{wu} + \dfrac{w}{uv}$

18. $\dfrac{b - c}{bc} + \dfrac{c - a}{ca} + \dfrac{a - b}{ab}$

Simplify.

19. $\dfrac{3}{t-2}+\dfrac{2}{2-t}$

20. $\dfrac{x}{x-1}-\dfrac{1}{1-x}$

21. $\dfrac{1}{x-2}+\dfrac{1}{x+2}$

22. $\dfrac{2}{t}-\dfrac{1}{t+2}$

23. $\dfrac{1}{x^2}-\dfrac{1}{x^2+x}$

24. $\dfrac{1}{2z-1}-\dfrac{1}{2z+1}$

25. $\dfrac{2}{u^2-1}-\dfrac{1}{u^2-u}$

26. $\dfrac{2}{x^2-4}+\dfrac{3}{x^2+4x+4}$

If $f(x)=\dfrac{x}{x+1}$ and $g(x)=\dfrac{1}{x-1}$, find and simplify:

B **27.** $f(x)+g(x)$

28. $f(x)-g(x)$

If $f(x)=x+1$ and $g(x)=\dfrac{1}{x+1}$, find and simplify:

29. $f(x)+g(x)$

30. $f(x)-g(x)$

Simplify.

31. $\dfrac{3}{x^2-ax-6a^2}-\dfrac{2}{x^2-4a^2}$

32. $\dfrac{1}{t^2+3ct}+\dfrac{2}{t^2-9c^2}$

33. $\dfrac{1}{a+b}+\dfrac{1}{a-b}+\dfrac{2a}{a^2-b^2}$

34. $\dfrac{1}{a-x}-\dfrac{3x}{a^2-x^2}-\dfrac{a}{ax+x^2}$

35. $3(u+1)^{-1}+3(1-u)^{-1}-6(u^2-1)^{-1}$

36. $t(t-c)^{-1}+(t^2+c^2)(c^2-t^2)^{-1}+c(t+c)^{-1}$

Find constants A and B that make the given equations true.

SAMPLE $\quad \dfrac{x+4}{x^2-x-2}=\dfrac{A}{x-2}+\dfrac{B}{x+1}$

SOLUTION $\quad \dfrac{x+4}{(x-2)(x+1)}=\dfrac{A(x+1)+B(x-2)}{(x-2)(x+1)}=\dfrac{(A+B)x+(A-2B)}{(x-2)(x+1)}$

$$\therefore\ x+4=(A+B)x+(A-2B)$$
$$1=A+B$$
$$4=A-2B$$

Solving the system gives: $A=2$; $B=-1$. ***Answer***

C **37.** $\dfrac{4x-3}{x^2-x}=\dfrac{A}{x}+\dfrac{B}{x-1}$

38. $\dfrac{1}{x^2-4}=\dfrac{A}{x-2}+\dfrac{B}{x+2}$

39. Explain why the set of rational numbers is closed under addition.

40. Explain why the set of rational expressions is closed under addition.

5-8 *Complex Fractions*

OBJECTIVE   To simplify complex fractions.

A **complex fraction** is one whose numerator or denominator, or both, contains one or more fractions or powers with negative exponents. For example,

$$\frac{\frac{3}{2} - \frac{1}{9}}{1 - \frac{1}{6}} \quad \text{and} \quad \frac{a^{-1} - x^{-1}}{a^{-2} - x^{-2}}$$

are complex fractions. Either of two methods may be used to simplify such fractions.

> Method 1: Express the fraction as a quotient, using the sign $\div$.
>
> Method 2: Multiply the numerator and denominator by the LCD of all the fractions within the numerator and denominator.

EXAMPLE 1   Simplify $\dfrac{\frac{3}{2} - \frac{1}{9}}{1 - \frac{1}{6}}$.

SOLUTION   Method 1

$$\frac{\frac{3}{2} - \frac{1}{9}}{1 - \frac{1}{6}} = \left(\frac{3}{2} - \frac{1}{9}\right) \div \left(1 - \frac{1}{6}\right)$$

$$= \frac{27 - 2}{18} \div \frac{6 - 1}{6}$$

$$= \frac{25}{18} \div \frac{5}{6}$$

$$= \frac{25}{18} \cdot \frac{6}{5} = \frac{5}{3} \quad \textbf{\textit{Answer}}$$

Method 2

$$\frac{\frac{3}{2} - \frac{1}{9}}{1 - \frac{1}{6}} = \frac{\left(\frac{3}{2} - \frac{1}{9}\right) \cdot 18}{\left(1 - \frac{1}{6}\right) \cdot 18}$$

$$= \frac{27 - 2}{18 - 3}$$

$$= \frac{25}{15} = \frac{5}{3} \quad \textbf{\textit{Answer}}$$

EXAMPLE 2 Simplify $\dfrac{a^{-1} - x^{-1}}{a^{-2} - x^{-2}}$.

SOLUTION

Method 1

$$\frac{a^{-1} - x^{-1}}{a^{-2} - x^{-2}} = \left(\frac{1}{a} - \frac{1}{x}\right) \div \left(\frac{1}{a^2} - \frac{1}{x^2}\right)$$

$$= \frac{x - a}{ax} \div \frac{x^2 - a^2}{a^2 x^2}$$

$$= \frac{x - a}{ax} \cdot \frac{a^2 x^2}{x^2 - a^2}$$

$$= \frac{a^2 x^2 (x - a)}{ax(x + a)(x - a)}$$

$$= \frac{ax}{x + a} \quad \textbf{\textit{Answer}}$$

Method 2

$$\frac{a^{-1} - x^{-1}}{a^{-2} - x^{-2}} = \frac{\left(\dfrac{1}{a} - \dfrac{1}{x}\right) a^2 x^2}{\left(\dfrac{1}{a^2} - \dfrac{1}{x^2}\right) a^2 x^2}$$

$$= \frac{ax^2 - a^2 x}{x^2 - a^2}$$

$$= \frac{ax(x - a)}{(x + a)(x - a)}$$

$$= \frac{ax}{x + a} \quad \textbf{\textit{Answer}}$$

If a fraction in the numerator or denominator of a complex fraction is itself complex, it should first be simplified independently. For example,

$$\frac{\dfrac{1}{b} + \dfrac{1 + \dfrac{1}{b}}{a}}{\dfrac{1}{a} + \dfrac{1}{b}} = \frac{\dfrac{1}{b} + \dfrac{1 + \dfrac{1}{b}}{a} \cdot \dfrac{b}{b}}{\dfrac{1}{a} + \dfrac{1}{b}} = \frac{\dfrac{1}{b} + \dfrac{b + 1}{ab}}{\dfrac{1}{a} + \dfrac{1}{b}}$$

$$= \frac{\left(\dfrac{1}{b} + \dfrac{b + 1}{ab}\right) \cdot ab}{\left(\dfrac{1}{a} + \dfrac{1}{b}\right) \cdot ab} = \frac{a + b + 1}{b + a}$$

Written Exercises

Simplify.

A **1.** $\dfrac{1 + \dfrac{1}{6}}{1 - \dfrac{1}{3}}$

2. $\dfrac{\dfrac{1}{2} - \dfrac{1}{12}}{1 - \dfrac{1}{6}}$

3. $\dfrac{\dfrac{3}{4} - \dfrac{3}{5}}{\dfrac{1}{2} - \dfrac{1}{10}}$

4. $\dfrac{1 - \dfrac{1}{6}}{\dfrac{3}{4} - \dfrac{1}{3}}$

5. $\dfrac{a + 1}{1 + \dfrac{1}{a}}$

6. $\dfrac{\dfrac{1}{x} + \dfrac{1}{2}}{\dfrac{1}{x} + 1}$

7. $\dfrac{a - b}{a^{-1} - b^{-1}}$

8. $\dfrac{m^{-1} + n^{-1}}{1 + mn^{-1}}$

9. $\dfrac{1 - \dfrac{1}{t^2}}{1 + \dfrac{1}{t}}$

10. $\dfrac{\dfrac{4}{x^2} - 1}{x - 2}$

11. $\dfrac{\dfrac{1}{u^2} - \dfrac{2}{uv} + \dfrac{1}{v^2}}{\dfrac{1}{u^2} - \dfrac{1}{v^2}}$

12. $\dfrac{\dfrac{1}{a^2} - \dfrac{1}{b^2}}{\dfrac{1}{a^2} - \dfrac{2}{ab} - \dfrac{3}{b^2}}$

13. $\dfrac{x^{-1} + y^{-1}}{x^{-2} - y^{-2}}$

14. $\dfrac{a^{-2} - b^2}{a^{-1} - b}$

15. $\dfrac{t + t^{-2}}{1 + t^{-1}}$

16. $\dfrac{8x^{-2} - x}{2x^{-1} - 1}$

17. $(u^{-1} - v^{-1})(u^2 - v^2)^{-1}$

18. $(u^{-2} - v^{-2})(u - v)^{-1}$

B **19.** $\dfrac{1 + \dfrac{1}{a + 1}}{1 + \dfrac{3}{a - 1}}$

20. $\dfrac{1 + \dfrac{a}{b + 1}}{1 + \dfrac{1}{b + a}}$

21. $\left(\dfrac{1}{x^2 - 1} + 1\right)\left(\dfrac{1}{x - 1} + 1\right)^{-1}$

22. $\left(1 + \dfrac{t}{t - 1}\right)\left(4 + \dfrac{3}{t^2 - 1}\right)^{-1}$

23. $\dfrac{1 + \dfrac{2 + \dfrac{1}{a}}{a}}{1 + \dfrac{1}{a}}$

24. $\dfrac{\dfrac{1}{x + 1}}{x + \dfrac{1}{x - \dfrac{1}{x}}}$

25. $1 + \dfrac{1}{1 + \dfrac{1}{1 + \dfrac{1}{1 + \dfrac{1}{1}}}}$

26. $1 + \dfrac{1}{2 + \dfrac{1}{2 + \dfrac{1}{2 + \dfrac{1}{2}}}}$

In Exercises 27–30, express $\dfrac{f(x + h) - f(x)}{h}$ as a single simplified fraction. (These exercises might be met in calculus.)

SAMPLE $f(x) = \dfrac{1}{x^2}$

SOLUTION $\dfrac{f(x + h) - f(x)}{h} = \dfrac{\dfrac{1}{(x + h)^2} - \dfrac{1}{x^2}}{h}$

$= \dfrac{x^2 - (x + h)^2}{hx^2(x + h)^2}$

$= \dfrac{x^2 - x^2 - 2xh - h^2}{hx^2(x + h)^2}$

$= \dfrac{-2x - h}{x^2(x + h)^2}$

27. $f(x) = \dfrac{1}{x}$

28. $f(x) = \dfrac{x + 1}{x}$

29. $f(x) = \dfrac{1}{x + 1}$

30. $f(x) = \dfrac{1 - x}{x}$

Simplify.

C 31. $[(x + y)(x - y)^{-1} + xy^{-1}][xy(x^2 - y^2)^{-1} + x(x + y)^{-1}]^{-1}$

32. $[(a + b)a^{-1} - 2b(a + b)^{-1}][(a - b)b^{-1} + 2a(a - b)^{-1}]^{-1}$

Self-Test 2

VOCABULARY   rational algebraic expression (p. 177)
rational expression (p. 177)
rational function (p. 178)
mixed expression (p. 180)
least common denominator (p. 186)
complex fraction (p. 189)

Simplify.

1. $(a^2 - x^2)(a + x)^{-1}$

2. $\dfrac{2t^2 + 5t - 3}{1 - 4t^2}$ Obj. 5-4, p. 177

3. Find the quotient and the remainder.   Obj. 5-5, p. 180

$$\frac{x^3 - 5x^2 + 18}{x - 3}$$

Perform the indicated operations and simplify.

4. $\dfrac{6st^2}{5u} \cdot \left(\dfrac{2t^3}{15su^2}\right)^{-1}$

5. $\dfrac{x + 3a}{x^2 - a^2} \div \dfrac{x - 3a}{x^2 - 2ax - 3a^2}$ Obj. 5-6, p. 183

6. $\dfrac{1}{2ab^2} - \dfrac{1}{a^2b} + \dfrac{1}{2a^3}$

7. $\dfrac{1}{t^2 + 2t} - \dfrac{2}{t^2 - 4}$ Obj. 5-7, p. 186

8. $\dfrac{2 - \dfrac{5}{6}}{\dfrac{3}{4} - \dfrac{2}{3}}$

9. $\dfrac{x^{-2} - y^{-2}}{x^{-1} - y^{-1}}$ Obj. 5-8, p. 189

Check your answers with those at the back of the book.

Computer Key-In

The least common denominator of two fractions is the least common multiple of the denominators. One way to find this number is to find multiples of one denominator and then test to find out if the other denominator is a factor of each multiple.

To find the LCM of 6 and 9, proceed as follows:

$9 \times 1 = 9$, which is not divisible by 6
$9 \times 2 = 18$, which is divisible by 6; hence 18 is the LCM.

Working the other way:

$6 \times 1 = 6$, which is not divisible by 9
$6 \times 2 = 12$, which is not divisible by 9
$6 \times 3 = 18$, which is divisible by 9; hence 18 is the LCM.

Notice that there are fewer steps if you find multiples of the larger number. This method is used in the following computer program.

```
10   PRINT "TO FIND THE LEAST COMMON DENOMINATOR,"
20   PRINT "INPUT D1, D2:";
30   INPUT D1,D2
40   FOR M=1 TO D1
50   LET Q=D2*M/D1
60   IF Q=INT(Q) THEN 80
70   NEXT M
80   PRINT "LCD(";D1;",";D2;") =";D2;" ×";M;" =";D2*M
90   END
```

Exercises

Use the program given above to find the following.

1. a. LCD (6,20)   b. LCD(20,6)   c. LCD(12,15)   d. LCD(15,12)
2. a. LCD (8,16)   b. LCD(16,8)   c. LCD(16,25)   d. LCD(25,16)

ḣistorical ṅote Calculators

In the early seventeenth century, while he was still a young man, the French mathematician Blaise Pascal developed a mechanical calculator to aid his father in doing accounts. (See the picture below.) This machine used a sequence of mechanical dials to add numbers with as many as six digits.

Compare this calculator with the ones that are available today.

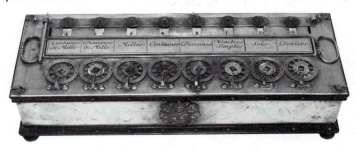

FRACTIONAL EQUATIONS

5-9 *Fractional Coefficients*

OBJECTIVE To solve equations and inequalities that have fractional coefficients.

EXAMPLE 1 Solve $\frac{x^2}{4} - \frac{5x}{6} - \frac{2}{3} = 0$.

SOLUTION

$$\frac{x^2}{4} - \frac{5x}{6} - \frac{2}{3} = 0$$

$$\frac{3x^2}{12} - \frac{10x}{12} - \frac{8}{12} = 0 \quad \left\{ \begin{array}{l} \text{Express the fractions} \\ \text{in terms of their LCD.} \end{array} \right.$$

$$\frac{1}{12}(3x^2 - 10x - 8) = 0$$

$$\frac{1}{12}(3x + 2)(x - 4) = 0$$

$$x = -\frac{2}{3} \quad \text{or} \quad x = 4$$

$\therefore$ the solution set is $\left\{ -\frac{2}{3}, 4 \right\}$. *Answer*

EXAMPLE 2 Solve the inequality $\frac{2x - 35}{15} < \frac{3x}{10} - 2$.

SOLUTION

$$\frac{2x - 35}{15} < \frac{3x}{10} - 2$$

$$30\left(\frac{2x - 35}{15}\right) < 30\left(\frac{3x}{10} - 2\right) \quad \left\{ \begin{array}{l} \text{Multiply both sides by} \\ \text{the LCD of the fractions.} \end{array} \right.$$

$$4x - 70 < 9x - 60$$

$$-10 < 5x$$

$$-2 < x$$

$\therefore$ the solution set is $\{x : x > -2\}$. *Answer*

EXAMPLE 3 Water purification plant A can process a day's water supply in 18 h; plant B can perform the same operation in 12 h. How long does it take to process a day's water when both plants are in operation?

SOLUTION

Step 1 The problem asks for the number of hours required by the two plants to process a day's supply of water.

Step 2 Let t = number of hours required by the two plants to process a day's supply of water.

The part of one day's supply processed by plant A in 1 h is $\frac{1}{18}$. Thus, the part of one day's supply processed by plant A in t h is $t \cdot \frac{1}{18} = \frac{t}{18}$. Similarly, the part of one day's supply processed by plant B in t h is $t \cdot \frac{1}{12} = \frac{t}{12}$.

Step 3 The combined output of the plants is to be one day's supply.

Part processed by Plant A	Plus	Part processed by Plant B	Is	One day's supply
$\frac{t}{18}$	$+$	$\frac{t}{12}$	$=$	1

Step 4 $\frac{t}{18} + \frac{t}{12} = 1$

$2t + 3t = 36; \quad 5t = 36; \quad t = \frac{36}{5} = 7.2 \text{ h}$

Step 5 In 7.2 h Plant A will process $7.2\left(\frac{1}{18}\right)$, or 0.4, of a day's supply of water. In 7.2 h Plant B will process $7.2\left(\frac{1}{12}\right)$, or 0.6, of a day's supply of water. Because $0.4 + 0.6 = 1$, the solution is correct.

$\therefore$ it will require the two plants 7.2 h to process a day's supply of water. ***Answer***

Percentage problems often involve fractional coefficients. The word **percent** means "hundredths" and is denoted by %. When working with percents the word "of" usually indicates multiplication. For example, "75% of 200" means "0.75×200," which equals 150.

EXAMPLE 4 A chemist wishes to mix 70% and 20% solutions of hydrochloric acid to produce 200 L of a 40% solution of hydrochloric acid. How much of each solution should the chemist use?

SOLUTION

Step 1 The problem asks for the number of liters of the 70% solution and the number of liters of the 20% solution that must be used.

Step 2 Let x = number of liters of the 70% solution.
Then $200 - x$ = number of liters of the 20% solution.

Represent the known facts in a chart.

	Liters of Solution	$\times$ % Acid $=$	Liters of Acid
70% Solution	x	70%	$0.70x$
20% Solution	$200 - x$	20%	$0.20(200 - x)$
Resulting 40% Solution	200	40%	$0.40(200)$

(*Solution continued on page 196*)

Step 3

Acid in 70% sol.	And	Acid in 20% sol.	Is	Acid in resulting sol.
$0.70x$	$+$	$0.20(200 - x)$	$=$	$0.40(200)$

Step 4
$$0.7x + 0.2(200 - x) = 0.4(200)$$
$$0.7x + 40 - 0.2x = 80$$
$$0.5x = 40$$
$$x = 80; \ 200 - x = 120$$

Step 5 The check is left for you.

∴ the chemist should use 80 L of the 70% solution and 120 L of the 20% solution. ***Answer***

Oral Exercises

State the LCD of the terms of each open sentence and read the sentence after multiplying by the LCD.

1. $\dfrac{x}{4} - 1 = \dfrac{1}{2}$

2. $1 - \dfrac{t}{6} = \dfrac{2}{3}$

3. $\dfrac{z}{2} + 2 < \dfrac{z}{3}$

4. $\dfrac{x}{5} - \dfrac{1}{2} > \dfrac{3x}{10}$

5. $\dfrac{t}{3} - \dfrac{t}{4} = 2$

6. $\dfrac{n}{3} - \dfrac{n}{12} = \dfrac{5}{6}$

7. $\dfrac{x^2}{4} + \dfrac{x}{2} - \dfrac{3}{8} = 0$

8. $\dfrac{y^2}{4} - \dfrac{1}{2} < \dfrac{y}{3}$

9. $\dfrac{t^2}{15} + \dfrac{1}{2} > \dfrac{t}{5}$

Written Exercises

Solve each open sentence.

A

1. $\dfrac{5x^2}{14} - \dfrac{x}{7} - \dfrac{1}{2} = 0$

2. $\dfrac{t^2}{5} - \dfrac{3t}{10} - \dfrac{1}{2} = 0$

3. $\dfrac{z^2}{2} - \dfrac{7z}{4} - 1 = 0$

4. $x^2 + \dfrac{5x}{12} - \dfrac{1}{4} = 0$

5. $\dfrac{3m^2}{10} - \dfrac{m}{2} - \dfrac{1}{5} = 0$

6. $\dfrac{t^2}{6} - \dfrac{t}{12} - \dfrac{1}{2} = 0$

7. $\dfrac{r^2}{8} - \dfrac{3r}{4} - 2 = 0$

8. $\dfrac{n^2}{2} - \dfrac{5n}{6} - 2 = 0$

9. $\dfrac{x^2}{6} + \dfrac{x}{3} = \dfrac{1}{2}$

10. $\dfrac{3t^2}{2} + \dfrac{17t}{12} = \dfrac{5}{4}$

11. $\dfrac{2y^2}{5} = \dfrac{5(y - 1)}{3}$

12. $\dfrac{2}{3}x(x - 2) = \dfrac{7}{2}$

13. $\dfrac{x - 7}{3} + \dfrac{5}{2} < 0$

14. $\dfrac{t + 2}{5} > \dfrac{3}{2}$

15. $\dfrac{z}{2} > \dfrac{2z}{3} + 1$

16. $\dfrac{2x + 1}{6} - 1 < \dfrac{x}{8}$

17. $\dfrac{x + 7}{10} - \dfrac{x}{25} \leq 1$

18. $\dfrac{u + 5}{12} - \dfrac{u + 3}{8} \geq 1$

Problems

Solve.

A 1. If $\frac{1}{2}$ is $\frac{3}{4}$ of $\frac{5}{6}$ of a certain number, what is that number?

2. If 7 is $\frac{3}{2}$ of $\frac{7}{6}$ of a certain number, what is that number?

3. If 30 is 20% of 75% of a certain number, what is that number?

4. Forty percent of 350 is what percent of 200?

5. In a college with an enrollment of 1520, the ratio of women to men is 10 to 9. How many women and how many men are there?

6. The average of two numbers is 21. Find the numbers if the smaller is three-fourths the larger.

7. A framed print costs a dealer $24. At what price should the dealer sell the print in order to make a profit of 20% of the selling price?

8. Grandstand seats for a baseball game cost $8.00 and bleacher seats cost $4.25. At Friday's game the receipts from the sale of 9000 tickets were $60,000. How many tickets of each type were sold?

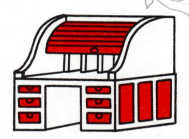

9. Will, Myrna, and Jim went to an antiques auction and spent a total of $184. If Will spent $\frac{2}{3}$ as much as Myrna and $\frac{3}{4}$ as much as Jim, how much did each person spend?

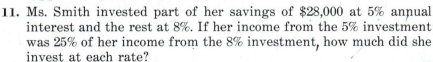

B 10. One way to estimate the size of a population is to tag a sample. Of the Lake Nakuru flock of flamingos, 1500 birds were tagged. If, at a later date, a sample of 600 flamingos was found to contain 30 tagged ones, about how many birds are in the flock?

11. Ms. Smith invested part of her savings of $28,000 at 5% annual interest and the rest at 8%. If her income from the 5% investment was 25% of her income from the 8% investment, how much did she invest at each rate?

12. How much pure alcohol must be added to 300 g of a 25% (by mass) solution of alcohol in water to produce a 40% solution?

13. Computer A can process a payroll in 30 h and computer B can do the job in 20 h. How long would it take both of them together to process the payroll?

14. An elevator went from bottom to top of a tower at an average speed of 3 m/s, remained at the top for 30 s, and then returned to the bottom at 4 m/s. If the elapsed time was 4 min, how tall is the tower?

15. How much of a 10% solution of boric acid should be added to 60 mL of a 3% boric acid solution to produce a 5% solution?

16. Three water supply pipes can individually fill a reservoir in 6 d, 8 d, and 12 d, respectively. How long would it take to fill the reservoir if all three were running?

17. One paving machine can surface 1 km of highway in 6 h. Another can surface 1 km in 8 h. How long will it take them to surface a 10 km stretch of highway if they start at opposite ends and work day and night?

18. Two equal masses of rocket fuel are fired simultaneously and burn at constant but different rates. If the first mass is consumed in 4 min and the second in 5 min, when was the first mass equal to half the second?

19. A chemist needs to make 600 g of a 45% (by mass) solution of alcohol by mixing 25% and 55% solutions. How much of each should be used?

20. A dog food company wishes to produce a product by mixing ingredients A, containing 55% protein, and B, containing 30% protein. What proportion of ingredients A and B should be used if the final product is to contain 40% protein?

C 21. A fertilizer company wishes to make a mixture containing 60% nutrient by mixing together quantities of a mixture containing 50% nutrient and costing 30 cents per kilogram and a mixture containing 80% nutrient and costing 50 cents per kilogram. How much of each should be used: (a) in 1 kg of the final mixture; (b) in $280 worth of the final mixture?

22. Pipe A can fill a tank in 3 h and pipe B can fill it in 2 h. With the tank empty, pipe A is turned on, and one hour later, pipe B is turned on. At the time the tank is full, how long has each pipe run?

23. The road between two towns consists of two segments, one 75 km longer than the other. Jean drove the shorter segment at 45 km/h and the longer at 90 km/h. If she averaged 75 km/h for the entire trip, how far apart are the towns?

24. In a Grand Prix race, a Bugari started at 9 A.M. and averaged 195 km/h. A Ferratti started 2 min later and averaged 205 km/h. If a lap is 25 km, on which lap was the Bugari overtaken?

25. A car radiator contains 5 L of a 25% antifreeze solution. How many liters must be removed and replaced by a 75% antifreeze solution to leave the radiator filled with a 55% antifreeze solution?

26. Two front-end loaders can remove three quarters of the dirt from a certain excavation in $1\frac{4}{5}$ days. Working alone, loader A would take 2 days longer than loader B to remove all the dirt. How long would loader A take to do the entire excavation alone?

Time upriver	Plus	Time at bridge	Plus	Time downriver	Equals	Elapsed time
$\dfrac{18}{15-v}$	$+$	$\dfrac{3}{2}$	$+$	$\dfrac{18}{15+v}$	$=$	4

$$\frac{18}{15-v} + \frac{18}{15+v} = \frac{5}{2}$$

Do you see how we have combined Steps 1, 2, and 3 of our problem-solving method? Solving the equation and checking the roots are left for you.

You should find that the rate of the current is 3 km/h. ***Answer***

0 in denominator = undefined

Written Exercises

Solve and check. If no solution exists, so state.

A 1. $\dfrac{1}{2t} + \dfrac{2}{t} = 10$

2. $\dfrac{1}{x} - \dfrac{2}{3} = \dfrac{1}{3x}$

3. $\dfrac{x}{2x-1} = \dfrac{2}{3}$

4. $\dfrac{u+1}{u-1} = \dfrac{7}{3}$

5. $\dfrac{z+2}{z-2} = \dfrac{z-2}{z-4}$

6. $\dfrac{x+1}{x-1} = \dfrac{x-1}{x+3}$

7. $\dfrac{x+1}{2x} = \dfrac{x-1}{2x-1}$

8. $\dfrac{3t}{t-5} = \dfrac{3t+1}{t-4}$

9. $\dfrac{2x^2 + x + 2}{x^2 - 2x + 1} = 2$

10. $\dfrac{x^2 - x + 2}{2x^2 + x - 2} = \dfrac{1}{2}$

11. $\dfrac{2}{t+2} + \dfrac{1}{t-2} = \dfrac{1}{t^2-4}$

12. $\dfrac{x}{x+5} + \dfrac{5}{x-5} = \dfrac{x^2}{x^2-25}$

13. $\dfrac{3}{z-3} + \dfrac{2}{z+3} = \dfrac{z^2+9}{z^2-9}$

Method Find C.D.

14. $\dfrac{1}{t-3} = \dfrac{6}{t^2-9} + \dfrac{8}{7}$

15. $\dfrac{3}{u} + \dfrac{6}{1-u} = \dfrac{u^2+13}{u^2-u}$

16. $\dfrac{3}{x-1} + 4 = \dfrac{1}{1-x^2}$

17. $\dfrac{1}{t^2-3t+2} + \dfrac{t}{t-1} = \dfrac{2}{t-2}$

18. $\dfrac{2}{m^2+3m-4} = \dfrac{2}{3m+12} - \dfrac{m}{m-1}$

19. $3(x+1)^{-1} + 3(x-1)^{-1} = 4$

20. $8(y+2)^{-1} + 8(y-2)^{-1} = 3$

B 21. $\dfrac{3}{4x^2-7x-2} + \dfrac{2}{2-x} = \dfrac{4}{28x+7}$

22. $\dfrac{2}{2x^2-11x+15} + \dfrac{12}{9-x^2} = \dfrac{1}{2x^2+x-15}$

23. $\dfrac{2x-1}{x+3} + \dfrac{1}{x^2+x-6} + \dfrac{x-4}{x-2} = 0$

24. $\dfrac{y+3}{3-y} + \dfrac{3y+1}{y^2-9} = \dfrac{1-5y}{y+3}$

25. $\left(\dfrac{x+2}{x-1}\right)^2 + 6 = \dfrac{5x+10}{x-1}$

26. $\left(\dfrac{t}{t-1}\right)^2 + 4 = \dfrac{5t}{t-1}$

Problems

A

1. What number must be added to both numerator and denominator of $\frac{3}{17}$ to produce a fraction equivalent to $\frac{3}{5}$?

2. When the same number is subtracted from the numerator of $\frac{13}{2}$ and added to its denominator, the resulting fraction is equal to $\frac{2}{3}$. Find the number.

3. One pipe can fill a reservoir in 3 d. With second pipe also in operation, the reservoir can be filled in 2 d. How long would it take the second pipe alone to fill the reservoir?

4. The intake pipe of a tank can fill it in 4 h. One day, however, the intake pipe took 6 h to fill the tank because the drain pipe had been left open by mistake. How long would it take the drain pipe to empty a full tank?

5. Two positive integers differ by 4 and their reciprocals differ by $\frac{1}{15}$. Find the integers.

6. The sum of two integers is 18 and the sum of their reciprocals is $\frac{1}{4}$. Find the integers.

7. Since the average speed of a passenger train was increased by 10 km/h over a 300 km route, the trip takes 1 h less than previously. What is the new speed?

8. Jan can bicycle 50% faster than her younger brother, and she rides the 6 km distance between their home and school in 10 min less time. What are their speeds?

9. Maria drove for 100 km in the city, getting 10 km/L, and then drove 250 km on a throughway. If her fuel consumption for the whole trip was 15 km/L, what was her fuel consumption on the throughway?

10. A light plane flew for 576 km directly into a strong wind and then flew back with the same wind. If the total flying time was 5 h, and the plane's airspeed was 250 km/h, what was the speed of the wind?

11. The riverboat *Pixie* goes 20 km upriver against a 5 km/h current and back again in 3 h. What is the *Pixie*'s speed in still water?

12. The members of an outing club were to contribute equally to raise $240 for a day's trip. When 4 members had to stay home, each of the others had to pay $5 more than originally planned. How many members of the club are there?

13. The members of the soccer team are to share the $540 cost of a banquet. When 5 students were unable to attend, the cost per student was $1.50 greater. How many attended?

14. Joe can mow the 18th fairway in 4 h, Jan can do it in 3 h, and Joe, Jan, and John, working together, can do it in 1 h 20 min. How long would it take John, working alone, to do the job?

B **15.** Pipe A can fill a tank in 4 h, and pipe B can fill the tank in half the time required for pipe C, a drain pipe, to empty the tank. When all three pipes are open, the tank can be filled in 2.4 h. How much time is required for pipe C to empty the tank?

16. A plane had a 100 km/h tail wind on its flight from airport A to airport B, 600 km away. The pilot waited 2 h at B for the wind to abate and then flew back to A in a dead calm. If the total elapsed time was 7 h, what was the plane's airspeed?

17. An elevator went from the bottom to the top of a 144 m tower, remained at the top for 30 s, and then returned to the bottom. The elevator traveled 1 m/s faster on the way down, and the trip up lasted 2 s longer than the trip down. Find the speed of the elevator when it was going up.

18. A boat whose speed in still water is 20 km/h traveled upriver 24 km to Stillwater Lake, crossed to the other side, 5 km away, and then retraced its route back to its starting point. If the entire trip took 3 h, what is the speed of the river current?

19. Mary drove halfway from A to B at 40 km/h and the rest of the way at 80 km/h. What was her average speed for the whole trip?

20. Luis drove halfway from A to B at 20 km/h. At what speed must he drive the rest of the way in order to average 30 km/h for the whole trip?

21. Simple interest on a certain amount of money for one year was $720. If the interest rate were 1% higher, $1000 less would have to be invested to produce the same yield. Find the amount that was invested and the interest rate.

22. A store bought a shipment of dresses for $2000 and offered them for sale after a markup of $20 each. All but 5 were sold, and the store made a profit of $700. How many dresses were in the original shipment?

23. In going between two floors, a postal worker took a freight elevator up and a passsenger elevator down. What was the average speed for the round trip if the freight elevator requires 3 s to travel 1 m and the passenger elevator travels at 3 m/s?

24. Lucy Jones takes 3 min less time than Ben Smith to assemble a TV set. One day, after Lucy had spent 8 min on a set, she was called away, and Ben finished assembling it in 5 min. How long does it take each of them to assemble a set?

C **25.** The number x is the *harmonic mean* of the numbers a and b if $\frac{1}{x}$ is the average of $\frac{1}{a}$ and $\frac{1}{b}$.

  a. Find the harmonic mean of 2 and 6.
  b. Find a formula for the harmonic mean of a and b.

Self-Test 3

VOCABULARY   fractional equation (p. 199)

Solve.

1. $\dfrac{t^2}{14} + \dfrac{t}{6} = \dfrac{1}{7}$

2. $\dfrac{1}{5} - \dfrac{t}{10} = t^2$

Obj. 5-9, p. 194

3. How many liters of a 50% solution of acid should be added to 6 L of a 25% solution to obtain a 40% solution?

Solve and check.

4. $\dfrac{x-2}{5x} + \dfrac{4}{15x} = \dfrac{1}{6}$

5. $\dfrac{1}{t^2 + t} - \dfrac{2}{t+1} = \dfrac{1-t}{t}$

Obj. 5-10, p. 199

6. Working alone, one computer requires 3 h more time than another to process a payroll. If they operate together, they can do the job in 2 h. How long does it take the slower computer to do the job alone?

Check your answers with those at the back of the book.

Chapter Summary

1. The definitions

$$a^{-n} = \frac{1}{a^n} \text{ and } a^0 = 1$$

permit negative integers and zero to be used as exponents when $a \neq 0$. The laws of exponents continue to hold.

2. A number may be written in *scientific notation*: $m \times 10^n$, where $1 \le |m| < 10$ and n is an integer. The digits in m should all be *significant*.

3. A *rational algebraic expression* is a quotient of polynomials. To simplify such an expression, divide its numerator and denominator by their GCF.

4. To *divide* one polynomial by another, find the quotient and remainder in the algorithm

$$\frac{\text{Dividend}}{\text{Divisor}} = \text{Quotient} + \frac{\text{Remainder}}{\text{Divisor}}$$

5. Products and quotients of rational expressions can be found using the multiplication rule for fractions or the division rule for fractions, which are shown below.

$$\frac{p}{q} \cdot \frac{r}{s} = \frac{pr}{qs} \qquad \frac{p}{q} \div \frac{r}{s} = \frac{p}{q} \cdot \frac{s}{r}$$

6. To find a sum or a difference of rational expressions, find their LCD, express each as an equivalent fraction having the LCD as denominator, combine, and simplify.

7. To simplify a *complex fraction* that has no complex fractions in its numerator or denominator, use either of the following methods. *Method 1:* Express the fraction as a quotient, using the sign $\div$. *Method 2:* Multiply the numerator and denominator by the LCD of all the simple fractions within the numerator and denominator.

8. To solve an equation having fractional coefficients, multiply each side by the LCD of all the fractions. To solve a *fractional equation* (one in which a variable appears in a denominator), proceed the same way but check the results because extra roots may be introduced.

Chapter Review

Give the letter of the correct answer.

1. Simplify $\dfrac{6a^2x^4}{2a^3x^3}$ using positive exponents only.   **5-1**

  a. $3ax$ **b.** $3a^5x^7$ **c.** $\dfrac{3x}{a}$ **d.** $\dfrac{3}{ax}$

2. Simplify $\dfrac{(-2s^2t)^3}{(-4st^2)^2}$ using positive exponents only.

  a. $-\dfrac{s^3}{2t}$ **b.** $-\dfrac{s^4}{2t}$ **c.** $\dfrac{s^5}{2t^3}$ **d.** $\dfrac{s^4}{t}$

3. Simplify $\dfrac{(2ab^{-2})^0}{3^0a^{-2}b}$ using positive exponents only.   **5-2**

  a. $\dfrac{a^3}{3b^3}$ **b.** a^2 **c.** 1 **d.** $\dfrac{a^2}{b}$

4. Express $\left(\dfrac{m^2}{n^{-3}}\right)^{-1}\left(\dfrac{3m^{-2}}{n^{-2}}\right)^{-2}$ in simplest form without negative or zero exponents.

  a. $\dfrac{9m^2}{n^7}$ **b.** $\dfrac{m^2}{9n^7}$ **c.** $\dfrac{m^2}{9n}$ **d.** $\dfrac{9m^6}{n}$

5. Which number is greatest?   **5-3**

  a. 6.3×10^5 **b.** 9.8×10^4 **c.** 5.2×10^5

6. Write 2.37×10^{-4} in decimal form.

  a. 0.0000237 **b.** $23{,}700$ **c.** 0.000237 **d.** 0.00237

7. Simplify $\dfrac{a - 4a^3}{a - 4a^2 + 4a^3}$.   **5-4**

  a. $\dfrac{1}{4a^2}$ **b.** $\dfrac{1 - 4a^2}{1 - 4a + 4a^2}$ **c.** -1 **d.** $\dfrac{1 + 2a}{1 - 2a}$

8. Find the zeros of the function $f(x) = \dfrac{x^2 - x - 6}{x^2 + 7x + 10}$.

 a. 3   **b.** $-2, 3$ **c.** $-5, -2, 3$ **d.** $-5, -2$

9. Divide: $\dfrac{a^3 - 2a^2 + 3a - 4}{a - 2}$. 5-5

 a. $a^2 + 3 - \dfrac{10}{a - 2}$ **b.** $a^2 + 3 + \dfrac{2}{a - 2}$

 c. $a^2 - 4a - 5 - \dfrac{14}{a - 2}$ **d.** $a^2 + 4a + 11 + \dfrac{18}{a - 2}$

10. Simplify $\dfrac{t + 2}{t^2 + 3t} \cdot \dfrac{t^2 - 5t + 6}{4 - t^2}$. 5-6

 a. $\dfrac{(t - 6)(t + 1)}{t(t + 3)(2 - t)}$ **b.** $\dfrac{3 - t}{t(t + 3)}$ **c.** $\dfrac{1}{t}$ **d.** $\dfrac{t - 3}{t(t + 3)}$

11. Simplify $\dfrac{6c^2d}{5x^3} \div \dfrac{9cd}{10x^2}$.

 a. $\dfrac{4c}{3}$ **b.** $\dfrac{27c^3d^2}{25x^5}$ **c.** $\dfrac{4c^3}{3x^3}$ **d.** $\dfrac{4c}{3x}$

12. Simplify $\dfrac{2x}{3y} + \dfrac{5x}{6y}$. 5-7

 a. $\dfrac{3xy}{2y^2}$ **b.** $\dfrac{7x}{9y}$ **c.** $\dfrac{3x}{2y}$ **d.** $\dfrac{7x}{6y}$

13. Simplify $\dfrac{2}{a - 2} - \dfrac{3}{a - 1}$.

 a. $\dfrac{-a + 4}{(a - 2)(a - 1)}$ **b.** $\dfrac{-a - 8}{(a - 2)(a - 1)}$ **c.** $\dfrac{-1}{(a - 2)(a - 1)}$ **d.** $\dfrac{5a - 8}{(a - 2)(a - 1)}$

14. Simplify $\dfrac{1 - a^{-2}}{1 + a^{-1}}$. 5-8

 a. $\dfrac{a^2 - 1}{a^2 + 1}$ **b.** $\dfrac{a}{a + 1}$ **c.** $\dfrac{a - 1}{a}$ **d.** $\dfrac{a^2 - 1}{a^2 + 1}$

15. Solve $\dfrac{-3x + 5}{2} < 2 - \dfrac{4x}{3}$. 5-9

 a. $x > 13$ **b.** $x < 3$ **c.** $x < 13$ **d.** $x > 3$

16. How much pure hydrochloric acid should be added to 5 L of a 40% solution to produce a 75% solution?

 a. 7 L   **b.** 13 L   **c.** 2.3 L   **d.** 15 L

17. Solve $\dfrac{-8}{w^2 - 4} + 2 = \dfrac{2}{w + 2}$. 5-10

 a. $\{-2, 3\}$ **b.** $\{3\}$ **c.** $\{-1\}$ **d.** $\{-3, 3\}$

18. A boat went 8 km upstream and returned, all in 2 h. If the current was running at 3 km/h, what is the boat's speed in still water?

 a. 8 km/h   **b.** 10 km/h   **c.** 7 km/h   **d.** 9 km/h

Chapter Test

Write in simplest form using only positive exponents.

1. $\dfrac{s^2 t}{s} \left(\dfrac{t^2}{2s} \right)^3$ 5-1

2. $\dfrac{a^{-1}}{b^2} \left(\dfrac{a^{-1}}{2b^2} \right)^{-2}$ 5-2

3. Simplify and write in both scientific notation and decimal form: 5-3

$$\frac{(2.4 \times 10^{-3})(6.0 \times 10^5)}{8.0 \times 10^{-1}}$$

4. Reduce $\dfrac{x - 4x^3}{2x^2 + 5x - 3}$ to lowest terms. 5-4

5. Find the quotient and remainder: $\dfrac{6x^3 + 5x^2 + 9}{2x + 3}$. 5-5

Perform the indicated operations and simplify.

6. $\dfrac{(x - y)^2}{x^2 y} \div \dfrac{x^2 - y^2}{xy^2}$ 7. $\dfrac{2t - 3}{t^2 + 4t - 12} \cdot \dfrac{4t^3 + 24t^2}{2t^2 + t - 6} \div \dfrac{2t^4 - 8t^2}{8t^3}$ 5-6

8. $\dfrac{a}{a - 1} - \dfrac{a + 1}{a}$ 9. $\dfrac{x + a}{4x + 2a} - \dfrac{ax}{4x^2 - a^2}$ 5-7

10. Simplify $\dfrac{4x^{-1} - x}{2x^{-1} - 1}$. 5-8

11. Solve $\dfrac{x^2}{6} = \dfrac{x}{3} + \dfrac{1}{2}$. 5-9

12. Eight liters of a 50% solution of alcohol is to be made by mixing 25% and 65% solutions. How much of each should be used?

13. Solve and check: $\dfrac{4}{x^2 - 4} = \dfrac{1}{x - 2} + 1$. 5-10

14. An elevator went from bottom to top of a 180 m building, stayed there for 1 min, and then came back down, the total elapsed time being 3.5 min. If the speed of the elevator when it went up was 1 m/s less than when it came down, find these speeds.

Shown above is a basic electric arc furnace. It can be used to produce
all the known grades of steel including the special alloys used in high-
temperature applications. The equations used in the study of heat
require the use of complex numbers.

6

IRRATIONAL AND COMPLEX NUMBERS

Hi roomie

ROOTS AND RADICALS

6-1 *Roots of Real Numbers*

OBJECTIVE **To identify roots of real numbers.**

Consider the function defined by the equation $y = x^2$. If an ordered pair (x, y) satisfies this equation, x is called a **square root** of y.

To find the square root of 9, solve this equation:

$$x^2 = 9$$
$$x^2 - 9 = 0$$
$$(x + 3)(x - 3) = 0$$
$$x + 3 = 0 \quad \text{or} \quad x - 3 = 0$$
$$x = -3 \qquad\qquad x = 3$$

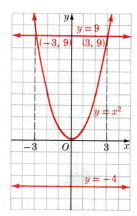

Figure 6-1

You say that -3 and 3 are the square roots of 9.

Now look at the graph of $y = x^2$ in Figure 6-1. The graph of $y = 9$ intersects the graph of $y = x^2$ at $(-3, 9)$ and $(3, 9)$. So -3 and 3 are solutions of $x^2 = 9$, confirming that -3 and 3 are the square roots of 9.

Consider a second example.

$$x^2 = -4$$
$$x^2 + 4 = 0$$

This quadratic equation cannot be solved over the real numbers. That is, -4 has no real-valued square roots. Looking at Figure 6-1 again will confirm this result. The graph of $y = -4$ does not intersect the graph of $y = x^2$, so you may conclude that there are no real-valued square roots of -4.

209

Note also from Figure 6-1 that the graphs of $y = 0$ and $y = x^2$ intersect at the origin. The square root of 0 is 0.

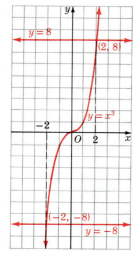

Figure 6-2

If an ordered pair (x, y) satisfies the equation $y = x^3$, x is called a **cube root** of y. The graph of $y = x^3$ is shown in Figure 6-2. The graphs of $y = 8$ and $y = x^3$ intersect in one point, namely $(2, 8)$, so 2 is the cube root of 8. Similarly, note that -2 is the cube root of -8. The graphs of $y = 0$ and $y = x^3$ intersect at the origin, so the cube root of 0 is 0.

Functions defined by equations of the form $y = x^n$ are called **power functions.** The graphs of power functions of degree 4, 5, 6, and 7 are shown in Figures 6-3, 6-4, 6-5, and 6-6, respectively.

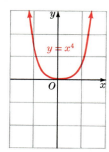

Figure 6-3

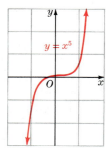

Figure 6-4

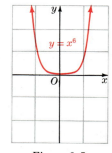

Figure 6-5

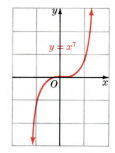

Figure 6-6

The graph of $y = x^n$ resembles that of $y = x^2$ if n is even (Figures 6-3 and 6-5) and resembles that of $y = x^3$ if n is odd (Figures 6-4 and 6-6).

In general, let n be any positive integer. Then a is called an **nth root** of b if $a^n = b$. The following chart summarizes the facts about the real nth roots of b suggested by considering points common to the graphs of $y = x^n$ and $y = b$.

Number and Sign of the nth Roots of b

	$b > 0$	$b < 0$	$b = 0$
n even	one positive root one negative root	no real roots	one root, 0
n odd	one positive root	one negative root	one root, 0

The symbol $\sqrt[n]{b}$ (read "the nth root of b") denotes the **principal** nth root of b, as follows:

1. If n is odd, $\sqrt[n]{b}$ denotes the single nth root of b.

   EXAMPLES $\sqrt[5]{32} = 2$, $\sqrt[3]{-\dfrac{1}{8}} = -\dfrac{1}{2}$, $\sqrt[3]{0.008} = 0.2$

2. a. If n is even and $b \geq 0$, $\sqrt[n]{b}$ denotes the nonnegative nth root of b.

   EXAMPLES $\sqrt[4]{16} = 2$, $\sqrt[6]{0} = 0$, $\sqrt[2]{9} = \sqrt{9} = 3$, $-\sqrt[4]{16} = -2$

   b. If n is even and $b < 0$, $\sqrt[n]{b}$ has no meaning in the system of real numbers.

   EXAMPLES $\sqrt[2]{-9}$ and $\sqrt[4]{-16}$ are not real numbers.

The symbol $\sqrt[n]{b}$ is called a **radical.** Other terms are:

$$\textbf{index} \longrightarrow \ \ \sqrt[n]{b} \quad \begin{matrix} \longleftarrow \textbf{radical sign} \\ \\ \longleftarrow \textbf{radicand} \end{matrix}$$

The index must be a positive integer. The index 2 is usually omitted from the radical—the second root of a number is simply its square root. (The third root is the cube root.) In writing a radical, be sure that the radical sign extends over the entire radicand. For example,

$$\sqrt{9 + 7} = \sqrt{16} = 4, \text{ but } \sqrt{9} + 7 = 3 + 7 = 10.$$

By the definition of the nth root of b,

$$\left(\sqrt[n]{b}\right)^n = b.$$

For example, $\left(\sqrt[3]{8}\right)^3 = 8$ and $\left(\sqrt{7}\right)^2 = 7$. It is not always true, however, that $\sqrt[n]{b^n} = b$ because the radical denotes the *principal* root. For example, if $n = 4$ and $b = -2$, you have $\sqrt[4]{(-2)^4} = \sqrt[4]{16} = 2$, not -2. The general rules are these:

$$\text{If } n \text{ is odd, } \sqrt[n]{b^n} = b.$$
$$\text{If } n \text{ is even, } \sqrt[n]{b^n} = |b|.$$

Thus, $\sqrt[3]{(-5)^3} = -5$, $\sqrt{(-5)^2} = |-5| = 5$, and $\sqrt[4]{5^4} = |5| = 5$.

Oral Exercises

Give the value of each radical. If the radical does not denote a real number, so state.

1. $\sqrt{25}$
2. $\sqrt[3]{-27}$
3. $\sqrt[3]{-1}$
4. $\sqrt[4]{0}$
5. $\sqrt[6]{-16}$
6. $\sqrt[4]{(-3)^4}$
7. $\sqrt[3]{(-7)^3}$
8. $\sqrt{(-1)^3}$

Find the real roots of each equation. If there are none, so state.

SAMPLE $25x^2 - 9 = 0$

SOLUTION $25x^2 = 9$, $x^2 = \dfrac{9}{25}$

$\therefore$ the roots are $\dfrac{3}{5}$ and $-\dfrac{3}{5}$.

9. $x^2 - 36 = 0$ 10. $x^3 + 8 = 0$
11. $x^4 + 16 = 0$ 12. $x^2 + 1 = 0$
13. $4x^2 - 9 = 0$ 14. $8x^3 - 1 = 0$

Written Exercises

Evaluate each radical. If the radical does not represent a real number, so state.

A 1. $\sqrt[3]{125}$ 2. $\sqrt{121}$ 3. $\sqrt[4]{256}$ 4. $\sqrt[3]{-1000}$
   5. $\sqrt{-64}$ 6. $-\sqrt{64}$ 7. $\sqrt[3]{-64}$ 8. $-\sqrt[3]{64}$
   9. $\sqrt{\dfrac{1}{9}}$ 10. $\sqrt{\dfrac{25}{4}}$ 11. $\sqrt[3]{\dfrac{27}{8}}$ 12. $\sqrt[3]{-\dfrac{1}{125}}$
   13. $\sqrt{0.16}$ 14. $\sqrt{1.21}$ 15. $\sqrt[3]{0.027}$ 16. $\sqrt[3]{-0.064}$
   17. $\sqrt{a^2}$ 18. $\sqrt{a^4}$ 19. $\sqrt[3]{a^6}$ 20. $\sqrt{a^6}$

Find the real roots of each equation. If there are none, so state.

21. $4x^2 + 36 = 0$ 22. $27x^3 - 8 = 0$
23. $27x^3 + 64 = 0$ 24. $81x^4 + 16 = 0$
25. $\dfrac{x^4}{16} - 81 = 0$ 26. $1000x^3 + 27 = 0$

For what values of the variable are the following statements true?

SAMPLE $\sqrt{(x - 4)^2} = x - 4$

SOLUTION $x - 4 \geq 0$, or $x \geq 4$.
             (If $x - 4 < 0$, then $\sqrt{(x - 4)^2} = |x - 4| = 4 - x$).

27. $\sqrt{(2 - x)^2} = 2 - x$ 28. $\sqrt[4]{(x + 1)^4} = x + 1$
29. $\sqrt[5]{(x + 3)^5} = x + 3$ 30. $\sqrt{x^4} = x^2$
31. $\sqrt{x - 3}$ denotes a real number.   32. $\sqrt[3]{x - 3}$ denotes a real number.

B 33. $\sqrt[4]{x^2 + 1}$ denotes a real number.
   34. $\sqrt[3]{4 - x^2}$ denotes a real number.
   35. $\sqrt{4 - x^2}$ denotes a real number.
   36. $\sqrt[4]{x^2 - 9}$ denotes a real number.

In Exercises 37 and 38, graph the given equation. (*Hint*: Consider the cases $x \geq 0$ and $x < 0$ separately.)

37. $y = \sqrt{x^2} + x$ **38.** $y = \sqrt[3]{x^3} - \sqrt{x^2}$

C **39.** Explain why the graphs of $y = x^2$ and $y = x^3$ lie below the graph of $y = x$ when $0 < x < 1$. It will be sufficient to show that if $0 < x < 1$, then $0 < x^2 < x$ and $0 < x^3 < x$.

40. Explain why the graphs of $y = x^2$ and $y = x^3$ lie above the graph of $y = x$ when $x > 1$. It will be sufficient to show that if $x > 1$, then $x^2 > x$ and $x^3 > x$.

41. Show that if $\sqrt{a} > \sqrt{b}$, then $a > b$. (*Hint*: Show first that $a > \sqrt{a}\,\sqrt{b}$ and $\sqrt{a}\,\sqrt{b} > b$.)

42. Show that if $a > b \geq 0$, then $\sqrt{a} > \sqrt{b}$.

Career Note   Systems Analyst

Systems analysts analyze and solve problems in a variety of fields. They may work full time for one employer or may be hired as consultants by business executives, scientists, or engineers with specific problems to solve.

After identifying the exact problem, the analyst breaks it down into its logical components. Then the analyst determines what data and hardware (computer machinery) are needed to solve it. At this point the analyst creates a solution, often using the techniques of cost accounting, sampling, and mathematical model building. Next, the analyst has programmers devise the software (computer programs) that the system requires. Then the analyst prepares charts and diagrams describing the system's operation in terms the customer can understand.

Preparation for a career as a systems analyst requires a bachelor's degree in a field such as mathematics, science, engineering, accounting, or business administration. Because computers are so frequently used as a tool in solving problems, previous programming experience is helpful. Constant technological advances in computer products require systems analysts to continue their education. They may do this by taking courses offered by their employers and software vendors.

6-2 *Properties of Radicals*

OBJECTIVE   To simplify radicals.

Because

$$\sqrt[3]{8 \cdot 125} = \sqrt[3]{1000} = 10 \text{ and } \sqrt[3]{8} \cdot \sqrt[3]{125} = 2 \cdot 5 = 10,$$

you can see that

$$\sqrt[3]{8 \cdot 125} = \sqrt[3]{8} \cdot \sqrt[3]{125}.$$

Similarly, from $\sqrt{\dfrac{144}{9}} = \sqrt{16} = 4$ and $\dfrac{\sqrt{144}}{\sqrt{9}} = \dfrac{12}{3} = 4$, you see that

$$\sqrt{\frac{144}{9}} = \frac{\sqrt{144}}{\sqrt{9}}.$$

These examples illustrate the next theorem.

THEOREM 1   If $\sqrt[n]{a}$ and $\sqrt[n]{b}$ are real numbers, then:

$$\text{1. } \sqrt[n]{ab} = \sqrt[n]{a} \cdot \sqrt[n]{b} \qquad \text{2. } \sqrt[n]{\frac{a}{b}} = \frac{\sqrt[n]{a}}{\sqrt[n]{b}}$$

PROOF OF PART (1):

By Law 2 of Exponents (page 165),

$$(\sqrt[n]{a} \cdot \sqrt[n]{b})^n = (\sqrt[n]{a})^n \cdot (\sqrt[n]{b})^n = ab.$$

Therefore $\sqrt[n]{a} \cdot \sqrt[n]{b}$ is *one* of the nth roots of ab. Is it the *principal* nth root? It certainly is if n is odd because then ab has only *one* real nth root. If n is even, then $\sqrt[n]{a} \geq 0$ and $\sqrt[n]{b} \geq 0$. Therefore, $\sqrt[n]{a} \cdot \sqrt[n]{b} \geq 0$ and again is the principal root. Hence, whether n is even or odd, $\sqrt[n]{a} \cdot \sqrt[n]{b} = \sqrt[n]{ab}$.

The proof of part (2) is similar (Exercise 49).

With the help of the next theorem (proved in Exercise 50) you can sometimes replace the index of a radical by a smaller one.

THEOREM 2   If each radical denotes a real number, then

$$\sqrt[nq]{b} = \sqrt[n]{\sqrt[q]{b}}.$$

For example:

$$\sqrt[6]{64} = \sqrt[3 \cdot 2]{64} = \sqrt[3]{\sqrt{64}} = \sqrt[3]{8} = 2.$$

$$\sqrt[4]{x^2} = \sqrt[2 \cdot 2]{x^2} = \sqrt{\sqrt{x^2}} = \sqrt{|x|}$$

A radical is in **simplest form** when
1. the index n is as small as possible,
2. the radicand contains no factor (other than 1) that is the nth power of an integer or polynomial, and
3. the radicand contains no fraction or power with a negative exponent.

For example, to make $\sqrt[3]{\dfrac{5}{2}}$ satisfy condition (2), you create a perfect cube in the denominator, as follows:

$$\sqrt[3]{\frac{5}{2}} = \sqrt[3]{\frac{5}{2} \cdot \frac{4}{4}} = \sqrt[3]{\frac{20}{8}} = \frac{\sqrt[3]{20}}{\sqrt[3]{8}} = \frac{\sqrt[3]{20}}{2}, \text{ or } \frac{1}{2}\sqrt[3]{20}$$

This process is called **rationalizing the denominator.**

EXAMPLE 1 Simplify: **a.** $\sqrt[3]{16a^5}$ **b.** $\sqrt[4]{36x^6}$

c. $\sqrt{\dfrac{12}{5a}}\ (a > 0)$ **d.** $\sqrt{a^{-2} + b^{-2}}$

SOLUTION **a.** $\sqrt[3]{16a^5} = \sqrt[3]{8a^3 \cdot 2a^2} = \sqrt[3]{8a^3} \cdot \sqrt[3]{2a^2} = 2a\sqrt[3]{2a^2}$

b. $\sqrt[4]{36x^6} = \sqrt{\sqrt{36x^6}} = \sqrt{|6x^3|} = \sqrt{x^2 \cdot 6|x|} = \sqrt{x^2} \cdot \sqrt{6|x|} = |x|\sqrt{6|x|}$

c. $\sqrt{\dfrac{12}{5a}} = \dfrac{\sqrt{12}}{\sqrt{5a}} = \dfrac{\sqrt{12}}{\sqrt{5a}} \cdot \dfrac{\sqrt{5a}}{\sqrt{5a}} = \dfrac{2\sqrt{3} \cdot \sqrt{5a}}{5a} = \dfrac{2}{5a}\sqrt{15a}$

d. $\sqrt{a^{-2} + b^{-2}} = \sqrt{\dfrac{1}{a^2} + \dfrac{1}{b^2}} = \sqrt{\dfrac{b^2 + a^2}{a^2b^2}} = \dfrac{\sqrt{b^2 + a^2}}{\sqrt{a^2b^2}} = \dfrac{\sqrt{a^2 + b^2}}{|ab|}$

One must be careful when writing radical expressions. To avoid confusing $\sqrt{2x}$ with $\sqrt{2}x$, for example, you can write $\sqrt{2}x$ as $x\sqrt{2}$. And you can write $\dfrac{1}{2}\sqrt{a}$ instead of $\dfrac{\sqrt{a}}{2}$ to avoid confusion with $\sqrt{\dfrac{a}{2}}$.

$\dfrac{1}{a^2} + \dfrac{1}{b^2} = \dfrac{b^2 + a^2}{a^2 b^2}$

The next theorem (proved in Exercise 51) is often useful in numerical work.

THEOREM 3   If b and $\sqrt[n]{b}$ are real numbers, then
$$\sqrt[n]{b^m} = (\sqrt[n]{b})^m.$$

For example:

$$\sqrt[4]{16^3} = (\sqrt[4]{16})^3 = 2^3 = 8$$
$$\sqrt[3]{(-27)^2} = (\sqrt[3]{-27})^2 = (-3)^2 = 9$$

When a radical cannot be expressed as an integer, you can use a table of roots or a calculator to obtain estimates. Table 1, Squares and Square Roots, on page 638 and Table 2, Cubes and Cube Roots, on page 639 are provided for this purpose.

EXAMPLE 2 Estimate to four significant digits:

   a. $\sqrt{53}$ **b.** $\sqrt{710}$ **c.** $\sqrt[4]{121}$ **d.** $\dfrac{1}{\sqrt[3]{5}}$

SOLUTION   **a.** In Table 3, find 5.3 and look under $\sqrt{10N}$. $\sqrt{53} \approx 7.280$

   b. $\sqrt{710} = \sqrt{100} \cdot \sqrt{7.1} \approx 10(2.665) = 26.65$

   c. $\sqrt[4]{121} = \sqrt{\sqrt{121}} = \sqrt{11} \approx 3.317$

   d. $\dfrac{1}{\sqrt[3]{5}} = \dfrac{1}{\sqrt[3]{5}} \cdot \dfrac{\sqrt[3]{5^2}}{\sqrt[3]{5^2}} = \dfrac{\sqrt[3]{5^2}}{\sqrt[3]{5^3}} = \dfrac{1}{5}\sqrt[3]{25} \approx (0.2)(2.924) = 0.5848$

Rationalizing the denominator in Example 2(d) simplified the numerical calculation. When you are using a calculator, however, it is usually more efficient to evaluate an expression directly.

Oral Exercises

Simplify. Assume that variables denote positive numbers.

1. $\sqrt{12}$ **2.** $\sqrt{27}$ **3.** $\sqrt{\dfrac{9a^2}{25}}$ **4.** $\sqrt[3]{-\dfrac{27}{1000}}$

5. $\sqrt[3]{-16}$ **6.** $\sqrt[3]{54}$ **7.** $\sqrt[4]{25}$ **8.** $\sqrt[6]{8c^3}$

Written Exercises

Simplify. Assume that the given radicals denote real numbers.

A **1.** $\sqrt[3]{-54}$ **2.** $\sqrt[3]{-32}$ **3.** $\sqrt[3]{\dfrac{8}{25}}$

   4. $\sqrt[4]{\dfrac{16}{27}}$ **5.** $\sqrt[4]{\dfrac{9}{25}}$ **6.** $\sqrt[6]{\dfrac{27}{8}}$

   7. $\sqrt[5]{64a^6}$ **8.** $\sqrt[3]{81x^5}$ **9.** $\sqrt{32a^3c^5}$

   10. $\sqrt[4]{9u^6v^8}$ **11.** $\sqrt{\dfrac{ab^2}{2c^3}}$ **12.** $\sqrt[3]{-\dfrac{s^2}{2t^2}}$

Estimate to four significant digits. Use the tables on pages 638 and 639 as needed.

13. $\sqrt{47}$ **14.** $\sqrt{7.3}$ **15.** $\sqrt{920}$ **16.** $\sqrt{1400}$

17. $\sqrt[4]{324}$ **18.** $\sqrt[6]{64}$ **19.** $\dfrac{1}{\sqrt[3]{9}}$ **20.** $\dfrac{\sqrt[3]{45}}{\sqrt[3]{3}}$

Simplify. Assume the given radicals denote real numbers.

21. $\sqrt[3]{16x^{-1}y^{-2}z^{-3}}$ **22.** $\sqrt[4]{121x^5y^{-6}}$ **23.** $\sqrt[3]{2a^2} \cdot \sqrt[3]{4a}$

24. $\sqrt{20a^3b} \cdot \sqrt{5ab^3}$ **25.** $\dfrac{\sqrt{20u^3v}}{\sqrt{5uv^3}}$ **26.** $\dfrac{\sqrt[3]{-5x^4}}{\sqrt[3]{40xy^6}}$

27. $\sqrt[4]{4a^2b^4} \cdot \sqrt{ab^{-2}}$ **28.** $\sqrt{cd^{-2}} \cdot \sqrt[6]{27c^9d^3}$ **29.** $\sqrt{x^{-1} + y^{-1}}$

30. $\sqrt[3]{x^{-3} + y^{-3}}$ **31.** $\sqrt{a^2 + 4a + 4}$ **32.** $\sqrt{x^2 - 6x + 9}$

B 33. $\sqrt{u^3 + 2u^2 + u}$ **34.** $\sqrt{\dfrac{a^2 - 4a + 4}{a}}$ **35.** $\sqrt{\dfrac{t - 1}{t^2 + 2t + 1}}$

36. $\sqrt{\dfrac{u}{u - 2}}$ **37.** $\sqrt{\dfrac{x - 1}{x + 1}}$ **38.** $\sqrt[3]{\dfrac{1}{x^3 + x^4}}$

39. $\sqrt[3]{\dfrac{a^2 - 2a + 1}{a^2 + a - 2}}$ $\dfrac{(a-2)(a+1)}{a = 2, \; a = -1}$ **40.** $\sqrt[3]{\dfrac{(x - 1)^2}{x^2 - 1}}$ **41.** $\sqrt[3]{\dfrac{1 - 2v + v^2}{v - v^3}}$

Express as a single radical.

SAMPLE $\sqrt{a} \cdot \sqrt[3]{a^2}$

SOLUTION $\sqrt{a} \cdot \sqrt[3]{a^2} = \sqrt[6]{a^3} \cdot \sqrt[6]{a^4} = \sqrt[6]{a^7} = a\sqrt[6]{a}$

C 42. $\sqrt{x}\sqrt[4]{x^3}$ **43.** $\sqrt[6]{a^5} \cdot \sqrt{a}$

44. $\sqrt{2t} \cdot \sqrt[3]{4t^2}$ **45.** $\sqrt[3]{x^2} \cdot \sqrt[4]{x^3}$

46. $\dfrac{\sqrt[3]{c}}{\sqrt{c}}$ **47.** $\dfrac{\sqrt[5]{a}}{\sqrt{a}}$

48. a. By setting $a = 3$ and $b = 4$, show that the equation $\sqrt{a^2 + b^2} = a + b$ is *not* an identity.
  b. Under what conditions *does* $\sqrt{a^2 + b^2}$ equal $a + b$?

49. Prove part (2) of Theorem 1 on page 214. (*Hint*: Follow the pattern of the proof of part (1).)

50. Prove Theorem 2 on page 214. (*Hint*: Show that $\sqrt[n]{\sqrt[q]{b}}$ is *an* nqth root of b by justifying these statements:

$$(\sqrt[n]{\sqrt[q]{b}})^{nq} = [(\sqrt[n]{\sqrt[q]{b}})^n]^q = (\sqrt[q]{b})^q = b$$

Then show that $\sqrt[n]{\sqrt[q]{b}}$ is the principal nqth root by considering the cases $b \geq 0$ and $b < 0$. Note that if $b < 0$, then q and n are both odd.)

51. Prove Theorem 3 on page 215. (*Hint*: Show that $(\sqrt[n]{b})^m$ is *an* nth root of b^m by justifying these statements:

$$[(\sqrt[n]{b})^m]^n = [(\sqrt[n]{b})^n]^m = b^m$$

Then show that it is the principal nth root by considering the cases n even and n odd.)

6-3 *Radical Expressions*

OBJECTIVE   **To simplify radical expressions.**

The distributive axiom enables you to simplify any sum or difference of radicals that have the same index and radicand. For example:

$$8\sqrt[3]{x} - 3\sqrt[3]{x} = (8 - 3)\sqrt[3]{x} = 5\sqrt[3]{x}$$

On the other hand, radicals with different indexes or different radicands cannot be combined. Thus, $\sqrt{6} + \sqrt[3]{6} + \sqrt[3]{4}$ cannot be simplified.

To simplify sums or differences of radicals.
1. Express each radical in simplest form.
2. Combine terms in which the radicals have the same index and radicand.

EXAMPLE 1   Simplify $4\sqrt{3a} + \sqrt[4]{9a^2} - \sqrt{12a^3}$.

SOLUTION $4\sqrt{3a} + \sqrt[4]{9a^2} - \sqrt{12a^3} = 4\sqrt{3a} + \sqrt{\sqrt{9a^2}} - \sqrt{4a^2 \cdot 3a}$
$$= 4\sqrt{3a} + \sqrt{3a} - 2a\sqrt{3a}$$
$$= (5 - 2a)\sqrt{3a}$$

You can also simplify products of sums of radicals.

EXAMPLE 2   Simplify: **a.** $(5 - \sqrt{3})(3 + 2\sqrt{3})$
             b. $(\sqrt{x + 1} + \sqrt{2})(\sqrt{x + 1} - \sqrt{2})$

SOLUTION   **a.** $(5 - \sqrt{3})(3 + 2\sqrt{3}) = 5 \cdot 3 + 10\sqrt{3} - 3\sqrt{3} - 2(\sqrt{3})^2$
$$= 15 + 7\sqrt{3} - 2 \cdot 3$$
$$= 9 + 7\sqrt{3}$$
b. $(\sqrt{x + 1} + \sqrt{2})(\sqrt{x + 1} - \sqrt{2}) = (\sqrt{x + 1})^2 - (\sqrt{2})^2$
$$= (x + 1) - 2$$
$$= x - 1$$

When simplifying radical expressions, you must simplify each radical and simplify sums and differences. You must also make sure there are no radicals in denominators. The result in the next paragraph is often useful in this regard.

Notice in Example 2(a) that the product of the two radical expressions is an integer. In general, if a and c are integers and b and d are positive integers, the product

$$(a\sqrt{b} + c\sqrt{d})(a\sqrt{b} - c\sqrt{d})$$

is an integer. This result is used to rationalize the denominator in Example 3.

EXAMPLE 3   Simplify $\dfrac{1 - 2\sqrt{2}}{3 + \sqrt{2}}$.

SOLUTION $\dfrac{1 - 2\sqrt{2}}{3 + \sqrt{2}} = \dfrac{1 - 2\sqrt{2}}{3 + \sqrt{2}} \cdot \dfrac{3 - \sqrt{2}}{3 - \sqrt{2}}$ $\left\{ \begin{array}{l} \text{Multiply the numerator and} \\ \text{denominator by a factor that} \\ \text{will rationalize the denominator.} \end{array} \right.$

$$= \frac{3 - \sqrt{2} - 6\sqrt{2} + 2(\sqrt{2})^2}{9 - (\sqrt{2})^2}$$

$$= \frac{3 - 7\sqrt{2} + 4}{9 - 2}$$

$$= \frac{7 - 7\sqrt{2}}{7}$$

$$= 1 - \sqrt{2}$$

Using radicals you can factor certain polynomials that are irreducible over the set of polynomials with integral coefficients. For example:

$$x^2 - 12 = x^2 - (\sqrt{12})^2 = (x + \sqrt{12})(x - \sqrt{12})$$

$$\therefore x^2 - 12 = (x + 2\sqrt{3})(x - 2\sqrt{3}).$$

Oral Exercises

Simplify. If no further simplification is possible, so state.

1. $3\sqrt{5} - \sqrt{5} + 2\sqrt{5}$
2. $6\sqrt[3]{2} - \sqrt[3]{2} - 2\sqrt[3]{2}$
3. $4\sqrt{3} - \sqrt{4 \cdot 3}$
4. $3\sqrt{6} + \sqrt[3]{6}$
5. $\sqrt[3]{2} + \sqrt[3]{4}$
6. $\sqrt[4]{4} - \sqrt{2}$
7. $\sqrt{2}(\sqrt{2} - 1)$
8. $\sqrt[3]{4}(\sqrt[3]{8} - 1)$
9. $(\sqrt{2} + 1)(\sqrt{2} - 1)$
10. $(2 - \sqrt{3})(2 + \sqrt{3})$

Written Exercises

Simplify. Assume that all radicals denote real numbers.

A **1.** $\sqrt{75} - 2\sqrt{12}$
2. $2\sqrt{45} - \sqrt{20}$
3. $\sqrt{12} + 2\sqrt{27} - \sqrt{48}$
4. $\sqrt{28} - 2\sqrt{98} + \sqrt{63}$
5. $\sqrt[3]{81} + 2\sqrt[3]{16} - \sqrt[3]{24}$
6. $\sqrt[3]{128} - 3\sqrt[3]{16} + \sqrt[3]{54}$
7. $\sqrt{18a^3} + \sqrt{2a^3} + a\sqrt{8a}$
8. $\sqrt[3]{54x^5} - \sqrt[3]{16x^5}$
9. $\sqrt{\dfrac{2}{3}} + \sqrt{\dfrac{3}{2}}$
10. $2\sqrt{\dfrac{a}{2}} + a\sqrt{\dfrac{2}{a}}$
11. $\sqrt{a}(\sqrt{a} - 1)$
12. $\sqrt[3]{a}(\sqrt[3]{a^2} - 1)$

Simplify. Assume that all radicals denote real numbers.

13. $(\sqrt{3} + \sqrt{2})(\sqrt{3} - \sqrt{2})$

14. $(2\sqrt{2} + \sqrt{5})(2\sqrt{2} - \sqrt{5})$

15. $(\sqrt{3} - 1)(\sqrt{3} + 2)$

16. $(\sqrt{2} + \sqrt{3})(2\sqrt{2} - \sqrt{3})$

17. $(\sqrt{6} - \sqrt{3})^2$

18. $(\sqrt{10} - 2\sqrt{5})(\sqrt{10} + \sqrt{5})$

19. $(4 + \sqrt[4]{4})(4 - \sqrt[4]{4})$

20. $(\sqrt[4]{8} - 2)(\sqrt[4]{8} + 2)$

Rationalize the denominator and simplify. Assume that all radicals denote real numbers.

21. $\dfrac{1 - \sqrt{2}}{2 + \sqrt{2}}$

22. $\dfrac{2}{\sqrt{5} + 2}$

23. $\dfrac{\sqrt{3}}{\sqrt{5} - \sqrt{3}}$

24. $\dfrac{\sqrt{3} - \sqrt{2}}{\sqrt{3} + \sqrt{2}}$

25. $\dfrac{1}{\sqrt{x} - 2}$

26. $\dfrac{3}{\sqrt{t} + \sqrt{3}}$

B 27. $\dfrac{2}{\sqrt{x + 1} + 1}$

28. $\dfrac{\sqrt{x + 4} + 2}{\sqrt{x + 4} - 2}$

29. $\dfrac{2}{\sqrt{a + 2} - \sqrt{a}}$

30. $\dfrac{2c}{-b + \sqrt{b^2 - 4ac}}$

Express each of the following as a single fraction in simplest form.

31. $\sqrt{x - 1} + \dfrac{x}{2\sqrt{x - 1}}$

32. $\sqrt{1 - x^2} - \dfrac{x^2}{\sqrt{1 - x^2}}$

33. $\dfrac{t}{\sqrt{1 - t^2}} + \dfrac{\sqrt{1 - t^2}}{t}$

34. $\dfrac{\sqrt{1 + x^2}}{\sqrt{1 - x^2}} - \dfrac{\sqrt{1 - x^2}}{\sqrt{1 + x^2}}$

Factor each of the following over the set of polynomials with real coefficients.

35. $x^2 - 27$

36. $t^2 - 1000$

37. $x^2 + 2\sqrt{3}x + 3$

38. $x^2 - 4\sqrt{2}x + 8$

39. $u^2 + \sqrt{3}u - 6$

40. $x^2 - \sqrt{5}x - 30$

   (*Hint:* $6 = 2 \cdot \sqrt{3} \cdot \sqrt{3}$)

In each of Exercises 41–44 you are given two expressions. Show that the two expressions are not equivalent by substituting values for the variable(s) involved.

41. $\sqrt{a} + \sqrt{4a};\ \sqrt{5a}$

42. $\sqrt{a + b};\ \sqrt{a} + \sqrt{b}$

43. $\sqrt[3]{a} - \sqrt[3]{b};\ \sqrt[3]{a - b}$

44. $\dfrac{1}{\sqrt{a}} + \dfrac{1}{\sqrt{b}};\ \dfrac{1}{\sqrt{a} + \sqrt{b}}$

6-4 Radical Equations

An equation that has a variable in a radicand is called a **radical equation.**
To solve the simple radical equation

$$\sqrt[3]{x-2} = 2,$$

just cube both sides:

$$(\sqrt[3]{x-2})^3 = 2^3 \qquad \textit{Check: } \sqrt[3]{10-2} \overset{?}{=} 2$$
$$x - 2 = 8 \qquad\qquad\qquad \sqrt[3]{8} = 2 \;\checkmark$$
$$x = 10$$

Therefore, the solution is 10.

To solve an equation having a term with a variable in a radicand, start by "isolating" such a term in one side of the equation. Then raise each member to the power equal to the index of the radical.

EXAMPLE 1   Solve $x + 2\sqrt{x-3} = 6$.

SOLUTION

1. Isolate the term containing the radical.

$$2\sqrt{x-3} = 6 - x$$
$$(2\sqrt{x-3})^2 = (6-x)^2$$

2. Square both sides.

$$4(x-3) = 36 - 12x + x^2$$
$$x^2 - 16x + 48 = 0$$

3. Solve the resulting equation.

$$(x-4)(x-12) \overset{?}{=} 0$$
$$x = 4 \text{ or } x = 12$$

4. *Check:* $4 + 2\sqrt{4-3} \overset{?}{=} 6 \qquad 12 + 2\sqrt{12-3} \overset{?}{=} 6$
$$4 + 2 \cdot 1 \quad = 6 \;\checkmark \qquad 12 + 2 \cdot 3 \qquad \neq 6$$

∴ the solution is 4.   ***Answer***

In the solution of Example 1, steps 1, 2, and 3 show that if x is a solution of the given equation, then $x = 4$ or $x = 12$. Step 4 shows that 4 (but not 12) actually *is* a solution. Usually when you solve an equation, each step involves equations equivalent to the original equation, and the check merely guards against mistakes. In step 2 of this example, however, the equation is not equivalent to the original equation. (From $(2\sqrt{x-3})^2 = (6-x)^2$, you obtain not only the solutions to $2\sqrt{x-3} = 6 - x$, but also the solutions to $2\sqrt{x-3} = -(6-x)$.) Thus, "extraneous roots" may be introduced, and a check is essential.

If a radical equation has more than one term with a variable in a radicand, you may have to "isolate and raise to a power" more than once. Two steps of this kind are shown in the solution of Example 2 on the following page.

EXAMPLE 2 Solve $\sqrt{2x + 5} - \sqrt{x - 1} = 2$.

SOLUTION
$$\sqrt{2x + 5} = 2 + \sqrt{x - 1}$$
$$(\sqrt{2x + 5})^2 = (2 + \sqrt{x - 1})^2$$
$$2x + 5 = 4 + 4\sqrt{x - 1} + (x - 1)$$
$$x + 2 = 4\sqrt{x - 1}$$
$$(x + 2)^2 = (4\sqrt{x - 1})^2$$
$$x^2 + 4x + 4 = 16(x - 1)$$
$$x^2 - 12x + 20 = 0$$
$$(x - 2)(x - 10) = 0$$
$$x = 2 \text{ or } x = 10$$

Check: $\sqrt{2 \cdot 2 + 5} - \sqrt{2 - 1} \overset{?}{=} 2$ $\sqrt{2 \cdot 10 + 5} - \sqrt{10 - 1} \overset{?}{=} 2$

$\sqrt{9} - \sqrt{1} \overset{?}{=} 2$ $\sqrt{25} - \sqrt{9} \overset{?}{=} 2$

$3 - 1 = 2$ ✓ $5 - 3 = 2$ ✓

$\therefore$ the solution set is $\{2, 10\}$. **Answer**

Oral Exercises

Solve. If there is no real solution, so state.

1. $\sqrt{x} = 3$ **2.** $\sqrt[3]{t} = 2$ **3.** $\sqrt[3]{x} + 2 = 0$
4. $\sqrt{x} + 2 = 0$ **5.** $2\sqrt{t} - 10 = 0$ **6.** $\sqrt[5]{x} + 1 = 0$

Written Exercises

Solve. If there are no solutions, so state.

A **1.** $\sqrt[3]{x} + 4 = 0$ **2.** $\sqrt[4]{t} - 2 = 0$ **3.** $\sqrt{t - 1} = 5$
  4. $\sqrt[3]{x + 3} = 2$ **5.** $\sqrt{x - 2} + 2 = 0$ **6.** $\sqrt{2t - 1} - 3 = 0$

  7. $\sqrt{\dfrac{x^3}{2}} = 2$ **8.** $2\sqrt{x^{-1}} = 3$ **9.** $\sqrt{u^5} = 32$

  10. $\sqrt[3]{z^2} - 1 = 15$ **11.** $\sqrt{2t^2 - 9} = t$ **12.** $\sqrt{t^2 - 12} = 2t$
  13. $\sqrt[3]{z^2 + 2} - 3 = 0$ **14.** $\sqrt[4]{x^3 + 7} = 2$ **15.** $\sqrt{x + 2} = x$
  16. $\sqrt{5x - 4} = x$ **17.** $\sqrt{2s + 3} = s$ **18.** $\sqrt{2s + 3} = \sqrt{s^2}$
  19. $\sqrt{x - 2} = 4 - x$ **20.** $\sqrt{x - 5} = x - 7$ **21.** $x - 2\sqrt{x - 1} = 1$
  22. $\sqrt{t^2 - 3} - t = 1$ **23.** $2 + \sqrt{4u - 3} = u$ **24.** $2z = 3 + \sqrt{7z - 3}$

  25. $\sqrt[3]{x - 3} + 1 = 4$ **26.** $\sqrt[3]{2t + 1} - 1 = 2$ **27.** $\sqrt[4]{\dfrac{z}{2}} + 4 = 6$

  28. $\sqrt[4]{\dfrac{x}{3}} - 2 = 1$ **29.** $\sqrt[4]{y^2 + y + 4} = 2$ **30.** $\sqrt[3]{n^2 + 2} - 3 = 0$

B 31. $\sqrt{x} + \sqrt{x+5} = 5$

32. $\sqrt{t+6} - \sqrt{t} = \sqrt{2}$

33. $\sqrt{x-3} + \sqrt{x} = \sqrt{2}$

34. $\sqrt{x} + \sqrt{2} = \sqrt{x+2}$

35. $\sqrt{2t+1} - \sqrt{t} = 1$

36. $\sqrt{3x-2} - \sqrt{2x-3} = 1$

37. $\sqrt{x} + \sqrt{x-3} = \dfrac{3}{\sqrt{x-3}}$

38. $\sqrt{x+1} + \dfrac{2}{\sqrt{x+1}} = \sqrt{x+6}$

39. $\sqrt{t^2 + 3t + 3} + \sqrt{t^2 + t - 1} = 2$

40. $\sqrt{u^2 + 5u + 3} - \sqrt{u^2 + 3u} = 1$

Solve each formula for the symbol printed in red.

41. $v = \sqrt{\dfrac{2k}{m}}$

42. $P = \pi \sqrt{\dfrac{l}{g}}$

43. $s = \dfrac{1}{\sqrt{1 - t^2}}$

44. $\dfrac{1}{\sqrt{a}} + \dfrac{1}{\sqrt{b}} = \dfrac{1}{\sqrt{c}}$

Self-Test 1

VOCABULARY square root (p. 209)
cube root (p. 210)
power function (p. 210)
nth root (p. 210)
principal nth root (p. 211)
radical (p. 211)

radical sign (p. 211)
index of a radical (p. 211)
radicand (p. 211)
simplest form of a radical
(p. 215)
radical equation (p. 221)

1. Evaluate: **a.** $\sqrt{0.25}$ **b.** $\sqrt[3]{-125}$

Obj. 6-1, p. 209

2. For what values of x does $\sqrt{9 - x}$ denote a real number?

Simplify.

3. $\sqrt[3]{\dfrac{4}{3} ab^{-5}c^4}$

4. $\sqrt{\dfrac{x}{x+1}}$

Obj. 6-2, p. 214

5. $\sqrt[3]{54} - \sqrt[3]{16} + \sqrt[3]{\dfrac{1}{4}}$

6. $(\sqrt{x} + \sqrt{a})(\sqrt{x} - \sqrt{a})$

Obj. 6-3, p. 218

7. Rationalize the denominator: $\dfrac{2}{1 + \sqrt{3}}$.

Solve.

8. $\sqrt[3]{t+2} + 2 = 0$

9. $2 + \sqrt{12 - 2x} = x$

Obj. 6-4, p. 221

Check your answers with those at the back of the book.

6-5 *Rational and Irrational Roots*

OBJECTIVE   **To determine rational and irrational roots of polynomial equations.**

In this section you will learn how to determine which roots of a polynomial equation with integral coefficients are rational numbers. Recall that a **rational number** is one that can be expressed in the form $\frac{a}{b}$ where a is an integer and b is a nonzero integer. The rational numbers are closed under addition, subtraction, and multiplication.

The following useful theorem will enable us to show that such roots as $\sqrt{2}$, $\sqrt[3]{5}$, and $\sqrt[4]{9}$ are not rational numbers. (The theorem is proved in Exercises 24 and 25.)

THEOREM   Consider a polynomial equation with integral coefficients and suppose that it has the root $\frac{p}{q}$, where p and q are integers and $\frac{p}{q}$ is in simplest form. Then p must be a factor of the constant term and q a factor of the coefficient of the term of highest degree.

For example, consider the equation

$$4x^4 - 2x^3 - 4x^2 - x - 3 = 0.$$

The numerator of a rational root of this equation must be a factor of 3, and the denominator must be a factor of 4. Thus, the only possible rational roots are

$$1, 3, \frac{1}{2}, \frac{3}{2}, \frac{1}{4}, \frac{3}{4},$$

and their negatives. You can verify that the rational roots are -1 and $\frac{3}{2}$.

EXAMPLE 1   Show that $\sqrt{2}$ is not rational.

SOLUTION   Since $\sqrt{2}$ is a root of $x^2 = 2$, or

$$x^2 - 2 = 0,$$

it is sufficient to show that this equation has no rational roots. By the theorem, the only possible rational roots are 1, -1, 2, and -2. Since none of these satisfies the equation, $\sqrt{2}$ is not rational.

Real numbers that are not rational are called **irrational.** You can show (Exercise 26) that *if b is an integer, then* $\sqrt[n]{b}$ *is irrational unless b is the nth power of an integer.* Thus, $\sqrt[3]{4}$, $\sqrt{8}$ and $\sqrt[4]{15}$ are irrational numbers.

In Example 2, the method of proof is called **indirect argument.**

EXAMPLE 2   Show that $3 - \sqrt{2}$ is irrational.

SOLUTION   (*Plan:* To show that the assumption that $3 - \sqrt{2}$ is rational leads to a contradiction and so must be false.)

Suppose that $3 - \sqrt{2} = r$, where r is rational. Then $\sqrt{2} = 3 - r$. Since 3 and r are both rational, their difference, $3 - r$, is rational. But we know that $\sqrt{2}$ is not rational, and so we have a contradiction. Our assumption that $3 - \sqrt{2}$ is rational must be false. It follows that $3 - \sqrt{2}$ is irrational.

The method employed in this example can be used to show that *any sum or difference of a rational and an irrational number is an irrational number.* Similar reasoning will prove that *the product or quotient of a nonzero rational and an irrational number will always be irrational.* Thus, from the fact that $\sqrt{2}$ is irrational, it follows that every number in this list is irrational:

$$1 + \sqrt{2}, \quad 2.5 + \sqrt{2}, \quad \sqrt{2} - 2, \quad 3\sqrt{2}, \quad \frac{1}{\sqrt{2}}, \quad -\tfrac{3}{2}\sqrt{2}, \quad 1 - \frac{1}{\sqrt{2}}$$

The following illustrations show that the *additions, subtractions, multiplications, and divisions performed with irrational numbers may result in either a rational or an irrational number.*

The result is *rational.*	The result is *irrational.*
$\sqrt{2} + (1 - \sqrt{2}) = 1$	$\sqrt[4]{5} + \sqrt[4]{5} = 2\sqrt[4]{5}$
$\sqrt{2} \times \sqrt{2} = 2$	$\sqrt{2}(1 - \sqrt{2}) = \sqrt{2} - 2$
$\sqrt[5]{6} - \sqrt[5]{6} = 0$	$2\sqrt[3]{11} - \sqrt[3]{11} = \sqrt[3]{11}$
$\dfrac{\sqrt[3]{7}}{\sqrt[3]{7}} = 1$	$\dfrac{\sqrt{2} - 2}{\sqrt{2}} = 1 - \sqrt{2}$

Oral Exercises

Give a polynomial equation with integral coefficients that has the given number as a root.

1. $\sqrt{5}$ **2.** $-\sqrt{10}$ **3.** $-2\sqrt{3}$ **4.** $3\sqrt{2}$

5. $\sqrt[3]{4}$ **6.** $\sqrt[5]{-2}$ **7.** $\sqrt[5]{-\dfrac{2}{3}}$ **8.** $-\sqrt[4]{9}$

List the numbers that, according to the theorem on page 224, could be rational roots of the given equation.

9. $x^3 - 4x^2 + x + 6 = 0$

10. $x^4 - 5x^2 + 4 = 0$

11. $x^4 + 3x^2 - 4 = 0$

12. $x^3 - 5x^2 + 2x - 10 = 0$

13. $2x^3 - x^2 - 2x + 1 = 0$

14. $6x^3 + 7x^2 - 1 = 0$

15. $6x^3 - 4x^2 + 3x - 2 = 0$

16. $2x^3 - 5x^2 - 4x + 3 = 0$

Explain why the given equation has no rational roots.

17. $x^4 + x + 1 = 0$

18. $x^4 - 9x^2 + 1 = 0$

19. $x^3 + x + 3 = 0$

20. $5x^3 + 1 = 0$

Written Exercises

A **1–8.** Use the method of Example 1 to show that the numbers listed in Oral Exercises 1–8 are irrational.

9–16. Find the rational roots of the equations in Oral Exercises 9–16.

The given number is a root of the equation. Use this fact to show that the number is irrational.

17. $\sqrt{3} - \sqrt{2};\ x^4 - 10x^2 + 1 = 0$

18. $2 - \sqrt[3]{2};\ x^3 - 6x^2 + 12x - 6 = 0$

Use the method of Example 2 to show that the given numbers are irrational. (Assume it is known that $\sqrt{2}$, $\sqrt{3}$, and $\sqrt[3]{4}$ are irrational.)

B **19.** $\sqrt{3} - 1$

20. $\sqrt[3]{4} + 3$

21. $\dfrac{4 + \sqrt{2}}{3}$

22. $\dfrac{2\sqrt{3} + 1}{5}$

C **23.** We know that the set of rational numbers is closed under both addition and multiplication. Show that this is not true of the set of irrational numbers by considering $3 + \sqrt{2}$ and $3 - \sqrt{2}$.

The proof of the theorem on page 224 is essentially the same whatever the degree of the polynomial. The proof for degree 3 is outlined in Exercises 24 and 25 on the following page. Consider the polynomial equation

$$0 = ax^3 + bx^2 + cx + d,$$

where a, b, c, and d are integers. You must show that p is a factor of d and q is a factor of a.

24. Justify the following steps:

$$a\left(\frac{p}{q}\right)^3 + b\left(\frac{p}{q}\right)^2 + c\left(\frac{p}{q}\right) + d = 0$$

$$ap^3 + bp^2q + cpq^2 + dq^3 = 0$$

$$dq^3 = -ap^3 - bp^2q - cpq^2$$

$$\frac{dq^3}{p} = -ap^2 - bpq - cq^2$$

$$\frac{dq^3}{p} \text{ is an integer.}$$

The proof is completed as follows: Since $\frac{dq^3}{p}$ is an integer, each prime factor h of p must cancel with a factor of dq^3. But p and q have no common prime factor. Thus h, and therefore p, must be a factor of d.

25. Modify the proof in Exercise 24 to show that q is a factor of a.

26. Show that if b is an integer and $\sqrt[n]{b}$ is rational, then b is the nth power of an integer. (*Hint:* $\sqrt[n]{b}$ is a solution of $x^n - b = 0$. What sort of rational roots does this equation have?)

Calculator Key-In _____

Most calculators have a square-root key. Many other calculators have a key that enables you to enter a radical index as well as the radicand. Thus, you can evaluate radicals such as $\sqrt[5]{11}$ and $\sqrt[13]{147}$ quickly and easily.

Exercises

Use a calculator to evaluate each radical to four decimal places.

1. $\sqrt[3]{12}$ 2. $\sqrt[5]{17}$ 3. $\sqrt[6]{460}$ 4. $\sqrt[13]{1110}$ 5. $\sqrt[7]{930}$

6. $\sqrt[4]{0.63}$ 7. $\sqrt[3]{1.84}$ 8. $\sqrt[8]{12.46}$ 9. $\sqrt[10]{17.642}$ 10. $\sqrt[5]{0.096}$

Use a calculator to evaluate each expression to four decimal places.

11. $\sqrt[4]{2^6}$ 12. $(\sqrt[3]{3})^4$ 13. $\sqrt[5]{14^2}$ 14. $(\sqrt[8]{21})^5$ 15. $\sqrt[11]{17^7}$

16. $(\sqrt[3]{0.62})^2$ 17. $\sqrt[7]{1.68^3}$ 18. $\sqrt[5]{12.31^7}$ 19. $\sqrt[9]{15.94^5}$ 20. $\sqrt[10]{6.45^{12}}$

For each of the following expressions, evaluate the given radical and then raise it to the same power as the index.

21. $\sqrt[3]{7}$ 22. $\sqrt[7]{16}$ 23. $\sqrt[4]{21}$ 24. $\sqrt[6]{37}$ 25. $\sqrt[10]{59}$

6-6 *Decimals for Real Numbers*

OBJECTIVE   **To use the characteristics of decimal representations of real numbers.**

It is easy to see that every **finite,** or terminating, **decimal** represents a real number. In fact each such decimal represents a rational number. For example,

$$3.875 = \frac{3875}{1000} = \frac{31}{8}.$$

The fact that **infinite decimals,** for example,

$$4.7161616 \ldots \text{ and } 2.30300300030 \ldots ,$$

also represent real numbers, is taken as an axiom.

AXIOM OF COMPLETENESS

Every decimal represents a real number, and every real number has a decimal representation.

To find decimal representations of *rational* numbers, you can use the division process:

$$\frac{37}{16} = 37 \div 16 \qquad\qquad \frac{19}{22} = 19 \div 22$$

```
        2.3125                          0.86363
   16)37.0000                       22)19.00000
      32                               17 6
       5 0                             1 40
       4 8                             1 32
         20                              80
         16                              66
         40          Recurring ←       140      → Recurring
         32          remainders        132        remainders
          80                            80
          80                            66
           0                            14
```

$$\therefore \frac{37}{16} = 2.3125 \qquad\qquad \therefore \frac{19}{22} = 0.8636363 \ldots$$

Notice that the representation for $\frac{19}{22}$ is a **repeating infinite decimal,** the recurring remainders 14 and 8 producing the repeating block 63.

For brevity, you can use a bar to indicate the block of digits that repeats. For example,

$$0.8636363\ldots = 0.8\overline{63}.$$

The conversion of $\frac{37}{16}$ and $\frac{19}{22}$ to decimals illustrates what happens when a rational number is expressed as a decimal. When an integer p is divided by a positive integer q, the remainder at each stage is one of $0, 1, 2, \ldots, q - 1$. Therefore, within $q - 1$ steps after only zeros are left in the dividend, either 0 occurs as a remainder and the division process ends, or a nonzero remainder recurs, and the division process produces a repeating sequence of remainders with a repeating block in the quotient.

The decimal representation of any rational number is either finite or repeating.

The converse of this statement is true as well. (See Exercise 37.)

Every finite or repeating decimal represents a rational number. (Thus, every finite or repeating decimal can be written in the form $\frac{n}{d}$ where n is an integer and d is a positive integer.)

The following examples show how to convert a repeating decimal into a common fraction.

EXAMPLE 1 Write as a common fraction:

a. $0.3\overline{27}$ **b.** $1.89\overline{189}$

SOLUTION In each case let N be the number. Multiply the given number by 10^n where n is the number of digits in the block of repeating digits. Then subtract.

a. Let $N = 0.3\overline{27}$

$100N = 32.7\overline{27}$

Subtract $N = 0.3\overline{27}$

$99N = 32.4$

$N = \frac{32.4}{99} = \frac{324}{990} = \frac{18}{55}$

$\therefore 0.3\overline{27} = \frac{18}{55}$ *Answer*

b. Let $N = 1.89\overline{189}$

$1000N = 1891.89\overline{189}$

Subtract $N = 1.89\overline{189}$

$999N = 1890$

$N = \frac{1890}{999} = \frac{70}{37}$

$\therefore 1.89\overline{189} = \frac{70}{37}$ *Answer*

A calculator gives us this approximation:

$$\sqrt{2} \approx 1.4142136$$

Does the actual decimal for $\sqrt{2}$ ever end or begin repeating? No, because every such decimal represents a rational number, and $\sqrt{2}$ is irrational. If

$$x = 0.2020020002000020\ldots,$$

is x rational or irrational? Since every rational number is represented by a finite or repeating decimal, x must be irrational.

> Irrational numbers are precisely those real numbers represented by infinite, nonrepeating decimals.

A set S of real numbers is **dense** if between every two real numbers there is a member of S. Both the set of rational numbers and the set of irrational numbers are dense. We can use decimals to illustrate these facts.

EXAMPLE 2   Find a rational number r and an irrational number s between 1.4 and $\sqrt{2}$.

SOLUTION   Since $1.414 < \sqrt{2}$, choose r and s so that

$$1.4 < r < 1.414 \qquad \text{and} \qquad 1.4 < s < 1.414.$$

Two possible solutions are shown below; there are many others.

$$r = 1.41 \qquad s = 1.41010010001000010\ldots$$

$$r = 1.4\overline{13} \qquad s = \frac{1.4 + \sqrt{2}}{2}$$

Oral Exercises

At most, how many digits are in the repeating block of the decimal for the given number?

1. $\dfrac{13}{7}$ 2. $\dfrac{7}{13}$ 3. $\dfrac{41}{37}$ 4. $\dfrac{125}{411}$

State whether each of the following is rational or irrational.

5. $2.61\overline{43}$ 6. $6 - 4.\overline{61}$ 7. $\sqrt{2} + 6.\overline{49}$ 8. $\dfrac{4.\overline{4}}{\sqrt[3]{4}}$

9. $4.757557555755557\ldots$ 10. $3.020220222022220\ldots$

11. The sum of the numbers in Exercises 9 and 10.

12. The difference of the numbers in Exercises 9 and 10.

Written Exercises

A Write as finite or repeating decimals.

1. $\dfrac{7}{16}$ 2. $\dfrac{41}{125}$ 3. $\dfrac{5}{9}$ 4. $\dfrac{4}{11}$

5. $\dfrac{131}{40}$ 6. $\dfrac{92}{160}$ 7. $\dfrac{9}{22}$ 8. $\dfrac{7}{27}$

9. $\dfrac{25}{44}$ 10. $\dfrac{97}{220}$ 11. $\dfrac{1}{13}$ 12. $\dfrac{5}{14}$

Write as a common fraction in simplest form.

13. 1.875 14. 0.4375 15. $0.\overline{1}$ 16. $0.0\overline{1}$

17. $0.\overline{01}$ 18. $3.\overline{21}$ 19. $0.7\overline{11}$ 20. $0.\overline{074}$

21. $0.5\overline{12}$ 22. $0.02\overline{13}$ 23. $0.0\overline{213}$ 24. $0.\overline{0213}$

Find a rational number and an irrational number between the given numbers.

25. $\dfrac{1}{2}, \dfrac{5}{8}$ 26. $\dfrac{2}{3}, \dfrac{5}{6}$ 27. $-1.6, -1\dfrac{5}{8}$

28. $-1.4, -1.\overline{4}$ 29. $1.7, \sqrt{3}$ 30. $2\sqrt{6}, 5$

B 31. $\pi, \dfrac{22}{7}$ 32. $\pi, \dfrac{157}{50}$ 33. $\pi, \dfrac{355}{113}$

(Note: $\pi = 3.14159265\ldots$ and is irrational.)

34. Is the set of integers dense? Explain.

C 35. Is the set of numbers having finite decimal representations dense? Explain.

36. **a.** Suppose that the denominator of a common fraction has no prime factors other than 2 and 5. $\left(\text{The fractions } \dfrac{144}{125} \text{ and } \dfrac{27}{200} \text{ are examples because } 125 = 5^3 \text{ and } 200 = 2^3 \cdot 5^2.\right)$ Show that the fraction has a finite decimal representation.

   b. If a common fraction has a finite decimal representation, what can be said of the prime factors of its denominator? Explain.

37. Show that each repeating decimal represents a rational number as follows: Let $N =$ the number. Let $P =$ the number of digits in the repeating block of N. Justify the following statements.

   a. $N \cdot 10^p$ has the same repeating block as N.
   b. $N \cdot 10^p - N$ is a terminating decimal.
   c. $N(10^p - 1)$ is rational.
   d. $\dfrac{N(10^p - 1)}{10^p - 1}$ is rational.

Computer Key-In _____

The computer can be used to investigate repeating decimals. The following program is the basis for some of the exercises below.

```
10   PRINT "TO FIND A DECIMAL FOR N/D:"
20   PRINT "INPUT N, D (0 < N < D)";
30   INPUT N,D
40   IF N<0 OR D<0 OR N >= D THEN 20
50   PRINT N;" /";D;" = 0 .";
55   REM***THE NUMERATOR IS THE FIRST 'REMAINDER'
56   REM*** IN THE LOOP BELOW.
60   LET R=N
65   REM***THIS LOOP COMPUTES AND PRINTS ONE DIGIT OF
66   REM*** THE QUOTIENT AT A TIME.
70   FOR I=1 TO 25
80   LET D1=R*10
90   LET Q=D1/D
95   REM***Q1 IS A DIGIT IN THE QUOTIENT.
100  LET Q1=INT(Q)
110  PRINT Q1;
115  REM***R IS THE NEW REMAINDER.
120  LET R=R*10-Q1*D
130  IF R=0 THEN 170
140  NEXT I
150  PRINT "..."
160  STOP
170  PRINT " TERMINATES"
180  END
```

Exercises

1. RUN the program above to find decimal representations of unit fractions from $1/2$ to $1/25$. (Note that these fractions are written the way the computer writes them.)

2. Find and mark off the repetend for each repeating decimal. Note the number of digits in each repetend.

3. Compare the repetends of $1/7$, $1/14$, and $1/21$.

4. Explain why the repetend for a divisor D can have no more than $D - 1$ digits. (*Hint*: Divide $1/7$ by hand and study the remainders.)

5. Study the computer print-out for Exercise 1, and find the repetends that have the maximum number (D-1) of digits.

6. List the fractions that have terminating decimal representations in Exercise 1. Factor each denominator. What do you discover?

Self-Test 2

VOCABULARY   rational number (p. 224)   infinite decimal (p. 228)
                   irrational number (p. 225)   repeating decimal (p. 228)
                   indirect argument (p. 225)   dense set (p. 230)
                   finite decimal (p. 228)

1. Find a polynomial with integral coefficients having $\sqrt[5]{-3}$ as a root.   **Obj. 6-5, p. 224**

2. Explain how you know that $x^4 + x + 2 = 0$ has no rational roots.

3. Show that $\sqrt[3]{2}$ is irrational.

4. Find the decimal representation of $\frac{17}{44}$.   **Obj. 6-6, p. 228**

5. Express $4.9\overline{90}$ as a common fraction.

6. Find an irrational number between $\sqrt{3}$ and $\frac{7}{4}$.

Check your answers with those at the back of the book.

ḣistorical ṅote Radical Signs

What do the four symbols shown at the right have in common? They are all symbols that have been used to mean "the square root of 5." These symbols appeared in Europe during the twelfth century when Arabic mathematics texts became generally available there. The top two symbols stand for the Latin word *radix*, from which the English word *radical* was derived.

R_x 5

$ra.$ 5

$\sqrt{x}$ 5

l 5

All four of these symbols were used to some extent, different ones in different parts of Europe. As communications improved, notation became more uniform. By the end of the 17th century $\sqrt{5}$ had become predominant. It was first introduced in 1525 by Christoff Rudolff.

Square roots were nothing new in the twelfth century. Ancient Egyptians and Babylonians, for example, worked with square roots. The Egyptians are known to have used the symbol shown at the right as a square root sign.

Calculator Key-In

By dividing 1 by 7 on a calculator, you can find the decimal equivalent of $\frac{1}{7}$. If your calculator gives 8 significant digits, it will show 0.14285714. Since you know that $\frac{1}{7}$ must repeat after 7 − 1, or 6, digits, you can write $\frac{1}{7} = 0.\overline{142857}$.

Which of the numbers $\frac{2}{3}, \frac{1}{6}, \frac{4}{9}, \frac{1}{17}, \frac{7}{24}$ have repetends which are *certain* to be found using a calculator with 8 significant digits? Test your hypothesis by performing the indicated divisions on such a calculator. Can you *guess* the repetend of any of the remaining numbers?

6-7 *The Number i*

OBJECTIVE   **To use the number i to simplify square roots of negative numbers.**

The equation $z^2 + 1 = 0$ has no solution over the set of real numbers because if z is real, $z^2 + 1$ is *positive*. We wish to enlarge the domain of z to obtain a set over which $z^2 + 1 = 0$ does have a solution. We do this by introducing a new number, i, called the **imaginary unit,** with the property that

$$i^2 = -1.$$

Thus, i is a solution of $z^2 + 1 = 0$. We shall operate with i as we do with any other constant, remembering that $i^2 = -1$. Thus,

$$(-i)^2 = [-1(i)]^2 = (-1)^2 i^2 = 1(-1) = -1,$$

and so $-i$ is also a root of $z^2 + 1 = 0$.

In order to combine i in a natural way with real numbers, we introduce complex numbers such as

$$3i, \quad -7i, \quad 2 + 5i, \quad \text{and} \quad 6 - i.$$

In general, a **complex number** is a number of the form

$$a + bi$$

where a and b are real. The set of complex numbers will be denoted by $\mathcal{C}$, and the set of real numbers will be denoted by $\mathcal{R}$.

The fact that $i^2 = -1$ enables you to write

$$i = \sqrt{-1}$$

and call i a "square root of -1." You can use i to find square roots of other negative numbers. For example, since

$$(3i)^2 = 3^2 i^2 = 9(-1) = -9,$$

you have

$$\sqrt{-9} = 3i.$$

In general,

If $r > 0$:

$$\sqrt{-r} = i\sqrt{r}$$

It is customary to write $i\sqrt{r}$ rather than $\sqrt{r}i$ to avoid confusion with $\sqrt{ri}$.

EXAMPLE 1 Simplify.

      a. $\sqrt{-18}$ **b.** $7\sqrt{-5} - \sqrt{-125}$ **c.** $\sqrt{-2} \cdot \sqrt{-8}$

SOLUTION   **a.** $\sqrt{-18} = i\sqrt{18} = i \cdot 3\sqrt{2} = 3i\sqrt{2}$

              b. $7\sqrt{-5} - \sqrt{-125} = 7i\sqrt{5} - i\sqrt{125} = 7i\sqrt{5} - 5i\sqrt{5} = 2i\sqrt{5}$

              c. $\sqrt{-2} \cdot \sqrt{-8} = i\sqrt{2} \cdot i\sqrt{8} = i^2\sqrt{16} = -1 \cdot 4 = -4$

As Example 1 indicates, you must now eliminate negative radicands when simplifying radical expressions.

Warning: In part (c) of Example 1, it would be incorrect to write

$$\sqrt{-2} \cdot \sqrt{-8} = \sqrt{(-2)(-8)}$$
$$= \sqrt{16} = 4$$

because the rule $\sqrt{a}\sqrt{b} = \sqrt{ab}$ does not hold if a and b are negative.

Because $-i^2 = 1$, you can see that $(-i)i = 1$ and $i(-i) = 1$. Thus, i and $-i$ are reciprocals:

$$\frac{1}{i} = -i \quad \text{and} \quad \frac{1}{-i} = i.$$

EXAMPLE 2 Simplify $\dfrac{2}{\sqrt{-18}}$.

SOLUTION $\dfrac{2}{\sqrt{-18}} = \dfrac{2}{3i\sqrt{2}} = -\dfrac{2i}{3\sqrt{2}} \cdot \dfrac{\sqrt{2}}{\sqrt{2}}$

                   $= -\dfrac{2i\sqrt{2}}{6} = -\dfrac{i\sqrt{2}}{3}$

Because $\sqrt{-r} = i\sqrt{r}$ if $r > 0$, every equation of the form $x^2 + r = 0$ has the solution set $\{-i\sqrt{r}, i\sqrt{r}\}$ when solved over the set of complex numbers. In Chapter 8 you will learn that *every* polynomial equation has a solution when solved over $\mathbb{C}$.

Oral Exercises

Simplify, that is, express in the form a or bi with all radicals in simple form.

1. $\sqrt{-16}$ 2. $-\sqrt{-100}$ 3. $\sqrt{-200}$ 4. $\sqrt{-75}$

5. $i\sqrt{-1}$ 6. $-\sqrt{-1}$ 7. $(\sqrt{-1})^2$ 8. $\sqrt{(-1)^2}$

9. $\dfrac{\sqrt{-12}}{2}$ 10. $\dfrac{\sqrt{-12}}{\sqrt{3}}$ 11. i^3 12. i^4

Name two roots of each equation.

SAMPLE $z^2 + 25 = 0$

SOLUTION $z^2 = -25$; $z = \sqrt{-25} = 5i$ and $z = -\sqrt{-25} = -5i$.

13. $z^2 + 4 = 0$ **14.** $z^2 = -100$

15. $z^2 = -64$ **16.** $z^2 + 16 = 0$

[handwritten: 1-23 odd]

Written Exercises

Simplify. *[handwritten: $i\sqrt{32} = 4i\sqrt{2}$, $16\cdot 2$]*

A 1. $\sqrt{-32}$ *[handwritten: $= i\sqrt{32}$, $4i\sqrt{2}$, $16\cdot2$]* **2.** $\sqrt{-50}$ *[handwritten: $= i\sqrt{50}$, $5i\sqrt{2}$]* **3.** $\sqrt{\dfrac{-1}{16}}$ *[handwritten: $= \dfrac{\sqrt{-1}}{\sqrt{16}} = \dfrac{i}{4}$]* **4.** $\sqrt{\dfrac{-4}{25}}$

5. $\sqrt{-\dfrac{1}{3}}$ **6.** $\sqrt{-\dfrac{5}{12}}$ **7.** $\sqrt{(-3)^2}$ **8.** $\sqrt{-3^2}$

9. $(\sqrt{-3})^2$ **10.** $\dfrac{6}{\sqrt{-8}}$ **11.** $\dfrac{3}{\sqrt{-18}}$ **12.** $\sqrt{-8}\sqrt{-18}$

13. $\sqrt{-12}\sqrt{-27}$ **14.** $\sqrt{-2}\sqrt{50}$ **15.** $\sqrt{18}\sqrt{-8}$ **16.** $\dfrac{7}{\sqrt{-7}}$

17. $\dfrac{12}{\sqrt{-12}}$ **18.** $\sqrt{-\dfrac{1}{12}}\sqrt{3}$ **19.** $\sqrt{-\dfrac{4}{7}}\sqrt{\dfrac{7}{4}}$ **20.** $\dfrac{\sqrt{48}}{\sqrt{-12}}$

[handwritten near 19: $\dfrac{\sqrt{-4}}{\sqrt{7}}, \dfrac{\sqrt{7}}{\sqrt{4}}$]

21. $\dfrac{\sqrt{12}}{i\sqrt{-2}}$ **22.** $\sqrt{-128} - \sqrt{-48}$ *[handwritten: $\dfrac{\sqrt{-28}}{\sqrt{28}} = \dfrac{2i\sqrt{7}}{2\sqrt{7}} = i$]*

23. $\sqrt{-98} + 2\sqrt{-18}$ *[handwritten: $i\sqrt{98} + 2i\sqrt{18}$, $7\cdot2$, $9\cdot2$, $7i\sqrt{2} + 6i\sqrt{2}$, $13i\sqrt{2}$]* **24.** $\sqrt{48} + i\sqrt{-12}$

Solve over $\mathbb{C}$.

B 25. $z^2 + 8 = 0$ **26.** $z^2 + 20 = 0$ **27.** $z^2 + 20 = 4$

28. $z^2 + 16 = 4$ **29.** $4z^2 + 1 = 0$ **30.** $9z^2 + 4 = 0$

Simplify. Assume that the variables denote positive real numbers.

31. $\sqrt{-9a} \cdot \sqrt{-4a}$ **32.** $\sqrt{18c}\sqrt{-2c^3}$

33. $\sqrt{-\dfrac{r}{5}} \cdot \sqrt{-\dfrac{20}{r}}$ **34.** $\sqrt{\dfrac{-a^5}{b}}\sqrt{-\dfrac{b}{a^3}}$

35. $\sqrt{-9c^2} + \sqrt{-49c^2} - 2\sqrt{-c^2}$ **36.** $\sqrt{-25a^3} - \sqrt{-225a^3} + 20a\sqrt{-a}$

37. $\sqrt{-r^3} + \sqrt{-4r^3} - \sqrt{-9r^3}$ **38.** $\sqrt{-2t^5} + \sqrt{-8t^5} - \sqrt{-18t^5}$

39. $\sqrt{-x^5} + x\sqrt{-25x^3} - \sqrt{-25x^5}$ **40.** $\sqrt{-m^7} - 2m\sqrt{-9m^5} + 3\sqrt{-m^5}$

41. $\dfrac{1}{i} - \dfrac{i}{2} + \dfrac{3}{2i}$ **42.** $\dfrac{\sqrt{3}}{i} + \dfrac{i}{\sqrt{3}} - \dfrac{\sqrt{3}}{3i}$

43. $ti\sqrt{-4t^2} + \sqrt{4t^4} - t^2 i\sqrt{-9}$ **44.** $i\sqrt{-27m^7} - m^2 i\sqrt{-3m^3} - m\sqrt{12m^5}$

6-8 *Operating with Complex Numbers*

When a complex number is written in the form $a + bi$, it is understood that a and b are real numbers. The number a is called the **real part** of $a + bi$, and b (not bi) is called the **imaginary part.** Two complex numbers are **equal** if and only if their real parts are equal and their imaginary parts are equal. Thus, if $x + yi = 4 - i$, then $x = 4$ and $y = -1$.

A complex number $a + bi$ is **imaginary** if $b \neq 0$ and is **pure imaginary** if it is of the form bi ($b \neq 0$). For example,

$$-3 + 5i, \quad 2 + i, \quad \text{and} \quad -3i$$

are imaginary, and $-3i$ is pure imaginary. Those complex numbers having imaginary parts 0 are the real numbers. It should be apparent that any real number is also a complex number.

To add or subtract two complex numbers, treat them as ordinary binomials. For example:

$$(4 + i) + (3 - 2i) = (4 + 3) + (i + [-2i]) = 7 - i$$
$$(4 + i) - (3 - 2i) = (4 - 3) + \quad (i + 2i) \quad = 1 + 3i$$

To multiply two complex numbers, first multiply them as ordinary binomials and then use the fact that $i^2 = -1$.

$$\begin{aligned} (4 + i)(3 - 2i) &= 12 - 8i + 3i - 2i^2 \\ &= 12 - 5i - 2(-1) \\ &= 14 - 5i \end{aligned}$$

Whenever you operate with complex numbers, you should express the result in the form $a + bi$ unless told to do otherwise. Real numbers are written as usual, and pure imaginary numbers are written in the form bi.

The general definitions of the sum and product of two complex numbers are given below.

$$\boxed{\begin{aligned} (a + bi) + (c + di) &= (a + c) + (b + d)i \\ (a + bi)(c + di) &= (ac - bd) + (ad + bc)i \end{aligned}}$$

The definition of the product is motivated by the following:

$$\begin{aligned} (a + bi)(c + di) &= ac + adi + bci + bdi^2 \\ &= ac + (ad + bc)i + bd(-1) \\ &= (ac - bd) + (ad + bc)i. \end{aligned}$$

It can be shown that addition and multiplication of complex numbers satisfy the commutative, associative, and distributive axioms. (See Exercises 33–37.)

Example 1 illustrates how to find the quotient of two complex numbers.

EXAMPLE 1 Simplify $(2 + i) \div (3 + 4i)$.

SOLUTION $(2 + i) \div (3 + 4i) = \dfrac{2 + i}{3 + 4i}$

$$= \frac{2 + i}{3 + 4i} \cdot \frac{3 - 4i}{3 - 4i}$$

$$= \frac{6 - 8i + 3i - 4i^2}{9 - 16i^2}$$

$$= \frac{6 - 5i - 4(-1)}{9 - 16(-1)}$$

$$= \frac{10 - 5i}{25} = \frac{2}{5} - \frac{1}{5}i$$

Notice in Example 1 that both the numerator and the denominator were multiplied by the number $3 - 4i$, called the conjugate of the denominator $3 + 4i$. It was obtained from $3 + 4i$ by changing the sign of its imaginary part. In general, the **conjugate** of $a + bi$ is $a - bi$. Because

$$(a + bi)(a - bi) = a^2 - b^2i^2 = a^2 - b^2(-1) = a^2 + b^2,$$

you can see that the product of two conjugate complex numbers is always a nonnegative real number.

EXAMPLE 2 Find the reciprocal of $3 - i$.

SOLUTION $\dfrac{1}{3 - i} = \dfrac{1}{3 - i} \cdot \dfrac{3 + i}{3 + i} = \dfrac{3 + i}{9 - i^2}$

$$= \frac{3 + i}{9 - (-1)}$$

$$= \frac{3 + i}{10} = \frac{3}{10} + \frac{1}{10}i$$

Oral Exercises

Give the values of the variables.

1. $x + yi = 3 - 2i$

2. $u + vi = -2 + i$

3. $s + ti = 3i$

4. $x + yi = -5$

5. $x + 2i = 5 + yi$

6. $6 + ti = s - i$

7. $x + yi = 2 + 2yi$

8. $u + vi = 2u + 2vi$

Simplify each sum or difference.

9. $(3 + 4i) + (2 + i)$

10. $(3 + 4i) - (2 + i)$

11. $(6 - i) - (2 - 3i)$

12. $(-3 + i) + (1 - 3i)$

13. $(2 - i) + (2 + i)$

14. $(2 + 3i) - (2 - 3i)$

15. $(2 + 3i) - 4i$

16. $(3 - i) - 5$

Using such terms as "conjugate" and "real part," state the following facts in words.

17. $(a + bi) + (a - bi) = 2a$

18. $(a + bi) - (a - bi) = 2bi$

Written Exercises

Simplify each expression.

A

1. $(6 + 7i) + (-1 + 3i)$

2. $(10 - 6i) - (7 - 3i)$

3. $(3 + i) + 4i - (1 + 2i)$

4. $(6 - 2i) - (6 + 2i) + 4i$

5. $5 + (2 + 3i) - 5i$

6. $(4 + i) - (3 + 2i) - (2 + 3i)$

7. $2(3 - i) + (4 + 2i)$

8. $(5 + 3i) - 3(1 - i)$

9. $(1 + i)(2 + i)$

10. $(3 + i)(1 - i)$

11. $(5 + 2i)(1 - 3i)$

12. $(4 - 3i)(3 - 4i)$

13. $(1 + i)^2$

14. $(1 - i)^2$

15. $(1 + i)^3$

16. $(1 - i)^3$

17. $(1 + i)^4$

18. $(1 - i)^4$

19. $(\sqrt{2} + i)(\sqrt{2} - i)$

20. $(2 - \sqrt{-3})(2 + \sqrt{-3})$

Find the reciprocal of the given complex number.

21. $2 + i$

22. $3 - 4i$

23. $2 + 4i$

24. $1 - 3i$

25. $6 + 3i$

26. $4 - 6i$

Simplify the given quotient.

27. $(2 + i) \div (1 + i)$

28. $(3 - i) \div (2 - i)$

29. $\dfrac{2 + 2i}{3 - i}$

30. $\dfrac{3i}{1 - 2i}$

31. $\dfrac{4 + 5i}{1 + i}$

32. $\dfrac{1 - i}{2 + 2i}$

Show that the following statements are true. (Exercises 33-37 show that addition and multiplication of complex numbers satisfy the commutative, associative and distributive properties.)

B **33.** $(a + bi) + (c + di) = (c + di) + (a + bi)$

34. $(a + bi)(c + di) = (c + di)(a + bi)$

Show that the following statements are true.

C **35.** $[(a + bi) + (c + di)] + (e + fi) = (a + bi) + [(c + di) + (e + fi)]$

36. $[(a + bi)(c + di)](e + fi) = (a + bi)[(c + di)(e + fi)]$

37. $(a + bi)[(c + di) + (e + fi)] = (a + bi)(c + di) + (a + bi)(e + fi)$

38. It is easy to see that the complex numbers 0 and 1 are, respectively, the additive and multiplicative identities in $\mathcal{C}$. Also, $-a - bi$ is the additive inverse of $a + bi$. Verify that if $a + bi \neq 0$, then its multiplicative inverse is $\dfrac{a}{a^2 + b^2} - \dfrac{b}{a^2 + b^2} i$.

Self-Test 3

VOCABULARY   imaginary unit (p. 234)
complex number (p. 234)
real part (p. 237)
imaginary part (p. 237)
imaginary number (p. 237)
pure imaginary number (p. 237)
conjugate (p. 238)

1. Simplify: **a.** $\sqrt{-\dfrac{3}{8}}$ **b.** $\sqrt{-48} - \sqrt{-27}$ **Obj. 6-7, p. 234**

2. Solve $9z^2 + 1 = 0$ over $\mathcal{C}$.

Simplify.

3. $(4 - i) - (3 - 2i)$ **4.** $(3 - 2i)^2$ **Obj. 6-8, p. 237**

5. $\left(\sqrt{3} + i\sqrt{2}\right)\left(\sqrt{3} - i\sqrt{2}\right)$ **6.** $\dfrac{2 + i}{3 - 2i}$

Check your answers with those at the back of the book.

EXTRA

Part 1. More About Roots

It is easy to check that successive powers of i repeat in cycles of four according to the pattern

$$i^1 = i, \ i^2 = -1, \ i^3 = -i, \ i^4 = 1, \ i^5 = i, \ i^6 = -1, \ \ldots.$$

Thus, $i^{75} = i^{72} \cdot i^3 = (i^4)^{18} i^3 = 1^{18}(-i) = -i$.

Since $1^4 = 1$, $(-1)^4 = 1$, $i^4 = 1$, and $(-i)^4 = 1$, the four fourth roots of 1 are 1, -1, i, and $-i$.

EXAMPLE Show that $1 + i\sqrt{3}$ is a cube root of -8.

SOLUTION It is necessary to show that $(1 + i\sqrt{3})^3 = -8$.

$$(1 + i\sqrt{3})^2 = 1 + 2i\sqrt{3} + 3i^2 = -2 + 2i\sqrt{3}$$
$$(1 + i\sqrt{3})^3 = (1 + i\sqrt{3})^2(1 + i\sqrt{3}) = (-2 + 2i\sqrt{3})(1 + i\sqrt{3})$$
$$= -2 - 2i\sqrt{3} + 2i\sqrt{3} + 2i^2 \cdot 3 = -2 - 6 = -8$$

We can show in a similar way that $1 - i\sqrt{3}$ is also a cube root of -8 (Exercise 15). The three cube roots of -8 are $-2, 1 + i\sqrt{3}, 1 - i\sqrt{3}$. It can be shown that *in* $\mathcal{C}$, *every nonzero number has n nth roots.*

Exercises

Express as one of $0, 1, -1, i$, or $-i$.

A 1. i^{20} 2. i^{21} 3. i^{22} 4. i^{23}

   5. $i^8 + i^{10}$ 6. $i^{17} + i^{19}$ 7. $i + i^2 + i^3$ 8. $i^9 + i^{11} + i^{19}$

   9. $i + i^2 + i^3 + i^4$ 10. $\dfrac{1}{i} + \dfrac{1}{i^2} + \dfrac{1}{i^3} + \dfrac{1}{i^4}$

   11. $i^9 \cdot i^7$ 12. $i^{37} \div i^{35}$

   13. $i^{102} \cdot i^{-98}$ 14. $i^{-36} \cdot i^{-64}$

   15. Show that $1 - i\sqrt{3}$ is a cube root of -8.

   16. Show that $-1 + i\sqrt{3}$ is a cube root of 8.

   17. Show that $-1 - i\sqrt{3}$ is a cube root of 8.

   18. Show that $\dfrac{\sqrt{3}}{2} + \dfrac{1}{2}i$ is a cube root of i.

   19. Show that $-\dfrac{\sqrt{3}}{2} + \dfrac{1}{2}i$ is a cube root of i.

B 20. What are the three cube roots of i? (See Exercises 18 and 19.)

   21. Show that the four fourth roots of -4 are $1 + i, -1 + i, -1 - i$, and $1 - i$.

C 22. Use Exercise 21 to find the four fourth roots of -1.

   23. Show that if $b \geq 0$, then

$$z = \sqrt{\frac{\sqrt{a^2 + b^2} + a}{2}} + i\sqrt{\frac{\sqrt{a^2 + b^2} - a}{2}}$$

   is a square root of $a + bi$.

   24. Show that the two imaginary cube roots of a real number are conjugates of each other.

Part 2. More on Conjugates and Absolute Values

When studying complex numbers, it is often convenient to represent a complex number by a single letter. For example, let

$$z = x + yi.$$

The conjugate of z is denoted by $\bar{z}$, that is,

$$\bar{z} = x - yi.$$

Properties of the conjugate are summed up in the next theorem.

THEOREM 1   Let w and z be complex numbers.

a. $\overline{w + z} = \bar{w} + \bar{z}$ **b.** $\overline{w - z} = \bar{w} - \bar{z}$

c. $\overline{wz} = \bar{w}\,\bar{z}$ **d.** $\overline{\left(\dfrac{w}{z}\right)} = \dfrac{\bar{w}}{\bar{z}}$ $(z \neq 0)$

Proof of part (c): Let $w = u + vi$ and $z = x + yi$. Then

$$\overline{wz} = \overline{(u + vi)(x + yi)} = \overline{(ux - vy) + (uy + vx)i}$$
$$= (ux - vy) - (uy + vx)i$$
$$\bar{w}\,\bar{z} = (u - vi)(x - yi) = [ux - (-v)(-y)] + [u(-y) + (-v)x]i$$
$$= (ux - vy) - (uy + vx)i$$
$$\therefore \overline{wz} = \bar{w}\,\bar{z}$$

Proofs of the other parts of Theorem 1 are left as exercises.

To measure the "size" of the complex number $z = x + yi$, you can use its **absolute value,** defined by

$$|z| = \sqrt{x^2 + y^2}.$$

For example, if $z = 4 - 3i$, then $|z| = \sqrt{4^2 + (-3)^2} = \sqrt{25} = 5$. If $w = -6i$, then $|w| = \sqrt{0^2 + (-6)^2} = 6$.

A useful relationship between absolute value and conjugate is given by the following theorem.

THEOREM 2.   If z is a complex number, then $|z|^2 = z\bar{z}$.

Proof: Let $z = x + yi$. Then

$$|z|^2 = \left(\sqrt{x^2 + y^2}\right)^2 = x^2 + y^2, \text{ and } z\bar{z} = (x + iy)(x - yi) = x^2 + y^2$$
$$\therefore |z|^2 = z\bar{z}.$$

If you divide both members of $|z|^2 = z\bar{z}$ by $|z|^2 z$, you obtain this convenient expression for the reciprocal of a nonzero complex number:

$$\frac{1}{z} = \frac{\bar{z}}{|z|^2}$$

For example, since $|3 - 2i|^2 = 3^2 + (-2)^2 = 13$, you have

$$\frac{1}{3 - 2i} = \frac{3 + 2i}{13}.$$

Some properties of the absolute value are given below.

THEOREM 3. Let w and z be complex numbers.

a. $|wz| = |w|\,|z|$ **b.** $\left|\dfrac{w}{z}\right| = \dfrac{|w|}{|z|}$ $(z \neq 0)$

c. $|w + z| \leq |w| + |z|$

Proof of part (a): By Theorems 1 and 2 and the commutative and associative properties:

$$|wz|^2 = (wz)(\overline{wz}) = wz\bar{w}\,\bar{z} = w\bar{w}z\bar{z} = |w|^2|z|^2$$

Since $|wz|$, $|w|$, and $|z|$ are all nonnegative, when you take principal square roots, you obtain

$$|wz| = |w|\,|z|.$$

The proof of part (c) of Theorem 3 is more difficult and is outlined in Exercises 19 and 20 on the following page.

Exercises

Express each of the following as a real number.

A **1.** $|-3i|$ **2.** $|-4 - 3i|$ **3.** $|12 - 5i|$ **4.** $|-12 + 5i|$

  5. $|1 + i|$ **6.** $|\sqrt{3} - i|$ **7.** $\left|\dfrac{\sqrt{2}}{2} + \dfrac{\sqrt{2}}{2}i\right|$ **8.** $\left|\dfrac{\sqrt{2}}{2} - \dfrac{1}{2}i\right|$

  9. a. $|4 + 3i| + |4 - 3i|$ **b.** $|(4 + 3i) + (4 - 3i)|$
  10. a. $|\sqrt{3} + i| + |-\sqrt{3} + i|$ **b.** $|(\sqrt{3} + i) + (-\sqrt{3} + i)|$

  11. Show that $|\bar{z}| = |z|$.
  12. Show that $z + \bar{z}$ is twice the real part of z.

B **13.** Express the imaginary part of z in terms of z and $\bar{z}$.
  14. Prove part (a) of Theorem 1.
  15. Prove part (b) of Theorem 1.

16. Prove that $\overline{\left(\dfrac{1}{z}\right)} = \dfrac{1}{\bar{z}}$.

17. Prove part (d) of Theorem 1 by combining part (c) and Exercise 16 above. (*Hint:* $\dfrac{w}{z} = w \cdot \dfrac{1}{z}$.)

18. Prove part (b) of Theorem 3. (*Hint:* Apply Theorem 2 to $\left|\dfrac{w}{z}\right|^2$. Then use part (d) of Theorem 1.)

The remaining exercises constitute a proof of part (c) of Theorem 3.

C 19. Show that $w\bar{z} + \bar{w}z \le 2|w||z|$.

(*Hint:* Show that $w\bar{z} + \bar{w}z = w\bar{z} + \overline{w\bar{z}}$ and therefore is twice the real part of $w\bar{z}$. How does the real part of a complex number compare in size with its absolute value?)

20. Show that $|w + z| \le |w| + |z|$. (*Hint:* Use the theorems of this section and the preceding exercise to justify these steps:

$$|w + z|^2 = (w + z)\overline{(w + z)} = (w + z)(\bar{w} + \bar{z})$$
$$= w\bar{w} + w\bar{z} + \bar{w}z + z\bar{z}$$
$$\le |w|^2 + 2|w||z| + |z|^2$$

$\therefore |w + z|^2 \le (|w| + |z|)^2$)

Chapter Summary

1. If $a^n = b$, then a is an nth root of b. The radical $\sqrt[n]{b}$ denotes the *principal* nth root of b. If n is odd $\sqrt[n]{b^n} = b$; if n is even, $\sqrt[n]{b^n} = |b|$.

2. In working with radicals, you can use the following results:

$$\sqrt[n]{ab} = \sqrt[n]{a} \cdot \sqrt[n]{b} \qquad\qquad \sqrt[n]{\dfrac{a}{b}} = \dfrac{\sqrt[n]{a}}{\sqrt[n]{b}}$$

$$\sqrt[nq]{b} = \sqrt[n]{\sqrt[q]{b}} \qquad\qquad \sqrt[n]{b^m} = (\sqrt[n]{b})^m$$

3. The distributive law enables you to write as a single term any sum of radicals having the same index and the same radicand. You can simplify products and quotients of expressions involving radicals with the help of the rules in item 2 above.

4. To solve a *radical equation*, isolate a radical in one member and raise both members to the power equal to the index of the radical. Repeat this operation if necessary. It is essential to check the possible solutions found in this way.

5. If a *rational* root of a simplified polynomial equation with integral coefficients is expressed as $\frac{p}{q}$, where p and q are integers and $\frac{p}{q}$ is in simplest form, then p is a factor of the constant term and q is a factor of the coefficient of the term of highest degree.

6. Decimals representing rational numbers are either *finite* or *repeating*. Thus, decimals representing *irrational numbers* are infinite and nonrepeating.

7. A *complex number* is one of the form $a + bi$, where a and b are *real* numbers and $i^2 = -1$. The number is *imaginary* if $b \neq 0$ and is *pure imaginary* if $a = 0$ and $b \neq 0$.

8. Complex numbers may be added and multiplied by treating them as ordinary binomials and using the fact that $i^2 = -1$. The *conjugate* of $a + bi$ is $a - bi$. To simplify a quotient, multiply both numerator and denominator by the conjugate of the denominator.

Chapter Review

Give the letter of the correct answer.

1. Evaluate $\sqrt[3]{-\frac{1}{64}}$.

    a. $-\frac{1}{8}$ **b.** -4 **c.** $-\frac{1}{4}$ **d.** undefined

    6-1

2. Find the real roots of the equation $4x^2 - 16 = 0$.

    a. $\{2\}$ **b.** $\{2, -2\}$
    c. $\{-2, 2, -2i, 2i\}$ **d.** no real roots

3. Simplify $\sqrt{32y^9z^{16}}$.

    a. $4y^4z^8\sqrt{2y}$ **b.** $16y^4z^8\sqrt{2y}$ **c.** $4y^3z^4\sqrt{2}$ **d.** $16y^3z^4$

    6-2

4. Simplify $\sqrt[4]{9x^2y^3}\ \sqrt[4]{9x^3y^2}$.

    a. $9xy\sqrt[4]{xy}$ **b.** $3xy\sqrt[4]{x^2y^2}$ **c.** $3xy\sqrt[4]{xy}$ **d.** $9\sqrt[4]{x^2y^2}$

5. Simplify $\sqrt{x^2 - 8x + 16}$.

    a. $4 - x$ **b.** $x - 4$ **c.** $|x - 4|$ **d.** cannot be simplified

6. Simplify $2\sqrt{18} - 5\sqrt{32} + \sqrt{12}$.

    a. $2\sqrt{3} - 4\sqrt{2}$ **b.** $-12\sqrt{2}$
    c. $2\sqrt{3} + 24\sqrt{2}$ **d.** $2\sqrt{3} - 14\sqrt{2}$

    6-3

7. Simplify $(2\sqrt{5} - \sqrt{3})^2$.

    a. $23 - 4\sqrt{15}$ **b.** $13 - 4\sqrt{15}$ **c.** $7 - 4\sqrt{15}$ **d.** $23 + 4\sqrt{5} - 2\sqrt{3}$

8. Rationalize the denominator and simplify: $\dfrac{4}{\sqrt{6}-5}$

   a. $\dfrac{20+4\sqrt{6}}{19}$ **b.** $\dfrac{-20-4\sqrt{6}}{19}$ **c.** $\dfrac{20+4\sqrt{6}}{11}$ **d.** $\dfrac{4\sqrt{6}-20}{11}$

9. Solve $\sqrt{x^2-7}+3=0$. 6-4

   a. $\{4\}$ **b.** $\{-4,4\}$ **c.** $\{-4\}$ **d.** no solution

10. Which of the following could *not* be a rational root of $4x^3+2x^2-7x+6=0$ according to the theorem on p. 224? 6-5

   a. $\dfrac{3}{4}$ **b.** -3 **c.** $-\dfrac{3}{2}$ **d.** $\dfrac{2}{3}$

11. Write $0.1\overline{7}$ as a common fraction in simplest form. 6-6

   a. $\dfrac{17}{99}$ **b.** $\dfrac{1}{10}$ **c.** $\dfrac{16}{99}$ **d.** $\dfrac{8}{45}$

12. Which of the following is not a rational number?

   a. 0.3862731 **b.** $\sqrt[3]{125}$

   c. $2.2121121112\ldots$ **d.** $0.46\overline{32}$

13. Simplify $\sqrt{-32}\sqrt{-2}$. 6-7

   a. 8 **b.** $8i$ **c.** -8 **d.** $-8i$

14. Solve $3x^2+18=0$ over the complex numbers.

   a. $\{-\sqrt{6},\sqrt{6}\}$ **b.** $\{-i\sqrt{6},i\sqrt{6}\}$ **c.** $\{-6i,6i\}$ **d.** $\{i\sqrt{6}\}$

15. Find real numbers x and y such that $2x-yi=-3+5yi$. 6-8

   a. $x=-\dfrac{3}{2}, y=-5$ **b.** $x=-3, y=-5$

   c. $x=-\dfrac{3}{2}, y=0$ **d.** $x=-3, y=0$

16. Simplify $(5-6i)(4+3i)$.

   a. $38-9i$ **b.** $38-11i$ **c.** $2-9i$ **d.** $20-27i$

17. Which of the following is the reciprocal of $4+2i$?

   a. $\dfrac{1}{3}+\dfrac{1}{6}i$ **b.** $\dfrac{1}{3}-\dfrac{1}{6}i$ **c.** $\dfrac{1}{5}-\dfrac{1}{10}i$ **d.** $\dfrac{1}{5}+\dfrac{1}{10}i$

Chapter Test

1. Evaluate $\sqrt[3]{\dfrac{27}{1000}}$. 6-1

2. Find the real roots of $16x^4-1=0$.

Simplify.

   3. $\sqrt[4]{9a^6b^{-8}}$ **4.** $\sqrt{x^3-4x^2+4x}$ 6-2

Simplify.

5. $3t\sqrt{3t} + \sqrt{12t^3} - \sqrt{27t^3}$ **6.** $\dfrac{\sqrt{3}+1}{\sqrt{3}-1}$

6-3

Solve.

7. $\sqrt[3]{x^2 - 9} = 3$ **8.** $x + \sqrt{2x - 6} = 3$

6-4

9. Find the rational roots of the equation $4x^3 + 2x^2 + x - 7 = 0$.

6-5

10. Express $0.8\overline{409}$ as a common fraction.

6-6

11. Find an irrational number between $\dfrac{3}{5}$ and $\dfrac{2}{3}$.

Simplify.

12. $\sqrt{-20} \cdot \sqrt{-45}$ **13.** $\dfrac{9}{\sqrt{-27}}$

6-7

14. $(\sqrt{3} - 2i)(\sqrt{3} + 2i)$ **15.** $\dfrac{3 - 2i}{4 - 3i}$

6-8

*Shown above is the Metropolitan Opera House at Lincoln Center in
New York. The face of the building is very nearly a golden rectangle, as
described in Problem 11 on page 257.*

7

QUADRATIC EQUATIONS AND FUNCTIONS

SOLVING QUADRATIC EQUATIONS

7-1 *Completing the Square*

OBJECTIVE **To solve quadratic equations by completing the square.**

An equation of the form

$$ax^2 + bx + c = 0 \ (a \neq 0)$$

is called a **quadratic equation.** Because of their frequent occurrence in diverse fields of study and work, it is important to be able to solve quadratic equations. You learned earlier to solve some of these equations by factoring. In this chapter you will learn methods for solving *all* quadratics.

In Chapter 6 you learned to solve any equation of the form

$$z^2 = q.$$

This equation is equivalent to the compound sentence

$$z = \sqrt{q} \quad \text{or} \quad z = -\sqrt{q},$$

which can be written in combined form as

$$z = \pm\sqrt{q}$$

(read "z equals plus or minus $\sqrt{q}$"). These facts can be used to solve more general equations.

EXAMPLE 1   Solve: **a.** $(x + 2)^2 = 5$ **b.** $x^2 - 2x + 1 = 3$

SOLUTION   **a.** Use the facts stated above with $x + 2$ playing the role of z.

$$(x + 2)^2 = 5$$
$$x + 2 = \pm \sqrt{5}, \quad \text{or} \quad x = -2 \pm \sqrt{5}$$

∴ the solution set is $\{-2 + \sqrt{5}, -2 - \sqrt{5}\}$.   ***Answer***

b. $x^2 - 2x + 1 = 3$

$$(x - 1)^2 = 3$$

Now use the method of part (a) with $x - 1$ playing the role of z.

$$x - 1 = \pm\sqrt{3}$$
$$x = 1 \pm \sqrt{3}$$

∴ the solution set is $\{1 + \sqrt{3}, 1 - \sqrt{3}\}$.   ***Answer***

Example 1 suggests that any quadratic equation can be solved readily if it can be written in the form

$$(x + p)^2 = q.$$

Examples 2 and 3 illustrate how to take advantage of this fact by completing the trinomial square suggested by the coefficient of the linear term. The method of solution presented in these examples is called **completing the square.**

EXAMPLE 2   Solve $t^2 - 7t + 11 = 0$.

SOLUTION

1. Subtract the constant term from both sides.

$$t^2 - 7t + 11 = 0$$
$$t^2 - 7t \qquad = -11$$

2. Add the square of half the coefficient of t to both sides.

$$t^2 - 7t + \left(\frac{7}{2}\right)^2 = -11 + \left(\frac{7}{2}\right)^2$$

$$= -11 + \frac{49}{4}$$

$$= \frac{5}{4}$$

3. Factor the left side as the square of a binomial.

$$\left(t - \frac{7}{2}\right)^2 = \frac{5}{4}$$

4. Proceed as in Example 1.

$$t - \frac{7}{2} = \pm \sqrt{\frac{5}{4}}$$

$$t = \frac{7}{2} \pm \frac{\sqrt{5}}{2} = \frac{7 \pm \sqrt{5}}{2}$$

∴ the solution set is $\left\{\dfrac{7 + \sqrt{5}}{2}, \dfrac{7 - \sqrt{5}}{2}\right\}$.   ***Answer***

Completing the square will also enable you to find any complex roots of an equation.

EXAMPLE 3   Solve $3x^2 - 2x + 1 = 0$ over the complex numbers.

SOLUTION   First divide both sides by 3; then proceed as in Example 2.

$$3x^2 - 2x + 1 = 0$$

$$x^2 - \frac{2}{3}x + \frac{1}{3} = 0$$

$$x^2 - \frac{2}{3}x \qquad = -\frac{1}{3}$$

$$x^2 - \frac{2}{3}x + \left(\frac{1}{3}\right)^2 = -\frac{1}{3} + \left(\frac{1}{3}\right)^2$$

$$\left(x - \frac{1}{3}\right)^2 = -\frac{2}{9}$$

$$x - \frac{1}{3} = \pm\sqrt{-\frac{2}{9}}$$

$$= \pm\frac{i\sqrt{2}}{3}$$

$$x = \frac{1}{3} \pm \frac{i\sqrt{2}}{3}$$

$$= \frac{1 \pm i\sqrt{2}}{3}$$

$\therefore$ the solution set is $\left\{\dfrac{1 + i\sqrt{2}}{3}, \dfrac{1 - i\sqrt{2}}{3}\right\}$.   **Answer**

Oral Exercises

What two numbers are represented by each of the following?

1. 3 ± 2

2. 1 ± 3

3. 5 ± 5

4. $\frac{3}{2} \pm \frac{1}{2}$

5. $1 \pm \frac{1}{3}$

6. $-1 \pm \frac{3}{2}$

For what value(s) of k is the given expression a trinomial square?

7. $x^2 + 2x + k$

8. $t^2 + 4t + k$

9. $w^2 + 10w + k$

10. $x^2 - 6x + k$

11. $t^2 + t + k$

12. $x^2 - 3x + k$

13. $x^2 - \frac{2}{5}x + k$

14. $u^2 + \frac{4}{3}u + k$

15. $z^2 - 7z + k$

16. $y^2 + ky + 25$

17. $r^2 + kr + 49$

18. $s^2 + ks + \frac{9}{4}$

19. $z^2 + kz + 121$

20. $x^2 + kx + \frac{25}{16}$

21. $x^2 + kx + \frac{16}{25}$

Written Exercises

Solve.

A   **1.** $(x - 2)^2 = 3$ **2.** $(x - 3)^2 = 2$ **3.** $(t + 2)^2 = 5$

4. $(y + 4)^2 = 7$ **5.** $(z + 3)^2 - 12 = 0$ **6.** $(z - 3)^2 - 18 = 0$

Solve by the method of completing the square.

7. $x^2 - 4x - 5 = 0$ **8.** $x^2 + 6x + 2 = 0$ **9.** $x^2 - 2x - 10 = 0$

10. $t^2 - 4t + 3 = 0$ **11.** $u^2 + 8u + 8 = 0$ **12.** $x^2 - x - 6 = 0$

13. $x^2 + x - 1 = 0$ **14.** $z^2 + 5z = 4$ **15.** $t^2 - 9 = 3t$

16. $2x^2 + 6x + 1 = 0$ **17.** $3v^2 + 6v - 2 = 0$ **18.** $6t^2 + 10t + 4 = 0$

B   **19.** $\dfrac{t^2}{3} + \dfrac{t}{2} + \dfrac{1}{6} = 0$ **20.** $\dfrac{x^2}{4} + \dfrac{x}{3} = 1$

21. $\dfrac{x^2}{2} - \dfrac{x}{5} = \dfrac{1}{10}$ **22.** $\dfrac{u^2}{5} - \dfrac{u}{6} = \dfrac{1}{30}$

23. $2t(t - 2) = 3(4 - t)$ **24.** $5x(x + 2) = 4(3x + 1)$

Solve over the set of complex numbers.

25. $x^2 + 2x + 4 = 0$ **26.** $z^2 + 3z + 6 = 0$ **27.** $4x^2 + 2x + 5 = 0$

28. $2x^2 + 5x + 3 = 0$ **29.** $3t^2 + 3t + 4 = 0$ **30.** $6x^2 + 5x + 1 = 0$

Solve each equation.

31. $\dfrac{1}{x + 1} + \dfrac{1}{x - 1} = 1$ **32.** $\dfrac{1}{t + 2} + \dfrac{1}{t + 6} = 1$

33. $\dfrac{2}{z + 2} + \dfrac{1}{z - 2} = 2$ **34.** $\dfrac{2x + 3}{x + 1} - \dfrac{x}{x - 3} = \dfrac{1}{x^2 - 2x - 3}$

35. $\sqrt{x + 3} = 2x$ **36.** $\sqrt{2x^2 + 1} = x + 3$

37. $\sqrt{x - 4} - \dfrac{2}{\sqrt{x - 4}} = 1$ **38.** $\dfrac{1}{\sqrt{x}} - 2\sqrt{x} = 2$

Write each equation in the form $(x - h)^2 + (y - k)^2 = c$. (*Hint:* Complete the square twice, once using the terms in x and once using the terms in y.)

C   **39.** $x^2 + y^2 - 4x - 2y - 4 = 0$ **40.** $x^2 + y^2 + 2x - 8y + 8 = 0$

41. $x^2 + y^2 + 10x - 10y = 0$ **42.** $x^2 + y^2 - 3x + y + 1 = 0$

Write each equation in the form $y = (x - h)^2 + k$.

43. $y = x^2 + 8x + 3$ **44.** $y = x^2 - 6x + 12$

45. $y = x^2 + 3x + 2$ **46.** $y = x^2 + 7x + 4$

7-2 *The Quadratic Formula*

OBJECTIVE To solve quadratic equations by using the quadratic formula.

Quadratic equations arise so frequently that it is useful to have a formula that gives their solutions directly from the coefficients. You can derive this formula by applying the method of completing the square to the general quadratic equation:

$$ax^2 + bx + c = 0 \quad \text{(Recall that } a \neq 0.\text{)}$$

$$x^2 + \frac{b}{a}x + \frac{c}{a} = 0$$

$$x^2 + \frac{b}{a}x = -\frac{c}{a}$$

$$x^2 + \frac{b}{a}x + \left(\frac{b}{2a}\right)^2 = -\frac{c}{a} + \left(\frac{b}{2a}\right)^2$$

$$\left(x + \frac{b}{2a}\right)^2 = \frac{-4ac + b^2}{4a^2}$$

$$x + \frac{b}{2a} = \pm\sqrt{\frac{b^2 - 4ac}{4a^2}} = \pm\frac{\sqrt{b^2 - 4ac}}{2a}$$

$$x = -\frac{b}{2a} \pm \frac{\sqrt{b^2 - 4ac}}{2a} = \frac{-b \pm \sqrt{b^2 - 4ac}}{2a}$$

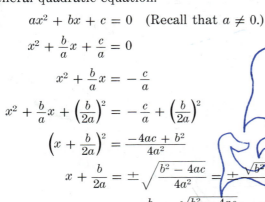

THE QUADRATIC FORMULA

The solutions of the quadratic equation

$$ax^2 + bx + c = 0 \quad (a \neq 0)$$

are given by the formula

$$x = \frac{-b \pm \sqrt{b^2 - 4ac}}{2a}.$$

EXAMPLE 1 Solve $3x^2 + 2x - 4 = 0$.

SOLUTION For the equation $3x^2 + 2x - 4 = 0$, you see that $a = 3$, $b = 2$, and $c = -4$. Substituting into the quadratic formula, you have:

$$x = \frac{-2 \pm \sqrt{2^2 - 4 \cdot 3 \cdot (-4)}}{2 \cdot 3}$$

$$= \frac{-2 \pm \sqrt{52}}{6} = \frac{-2 \pm 2\sqrt{13}}{6} = \frac{-1 \pm \sqrt{13}}{3}$$

$\therefore$ the solution set is $\left\{\dfrac{-1 + \sqrt{13}}{3}, \dfrac{-1 - \sqrt{13}}{3}\right\}$. ***Answer***

EXAMPLE 2 Solve $2t^2 - 3t + 5 = 0$ over the complex numbers.

SOLUTION You can see that $a = 2, b = -3,$ and $c = 5.$ Substitute in the quadratic formula:

$$t = \frac{-(-3) \pm \sqrt{(-3)^2 - 4(2)(5)}}{2(2)}$$

$$= \frac{3 \pm \sqrt{9 - 40}}{4} = \frac{3 \pm \sqrt{-31}}{4}$$

$$= \frac{3 \pm i\sqrt{31}}{4}$$

$$= \frac{3}{4} \pm \frac{\sqrt{31}}{4}i$$

Checking these roots is left for you.

$\therefore$ the solution set is $\left\{ \frac{3}{4} + \frac{\sqrt{31}}{4}i, \frac{3}{4} - \frac{\sqrt{31}}{4}i \right\}.$ *Answer*

EXAMPLE 3 A rug is to cover two thirds of the floor area of an 8 m by 12 m room. The uncovered part of the floor is to form a strip of uniform width around the rug. Find the width of this strip.

SOLUTION

1. Let x = width of strip in meters. Then the dimensions of the rug are $8 - 2x$ by $12 - 2x$.

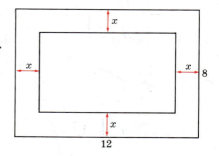

2.

The rug area	is two thirds of	the floor area.
$(8 - 2x)(12 - 2x)$	$= \frac{2}{3} \times$	(8×12)

3. $2(4 - x) \cdot 2(6 - x) = 64$

$\quad (4 - x)(6 - x) = 16$

$\quad 24 - 10x + x^2 = 16$

$\quad x^2 - 10x + 8 = 0$

$$x = \frac{-(-10) \pm \sqrt{(-10)^2 - 4 \cdot 1 \cdot 8}}{2 \cdot 1} = \frac{10 \pm \sqrt{68}}{2}$$

$$= \frac{10 \pm 2\sqrt{17}}{2} = 5 \pm \sqrt{17}$$

$\therefore$ the width of the strip is $(5 - \sqrt{17})$ m, which is approximately equal to 0.877 m.

Answer

Check: The dimensions of the rug are $8 - 2(5 - \sqrt{17})$ m by $12 - 2(5 - \sqrt{17})$ m, or $-2 + 2\sqrt{17}$ m by $2 + 2\sqrt{17}$ m. The rug area is $(-2 + 2\sqrt{17})(2 + 2\sqrt{17})$, or 64 m². The area of the room is 8×12, or 96 m². Thus, the solution is correct because $\frac{2}{3}(96) = 64.$ (Reject the root $5 + \sqrt{17}$ because the room is 8 m wide, so that the width of the strip must be less than 4 m.)

Oral Exercises

Read each equation in the form $ax^2 + bx + c = 0$ with the value of a positive.

1. $x^2 + 2x = 3$ **2.** $x^2 - 4 = 2x$ **3.** $1 - x^2 = 4x$

4. $4 - 4x = 3x^2$ **5.** $x(x - 2) = 4$ **6.** $(x + 1)(x - 1) = 2x$

Give the values that you would use for a, b, and c in the quadratic formula.

7. $x^2 + x - \sqrt{2} = 0$ **8.** $3x^2 - 3 + 2x = 0$ **9.** $4 - x + 2x^2 = 0$

10. $3x^2 = 10$ **11.** $2x^2 - 5x = 0$ **12.** $x(2x - 1) = 6$

Written Exercises

Solve each equation.

A **1.** $x^2 + 6x + 4 = 0$ **2.** $x^2 - 2x + 5 = 0$ **3.** $t^2 + 4t + 8 = 0$

4. $u^2 + 6u + 6 = 0$ **5.** $x^2 + x + 1 = 0$ **6.** $x^2 + 2x + 3 = 0$

7. $z^2 + 6z = 5$ **8.** $t^2 + 7 = 4t$ **9.** $2x^2 + 8x + 5 = 0$

10. $3v^2 - 6v - 4 = 0$ **11.** $5t^2 + 12t + 8 = 0$ **12.** $3t^2 + 2t + 1 = 0$

13. $16 - 15x^2 = 14x$ **14.** $8x^2 = 14x + 15$ **15.** $\dfrac{t^2}{2} + \dfrac{t}{5} + 1 = 0$

16. $\dfrac{x^2}{4} - 1 = \dfrac{x}{3}$ **17.** $\dfrac{u^2}{5} - \dfrac{u}{3} = \dfrac{2}{15}$ **18.** $x^2 = \dfrac{1}{6} - \dfrac{x}{6}$

19. $2t(t + 2) = 3(1 - t)$ **20.** $3x(x - 4) = 5(2 - x)$

21. $\dfrac{1}{x + 2} + \dfrac{1}{x - 2} = 1$ **22.** $\dfrac{1}{t + 2} + \dfrac{1}{t + 4} = 1$

23. $\dfrac{2}{x + 3} + \dfrac{1}{x - 3} = 2$ **24.** $\dfrac{2x - 1}{x - 1} - \dfrac{x}{x + 2} = \dfrac{1}{x^2 + x - 2}$

Solve for x in terms of a, b, and c.

B **25.** $bx^2 + cx + a = 0$ **26.** $cx^2 + ax + b = 0$

Solve.

27. $x^2 - x\sqrt{2} - 1 = 0$ **28.** $x^2 - x\sqrt{5} - 1 = 0$

29. $t^2 - 2t\sqrt{2} + 1 = 0$ **30.** $u^2 + 2u\sqrt{3} - 3 = 0$

31. $\sqrt{2}\,x^2 + 5x + 2\sqrt{2} = 0$ **32.** $\sqrt{3}\,x^2 - 2x + 2\sqrt{3} = 0$

33. $z^2 + iz + 2 = 0$ **34.** $z^2 + 2iz - 1 = 0$

35. $z^2 - (3 + 2i)z + (1 + 3i) = 0$ **36.** $iz^2 + (2 - 3i)z - (3 + i) = 0$

37. $\dfrac{2w + i}{w - i} = \dfrac{3w + 4i}{w + 3i}$ **38.** $\dfrac{1}{2z + i} + \dfrac{1}{2z - i} = \dfrac{4}{z + 2i}$

In Exercises 39–42:
a. Solve for u in terms of v, assuming that $v > 0$.
b. Solve for v in terms of u.

SAMPLE $2u^2 - 2uv - v^2 = 0$

SOLUTION   **a.** $u = \dfrac{2v \pm \sqrt{4v^2 + 8v^2}}{4}$

$$= \dfrac{2v \pm \sqrt{12v^2}}{4}$$

$$= \dfrac{2v \pm 2v\sqrt{3}}{4} = \dfrac{1 \pm \sqrt{3}}{2}\,v \quad \textbf{\textit{Answer}}$$

b. From part (a): $v = \dfrac{2}{1 \pm \sqrt{3}}\,u = (-1 \pm \sqrt{3})\,u \quad \textbf{\textit{Answer}}$

C 39. $u^2 - 4uv - v^2 = 0$ **40.** $u^2 - 4uv + v^2 = 0$
41. $2u^2 + 5uv + 2v^2 = 0$ **42.** $u^2 - 4uv + 2v^2 = 0$

43. Show that if $c \neq 0$, then the roots of $ax^2 + bx + c = 0$ are given by

$$x = \dfrac{2c}{-b \pm \sqrt{b^2 - 4ac}}.$$

(*Hint:* Use the quadratic formula and rationalize the numerator.)

Problems

Solve each problem. For radicals in answers, simplify the radicals and give decimal approximations.

A 1. If 400 m of fencing encloses a rectangular field having area 8000 m², find the dimensions of the field.

2. The area of the right trapezoid pictured is 32. Find the value of x.

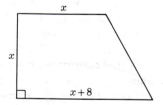

3. When mineral deposits formed a coating 3 mm thick on the inside of a pipe, its cross-sectional area was reduced by 50%. What was the original inside diameter of the pipe?

4. On a 24 cm by 16 cm page the printed part is surrounded by a uniform margin. How wide is the margin if the printed part has area 160 cm²?

5. A large pipe can fill a tank in 2 h less time than a smaller pipe, and the two together can fill the tank in 2 h. How long would it take each pipe alone to fill the tank?

6. The volumes of two spheres differ by 336π cm³, and the radii of the spheres differ by 6 cm. Find the radii. $(V = \tfrac{4}{3}\pi r^3)$

B 7. A lidless box is made from a square piece of metal by cutting 3 cm squares from the corners and bending up the sides. If the volume of the box is 60 cm³, find the dimensions of the square piece of metal.

8. A hydrofoil made a round trip of 180 km in 5 h. Because of adverse winds, the speed on the return leg was 15 km/h less than the average speed going out. Find the two speeds.

9. A gutter with open top and rectangular cross section is formed from a long sheet of metal 30 cm wide by bending up equal strips along the edges. How deep is the gutter if its cross-sectional area is 50 cm²?

10. Martha Nichols collected $270 in weekly rentals over a period of time for the smaller of two apartments and $320 for the larger. The larger apartment rented for $10 per week more than the other, but it was vacant for 1 week during the period. What was the weekly rental for each apartment?

C 11. In a *golden rectangle* the ratio of the length to the width equals the ratio of the length plus width to the length. Find the value of this *golden ratio*. (Since the Greek classical period, in the fifth century B.C., such rectangles have been considered the most pleasing; hence the name.)

ꜰistorical ꞑote Irrational Numbers

Irrational numbers were found to exist by members of the School of Pythagoras in the fifth century B.C. This school, or brotherhood, was established primarily for the study of mathematics. The Greeks who were members of the school considered the study of numbers to be of basic importance in the understanding of life's great mysteries. Some of the Pythagoreans tried to find the geometric mean of two numbers that they considered to be sacred, 1 and 2. In doing so, they found that the ratio of a side and a diagonal of a square could not be expressed in terms of rational numbers. As shown in the diagram, a diagonal of a square with side 1 is $\sqrt{2}$, an irrational number.

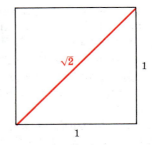

You know, of course, that the real numbers consist of rational and irrational numbers. Interestingly enough, it can be proved that there are more irrational numbers than rational ones.

7-3 Equations in Quadratic Form

OBJECTIVE   To recognize and solve equations in quadratic form.

The equation

$$x^4 - 13x^2 + 36 = 0$$

is not a quadratic equation, but it can be written in the form

$$(x^2)^2 - 13(x^2) + 36 = 0.$$

For this reason, it is said to be *quadratic in x^2*. Solve first for x^2 and then solve the resulting equations for x:

$$x^4 - 13x^2 + 36 = 0$$
$$(x^2 - 4)(x^2 - 9) = 0$$
$$x^2 = 4 \qquad \text{or} \qquad x^2 = 9$$
$$x = \pm 2 \qquad\qquad x = \pm 3$$

Thus, the roots of the given equation are 2, -2, 3, and -3.

In general, an equation is in **quadratic form** if it can be written as

$$a[f(x)]^2 + b[f(x)] + c = 0,$$

where $a \neq 0$ and $f(x)$ is some expression in x. You can solve such an equation for $f(x)$, and sometimes the resulting equations can be solved for x. It often is helpful to start by making a substitution of the form $z = f(x)$.

EXAMPLE 1   Solve $3x + 2\sqrt{3x} - 8 = 0$ over the real numbers.

SOLUTION   Let $z = \sqrt{3x}$; then $z^2 = 3x$, and the equation becomes quadratic in $\sqrt{3x}$.

$$z^2 + 2z - 8 = 0$$
$$(z + 4)(z - 2) = 0$$
$$z = -4 \qquad \text{or} \qquad z = 2$$
$$\sqrt{3x} = -4 \qquad\qquad \sqrt{3x} = 2$$
$$\text{no solution} \qquad\qquad 3x = 4$$
$$x = \tfrac{4}{3}$$

$$\text{Check: } 3 \cdot \tfrac{4}{3} + 2\sqrt{3 \cdot \tfrac{4}{3}} - 8 \overset{?}{=} 0$$
$$4 + 2\sqrt{4} - 8 \overset{?}{=} 0$$
$$4 + 4 - 8 = 0 \quad \checkmark$$

$\therefore$ the only solution is $\tfrac{4}{3}$. ***Answer***

EXAMPLE 2   Solve $x^4 + x^2 - 12 = 0$ over the complex numbers.

SOLUTION

$$x^4 + x^2 - 12 = 0$$
$$(x^2 - 3)(x^2 + 4) = 0$$

$$x^2 - 3 = 0 \qquad \text{or} \qquad x^2 + 4 = 0$$
$$x = \pm\sqrt{3} \qquad\qquad x^2 = -4$$
$$x = \pm 2i$$

The check is left for you.

$\therefore$ the solution set is $\{-\sqrt{3}, \sqrt{3}, -2i, 2i\}$.   *Answer*

Oral Exercises

State the variable expression in which the given equation is quadratic.

1. $u^4 - 5u^2 + 4 = 0$

2. $x - 3\sqrt{x} + 2 = 0$

3. $4x^6 - 3x^3 - 1 = 0$

4. $3x^{-2} - 4x^{-1} + 1 = 0$

5. $t - 5\sqrt{t} + 6 = 0$

6. $\dfrac{9}{x^2} - \dfrac{8}{x} - 1 = 0$

7. $2t^{-2} + 3t^{-1} = 2$

8. $4x^4 - 37x^2 + 9 = 0$

9. $x^6 + 4x^3 + 3 = 0$

10. $(u^2 - 2)^2 - (u^2 - 2) - 2 = 0$

11. $\left(\dfrac{x+2}{x}\right)^2 - 2\left(\dfrac{x+2}{x}\right) - 3 = 0$

12. $2\left(\dfrac{1-t}{t}\right)^2 - \left(\dfrac{1-t}{t}\right) - 1 = 0$

Written Exercises

A 1–12. Solve the equations in Oral Exercises 1–12 over the real numbers.

Solve over the complex numbers.

13. $x^4 - 1 = 0$

14. $u^4 - 5u^2 - 36 = 0$

15. $m^5 - 11m^3 + 10m = 0$

16. $x^4 - 3x^2 - 10 = 0$

17. $w^8 - 17w^4 + 16 = 0$

18. $c^8 - 13c^4 + 36 = 0$

19. $2t + 3\sqrt{t} - 2 = 0$

20. $2t + 5\sqrt{t} + 3 = 0$

21. $\dfrac{2}{x} + \dfrac{1}{\sqrt{x}} = 1$

22. $\dfrac{3}{n} - \dfrac{7}{\sqrt{n}} = 6$

B 23. $(x^2 - 2x)^2 - 2(x^2 - 2x) - 3 = 0$

24. $(1 + 2u^2)^2 + 6(1 + 2u^2) - 7 = 0$

25. $\left(\dfrac{1}{x-1}\right)^2 - \dfrac{1}{x-1} = 2$

26. $\dfrac{6}{(x-1)^2} = \dfrac{1}{x-1} + 1$

C 27. $\left(\dfrac{t^2-6}{t}\right)^2 - 4\left(\dfrac{t^2-6}{t}\right) = 5$

28. $\left(\dfrac{x-1}{x+3}\right)^2 = 4\left(\dfrac{1-x}{x+3}\right) - 3$

29. $\sqrt{x-2} + \sqrt{\sqrt{x-2}} = 2$

30. $\sqrt{t+3} - 6\sqrt[4]{t+3} + 5 = 0$

Self-Test 1

Solve by completing the square.

1. $x^2 - 4x = 2$

2. $t^2 + 5t - 5 = 0$

Obj. 7-1, p. 249

Solve by using the quadratic formula.

3. $r^2 - r = 1$

4. $4z^2 - 8z + 13 = 0$

Obj. 7-2, p. 253

5. Find the dimensions of a rectangle whose perimeter is 8 cm and whose area is 2 cm².

6. Solve $(x^2 - 4)^2 + 2(x^2 - 4) = 3$.

Obj. 7-3, p. 258

Check your answers with those at the back of the book.

Historical Note Solving Equations

People have been able to solve linear and quadratic equations for a very long time. As early as 1800–1600 B.C., the Babylonians solved equations of the form $x + x^{-1} = a$. (Do you see that this is just another way of writing $x^2 - ax + 1 = 0$?)

Methods for solving quadratic equations have varied. For example, the Egyptians solved them arithmetically, the Greeks, geometrically, and the Hindus, algebraically. Generally, negative and irrational numbers and zero were not considered legitimate solutions.

Various people have been given credit for discovering solutions of equations of higher degree. The Italian mathematician Del Ferro is said to have solved a cubic equation around A.D. 1510. Later in the same century another Italian, Ludovico Ferrari, solved a fourth-degree equation by reducing it to a cubic. Another 300 years later, Ruffini, a third Italian, proved that in general the roots of equations of the fifth degree and higher cannot be expressed using radicals and the coefficients of the equations. Note that more than 3000 years separate these solutions from the Babylonian achievements!

7-4 *The Discriminant*

OBJECTIVE To determine the nature of the roots of a quadratic equation by using its discriminant.

Using the quadratic formula, you can write the roots of the quadratic equation

$$ax^2 + bx + c = 0$$

in the form

$$r_1 = \frac{-b + \sqrt{D}}{2a} \quad \text{and} \quad r_2 = \frac{-b - \sqrt{D}}{2a},$$

where

$$D = b^2 - 4ac.$$

The following examples illustrate how D is related to the nature of the roots.

EXAMPLE 1 $x^2 + 6x + 7 = 0$

$D = 6^2 - 4 \cdot 1 \cdot 7 = 36 - 28 = 8 \longleftarrow$ D is positive.

$r_1 = \dfrac{-6 + \sqrt{8}}{2} = -3 + \sqrt{2}$

$r_2 = \dfrac{-6 - \sqrt{8}}{2} = -3 - \sqrt{2}$ $\longleftarrow$ The roots are real and unequal.

EXAMPLE 2 $3x^2 - 4\sqrt{3}\,x + 4 = 0$

$D = \left(-4\sqrt{3}\right)^2 - 4 \cdot 3 \cdot 4 = 48 - 48 = 0 \longleftarrow$ D is zero.

$r_1 = \dfrac{-\left(-4\sqrt{3}\right) + \sqrt{0}}{2 \cdot 3} = \dfrac{2\sqrt{3}}{3}$

$r_2 = \dfrac{-\left(-4\sqrt{3}\right) - \sqrt{0}}{2 \cdot 3} = \dfrac{2\sqrt{3}}{3}$ $\longleftarrow$ There is a double root, which is real.

EXAMPLE 3 $x^2 - 2x + 5 = 0$

$D = (-2)^2 - 4 \cdot 1 \cdot 5 = 4 - 20 = -16 \longleftarrow$ D is negative.

$r_1 = \dfrac{-(-2) + \sqrt{-16}}{2} = 1 + 2i$ $\longleftarrow$ The roots are imaginary conjugates.

$r_2 = \dfrac{-(-2) - \sqrt{-16}}{2} = 1 - 2i$

Because the value of $D = b^2 - 4ac$ distinguishes among the three cases, D is called the **discriminant** of the quadratic equation, and also of the quadratic function defined by $f(x) = ax^2 + bx + c$.

The following general result can be stated:

Let $ax^2 + bx + c = 0$ be a quadratic equation with *real* coefficients.

1. If $b^2 - 4ac > 0$, there are two real roots.
2. If $b^2 - 4ac = 0$, there is a real, double root.
3. If $b^2 - 4ac < 0$, there are two imaginary, conjugate roots.

The discriminant also enables you to tell whether the roots of a quadratic equation with *integral* coefficients are rational numbers. If a, b, and c are integers, then the numbers

$$\frac{-b + \sqrt{b^2 - 4ac}}{2a} \quad \text{and} \quad \frac{-b - \sqrt{b^2 - 4ac}}{2a}$$

are rational if and only if $\sqrt{b^2 - 4ac}$ is rational. The radical expression $\sqrt{b^2 - 4ac}$ is rational if and only if $b^2 - 4ac$ is the square of an integer (Section 6-5). Therefore, the following general result can be stated:

A quadratic equation with *integral* coefficients has rational roots if and only if its discriminant is the square of an integer.

EXAMPLE 4 Without solving the equation, determine the nature of its roots.

a. $5x^2 - 8x + 4 = 0$

b. $x^2 + \frac{9}{2}x + 2 = 0$

c. $x^2 + 2\sqrt{3}\,x - 1 = 0$

SOLUTION

a. $D = (-8)^2 - 4 \cdot 5 \cdot 4 = 64 - 80 = -16 < 0$.
The roots are imaginary conjugates. ***Answer***

b. The given equation is equivalent to $2x^2 + 9x + 4 = 0$, which has integral coefficients.
$D = 9^2 - 4 \cdot 2 \cdot 4 = 81 - 32 = 49 = 7^2 > 0$
The roots are real, unequal, and rational. ***Answer***

c. $D = (2\sqrt{3})^2 - 4 \cdot 1 \cdot (-1) = 12 + 4 = 16 > 0$. The roots are real and unequal. ***Answer***

(Note that even though $16 = 4^2$, you cannot conclude that the roots are rational, because the equation does not have *integral* coefficients. Indeed, the roots are the irrational numbers $-\sqrt{3} + 2$ and $-\sqrt{3} - 2$, as you can easily verify.)

Oral Exercises

Determine the nature of the roots of each equation.

1. $x^2 + 6x + 6 = 0$ **2.** $x^2 + 4x + 6 = 0$ **3.** $t^2 - 3t - 4 = 0$
4. $w^2 + 9 = 6w$ **5.** $u^2 + \sqrt{10}u + 2 = 0$ **6.** $3c^2 - 7c + 5 = 0$

Written Exercises

Determine the nature of the roots of each equation.

A **1.** $x^2 - 5x + 3 = 0$ **2.** $u^2 - 3u = 5$ **3.** $t^2 - 3t + 5 = 0$

4. $4m^2 - 12m + 9 = 0$ **5.** $t^2 - t + \frac{5}{4} = 0$ **6.** $3x^2 - 7x + 4 = 0$

7. $x^2 + \frac{7}{3}x = 2$ **8.** $\frac{1}{4}y^2 + 1 = y$ **9.** $2s^2 + 7s + 5 = 0$

10. $7u^2 + 2 = 2\sqrt{14}u$ **11.** $\sqrt{5}x^2 - 6x + \sqrt{5} = 0$ **12.** $\sqrt{3}x^2 - 4\sqrt{3} = 0$

Find the real values of k for which the given equation will have roots of the specified nature.

SAMPLE $3x^2 - 4x + k = 0$; two real roots

SOLUTION There are two real roots if and only if the discriminant, D, is positive.

$$D = b^2 - 4ac = (-4)^2 - 4 \cdot 3 \cdot k = 16 - 12k$$

Thus for $16 - 12k > 0$, or $k < \frac{4}{3}$, there are two real roots. ***Answer***

B **13.** $3x^2 + 6x + k = 0$; roots are imaginary conjugates.
14. $2x^2 - 3x + k = 0$; two real roots.
15. $3z^2 - kz + 4 = 0$; a double root.
16. $kw^2 + 8w = 4$; roots are imaginary conjugates.
17. $2x^2 - 3x + (k + 1) = 0$; two real roots.
18. $kt^2 + 6t + k = 0$; a double root.

C **19.** $x^2 + kx + (k + 3) = 0$; a double root.
20. $3x^2 + (k + 2)x + 3 = 0$; a double root.

If r is a real constant, show that the equation has no real roots.

21. $\dfrac{1}{x + r} = \dfrac{1}{x} + \dfrac{1}{r}$ **22.** $\dfrac{1}{x - r} = \dfrac{1}{x} - \dfrac{1}{r}$

In Exercises 23 and 24, h and k are integers. Show that the roots of the equations are rational.

23. $x^2 + hx + h - 1 = 0$ **24.** $hx^2 + (h + k)x + k = 0$

7-5 *Relationships between Roots and Coefficients*

OBJECTIVE **To learn how the roots and coefficients of a quadratic equation are related.**

Recall that the roots of the quadratic equation

$$ax^2 + bx + c = 0$$

are given by

$$r_1 = \frac{-b + \sqrt{D}}{2a} \quad \text{and} \quad r_2 = \frac{-b - \sqrt{D}}{2a}$$

where $D = b^2 - 4ac$. Thus,

$$r_1 + r_2 = \frac{-b + \sqrt{D}}{2a} + \frac{-b - \sqrt{D}}{2a} = \frac{-2b}{2a} = -\frac{b}{a},$$

and

$$r_1 r_2 = \frac{-b + \sqrt{D}}{2a} \cdot \frac{-b - \sqrt{D}}{2a} = \frac{b^2 - D}{4a^2} = \frac{b^2 - (b^2 - 4ac)}{4a^2} = \frac{c}{a}.$$

The discussion above proves the "only if" part of the following theorem (for a proof of the "if" part, see Exercise 33):

THEOREM

The numbers r_1 and r_2 are the roots of the quadratic equation

$$ax^2 + bx + c = 0 \quad (a \neq 0)$$

if and only if

$$r_1 + r_2 = -\frac{b}{a} \quad \text{and} \quad r_1 r_2 = \frac{c}{a}.$$

EXAMPLE 1 Show that $\dfrac{5 + \sqrt{11}}{2}$ and $\dfrac{5 - \sqrt{11}}{2}$ are the roots of $2x^2 - 10x + 7 = 0$.

SOLUTION You have three methods to show this fact.

1. Solve the equation using the quadratic formula to get $\dfrac{5 \pm \sqrt{11}}{2}$ for roots.

2. Substitute $\dfrac{5 \pm \sqrt{11}}{2}$ for x, and show that each value makes the equation true.

3. Use the theorem.

Method 3 is used here. It is generally considered the easiest method. In $2x^2 - 10x + 7$, $a = 2$, $b = -10$ and $c = 7$. Thus,

$$-\frac{b}{a} = -\frac{-10}{5} = 2 \quad \text{and} \quad \frac{c}{a} = \frac{7}{2}.$$

It will be sufficient to show that the sum of the prospective roots is 2 and that their product is $\frac{7}{2}$. Letting

$$r_1 = \frac{5 + \sqrt{11}}{2} \quad \text{and} \quad r_2 = \frac{5 - \sqrt{11}}{2}, \text{ you have}$$

$$r_1 + r_2 = \frac{5 + \sqrt{11}}{2} + \frac{5 - \sqrt{11}}{2} = \frac{10}{2} = 5$$

$$r_1 r_2 = \frac{5 + \sqrt{11}}{2} \cdot \frac{5 - \sqrt{11}}{2} = \frac{25 - 11}{4} = \frac{14}{4} = \frac{7}{2}$$

$\therefore$ according to the theorem, $\dfrac{5 + \sqrt{11}}{2}$ and $\dfrac{5 - \sqrt{11}}{2}$ are the roots. *Answer*

EXAMPLE 2 Find a quadratic equation whose roots are $\dfrac{3 + i}{2}$ and $\dfrac{3 - i}{2}$.

SOLUTION Let the required equation be $ax^2 + bx + c = 0$.

$$-\frac{b}{a} = \frac{3 + i}{2} + \frac{3 - i}{2} = \frac{6}{2} = 3, \quad \text{or} \quad b = -3a$$

$$\frac{c}{a} = \frac{3 + i}{2} \cdot \frac{3 - i}{2} = \frac{9 - i^2}{4} = \frac{10}{4} = \frac{5}{2}, \quad \text{or} \quad c = \frac{5}{2}a.$$

Any combination of values of a, b, and c that satisfies these conditions determines an equation having the given roots. To avoid fractions, choose $a = 2$, so that $b = -6$ and $c = 5$.

$\therefore$ an equation with the given roots is $2x^2 - 6x + 5 = 0$. *Answer*

In problems like Example 2, you may decide to let $a = 1$. Then $r_1 + r_2 = -b$, and $r_1 r_2 = c$. If you had done so in Example 2, you would have

$$-b = r_1 + r_2 = 3; \; b = -3$$

$$c = r_1 r_2 = \frac{5}{2}$$

Thus, an equation having the required roots is

$$x^2 - 3x + \frac{5}{2} = 0,$$

which is equivalent to the equation given in the solution above.

Oral Exercises

Give the sum and product of the roots of each equation.

1. $x^2 - 3x + 6 = 0$ **2.** $x^2 + 4x - 2 = 0$ **3.** $t^2 + t + 2 = 0$

4. $u^2 - u + 5 = 0$ **5.** $2x^2 - 6x + 1 = 0$ **6.** $2z^2 + 2 = 3z$

Find a quadratic equation whose roots have the given sum and product.

7. $r_1 + r_2 = 3,\ r_1 r_2 = 4$ **8.** $r_1 + r_2 = -2,\ r_1 r_2 = -2$

9. $r_1 + r_2 = 0,\ r_1 r_2 = 6$ **10.** $r_1 + r_2 = -4,\ r_1 r_2 = 0$

Written Exercises

Find a quadratic equation with *integral coefficients* having the given roots.

A **1.** $-3, 1$ **2.** $-\sqrt{5}, \sqrt{5}$ **3.** $-2, \dfrac{7}{2}$

4. $\dfrac{3}{2}, -1$ **5.** $\dfrac{3}{2}, -\dfrac{1}{2}$ **6.** $\dfrac{2}{3}, \dfrac{4}{3}$

7. $-7, 0$ **8.** $0, \dfrac{4}{5}$ **9.** $2 + \sqrt{2}, 2 - \sqrt{2}$

10. $2 + \sqrt{3}, 2 - \sqrt{3}$ **11.** $\dfrac{3 + \sqrt{5}}{2}, \dfrac{3 - \sqrt{5}}{2}$ **12.** $\dfrac{\sqrt{5}}{3}, -\dfrac{\sqrt{5}}{3}$

13. $3 + i, 3 - i$ **14.** $3 + 4i, 3 - 4i$

15. $i\sqrt{5}, -i\sqrt{5}$ **16.** $-2 + i\sqrt{2}, -2 - i\sqrt{2}$

17. $\dfrac{1 - i\sqrt{2}}{3}, \dfrac{1 + i\sqrt{2}}{3}$ **18.** $\dfrac{2 + i\sqrt{3}}{2}, \dfrac{2 - i\sqrt{3}}{2}$

Find a quadratic equation having the given roots.

B **19.** $\sqrt{3} + \sqrt{2}, \sqrt{3} - \sqrt{2}$ **20.** $\sqrt{5} - 2, \sqrt{5} + 2$

21. $1 + \sqrt[4]{2}, 1 - \sqrt[4]{2}$ **22.** $1 + \sqrt[3]{2} + \sqrt[3]{4}, 1 - \sqrt[3]{2}$

23. If 2 is one root of $x^2 - 5x + c = 0$, find the other root and the value of c.

24. If $\dfrac{3}{2}$ is one root of $4x^2 + bx - 3 = 0$, find the other root and the value of b.

25. If $1 + i$ is one root of $x^2 + bx + 2i = 0$, find the other root and the value of b.

26. If $2 - \sqrt{3}$ is one root of $3x^2 - 12x + c = 0$, find the other root and the value of c.

27. If the difference of the roots of $2x^2 - 6x + c = 0$ is 5, find the roots and the value of c.

28. If $2x^2 + 6ix + c = 0$ has a double root, find the root and the value of c.

C 29. Show that if both roots of $x^2 + bx + c = 0$ are real, then both b and c are real. Is the converse of this statement true?

30. Show that if both roots of $x^2 + bx + c = 0$ are rational, then both b and c are rational. Is the converse of this statement true?

31. Show that the roots of $ax^2 + bx + c = 0$ are reciprocals of each other if and only if $a = c$.

32. Show that the sum of the reciprocals of the roots of $ax^2 + bx + c = 0$ is $-\dfrac{b}{c}$.

33. Prove: If $p + q = -\dfrac{b}{a}$ and $pq = \dfrac{c}{a}$, then p and q are the roots of $ax^2 + bx + c = 0$. (*Hint*: Eliminate q from the given equations and show that $ap^2 + bp + c = 0$ and $aq^2 + bq + c = 0$.)

34. Show that the sum of the squares of the roots of $ax^2 + bx + c = 0$ is $\dfrac{b^2 - 2ac}{a^2}$.

$$r_1 + r_2 = -b/A$$
$$r_1 r_2 = c/A$$

Self-Test 2

VOCABULARY   discriminant (p. 262)

Without solving the equation, determine the nature of its roots.

1. $2x^2 - 6x + 5 = 0$ **2.** $7t^2 - 9t + 2 = 0$ Obj. 7-4, p. 261

3. Find all real values of k for which $3z^2 - 4z + k = 0$ has imaginary roots.

Give the sum and product of the roots.

4. $6x^2 - 3x - 2 = 0$ **5.** $u^2 - 4 = 3u$ Obj. 7-5, p. 264

6. Find a quadratic equation having the roots $-2 + i\sqrt{3}$ and $-2 - i\sqrt{3}$.

Check your answers with those at the back of the book.

QUADRATIC FUNCTIONS AND THEIR GRAPHS

7-6 *Graphing* $y = a(x - h)^2 + k$

OBJECTIVE To graph parabolas with equations of the form $y = a(x - h)^2 + k$, and to find the vertices and axes of symmetry.

As a simple example of a nonlinear equation in two variables, consider the equation

$$y = x^2.$$

To graph the equation, first construct a table of pairs of coordinates for x and y that satisfy the equation. Then plot the graph of each pair of coordinates as shown in Figure 7-1. If you plotted more points, you would see that they all lie on the smooth curve shown in Figure 7-2. This curve is the graph of $y = x^2$.

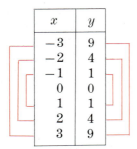

x	y
-3	9
-2	4
-1	1
0	0
1	1
2	4
3	9

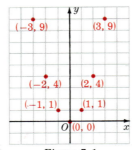

Figure 7-1

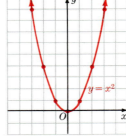

Figure 7-2

The graph of $y = x^2$ is called a **parabola.** You will notice that each point (p, q) on the parabola has a "mirror image" in the y-axis, the point $(-p, q)$, which also lies on the parabola. This property can also be seen in the table; the coordinate pairs connected by red lines are the mirror images. Because of this property, the y-axis is called the **axis of symmetry,** or simply the **axis,** of the parabola. The **vertex** of a parabola is the point where the parabola crosses its axis. Thus, the origin is the vertex of the parabola $y = x^2$.

The graphs of several equations of the form $y = ax^2$ are shown in Figures 7-3, 7-4, and 7-5 on the next page.

Notice that the origin is the vertex of each of these parabolas, and the y-axis is the axis of symmetry. Notice, also, that the parabola $y = ax^2$ opens upward if $a > 0$ and downward if $a < 0$. The "flatness" of the parabola depends on the value of $|a|$. The smaller $|a|$ is, the "flatter" the parabola is.

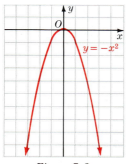

Figure 7-3

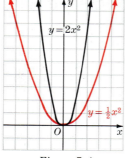

Figure 7-4

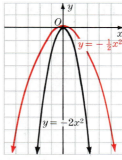

Figure 7-5

Now consider the graphs shown in Figures 7-6, 7-7, and 7-8 below. Each of these parabolas has an equation of the form $y = a(x - h)^2$. The graph of $y = \frac{1}{2}(x - 2)^2$ is the same as the graph of $y = \frac{1}{2}x^2$ shifted 2 units to the right, making the vertex $(2, 0)$ and the axis of symmetry the vertical line $x = 2$. The graph of $y = \frac{1}{2}(x + 1)^2$ is the same as the graph of $y = \frac{1}{2}x^2$ shifted 1 unit to the *left*, making the vertex $(-1, 0)$ and the axis the vertical line $x = -1$.

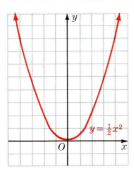

Figure 7-6

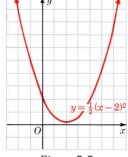

Figure 7-7

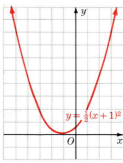

Figure 7-8

In general, the parabola $y = a(x - h)^2$ is the same as the parabola $y = ax^2$ shifted *horizontally* by $|h|$ units; the shift is to the right when $h > 0$ and to the left when $h < 0$.

The graphs of the equations $y = \frac{1}{2}x^2 + 3$ and $y = \frac{1}{2}x^2 - 2$ are shown in Figure 7-9. Each of these parabolas has an equation of the form $y = ax^2 + k$. The graph of $y = \frac{1}{2}x^2 + 3$ is the same as the graph of $y = \frac{1}{2}x^2$ shifted 3 units *up*, making the vertex $(0, 3)$ and the axis the y-axis. The graph of $y = \frac{1}{2}x^2 - 2$ is the same as the graph of $y = \frac{1}{2}x^2$ shifted 2 units *down*, making the vertex $(0, -2)$ and the axis, again, the y-axis.

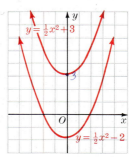

Figure 7-9

In general, the parabola $y = ax^2 + k$ is the same as the parabola $y = ax^2$ shifted *vertically* by $|k|$ units; the shift is up when $k > 0$ and down when $k < 0$.

All of these factors must be considered when graphing parabolas with the general equation

$$y = a(x - h)^2 + k.$$

If $a > 0$, the parabola opens upward; if $a < 0$, the parabola opens downward. The parabola is the same as $y = ax^2$, shifted horizontally by h units and vertically by k units. Thus, the vertex is (h, k) and the axis of symmetry is the vertical line $x = h$. The smaller $|a|$ is, the "flatter" the parabola is.

EXAMPLE 1   Graph $y = -(x + 2)^2 + 5$.

SOLUTION $a = -1$; the parabola opens downward.

$h = -2$, $k = 5$; the vertex is $(-2, 5)$; the axis is $x = -2$. Calculate a few coordinate pairs and use symmetry to find their mirror images. Plot the points and sketch the parabola.

x	y
0	1
-1	4
-2	5

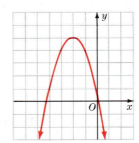

Figure 7-10

The graph is shown in Figure 7-10.   *Answer*

EXAMPLE 2   Find an equation of the parabola with vertical axis having vertex $(1, -2)$ and containing the point $(-1, 6)$.

SOLUTION   Substituting $(1, -2)$ for (h, k) in the general form, you obtain

$$y = a(x - 1)^2 - 2.$$

Since the parabola contains the point $(-1, 6)$, you can substitute -1 for x and 6 for y, and then solve for a.

$$6 = a(-1 - 1)^2 - 2$$
$$6 = 4a - 2$$
$$a = 2$$

$\therefore$ the equation is $y = 2(x - 1)^2 - 2$.   *Answer*

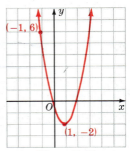

Figure 7-11

Sometimes it is important to find the *intercepts* of a parabola. The x-coordinate of a point where a parabola crosses the x-axis is called an **x-intercept** of the parabola. The y-coordinate of the point where a parabola crosses the y-axis is called the **y-intercept** of the parabola. A parabola may have no x-intercept, one x-intercept, or two x-intercepts. The x-intercepts of the parabola shown in Figure 7-11 are 0 and 2; the y-intercept is 0.

Oral Exercises

For each parabola, state **(a)** the coordinates of the vertex, **(b)** the equation of the axis, and **(c)** whether the parabola opens upward or downward.

1. $y = x^2 - 2$

2. $y = 2 + x^2$

3. $y = (x - 2)^2$

4. $y = (x + 2)^2$

5. $y = -2x^2$

6. $y = 2x^2 - 6$

7. $y = 2 - x^2$

8. $y = (x - 1)^2 + 1$

9. $y = 2(x - 1)^2 - 1$

10. $y = -2(x + 1)^2 + 2$

11. $y = 2 - \frac{1}{2}(x - 4)^2$

12. $y - 1 = x^2 - 2x$

Written Exercises

A **1–12.** Graph each equation in Oral Exercises 1–12.

Find an equation of the parabola with vertical axis, having the point V as vertex and containing the point P.

13. $V(0, 2);\ P(2, 0)$

14. $V(0, 0);\ P(2, -2)$

15. $V(2, 0);\ P(0, 2)$

16. $V(2, -2);\ P(0, 0)$

17. $V(4, 5);\ P(5, 3)$

18. $V(3, -2);\ P(1, 10)$

Find all values of a, h, or k for which the given parabola contains the given point.

19. $y = (x + 2)^2 + k;\ (-1, 3)$

20. $y = a(x - 3)^2 - 3;\ (1, 5)$

21. $y = a(x - 3)^2 + 6;\ (0, 0)$

22. $y = \frac{1}{2}(x + 1)^2 + k;\ (-3, 5)$

B **23.** $y = 3(x - h)^2 - 4;\ (3, 8)$

24. $y = \frac{1}{2}(x - h)^2 + 2;\ (1, 4)$

25. $y = \frac{1}{3}(x - h)^2 - 2;\ (2, 10)$

26. $y = (x - h)^2 + 3;\ (4, 1)$

Find all values for a and k for which the given parabola contains the given points.

27. $y = a(x - 1)^2 + k;\ (3, 11),\ (1, 3)$

28. $y = a(x + 3)^2 + k;\ (-5, 1),\ (1, 7)$

Find the x- and y-intercepts of the given parabola.

SAMPLE $y = -3(x - 2)^2 + 6$

SOLUTION   To find the y-intercept, set $x = 0$ and solve for y:
$$y = -3(0 - 2)^2 + 6 = -12 + 6 = -6$$
∴ the y-intercept is -6.   **Answer**

To find the x-intercepts, set $y = 0$ and solve for x:
$$0 = -3(x - 2)^2 + 6$$
$$-6 = -3(x - 2)^2$$
$$2 = (x - 2)^2$$
$$x - 2 = \pm\sqrt{2}$$
∴ the x-intercepts are $2 + \sqrt{2}$ and $2 - \sqrt{2}$.   **Answer**

29. $y = (x - 3)^2 - 1$ **30.** $y = -2(x + 1)^2 - 4$ **31.** $y = 2(x + 2)^2 + 8$

32. $y = \frac{1}{2}(x - 2)^2 - 8$ **33.** $y = -\frac{2}{3}(x - 1)^2 + 3$ **34.** $y = \frac{1}{4}(x + 1)^2 - 1$

C **35.** Find a condition involving a and k that is equivalent to the parabola $y = a(x - h)^2 + k$ having no x-intercepts.

36. Find a condition involving a, h, and k that is equivalent to the parabola $y = a(x - h)^2 + k$ passing through the origin.

37. Prove algebraically that if the point $(h + r, s)$ is on the parabola $y = a(x - h)^2 + k$, then so is the point $(h - r, s)$. What fact about the parabola is established by this proof?

38. Graph $y = |x^2 - 1|$.   **39.** Graph $y = |4 - x^2|$.

40. a. Using integral values of y from -3 to 3, make a table of values for the relation $x = y^2$.

b. Use the table in part (a) to draw the graph of $x = y^2$.

c. Is $x = y^2$ a function? Why?

41. Make a table of values for each relation below using the indicated values of y. Then draw the graph of the relation.

a. $x = -y^2$; -3 to 3 **b.** $x = y^2 + 2$; -3 to 3

c. $x = (y + 1)^2$; -4 to 2 **d.** $x = (y + 1)^2 + 2$; -4 to 2

e. $x = -\frac{1}{2}(y - 2)^2 + 3$; -1 to 5

42. State the coordinates of the vertex and the equation of the axis for each parabola in Exercise 41.

43. a. State the general equation that represents all parabolas that have a horizontal axis.

b. How many x-intercepts does a parabola with a horizontal axis have? How many y-intercepts?

7-7 Some Properties of Quadratic Functions

OBJECTIVE To draw the graphs and find the extreme values of quadratic functions.

A function f of the form

$$f(x) = ax^2 + bx + c \qquad (a \neq 0)$$

is called a **quadratic function.** By completing the square you can show
that the graph of any quadratic function is a parabola.

EXAMPLE 1 Let $f(x) = 2x^2 - 4x - 1$. Show that the graph of f is a parabola, find
the vertex, and graph the parabola.

SOLUTION The graph is the same as the graph of the equation $y = 2x^2 - 4x - 1$.

$$y = 2x^2 - 4x - 1$$
$$y = 2(x^2 - 2x \qquad) - 1$$
$$y = 2(x^2 - 2x + 1) - 1 - 2 \cdot 1$$
$$y = 2(x - 1)^2 - 3$$

The function is now expressed in the form

$$y = a(x - h)^2 + k.$$

$\therefore$ you see that the graph is a parabola opening
upward with vertex at $(1, -3)$ as shown in Figure 7-12. **Answer**

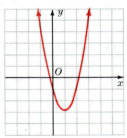

Figure 7-12

The method of Example 1 can be used to put the equation for any
quadratic function

$$y = ax^2 + bx + c$$

into the form

$$y = a\left(x + \frac{b}{2a}\right)^2 + \frac{4ac - b^2}{4a}.$$

You will be asked to do this in Exercise 18.
Comparing the latter equation with $y = a(x - h)^2 + k$, you see that
the graph of the quadratic function

$$f(x) = ax^2 + bx + c$$

is a parabola with vertex $\left(-\dfrac{b}{2a}, \dfrac{4ac - b^2}{4a}\right)$. You can verify by substitu-

tion that $\dfrac{4ac - b^2}{4a} = f\left(-\dfrac{b}{2a}\right)$. A convenient way to find the vertex (h, k)

is to use the equations $h = -\dfrac{b}{2a}$ and $k = f(h)$.

EXAMPLE 2 Graph the function $f(x) = 2 + 6x - x^2$, and find the vertex.

SOLUTION $a = -1$, and $b = 6$. Thus,

$$-\frac{b}{2a} = -\frac{6}{2(-1)} = 3.$$

The vertex is $(3, f(3))$, or $(3, 11)$, and the parabola is shown in Figure 7-13. ***Answer***

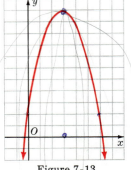

Figure 7-13

If $a > 0$, the graph of

$$f(x) = ax^2 + bx + c$$

is a parabola that opens upward; therefore, the vertex is at its lowest point. The y-coordinate of the vertex is the **minimum** value of f. Thus, in Example 1, the minimum value of f is -3. If $a < 0$, the parabola opens downward, and f has a **maximum** value. In Example 2, the maximum value of f is 11. In general, the **extreme value** of a quadratic function is the y-coordinate of its vertex and is given by $f\left(-\frac{b}{2a}\right)$.

EXAMPLE 3 If $g(x) = -4x^2 + 12x - 11$, find the extreme value of $g(x)$, and determine whether it is a maximum or a minimum.

SOLUTION $a = -4$, and $b = 12$. Since $a < 0$, g has a maximum value. Since $-\frac{b}{2a} = \frac{3}{2}$, this maximum value is $g\left(\frac{3}{2}\right)$.

$$g\left(\frac{3}{2}\right) = -4\left(\frac{3}{2}\right)^2 + 12\left(\frac{3}{2}\right) - 11 = -2$$

$\therefore$ the maximum value of $g(x)$ is -2. ***Answer***

EXAMPLE 4 A gutter with an open top and rectangular cross section is to be formed from a long sheet of metal 30 cm wide by bending up equal strips along the edges. In order to carry the most water, the cross-sectional area of the gutter must be a maximum. What should the dimensions of the gutter be?

SOLUTION

Step 1 The problem asks for the depth and width of the gutter for maximum cross-sectional area.

Step 2 Let x = depth in cm. Then $30 - 2x$ = width in cm.

Step 3 Express the cross-sectional area A as a function of depth:

$$A(x) = x(30 - 2x) = -2x^2 + 30x$$

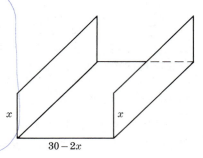

Step 4 This function has its maximum value when $x = -\dfrac{30}{2(-2)}$, or 7.5.

$$A(7.5) = 30 - 2(7.5) = 15$$

Step 5 (Checking the previous steps is left for you.) The gutter should be 7.5 cm deep and 15 cm wide. ***Answer***

Oral Exercises

Give the value of x for which the given function has its extreme value and state whether the extreme value is a maximum or a minimum.

1. $f(x) = 2 - x^2$

2. $f(x) = x^2 - 2$

3. $f(x) = 2x - x^2$

4. $f(x) = x^2 - 2x$

5. $f(x) = (2 - x)^2$

6. $f(x) = (x - 2)^2$

Written Exercises

Find the extreme value of the given function and determine whether it is a maximum or a minimum. Then graph the function.

A **1–6.** Use the functions in Oral Exercises 1–6.

7. $f(x) = x^2 - 4x + 3$

8. $f(x) = x^2 + 6x + 6$

9. $f(x) = 6x - x^2 - 2$

10. $f(x) = 1 + 6x - 3x^2$

11. $f(x) = \frac{1}{2}x^2 - 2x + 1$

12. $f(x) = \frac{1}{2}x^2 + 3x + \frac{1}{2}$

Express the given equation in the form $y = a(x - h)^2 + k$.

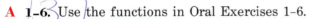

13. $y = x^2 - 4x - 5$

14. $y = (x^2 + 6x) + 1$

15. $y = 2x^2 + 6x - 2$

16. $y = 3x^2 - 6x + 5$

17. $y = x^2 + bx + c$

18. $y = ax^2 + bx + c$

Without drawing the graph of the given function, determine how many x-intercepts it has.

SAMPLE $f(x) = 2x^2 - 6x + 5$

SOLUTION Recall that the x-intercepts of the graph of f are the real roots of the equation $f(x) = 0$. The discriminant of $f(x)$ is

$$(-6)^2 - 4 \cdot 2 \cdot 5 = -4 < 0.$$

Therefore, the equation $f(x) = 0$ has no (real) roots, and the graph of f has no x-intercepts.

B **19.** $F(x) = 2x^2 - 8x + 9$

20. $g(x) = 3x^2 + 5x + 2$

21. $f(x) = 12x - 4x^2 - 9$

22. $G(x) = 9x - 3x^2 - 7$

23. $h(x) = 4x^2 - 7x + 3$

24. $f(x) = 24x - 9x^2 - 16$

Determine how many times the graph of the given function intersects the given horizontal line.

25. $f(x) = -x^2 - 6x - 10$; $y = 1$

26. $g(x) = x^2 - 6x + 7$; $y = -2$

27. $h(x) = 2x^2 + 20x + 51$; $y = 3$

28. $m(x) = 2x - 4 - \frac{1}{2}x^2$; $y = -1.8$

Find the domain and range of each function.

SAMPLE $f(x) = x^2 - 3x + 1$

SOLUTION   For every real number a, $f(a) = a^2 - 3a + 1$. Thus, $f(a)$ is a real number.

∴ the domain is all real numbers.   *Answer*

The minimum of f is $f\left(\frac{3}{2}\right) = -\frac{5}{4}$.

∴ the range is $\left\{y{:}y \geq -\frac{5}{4}\right\}$.   *Answer*

29. $f(x) = -x^2 + 6x - 11$ 30. $g(x) = 2x^2 - 3x + 1$

C 31. Let $f(x) = ax^2 + bx + c$. Prove that $f(-x) = f(x)$ for all x ($x \neq 0$) if and only if $b = 0$.

32. Prove that the graph of every quadratic function intersects every vertical line exactly once.

Problems

A 1. Find the dimensions of the rectangle of greatest area whose perimeter is 20 cm.

2. The sum of two numbers is 12. Find their greatest possible product.

Use this fact in Exercises 3 and 4: If an object is projected vertically upward with initial speed k m/s, its height in meters after t seconds is given by $h = kt - 4.9t^2$.

B 3. A rifle bullet is fired vertically upward with initial speed 490 m/s. How long does it take the bullet to reach its greatest height?

4. A baseball is thrown vertically upward with initial speed 24.5 m/s. How high does it go?

5. In a 120 V circuit having resistance of 16 Ω the available power in watts (W) when a current of I amperes is flowing is given by $W = 120I - 16I^2$. Find the maximum power that can be delivered in the circuit.

6. A rectangular field is to be enclosed by a fence and divided into two parts by another fence. Find the dimensions of the field of greatest area that can be enclosed and partitioned in this manner with 1200 m of fencing.

7. A parking lot is to be formed by fencing in a rectangular plot of land except for an entrance 12 m wide. Find the dimensions of the lot of greatest area if 300 m of fencing is to be used. (*Hint*: Solve for y in terms of x.)

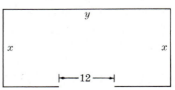

8. At what first-quadrant point on the parabola $y = 4 - x^2$ is the sum of the distances to the coordinate axes greatest?

9. A rectangle is to be inscribed in an isosceles triangle of height 8 and base 10, as shown. Find the greatest area of such a rectangle. (*Hint*: Triangle APQ is similar to triangle ABC. Use this fact to express y in terms of x.)

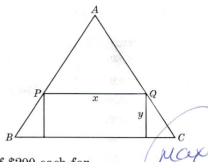

10. A charter company will provide a plane for a fare of $200 each for 80 or fewer passengers. For each passenger in excess of 80, the fare is decreased $2 per person for everyone. What number of passengers would produce the greatest revenue for the company?

11. Let a_1, a_2, and a_3 be real numbers. For what value of x will

$$(x - a_1)^2 + (x - a_2)^2 + (x - a_3)^2$$

have its least value? By generalizing the above result, find the value of x for which

$$(x - a_1)^2 + (x - a_2)^2 + (x - a_3)^2 + \cdots + (x - a_n)^2$$

is a minimum.

Self-Test 3

1. Find the vertex and axis of the parabola $y = (x - 2)^2 - 4$. Then draw its graph.   Obj. 7-6, p. 268

2. Find an equation of the parabola with vertical axis having $(-2, 3)$ as vertex and containing the point $(0, 1)$.

3. Find the extreme value of the quadratic function $f(x) = 3 + 4x - x^2$. Then graph the function. Is the extreme value a maximum or a minimum?   Obj. 7-7, p. 273

4. If two numbers differ by 6, what is the least possible value of their product?

Check your answers with those at the back of the book.

Chapter Summary

1. The solution of the general quadratic equation, $ax^2 + bx + c = 0$ $(a \neq 0)$ is given by the *quadratic formula:*

$$x = \frac{-b \pm \sqrt{b^2 - 4ac}}{2a}$$

2. To solve an equation in *quadratic form,* $a[f(x)]^2 + b[f(x)] + c = 0$, first solve for $f(x)$ and then for x.

3. The discriminant, $b^2 - 4ac$, can be used to determine the number and nature of the roots of a quadratic equation: real or imaginary; rational or irrational; zero, one, or two roots.

4. The sum of the roots of a quadratic equation is $-\frac{b}{a}$; the product of the roots is $\frac{c}{a}$.

5. The graph of the equation $y = a(x - h)^2 + k$ is a *parabola* having a vertical *axis* of symmetry, the line $x = h$. The point (h, k), where it crosses its axis, is the *vertex* of the parabola.

6. The graph of the *quadratic function* $f(x) = ax^2 + bx + c$ is a parabola. The function f takes on its *extreme value* when $x = -\frac{b}{2a}$. This value is a *maximum* if $a < 0$, a *minimum* if $a > 0$.

Chapter Review

Give the letter of the correct answer.

1. Solve $(x - 4)^2 - 2 = 0$.   **7-1**
   a. $\{2 + \sqrt{2}, 2 - \sqrt{2}\}$ **b.** $\{2 + i\sqrt{2}, 2 - i\sqrt{2}\}$
   c. $\{0, 4\}$ **d.** $\{4 + \sqrt{2}, 4 - \sqrt{2}\}$

2. If $2x^2 - 6x + c$ is a trinomial square, find c.

   a. $\frac{9}{4}$ **b.** $\frac{9}{2}$ **c.** 9   **d.** 18

3. If $x^2 - 4x = 9$, find the value of $(x - 2)^2$.

   a. 1   **b.** 13   **c.** 4   **d.** 9

4. Which of the following numbers is a root of $4x^2 - 9x - 9 = 0$?   **7-2**

   a. $-\frac{3}{4}$ **b.** $\frac{3}{4}$ **c.** $\frac{3}{2}$ **d.** -3

5. Which of the following numbers is a root of $2x^2 - 4x + 3 = 0$?

    a. $1 + i\sqrt{2}$ **b.** $1 + \dfrac{i\sqrt{2}}{2}$

    c. $1 + 2\sqrt{10}$ **d.** $-1 + 2\sqrt{10}$

6. If the length x of each edge of a cube is increased by 2 cm, its volume is increased by 12 cm³. Which equation expresses this information?

    a. $x^2 + 2x - 6 = 0$ **b.** $x^2 + 2x - 12 = 0$ **c.** $3x^2 + 6x - 2 = 0$

7. Which of the following numbers is a root of   7-3
$$(x^2 - 2x)^2 + 2(x^2 - 2x) - 3 = 0?$$

    a. $1 + \sqrt{2}$ **b.** $1 + 2i$ **c.** 2 **d.** $1 - 2i$

8. Describe the roots of $5x^2 - 8x + 5 = 0$.   7-4

    a. real, unequal, rational   **b.** real, unequal, irrational
    c. real, equal, rational   **d.** imaginary conjugates

9. Describe the roots of $4x^2 - 4x\sqrt{3} + 3 = 0$.

    a. real, unequal, rational   **b.** real, unequal, irrational
    c. real, equal, irrational   **d.** imaginary conjugates

10. If k is a real number, then for what values of k are the roots of $kx^2 - 6x + 3 = 0$ imaginary?

    a. $k > 6$ **b.** $k > 3$ **c.** $k \neq 0$ **d.** $k < -3$

11. Find the sum and product of the roots of $2x^2 - 8x - 6 = 0$.   7-5

    a. -4 and -3 **b.** -4 and 3 **c.** 4 and -3

12. Which equation has $\dfrac{-1 \pm 3i}{2}$ as roots?

    a. $2x^2 + 2x + 5 = 0$ **b.** $x^2 + x + 5 = 0$ **c.** $2x^2 - 2x + 5 = 0$

13. If one root of $2x^2 + 5x + k = 0$ is $\frac{1}{2}$, find the other root.

    a. -3 **b.** -2 **c.** 2 **d.** 3

14. Find an equation of the parabola shown at the right.   7-6

    a. $y = x^2 + 2$ **b.** $y = (x + 1)^2 + 2$
    c. $y = 2(x + 1)^2$ **d.** $y = 2(x - 1)^2$

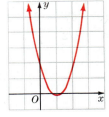

15. Find the vertex of the parabola $y = 2(x - 1)^2 + 3$.

    a. $(2, 3)$ **b.** $(1, 3)$ **c.** $(-1, 3)$ **d.** $(2, -3)$

16. Find the minimum value of the function $f(x) = 3x^2 - 6x + 7$.   7-7

    a. 2 **b.** 4 **c.** 7 **d.** 1

17. Which curve is the graph of $f(x) = -2 - x^2$?

a. 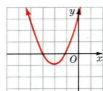 **b.** 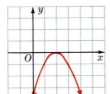 **c.** 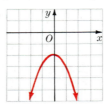 **d.**

18. A rectangular pen is to be built against a wall using 60 m of fencing for the three sides which need fencing. If the area of the pen is to be as large as possible, find the length of the longest side.

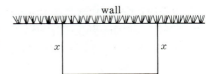

a. 10 m   **b.** 20 m   **c.** 25 m   **d.** 30 m

Chapter Test

1. Solve $(x - 3)^2 = 3$.   7-1

2. Solve by completing the square: $x^2 - 6x - 13 = 0$.

3. Use the quadratic formula to solve $2x^2 - 6x + 7 = 0$.   7-2

4. The area of a right triangle is $1\ \mathrm{m}^2$ and one of its legs is 8 m longer than the other. Find the lengths of the legs.

5. Find all four roots of $z^4 - 8z^2 - 9 = 0$.   7-3

6. Without solving the equation, determine the nature of its roots.   7-4
     a. $5x^2 - 6x + 5 = 0$ **b.** $6x^2 - 7x - 10 = 0$

7. Find a quadratic equation with integral coefficients that has $1 + i\sqrt{3}$ as a root.   7-5

8. One root of $2x^2 - 3x + c = 0$ is twice the other. Find the roots and the value of c.

9. Find an equation of the parabola with vertical axis whose vertex is $(-3, -5)$ and that contains the point $(-1, 3)$. Then draw the parabola.   7-6

10. When an automobile dealer's markup over factory price is x dollars per car, the dealer sells $\left(300 - \frac{2}{3}x\right)$ cars per month. Thus, the monthly profit will be $\left[x\left(300 - \frac{2}{3}x\right)\right]$ dollars. For what value of x will the profit be the greatest?   7-7

Cumulative Review (Chapters 4-7)

Express as a polynomial in simplest form.

1. $(-2a^4)(4a^3)^2$ **2.** $(5c-4)^2$ **3.** $3x(2x+5)(3x-7)$

Find **(a)** the GCF and **(b)** the LCM of each pair of monomials.

4. $18, 32$ **5.** $-3p^2q^4, 7p^5qr^2$ **6.** $16a^5b^7, 4a^2b^5$

7. A rectangular swimming pool has an area of 300 m². If the length is 5 m longer than the width, find the dimensions of the pool.

8. Find and graph the solution set of the inequality $x^2 - 8x - 9 < 0$.

Express in simplest form without negative exponents.

9. $\dfrac{5x^{-2}y}{xy^{-1}}$ **10.** $\dfrac{12x^2 - 11x - 15}{9x^2 - 25}$ **11.** $\dfrac{rs + 3s - 2r - 6}{r^3 + 27}$

12. $\dfrac{1 - t^4}{t^3 - t} \cdot \dfrac{t^2}{t^4 + 2t^2 + 1}$ **13.** $\dfrac{4}{x^2 - 3x} - \dfrac{3}{x^2 - 9}$ **14.** $\dfrac{4 - \dfrac{1}{x^2}}{2 + \dfrac{3}{x} - \dfrac{2}{x^2}}$

15. Solve $\dfrac{1}{4x^2 - 9x + 2} = \dfrac{5}{4x - 1} + \dfrac{2}{x - 2}$.

Simplify. Rationalize denominators where applicable.

16. $\sqrt[4]{32a^7}$ **17.** $(3\sqrt{2} - 5)^2$ **18.** $\dfrac{3}{2\sqrt{7} - 1}$

19. Solve $\sqrt{x + 2} = 10 - x$.

20. Simplify $\dfrac{4 - i}{3 + 2i}$.

Solve by completing the square.

21. $x^2 - 10x = -17$ **22.** $x^2 - 5x + 2 = 0$ **23.** $3y^2 = 3y + 1$

24. One leg of a right triangle is 2 cm longer than the other. The hypotenuse is 8 cm long. Using the quadratic formula, find the lengths of the legs.

25. Determine the nature of the roots of the quadratic equation $2x^2 + 8x + 2 = 0$.

26. The graph of $f(x) = x^2 + 6x + 5$ is a parabola.
     a. Express f in the form $y = a(x - h)^2 + k$.
     b. Find the x- and y-intercepts of the graph.
     c. State the vertex and the equation of the axis and sketch the graph.

27. Find the maximum value of p if $p = 1 - 5x - 2x^2$.

Shown above is a bamboo thicket. Bamboo shoots are edible, and the woody stems of the mature plant are used in furniture making and a variety of other crafts. See the Example on page 319 for a mathematical description of the growth rates of bamboo plants.

8

EQUATIONS AND NUMERICAL METHODS

LINEAR SYSTEMS

8-1 *Two Equations in Two Variables*

OBJECTIVE To find the solution set of a pair of linear equations in two variables.

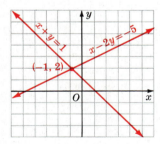
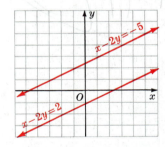
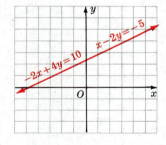

(a) $x - 2y = -5$
$x + \ y = 1$

(b) $x - 2y = -5$
$x - 2y = 2$

(c) $\quad x - 2y = -5$
$-2x + 4y = 10$

Figure 8-1

When two linear equations in two variables are graphed in the same coordinate plane (Figure 8-1), the graphs of the equations relate in just one of the following ways:

(a) The graphs intersect in exactly one point.
(b) The graphs are parallel to each other, and intersect in no point.
(c) The graphs coincide, and thus have every point in common.

In terms of the equations, these geometric relationships mean:

(a) Exactly one ordered pair of numbers satisfies both equations.
(b) No ordered pair of numbers satisfies both equations.
(c) Every ordered pair of numbers that satisfies either equation also satisfies the other.

Two equations in the same variables form a **system,** or **pair,** of **simultaneous equations.** The ordered pairs of numbers that satisfy both equations are called **common,** or **simultaneous, solutions.** The set of all simultaneous solutions is called the **solution set** of the system. For example, the solution set of the system

$$x - 2y = -5$$
$$x + y = 1$$

is $\{(-1, 2)\}$ (see Figure 8-1(a)). To check that $(-1, 2)$ satisfies both equations, substitute -1 for x and 2 for y in each equation to find:

$$-1 - 2(2) = -5 \quad \text{or} \quad -5 = -5 \; \checkmark$$
$$-1 + 2 = 1 \quad \text{or} \quad 1 = 1 \; \checkmark$$

If two systems of equations have the same solution set, then the systems are **equivalent.** For example, Figure 8-2 illustrates the fact that the systems

$$\begin{array}{cc} x - 2y = -5 \\ x + y = 1 \end{array} \quad \text{and} \quad \begin{array}{cc} x = -1 \\ y = 2 \end{array}$$

Figure 8-2

are equivalent. To solve a system of equations algebraically, you transform it into an equivalent system whose solution set is easily seen—for example,

$$x = -1$$
$$y = 2.$$

The following transformations are helpful in solving systems:

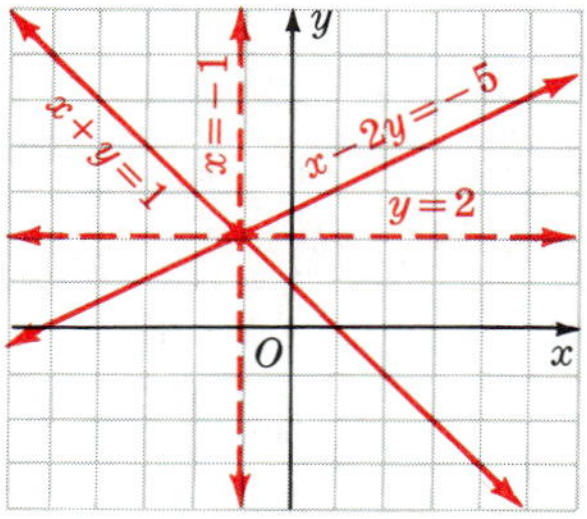

TRANSFORMATIONS THAT PRODUCE AN EQUIVALENT SYSTEM
OF LINEAR EQUATIONS

1. Replacing any equation of the system by an equivalent equation in the same variables (see page 49).
2. Substituting for one variable in any equation either
    (a) the actual value of the variable, or
    (b) an equivalent expression for that variable obtained from another equation of the system.
3. Replacing any equation by the *sum* of that equation and a *constant multiple* of another one of the equations of the system. (The replacement is called a **linear combination** of the two equations.)

A *constant multiple* of an equation results when you multiply each side of the equation by the same number. To *add equations*, you add their left sides, add their right sides, and set these sums equal to each other.

EXAMPLE 1 Solve the system: $\quad 2x - y = 6 \quad$ (equation 1)
$$3x + 5y = 22 \quad \text{(equation 2)}$$

SOLUTION 1 (Substitution Method)

1. Transform equation 1 to express y in terms of x since the coefficient of y has absolute value 1. (Transformation 1)

$$2x - y = 6$$
$$-y = -2x + 6$$
$$y = 2x - 6$$

2. Substitute this expression for y in equation 2. (Transformation 2)

$$3x + 5y = 22$$
$$3x + 5(2x - 6) = 22$$

3. Solve the result for x. (Transformation 1)

$$3x + 10x - 30 = 22$$
$$13x = 52$$
$$x = 4$$

4. Substitute the value of x in the expression for y. (Transformation 2)

$$y = 2(4) - 6$$
$$= 8 - 6$$

5. Solve for y. (Transformation 1)

$$y = 2$$

6. Check that $(4, 2)$ satisfies *both original equations*.

$$2(4) - (2) = 8 - 2 = 6 \quad \checkmark$$
$$3(4) + 5(2) = 12 + 10 = 22 \quad \checkmark$$

∴ the solution set is $\{(4, 2)\}$. ***Answer***

SOLUTION 2 (Linear-Combination Method)

1. a. To obtain equations in which the coefficients of y have the same absolute value, multiply both sides of the first equation by 5.

$$10x - 5y = 30$$
$$3x + 5y = 22$$

b. Add the result to equation 2.

$$13x \qquad = 52$$

c. Keep the original first equation, but replace the second equation by the sum of the equations in Step 1 (b). (Transformation 3)

$$2x - y = 6$$
$$13x \qquad = 52$$

2. Solve $13x = 52$ for x. (Transformation 1)

$$x = 4$$

3. Substitute 4 for x in the *original* first equation. (Transformation 2)

$$2(4) - y = 6$$
$$8 - y = 6$$

4. Solve for y. (Transformation 1)

$$y = 2$$

5. The check is the same as Step 6 in Solution 1.

∴ the solution is $(4, 2)$. ***Answer***

EXAMPLE 2   Solve and graph the system of equations $2x - 4y = 3$ and $3x - 6y = 8$.

SOLUTION   (Linear-Combination Method)

1. To obtain equations having the coefficients of x the same, multiply the first equation by 3 and the second by 2. (Transformation 1)

$$6x - 12y = 9$$
$$6x - 12y = 16$$

2. Multiply either equation by -1 and add the result to the other equation (equivalently, subtract one from the other). (Transformation 3)

$$\begin{array}{r} 6x - 12y = 9 \\ -6x + 12y = -16 \\ \hline 0 = -7 \quad \text{False!} \end{array}$$

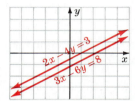

3. The resulting equation is a false statement.

   $\therefore$ the given system has no solutions; the graph is shown at the right.   ***Answer***

In Example 2, notice that the graphs of the given equations do not intersect, and have the same slope and, therefore, are parallel lines. Example 2 suggests the following statement and converse.

In a plane:

1. Parallel lines are nonintersecting.
2. Nonintersecting lines are parallel.

EXAMPLE 3   Solve the equations $-7x + 5y = -3$ and $21x - 15y = 9$ simultaneously.

SOLUTION   If you multiply the first equation by -3, you obtain the second equation. Thus, the given system is equivalent to one in which both equations are the same. Therefore, the solution set of the system is the same as the solution set of one of the equations, namely,

$$\{(x, y)\colon -7x + 5y = -3\}. \quad \textit{Answer}$$

The solution set in Example 3 has an unlimited number of members and is, therefore, called an **infinite set.** In general, the solution set of a system of two linear equations in two variables contains either one member (Example 1), no members (Example 2), or infinitely many members (Example 3). The equations in a system with at least one solution (Examples 1 and 3) are called **consistent.** When the system has no solution (Example 2), the equations are called **inconsistent.** When a system has an infinite solution set (Example 3) the equations are **dependent.**

Oral Exercises

State whether or not the given ordered pair of numbers is a solution of the given system of equations.

1. $(4, 1)$
$x + 7y = 11$
$3x - y = 5$

2. $(2, 3)$
$4x - y = 5$
$x + y = 5$

3. $(2, 5)$
$5x + 2y = 20$
$3x - 2y = -4$

4. $(-2, 1)$
$x - y = 3$
$6x + 13y = 1$

State whether or not the given systems are equivalent.

5. $x = -1 \quad -x + y = 3$
$y = 2 \qquad 3x - y = 5$

6. $4x - 3y = 10 \quad 4x - 6y = 10$
$y = 2 \qquad\qquad y = 2$

7. $2x - 5y = 9 \quad 2x - 5y = 9$
$x - y = 4 \qquad y = 4 - x$

8. $9r - 8s = 19 \qquad 10r = 20$
$r + 8s = 1 \qquad r + 8s = 1$

Tell how to combine the given equations to obtain an equation in which the specified variable has been eliminated.

SAMPLE $4x + 7y = 15; y$
$3x + 2y = 8$

SOLUTION   Multiply the first equation by 2 and the second by -7, and then add the resulting equations.

9. $5x + 3y = 8; x$
$x - 2y = 4$

10. $6x - y = 2; y$
$-2x + 9y = 15$

11. $4a + 2b = 4; a$
$2a - 9b = -3$

12. $3s - 35t = 79; t$
$8s - 7t = 1$

13. $2m + 5n = -8; n$
$7m + 3n = 2$

14. $4c - 9d = 2; c$
$10c + 13d = 76$

Written Exercises

Graph each system of equations and state whether the equations are consistent or inconsistent.

A **1.** $6x - y = 11$
$2x + y = 5$

2. $2x + 3y = 6$
$4x + 6y = 3$

3. $6m - 9n = 24$
$2m - 3n = 8$

4. $7r - 3s = -6$
$3r - s = -6$

5. $x - y = 21$
$3y - 3x = 7$

6. $15x - 6y = 9$
$-10x + 4y = -6$

7. $2a - b = 1$
$3a + b = -11$

8. $3x - 7y = 4$
$6x + 14y = 1$

For each of the following systems that contains consistent equations, find the solution set.

9. $x + 3y = 8$
$y = x$

10. $5x + y = 12$
$x = y$

11. $t + v = 6$
$-t + v = 10$

12. $4x - y = 10$
$2x + 3y = -2$

13. $x + 3y = 10$
$x + 9y = 22$

14. $2k - 3m = 4$
$3k + m = 17$

For each of the following systems that contains consistent equations, find the solution set.

15. $8m + 15n = 13$
$\quad\ \ 2m -\ \ 5n = -1$

16. $6p - 3q = 11$
$\quad\ \ 4p + 5q = -9$

17. $\quad 7r = 8 + 3s$
$\quad 21r - 9s = 42$

18. $\quad 18x -\ \ 5y = -4$
$\quad -9x + 2.5y = 2$

19. $-4x +\ \ 9y = 7$
$\quad 12x - 27y = -21$

20. $\quad 3a = 8 + 5b$
$\quad 12a - 20b = 24$

21. $9s + 5t + 6 = 0$
$\quad 4s + 3t - 2 = 0$

22. $\quad 2x + 3y + 17 = 0$
$\quad -9x + 5y + 16 = 0$

23. $3a + 8b = 1$
$\quad 5a + 4b = 1$

24. $\quad 6c -\ \ 5d = -3$
$\quad -4c + 23d = 2$

25. $\quad 9x +\ \ 8y = -3$
$\quad -3x + 13y = 1$

26. $3x + 10y = 11$
$\quad 4x -\ \ 6y = 5$

27. $8x - 3y = 3$
$\quad 3x - 2y = -5$

28. $\quad 3r +\ \ s = 1$
$\quad 21r + 3s = -2$

29. $\quad 15a + 3b = -10$
$\quad -5a + 2b = 2$

30. $27a + 20b + 14 = 0$
$\quad\ \ 8b - 15a -\ \ 3 = 0$

31. $12 - 4t + 21s = 0$
$\quad 19 + 6t + 35s = 0$

32. $5m + 3n +\ \ 4 = 0$
$\quad 2m + 7n - 10 = 0$

Solve. Note that the equations in Exercises 33–39 are not linear in the original variables. Their graphs are not straight lines.

B 33. $\dfrac{2}{r} + \dfrac{3}{s} = 16$ *Hint:* Let $x = \dfrac{1}{r}$ and $y = \dfrac{1}{s}$, and rewrite: $2x + 3y = 16$
$\qquad\qquad\qquad\qquad\qquad\qquad\qquad\qquad\qquad\qquad\qquad\ \ \ x - 2y = 1$

$\quad\ \ \dfrac{1}{r} - \dfrac{2}{s} = 1$

34. $\quad \dfrac{3}{r} - \dfrac{4}{s} = -1$

$\quad -\dfrac{1}{r} + \dfrac{2}{s} = 3$

35. $\dfrac{3}{x} - \dfrac{8}{y} = 2$

$\quad \dfrac{1}{x} - \dfrac{5}{y} = 2$

36. $\dfrac{1}{x} - \dfrac{4}{y} = -1$

$\quad \dfrac{4}{x} - \dfrac{1}{y} = 3$

37. $\dfrac{1}{r} + \dfrac{2}{s} = 8$

$\quad \dfrac{5}{r} + \dfrac{1}{s} = 7$

38. $\dfrac{7}{x} - \dfrac{5}{y} = 1$

$\quad \dfrac{1}{x} + \dfrac{1}{y} = 4$

39. $\dfrac{3}{x} + \dfrac{2}{y} = 3$

$\quad \dfrac{2}{x} + \dfrac{3}{y} = 1$

Determine A and B so that the graph of the given equation will contain the points whose coordinates are given.

C 40. $Ax + By = 10$; $(2, -1)$ and $(6, 2)$

41. $Ax + By = 5$; $(3, -1)$ and $(-8, 13)$

42. $y = Ax^2 + Bx$; $(1, -1)$ and $(-2, -10)$

43. $y = Ax^2 + B$; $(-1, -4)$ and $(2, 5)$

In each system, solve for x and y in terms of a and b. Assume $a \neq 0$ and $b \neq 0$.

44. $\quad ax +\ \ by = a + b$
$\quad abx + aby = a^2 + b^2$

45. $\quad ax +\ \ by = a$
$\quad a^2x + b^2y = a^2$

8-2 *Problem Solving with Two Variables*   23-01-86

OBJECTIVE   To use pairs of linear equations in two variables to solve problems.

You may find it helpful to use two variables in solving some problems.

EXAMPLE 1   For delivering newspapers, a delivery service charges a fixed amount for the first 50 g and a fixed rate for each additional 10 g. If the charge for a 150 g newspaper is 72¢ and that for a 220 g newspaper is $1, what are the rates?

SOLUTION

Step 1   The problem asks for the charge for the first 50 g and the charge for each additional 10 g.

Step 2   Let x = the charge in cents for the first 50 g,
and y = the charge in cents for each additional 10 g.

x = 50 g
y = each additional 10 g.

Step 3   Since $220 - 50 = 170$ and $170 \div 10 = 17$:

Charge for a 220 g paper is 100 cents

$$x + 17y \qquad = \qquad 100$$

Similarly:

Charge for a 150 g paper   is   72¢

$$x + 10y \qquad = \qquad 72$$

Step 4   Solve the system: $x + 17y = 100$
                    $x + 10y = 72$

Subtract: $7y = 28$ $\longrightarrow$ Substitute: $x + 17(4) = 100$
              $y = 4$ $\qquad\qquad\qquad\qquad x + 68 = 100$
              $\qquad\qquad\qquad\qquad\qquad\qquad x = 32$

Step 5   The check is left to you.

∴ the charge for the first 50 g is 32¢, and the charge for each additional 10 g is 4¢. *Answer*

To solve problems about airplanes flying with or against the wind, you should know what the following terms mean:

air speed: the speed of the airplane in still air

wind speed: the speed of the wind

ground speed: the speed of the airplane in terms of the distance traveled over the ground   MPH

tail wind: a wind blowing in the same direction as the one in which the airplane is heading   ADD TO MPH

head wind: a wind blowing in the direction opposite to the one in which the airplane is heading   WIND BLOWING AGAINST YOU

You also need to know these facts:

1. With a tail wind: ground speed = air speed + wind speed

2. With a head wind: ground speed = air speed − wind speed

EXAMPLE 2 Flying with a tail wind, an airplane can fly 3625 km in 6.25 h. Flying at the same air speed, however, it takes the airplane 1 h longer to make the return flight against the wind. Find the wind speed and the air speed of the airplane.

SOLUTION

Step 1 The problem asks for the wind speed and the air speed of the airplane.

Step 2 Let x = air speed of the airplane in kilometers per hour and y = wind speed in kilometers per hour.

Step 3

	ground speed r (km/h)	time t (h)	distance $d = rt$ (km)
with tail wind	$x + y$	6.25	$6.25(x + y)$
with head wind	$x - y$	7.25	$7.25(x - y)$

The distance with a tail wind is 3625 km.

$$6.25(x + y) = 3625$$

The distance with a head wind is 3625 km.

$$7.25(x - y) = 3625$$

Step 4 Solve the system:

$$\begin{aligned} 6.25(x + y) &= 3625 \\ 7.25(x - y) &= 3625 \end{aligned} \quad \text{or} \quad \begin{aligned} x + y &= 580 \\ x - y &= 500 \end{aligned}$$

Completing and checking the solution is left to you.

You should find that the air speed = 540 km/h and the wind speed = 40 km/h. **Answer**

Problems

Solve.

A 1. Twice one number is 20 more than another number. One fourth the first number is 2 less than one fourth the second number. Find the numbers.

2. One third of the sum of two numbers is $-\frac{1}{3}$, while one third of their difference is 3. Find the numbers.

3. An isosceles triangle has a perimeter of 8.5 cm. A second isosceles triangle, whose base is equal to that of the first but whose legs are twice as long as those of the first, has a perimeter of 15.5 cm. Find the lengths of the sides of each triangle.

$y = 24 - 3x +$

4. A collection of quarters and dimes contains 44 coins and has a total value of $6.50. How many coins of each kind are there in the collection?

5. There are 28 students in a history class. The number of juniors is 24 less than three times the number of seniors. How many juniors and how many seniors are in the class?

6. Tickets for a band concert cost $8.00 for the main floor and $6.00 for the balcony. If 1125 tickets were sold, and the ticket sales totaled $7700, how many tickets of each kind were sold?

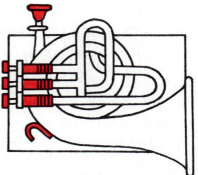

7. Martha earns $5.50 per hour and Joan earns $6.50 per hour. Together they worked a total of 45 hours one week and earned a total of $266.50. How many hours did each work?

8. For some long distance calls, a fixed amount is charged for the first three minutes, and a fixed *rate* is charged for each additional minute. If the charge for a fifteen-minute call from New York to Chicago is $2.94, and the charge for a ten-minute call is $1.99, find the fixed amount that is charged for the first three minutes and the fixed *rate* that is charged for each additional minute.

9. Three dozen eggs and five loaves of bread cost $6.10; four dozen eggs and two loaves of bread cost $5.10. Find the prices for a dozen eggs and for a loaf of bread.

10. Flying with the wind, an airplane can travel 1500 km in 2.5 h, but flying against the wind, the airplane requires 0.5 h more to make the return trip. Find the wind speed and the air speed.

B 11. Write an equation in the form $y = mx + b$ for the line passing through the points $(6, -1)$ and $(-9, 11)$.

$\frac{12}{3}$

12. Two temperature scales are established: one, the M scale, where, under fixed conditions, water freezes at 12° and boils at 509°; and the other, the N scale, where water freezes at 4° and boils at 75°. If the M and N scales are linearly related, find an expression for any temperature M in terms of a temperature N.

13. The final velocity of a uniformly accelerated particle is linearly related to the elapsed time by the equation

$$v = v_0 + at$$

where a and v_0 are constants. If $v = 34.5$ when $t = 4$, and $v = 54$ when $t = 7$, find values for v_0 and a.

In Problems 14 and 15, the original number is a positive integer whose decimal numeral contains two places. Find this integer in each case.

14. The tens' digit exceeds the units' digit by one. The difference between the original number and the number represented when the digits are reversed is equal to the tens' digit of the original number.

15. The units' digit is one more than twice the tens' digit. The sum of the original number and the number represented when the digits are reversed is 77.

16. A river steamer travels 48 km downstream in the same time that it takes to travel 32 km upstream. The steamer's engines drive it in still water at a rate that is 16 km/h greater than the rate of the current. Find the rate of the current.

C 17. Savings Rent-A-Car charges a fixed amount for each day a car is rented and a fixed amount for each kilometer the car is driven. Toshiro spent $134 to rent a compact car for 5 days and drive it 450 km; Louise spent $106 to rent the same kind of car for 4 days and drive it 350 km. Find the daily charge in dollars and the charge per kilometer in cents.

18. In calm water, a motorboat can travel 5 times as fast as the current in the Rolling River. A trip upriver and back totaling 96 km takes 5 h. Find the rate of the current.

19. One hour after Jill Nussbaum's plane, flying with a tail wind, left on a 350 km trip east to Ashford, it developed engine trouble and had to fly the remaining 2 h of the trip at half of its original air speed. Repairs were made in Ashford, and the return flight of 2.75 h was made at the original air speed but with a head wind $\frac{1}{11}$ the speed of the original tail wind. Find the air speed of the plane.

20. When Marvin was 2 km upstream from where he started his canoe trip, he passed a log floating with the current. After paddling upstream for one more hour, he paddled back and reached his starting point just as the log arrived. How fast was the current flowing?

8-3 *Linear Inequalities in Two Variables*

OBJECTIVE   To graph the solution set of a linear inequality in two variables or a system of such inequalities.

The line whose equation is

$$y = \frac{1}{3}x + 2$$

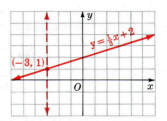

Figure 8-3

(Figure 8-3) separates the coordinate plane into two regions called **open half-planes**—one "above" the line and one "below" the line. The line itself is the *boundary* of each half-plane.

If you start at any point of the line, say $(-3, 1)$, and move vertically upward, the y-coordinate *increases*. Therefore, the upper open half-plane is the graph of

$$y > \frac{1}{3}x + 2.$$

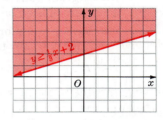

Figure 8-4

If you move vertically downward from $(-3, 1)$, the y-coordinate *decreases*, and the lower open half-plane is the graph of

$$y < \frac{1}{3}x + 2.$$

Figures 8-4, 8-5, 8-6, and 8-7 show partial graphs of four linear inequalities; each has as a boundary the line with equation $y = \frac{1}{3}x + 2$.

If the boundary is part of the graph, it is drawn as a solid line. If the boundary is not part of the graph, it is drawn as a dashed line. The equation $y = \frac{1}{3}x + 2$ is called the **associated equation** of each of the inequalities graphed in Figures 8-4, 8-5, 8-6, and 8-7.

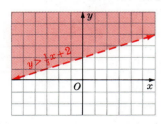

Figure 8-5

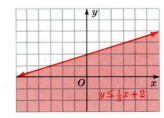

Figure 8-6

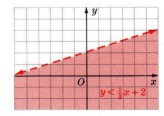

Figure 8-7

An open half-plane together with its boundary (Figures 8-4 and 8-6) is called a **closed half-plane.**

In general,

> A **linear inequality** is an inequality whose associated equation is a linear equation. In a coordinate plane, the graph of a linear inequality in two variables is an open or a closed half-plane.

EXAMPLE 1   Graph $2x + 3y \leq 12$.

SOLUTION

1. Transform the given inequality into an equivalent inequality (page 65) in which y is one side and an expression not containing y is the other side:

$$2x + 3y \leq 12$$
$$3y \leq -2x + 12$$
$$y \leq -\frac{2}{3}x + 4$$

2. Graph the associated equation

$$y = -\frac{2}{3}x + 4$$

and show it as a solid line.

3. The graph of the given inequality is that line and the half-plane below it.   ***Answer***

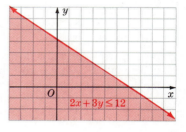

EXAMPLE 2   Graph $x < 2$.

SOLUTION   If you start at any point on the graph of $x = 2$ and move horizontally to the left, the x-coordinate decreases. Move to the right, and the x-coordinate increases.

∴ the graph of $x < 2$ is the open half-plane to the left of the graph of $x = 2$.   ***Answer***

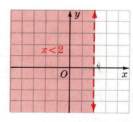

The next example shows how to graph a system of inequalities. The graph of the solution set of the system is the region where the graphs of the inequalities overlap.

EXAMPLE 3   Graph the solution set of the system:

$$x + y \geq 2$$
$$2x - y < 1$$

SOLUTION

1. Graph $x + y \geq 2$, or $y \geq 2 - x$, showing the boundary as a solid line.

2. In the same coordinate plane, graph $2x - y < 1$, or $y > 2x - 1$, showing the boundary as a dashed line.

3. The graph of the solution set of the system is the doubly shaded region above and on the graph of $x + y = 2$ and also above the graph of $2x - y = 1$. *Answer*

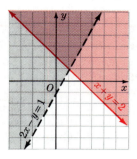

Oral Exercises

State whether the point whose coordinates are given lies above, on, or below the line with the given equation.

1. $(0, 2)$; $y = 3 - \frac{1}{2}x$ **2.** $(1, 3)$; $y = 3 - \frac{1}{2}x$ **3.** $(-1, -1)$; $y = 2x$

4. $(3, -5)$; $y = -x$ **5.** $(2, 2)$; $y = 3x - 4$ **6.** $(2, -3)$; $y = -4x + 5$

Which of the given points belong to the graph of the given inequality?

7. $y - x \leq 0$; $(4, 3)$, $(1, 1)$ **8.** $x + y > 0$; $(4, -3)$, $(-4, 3)$
9. $y - 2x > 6$; $(0, -1)$, $(-3, 1)$ **10.** $5x + y < 1$; $(0, 1)$, $(-2, 5)$

Transform each inequality into an equivalent one having y alone on one side.

11. $3x + y < 2$ **12.** $5y - x > 4$ **13.** $4x - y \leq 1$
14. $-2x - 5y \geq -1$ **15.** $-4 \geq x + 2y$ **16.** $9 \leq 3x - 2y$

Put IN
y - intercept down

Written Exercises

Graph the solution set of each inequality.

A **1.** $y > 3$ **2.** $y \leq -2$ **3.** $x \geq -1$ **4.** $x < 5$

5. $x \leq -y$ **6.** $y > x$ **7.** $y < 2x$ **8.** $y > \frac{1}{3}x$

9. $x < 3y$ **10.** $x \leq -2y$ **11.** $y - 4x \leq 5$ **12.** $y + 2x \leq -1$
13. $4x + 2y \leq 3$ **14.** $x + 3y > 7$ **15.** $-x > 0$ **16.** $-y \leq 0$
17. $5y - 4x \geq -20$ **18.** $2x + 3y > -6$ **19.** $-y < 4x - 9$ **20.** $-2y \geq 5x - 4$

Graph each system of inequalities.

21. $y < x$ **22.** $y \geq -x$ **23.** $x \leq 3$ **24.** $y < 2$
  $\quad\;\; y \geq 0$ $\quad\;\;\;\; x < 0$ $\quad\;\;\; y \leq x + 2$ $\quad\;\; y > 1 - x$

Graph each system of inequalities.

25. $y < x + 1$
　　$y > x - 2$

26. $y \geq -2 - x$
　　$y \leq \quad 2 - x$

27. $2x + 3y \leq 6$
　　$x + 2y < 3$

28. $\quad x + 3y < 4$
　　$-x + \;\; y > 4$

Graph the solution set of each inequality or system of inequalities.

SAMPLE　　$-5 \leq y \leq 3$

SOLUTION　The given inequality is equivalent to

$$y \geq -5 \quad \text{and} \quad y \leq 3.$$

The graph is the doubly shaded region shown below.

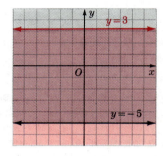

B **29.** $-2 \leq y \leq 6$

30. $-1 < x < 6$

31. $4 > x > 0$

32. $2 \geq y \geq 0$

33. $x - 3 \leq y < x + 3$

34. $1 - 3x < y < 3x + 1$

35. $|x| < 1$

36. $|x| > 2$

37. $|y| \geq 3$

38. $|y| \leq 4$

39. $y \geq 3 - x$
　　$-1 \leq x \leq 2$

40. $y \geq x - 2$
　　$-3 \leq y \leq 1$

C **41.** $|x - 1| \leq 2$

42. $|x - 2| \geq 1$

43. $|y + 1| > 3$

44. $|y + 4| < 1$

CHALLENGE

a. Choose two nonzero numbers r and s. Graph the following three equations to determine their apparent common solution.

$$2x + y = 5$$
$$x - y = -2$$
$$r(2x + y) + s(x - y) = r(5) + s(-2)$$

b. Verify that the apparent common solution is actually a common solution.

c. Why must any solution to the first two equations in part (a) be a solution to the third?

8-4 Systems of Equations in Three Variables

OBJECTIVE   **To find the solution set of a system of three equations in three variables.**

Suppose that -1, 4, and 2 are values of x, y, and z, respectively. The **ordered triple** $(x, y, z) = (-1, 4, 2)$ is called a solution of the equation

$$x + 2y - 3z = 1$$

because

$$-1 + 2(4) - 3(2) = 1$$

is a true statement.

    Any equation of the form

$$Ax + By + Cz = D$$

where A, B, C, and D are real numbers, with A, B, C not all zero, is called a **linear equation in three variables,** x, y, and z. (Although such equations are called "linear," their graphs are not lines, but planes in three-dimensional space.) Three-dimensional graphs can be constructed using a z-axis perpendicular to the x- and y-axes and passing through the origin. A **solution** of a linear equation in three variables is an ordered triple of values of the variables for which the equation is a true statement. You can find such solutions by assigning values to two of the variables and solving for the third.

    The transformations introduced in Section 8-1 can be used to solve systems of linear equations in three variables.

EXAMPLE 1   Solve the system: $x - 2y + 3z = 13$
$$y + 8z = 23$$
$$z = 3$$

SOLUTION   (Substitution Method)

1. The third equation tells the value of z, namely, 3. $\hfill z = 3$

2. Substitute 3 for z in the second equation, and solve for y. (Transformations 2 and 1)

$$\begin{aligned} y + 8z &= 23 \\ y + 8(3) &= 23 \\ y + 24 &= 23 \\ y &= -1 \end{aligned}$$

3. Substitute 3 for z and -1 for y in the first equation, and solve for x. (Transformations 2 and 1)

$$\begin{aligned} x - 2y + 3z &= 13 \\ x - 2(-1) + 3(3) &= 13 \\ x + 2 + 9 &= 13 \\ x &= 2 \end{aligned}$$

4. The check is left to you.

$\therefore$ the solution is $(2, -1, 3)$.   *Answer*

A system of linear equations like the one in Example 1 is called *triangular* because its shape suggests a triangle (Figure 8-8). Since triangular systems are easy to solve, an efficient way to solve any system is to transform it into an equivalent triangular system and then solve the triangular system. Example 2 illustrates this method.

$$x - 2y + 3z = 13$$
$$y + 8z = 23$$
$$z = 3$$

Figure 8-8

EXAMPLE 2   Solve the system: $3x + 2y - 2z = 11$
$$x + y + 2z = -1$$
$$2x - y + 2z = -4$$

SOLUTION   (Linear-Combination and Substitution Methods)

1. Interchange the first and second equations.

$$x + y + 2z = -1$$
$$3x + 2y - 2z = 11$$
$$2x - y + 2z = -4$$

2. Subtract three times the first equation from the second and twice the first equation from the third. (Transformation 3)

$$x + y + 2z = -1$$
$$- y - 8z = 14$$
$$- 3y - 2z = -2$$

3. In the new system, subtract three times the second equation from the third. The resulting system is triangular. (Transformation 3)

$$x + y + 2z = -1$$
$$- y - 8z = 14$$
$$22z = -44$$

4. Solve the third equation in Step 3 for z. (Transformation 1)

$$z = -2$$

5. Substitute -2 for z in the second equation in Step 3 and solve for y. (Transformations 2 and 1)

$$-y - 8(-2) = 14$$
$$-y + 16 = 14$$
$$y = 2$$

6. Substitute -2 for z and 2 for y in the first equation of Step 3. Solve for x. (Transformations 2 and 1)

$$x + 2 + 2(-2) = -1$$
$$x + 2 - 4 = -1$$
$$x = 1$$

7. The check is left to you.

∴ the solution is $(1, 2, -2)$. *Answer*

The method of Example 2 is called Gaussian elimination in honor of its inventor, Karl Friedrich Gauss. Gauss (1777–1855) was a German mathematician, astronomer, and physicist. The method can be applied to systems of linear equations in two, three, or even more equations.

EXAMPLE 3   A dealer carries three grades of oil. Three liters of the first grade, 2 L of the second, and 3 L of the third cost $8; 1 L of the first grade and 3 L of the third grade cost $4.20; and 2 L of the second grade and 3 L of the third grade cost $4.40. What is the cost of each grade of oil?

SOLUTION   Let x = the cost in cents of 1 L of the first grade;
y = the cost in cents of 1 L of the second grade;
z = the cost in cents of 1 L of the third grade.

An analysis of the problem leads to the system:

$$3x + 2y + 3z = 800$$
$$x \quad\quad + 3z = 420$$
$$2y + 3z = 440$$

Solving the system, you will find:

$$x = 120¢, \; y = 70¢, \; z = 100¢$$

Writing a complete solution of the problem is left to you.

∴ The first grade of oil costs \$1.20 per liter, the second grade costs \$.70 per liter, and the third grade costs \$1 per liter.   ***Answer***

Oral Exercises

Which of the given ordered triples is a solution of the given equation?

1. $x + y - z = 2$; $(1, -2, -3)$, $(0, -2, -4)$

2. $x - y + 2z = 3$; $(1, -1, -1)$, $(2, -3, -1)$

3. $x + 4y + 2z = 0$; $(0, 0, 4)$, $(0, -2, 8)$

4. $5x + y - z = 0$; $(-1, -1, 6)$, $(2, -6, 4)$

Find two ordered triples (x, y, z) that satisfy the given equation.

5. $y = 7$ **6.** $z = -4$ **7.** $x + 2y = 3$ **8.** $x - y = 1$

Tell how to combine the given equations to obtain an equation in which the coefficient of x is 0.

9. $x + 4y - 3z = 7$
$\quad\; 3x - y - z = 2$

10. $-x + 3y + 2z = -4$
$\quad\quad 2x - y - 3z = 6$

11. $2x - 5y + 2z = 13$
$\quad\;\; 3x + 4y + 7z = 4$

12. $\quad\;\; 6x - 4y + 5z = 16$
$\quad\quad -4x + 9y - 3z = 2$

Written Exercises

Solve each system of equations.

A **1.** $x + 2y - 4z = 2$
$\quad\quad\;\; y + z = 5$
$\quad\quad\quad\quad\; z = 3$

2. $x + 2y + z = 4$
$\quad\;\; 3y + z = 8$
$\quad\quad\quad\; z = -1$

3. $2x + y - 3z = 8$
$\quad\quad 5y + 2z = 6$
$\quad\quad\quad\; 4z = -8$

4. $-5x \quad\quad + 8z = 15$
$\quad\quad 7y + 4z = -11$
$\quad\quad\quad\; 2z = 5$

5. $\quad\;\; x - 3y - 2z = 3$
$\quad\quad 2x + y + 3z = -1$
$\quad\; -3x - 2y + z = 8$

6. $\quad x - y + 3z = 2$
$\quad\; 4x - 5y + 14z = 3$
$\quad\; 5x - 6y + 19z = 3$

Solve each system of equations.

7. $-2x + 19y + 8z = 27$
$x - 3y - 2z = -18$
$2x - 9y - 5z = -35$

8. $4x - 13y + 14z = 4$
$x - 4y + 5z = -2$
$6x - 22y + 27z = -6$

9. $5x + 7y - 17z = 28$
$2x + 4y - 9z = 17$
$x + y - 3z = 4$

10. $3x + 10y - 5z = -6$
$-3x + 5y - 2z = 5$
$x + 2y - z = -2$

11. $-z - y + 4x = 14$
$5y + 2x = -4$
$3x = 9$

12. $5z + 2y + 3x = 2$
$-3y + x = -8$
$4x = -20$

B 13. $2x - 3y + z = 3$
$5x - 5y + z = 8$
$6x - 7y + 2z = 9$

14. $7x + 7y - z = 0$
$9x + 3y - 4z = 4$
$10x + 4y - 3z = 2$

15. $2a + 6b - 3c = 5$
$3a + 5b - 5c = 2$
$2a + 3b - 4c = 1$

16. $7m + 6p + 7q = 0$
$2m + 2p + 3q = -1$
$8m + 3p + 5q = 3$

17. $\dfrac{6}{a} - \dfrac{2}{b} + \dfrac{2}{c} = 4$

$\dfrac{3}{a} - \dfrac{2}{b} + \dfrac{3}{c} = 5$

$\dfrac{3}{a} + \dfrac{1}{b} + \dfrac{3}{c} = -1$

18. $\dfrac{1}{r} + \dfrac{3}{s} + \dfrac{4}{t} = 6$

$-\dfrac{2}{r} - \dfrac{3}{s} + \dfrac{1}{t} = 12$

$\dfrac{3}{r} - \dfrac{6}{s} + \dfrac{3}{t} = 30$

Find A, B, and C so that the solution set of the equation $Ax + By + Cz = 1$ will contain the given ordered triples.

19. $(5, 3, -2)$, $(2, 2, -1)$, $(-2, 0, -3)$

20. $(0, 1, -8)$, $(1, 3, -3)$, $(2, 4, -2)$

Show that the equations of each system are *inconsistent* (that is, have no common solution). (*Hint:* Transform each system into an equivalent one in which one equation is a false statement.)

C 21. $2x - y + z = 2$
$3x - 2y - z = 0$
$5x - 3y = -2$

22. $x - 4y - 3z = 0$
$4x - 3y - 5z = -2$
$3x + y - 2z = 2$

Problems

Solve.

A 1. The sum of three numbers is 12. The second number is equal to the sum of the first and third numbers. Twice the first number exceeds the second number by 4. Find the numbers.

2. The sum of three numbers is -2. The sum of three times the first number, twice the second number, and the third number is 9. The difference between the second number and half the third number is 10. Find the numbers.

3. Marika has $1, $5, and $10 bills in her wallet that are worth $96. If she had 1 more $1 bill she would have just as many $1 bills as $5 and $10 bills combined. If she has 23 bills in all, how many of each denomination does she have?

4. Vincent has 32 coins made up of nickels, dimes, and quarters. The sum of the number of nickels and the number of quarters is three times the number of dimes. If the total value of the coins is $4.60, how many of each kind does he have?

5. The sum of the length, width, and height of a rectangular box is 75 cm. The length is twice the sum of the width and height, and twice the width exceeds the height by 5 cm. Find the dimensions of the box.

6. In a triangle whose perimeter is 52 cm, the length of the longest side is 2 cm less than the sum of the lengths of the other two sides. The difference between the length of the longest side and twice the length of the shortest side is 3 cm. How long is each side of the triangle?

B 7. One avocado, one bunch of celery, and one bag of radishes cost $1.59. Two bunches of celery, one avocado, and four bags of radishes cost $3.65. Three bunches of celery, two avocados, and one bag of radishes cost $3.12. Find the cost of each: an avocado; a bunch of celery; a bag of radishes.

8. An art museum charges $3 for admission tickets, but members receive a $.50 discount, and students are admitted for half price. One Saturday, 750 tickets were sold for a total of $1715. If 20 more student tickets than full-price tickets were sold, find the number of each type of tickets sold.

9. The Ultraclean Laundromat has regular washing machines, large washing machines, and dryers. Ned, Lena, and Will went there to do their laundry. Ned used 3 regular washers and two dryers; he spent $2.70. Lena used 2 regular washers, 1 large washer, and 3 dryers; she spent $3.55. Will used two large washers and two dryers. He also bought two packets of laundry soap that cost 50¢ apiece. He spent $3.70 in all. How much does it cost to run each machine?

10. Find the 3-digit integer for which all the following statements are true:
    (a) The sum of the three digits is 17.
    (b) The sum of the original integer and the integer represented when the digits are reversed is 1474.
    (c) The difference between the original integer and the integer represented when the digits are reversed is 198.

11. In a certain family with three children, the age of the eldest child is two years less than the sum of the ages of the other two children. Four years ago the eldest child was four times as old as the youngest; at the same time the middle child was twice as old as the youngest. How old are the children?

12. If Mrs. Zablocki were one year younger, she would be three times as old as her daughter Wanda. Three years ago, Mr. Zablocki, who is older than his wife, was four times as old as Wanda. Two years from now, the difference between the ages of the parents will be one fifth of Wanda's age. How old are Wanda and her parents?

Self-Test 1

VOCABULARY
system, or pair, of simultaneous equations (p. 284)
common, or simultaneous, solutions (p. 284)
solution set of a system (p. 284)
equivalent systems (p. 284)
linear combination (p. 284)
infinite set (p. 286)
consistent equations (p. 286)
inconsistent equations (p. 286)
dependent equations (p. 286)
open half-plane (p. 293)
associated equation (p. 293)
closed half-plane (p. 293)
linear inequality (p. 294)
ordered triple (p. 297)
linear equation in three variables (p. 297)
solution of a linear system in three variables
(p. 297)

1. Solve $8x + 3y = 5$
$5x + 4y = 18$

Obj. 8-1, p. 283

2. Adult tickets for a concert cost \$4.50 and student tickets cost \$3.75. If 400 people attended the concert and ticket sales amounted to \$1680, how many adult tickets and how many student tickets were sold?

Obj. 8-2, p. 289

3. Graph the solution set of the system: $x + 2y \leq 6$
$y - 3x \geq 4$

Obj. 8-3, p. 293

4. Solve the system: $x - 2y - z = -3$
$3x + y + 2z = 4$
$y + z = 1$

Obj. 8-4, p. 297

Check your answers with those at the back of the book.

8-5 *Synthetic Division*

The usual process of dividing $2x^3 - 9x^2 + 4x - 7$ by $x - 3$ is shown at the left below. At the right, the same process is shown compactly; only the coefficients of the terms of the polynomials are written.

$$
\begin{array}{r}
2x^2 - 3x - 5 \\
x - 3 \overline{\smash{\big)}\, 2x^3 - 9x^2 + 4x - 7} \\
\underline{2x^3 - 6x^2} \\
-3x^2 \\
\underline{-3x^2 + 9x} \\
-5x \\
\underline{-5x + 15} \\
-22
\end{array}
$$

$$\therefore \frac{2x^3 - 9x^2 + 4x - 7}{x - 3} =$$

$$2x^2 - 3x - 5 - \frac{22}{x - 3}$$

Call this c.   Coefficients of dividend

$$
\begin{array}{c|cccc}
3 & 2 & -9 & 4 & -7 \\
& & & & \\
\hline
& 2 & & &
\end{array}
$$

Bring down 2

Multiply 2 by c (or 3) and add this product to the next coefficient of the dividend. Repeat for each coefficient.

$$
\begin{array}{c|cccc}
3 & 2 & -9 & 4 & -7 \\
& & 6 & -9 & -15 \\
\hline
& 2 & -3 & -5 & -22
\end{array}
$$

Coefficients of   Remainder
the quotient

To divide $2x^3 - 9x^2 + 4x - 7$ by $x + 3$, you can proceed as follows: Since $x + 3 = x - (-3)$, $c = -3$.

$$
\begin{array}{c|cccc}
-3 & 2 & -9 & 4 & -7 \\
& & -6 & 45 & -147 \\
\hline
& 2 & -15 & 49 & -154
\end{array}
$$

$$2x^2 - 15x + 49 \quad \text{Rem.} = -154$$

$$\therefore \frac{2x^3 - 9x^2 + 4x - 7}{x + 3} = 2x^2 - 15x + 49 - \frac{154}{x + 3}$$

This method of detaching coefficients to display the process of dividing a polynomial in x by $x - r$ is called **synthetic division.** (In honor of the English mathematician W. G. Horner (1773-1827), this method is also called *Horner's algorithm*.) Synthetic division can be adapted for use with a divisor of the form $ax - b$.

EXAMPLE Divide $8x^3 + 2x^2 - 49$ by $4x - 7$.

SOLUTION $4x - 7 = 4\left(x - \dfrac{7}{4}\right)$.

$$\therefore \frac{8x^3 + 2x^2 - 49}{4x - 7} = \frac{1}{4}\left(\frac{8x^3 + 2x^2 - 49}{x - \frac{7}{4}}\right)$$

The quotient $(8x^3 + 2x^2 - 49) \div \left(x - \dfrac{7}{4}\right)$ can be found using the synthetic division below. Note that the coefficient 0 has been used for the missing power of x in the dividend.

$$\frac{7}{4} \;\bigg|\; \begin{array}{rrrr} 8 & 2 & 0 & -49 \\ & 14 & 28 & 49 \\ \hline 8 & 16 & 28 & 0 \end{array}$$

$$\therefore \frac{8x^3 + 2x^2 - 49}{4x - 7} = \frac{1}{4}(8x^2 + 16x + 28) = 2x^2 + 4x + 7. \quad \textbf{\textit{Answer}}$$

Written Exercises

Use synthetic division to find the quotient and remainder.

A **1.** $\dfrac{3x^3 - 4x^2 + x + 2}{x - 1}$

2. $\dfrac{5x^3 - 9x^2 + x + 6}{x - 4}$

3. $\dfrac{y^3 - 2y^2 - 2y - 3}{y + 2}$

4. $\dfrac{2z^3 - 3z^2 + 2z - 6}{z + 3}$

5. $\dfrac{2a^4 - 5a^3 + a^2 - 9a + 6}{a - 3}$

6. $\dfrac{b^4 + 2b^3 - b^2 - 10b + 15}{b - 2}$

7. $\dfrac{2x^3 + 11x^2 + 10x - 8}{x + 4}$

8. $\dfrac{6x^3 + 7x^2 - 7x + 6}{x + 2}$

9. $\dfrac{2z^4 - z^3 + 2z + 4}{z - 3i}$

10. $\dfrac{3z^4 - 3z^2 + 4z + 3}{z + 2i}$

B **11.** $\dfrac{6t^3 - 7t^2 + 14t - 6}{2t - 1}$

12. $\dfrac{15s^3 + s^2 + 12s + 12}{3s + 2}$

13. $\dfrac{4v^3 - 2v + 24}{2v + 3}$

14. $\dfrac{9n^3 + 3n - 2}{3n - 1}$

Find the polynomial $Q(x)$ and the constant r for each equation.

15. $2x^3 + 7x^2 - 10x - 32 = (x + 2)Q(x) + r$

16. $2x^3 - 3x^2 - 12x + 9 = (x - 3)Q(x) + r$

17. $3x^4 - 6x^3 + 3x + 4 = (x - 2i)Q(x) + r$

18. $2x^4 - 3x^2 + 7x + 3 = (x + i)Q(x) + r$

Determine k so that the first polynomial is a factor of the second.

C **19.** $x - 2$; $x^3 - 2x^2 + 3x + k$

20. $x + 4$; $2x^4 - 3x^2 + 2x + k$

8-6 *Remainder and Factor Theorems*

OBJECTIVE   **To use synthetic division to find the value of a given polynomial $P(x)$ at a given number c and to decide whether $x - c$ is a factor of $P(x)$, which is equivalent to determining whether c is a root of $P(x) = 0$.**

The synthetic division displayed at the right shows the division of the polynomial $P(x)$ by $x - 2$. Notice that the remainder 5 is equal to $P(2)$, the value of the polynomial at 2.

$$P(x) = x^3 - 4x^2 + 13$$

$$
\begin{array}{r|rrrr}
2 & 1 & -4 & 0 & 13 \\
  &   & 2 & -4 & -8 \\
\hline
  & 1 & -2 & -4 & 5
\end{array}
$$

$$P(2) = 8 - 16 + 13 = 5$$

The following equations show why $P(2)$ will always equal the remainder when $P(x)$ is divided by $x - 2$.

$$P(x) = (x^2 - 2x - 4)(x - 2) + 5$$

Thus,
$$
\begin{aligned}
P(2) &= (2^2 - 2 \cdot 2 - 4)(2 - 2) + 5 \\
&= (2^2 - 2 \cdot 2 - 4)(0) + 5 \\
&= 0 + 5 \\
&= 5
\end{aligned}
$$

In general, if $Q(x)$ is the quotient and R the remainder when a polynomial $P(x)$ is divided by $x - c$, you can reason as follows:

$$P(x) = Q(x)(x - c) + R$$

Thus,
$$
\begin{aligned}
P(c) &= Q(c)(c - c) + R \\
&= Q(c)(0) + R \\
&= 0 + R \\
&= R
\end{aligned}
$$

The result just proved is called the *remainder theorem:*

REMAINDER THEOREM

For every polynomial $P(x)$ of positive degree n over the set of complex numbers and for every complex number c, there exists a polynomial $Q(x)$ of degree $n - 1$ such that

$$P(x) = Q(x)(x - c) + P(c).$$

Because the remainder on dividing $P(x)$ by $x - c$ is $P(c)$, you can use synthetic division as a convenient way to find $P(c)$. For this reason synthetic division is also called **synthetic substitution.**

EXAMPLE 1 Use synthetic division to find the value of
$P(x) = x^3 + 3x^2 - 5x - 1$ at -2.

SOLUTION

$$
\begin{array}{c}
\quad\ c \\
\quad\ \downarrow \\
\underline{-2}\ \big|\ \ 1 \qquad 3 \qquad -5 \qquad -1 \\
\qquad\qquad\ \ -2 \quad -2 \qquad 14 \\
\underline{} \\
\qquad\ \ 1 \qquad 1 \qquad -7 \qquad 13 \\
\qquad\qquad\qquad\qquad\qquad\ \uparrow \\
\qquad\qquad\qquad\qquad\ \ P(c)
\end{array}
$$

$\therefore$ the value of $x^3 + 3x^2 - 5x - 1$ at -2 is 13. ***Answer***

You can check the answer to Example 1 by directly substituting -2
for x in $x^3 - 3x^2 - 5x - 1$, as follows:

$$(-2)^3 + 3(-2)^2 - 5(-2) - 1 = -8 + 12 + 10 - 1 = 13. \quad \checkmark$$

The following assertion is an important corollary of the remainder
theorem.

FACTOR THEOREM

$x - r$ is a factor of a polynomial $P(x)$ if and only if r is a root of the
equation $P(x) = 0$.

PROOF

If r is a root of $P(x) = 0$, then by the definition of root, $P(r) = 0$. Therefore, by the remainder theorem,

$$P(x) = (x - r)Q(x) + P(r) = (x - r)Q(x) + 0 = (x - r)Q(x)$$

and $(x - r)$ is a factor of $P(x)$. Conversely, if $(x - r)$ is a factor of $P(x)$,
then

$$P(x) = (x - r)Q(x), \text{ so that } P(r) = (r - r)Q(r) = 0 \cdot Q(r) = 0.$$

This theorem can help you identify factors of polynomials.

EXAMPLE 2 Is $x - 3$ a factor of $P(x) = x^4 - 5x^2 - 17x + 15$?

SOLUTION If $P(3) = 0$, then $x - 3$ is a factor. Use synthetic division to find $P(3)$.

$$
\begin{array}{c}
\underline{3}\ \big|\ \ 1 \qquad 0 \qquad -5 \qquad -17 \qquad 15 \\
\qquad\qquad\ \ \ 3 \qquad 9 \qquad 12 \qquad -15 \\
\underline{} \\
\qquad\ \ 1 \qquad 3 \qquad 4 \qquad -5 \qquad 0
\end{array}
$$

$\therefore x - 3$ is a factor of $P(x)$. ***Answer***

Whenever r is a root of the polynomial equation $P(x) = 0$, you find the remaining roots by solving the **depressed equation**

$$P(x) \div (x - r) = 0.$$

EXAMPLE 3   Solve $P(x) = 0$ if $P(x) = 2x^3 + x^2 - 10x - 5 = 0$.

SOLUTION

1. The coefficients are integers.

   Therefore, you can use the theorem on page 224 to identify possible rational roots.

   $2x^3 + x^2 - 10x - 5 = 0$

   The only rational numbers that can be roots are

   $\frac{1}{2}, -\frac{1}{2}, \frac{5}{2}, -\frac{5}{2}, 1, -1, 5, -5.$

2. Use the factor theorem and synthetic substitution to test each possibility. By mentally doing the addition steps in the process, you can arrange the work conveniently, as shown. Row Ⓐ shows the coefficients of the polynomial. Row Ⓑ shows the results of synthetic substitution of $\frac{1}{2}$ for x. Row Ⓒ shows the results of synthetic substitution of $-\frac{1}{2}$ for x.

x				$P(x)$	
	2	1	-10	-5	← Ⓐ
$\frac{1}{2}$	2	2	-9	$-9\frac{1}{2}$	← Ⓑ
$-\frac{1}{2}$	2	0	-10	0	← Ⓒ

$$\therefore P(x) = (x + \tfrac{1}{2})(2x^2 - 10)$$

(x-C)

3. Solve the depressed equation $2x^2 - 10 = 0$:

$$x^2 = 5; \quad x = \sqrt{5} \text{ or } x = -\sqrt{5}$$

$\therefore$ the solution set is $\{-\frac{1}{2}, -\sqrt{5}, \sqrt{5}\}$.   ***Answer***

Oral Exercises

1. The synthetic division of $P(x) = x^3 - 5x^2 + 8$ by $x - 2$ is shown below.

   a. State:
   (i) the quotient;
   (ii) the remainder.
   b. Find $P(2)$.

   $$\begin{array}{r|rrrr} 2 & 1 & -5 & 0 & 8 \\ & & 2 & -6 & -12 \\ \hline & 1 & -3 & -6 & -4 \end{array}$$

2. The synthetic division of $T(x) = x^4 - 6x^2 + 4x - 7$ by $x + 1$ is shown below.

   a. State:
   (i) the quotient;
   (ii) the remainder.
   b. Find $T(-1)$.

   $$\begin{array}{r|rrrrr} -1 & 1 & 0 & -6 & 4 & -7 \\ & & -1 & 1 & 5 & -9 \\ \hline & 1 & -1 & -5 & 9 & -16 \end{array}$$

Written Exercises

Use synthetic division and the remainder theorem to find $P(c)$ for the given polynomial $P(x)$ and number c.

A   **1.** $P(x) = x^3 - 2x^2 + 14x - 23; \; c = 2$

     2. $P(x) = x^4 - 3x^2 + 7x + 2; \; c = 3$

     3. $P(x) = 2x^4 + 9x^3 - x - 1; \; c = -5$

     4. $P(x) = -2x^3 - 15x^2 + 7; \; c = -6$

     5. $P(x) = x^2 + 3x^5 - x; \; c = -3$

     6. $P(x) = x^3 - x^4 + 2x + 1; \; c = -2$

Use the factor theorem to determine whether the first polynomial in each pair is a factor of the second.

     7. $t - 1; \; t^4 - 3t^2 - 2t - 4$ **8.** $s - 3; \; 6 + s + s^3 - 2s^2$

     9. $a + 5; \; 725 - 80a^2 - 16a^3 - a^4$ **10.** $b + 2; \; b^4 + 3b^3 - 3b^2 - 2b + 16$

     11. $x - \sqrt{5}; \; x^3 + 5x + 3x^2 + 15$ **12.** $x + \sqrt{2}; \; x^3 - 2x - x^2 + 2$

     13. $x - 1; \; x^{100} + 5x^{99} - 6$ **14.** $x + 1; \; x^{200} + 1$

Find the solution set of each of the following equations.

     15. $x^3 - 4x^2 + 8x - 5 = 0$ 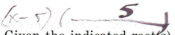   **16.** $x^3 + 6x^2 + 11x + 6 = 0$

     17. $3y^3 + 2y^2 - 8y + 3 = 0$ **18.** $2z^3 + 13z^2 - 13z + 15 = 0$

     19. $2t^4 + 7t^3 + 4t^2 - 7t - 6 = 0$ **20.** $6s^4 + 29s^3 + 40s^2 + 7s - 12 = 0$

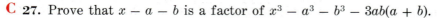

Given the indicated root(s), find the other roots of the equation.

B   **21.** $z^3 + 2z^2 - 3z - 6 = 0; \; -2$ **22.** $z^4 + 2z^3 + 2z - 1 = 0; \; i$ and $-i$

     23. Show that if $P(x) = x^5 + 4x^4 + 4x^3 - x^2 - 4x - 4$, then $x + 2$ is a factor of $P(x)$ and also of $P(x) \div (x + 2)$.

     24. Show that if $P(y) = 2y^4 - 4y^3 + 3y^2 - 2y + 1$, then $y - 1$ is a factor of $P(y)$ and also of $P(y) \div (y - 1)$.

     25. Determine k so that $t + 2$ shall be a factor of
$$3t^3 - 2kt^2 + (k - 1)t + 10.$$

     26. Determine k so that $v - 1$ shall be a factor of
$$2v^3 + (k + 1)v^2 + 6kv + 11.$$

C   **27.** Prove that $x - a - b$ is a factor of $x^3 - a^3 - b^3 - 3ab(a + b)$.

     28. Prove that for every number a and every positive integer n, $x(x - a)$ is a factor of $ax^n - a^n x$.

Computer Key-In

Synthetic division can be done by using a computer. First, the coefficients of the polynomial must be entered and stored in a list. In the program below, this is done by using a *subscripted variable*, C[I]. The coefficients are INPUT in lines 30–80 below.

The synthetic division occurs in lines 150–200. The final value of P is the value of the polynomial. For the polynomial (Section 8-5)

$$2x^3 - 9x^2 + 4x - 7$$

$$C[1] = 2, \quad C[2] = -9, \quad C[3] = 4, \quad C[4] = -7.$$

When the value of x is 3, P begins with the value 2 and takes on values as shown below.

$$P = C[1] = 2$$
$$P = P * X = 2 \times 3 = 6 \longrightarrow P = P + C[2] = 6 + (-9) = -3$$
$$P = P * X = -3 \times 3 = -9 \longrightarrow P = P + C[3] = -9 + 4 = -5$$
$$P = P * X = -5 \times 3 = -15 \longrightarrow P = P + C[4] = -15 + (-7) = -22$$

See if you can determine how these values for P relate to the corresponding synthetic division, which is shown at the bottom on page 303.

```
10   PRINT "WHAT IS THE DEGREE OF YOUR POLYNOMIAL (<=9)";
20   INPUT D
30   FOR I=1 TO D
40   PRINT "INPUT COEFFICIENT OF X↑";D+1-I;
50   INPUT C[I]
60   NEXT I
70   PRINT "INPUT CONSTANT TERM";
80   INPUT C[D+1]
90   PRINT "INPUT X";
100  INPUT X
145  REM***THIS IS SYNTHETIC DIVISION.
150  LET P=C[1]
160  FOR I=2 TO D+1
170  LET P=P*X
180  LET P=P+C[I]
190  NEXT I
200  PRINT "P = ";P
320  PRINT
330  END
```

Exercises

1. RUN the preceding program for $x = 3$, $x = 4$, and $x = 5$. What do you discover?

2. Make changes and additions in the preceding program to make the program on the following page. This program can be used to search for real roots of a polynomial equation.

```
10   PRINT "WHAT IS THE DEGREE OF YOUR POLYNOMIAL (<=9)";
20   INPUT D
30   FOR I=1 TO D
40   PRINT "INPUT COEFFICIENT OF X↑";D+1-I;
50   INPUT C[I]
60   NEXT I
70   PRINT "INPUT CONSTANT TERM";
80   INPUT C[D+1]
90   REM***SEARCH FOR REAL ROOTS (F COUNTS THEM).
100  LET F=0
110  PRINT "FOR X=X1 TO X2 STEP X3;"
120  PRINT "INPUT X1, X2, X3";
130  INPUT X1,X2,X3
140  FOR X=X1 TO X2 STEP X3
150  LET P=C[1]
160  FOR I=2 TO D+1
170  LET P=P*X
180  LET P=P+C[I]
190  NEXT I
200  IF P <> 0 THEN 230
210  PRINT X;" IS A ROOT."
220  GOTO 270
230  IF X <> X1 THEN 250
240  GOTO 280
250  IF Q*P >= 0 THEN 280
260  PRINT "ROOT BETWEEN ";X-X3;" AND ";X
270  LET F=F+1
280  LET Q=P
290  NEXT X
300  IF F>0 THEN 320
310  PRINT "NO REAL ROOTS FOUND"
320  PRINT
330  END
```

Lines 250–260 use the fact that if two values of P have opposite signs, there must be at least one root between the corresponding values of x.

Use this program to locate real roots of $2x^3 + x^2 - 10x - 5 = 0$ (Example 3, Section 8-6). Use -10, 10, 1 for X1, X2, X3.

3. Use the preceding program to locate real roots of

$$x^3 + 6x^2 + 11x + 6 = 0,$$

with $X1 = -10$, $X2 = 10$, $X3 = 1$.

4. Use the preceding program to locate real roots of

$$3x^3 + 2x^2 - 8x + 3 = 0, \text{ with:}$$

a. $X1 = -10$, $X2 = 10$, $X3 = 1$

b. $X1 = -5$, $X2 = 5$, $X3 = 0.1$

What do you discover?

8-7 *Equations with Real Coefficients*

OBJECTIVE   To solve polynomial equations of degree n with real coefficients by using these facts:
1. there are exactly n roots to be found;
2. the imaginary roots occur in conjugate pairs;
3. Descartes' rule of signs can be applied.

The problem of finding the roots of a polynomial equation with *real* coefficients occurs frequently in mathematics and science. In searching for the roots, you can use theorems that you already know, like the one on page 224. It is also useful to know the theorems stated below.

> **THEOREM** (Fundamental Theorem of Algebra)
> Every polynomial equation of positive degree n has exactly n roots.

Some examples are shown in the chart below.

Equation	Degree = Number of Roots	The Roots
1. $x^2 - 6x + 9 = 0$	2	3 and 3
2. $x^3 - 4x^2 + 21x - 34 = 0$	3	$2, 1 + 4i$, and $1 - 4i$
3. $x^4 + 64 = 0$	4	$2 + 2i, 2 - 2i, -2 + 2i$, and $-2 - 2i$
4. $x^5 - 16x = 0$	5	$0, -2, 2, -2i$, and $2i$

In counting the roots of an equation, you may have to count a root more than once. In Equation 1, the root 3 is counted *twice* because $(x - 3)$ can be factored from the polynomial *twice*. Also, some of the roots may be imaginary numbers, as in Equations 2 and 3, even though all the coefficients of the equation are real. In such equations, the imaginary roots occur in conjugate pairs.

> **THEOREM**   If a polynomial equation with real coefficients has $a + bi$ as a root (a and b real, $b \neq 0$), then $a - bi$ is also a root.

The proof of this theorem is outlined in Exercises 22–24, page 314.

EXAMPLE 1   Given that $2 - i$ is a root of
$$P(x) = x^4 - 4x^3 + 13x^2 - 32x + 40 = 0,$$
find the solution set of the equation.

SOLUTION   1. Since the given equation has real coefficients, *both $2 - i$ and $2 + i$* are roots. Therefore, *both $x - (2 - i)$ and $x - (2 + i)$* are factors of $P(x)$. Since they have no factor in common, their product,
$$[(x - 2) + i][(x - 2) - i], \text{ or } x^2 - 4x + 5,$$
is a factor of $P(x)$.

2. $P(x) \div (x^2 - 4x + 5) = x^2 + 8$.

3. $x^2 + 8 = 0$ is the depressed equation, and its roots are $2i\sqrt{2}$ and $-2i\sqrt{2}$.

∴ the solution set of the given equation is
$$\{2 - i, 2 + i, 2i\sqrt{2}, -2i\sqrt{2}\}. \quad \textit{Answer}$$

Some information about the *number* of real roots of a polynomial equation with real coefficients can be obtained from a theorem called **Descartes' rule of signs.** Suppose that you write a polynomial, $P(x)$, in simple form in order of decreasing powers of x and ignore missing terms. If the coefficients of two successive terms are opposite in sign (one positive, the other negative), you say that $P(x)$ has a **variation in sign.** Thus,

$$5x^4 - 3x^2 + 6x - 8$$
$$1 \qquad 2 \qquad 3$$

has 3 variations in sign. Here is Descartes' rule:

THEOREM   The number of positive roots of $P(x) = 0$ where $P(x)$ is a polynomial with real coefficients is equal to the number of variations in sign in $P(x)$, or else is fewer than this number by a positive even integer. The number of negative roots of $P(x) = 0$ is equal to the number of variations in sign in $P(-x)$, or else is fewer than this number by a positive even integer.

EXAMPLE 2   Determine the possible number of **(a)** positive roots, and **(b)** negative roots of $x^3 - x^2 - 5x - 4 = 0$.

SOLUTION   **a.** $x^3 - x^2 - 5x - 4$ has 1 variation in sign.
$$1$$

So $x^3 - x^2 - 5x - 4 = 0$ has 1 positive root. *Answer*

b. Replacing x by $-x$, you have
$$(-x)^3 - (-x)^2 - 5(-x) - 4, \text{ or } -x^3 - x^2 + 5x - 4.$$

This polynomial has 2 variations in sign, so $x^3 - x^2 - 5x - 4 = 0$ has either 2 negative roots or 0 negative roots. ***Answer***

Because an equation of degree 3 like the one in Example 2 has exactly 3 roots, there are only two possibilities for the nature of the roots of $x^3 - x^2 - 5x - 4 = 0$ as shown in the rows of the following chart:

Number of Positive Real Roots	Number of Negative Real Roots	Number of Imaginary Roots
1	2	0
1	0	2

Written Exercises

Apply Descartes' rule of signs to state the possibilities for the nature of the roots of each equation.

A **1.** $x^4 + x^3 + x^2 + x + 1 = 0$ **2.** $x^7 - x^2 + 1 = 0$

   3. $w^4 + w^2 - 1 = 0$ **4.** $3x^6 + x^4 + x^2 + 5 = 0$

   5. $t^5 - t^3 - 2t + 3 = 0$ **6.** $r^5 + 2 = 0$

   7. $y^7 - 9 = 0$ **8.** $v^6 - v^4 - 3 = 0$

   9. If two roots of $x^3 + x^2 + 2x + 2 = 0$ are -1 and $-\sqrt{2}i$, what must be the other root? Verify your answer.

   10. If two roots of $x^3 - 5x^2 + 9x - 5 = 0$ are 1 and $2 + i$, what must be the other root? Verify your answer.

B **11.** A cubic equation with real coefficients has roots 2 and $1 - 3i$. What must be the third root? Find such an equation.

   12. A cubic equation with real coefficients has roots -3 and $5i$. What must be the third root? Find such an equation.

   13. Given that one root of $2x^3 - 11x^2 + 62x + 34 = 0$ is $3 - 5i$, solve the equation.

   14. Given that one root of $y^3 + 3y^2 + 4y + 2 = 0$ is $-1 + i$, solve the equation.

   15. Given that one root of $t^4 + 3t^3 + 6t^2 - 2t - 60 = 0$ is $-1 + 3i$, solve the equation.

   16. Given that one root of $v^4 + 10v^3 + 35v^2 + 50v + 34 = 0$ is $-4 + i$, solve the equation.

State whether each assertion is true. Justify your answer.

17. If $3 + 5i$ is a root of a polynomial equation, then so is $3 - 5i$.

18. Every polynomial with real coefficients and odd degree has at least one real root.

19. There exists a polynomial of degree 2 having $1 + 4i$, $1 - 4i$, and 3 as its roots.

20. Every cubic polynomial with real coefficients can be expressed as the product of three linear polynomials with real coefficients.

C 21. Explain why the conjugate of a real number is the number itself.

Let a, b, c, d, and e denote real numbers. Prove that each statement in Exercises 22–24 is true.

You can use the following two results in your proofs (see the proof on page 242 and Exercise 14 on page 243): The conjugate of the sum of $a + bi$ and $c + di$ is the sum of the conjugates of the numbers. The conjugate of the product of $a + bi$ and $c + di$ is the product of the conjugates of the numbers.

22. For each positive integer k, the conjugate of $e \cdot (a + bi)^k$ is $e \cdot (a - bi)^k$. (*Hint:* Use Exercise 21.)

23. If $P(x) = a_0x^n + a_1x^{n-1} + \cdots + a_n$ is a polynomial with *real* coefficients, then the conjugate of $P(a + bi)$ is $P(a - bi)$. (*Hint:* Use Exercise 22.)

24. If $P(x)$ is the polynomial described in Exercise 23, and if $P(a + bi) = 0$, then $P(a - bi) = 0$.

25. Find one real root of $x^5 - x^4 + 3x^3 - 3x^2 + 2x - 2 = 0$ and then apply Descartes' rule to the depressed equation to show that there are no other real roots.

Self-Test 2

1. Use synthetic division to find the quotient and remainder when $6x^4 - 3x^3 + 4x - 8$ is divided by $x - 3$.   Obj. 8-5, p. 303

2. Find the roots of $x^3 - 5x^2 - 4x + 20 = 0$.   Obj. 8-6, p. 305

3. Given that one root of $x^4 - 6x^3 + 8x^2 + 12x - 20 = 0$ is $3 + i$, solve the equation.   Obj. 8-7, p. 311

Check your answers with those at the back of the book.

8-8 *Estimating Real Roots*

OBJECTIVE To use the graph of a polynomial function, P, to find estimates of the real roots of the equation $P(x) = 0$.

Some idea of the nature of the roots of the equation

$$x^3 - x^2 - 5x - 4 = 0$$

was obtained in Example 2, pages 312–313. More information can be found from the graph of the polynomial function P, where $P(x) = x^3 - x^2 - 5x - 4$.

EXAMPLE 1 Graph $P(x) = x^3 - x^2 - 5x - 4$.

SOLUTION Use synthetic division to find some values for $P(x)$. When the points $(x, P(x))$ are connected by a smooth curve, you obtain the graph below.

x				$P(x)$
0	1	-1	-5	-4
1	1	0	-5	-9
2	1	1	-3	-10
3	1	2	1	-1
4	1	3	7	24
-1	1	-2	-3	-1
-2	1	-3	1	-6
-3	1	-4	7	-25

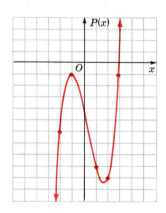

The graph in Example 1 meets the x-axis exactly once. The x-coordinate of the point where it intersects the x-axis (the **x-intercept** of the graph) is between 3 and 4, but is closer to 3. Thus, the equation $P(x) = 0$, or

$$x^3 - x^2 - 5x - 4 = 0,$$

has exactly one real root, which is a number greater than, but close to, 3. The other two roots of the equation must, therefore, be conjugate imaginary numbers.

In drawing the graphs of polynomial functions as smooth unbroken curves, you assume that $P(x)$ takes on every value between any two of its values. This fact is expressed formally as the *property of continuity*, stated on the following page.

> ### PROPERTY OF CONTINUITY
>
> If P is a polynomial function with real coefficients, and if m is any number between $P(a)$ and $P(b)$, then there is at least one number c between a and b for which $P(c) = m$.

Recall that a *root* of a polynomial equation

$$P(x) = 0$$

is also called a *zero* of the function, P. Thus, finding the zeros of the function P is equivalent to finding the roots of the equation $P(x) = 0$.

EXAMPLE 2   Use a graph to estimate to the nearest half unit each of the zeros of P for $P(x) = -x^3 + 2x^2 + 4x - 7$.

SOLUTION   1. Compute a table of values of the polynomial, plot the corresponding points, and sketch the graph.

x				$P(x)$
0	-1	2	4	-7
1	-1	1	5	-2
2	-1	0	4	1
3	-1	-1	1	-4
4	-1	-2	-4	-23
-1	-1	3	1	-8
-2	-1	4	-4	1
-3	-1	5	-11	26

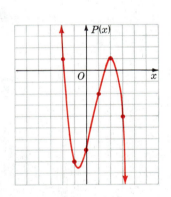

2. Reading the graph to the nearest half unit, you find the zeros of P to be, approximately, -2, 1.5, and 2.5.   *Answer*

Written Exercises

Graph each polynomial function, P, and estimate any real zeros to the nearest half unit.

A **1.** $P(x) = 2x^3$

2. $P(x) = -x^3$

3. $P(x) = x^3 - 1$

4. $P(x) = x^3 + 2$

5. $P(x) = x^3 - 9x$

6. $P(x) = x^3 + 9x$

7. $P(x) = x^3 + 4x^2$

8. $P(x) = x^3 - 4x^2$

9. $P(x) = x^3 + 5x^2 + 2x - 8$

10. $P(x) = 3x^3 - 7x^2 - 11x + 15$

11. $P(x) = x^4 + 4x^3 - 4x^2 - 16x$

12. $P(x) = x^5 + 2x^4 + x^3 + 1$

B 13. Observe that if $P(x) = x^2 + 3x + 2$, then $P(0) = 2$ and $P(5) = 42$. The principle of continuity assures you that there must be a number c between 0 and 5 such that $P(c) = 6$. Find c.

14. In Exercise 13, $P(-7) = 30$ and $P(-1) = 0$. Find a number c, $-7 < c < -1$, such that $P(c) = 12$.

15. If $P(x) = x^2 - 4x - 8$, then $P(0) = -8$ and $P(6) = 4$. Find a number c, $0 < c < 6$, such that $P(c) = 0$.

16. In Exercise 15, $P(-4) = 24$. Find a number c, $-4 < c < 0$, such that $P(c) = 0$.

Biography Benjamin Banneker

Benjamin Banneker was born on a farm in Baltimore County, Maryland, in 1731. He attended a Friends school, where his mathematical skill soon became evident. Banneker's fascination with mathematics was so strong that, while working on the family farm, he would create and then solve his own mathematical problems.

In 1753 Banneker applied his mathematical expertise to the construction of a clock. His only tools were a geometry book, a copy of Newton's *Principia*, a picture of a clock, and an old pocket watch which he used as a model. Banneker made all the necessary mathematical calculations, carried out all measurements with a compass and ruler, and hand-carved each gear for his clock. It was the first clock ever to be constructed in America, and it kept perfect time for more than forty years!

During the Revolutionary War, Banneker began to study astronomy. He was soon able to make astronomical calculations with great accuracy. Contradicting the predictions of two eminent mathematicians of the day, Banneker correctly predicted the solar eclipse of 1789. Three years later he began publishing a series of ten almanacs which became popular throughout the mid-Atlantic states. Banneker's almanacs included weather forecasts, tide tables, information about phases of the moon, and times for sunrise and sunset. Banneker made all his own calculations for these almanacs.

In addition to being a skillful mathematician and astronomer, Benjamin Banneker was an adept surveyor. Along with Pierre L'Enfant and Andrew Ellicott, Banneker is credited with designing the nation's new capital, Washington, D.C.

8-9 *Linear Interpolation*

OBJECTIVE   **Given a function $y(x)$ defined by a table, to use linear interpolation to approximate the value of y for x not in the table, or to estimate x for y not in the table.**

Many applications of mathematics in business, engineering, and science involve functions whose values are given in tables rather than calculated from formulas. The square root function whose values are given in Table 1, page 638, is an example.

To work with such functions, you use **linear interpolation** to find approximations for function values that are *not* given in the tables. Here is how the process works. Suppose that you are given two points $P(x_1, y_1)$ and $Q(x_2, y_2)$ on the graph of a function (Figure 8-9). Suppose also that you are *not* given any points on the graph between P and Q.

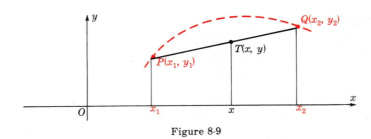

Figure 8-9

Since you do not know what curve connecting P and Q is the actual graph of the function (the dashed red curve is just one of many possibilities), you might as well make the simplest choice, namely, $\overline{PQ}$, the line segment joining P and Q. Of course, for the square root function and virtually every other function given in tables, the line segment choice is in error. But, for x_1 and x_2 close to each other, the error is usually small enough to be acceptable.

Now, to find an approximation to the function at x between x_1 and x_2, you need only compute y at the point $T(x, y)$ on the line segment $\overline{PQ}$. Since P, T, and Q are collinear, you have

slope of $\overline{PT}$ = slope of $\overline{PQ}$

$$\frac{y - y_1}{x - x_1} = \frac{y_2 - y_1}{x_2 - x_1}$$

Let $y - y_1 = d$ and $x - x_1 = c$ (Figure 8-10), and you have

$$\frac{d}{c} = \frac{y_2 - y_1}{x_2 - x_1}$$

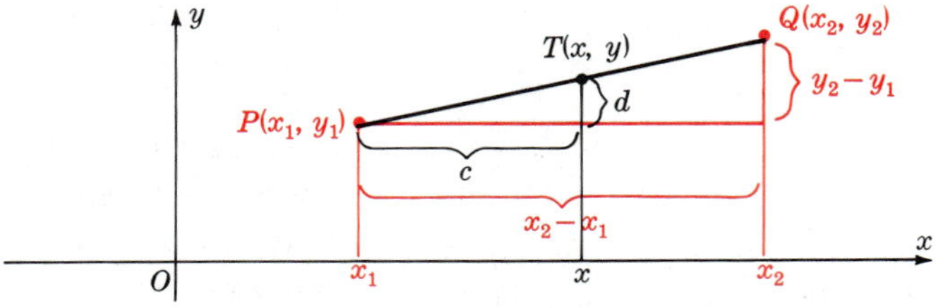

Figure 8-10

Thus:

$$d = \frac{c}{x_2 - x_1}(y_2 - y_1) \quad \text{and} \quad c = \frac{d}{y_2 - y_1}(x_2 - x_1),$$

where

$$y = y_1 + d \quad \text{and} \quad x = x_1 + c.$$

In actual calculations, you arrange the work as follows:

Number	Function Value
$x_2 - x_1 \begin{bmatrix} x_2 \\ c\begin{bmatrix} x \\ x_1 \end{bmatrix} \end{bmatrix}$	$\begin{bmatrix} y_2 \\ y \\ y_1 \end{bmatrix}d\end{bmatrix} y_2 - y_1$

For example, to use linear interpolation in Table 1 to find an approximation of $\sqrt{2.37}$, take $x_1 = 2.3$ and $x_2 = 2.4$, and proceed as follows:

Number	Square Root
$0.1 \begin{bmatrix} 2.4 \\ 0.07\begin{bmatrix} 2.37 \\ 2.3 \end{bmatrix} \end{bmatrix}$	$\begin{bmatrix} 1.549 \\ \sqrt{2.37} \\ 1.517 \end{bmatrix}d\end{bmatrix} 0.032$

$$d = \frac{0.07}{0.1}(0.032) = 0.7(0.032) = 0.0224$$

$\therefore \ \sqrt{2.37} \approx 1.517 + d = 1.517 + 0.0224.$

$\therefore \ \sqrt{2.37} \approx 1.539$ (correct to three decimal places).

If you are given a value y of the function, $y(x)$, defined by a table, the process of finding the corresponding number x is called **inverse interpolation.**

EXAMPLE The following table* shows the height of a stem of bamboo, measured from the time the sprout came up.

Age x in Weeks	1	2	3	4	5	6	7	8	9	10	11	12
Height y in Meters	0.7	1.5	2.5	4.0	6.2	8.3	10.2	12.0	13.2	13.8	14.1	14.2

Use inverse linear interpolation to find the age to the nearest tenth of a week when the stem was 7.0 m tall. (See next page for solution.)

*Biological Sciences Curriculum Study: BIOLOGICAL SCIENCE: MOLECULES TO MAN, Revised Edition, p. 765. Copyright © 1968, 1963 by The Regents of the University of Colorado.

SOLUTION The height, 7.0, falls between 6.2 and 8.3 in the table. Therefore, make the following chart.

Age	Height
6	8.3
x	7.0
5	6.2

$$c = \frac{0.8}{2.1}(1) \approx 0.38$$

$$\therefore x \approx 5 + c \approx 5 + 0.4, \text{ or } 5.4 \text{ weeks.}$$

Answer

Written Exercises

Use linear interpolation in Table 1, page 638, to find a three-decimal-place approximation to the indicated square root.

A **1.** $\sqrt{1.72}$　　　　**2.** $\sqrt{2.15}$　　　　**3.** $\sqrt{4.68}$　　　　**4.** $\sqrt{5.31}$

　　5. $\sqrt{6.03}$　　　　**6.** $\sqrt{8.36}$　　　　**7.** $\sqrt{9.14}$　　　　**8.** $\sqrt{7.59}$

Use linear interpolation in Table 2, page 639, to find three-decimal-place approximations to the indicated cube roots.

9. $\sqrt[3]{1.33}$　　　　**10.** $\sqrt[3]{3.67}$　　　　**11.** $\sqrt[3]{5.15}$　　　　**12.** $\sqrt[3]{8.72}$

Use inverse linear interpolation in Table 2, page 639, to find a two-decimal-place approximation of the number whose cube root is given.

13. 1.550　　　　**14.** 1.842　　　　**15.** 1.085　　　　**16.** 2.151

17. Given the following entries from a table for a function f:

x	8.2	8.4	8.6	8.8
$f(x)$	30.38	32.64	32.92	33.19

  a. Use linear interpolation to estimate $f(8.52)$.
  b. Use inverse linear interpolation to estimate x, if $f(x) = 32.50$.

18. Given the following entries from a table for a function E:

x	0.20	0.25	0.30	0.35
$E(x)$	1.221	1.284	1.350	1.419

  a. Use linear interpolation to estimate $E(0.28)$.
  b. Use inverse linear interpolation to estimate x, if $E(x) = 1.375$.

B **19.** The table* at the top of the next page shows the average mass of a large number of corn seedlings, recorded every two weeks.

*Biological Sciences Curriculum Study: BIOLOGICAL SCIENCE: MOLECULES TO MAN, Revised Edition, p. 765. Copyright © 1968, 1963 by The Regents of the University of Colorado.

Age in Weeks	2	4	6	8	10	12	14	16	18	20
Average Mass in Grams	21	28	58	76	170	422	706	853	924	966

a. Estimate the average mass of the seedlings at age 6.5 weeks.
b. Estimate the age of the seedlings when their average mass was 300 g.

20. The temperature of a beaker of water is read every 0.1 min as it is heated, with the results shown in the following table.

Time in Minutes	0.0	0.1	0.2	0.3	0.4
Temperature (°C)	30.2	31.5	32.7	34.0	35.1

a. Estimate the temperature 0.37 min after the heating began.
b. Estimate how long it took the temperature to rise to 31.9°C.

Self-Test 3

VOCABULARY   linear interpolation (p. 318)
inverse interpolation (p. 319)

Graph each polynomial function, P, and estimate any real zeros to the nearest half unit.

1. $P(x) = x^3 - 4x$ **2.** $P(x) = 3x^3 - 16x^2 + 12x + 16$ Obj. 8-8, p. 315

3. Given that $\sqrt[3]{5.2} \approx 1.732$ and $\sqrt[3]{5.3} \approx 1.744$, use linear interpolation to find a three-decimal-place approximation of $\sqrt[3]{5.27}$.   Obj. 8-9, p. 318

Check your answers with those at the back of the book.

Chapter Summary

1. The *solution set* of a system of linear equations in two variables is the set of ordered pairs that satisfy both equations. The solution set of a system of linear equations in three variables is the set of ordered triples that satisfy all three equations.

2. For a system of linear equations in two variables, either the graphs of the equations intersect, or the graphs are parallel, or the graphs coincide. Correspondingly, the system has one solution, no solution, or an infinite number of solutions. A system that has at least one solution is *consistent*, and a system that has no solution is *inconsistent*.

3. Systems of linear equations can be solved by the *substitution method* or the *linear-combination* method. Systems of linear equations are useful for solving word problems.

4. In a coordinate plane, the graph of a linear inequality in two variables is an *open* or a *closed half-plane*. The graph of the solution set of a system of linear inequalities in two variables is the intersection of the open or closed half-planes representing the inequalities.

5. Synthetic division may be used to divide a polynomial $P(x)$ by $x - c$.

6. The remainder theorem states that for every polynomial $P(x)$ of degree n $(n \geqslant 1)$ over the set of complex numbers, and for every complex number c, there exists a polynomial $Q(x)$ of degree $n - 1$, such that $P(x) = Q(x)(x - c) + P(c)$. The factor theorem states that $x - r$ is a factor of $P(x)$ if and only if r is a root of the equation $P(x) = 0$.

7. Every polynomial equation, $P(x) = 0$, of degree n $(n \geqslant 1)$ with real coefficients has exactly n roots; if $a + bi$ is a root of $P(x) = 0$, then $a - bi$ is also a root.

8. Descartes' rule of signs states that the number of positive roots of $P(x) = 0$, where $P(x)$ is a polynomial with real coefficients, is equal to the number of variations in sign in $P(x)$, or else is fewer than this number by a positive even integer. The number of negative roots of $P(x) = 0$ is equal to the number of variations in sign in $P(-x)$, or else is fewer than this number by a positive even integer.

Chapter Review ———————————

Give the letter of the correct answer.

1. Solve the system: $x + 2y = 10$ 8-1
$3x + 4y = 8$

  a. $(12, -11)$ **b.** $(11, -12)$ **c.** $(-12, 11)$ **d.** $(-12, -11)$

2. A barge can travel 96 km downstream in 4 h, but it requires 6 h to travel the same distance upstream. Find the rate of the current. 8-2

  a. 6 km/h   **b.** 4 km/h   **c.** 2 km/h   **d.** 10 km/h

3. Tell which of the following points does *not* lie on the graph of the system: 8-3

$$y \leq 3x + 2$$
$$y \geq 2 - x$$

  a. $(2, 0)$ **b.** $(1, 0)$ **c.** $(0, 2)$ **d.** $(2, 2)$

4. Solve the system:
$$x + 2y = 8$$
$$2x + y + z = 11$$
$$x + y + 2z = 13$$

8-4

  a. $(-2, 3, 4)$ **b.** $(2, -3, 4)$ **c.** $(2, 3, 4)$ **d.** $(-2, -3, 4)$

5. When $6x^5 - 3x^4 + 2x^2 - 1$ is divided by $x - 2$, what is the remainder?

8-5

  a. -41 **b.** -153 **c.** 39 **d.** 151

6. Find $P(-2)$, given that $P(x) = x^5 - 3x^3 + 4x^2 - 10$.

8-6

  a. -6 **b.** -2 **c.** -38 **d.** 54

7. Given that one root of $x^3 - 6x^2 + 13x - 10 = 0$ is $2 + i$, find the solution set.

8-7

  a. $\{2 + i, 2 - i, -2\}$ **b.** $\{i + 2, i - 2, 2\}$ **c.** $\{2 - i, 2 + i, 2\}$

8. Given that $P(x) = x^3 - 4x^2 + 4$, determine the number of zeros between 0 and 5.

8-8

  a. 0 **b.** 1 **c.** 2 **d.** 3

9. Given that $P(2.1) = 8.523$ and $P(2.2) = 9.629$, find a three-decimal-place approximation for $P(2.16)$ using linear interpolation.

8-9

  a. 9.187 **b.** 10.293 **c.** 15.159 **d.** 8.187

Chapter Test

1. Solve the system: $\quad 4a - b = 10$
$$3a + 5b = 19$$

8-1

2. Adult tickets for a concert cost $5.00 each, and student tickets cost $3.50. Receipts from ticket sales totaled $870. If 210 tickets were sold in all, how many were sold at each rate?

8-2

3. Graph the solution set of the system: $\quad 2x + 3y < 12$
$$3x - 2y \geq 6$$

8-3

4. Solve the system: $\quad 2x + y - z = 0$
$$x + y + 2z = 4$$
$$x + 2y + z = 6$$

8-4

5. Find the quotient and remainder when $2a^3 - 5a^2 + 5a - 1$ is divided by $a - 3$.

8-5

6. Given that $P(x) = 6x^3 - 4x^2 + 2x - 1$, find $P(-2)$.

8-6

7. Given that $i\sqrt{2}$ is a root of $x^4 + x^3 - 10x^2 + 2x - 24 = 0$, find the solution set.

8-7

8. Graph the function $P(x) = x^3 - 2x^2$ and estimate any real zeros to the nearest half unit.

8-8

9. Given that $P(-1) = 2.56$ and $P(1) = 8.42$, approximate $P(0)$ to the nearest hundredth using linear interpolation.

8-9

The conic sections studied in analytic geometry are often used by architects. In Montreal's Olympic Stadium shown above, several ellipses are readily seen. Note the circular structure shown at the upper left.

9

ANALYTIC GEOMETRY

07-02-86

DISTANCE AND SLOPE RELATIONSHIPS

9-1 *Distance and Midpoint Formulas*

OBJECTIVE To find the distance between any two points and the midpoint of the line segment joining them.

To find the distance between two points on a number line, simply take the absolute value of the difference of their coordinates. To denote the distance from A to B, write AB. Thus, for the points shown in Figure 9-1,

$$RS = |-3 - 1| = 4 \qquad ST = |6 - (-3)| = 9 \qquad TR = |1 - 6| = 5$$

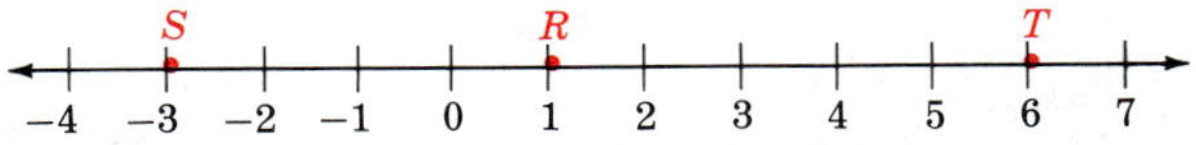

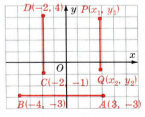

Figure 9-1

Since $|a - b| = |b - a|$, the order in which the coordinates are subtracted does not matter.

Use a similar method to find the distance between two points in a coordinate plane if they lie on the same horizontal or vertical line. For example, the distances between the pairs of points shown in Figure 9-2 are:

$$AB = |-4 - 3| = 7$$
$$CD = |4 - (-1)| = 5$$
$$PQ = |y_2 - y_1| = |y_1 - y_2|$$

Figure 9-2

325

A formula for the distance between *any* two points in a coordinate plane is a consequence of the familiar Pythagorean theorem:

PYTHAGOREAN THEOREM

If the length of the hypotenuse of a right triangle is c, and the lengths of the other two sides (the legs) are a and b, then

$$c^2 = a^2 + b^2.$$

The converse of this theorem is true as well:

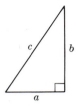

If the lengths a, b, and c of the sides of a triangle satisfy the equation $c^2 = a^2 + b^2$, then the triangle is a right triangle.

Now, let $P_1(x_1, y_1)$ and $P_2(x_2, y_2)$ be any two points not on the same horizontal or vertical line. Then $\overline{P_1 P_2}$ is the hypotenuse of the right triangle having vertices P_1, P_2, and $Q(x_2, y_1)$ (see Figure 9-3). The lengths of the legs are given by

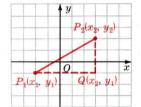

Figure 9-3

$$P_1 Q = |x_2 - x_1| \quad \text{and} \quad QP_2 = |y_2 - y_1|.$$

Therefore, by the Pythagorean theorem,

$$(P_1 P_2)^2 = (P_1 Q)^2 + (QP_2)^2$$
$$(P_1 P_2)^2 = |x_2 - x_1|^2 + |y_2 - y_1|^2$$
$$(P_1 P_2)^2 = (x_2 - x_1)^2 + (y_2 - y_1)^2.$$

Taking the principal square root of each side (since lengths must be nonnegative), you have:

DISTANCE FORMULA

The distance between the points $P_1(x_1, y_1)$ and $P_2(x_2, y_2)$ is

$$\boldsymbol{P_1 P_2 = \sqrt{(x_2 - x_1)^2 + (y_2 - y_1)^2}.}$$

It is easy to see that the formula is valid even if P_1 and P_2 are on the same horizontal or vertical line.

EXAMPLE 1 Find the distance between $P_1(5, 4)$ and $P_2(-3, 0)$.

SOLUTION $P_1 P_2 = \sqrt{(-3 - 5)^2 + (0 - 4)^2}$

$\qquad\qquad\quad = \sqrt{64 + 16} = \sqrt{80} = 4\sqrt{5}.$ *Answer*

A formula for the distance r from the origin to any given point (a, b) is $r = \sqrt{a^2 + b^2}$ (see Problem 1 on page 328).

The distance formula can be used to prove a formula for the coordinates of the midpoint of a segment (see Problem 4 on page 328):

MIDPOINT FORMULA

The midpoint of the line segment joining the points $P_1(x_1, y_1)$ and $P_2(x_2, y_2)$ is

$$M\left(\frac{x_1 + x_2}{2}, \frac{y_1 + y_2}{2}\right).$$

EXAMPLE 2 Find the midpoint of the line segment joining $(1, 3)$ and $(-3, 4)$.

SOLUTION The midpoint is $\left(\dfrac{1 + (-3)}{2}, \dfrac{3 + 4}{2}\right)$, or $\left(-1, \dfrac{7}{2}\right)$. *Answer*

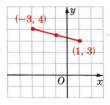

EXAMPLE 3 Prove that the diagonals of a rectangle bisect each other.

SOLUTION Any rectangle can be placed with a vertex at the origin and adjacent sides on the x- and y-axes, and with the vertices labeled as shown.

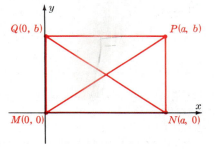

Midpoint of $\overline{MP}$ is $\left(\dfrac{0 + a}{2}, \dfrac{0 + b}{2}\right) = \left(\dfrac{a}{2}, \dfrac{b}{2}\right)$.

Midpoint of $\overline{NQ}$ is $\left(\dfrac{a + 0}{2}, \dfrac{0 + b}{2}\right) = \left(\dfrac{a}{2}, \dfrac{b}{2}\right)$.

Since the diagonals have a common midpoint, they bisect each other.

Oral Exercises

Find the distance between the given points.

1. $(2, 1)$, $(2, 6)$ **2.** $(4, -3)$, $(0, -3)$ **3.** $(-3, 2)$, $(1, 2)$

4. $(1, -2)$, $(1, -6)$ **5.** $(0, -3)$, $(4, 0)$ **6.** $(0, 0)$, $(-4, 3)$

7–12. Find the midpoint of the segment joining each pair of points in Exercises 1–6.

Written Exercises

Find **(a)** the length of the line segment joining the given points and **(b)** the midpoint of the segment. Express all radicals in simplest form.

A **1.** $(2, -3), (-2, 0)$ **2.** $(3, 2), (-1, -2)$ **3.** $(5, -1), (-1, 5)$

4. $(4, -6), (-1, 6)$ **5.** $(-1, 3), \left(\frac{1}{2}, 1\right)$ **6.** $\left(1, -\frac{2}{5}\right), \left(\frac{3}{5}, \frac{2}{5}\right)$

7. $(4, \sqrt{3}), (2, -\sqrt{3})$ **8.** $(3\sqrt{2}, \sqrt{3}), (\sqrt{2}, 3\sqrt{3})$

9. $(\sqrt{3}, 1), (1, \sqrt{3})$ **10.** $(\sqrt{2}, \sqrt{3} + \sqrt{2}), (-\sqrt{2}, \sqrt{3} - \sqrt{2})$

11. $(3a, -2b), (-a, 2b)$ **12.** $(3p + q, q), (p + q, -q)$

If M is the midpoint of the segment $\overline{PQ}$, find the coordinates of P.

13. $M(1, 3), Q(0, 0)$ **14.** $M(0, 0), Q(1, 3)$ **15.** $M(1, -4), Q(3, 2)$

16. $M(-6, 1), Q(-2, -5)$ **17.** $M(a, b), Q(0, 0)$ **18.** $M(0, 0), Q(a, b)$

The vertices of a triangle are given. For each triangle, find **(a)** whether it is isosceles, and **(b)** whether it is a right triangle. If it is a right triangle, find its area.

B **19.** $A(-3, 5), B(-1, -3), C(7, -1)$ **20.** $A(1, 0), B(9, -8), C(2, -7)$

21. $A(0, 1), B(6, 1), C(3, 4)$ **22.** $A(-1, 6), B(8, -6), C(-4, 0)$

23. $A(3, 0), B(-1, 2), C(-4, -3)$ **24.** $A(0, 3), B(2, -1), C(-4, -4)$

Problems

A **1.** Prove that the distance from any point (a, b) to the origin is $\sqrt{a^2 + b^2}$.

2. $A(0, 0), B(6, 0),$ and $C(0, 8)$ are the vertices of a right triangle. Prove that the midpoint of the hypotenuse is equidistant from the three vertices.

3. Write a linear equation expressing the condition that a point (x, y) is equidistant from the given points.
a. $(0, 0)$ and $(1, -3)$ **b.** $(1, -3)$ and $(3, 5)$

B **4.** Use the distance formula to prove the midpoint formula. That is, for $P_1(x_1, y_1), P_2(x_2, y_2),$ and $M\left(\dfrac{x_1 + x_2}{2}, \dfrac{y_1 + y_2}{2}\right)$, prove that

$$MP_1 = MP_2 = \frac{1}{2}P_1P_2.$$

5. Find all values of a for which the point $(a, 4)$ is 5 units from $(3, 1)$.

C **6.** Prove that the segment joining the midpoints of two sides of a triangle is parallel to, and half as long as, the third side.

9-2 *Perpendicular Lines*

OBJECTIVE   To determine the relationship between the slopes of perpendicular lines.

Recall from Section 3-5 that two nonvertical lines are parallel if and only if their slopes are equal. Thus, you can tell that the lines

$$3x - 2y = 4 \quad \text{and} \quad 6x - 4y + 1 = 0$$

are parallel by rewriting their equations in slope-intercept form,

$$y = \tfrac{3}{2}x - 2 \quad \text{and} \quad y = \tfrac{3}{2}x + \tfrac{1}{4},$$

and noting that the slope of each line is $\tfrac{3}{2}$.

Two lines are **perpendicular** if they intersect at right angles. Thus, any horizontal line, such as $y = 3$ in Figure 9-4, is perpendicular to any vertical line, for example, $x = -2$.

The lines shown in Figure 9-5 also are perpendicular. Their equations are

$$y = \tfrac{1}{2}x + \tfrac{3}{2} \quad \text{and} \quad y = -2x + 5,$$

and their slopes are $\tfrac{1}{2}$ and -2. Notice that the product of their slopes is -1.

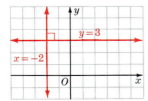

Figure 9-4

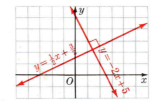

Figure 9-5

This relationship is true for all pairs of perpendicular lines neither of which is vertical. (Of course, if neither line is vertical, then neither line is horizontal.) The proof of the following theorem is outlined in Exercises 23–26.

> Two nonvertical lines are perpendicular if and only if the product of their slopes is -1.

Represent the lines by L_1 and L_2 and their slopes by m_1 and m_2, respectively. The theorem is equivalent to the two if-then statements at the top of the next page. Notice that the two statements are converses of each other:

> 1. If L_1 and L_2 are perpendicular, then $m_1m_2 = -1$.
> 2. If $m_1m_2 = -1$, then L_1 and L_2 are perpendicular.

Notice that $m_1m_2 = -1$ is equivalent to $m_1 = -\dfrac{1}{m_2}$ and $m_2 = -\dfrac{1}{m_1}$. (Since neither line is horizontal, $m_1 \neq 0$ and $m_2 \neq 0$.) Thus, nonvertical lines are perpendicular if and only if their slopes are the negatives of the reciprocals of each other.

EXAMPLE 1 Find an equation of the line that passes through $(2, -4)$ and is perpendicular to the line $2x + 5y = 3$.

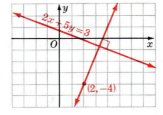

SOLUTION

1. Write $2x + 5y = 3$ in slope-intercept form:

$$y = -\tfrac{2}{5}x + \tfrac{3}{5}$$

∴ the given line has slope $-\tfrac{2}{5}$. Any line perpendicular to it has slope $-\dfrac{1}{-\frac{2}{5}} = \tfrac{5}{2}$.

2. The required line passes through $(2, -4)$ and has slope $\tfrac{5}{2}$. Use point-slope form.

$$y - y_1 = m(x - x_1)$$
$$y + 4 = \tfrac{5}{2}(x - 2)$$
$$5x - 2y = 18. \quad \textbf{\textit{Answer}}$$

The distance from a point P to a line L means the distance between P and the point of L nearest to P. This distance is the length of the segment, perpendicular to L, joining P to L.

EXAMPLE 2 Find the distance from $P(-5, 0)$ to the line L_1 whose equation is $2x + y = 5$.

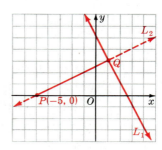

SOLUTION

1. Since the slope of L_1 is -2, the slope of the line L_2 through P perpendicular to L_1 is $\tfrac{1}{2}$. Use the point-slope form to write the equation of L_2:

$$y = \tfrac{1}{2}(x + 5).$$

2. Solve the system $2x + y = 5$
$$y = \tfrac{1}{2}(x + 5)$$

to find the point Q where lines L_1 and L_2 intersect.

Substitute $\frac{1}{2}(x + 5)$ for y in the first equation:

$$2x + \tfrac{1}{2}(x + 5) = 5$$
$$\tfrac{5}{2}x = \tfrac{5}{2}$$
$$x = 1$$
$$y = \tfrac{1}{2}(1 + 5) = 3$$

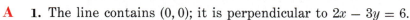

$\therefore$ lines L_1 and L_2 intersect at $Q(1, 3)$.

3. The distance from P to L_1 is PQ.

$$PQ = \sqrt{(1 - (-5))^2 + (3 - 0)^2} = \sqrt{36 + 9} = \sqrt{45} = 3\sqrt{5}. \quad \textit{Answer}$$

Oral Exercises

Give an equation of the line through the origin that is perpendicular to the given line.

1. $y = -2x$
2. $y = 2x + 3$
3. $x = 6$
4. $y = -2$
5. $y = -x + 2$
6. $y = x$
7. $y = -\frac{1}{3}x + 2$
8. $y = \frac{1}{2}x - 3$
9. $3x = 2y - 5$

10. Give an equation of the line perpendicular to $y = 4x + 5$ and having the same y-intercept.

Determine whether or not the lines with the given equations are perpendicular.

11. $y = 2x - 3$
    $y = \frac{1}{2}x + 2$

12. $y = 5 - 3x$
    $x + 3y = 2$

13. $6x - 3y = 8$
    $x + 2y = 4$

Written Exercises

4×4

Find an equation of the line that satisfies the stated conditions.

A 1. The line contains $(0, 0)$; it is perpendicular to $2x - 3y = 6$.
2. The line contains $(0, 2)$; it is perpendicular to $x + y = 5$.
3. The line contains $(-1, 0)$; it is perpendicular to $x - 2y = 1$.
4. The line contains $(2, -3)$; it is perpendicular to $2x - 3y = 4$.
5. The line is perpendicular to $3x - y = 1$ at $(1, 2)$.
6. The line is perpendicular to $5x + 3y = 2$ at $(1, -1)$.
7. The line contains $(0, 4)$; it is perpendicular to the line through $(3, 1)$ and $(1, 5)$.
8. The line contains $(1, 0)$; it is perpendicular to the line through $(2, 0)$ and $(0, 3)$.

Find an equation of the line that satisfies the stated conditions.

9. The line is perpendicular to the line $2x - 5y = 4$ at the point where it crosses the x-axis.

10. The line is perpendicular to the line $x + 3y = 6$ at the point where it crosses the y-axis.

11. The line is the perpendicular bisector of the segment joining $(0, -2)$ and $(4, 6)$.

12. The line is the perpendicular bisector of the segment joining $(1, -3)$ and $(7, 5)$.

$$\frac{-2+2}{3-4} = \frac{0}{-1}$$

Use slopes to show that the given points are the vertices of a right triangle. Which point is the vertex of the right angle?

B 13. $(4, 2), (3, -2), (-20, 8)$ **14.** $(4, 10), (-5, 3), (1, 1)$

    15. $(0, 2), (2, -2), (3, 1)$ $(0, 2)$ **16.** $(5, -6), (7, -5), (3, -2)$

Use slopes to determine whether the given points are the vertices of a rectangle.

17. $(-6, 0), (3, -3), (6, 6), (0, 8)$ **18.** $(-5, 9), (-4, -4), (9, -3), (8, 10)$

Find the distance from the point P to the given line.

19. $P(0, 0); \; 2x - y = 8$ **20.** $P(0, 0); \; x - 2y + 10 = 0$

21. $P(5, 0); \; 3x - y + 5 = 0$ **22.** $P(-5, 6); \; 3x + y = 11$

In Exercises 23-26, L_1 and L_2 are lines having slopes m_1 and m_2, respectively; $P(r, s)$ is their point of intersection; and T_1 and T_2 are the points in which the vertical line $x = r + 1$ intersects L_1 and L_2, respectively. Exercises 23-26 are a proof of the theorem on page 329.

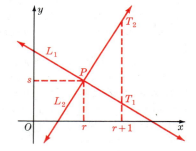

C 23. Write the equations of lines L_1 and L_2.

24. Find the coordinates of T_1 and T_2.

25. Find the distances T_1T_2, PT_1, and PT_2 in terms of m_1 and m_2.

26. a. Suppose L_1 and L_2 are perpendicular. Then triangle T_1PT_2 is a right triangle. Apply the Pythagorean theorem and simplify to obtain $m_1m_2 = -1$.

     b. Suppose, instead, that $m_1m_2 = -1$.
Prove that $(T_1T_2)^2 = (PT_1)^2 + (PT_2)^2$. It follows from the converse of the Pythagorean theorem that triangle T_1PT_2 has a right angle at P. Hence L_1 and L_2 are perpendicular.

Self-Test 1

VOCABULARY   Pythagorean theorem (p. 326)   midpoint formula (p. 327)
distance formula (p. 326)   perpendicular (p. 329)

1. Find the distance between $(-3, 2)$ and $(9, -3)$.

2. Find the midpoint of the segment having endpoints $(1, -2)$ and $(-5, 6)$.

Obj. 9-1, p. 325

Find an equation of each line described below.

3. The line contains the point $(3, -1)$ and is perpendicular to the line $2x - 3y = 6$.

Obj. 9-2, p. 329

4. The line is the perpendicular bisector of the segment in Exercise 2.

Check your answers with those at the back of the book.

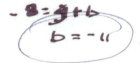

Career Note Mining Engineer

Mining engineers locate, extract, and process minerals for industrial use. They design and supervise the construction of mining facilities and devise methods for transporting minerals from mines to processing plants. Some mining engineers work with geologists to discover new deposits of minerals. Others are responsible for safe and efficient day-to-day mining operations.

Developments in recent years are creating new opportunities for mining engineers. The increasing emphasis on safe working conditions requires advances in the construction and operation of mines. Federal regulations governing strip mining have called for the reclamation of mined land. Mining engineers also have to devise methods for meeting more exacting regulation of air and water pollution. In addition, entirely new industries involving undersea mining and extraction of oil shale deposits are being developed.

Not all mining engineers work in remote mining areas. Those in research, teaching, or management positions often live and work near large urban areas.

Mining engineers should have at least a bachelor's degree, and some positions require advanced degrees as well. Jobs are available in industry, at universities, in government, or on a consulting basis.

SECOND-DEGREE CURVES

9-3 *Circles*

OBJECTIVE   To learn the relationship between the properties of a circle, such as center and radius, and the equation of the circle.

One of the purposes of analytic geometry is to use algebra to study various kinds of curves. In this section and the next three, you will study curves whose equations are of the second degree.

Recall that a **circle** is the set of all points in a plane that are at a given distance from a fixed point of the plane. The given distance is the *radius,* and the fixed point the *center,* of the circle. Thus, the circle having radius r and center C is the set of all points P such that $CP = r$.

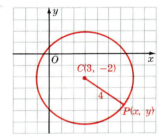

To find an equation of the circle having center $C(3, -2)$ and radius 4 (Figure 9-6), use the distance formula. For any point $P(x, y)$ on the circle,

$$\sqrt{(x - 3)^2 + (y + 2)^2} = 4,$$

which is equivalent to

$$(x - 3)^2 + (y + 2)^2 = 16.$$

Every circle has an equation of this form.

Figure 9-6

An equation of the circle with center (h, k) and radius r is

$$(x - h)^2 + (y - k)^2 = r^2.$$

As a special case, notice that every circle whose center is the origin has an equation of the form

$$x^2 + y^2 = r^2,$$

since h and k are both zero.

When the equation of a circle is given in the form $x^2 + y^2 + ax + by + c = 0$, you can find the center and radius of the circle by completing the square twice.

EXAMPLE 1   Find the center and radius of the circle $x^2 + y^2 + 4x - 8y + 11 = 0$.

SOLUTION   Complete the square twice; once using the terms in x, and once using the terms in y.

$$x^2 + y^2 + 4x - 8y + 11 = 0$$
$$x^2 + y^2 + 4x - 8y \quad = -11$$
$$(x^2 + 4x \quad) + (y^2 - 8y \quad) = -11$$
$$(x^2 + 4x + 4) + (y^2 - 8y + 16) = -11 + 4 + 16$$
$$(x + 2)^2 + (y - 4)^2 = 9.$$

$\therefore$ the center is $(-2, 4)$, and the radius is 3.   **Answer**

In the next example, use this fact: Let L be a line tangent to a circle at the point T (see Figure 9-7). Then the line perpendicular to L at T passes through the center of the circle.

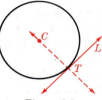

Figure 9-7

EXAMPLE 2   The center of a circle of radius 3 lies in the first quadrant. Find an equation of the circle if it is tangent to the x-axis at $(2, 0)$.

SOLUTION

Because of the fact stated above, the center of the circle lies on the line $x = 2$. Moreover, the center must be 3 units from the point $(2, 0)$, which is on the circle. Thus the center is $(2, 3)$, and the equation of the circle is

$$(x - 2)^2 + (y - 3)^2 = 3^2, \text{ or}$$
$$(x - 2)^2 + (y - 3)^2 = 9. \quad \textbf{Answer}$$

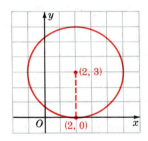

An equation of the form $x^2 + y^2 + ax + by + c = 0$ may not have a graph at all.

EXAMPLE 3   Graph $x^2 + y^2 - 2x - 4y + 9 = 0$.

SOLUTION   The equation $x^2 + y^2 - 2x - 4y + 9 = 0$ is equivalent to $(x - 1)^2 + (y - 2)^2 = -4$. Since the sum of two squares is nonnegative for all real values, the equation has no real solution and, therefore, no graph.   **Answer**

Oral Exercises

State an equation of the form $(x - h)^2 + (y - k)^2 = r^2$ for the circle with the given center and radius.

1. $(1, 2)$; 3

2. $(-2, 3)$; 4

3. $(2, -1)$; $\sqrt{2}$

4. $(0, 2)$; $\sqrt{3}$

5. $(-2, 0)$; 2

6. $(-1, -1)$; $\frac{1}{2}$

Give the center and radius of the circle having the given equation.

7. $(x - 3)^2 + (y - 2)^2 = 4$

8. $(x + 2)^2 + (y - 1)^2 = 9$

9. $(x + 1)^2 + (y + 1)^2 = 1$

10. $(x - 3)^2 + (y - 1)^2 = 5$

11. $(x + 1) + y^2 = 1$

12. $x^2 + (y - 1)^2 = \frac{1}{4}$

Written Exercises

Write an equation in the form $x^2 + y^2 + ax + by + c = 0$ for the circle with the given center and radius.

A **1.** $(0, 1); 1$ **2.** $(-3, 3); 3$ **3.** $(2, -2); 2\sqrt{2}$ **4.** $(-1, 0); 4$

If the given equation has a circle as its graph, find the center and radius. If the equation has no graph, so state.

5. $x^2 + y^2 - 16 = 0$

6. $x^2 + y^2 + 4 = 0$

7. $x^2 + y^2 - 4x = 0$

8. $x^2 + y^2 + 2x - 6y = 0$

9. $x^2 + y^2 = -4x$

10. $x^2 + y^2 = 2y$

11. $x^2 + y^2 - 4x + 2y + 6 = 0$

12. $x^2 + y^2 + 6x - 4y - 3 = 0$

13. $x^2 + y^2 - 3x + y = 0$

14. $x^2 + y^2 + 5x + 5y + 8 = 0$

B **15.** $2x^2 + 2y^2 - 6x - 2y + 3 = 0$

16. $3x^2 + 3y^2 + 2x - 4y = 0$

Find an equation of the circle having the given properties.

17. Center $(2, 0)$; passes through the origin.

18. Center $(0, 3)$; passes through $(0, 6)$.

19. Center in first quadrant; radius 3; tangent to y-axis at $(0, 1)$.

20. Center on the line $y = 2$; tangent to x-axis at $(3, 0)$.

21. Center on the line $x + y = 6$; tangent to x-axis at $(2, 0)$.

22. A diameter of the circle has endpoints $(-2, 3)$ and $(6, 5)$.

23. Radius 1; tangent to both coordinate axes. (Four answers)

24. Express the equation $x^2 + y^2 - 4x + 2y + 5 = 0$ in the form $(x - h)^2 + (y - k)^2 = r^2$; graph the equation.

In Exercises 25–28 on the next page, graph the given inequality.

SAMPLE $x^2 + y^2 > 9$

SOLUTION   1. The circle $x^2 + y^2 = 9$, shown at the top of the following page, separates the plane into two sets of points, those inside the circle and those outside the circle.

2. Choose a point that is clearly inside or outside the circle to test in the given inequality. The origin is inside the circle. Test $(0, 0)$ in the inequality.

$$0^2 + 0^2 > 9 \quad \text{False}$$

3. Since a point inside the circle does *not* satisfy the inequality, the graph consists of the points *outside* the circle. Draw the circle as a dashed curve, since the circle itself is not included in the graph, and shade the part of the plane outside the circle.

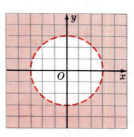

25. $x^2 + y^2 < 4$ **26.** $x^2 + y^2 \geq 1$

C 27. $x^2 + y^2 - 2y \leq 0$ **28.** $x^2 + y^2 \leq 2x$

Draw a semicircle that is the graph of the given equation. Recall that $\sqrt{a}$ is nonnegative.

29. $y = \sqrt{4 - x^2}$ **30.** $y = -\sqrt{4 - x^2}$

31. $x = \sqrt{9 - y^2}$ **32.** $x = -\sqrt{9 - y^2}$

33. $y = \sqrt{4x - x^2}$ **34.** $y = 2 + \sqrt{6x - x^2}$

35. Find the equation of a circle with radius 5 that is tangent to both branches of the graph of $y = |x|$.

36. Find an equation of the set of all points that are the centers of circles tangent to the line $y = 2x + 2$ at the point $(1, 4)$.

37. Find the equation of the circle that passes through $(5, 9)$ and $(7, -5)$ and whose center is on the line $y = 1$.

38. A point moves so that it is always twice as far from $(4, 0)$ as from $(1, 0)$. Describe the curve on which it travels and write the equation of the curve.

39. Find a condition involving a, b, and c that is equivalent to the graph of

$$x^2 + y^2 + ax + by + c = 0$$

being a circle.

40. Prove that any angle inscribed in a semicircle is a right angle. (*Hint:* Let the semicircle be the top half of the circle $x^2 + y^2 = r^2$, and $P(x, y)$ be any point on the semicircle. Solve for y in terms of x and r and use slopes to show that the segments $\overline{AP}$ and $\overline{BP}$ are perpendicular.)

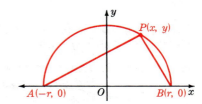

9-4 Parabolas

OBJECTIVE To learn the relationship between the properties of a parabola, such as focus, directrix, vertex, and axis, and the equation of the parabola.

Let a point $P(x, y)$ move so that its distance from the point $F(3, 0)$ is always equal to its distance PD from the line $y = -2$ (see Figure 9-8). To find an equation of the path of P, use the distance formula:

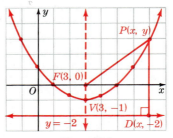

Figure 9-8

$$PF = PD$$
$$\sqrt{(x-3)^2 + (y-0)^2} = \sqrt{(x-x)^2 + (y+2)^2}$$
$$(x-3)^2 + y^2 = (y+2)^2$$
$$(x-3)^2 = 4y + 4$$
$$y = \tfrac{1}{4}(x-3)^2 - 1$$

Because the last equation is of the form $y = a(x-h)^2 + k$ (Section 7-6), the path of P is a parabola having vertex $(3, -1)$ and axis $x = 3$. This result suggests the definition of a parabola:

> A **parabola** is the set of all points equidistant from a fixed line, called the **directrix,** and a fixed point not on the line, called the **focus.**

The important features of a parabola are shown in Figure 9-9. Notice that the vertex is midway between the focus and the directrix.

Recall that a parabola is symmetric with respect to its axis and that all parabolas have the same shape. Because of these properties you can draw a parabola after plotting its vertex and only a few other points.

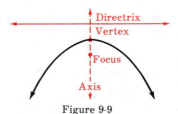

Figure 9-9

EXAMPLE Find an equation of the parabola whose focus is the point $(0, 3)$ and whose directrix is the line $x = 4$. Graph the parabola and label its focus F, vertex V, directrix, and axis of symmetry.

SOLUTION $P(x, y)$ is on the parabola if and only if $PF = PD$, where D is the point of the directrix nearest to P.

$$PF = PD$$
$$\sqrt{(x-0)^2 + (y-3)^2} = \sqrt{(x-4)^2 + (y-y)^2}$$
$$x^2 + (y-3)^2 = (x-4)^2$$

$$x^2 + (y - 3)^2 = x^2 - 8x + 16$$
$$(y - 3)^2 = -8x + 16$$
$$x = -\tfrac{1}{8}(y - 3)^2 + 2$$

Now substitute a few values for y, calculate the corresponding values of x, and graph the parabola, as shown below. ***Answer***

x	y
0	7
$\frac{3}{2}$	5
2	3
$\frac{3}{2}$	1
0	-1

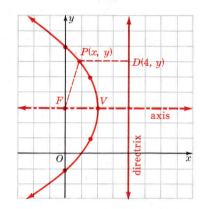

Notice that the parabola in the example has a *horizontal* axis, while all those you studied earlier had *vertical* axes. Furthermore, the equation for this parabola is similar to the form studied in Chapter 7 for parabolas with vertical axes, but the roles of x and y in the equation are reversed.

In general, a parabola with vertex (h, k) and a horizontal axis has an equation of the form

$$x = a(y - k)^2 + h.$$

The axis is the line $y = k$; the parabola opens to the right if $a > 0$ and to the left if $a < 0$.

Oral Exercises

For each of the following parabolas, state **(a)** the coordinates of its vertex, **(b)** an equation of the axis, and **(c)** whether the parabola opens to the right or to the left.

1. $x = y^2 + 2$
2. $x = -(y - 2)^2$
3. $x = -2(y - 1)^2 - 3$
4. $x = \tfrac{1}{4}(y + 3)^2 + 2$

In Oral Exercises 5–10, V denotes the vertex of a parabola, F its focus, and D its directrix. Two of these are given. Supply the third.

SAMPLE $V(3, 0)$, D: $x = 6$ ***SOLUTION***   Focus is $(0, 0)$.

5. $V(0, 0)$, D: $x = -2$
6. $F(0, 4)$, $V(0, 0)$
7. $F(0, 0)$, $V(0, -5)$
8. $F(6, 0)$, D: $x = -6$
9. $F(-1, 0)$, D: $x = 3$
10. $V(0, 1)$, D: $y + 1 = 0$

Written Exercises

Find an equation of the parabola with the given features; graph the parabola.

A 1. Focus $(0, 0)$; directrix $x = -2$

2. Focus $(0, 0)$; directrix $y = 2$

3. Focus $(2, 3)$; directrix $y + 3 = 0$

4. Focus $(-2, 3)$; directrix $x = 2$

5. Focus $(2, 0)$; vertex $(2, 2)$

6. Vertex $(3, -1)$; directrix $x + 1 = 0$

7. Vertex $(3, 0)$; directrix $y = 2$

8. Focus $(6, 2)$; vertex $(3, 2)$

Find the vertex and axis of the given parabola; graph the parabola.

SAMPLE $y^2 + 8y - 8x = 0$

SOLUTION   To find the vertex, complete the square in y.

$$y^2 + 8y = 8x$$
$$y^2 + 8y + 16 = 8x + 16$$
$$(y + 4)^2 = 8x + 16$$
$$x = \tfrac{1}{8}(y + 4)^2 - 2$$

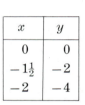

x	y
0	0
$-1\frac{1}{2}$	-2
-2	-4

$\therefore$ the vertex is $(-2, -4)$; the axis is $y = -4$.

Compute a few pairs of coordinates and use symmetry to sketch the graph.

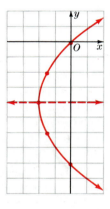

9. $4x = y^2$

10. $x + y^2 = 0$

11. $x = y^2 + 4y$

12. $y^2 - 2y + x = 0$

13. $y^2 - 4y + 4x = 0$

14. $x^2 - 6x + 3y = 0$

15. $x^2 = 2x + 2y$

16. $y^2 = 8(x + y)$

Graph each equation. Note that each graph is half of a parabola.

B 17. $y = \sqrt{x}$

18. $y = -\sqrt{4 - x}$

19. $y = -\sqrt{x + 4}$

20. $y = \sqrt{4x + 8}$

21. The line through the focus of a parabola perpendicular to its axis intersects the parabola in two points, P and Q. (The segment $\overline{PQ}$ is called the *latus rectum* of the parabola.) Explain why the length of $\overline{PQ}$ is twice the distance from the focus to the directrix. If the distance from the focus to the vertex is a, express PQ in terms of a.

22. A circle has its center on a parabola and passes through the focus of the parabola. What relationship does the circle have to the directrix of the parabola?

C 23. A *multiplication machine:* Draw the parabola $y = x^2$. Given any two positive numbers a and b, locate the points of the parabola having abscissas $-a$ and b. Explain why the line joining these points has y-intercept ab. (*Hint:* Find an equation of the line through $(-a, a^2)$ and (b, b^2).)

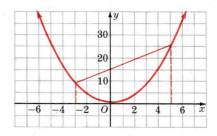

24. A parabola having vertex (h, k) and a horizontal axis has as focus a point of the form $(h + r, k)$ and as directrix the line $x = h - r$, $r \neq 0$. Show that an equation of the parabola is

$$x = \frac{1}{4r}(y - k)^2 + h.$$

EXTRA

Special Parabola Forms

The equations for parabolas developed thus far,

$$y = a(x - h)^2 + k \quad \text{and} \quad x = a(y - k)^2 + h,$$

are expressed in terms of the vertex of the parabola, (h, k) and (k, h), respectively, and a constant a associated with the direction and steepness of the parabola's curvature.

There are other equations, for parabolas with vertex at the origin, that are expressed in terms of the coordinates of the focus. Consider the parabola with vertex $(0, 0)$ and focus $(0, c)$. The directrix must be the line $y = -c$. For any point $P(x, y)$ on the parabola:

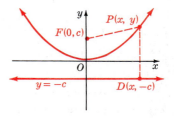

$$PF = PD$$

$$\sqrt{(x - 0)^2 + (y - c)^2} = \sqrt{(x - x)^2 + (y + c)^2}$$
$$x^2 + (y - c)^2 = (y + c)^2$$
$$x^2 + y^2 - 2cy + c^2 = y^2 + 2cy + c^2$$
$$x^2 = 4cy$$

Similarly, for a parabola with vertex at the origin and focus $(c, 0)$,

$$y^2 = 4cx.$$

Now given the focus (or directrix) of a parabola with vertex at the origin you can write its equation. On the other hand, if you can express the equation of a parabola in either form,

$$x^2 = 4cy \quad \text{or} \quad y^2 = 4cx,$$

you can conclude that its vertex is at the origin, its axis is either the x- or y-axis, and you can easily find its focus and directrix.

EXAMPLE 1 Find the vertex, axis, focus, and directrix of the parabola $x^2 - 2y = 0$.

SOLUTION $x^2 - 2y = 0$
$x^2 = 2y$

The equation is now in the form $x^2 = 4cy$, with $c = \frac{1}{2}$.

$\therefore$ the vertex is $(0, 0)$, the focus is $\left(0, \frac{1}{2}\right)$, the axis is the y-axis, and the directrix is $y = -\frac{1}{2}$. *Answer*

EXAMPLE 2 Write the equation of a parabola whose vertex is the origin and whose directrix is $x = 3$.

SOLUTION Since the directrix is $x = 3$, the focus is $(-3, 0)$, so that $c = -3$.
$\therefore$ the equation is of the form $y^2 = 4cx$. Since $c = -3$, the equation is $y^2 = -12x$. *Answer*

Exercises

Find the focus and directrix of each parabola. In which direction (left, right, up, down) does the parabola open?

A 1. $8x + y^2 = 0$
2. $3x^2 - 18y = 0$
3. $3x^2 - 4 = 4(3y - 1)$
4. $3(y^2 + 5) = 5(3 - 6x)$

Write the equation of a parabola with vertex at the origin and having the given properties.

5. The focus is $(-6, 0)$.
6. The directrix is $y = 5$.
7. a. The axis is the x-axis and the parabola contains the point $(5, 2)$.
   b. The axis is the y-axis and the parabola contains the point $(5, 2)$.
8. The directrix is $y = -0.01$.

B 9. Express the constant c in the form $x^2 = 4cy$ in terms of the constant a in the form $y = a(x - h)^2 + k$.

10. How does the appearance of a parabola whose equation is of the form $x^2 = 4cy$ change as successively larger values are assigned to c (that is, as the focus moves away from the vertex)?

9-5 *Ellipses*

OBJECTIVE   To learn the relationship between the properties of an ellipse, such as foci and intercepts, and the equation of the
ellipse.

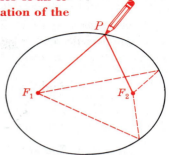

Imagine two points F_1 and F_2 with one end of a piece of
string fastened at each point. The point P of a moving
pencil that holds the string taut will trace out an oval
curve called an *ellipse*, as shown in Figure 9-10. Because
the sum of the distances PF_1 and PF_2 is the length of
the string, this sum, $PF_1 + PF_2$, is the same for all positions of P.

Figure 9-10

> An **ellipse** is a set of points in a plane such that for each point of
> the set, the sum of its distances to two fixed points is a given
> constant.

Each of the fixed points is called a **focus** (plural: *foci*) of the ellipse. If
the foci are F_1 and F_2, then for each point P of the
ellipse, PF_1 and PF_2 are the **focal radii** of P.

   To find an equation of the ellipse with foci $F_1\,(-4, 0)$
and $F_2\,(4, 0)$ and sum of focal radii 10, as shown in Figure 9-11, use the distance formula:

Figure 9-11

$$\begin{aligned}
PF_1 \quad + \quad PF_2 &= 10 \\
\sqrt{(x+4)^2 + (y-0)^2} + \sqrt{(x-4)^2 + (y-0)^2} &= 10 \\
\sqrt{(x+4)^2 + y^2} &= 10 - \sqrt{(x-4)^2 + y^2}
\end{aligned}$$

Square each side and simplify:

$$\begin{aligned}
(x+4)^2 + y^2 &= 100 - 20\sqrt{(x-4)^2 + y^2} + (x-4)^2 + y^2 \\
5\sqrt{(x-4)^2 + y^2} &= 25 - 4x
\end{aligned}$$

Square again, and simplify:

$$\begin{aligned}
25(x^2 - 8x + 16 + y^2) &= 625 - 200x + 16x^2 \\
9x^2 + 25y^2 &= 225
\end{aligned}$$

Divide both sides by 225:

$$\frac{x^2}{25} + \frac{y^2}{9} = 1$$

To make graphing the ellipse as easy as possible, first determine its
properties by analyzing the equation. A method of analysis is shown on
the following page.

1. Suppose (r, s) satisfies the equation; that is, $\frac{r^2}{25} + \frac{s^2}{9} = 1$.

   Since $(-r)^2 = r^2$ and $(-s)^2 = s^2$, then $(-r, s)$, $(r, -s)$, and $(-r, -s)$ also satisfy the equation.

   $\therefore$ *the curve is symmetric with respect to both coordinate axes and the origin.*

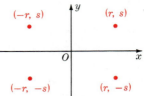

2. Replace y by 0; then $\frac{x^2}{25} + \frac{0}{9} = 1$; $x^2 = 25$; $x = \pm 5$.

   $\therefore$ *the x-intercepts of the ellipse are 5 and -5.*

3. Replace x by 0; then $\frac{0}{25} + \frac{y^2}{9} = 1$; $y^2 = 9$; $y = \pm 3$.

   $\therefore$ *the y-intercepts of the ellipse are 3 and -3.*

4. Solve the equation in turn for y and for x:
$$y = \pm \tfrac{3}{5}\sqrt{25 - x^2} \text{ and } x = \pm \tfrac{5}{3}\sqrt{9 - y^2}.$$

   Hence y is real if and only if $|x| \leq 5$, and x is real if and only if $|y| \leq 3$. This determines the *extent* of the curve.

   $\therefore$ *the ellipse lies entirely within the rectangle formed by the lines* $x = 5$, $x = -5$, $y = 3$, *and* $y = -3$.

With this information about symmetry, intercepts, and extent, and a table of coordinates, you can sketch the ellipse as shown in Figure 9-12. In the table, values are substituted for x; when necessary the resulting value of y is rounded to the nearest tenth.

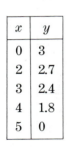

x	y
0	3
2	2.7
3	2.4
4	1.8
5	0

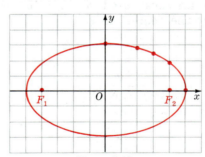

Figure 9-12

The preceding example suggests the following result:

The ellipse having foci $F_1(-c, 0)$ and $F_2(c, 0)$ and sum of focal radii $2a$ has the equation

$$\frac{x^2}{a^2} + \frac{y^2}{b^2} = 1, \text{ where } b^2 = a^2 - c^2.$$

An ellipse may, of course, have its foci on the y-axis. Study the following general results.

> The ellipse having foci $F_1(0, -c)$ and $F_2(0, c)$ and sum of focal radii $2a$ has the equation
>
> $$\frac{x^2}{b^2} + \frac{y^2}{a^2} = 1, \text{ where } b^2 = a^2 - c^2.$$

EXAMPLE   Graph the ellipse $4x^2 + y^2 = 4$ and find its foci.

SOLUTION   Divide both members by 4 to obtain

$$\frac{x^2}{1} + \frac{y^2}{4} = 1.$$

1. The ellipse is symmetric with respect to both coordinate axes and the origin.
2. The x-intercepts are 1 and -1.
3. The y-intercepts are 2 and -2.
4. Since $y = \pm 2\sqrt{1 - x^2}$, and $x = \pm\frac{1}{2}\sqrt{4 - y^2}$, then $|x| \leq 1$ and $|y| \leq 2$ for each point on the ellipse.

Construct a table of first-quadrant points and sketch the ellipse. In the table, values are substituted for x, and the corresponding values for y are calculated to the nearest tenth.

x	y
0.25	1.9
0.5	1.7
0.75	1.3

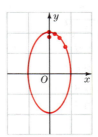

Since c is a coordinate of a focus, c is real and $c^2 > 0$. Also, since $c^2 = a^2 - b^2$, $a^2 - b^2 > 0$ or $a^2 > b^2$. For the equation

$$\frac{x^2}{1} + \frac{y^2}{4} = 1,$$

$a^2 = 4$ and $b^2 = 1$, and you see that the foci are on the y-axis. Thus, $c^2 = 4 - 1$, and $c = \pm\sqrt{3}$.

$\therefore$ the foci are $(0, -\sqrt{3})$ and $(0, \sqrt{3})$.   **Answer**

Oral Exercises

Give the x- and y-intercepts of each ellipse and state on which of the coordinate axes its foci lie.

1. $\dfrac{x^2}{4} + \dfrac{y^2}{9} = 1$

2. $\dfrac{x^2}{25} + \dfrac{y^2}{16} = 1$

3. $4x^2 + 9y^2 = 36$

4. $16x^2 + y^2 = 16$

5. $36x^2 + 100y^2 = 3600$

6. $4x^2 + y^2 = 16$

7. Two ellipses, E_1 and E_2, with foci on the x-axis have the same x-intercepts, but the foci of E_1 are closer together than those of E_2. Which ellipse looks more like a circle?

8. An ellipse has foci $(0, -99)$ and $(0, 99)$, and y-intercepts $(0, -100)$ and $(0, 100)$. Describe the appearance of such an ellipse.

Written Exercises

Graph each ellipse and find its foci.

A **1–6.** Use the equations in Oral Exercises 1–6.

7. $25x^2 + 9y^2 = 900$

8. $4x^2 + y^2 = 100$

9. $\dfrac{x^2}{100} + \dfrac{y^2}{25} = 4$

10. $\dfrac{x^2}{25} + \dfrac{y^2}{169} = 1$

11. $x^2 + 4y^2 = 1$

12. $9x^2 + 4y^2 = 4$

13. $\dfrac{x^2}{4} + \dfrac{y^2}{12} = 1$

14. $\dfrac{x^2}{25} + \dfrac{y^2}{16} = 2$

15. $4x^2 + y^2 = 1$

Write an equation of the ellipse having the given points as foci and the given number as sum of the focal radii.

16. $(-3, 0), (3, 0);\ 10$

17. $(0, -4), (0, 4);\ 12$

18. $(0, -5), (0, 5);\ 14$

Graph each inequality.

B **19.** $\dfrac{x^2}{4} + y^2 \le 1$

20. $16x^2 + 4y^2 > 64$

Graph the given semi-ellipse.

21. $y = 3\sqrt{1 - x^2}$

22. $x = -2\sqrt{4 - y^2}$

Use the definition to write an equation of the ellipse having the given points as foci and the given number as sum of the focal radii. Substitute $b^2 = a^2 - c^2$ at the appropriate point to simplify the equations.

C **23.** $(-c, 0), (c, 0);\ 2a$

24. $(0, -c), (0, c);\ 2a$

In Exercises 25 and 26 graph the ellipse whose equation is given; each ellipse has a center that is not the origin. Equations for ellipses with center at (h, k) and foci on the lines $y = k$ and $x = h$, respectively, are given in Figures 9-13 and 9-14.

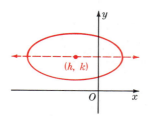

$$\frac{(x - h)^2}{a^2} + \frac{(y - k)^2}{b^2} = 1$$

Figure 9-13

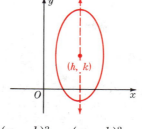

$$\frac{(x - h)^2}{b^2} + \frac{(y - k)^2}{a^2} = 1$$

Figure 9-14

25. $\dfrac{(x - 5)^2}{25} + \dfrac{(y - 3)^2}{9} = 1$

26. $\dfrac{x^2}{1} + \dfrac{(y - 2)^2}{16} = 1$

Biography Sonya Kovalevsky

As a young child, Sonya Corvin-Krukovsky Kovalevsky (1850–1891) displayed an ability in mathematics that amazed her teachers. Her father was a lecturer on differential and integral calculus. For this reason, some biographers attribute Kovalevsky's early interest in mathematics to her home environment.

Neither in Russia nor in Germany, where Kovalevsky later lived, were women allowed to attend college. Nevertheless, she pursued her studies. In Germany, she became the private student of Karl Weierstrass, an eminent mathematician. She produced research papers on various topics, including partial differential equations, Abelian integrals, and the rings of Saturn. So highly regarded was her work that she was granted a doctorate *in absentia* from the University of Göttingen.

Eventually Kovalevsky was appointed to the faculty of the University of Stockholm. She received the Prix Bordin of the French Academy of Sciences and was the first woman chosen as a Corresponding Member of the Russian Academy of Sciences. In addition to her mathematical studies, she published poetry, novels, and other literary works.

9-6 *Hyperbolas*

OBJECTIVE   To learn the relationship between the properties of a hyperbola, such as foci, intercepts, and asymptotes, and the equation of the hyperbola.

If one listening post (see Figure 9-15) hears an explosion 10 s before another post hears it, what can you conclude about the location P of the explosion? Since the sound of the explosion arrives at the first post 10 s before it arrives at the second post, and the speed of sound is about 350 m/s, then P is approximately 3500 m closer to the first post than to the second. The curve shown in Figure 9-15 is composed of all points that are 3500 m closer to one of the posts than to the other. This curve is called a *hyperbola*.

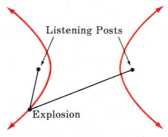

Figure 9-15

You see that, if you didn't know which post heard the sound first, the explosion must have occurred somewhere on one of the two branches of the hyperbola. By using more than two listening posts, the location of the explosion can be pinpointed accurately.

A **hyperbola** is a set of points in a plane such that for each point of the set, the difference of its distances to two fixed points is a given constant.

Each of the fixed points is called a **focus** of the hyperbola.

Suppose the foci of a hyperbola are $F_1(-5, 0)$ and $F_2(5, 0)$ as in Figure 9-16. Suppose, further, that the *focal radii*, PF_1 and PF_2, of any point $P(x, y)$ on the hyperbola differ by 6. then

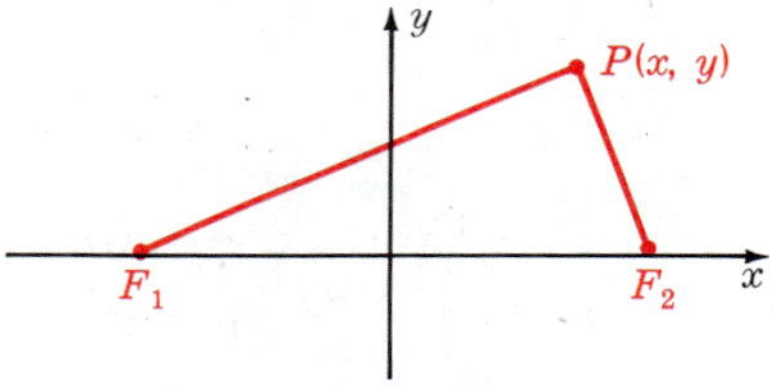

$$|PF_1 - PF_2| = 6$$

$$\left| \sqrt{(x + 5)^2 + y^2} - \sqrt{(x - 5)^2 + y^2} \right| = 6.$$

Figure 9-16

Eliminate the radicals and simplify.

$$\sqrt{(x + 5)^2 + y^2} - \sqrt{(x - 5)^2 + y^2} = \pm 6$$

$$\sqrt{(x + 5)^2 + y^2} = \sqrt{(x - 5)^2 + y^2} \pm 6$$

$$(x + 5)^2 + y^2 = (x - 5)^2 + y^2 \pm 12\sqrt{(x - 5)^2 + y^2} + 36$$

$$5x - 9 = \pm 3\sqrt{(x - 5)^2 + y^2}$$

$$25x^2 - 90x + 81 = 9[(x - 5)^2 + y^2]$$

$$16x^2 - 9y^2 = 144$$

$$\frac{x^2}{9} - \frac{y^2}{16} = 1$$

Several geometric properties of the hyperbola can be deduced from its equation.

1. Whenever (r, s) satisfies the equation, so do $(-r, s)$, $(r, -s)$, and $(-r, -s)$.

   $\therefore$ *the graph is symmetric with respect to both coordinate axes and the origin.*

2. Replace y by 0; then $\frac{x^2}{9} - \frac{0}{16} = 1$, $x^2 = 9$, $x = \pm 3$.

   $\therefore$ *the x-intercepts of the hyperbola are 3 and -3.*

3. Replace x by 0; then $\frac{0}{9} - \frac{y^2}{16} = 1$, or $y^2 = -16$. No real value of y satisfies this equation.

   $\therefore$ *the hyperbola has no y-intercepts.*

4. To determine the extent of the graph, solve the equation to express each variable in terms of the other:

$$y = \pm \frac{4}{3}\sqrt{x^2 - 9} \quad \text{and} \quad x = \pm \frac{3}{4}\sqrt{y^2 + 16}$$

   Hence y is real if and only if $|x| \geq 3$; x is real for all values of y.
   $\therefore$ *no part of the hyperbola lies between the lines* x $= -3$ *and* x $= 3$.

5. For $y = \pm \frac{4}{3}\sqrt{x^2 - 9}$, observe what happens as $|x|$ gets larger and larger. In the radicand $x^2 - 9$, the "-9" term will become less and less important, and the equation $y = \pm \frac{4}{3}\sqrt{x^2 - 9}$ becomes more and more nearly the same as $y = \pm \frac{4}{3}\sqrt{x^2}$, or simply $y = \pm \frac{4}{3}x$. These lines,

$$y = \frac{4}{3}x \quad \text{and} \quad y = -\frac{4}{3}x,$$

   are called the **asymptotes** of the hyperbola.
   $\therefore$ *the hyperbola approaches its asymptotes, the lines*

$$y = \frac{4}{3}x \quad \text{and} \quad y = -\frac{4}{3}x,$$

   as the value of $|x|$ *increases.*

With these facts and a short table of coordinates, you can sketch the graph of the hyperbola as shown in Figure 9-17. In the table, values are substituted for x and the resulting y-coordinates are rounded to tenths.

x	y
3	0
4	3.5
5	5.3

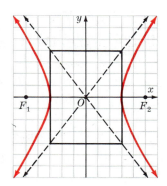

Figure 9-17

Figure 9-17 shows the rectangle formed by the lines $x = 3$, $x = -3$, $y = 4$, and $y = -4$. The asymptotes found earlier are the diagonals of this rectangle. They are useful guides in drawing the curve. Notice that the hyperbola lies entirely within two of the wedge-shaped regions into which the asymptotes divide the plane.

Generalizing on the preceding example, you have:

The hyperbola with foci $F_1(-c, 0)$ and $F_2(c, 0)$ and difference of focal radii $2a$ has an equation of the form

$$\frac{x^2}{a^2} - \frac{y^2}{b^2} = 1, \text{ where } b^2 = c^2 - a^2.$$

The equations of its asymptotes are $y = \frac{b}{a}x$ and $y = -\frac{b}{a}x$.

If the foci are on the y-axis at $F_1(0, -c)$ and $F_2(0, c)$, then the hyperbola has an equation of the form

$$\frac{y^2}{a^2} - \frac{x^2}{b^2} = 1, \text{ where } b^2 = c^2 - a^2.$$

In this case the equations of the asymptotes are $y = \frac{a}{b}x$ and $y = -\frac{a}{b}x$.

These equations are developed in Exercises 25 and 26 on page 352.

EXAMPLE Graph the hyperbola $y^2 = 4x^2 + 16$, showing its asymptotes.

SOLUTION

$y^2 = 4x^2 + 16$

$y^2 - 4x^2 = 16$

$\frac{y^2}{16} - \frac{x^2}{4} = 1$

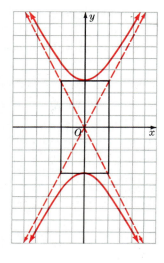

1. The graph is symmetric with respect to both axes.
2. There are no x-intercepts.
3. The y-intercepts are 4 and -4.
4. Determine the extent of the graph:

$$y = \pm 2\sqrt{x^2 + 4}, \ x = \pm\frac{1}{2}\sqrt{y^2 - 16}$$

$\therefore x$ is real if and only if $|y| \geq 4$.
5. The asymptotes are $y = 2x$ and $y = -2x$.

Construct a short table of coordinates, rounding y-coordinates to tenths, and sketch the graph.

x	y
0	4
1	4.5
2	5.7
3	7.2

There are hyperbolas that are not symmetric to the x- and y-axes. For example, the graph of an equation of the form

$$xy = k, \quad k \neq 0.$$

is a hyperbola symmetric to the lines $y = x$ and $y = -x$ and having the coordinate axes as asymptotes (see Exercises 27 and 28 on page 352). The graph of $xy = 4$ is shown in Figure 9-18.

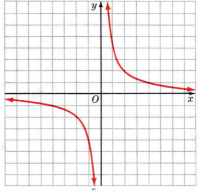

Figure 9-18

Oral Exercises

Give the intercepts of the hyperbola, the equations of its asymptotes, and state on which of the axes the foci lie.

1. $\dfrac{x^2}{16} - \dfrac{y^2}{9} = 1$ **2.** $\dfrac{y^2}{1} - \dfrac{x^2}{4} = 1$ **3.** $y^2 - 4x^2 = 4$

4. $4x^2 - y^2 = 4$ **5.** $49x^2 - 100y^2 = 4900$ **6.** $9x^2 - 100y^2 + 900 = 0$

7. What angle do the asymptotes of $x^2 - y^2 = 1$ make with each other?

8. Describe the graph of $xy = k$ for the case $k = 0$.

Written Exercises

In Exercises 1–12: **a.** Graph the given hyperbola. Show the asymptotes.
                   b. Find the foci of the hyperbola.

A   **1–6.** Use the equations in Oral Exercises 1–6.

7. $\dfrac{x^2}{25} - \dfrac{y^2}{144} = 1$ **8.** $\dfrac{y^2}{36} - \dfrac{x^2}{64} = 1$ **9.** $x^2 - y^2 + 100 = 0$

10. $3x^2 - y^2 = 12$ **11.** $\dfrac{x^2}{4} - 4y^2 = 1$ **12.** $25y^2 = 36x^2 + 900$

Graph the given half hyperbolas.

13. $y = \sqrt{x^2 + 4}$ **14.** $y = \sqrt{x^2 - 1}$

Write an equation of the hyperbola having the given properties.

15. Foci are $(0, -5)$ and $(0, 5)$; difference of focal radii is 6.

16. Foci are $(-3, 0)$ and $(3, 0)$; difference of focal radii is 4.

17. Intercepts are $(4, 0)$ and $(-4, 0)$; asymptotes are $y = \frac{1}{2}x$ and $y = -\frac{1}{2}x$.

18. Foci are $(0, 10)$ and $(0, -10)$; intercepts are $(0, 8)$ and $(0, -8)$.

Graph the given inequality.

B **19.** $x^2 - y^2 \leq 4$ **20.** $y^2 < x^2 - 1$

21. $4x^2 > 9y^2 + 36$ **22.** $9x^2 \geq 25y^2 - 225$

Use the definition to find an equation of the hyperbola having the given points as foci and the given number as the difference of the focal radii.

23. $(0, -6)$, $(0, 6)$; 4   **24.** $(-4, 0)$, $(4, 0)$; 6

C **25.** $(-c, 0)$, $(c, 0)$; $2a$ **26.** $(0, -c)$, $(0, c)$; $2a$
      (*Hint:* In Exercises 25 and 26, substitute b^2 for $c^2 - a^2$ at the appropriate point to simplify the equations.)

27. (a, a), $(-a, -a)$; $2a$ **28.** $(a, -a)$, $(-a, a)$; $2a$

29. Find a point in the first quadrant on the hyperbola $x^2 - y^2 = 1$ such that the vertical distance from the point to the nearest asymptote is less than 0.1.

ḫistorical Ṅote Analytic Geometry

The basic concepts of analytic geometry came about in the seventeenth century largely through the work of René Descartes and Pierre de Fermat. Descartes is probably most often associated with the Cartesian coordinate system. For this reason, it is interesting to note the difference between the original system Descartes used and the later system which was named in his honor. Descartes used a single horizontal axis as a guide and plotted only the positive values of an equation. At each point of the axis, he imagined constructing a segment whose length corresponded to the value of the equation at the given point. The segments were always parallel to each other, but were not always perpendicular to the axis. As a result, instead of plotting values on a fixed coordinate system, Descartes essentially made a new system with each new curve. Descartes published the first paper using methods of analytic geometry in 1637. Seven years earlier, Fermat had developed a method of representing equations with curves, using the vowels A and E to represent variables, and consonants to represent constants. Fermat's equations can be rewritten using familiar symbols. Fermat's equation for an ellipse and a modern translation are shown below.

Fermat's Equation	Translation
$\dfrac{B^2 - A^2}{E^2} =$ a constant	$\dfrac{r^2 - x^2}{y^2} = k$

9-7 *Inverse Variation*

When people play on a seesaw, they must choose their positions carefully if they want to balance each other. For example, suppose a 30 kg person sits 100 cm to the right of the fulcrum (the point where the seesaw is supported). Then a 20 kg person would have to sit 150 cm to the left of the fulcrum to create a balance, but a 60 kg person would need to sit only 50 cm to the left of the fulcrum to balance the 30 kg person.

The distance from each person to the fulcrum is called a *lever arm*. Notice that if the mass of the person on the left increases, then the lever arm must decrease; if the mass decreases, then the lever arm increases. Notice, too, that for each situation resulting in a balanced condition, for the person on the left

$$\text{mass} \times \text{lever arm} = 3000.$$

To balance a person on the right, the mass and lever arm of the person on the left are said to *vary inversely*, or to be *inversely proportional* to each other.

INVERSE VARIATION

Any function defined by an equation of the form

$$xy = k, \; k \neq 0,$$

is called an **inverse variation.**

Sometimes it is useful to express the variation $xy = k$ in the equivalent form

$$y = \frac{k}{x},$$

and to say that *y is inversely proportional to x*. The constant k is called the **constant of proportionality,** or the **constant of variation.**

The graph of an inverse variation is a hyperbola symmetric to the lines $y = x$ and $y = -x$, and having the axes for its asymptotes. The graph of $xy = 3000$, the equation defining the seesaw relationship on page 353, is shown in Figure 9-19. In many practical situations, including the seesaw example, consideration is limited to the branch of the hyperbola in the first quadrant, since $x > 0$, $y > 0$, and $k > 0$. If $k > 0$, the hyperbola lies in the first and third quadrants, as in Figure 9-19. If $k < 0$, the hyperbola lies in the second and fourth quadrants.

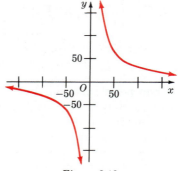

Figure 9-19

In solving problems involving inverse variations, it is often not necessary to determine k, the constant of proportionality. For any two pairs (x_1, y_1) and (x_2, y_2) of the variation,

$$x_1 y_1 = k \quad \text{and} \quad x_2 y_2 = k,$$

so that, by substitution,

$$x_1 y_1 = x_2 y_2.$$

By substituting values for any three terms, the remaining term can be readily determined.

EXAMPLE 1 To travel a given distance, the time required is inversely proportional to the speed of travel. If a trip can be made in 3.6 h at a speed of 70 km/h, how long will it take to make the same trip at 90 km/h?

SOLUTION Let s = speed and t = time.

$$s_1 t_1 = s_2 t_2$$
$$70(3.6) = 90 t_2$$
$$t_2 = \frac{70(3.6)}{90}$$
$$t_2 = 2.8$$

∴ the trip will take 2.8 h at 90 km/h. *Answer*

In some proportions, one quantity may vary in terms of others in more complicated ways. For example, if y varies inversely as the square of x, you write $y = \dfrac{k}{x^2}$. If y varies directly as x and inversely as z, you write $y = \dfrac{kx}{z}$. When one quantity varies directly as the product of two or more others, the variation is called a **joint variation.** Thus, if y varies jointly as x and z, you write $y = kxz$.

EXAMPLE 2 Weight is, essentially, a measure of the force of gravitational attraction between an object and the earth. The weight of an object is inversely proportional to the square of its distance from the center of the earth. If a person weighs 700 N on the surface of the earth, what is that person's weight aboard the Space Shuttle when it is 1600 km above the earth? The radius of the earth is about 6400 km.

SOLUTION Let w = weight and d = distance from center of earth. Then $w = \dfrac{k}{d^2}$, or $wd^2 = k$. For any two pairs (w_1, d_1) and (w_2, d_2) of the proportion,

$$w_1(d_1)^2 = w_2(d_2)^2.$$

Substitute $w_1 = 700$, $d_1 = 6400$, and $d_2 = 6400 + 1600 = 8000$.

$$700(6400)^2 = w_2(8000)^2$$

$$w_2 = \frac{700(6400)^2}{(8000)^2}$$

$$w_2 = 448$$

∴ the person weighs 448 N at a point 1600 km above the earth's surface. **Answer**

Problems

A 1. To earn a given return on an investment over a fixed time period, the interest rate and amount of the investment are inversely proportional to each other. If an investment of $20,000 at 9% interest yields the desired return, how much must be invested at 12% to produce the same return?

2. The frequency of a radio wave is inversely proportional to the wave length. If a wave 250 m long has a frequency of 1200 kHz, find the length of a wave with a frequency of 800 kHz.

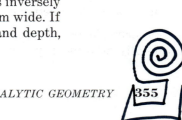

3. A pulley with diameter 8 cm is running at 1452 r/min (revolutions per minute) while belted to a 12 cm pulley. Find the speed of the larger pulley if the speeds of the pulleys are in inverse proportion to their diameters.

4. Two meshed gears have 35 and 56 teeth, respectively. If the speeds are inversely proportional to the numbers of teeth, at what speed should the second gear be driven so that the first gear will run at 1450 r/min?

5. For boxes with the same capacity and depth, the length is inversely proportional to the width. One box is 48 cm long and 30 cm wide. If a second box 40 cm long is to have the same capacity and depth, what must its width be?

6. The intensity of light, measured in lux (lx), varies inversely as the square of the distance between the source of the light and the object illuminated. If a light meter reads 18 lx at a distance of 2 m from a light source, what will it read at a distance of 6 m from the source?

B 7. A surface is now 10 m from a source of light. How far from the source would the surface have to be in order to receive twice as much illumination, if the intensity of illumination varies inversely as the square of the distance from the source of light?

8. The heat developed in a wire carrying a current for a specified time varies jointly as the resistance of the wire and the square of the current. If a current of 8 A produces 153.6 J of heat in a wire with a resistance of 10 Ω, how much heat is produced by a current of 6 A in a wire whose resistance is 15 Ω?

9. The electrical resistance of a wire varies directly as its length and inversely as the square of the diameter of the wire. Suppose 50 m of a wire of diameter 3 mm has a resistance of 8 Ω. What is the resistance of 40 m of the same type of wire if the diameter is 4 mm?

10. The kinetic energy of a moving body varies directly as the square of its velocity. If a body has an energy of 5 J at a velocity of 3 m/s, what is its energy when its velocity increases to 5 m/s?

C 11. The load that a wooden beam of given length can support varies jointly as its width and the square of its depth. If a beam whose width is 10 cm and whose depth is 5 cm can support a 420 kg object, find the load the beam can support when turned on its side.

12. If a satellite completes a circular orbit in 90 minutes flying 800 km above the earth at 28,000 km/h, how long would it take a space capsule flying 500 km above the earth at 30,000 km/h to complete one orbit? Consider 6400 km as the radius of the earth, and use the fact that the time required for a satellite to complete a circular orbit varies directly as the radius of orbit and inversely as the orbital velocity.

Self-Test 2

VOCABULARY

circle (p. 334)
parabola (p. 338)
directrix (p. 338)
focus (of a parabola) (p. 338)
ellipse (p. 343)
focus (of an ellipse) (p. 343)

focal radii (p. 343)
hyperbola (p. 348)
focus (of a hyperbola) (p. 348)
asymptotes (p. 349)
inverse variation (p. 353)
joint variation (p. 354)

1. Write the equation of the circle that is tangent to the y-axis and has its center at $(-3, 2)$.   **Obj. 9-3, p. 334**

2. Find the center and radius of the circle

$$x^2 + y^2 - 6x + 8y = 0.$$

3. Write an equation of the parabola having vertex $(0, 3)$ and directrix $x = -2$.　　　　　　　　　　　　Obj. 9-4, p. 338

Graph the following equations.

4. $x^2 + 4y^2 = 16$　　　　　　　　　　　　　　　Obj. 9-5, p. 343
5. $x^2 - 4y^2 = 16$　　　　　　　　　　　　　　　Obj. 9-6, p. 348

6. The power in an electric circuit with a constant voltage is inversely proportional to the resistance. If a circuit with a resistance of $20\ \Omega$ produces $605\ \text{W}$ of power, how much power is produced in a circuit with a resistance of $25\ \Omega$, if the voltage remains the same?　　　　　　Obj. 9-7, p. 353

Check your answers with those at the back of the book.

Career Note Purchasing Agent

Purchasing agents (or industrial buyers) maintain proper supply levels of those items organizations need to function smoothly and efficiently. One purchasing agent may secure machinery, raw materials, or product components for a manufacturing firm. Another may buy food or furnishings for a restaurant chain.

Purchasing agents must maintain communication with personnel in various parts of their organizations to keep abreast of supply needs. When placing orders, they consider the cost and quality of goods of different sellers, choosing the ones who offer the best terms. In the case of large orders, purchasing agents sometimes call for competitive bids in order to ensure the lowest possible price. After orders are placed, purchasing agents keep track of them to ensure prompt delivery. They authorize payment only after goods are received and inspected for damage.

Large firms often insist that purchasing agents have a master's degree in business administration. In smaller firms with less complicated purchasing needs, a clerical worker or technician may advance to the position of purchasing agent. Technical expertise will become more and more important for purchasing agents in the years to come.

9-8 *Graphical Analysis of Quadratic Systems*

OBJECTIVE   To use graphs to determine the number of real solutions of a quadratic system and to estimate the solutions.

A common real solution of two equations in two variables corresponds to a point of intersection of their graphs. Thus you can see from Figure 9-20 that a system of one quadratic and one linear equation may have 2, 1, or 0 real solutions.

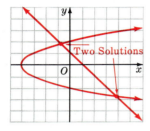
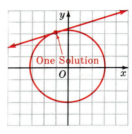
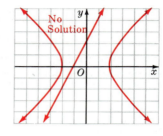

$$x - y^2 + 4 = 0$$
$$x + y = 1$$

$$x^2 + y^2 = 10$$
$$x - 3y + 10 = 0$$

$$x^2 - y^2 = 4$$
$$2x - y + 2 = 0$$

Figure 9-20

A system consisting of two quadratic equations may have 4, 3, 2, 1, or 0 real solutions. You can use graphs to find the number of real solutions of a quadratic system and to estimate the solutions. The more carefully the graphs are drawn, the better the estimates will be.

EXAMPLE   Use graphs to estimate the solutions of each system.

a. $y^2 = x + 4$
  $9x^2 + 4y^2 = 36$

b. $xy + 5 = 0$
  $x^2 + 5y = 20$

SOLUTION   Draw the graphs of the equations in each system and estimate the coordinates of their points of intersection.

a.

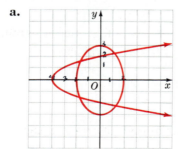

$$y^2 = x + 4$$
$$9x^2 + 4y^2 = 36$$

There are four solutions. The set of estimated solutions is

$\{(1.3, 2.3), (-1.7, 1.5), (-1.7, -1.5),$
$(1.3, -2.3)\}$.   ***Answer***

b.

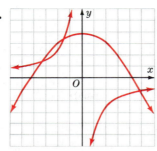

$$xy + 5 = 0$$
$$x^2 + 5y = 20$$

There are three solutions. The set of estimated solutions is

$$\{(-1.4, 3.6), (-3.6, 1.4), (5, -1)\}.$$
Answer

Actually, $(5, -1)$ is an *exact* solution of the system in part (b) of the example, as the following check shows.

$$5(-1) + 5 = 0 \quad \checkmark$$
$$5^2 + 5(-1) = 20 \quad \checkmark$$

The other solutions in the example are approximate. If you have a calculator, you might check to see how good they are.

Oral Exercises

Identify the kind of curve that is the graph of each equation in the given system.

SAMPLE $xy = 4$
$4x^2 + y^2 = 16$

every is circle an ellipse

in a circle/cents x & y coefficients have to be same.

SOLUTION   The graph of $xy = 4$ is a hyperbola. The graph of $4x^2 + y^2 = 16$ is an ellipse.

1. $x^2 + 4y^2 = 16$ *ELLIPSE*
   $x - 3y = 3$ *LINE*

2. $y^2 - x^2 = 4$ *hyperbola*
   $x - 2y + 2 = 0$ *line*

3. $xy = 9$ *hyperbola*
   $x + y = 6$ *line*

4. $x^2 + y^2 = 4$ *circle or ellipse*
   $y = x^2$ *parabola*

5. $4x^2 - 9y^2 = 36$ *hyperbola*
   $9x^2 + 25y^2 = 225$ *ellipse*

6. $y = 8 - x^2$ *parabola*
   $xy = 3$ *hyperbola*

7. $x^2 + 4y^2 = 16$ *ellipse*
   $x^2 + y^2 = 9$ *ellipse or circle*

8. $y = x^2$ *parabola (1 term squared other isn't+)*
   $y^2 = 8 - 2x$ *parabola*

9. $5x + y^2 = 20$ *parabola*
   $xy = 5$ *hyperbola*
   ($xy = k$)

List all the possible numbers of points of intersection for the given pair of curves.

10. A hyperbola and a line

11. An ellipse and a parabola

12. Two circles

13. Two parabolas

Written Exercises

A 1–8. By sketching the graphs, find the *number* of real solutions of each system in Oral Exercises 1–8.

B **9–16.** If necessary, draw the graphs of Exercises 1–8 more accurately. Then estimate the real solutions (if any) of each system in Written Exercises 1–8, page 359. Estimate coordinates to the nearest tenth.

Graph the following systems of inequalities.

SAMPLE $x^2 + y^2 \leq 4$
$y \geq x^2 - 1$

SOLUTION

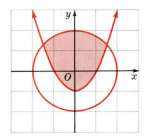

C **17.** $x^2 + y^2 \leq 4$
$xy \leq 1$

18. $x^2 + y^2 \geq 1$
$x^2 + y^2 \leq 4$

19. $x^2 + 4y^2 \leq 4$
$x \geq y^2 - 1$

20. Use the following procedure to show that no isosceles triangle has perimeter 4 and area 1.
   a. Write an equation for the area and an equation for the perimeter. (*Hint:* Let base $= 2x$ and height $= y$.)
   b. Simplify the perimeter equation to eliminate radicals.
   c. Graph the resulting system and use the graph to reach the required conclusion.

CHALLENGE

Using only the four operations of arithmetic and square root, write a numerical expression containing four 2's for as many of the whole numbers as you can.

Here are some examples to help you get started:

$$0 = (2 - 2) + (2 - 2)$$

$$1 = 2 - 2 + \frac{2}{2}$$

$$2 = \frac{2}{2} + \frac{2}{2}$$

$$3 = (2 \cdot 2) - \frac{2}{2}$$

9-9 *Solutions of Quadratic Systems*

OBJECTIVE   **To use algebraic methods to find exact solutions of quadratic systems.**

The substitution and linear-combination methods that you used earlier to solve linear systems of equations can also be used to solve quadratic systems. Please note that it is quite possible for quadratic systems to have solutions some or all of which are imaginary. In order to apply graphical as well as algebraic techniques to these systems, however, consideration is restricted to only their real solutions.

A system consisting of one quadratic and one linear equation, and some systems of two quadratic equations, can be solved by the substitution method. Solve one equation for one of the variables and substitute in the other equation.

EXAMPLE 1   Solve the system $x^2 + 4y^2 = 25$
$x + 2y = 1$

SOLUTION

1. Solve the linear equation for one of the variables, say x.

$$x = -2y + 1$$

2. Substitute $-2y + 1$ for x in the quadratic equation and solve the resulting equation.

$$(-2y + 1)^2 + 4y^2 = 25$$
$$4y^2 - 4y + 1 + 4y^2 = 25$$
$$8y^2 - 4y - 24 = 0$$
$$2y^2 - y - 6 = 0$$
$$(2y + 3)(y - 2) = 0$$
$$y = -\tfrac{3}{2} \quad \text{or} \quad y = 2$$

3. Substitute $-\tfrac{3}{2}$ and 2 for y in the linear equation to find the corresponding values of x.

If $y = -\tfrac{3}{2}$, then $x = -2(-\tfrac{3}{2}) + 1 = 4$.
$\therefore (4, -\tfrac{3}{2})$ is a solution.

If $y = 2$, then $x = -2(2) + 1 = -3$.
$\therefore (-3, 2)$ is a solution.

4. Check the ordered pairs $(4, -\tfrac{3}{2})$ and $(-3, 2)$ in both equations.

$$(4)^2 + 4(-\tfrac{3}{2})^2 \overset{?}{=} 25 \qquad\qquad 4 + 2(-\tfrac{3}{2}) \overset{?}{=} 1$$
$$16 + 9 = 25 \ \checkmark \qquad\qquad 4 - 3 = 1 \ \checkmark$$

$$(-3)^2 + 4(2)^2 \overset{?}{=} 25 \qquad\qquad -3 + 2(2) \overset{?}{=} 1$$
$$9 + 16 = 25 \ \checkmark \qquad\qquad -3 + 4 = 1 \ \checkmark$$

$\therefore$ the solution set is $\{(4, -\tfrac{3}{2}), (-3, 2)\}$.   ***Answer***

The effect of the substitution done in step 2 was to replace the ellipse by the pair of horizontal lines $y = -\tfrac{3}{2}$ and $y = 2$ (shown as dashed lines in Figure 9-21 on the following page).

Thus the original problem is now equivalent to solving the two systems

$$y \overset{.}{=} -\tfrac{3}{2}$$
$$x + 2y = 1$$

and

$$y = 2$$
$$x + 2y = 1.$$

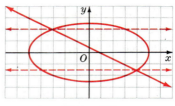

Figure 9-21

EXAMPLE 2 Solve the system $x^2 - y^2 = 5$
$$xy + 6 = 0.$$

SOLUTION

1. Solve the second equation for y. $\qquad y = -\dfrac{6}{x}$

2. Substitute $-\dfrac{6}{x}$ for y in the first equation. $\qquad x^2 - \left(-\dfrac{6}{x}\right)^2 = 5$

$$x^2 - \dfrac{36}{x^2} = 5$$

3. Solve the resulting equation, which is quadratic in x^2.

   Since $x^2 + 4 = 0$ has no real roots, consider only $x^2 - 9 = 0$.

   $x^4 - 5x^2 - 36 = 0$
   $(x^2 + 4)(x^2 - 9) = 0$
   $x^2 - 9 = 0$
   $x = -3 \quad \text{or} \quad x = 3$

4. Substitute -3 and 3 for x in $y = -\dfrac{6}{x}$.

   If $x = -3$, then $y = -\dfrac{6}{-3} = 2$.

   If $x = 3$, then $y = -\dfrac{6}{3} = -2$.

$\therefore$ the solution set is $\{(-3, 2), (3, -2)\}$. **Answer**

The system is graphed at the right. As you would expect, based on the solution set, the hyperbolas intersect in two points.

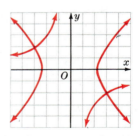

EXAMPLE 3 Solve the system $x^2 + 4y^2 = 49$
$$2x^2 - 3y^2 = -12$$

SOLUTION 1 (Substitution Method)

1. Solve the first equation for x^2. $\qquad x^2 = 49 - 4y^2$

2. Substitute $49 - 4y^2$ for x^2 in the second equation and solve the resulting equation.

   $2(49 - 4y^2) - 3y^2 = -12$
   $98 - 8y^2 - 3y^2 = -12$
   $-11y^2 = -110$
   $y^2 = 10$
   $y = \sqrt{10} \quad \text{or} \quad y = -\sqrt{10}$

3. Substitute $\sqrt{10}$ and $-\sqrt{10}$ for y in the first equation to find the corresponding values of x.

If $y = \sqrt{10}$:
$$x^2 + 4(\sqrt{10})^2 = 49$$
$$x^2 = 9$$
$$x = \pm 3.$$

If $y = -\sqrt{10}$:
$$x^2 + 4(-\sqrt{10})^2 = 49$$
$$x^2 = 9$$
$$x = \pm 3.$$

$\therefore$ the solution set is $\{(3, \sqrt{10}), (-3, \sqrt{10}), (3, -\sqrt{10}), (-3, -\sqrt{10})\}$. ***Answer***

The system is graphed at the right. Because both graphs are symmetric to both axes, checking $(3, \sqrt{10})$ would be sufficient, since if $(3, \sqrt{10})$ satisfies the equations, then the other points must also satisfy them.

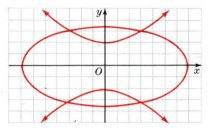

SOLUTION 2 (Linear-Combination Method)

1. Multiply the first equation by 2 and subtract the second equation from the multiplied first equation.

$$2x^2 + 8y^2 = 98$$
$$\underline{2x^2 - 3y^2 = -12}$$
$$11y^2 = 110$$

2. Solve the resulting equation.

$$y^2 = 10$$
$$y = \sqrt{10} \text{ or } y = -\sqrt{10}$$

3. Repeat Step 3 from Solution 1.

$\therefore$ the solution set is $\{(3, \sqrt{10}), (-3, \sqrt{10}), (3, -\sqrt{10}), (-3, -\sqrt{10})\}$. ***Answer***

Oral Exercises

State which of the given ordered pairs are solutions of the given system.

1. $x^2 + y^2 = 25$
   $x + y = 1$ $(-3, 4), (3, -4), (4, -3), (-4, 3)$

2. $x^2 - y^2 = 3$
   $x + y + 1 = 0$ $(1, -2), (-1, 2), (2, -1), (-2, 1)$

3. $y^2 - x^2 = 5$
   $xy + 6 = 0$ $(2, -3), (-2, 3), (3, -2), (-3, 2)$

4. $x^2 + y^2 = 5$
   $2x^2 + y = 0$ $(1, 2), (-1, 2), (-1, -2), (1, -2)$

Written Exercises

Find the real solutions of each system.

A 1. $x^2 - y = 4$
     $y = 3x$

2. $y = x^2 + 3$
     $3x - y + 1 = 0$

3. $xy + 2 = 0$
     $x - y = 3$

4. $x^2 - y^2 = 8$
     $x + y = 2$

5. $2s^2 + t^2 = 12$
     $2s + t = 2$

6. $4x^2 + y^2 = 13$
     $2x - y = 1$

7. $x^2 + y^2 = 25$
     $x - 2y = -5$

8. $x^2 + y^2 = 100$
     $x = y + 2$

9. $x^2 + y^2 = 5$
     $x^2 - y = 5$

10. $x^2 + y^2 = 13$
     $x^2 - y = 7$

11. $2x^2 + y^2 = 8$
     $x^2 - 2y^2 = 4$

12. $x^2 + y^2 = 13$
     $x^2 - y^2 = 5$

B 13. $y - 1 = (x - 2)^2$
     $(x - 2)^2 = 3 - y$

14. $5x^2 - y^2 = 3$
     $x^2 + 2y^2 = 5$

15. $2x^2 + 3y^2 = 23$
     $3x^2 - y^2 = 7$

16. $4x^2 + 9y^2 = 36$
     $y^2 = x + 3$

17. $x^2 + y^2 = 13$
     $xy = 6$

18. $x^2 - y^2 = 15$
     $xy = 4$

Find the square roots of the given complex number.

SAMPLE $5 - 12i$

SOLUTION   Let a square root be $x + yi$, where x and y are real.
Then $(x + yi)^2 = 5 - 12i$, or $(x^2 - y^2) + 2xyi = 5 - 12i$.
Equate real and imaginary parts to obtain the system

$$x^2 - y^2 = 5$$
$$2xy = -12$$

This system is equivalent to the system in Example 2, page 362. The real solutions of the system are $(-3, 2)$ and $(3, -2)$. Therefore the square roots are $-3 + 2i$ and $3 - 2i$. *Answer*

19. $3 - 4i$ 20. $-3 + 4i$ 21. $5 + 12i$ 22. $-5 - 12i$

Problems

A 1. Find the dimensions of a rectangle having area 10 cm² and perimeter 14 cm.

2. Find the dimensions of a rectangle having perimeter 34 and diagonal of length 13.

3. Find two numbers whose product is 4.9 and the sum of whose reciprocals is 1.

4. Find two numbers whose product is 3 and the difference of whose reciprocals is $\frac{1}{6}$.

5. A rectangular plot having area 1800 m² is to be fenced and divided into three pens, as shown. The entire job will use 240 m of fencing. Find the dimensions of the plot.

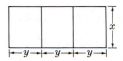

B **6.** Find the dimensions of a rectangle having area 10 cm² and diagonal of length 5 cm. (Give decimal approximations rounded to the nearest tenth.)

7. Find two numbers such that the difference of their squares is 2 and the difference of their fourth powers is 20.

8. Five-centimeter squares are cut from the corners of a rectangular sheet of metal having area 540 cm². The flaps are then bent up to form an open-topped box having volume 850 cm³. Find the dimensions of the original sheet of metal.

9. A circle whose center is on the x-axis passes through points $(3, 5)$ and $(6, 4)$. Write an equation of the circle.

10. A 20 m ladder and a 15 m ladder were leaned against a building. The bottom of the longer ladder was 7 m farther from the building than the bottom of the shorter ladder, but both ladders reached the same distance up the building. Find this distance.

C **11.** Find an equation of the ellipse with center at the origin and foci on the x-axis and that contains the points $(3, 1)$ and $(\sqrt{3}, \sqrt{3})$.

12. From the top of a vertical canyon wall 200 m high, a person throws a rock with a speed of 10 m/s toward the top of the opposite side of the canyon, which is at the same elevation but 510 m away. According to the laws of physics, the rock follows a path described approximately by the equation

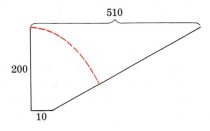

$$y = 200 - \frac{x^2}{20},$$

where y is the rock's height in meters above the canyon floor and x is the rock's horizontal distance in meters to the right of the vertical canyon wall. The opposite side of the canyon is steeply sloping and becomes level at a point 10 m from the base of the vertical wall. When the rock strikes the sloping side of the canyon, how far is it from where it was thrown? Express your answer rounded to the nearest tenth of a meter. (*Hint:* Introduce a coordinate system whose origin is the base of the vertical wall. Write an equation for the sloping side, and find a common solution of this equation and the equation of the rock's path.)

Self-Test 3

a. Graph the equations in each system.

b. Determine the number of real solutions of the system.

c. Estimate the solutions of the system.

1. $x^2 + y^2 = 25$ **2.** $x - 2y + 4 = 0$ **3.** $xy = -3$ Obj. 9-8, p. 358
$\quad\; x^2 - y^2 = 9$ $\quad\; 25x^2 + 9y^2 = 225$ $\quad\; x^2 + y^2 = 8$

Solve each system algebraically.

4. $x^2 + y^2 = 25$ **5.** $x^2 - y^2 = 35$ Obj. 9-9, p. 361
$\quad\; y = x^2 - 13$ $\quad\; x - y = 5$

6. Find two numbers the sum of whose reciprocals is 5 and the product of whose reciprocals is 4.

Check your answers with those at the back of the book.

Application

Conic Sections

Circles, parabolas, ellipses, and hyperbolas are usually called *conic sections,* because these curves are formed when a (hollow) double cone is sliced by a plane, as shown in Figure A. When the "slicing plane" is perpendicular to the axis of the cone, the resulting conic section is a circle. Can you describe the position of the "slicing plane" that forms each of the other conic sections?

The conic sections appear often in science and technology. Some applications of the properties of conic sections are described below.

An object that is thrown and allowed to fall to the ground under the force of gravity follows a path that is nearly a parabola. An example is the path of a baseball. The supporting cables of a suspension bridge form a curve that is theoretically a parabola. Parabolic reflectors are used in searchlights. The light from a source at the focus is reflected so that the light emerges in parallel rays, as shown in Figure B. The parabolic reflector in a telescope makes use of the reverse effect—parallel rays are gathered and concentrated at the focus.

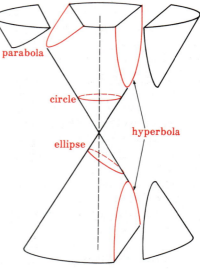

Figure A

Figure B

An ellipse has a reflective property similar to that of a parabola (see Figure C). If a source of sound is placed at one focus, the sound converges at the other focus. This property has been used in the design of "whispering chambers." A person whispering at one focus can be heard by someone standing at the other focus, but nowhere else in the chamber. You are probably familiar with another occurrence of ellipses. The orbits of the planets are elliptical paths with the sun at one focus.

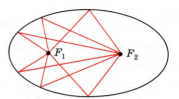

Figure C

One use of the hyperbola is a system of navigation called loran (for long-range navigation), which is illustrated in Figure D. Stations A and B send electronic signals to a ship at sea. From the time difference in which the signals are received, the difference in the ship's distances from the stations A and B can be computed. The ship can be located on a hyperbola with foci at A and B. Using signals from station B and a third station C, the ship can be located on a second hyperbola. Then its position can be determined from the intersection of the curves.

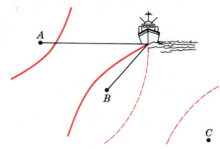

Figure D

Chapter Summary

1. The *distance* between the points $P_1(x_1, y_1)$ and $P_2(x_2, y_2)$ is given by
$$d = \sqrt{(x_2 - x_1)^2 + (y_2 - y_1)^2}.$$

The *midpoint* of the line segment $\overline{P_1 P_2}$ is
$$\left(\frac{x_1 + x_2}{2}, \frac{y_1 + y_2}{2} \right).$$

2. Two nonvertical lines are *perpendicular* if and only if the product of their slopes is -1.

3. An equation of the *circle* with center (h, k) and radius r is
$$(x - h)^2 + (y - k)^2 = r^2.$$

4. A *parabola* having vertex (h, k) has an equation of the form
$$y = a(x - h)^2 + k \text{ if its axis is vertical;}$$
$$x = a(y - k)^2 + h \text{ if its axis is horizontal.}$$

5. The *ellipse* with foci $(-c, 0)$ and $(c, 0)$ and sum of focal radii $2a$ has the equation
$$\frac{x^2}{a^2} + \frac{y^2}{b^2} = 1, \text{ where } b^2 = a^2 - c^2.$$

If the foci are $(0, -c)$ and $(0, c)$, then x and y are interchanged.

6. The *hyperbola* with foci $(-c, 0)$ and $(c, 0)$ and *difference* of focal radii $2a$ has the equation

$$\frac{x^2}{a^2} - \frac{y^2}{b^2} = 1, \text{ where } b^2 = c^2 - a^2.$$

If the foci are $(0, -c)$ and $(0, c)$, then x and y are interchanged.

7. A function defined by an equation of the form $xy = k$, $k \neq 0$, is called an *inverse variation*.

8. Graphical methods can be used to determine the number of real solutions of a quadratic system in two variables and to estimate these solutions. The *substitution method* or the *linear-combination method* often can be used to obtain exact solutions of a quadratic system.

Chapter Review _____

Give the letter of the correct answer.
In Questions 1–5, use the points $P(3, -1)$ and $Q(-1, 5)$.

1. The distance PQ is   9-1
   a. 10   **b.** 8   **c.** $2\sqrt{13}$ **d.** $4\sqrt{2}$

2. The midpoint of the segment PQ is
   a. $(2, 4)$ **b.** $(4, -1)$ **c.** $(-1, 4)$ **d.** $(1, 2)$

3. If Q is the midpoint of the segment PR, then R has coordinates
   a. $(-5, 7)$ **b.** $(5, -7)$ **c.** $(-5, 11)$ **d.** $(-7, 11)$

4. The slope of any line perpendicular to the line PQ is   9-2
   a. $\frac{3}{2}$ **b.** $\frac{2}{3}$ **c.** $-\frac{2}{3}$ **d.** $-\frac{3}{2}$

5. An equation of the perpendicular bisector of the segment PQ is
   a. $2x - 3y + 4 = 0$ **b.** $2x - 3y - 4 = 0$ **c.** $2x + 3y - 8 = 0$

6. An equation of the line perpendicular to the line $3x + 2y = 6$ at the point where it crosses the y-axis is
   a. $2x - 3y + 9 = 0$ **b.** $2x + 3y - 9 = 0$ **c.** $2x - 3y + 5 = 0$

7. An equation of the circle with center $(-3, 4)$ and passing through   9-3
   $(2, 4)$ is
   a. $x^2 + y^2 - 6x + 8y = 0$ **b.** $x^2 + y^2 + 6x - 8y = 0$
   c. $x^2 + y^2 + 6x - 8y - 25 = 0$ **d.** $x^2 + y^2 + 3x - 4y = 0$

8. The center and radius of the circle $x^2 + y^2 - 4x + 2y + 4 = 0$ are
   a. $(2, -1); 2$ **b.** $(-2, 1); 2$ **c.** $(2, -1); 1$ **d.** $(-2, 1); 1$

9. Find an equation of the circle shown at the right.

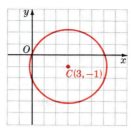

 a. $x^2 + y^2 - 6x + 2y - 10 = 0$
 b. $x^2 + y^2 + 6x - 2y + 10 = 0$
 c. $x^2 + y^2 - 6x + 2y = 0$
 d. $x^2 + y^2 + 6x - 2y = 0$

9-4

10. Find an equation of the parabola having focus $(0, 0)$ and directrix $x = 2$.

 a. $y^2 = -4x$ b. $y^2 = -4x + 4$ c. $x^2 = -8y$

11. Find the coordinates of the vertex of the parabola having equation $y^2 = 4y + 4x$.

 a. $(1, 2)$ b. $(-1, 2)$ c. $(2, -1)$ d. $(4, 2)$

12. Find an equation of the parabola shown at the right.

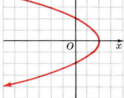

 a. $y^2 = 4 - 2x$
 b. $x^2 = -2(y - 2)$
 c. $y^2 = 2x - 4$
 d. $x^2 = 2y - 4$

13. Find an equation of the ellipse having foci $(0, -4)$ and $(0, 4)$ and sum of focal radii 12.

9-5

 a. $\dfrac{x^2}{36} + \dfrac{y^2}{16} = 1$ b. $\dfrac{x^2}{36} + \dfrac{y^2}{20} = 1$ c. $\dfrac{x^2}{20} + \dfrac{y^2}{36} = 1$

14. The equation of an ellipse is

$$\frac{x^2}{25} + \frac{y^2}{9} = 1.$$

Find the foci of the ellipse.

 a. $\left(\sqrt{34}, 0\right), \left(-\sqrt{34}, 0\right)$ b. $(4, 0), (-4, 0)$
 c. $(0, -4), (0, 4)$ d. $\left(0, -\sqrt{34}\right), \left(0, \sqrt{34}\right)$

15. Find an equation of the hyperbola having foci $(-4, 0)$ and $(4, 0)$ and difference of focal radii 6.

9-6

 a. $\dfrac{x^2}{16} - \dfrac{y^2}{9} = 1$ b. $\dfrac{x^2}{7} - \dfrac{y^2}{9} = 1$ c. $\dfrac{x^2}{9} - \dfrac{y^2}{7} = 1$

16. Find the foci of the hyperbola $3x^2 - y^2 + 12 = 0$.

 a. $\left(0, 2\sqrt{2}\right), \left(0, -2\sqrt{2}\right)$ b. $\left(2\sqrt{2}, 0\right), \left(-2\sqrt{2}, 0\right)$
 c. $(4, 0), (-4, 0)$ d. $(0, 4), (0, -4)$

17. If M is inversely proportional to V, and $M = 6$ when $V = 4$, find the value of V when M is 12.

9-7

 a. 18 b. 8 c. 2 d. 0.5

18. Suppose y varies directly as x and inversely as z. If $y = 12$ when $x = 4$ and $z = 3$, find y when $x = 12$ and $z = 18$.

   a. $\dfrac{2}{3}$ **b.** 6   **c.** 24   **d.** 216

19. How many solutions are there for the given system?   **9-8**

$$\frac{x^2}{4} + \frac{y^2}{25} = 1$$

$$y = 2x^2 - 5$$

   a. 1   **b.** 2   **c.** 3   **d.** 4

20. If (a, b) is a solution of the system

$$x^2 + y^2 = 16$$
$$y^2 - x = 2,$$

then which of the following is also a solution of the system?

   a. $(-a, b)$ **b.** $(a, -b)$ **c.** $(-a, -b)$

21. Find the solution set of the system   **9-9**

$$x^2 + y^2 = 39$$

$$\frac{x^2}{9} - y^2 = 1.$$

   a. $\{(6, 3), (-6, 3), (6, -3), (-6, -3)\}$
   b. $\{(5, \sqrt{14}), (-5, \sqrt{14}), (5, -\sqrt{14}), (-5, -\sqrt{14})\}$
   c. $\{(3, 0), (-3, 0)\}$
   d. $\{(6, \sqrt{3}), (-6, \sqrt{3}), (6, -\sqrt{3}), (-6, -\sqrt{3})\}$

Chapter Test

An isosceles triangle has vertices $(-4, 2)$, $(2, -2)$, and $(-2, 4)$.

1. Find the midpoints of the legs.   **9-1**
2. Find the length of the segment joining the midpoints of the legs.
3. Write an equation of the line that is perpendicular to the line $3x - 5y = 2$ at the point $(4, 2)$.   **9-2**
4. Find an equation of the circle having center $(-3, 1)$ and passing through the origin.   **9-3**
5. Find the center and radius of the circle

$$x^2 + y^2 - 8x + 4y + 4 = 0.$$

6. Find an equation of the parabola having the y-axis as directrix and $(4, 0)$ as focus.   **9-4**

7. Find the vertex of the parabola $y^2 = 2x - 4y$, and graph the parabola.

8. Find an equation of the ellipse having foci $(0, -2)$ and $(0, 2)$ and sum of focal radii 8.

9-5

9. Graph the ellipse $9x^2 + y^2 = 36$.

10. Graph the hyperbola $9x^2 - y^2 = 36$; show the asymptotes on the graph.

9-6

11. A manufacturer finds that the number of items sold is inversely proportional to the price of the item. If 4500 items are sold at a price of \$17, what price should be charged to raise sales to 6000 items?

9-7

Determine the number of solutions of each system.

12. $9x^2 - y^2 = 36$
    $y^2 = x + 1$

13. $9x^2 - y^2 = 36$
    $3x + y = 9$

9-8

Solve each system.

14. $xy + 1 = 0$
    $2x + 3y + 1 = 0$

15. $2x^2 + y^2 = 36$
    $x^2 - 2y^2 = 8$

9-9

16. Find the dimensions of a rectangle having area 60 cm^2 and perimeter 38 cm.

The pre-Columbian mask shown above was discovered at a site that is now part of Mexico City. The mask is a mosaic on a wooden base. See problem 10 on page 402 for a discussion of how exponential functions are used in carbon dating objects made of organic materials.

10

EXPONENTIAL AND LOGARITHMIC FUNCTIONS

EXPONENTIAL FUNCTIONS

10-1 *Rational Exponents*

OBJECTIVE **To extend the meaning of exponents to include rational numbers.**

You know the meaning of the power a^x ($a \neq 0$) if the exponent x is any *integer*. For example,

$$5^1 = 5, \quad 3^{-2} = \frac{1}{3^2} = \frac{1}{9}, \quad \text{and} \quad 7^0 = 1.$$

The definition of a power can be extended so that any *rational number* can serve as an exponent.

Consider first the special cases $5^{\frac{1}{2}}$ and $5^{\frac{1}{3}}$. If the laws of exponents (page 165) are to remain valid, the following equations must be true:

$$
\begin{aligned}
(5^{\frac{1}{2}})^2 &= 5^{\frac{1}{2} \cdot 2} \qquad \text{and} \qquad & (5^{\frac{1}{3}})^3 &= 5^{\frac{1}{3} \cdot 3} \\
&= 5^1 & &= 5^1 \\
&= 5 & &= 5
\end{aligned}
$$

Since $5^{\frac{1}{2}}$ is a number whose square is 5, $5^{\frac{1}{2}}$ is defined to be $\sqrt{5}$. The principal root, $\sqrt{5}$, is chosen, rather than $-\sqrt{5}$, so that the inequality $5^0 < 5^{\frac{1}{2}} < 5^1$ will be true. Also, since $5^{\frac{1}{3}}$ is a number whose cube is 5, $5^{\frac{1}{3}}$ is defined to be $\sqrt[3]{5}$. Reasoning in a similar way, you have:

$$
\begin{aligned}
5^{\frac{2}{3}} &= (5^{\frac{1}{3}})^2 \qquad\qquad & 5^{-\frac{3}{2}} &= (5^{\frac{1}{2}})^{-3} \\
&= (\sqrt[3]{5})^2 & &= (\sqrt{5})^{-3} \\
& & &= \frac{1}{(\sqrt{5})^3}
\end{aligned}
$$

These examples suggest the following definition:

If p is an integer, q is a positive integer, and a is a positive real number, then

$$a^{\frac{p}{q}} = (\sqrt[q]{a})^p.$$

Since $a > 0$, Theorem 3 on page 215 implies the equivalent statement

$$a^{\frac{p}{q}} = \sqrt[q]{a^p}.$$

EXAMPLE 1 Evaluate:

    a. $27^{\frac{2}{3}}$ **b.** $4^{-\frac{5}{2}}$ **c.** $81^{0.75}$

SOLUTION **a.** $27^{\frac{2}{3}} = (\sqrt[3]{27})^2$ **b.** $4^{-\frac{5}{2}} = (\sqrt{4})^{-5}$ **c.** $81^{0.75} = 81^{\frac{3}{4}}$

                      $= 3^2$ $= 2^{-5}$ $= (\sqrt[4]{81})^3$

                      $= 9$ *Answer* $= \dfrac{1}{32}$ *Answer* $= 3^3$

                                                           $= 27$ *Answer*

The laws of exponents established earlier for integral exponents continue to hold for powers with rational exponents. The laws of exponents can be used to write radical expressions in *exponential form*, that is, as a power or product of powers. Then you can use the laws to simplify the exponential expressions.

EXAMPLE 2 **a.** Evaluate $\left(\dfrac{1}{\sqrt{8}}\right)^{-\frac{2}{3}}$.

               b. Express $\sqrt{2} \cdot \sqrt[3]{4}$ in simplest radical form.

SOLUTION **a.** $\left(\dfrac{1}{\sqrt{8}}\right)^{-\frac{2}{3}} = (8^{-\frac{1}{2}})^{-\frac{2}{3}}$ **b.** $\sqrt{2} \cdot \sqrt[3]{4} = \sqrt{2} \cdot \sqrt[3]{2^2}$

                               $= 8^{(-\frac{1}{2})(-\frac{2}{3})}$ $= 2^{\frac{1}{2}} \cdot 2^{\frac{2}{3}}$

                               $= 8^{\frac{1}{3}}$ $= 2^{\frac{1}{2}+\frac{2}{3}}$

                               $= \sqrt[3]{8}$ $= 2^{\frac{7}{6}}$

                               $= 2$ *Answer* $= 2^1 \cdot 2^{\frac{1}{6}}$

                                                         $= 2\sqrt[6]{2}$ *Answer*

Oral Exercises

Evaluate each expression.

  1. $9^{\frac{1}{2}}$ **2.** $9^{-\frac{1}{2}}$ **3.** $32^{\frac{1}{5}}$ **4.** $32^{\frac{2}{5}}$

  5. $16^{-\frac{1}{2}}$ **6.** $16^{\frac{1}{4}}$ **7.** $16^{\frac{3}{4}}$ **8.** $16^{-\frac{3}{4}}$

Solve each equation.

9. $3^x = 27$ **10.** $4^x = 2$ **11.** $10^x = 1000$ **12.** $1000^x = 10$

13. $10^x = 0.01$ **14.** $16^x = 2$ **15.** $16^x = \frac{1}{4}$ **16.** $4^x = \frac{1}{8}$

Written Exercises

Write each expression without using radicals or negative exponents. Assume that all variables denote positive numbers.

A **1.** $\sqrt[3]{x^2 y^6}$ **2.** $\sqrt{ab^3}$ **3.** $\sqrt[4]{a^{-2}b^6}$

4. $\sqrt[3]{8x^6 y^{-6}}$ **5.** $\sqrt[6]{64a^2 b^{-2}}$ **6.** $\sqrt[5]{32a^2 b^{-10}}$

Evaluate.

7. $81^{\frac{3}{4}}$ **8.** $49^{-1.5}$ **9.** $\left(\frac{8}{125}\right)^{\frac{2}{3}}$

10. $\left(\frac{27}{8}\right)^{-\frac{4}{3}}$ **11.** $(9^{\frac{1}{2}} + 16^{\frac{1}{2}})^2$ **12.** $(16^{-\frac{1}{4}} - 16^{-\frac{1}{2}})^{-\frac{1}{2}}$

Express in simplest radical form.

13. $\sqrt{8} \cdot \sqrt[6]{8}$ **14.** $\sqrt[3]{4} \cdot \sqrt[6]{4}$ **15.** $\sqrt[6]{9} \cdot \sqrt[3]{3^5}$

16. $\sqrt[3]{9} \cdot \sqrt{27}$ **17.** $\sqrt{2} \cdot \sqrt[4]{8}$ **18.** $\sqrt[3]{4} \div \sqrt[6]{2}$

19. $\sqrt[5]{27^3} \div \sqrt[5]{9^2}$ **20.** $\sqrt[10]{32} \div \sqrt[6]{4}$ **21.** $\sqrt[6]{27} \div \sqrt[12]{9}$

Simplify. Leave answers in exponential form when necessary.

22. $4^{3.6} \cdot 4^{0.2} \div 4^{2.3}$ **23.** $3^{1.2} \cdot 3^{0.8} \div 3^{1.5}$ **24.** $3^{\frac{1}{2}} \cdot 9^{\frac{1}{3}} \div 27^{\frac{1}{4}}$

25. $2^{\frac{1}{5}} \cdot 4^{\frac{1}{5}} \div 8^{\frac{1}{5}}$ **26.** $(3^{-2} + 4^{-2})^{\frac{1}{2}}$ **27.** $(3^{-2})^{\frac{1}{2}} + (4^{-2})^{\frac{1}{2}}$

28. $(4^{\frac{3}{2}} + 9^{\frac{3}{2}})^{\frac{1}{3}}$ **29.** $(4^{\frac{3}{2}})^{\frac{1}{3}} + (9^{\frac{3}{2}})^{\frac{1}{3}}$ **30.** $\sqrt[3]{a^2} \sqrt{a^3}$

31. $\sqrt{c^{-1}} \cdot \sqrt[3]{c^2}$ **32.** $\sqrt[3]{\sqrt{8}} \cdot \sqrt[4]{4}$ **33.** $\sqrt{\sqrt[3]{9}} \cdot \sqrt[3]{\sqrt{3}}$

B **34.** $\sqrt[3]{\sqrt{\sqrt[3]{a^5}}}$ **35.** $\sqrt{\sqrt[6]{a^{10}}} \cdot \sqrt[4]{\sqrt[3]{\sqrt{a^7}}}$ **36.** $(x^{\frac{1}{2}} + y^{\frac{1}{2}})(x^{\frac{1}{2}} - y^{\frac{1}{2}})$

Solve.

37. $x^{-\frac{2}{3}} = 9$ **38.** $t^{-\frac{3}{4}} = 8$

39. $(t - 4)^{\frac{2}{5}} = 4$ **40.** $(y + 9)^{\frac{2}{3}} = 9$

C **41.** $x^{\frac{1}{2}} + 4x^{-\frac{1}{2}} = 5$ **42.** $z^{\frac{1}{4}} + 2z^{-\frac{1}{4}} = 3$

Express in simplest radical form.

43. $(a + 2\sqrt{ab} + b)^{\frac{1}{2}}$ **44.** $(a - 2\sqrt{ab} + b)^{\frac{1}{2}}$

10-2 *Real Number Exponents*

OBJECTIVE **To extend the meaning of exponents to include irrational numbers and to define exponential functions.**

Any power 2^x, where x is a rational number, has now been defined. For example,

$$2^{-4} = \frac{1}{16}, \quad 2^{\frac{5}{3}} = \sqrt[3]{2^5}, \quad \text{and} \quad 2^{1.7} = 2^{\frac{17}{10}} = \sqrt[10]{2^{17}}.$$

Now consider the problem of defining powers, such as $2^{\sqrt{3}}$, in which the exponent is irrational.

The graph of $y = 2^x$ for the rational values of x in the table below is shown in Figure 10-1. In the table irrational values of y are rounded to the nearest tenth. Figure 10-2 indicates what happens when you plot many more points of $y = 2^x$ for rational values of x.

x	-3	-2	-1	-0.5	0	0.5	1	1.5	2
$y = 2^x$	0.125	0.25	0.5	0.7	1	1.4	2	2.8	4

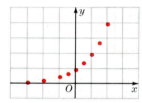

Figure 10-1

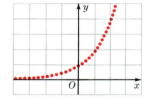

Figure 10-2

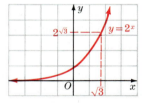

Figure 10-3

If the complete graph is to be a smooth curve as shown in Figure 10-3, there must be a point on the curve for every real value of x. In order for there to be no "breaks" in the curve, there must be a point where, for example, $x = \sqrt{3}$ and $y = 2^{\sqrt{3}}$. To find a decimal approximation of $2^{\sqrt{3}}$, evaluate the successive powers

$$2^1, \ 2^{1.7}, \ 2^{1.73}, \ 2^{1.732}, \ \ldots$$

in which the exponents are the rational numbers obtained by taking more and more decimal places in the rational approximation for $\sqrt{3}$. These powers increase steadily:

$$2^1 = 2, \quad 2^{1.7} \approx 3.2490, \quad 2^{1.73} \approx 3.3173, \quad 2^{1.732} \approx 3.3219.$$

The powers get closer and closer to a definite positive real number, which is defined to be $2^{\sqrt{3}}$. If you have a scientific calculator, you can check that $2^{\sqrt{3}} = 3.3220$ to four decimal places.

The method just discussed can be used to define a^x, where $a > 0$ and x is any real number. Moreover, it can be shown that the laws of exponents continue to hold for these powers.

EXAMPLE 1 Simplify: **a.** $3^{1+\pi} \cdot 3^{1-\pi}$ **b.** $(2^{3\sqrt{2}})^{\sqrt{2}}$ **c.** $\dfrac{5^{1+\sqrt{2}}}{5^{1-\sqrt{2}}}$

SOLUTION **a.** $3^{1+\pi} \cdot 3^{1-\pi} = 3^{(1+\pi)+(1-\pi)}$
$$= 3^2$$
$$= 9 \quad \textbf{\textit{Answer}}$$

b. $(2^{3\sqrt{2}})^{\sqrt{2}} = 2^{3\sqrt{2}\sqrt{2}}$
$$= 2^{3 \cdot 2}$$
$$= 2^6$$
$$= 64 \quad \textbf{\textit{Answer}}$$

c. $\dfrac{5^{1+\sqrt{2}}}{5^{1-\sqrt{2}}} = 5^{(1+\sqrt{2})-(1-\sqrt{2})}$
$$= 5^{2\sqrt{2}} \quad \textbf{\textit{Answer}}$$

Now that the meaning of exponents has been extended to include all real numbers, *exponential functions* can be defined.

If $a > 0$ and $a \neq 1$, the function defined by $y = a^x$ is called the **exponential function** with base a.

If $a > 1$, the graph of such a function has the general shape of the curve in Figure 10-3; it rises continuously with increasing x. The curve in Figure 10-4 is typical of the graph of $y = a^x$ for $0 < a < 1$; it falls as x increases. In each case, any vertical line and any horizontal line above the x-axis intersect the graph in just one point. This means that

$$a^p = a^q \text{ if and only if } p = q.$$

This fact can be used to solve equations in which a variable appears in an exponent.

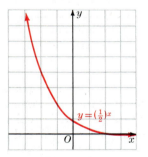

Figure 10-4

EXAMPLE 2 Solve $9^{t-1} = \left(\dfrac{1}{3}\right)^{4t-1}$.

SOLUTION
1. Express each power using the same base, 3, and simplify.

$$9^{t-1} = \left(\frac{1}{3}\right)^{4t-1}$$
$$(3^2)^{t-1} = (3^{-1})^{4t-1}$$
$$3^{2t-2} = 3^{-4t+1}$$

(*Solution continued on page 378*)

2. Equate exponents and solve.

$$2t - 2 = -4t + 1$$
$$6t = 3$$
$$t = \frac{1}{2}$$

3. Check by substituting in the original equation.

$$9^{\frac{1}{2}-1} \stackrel{?}{=} \left(\frac{1}{3}\right)^{4 \cdot \frac{1}{2}-1}$$
$$9^{-\frac{1}{2}} \stackrel{?}{=} \left(\frac{1}{3}\right)^{1}$$
$$\frac{1}{\sqrt{9}} \stackrel{?}{=} \frac{1}{3}$$
$$\frac{1}{3} = \frac{1}{3} \quad \checkmark$$

$\therefore$ the solution is $\frac{1}{2}$. ***Answer***

Oral Exercises

1. Through which point in the plane does the graph of every exponential function pass?
2. The graphs of all exponential functions have the same line as an asymptote. What is its equation?
3. What is the relationship between the graphs of $y = \left(\frac{1}{2}\right)^x$ and $y = 2^{-x}$?
4. What is the relationship between the graphs of $y = 2^x$ and $y = 2^{-x}$?

Which number of the given pair is greater?

5. $2^{\sqrt{3}}$, $2^{1.5}$

6. $\left(\frac{1}{2}\right)^{\sqrt{3}}$, $\left(\frac{1}{2}\right)^{1.5}$

7. $5^{-\pi}$, 5^{-3}

8. $3^{\sqrt{2}}$, $9^{0.7}$

9. $7^{-\pi}$, $49^{-1.5}$

10. $2^{\sqrt{15}}$, $\left(\frac{1}{4}\right)^{-2}$

11. The definition of the exponential function a^x specifies that $a \neq 1$. What is the reason for this?

Written Exercises

Simplify.

A 1. $(7^{\sqrt{2}})^{-\sqrt{2}}$

2. $5^{2-\sqrt{3}} \cdot 5^{2+\sqrt{3}}$

3. $10^{\pi+5} \div 10^{\pi+3}$

4. $(2^{\sqrt{12}})^{-\sqrt{3}}$

5. $10^{\sqrt{3}-2} \div 10^{\sqrt{3}+3}$

6. $3^{3-\pi} \cdot 3^{1+\pi}$

7. $9^\pi \cdot 3^{3-2\pi}$

8. $4^{3\sqrt{2}} \div 8^{2\sqrt{2}}$

9. $\frac{6^{\sqrt{3}}}{2^{\sqrt{3}}} \cdot 3^{1-\sqrt{3}}$

10. $\frac{10^{3+2\pi}}{5^{3+2\pi}} \cdot 4^{-\pi}$

11. $((\sqrt{2})^{\sqrt{6}})^{\sqrt{6}}$

12. $\frac{5^{\sqrt{12}}}{5^{\sqrt{27}}} \cdot 5^{2+\sqrt{3}}$

Solve.

13. $3^{2x-1} = 3^3$

14. $5^{3+x} = 5^{1+3x}$

15. $25^{2x} = 5^{x+6}$

16. $3^{2x+5} = 9^{x+1}$

17. $\left(\frac{1}{5}\right)^{2x-3} = 5^{3x-2}$

18. $\left(\frac{1}{4}\right)^x = 2^{x-9}$

B **19.** $\left(\frac{2}{5}\right)^{x+3} = \left(\frac{5}{2}\right)^{x+1}$

20. $\left(\frac{4}{9}\right)^{2x} = \left(\frac{3}{2}\right)^{6-x}$

21. $\left(\frac{1}{4}\right)^{x+2} = 8^{x-2} \cdot 8^{2x+1}$

Graph each pair of equations on the same set of axes.

22. $y = 2^x$, $y = 3^x$

23. $y = \left(\frac{1}{2}\right)^x$, $y = \left(\frac{1}{3}\right)^x$

24. $y = 3^x$, $y = 3^{-x}$

25. $y = 4^x$, $y = -4^x$

26. $y = 2^{x-1}$, $y = 2^x - 1$

27. $y = 2^{|x|}$, $y = 2^{-|x|}$

Solve each equation. Estimate solutions to the nearest tenth.

SAMPLE $2^{-x} = x + 4$

SOLUTION The solution of the equation is the x-coordinate of the point of intersection of the curves

$$y = 2^{-x} \text{ and } y = x + 4.$$

Graph the curves and estimate the x-coordinate of their point of intersection.

∴ the solution is, approximately, -1.4. **Answer**

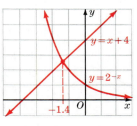

C **28.** $2^x = 4 - 2x$

29. $2^{-x} = x$

30. $2^{-x} = 2x + 4$

31. $2^{-x} = 2 - 2x$

32. $2^x = x + 2$

33. $x^2 = 2^x$

34. Prove that $y = 2^x$ and $y = \left(\frac{1}{2}\right)^x$ are reflections of each other in the y-axis.

Self-Test 1

VOCABULARY exponential function (p. 377)

1. Express in simple radical form.   **Obj. 10-1, p. 373**

    a. $\sqrt[3]{9} \div \sqrt[6]{9}$ **b.** $\sqrt[3]{a} \cdot \sqrt{a^{-\frac{1}{3}}}$

2. Write in simplest form, without using radicals or negative exponents.

    a. $\sqrt[6]{64x^4y^{-2}}$ **b.** $(a^{-\frac{1}{2}} + a^{-\frac{3}{2}})^2$

3. Simplify.   **Obj. 10-2, p. 376**

    a. $7^{2-\pi} \cdot 7^{1+\pi}$ **b.** $5^{3+2\sqrt{2}} \cdot 25^{-\sqrt{2}}$

4. Solve: $\left(\frac{1}{4}\right)^{x-1} = 2^{5-x}$.

Check your answers with those at the back of the book.

LOGARITHMIC FUNCTIONS

10-3 *Definition of Logarithms*

OBJECTIVE   To define logarithmic functions and to learn how they are related to exponential functions.

The graph of an exponential function can be used to approximate any power of the base. Consider the case where the base is 2. Using the graph in Figure 10-5, you can evaluate $2^{2.6}$ by drawing the vertical line shown in red, then the horizontal line. You see that $2^{2.6} \approx 6$. On the other hand, suppose you were given 6 and required to write it as a power of 2. By reversing the construction (Figure 10-6), you find that to express 6 as a power of 2, the exponent is approximately 2.6; that is, $6 \approx 2^{2.6}$. Figure 10-6 also shows that $0.4 \approx 2^{-1.3}$.

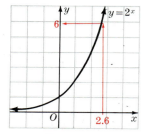

Figure 10-5

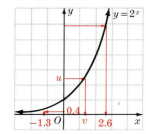

Figure 10-6

As Figure 10-6 suggests, given any positive number u, there is a unique number v such that

$$u = 2^v.$$

The exponent v is called the **logarithm** of u to the base 2, and you write

$$\log_2 u = v.$$

For example,

$$\log_2 8 = 3 \qquad \text{because} \quad 8 = 2^3;$$

$$\log_2 \frac{1}{4} = -2 \qquad \text{because} \quad \frac{1}{4} = 2^{-2};$$

$$\log_2 6 \approx 2.6 \qquad \text{because} \quad 6 \approx 2^{2.6};$$

$$\log_2 0.4 \approx -1.3 \quad \text{because} \quad 0.4 \approx 2^{-1.3}.$$

Of course, other bases besides 2 can be used. In fact, the base can be any positive number except 1, since every power of 1 is 1.

DEFINITION OF LOGARITHM

If a and u are positive numbers $(a \neq 1)$,

$$\log_a u = v \text{ if and only if } u = a^v.$$

The expression $\log_a u$ is read "the **logarithm** of u to the base a." For a given positive base a $(a \neq 1)$ and a given positive number u, there is a unique number v such that $u = a^v$. Therefore the value of $\log_a u$ exists and is unique.

Several properties of logarithms are readily apparent. Since the statements $\log_a u = v$ and $u = a^v$ are equivalent, by substitution

$$\log_a a^v = v \quad \text{and} \quad a^{\log_a u} = u.$$

Furthermore, since $a = a^1$ and $1 = a^0$ for all nonzero values of a, then it follows from the definition of a logarithm that

$$\log_a 1 = 0$$

and

$$\log_a a = 1.$$

EXAMPLE 1   **a.** Express the equation $\log_4 16 = 2$ in exponential form.

               b. Express the equation $6^3 = 216$ in logarithmic form.

SOLUTION   **a.** $\log_4 16 = 2$

                 $\therefore 16 = 4^2$ *Answer*

             b. $6^3 = 216$

                 $\therefore \log_6 216 = 3$ *Answer*

EXAMPLE 2   Simplify.

             a. $\log_5 125$ **b.** $\log_{\frac{1}{3}} 9$ **c.** $\log_{10} 0.01$ **d.** $4^{\log_4 5}$

SOLUTION   **a.** $\log_5 125 = \log_5 5^3 = 3$

             b. Let $\log_{\frac{1}{3}} 9 = v$. Then $\left(\dfrac{1}{3}\right)^v = 9$

$$(3^{-1})^v = 3^2$$
$$3^{-v} = 3^2$$
$$v = -2$$

               $\log_{\frac{1}{3}} 9 = -2$

             c. $\log_{10} 0.01 = \log_{10} 10^{-2} = -2$

             d. $4^{\log_4 5} = 5$

The function defined for $x > 0$ by the equation $y = \log_a x \, (a > 0,$ $a \neq 1)$ is the **logarithmic function with base a.** The fact that the following four statements are equivalent shows how the graphs of $y = \log_a x$ and $y = a^x$ are related:

1. (u, v) is on the graph of $y = \log_a x$
2. $v = \log_a u$
3. $u = a^v$
4. (v, u) is on the graph of $y = a^x$.

Because the points (u, v) and (v, u) are symmetric with respect to the line $y = x$, the graphs of

$$y = \log_a x \quad \text{and} \quad y = a^x$$

are mirror images of each other, with the line $y = x$ acting as a mirror. (This is illustrated for the case $a = 2$ in Figure 10-7.) Any two functions whose graphs are related in this way are inverses of each other. You will study inverse functions further in Section 10-4. Logarithmic functions have the property (suggested by Figure 10-7) that

$$\log_a p = \log_a q \text{ if and only if } p = q.$$

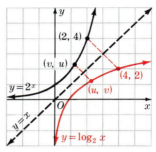

Figure 10-7

Oral Exercises

Express in exponential form.

1. $\log_5 25 = 2$

2. $\log_9 3 = \dfrac{1}{2}$

3. $\log_{\frac{1}{2}} 8 = -3$

4. $\log_{\frac{1}{3}} \left(\dfrac{1}{27} \right) = 3$

Express in logarithmic form.

5. $2^{-4} = \dfrac{1}{16}$

6. $7^2 = 49$

7. $25^{\frac{3}{2}} = 125$

8. $9^{-\frac{1}{2}} = \dfrac{1}{3}$

State two consecutive integers between which the given number lies.

9. $\log_2 10$

10. $\log_3 8$

11. $\log_{10} 0.4$

12. $\log_{10} 0.03$

Evaluate.

13. $\log_5 5^6$

14. $\log_2 2^{-3}$

15. $10^{\log_{10} 4}$

16. $8^{\log_8 2}$

17. Through which point in the plane does the graph of every logarithmic function pass?

18. If $a > 1$ and $0 < u < 1$, is $\log_a u$ positive or negative?

Written Exercises

Evaluate each logarithm.

A 1. $\log_3 27$ 2. $\log_2 32$ 3. $\log_7 7$

4. $\log_9 1$ 5. $\log_4 2$ 6. $\log_{27} 3$

7. $\log_{10} 0.001$ 8. $\log_{10} 10^{-6}$ 9. $\log_2 \frac{1}{8}$

10. $\log_{\frac{1}{2}} 16$ 11. $\log_4 8$ 12. $\log_9 27$

13. $\log_5 0.04$ 14. $\log_{\frac{1}{9}} 3$ 15. $\log_{\frac{1}{4}} \frac{1}{8}$

16. $\log_{\frac{1}{8}} \frac{1}{4}$ 17. $\log_{\sqrt{5}} 25$ 18. $\log_{\sqrt{2}} \frac{1}{4}$

Solve.

SAMPLE $\log_x 8 = \frac{3}{2}$ **SOLUTION** $\log_x 8 = \frac{3}{2}$

$$x^{\frac{3}{2}} = 8$$
$$(x^{\frac{3}{2}})^{\frac{2}{3}} = 8^{\frac{2}{3}}$$
$$x = 4 \quad \textit{Answer}$$

19. $\log_x 81 = 3$ 20. $\log_x 625 = 4$ 21. $\log_3 x = 3$

22. $\log_4 x = 3$ 23. $\log_{\frac{1}{2}} 8 = x$ 24. $\log_{\frac{1}{3}} 27 = x$

25. $\log_{\frac{1}{2}} x = -6$ 26. $\log_{\frac{1}{4}} x = -\frac{3}{2}$ 27. $\log_{\frac{1}{9}} x = -\frac{1}{2}$

28. $\log_{\frac{2}{3}} x = -2$ 29. $\log_x 27 = \frac{3}{2}$ 30. $\log_x 5 = -\frac{1}{2}$

B 31. $\log_{\sqrt{3}} x = 6$ 32. $\log_{\sqrt{2}} x = -8$

33. $\log_x \sqrt[3]{3} = \frac{1}{6}$ 34. $\log_x \sqrt{5} = -\frac{1}{2}$

35. $\log_{\sqrt{7}} \frac{1}{49} = x$ 36. $\log_{\sqrt{5}} 25 = x$

37. $\log_3(x^2 - 1) = 1$ 38. $\log_{10}(x^2 + 1) = 1$

Graph both equations using the same axes and the same scale on the two axes.

39. $y = 3^x$; $y = \log_3 x$ 40. $y = 10^x$; $y = \log_{10} x$

41. $y = \left(\frac{1}{2}\right)^x$; $y = \log_{\frac{1}{2}} x$ 42. $y = \left(\frac{3}{2}\right)^x$; $y = \log_{\frac{3}{2}} x$

Simplify each expression.

43. $\log_3 27 \cdot \log_{27} 3$

44. $\log_4 8 \cdot \log_8 4$

45. $\log_7(\log_3(\log_2 8))$

46. $\log_2(\log_2(\log_2 16))$

C **47.** $\log_a b \cdot \log_b a$
 (*Hint:* Let $\log_a b = x$. Express $\log_b a$ in terms of x.)

48. $\log_a(\log_a a)$

49. $\log_a(\log_a a^a)$

50. If $0 < a < 1$ and $0 < u < 1$, is $\log_a u$ positive or negative?

51. Show that the points (u, v) and (v, u) are symmetric with respect to the line $y = x$. (*Hint:* Two points P and Q are symmetric with respect to a line L if L is the perpendicular bisector of $\overline{PQ}$.)

52. Prove: $(\log_a b)(\log_b c) = \log_a c$.
 (*Hint:* Let $\log_a b = x$ and $\log_b c = y$.)

ḣistorical Ṅote Logarithms

Logarithms were first discovered at the end of the sixteenth century. Major work on logarithms was done by a Scotsman, John Napier. (Napier's kinsman, the Earl of Bothwell, married Mary, Queen of Scots.) Napier noticed that in certain pairs of arithmetic and geometric sequences, the sum of two terms from the arithmetic sequence and the product of the corresponding terms of the geometric sequence were themselves corresponding terms of each sequence. Consider these two sequences; the first is arithmetic, the second geometric.

$$
\begin{array}{ccccccccc}
0, & 1, & 2, & 3, & 4, & 5, & \cdots & , & n \\
\updownarrow & \updownarrow & & \updownarrow & \updownarrow & & & & \updownarrow \\
1, & 2, & 4, & 8, & 16, & 32, & \cdots & , & 2^n
\end{array}
$$

Observe, as Napier did, that

$$2 \cdot 8 = 16$$

and
$$\updownarrow$$
$$1 + 3 = 4.$$

Try matching other sums and products.

   Awareness of this correspondence made it possible to reduce complicated problems to simple computations using only addition and subtraction. Without the computational use of logarithms, many of the scientific discoveries of Kepler, Newton, and their contemporaries would have been much more difficult. Logarithmic principles were eventually applied in the development of the slide rule.

10-4 *Inverse Functions*

OBJECTIVE   **To find the inverse of a given function.**

Certain functions are related to each other in a special way. For example, consider the functions

$$f(x) = 2x - 3 \quad \text{and} \quad g(x) = \frac{x + 3}{2}.$$

A few of the values of f and g are:

$$f(0) = -3; \quad g(-3) = 0$$
$$g(5) = 4; \quad f(4) = 5$$
$$f(-2) = -7; \quad g(-7) = -2$$

In fact, you can see that whenever $f(u) = v$, it will be true that $g(v) = u$. This means that each of these functions "undoes" the other; f assigns -3 to 0, while g assigns 0 to -3, and so on.

To examine the relationship between $f(x)$ and $g(x)$ more fully, you can look at the expressions $f(g(x))$ and $g(f(x))$. This process of applying one function after another is called the **composition of functions** (see the Extra on page 389 for a fuller discussion of this topic). Before proceeding, it is important to recall that $f(g(x))$ does not necessarily equal $f(x)g(x)$.

Below are shown expressions for the composites of the functions $f(x)$ and $g(x)$, defined previously.

$$f(g(x)) = f\left(\frac{x + 3}{2}\right) \qquad\qquad g(f(x)) = g(2x - 3)$$

$$= 2\left(\frac{x + 3}{2}\right) - 3 \qquad\qquad = \frac{(2x - 3) + 3}{2}$$

$$= x + 3 - 3 \qquad\qquad\qquad = \frac{2x}{2}$$

$$= x \qquad\qquad\qquad\qquad\qquad = x$$

Thus, for a given value of x, if the functions f and g are applied one after the other the final result is the same as the original value of x. Once again you see that the functions f and g undo each other.

Functions related to each other in this way are called *inverse functions*.

Two functions f and g are **inverse functions** if

$f(g(x)) = x$ for all x in the domain of g and

$g(f(x)) = x$ for all x in the domain of f.

EXAMPLE 1 Are the functions $f(x) = \frac{1}{2}x + 1$ and $g(x) = 2x - 2$ inverses of each other?

SOLUTION
$$f(g(x)) = \frac{1}{2}(2x - 2) + 1$$
$$= x - 1 + 1$$
$$= x$$
$$g(f(x)) = 2\left(\frac{1}{2}x + 1\right) - 2$$
$$= x + 2 - 2$$
$$= x$$

$\therefore f(g(x)) = x$ and $g(f(x)) = x$; f and g are inverses of each other. ***Answer***

If two functions are inverses, then their graphs are mirror images of each other with respect to the line $y = x$. Figure 10-8 shows this relationship for the functions in Example 1.

You learned in Section 10-3 that the graphs of

$$y = \log_a x \text{ and } y = a^x$$

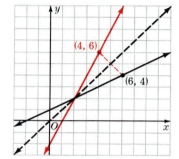

Figure 10-8

are also reflections of each other in $y = x$. This suggests that the functions

$$f(x) = \log_a x \text{ and } g(x) = a^x$$

are inverse functions. It is not difficult to verify that f and g are, indeed, inverses of each other.

$$f(g(x)) = \log_a a^x \qquad g(f(x)) = a^{\log_a x}$$
$$= x \qquad\qquad\qquad = x$$

The functions satisfy the definition of inverse functions.

It was noted earlier that if f and g are inverses, then the number pairs of g are obtained by interchanging the numbers in the pairs of f. Furthermore, the definition of inverse functions requires that f and g are both functions. Therefore some functions do not have inverses.

EXAMPLE 2 Does the function $h(x) = x^2$ have an inverse?

SOLUTION $(2, 4)$ and $(-2, 4)$ are pairs of h. If h had an inverse, then $(4, 2)$ and $(4, -2)$ would be pairs of the inverse function. But the definition of a function prohibits the assigning of two numbers, 2 and -2, in the range to one number, 4, in the domain.

$\therefore h$ does not have an inverse. ***Answer***

Example 2 suggests the generalizations stated at the top of the following page.

1. f does not have an inverse if there are numbers x_1 and x_2 such that $x_1 \neq x_2$ but $f(x_1) = f(x_2)$. (See Figure 10-9.)

2. f does have an inverse if, for all x_1 and x_2 such that $x_1 \neq x_2$, $f(x_1) \neq f(x_2)$. (See Figure 10-10.)

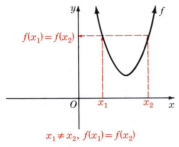

$x_1 \neq x_2,\ f(x_1) = f(x_2)$

Figure 10-9

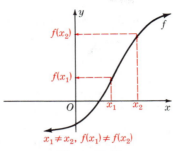

$x_1 \neq x_2,\ f(x_1) \neq f(x_2)$

Figure 10-10

If the function f has an inverse, the inverse function can be denoted by f^{-1}, which is read "f inverse." Notice that the superscript -1 is *not* an exponent. The symbol f^{-1} means the function that is the inverse of f; it does *not* mean $\dfrac{1}{f}$.

Sometimes it is possible to find the equation of the inverse of a given function. Since the numbers in the pairs of f are interchanged to produce the pairs of f^{-1}, there is a simple procedure for finding the equation of the inverse. Interchange the variables x and y in the equation of f, solve for y, and express the resulting function f^{-1} in function notation.

EXAMPLE 3 Let $g(x) = x^3 + 2$.

 a. Find $g^{-1}(x)$.

 b. Graph g and g^{-1} in the same coordinate system.

SOLUTION **a.** g is defined by the equation $y = x^3 + 2$.

Interchange x and y: $x = y^3 + 2$

Solve for y: $y^3 = x - 2$

$$y = \sqrt[3]{x - 2}$$

Express as a function: $g^{-1}(x) = \sqrt[3]{x - 2}$.

 b. To graph g^{-1}, first graph g, then reflect g in the line $y = x$.

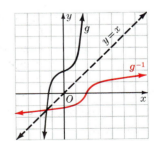

Oral Exercises

State the equation of the inverse of each function.

1. $f(x) = 5x$ **2.** $g(x) = x + 3$ **3.** $g(x) = x - 1$

4. $h(x) = -x$ **5.** $f(x) = \dfrac{1}{x}$ **6.** $k(x) = \sqrt[3]{x}$

7. State a rule for determining from its graph whether a function has an inverse.

8. Does any quadratic function have an inverse?

9. Simplify each expression.
     a. $f(f^{-1}(x))$ **b.** $f^{-1}(f(x))$ **c.** $(f^{-1})^{-1}(x)$

Written Exercises

In each exercise, determine whether the given functions are inverses of each other.

A   **1.** $f(x) = \dfrac{1}{2}x + 2$, $g(x) = 2x - 4$ **2.** $f(x) = \dfrac{1}{x - 1}$, $g(x) = \dfrac{x + 1}{x}$

     3. $f(x) = \dfrac{x}{3}$, $g(x) = \dfrac{3}{x}$ **4.** $f(x) = \dfrac{2}{3}x - 1$, $g(x) = \dfrac{3(x + 1)}{2}$

     5. $f(x) = -x + 3$, $g(x) = -x - 3$ **6.** $f(x) = x^3 + 1$, $g(x) = \sqrt[3]{x} - 1$

     7. $f(x) = \log_2(x - 1)$, $g(x) = 1 + 2^x$ **8.** $f(x) = \sqrt{x}$, $g(x) = x^2$

     9. $f(x) = \dfrac{1}{x}$, $g(x) = \dfrac{1}{x}$ **10.** $f(x) = \dfrac{1}{x^3}$, $g(x) = \sqrt[3]{\dfrac{1}{x}}$

If f has an inverse, find $f^{-1}(x)$ and graph f and f^{-1} in the same coordinate system. If f has no inverse, so state. (In Exercises 19–24 you may find it necessary to restrict the domain of f^{-1}.)

11. $f(x) = 3x - 1$ **12.** $f(x) = \dfrac{1}{2}x - 1$

13. $f(x) = x^2 - 1$ **14.** $f(x) = |x|$

15. $f(x) = -\dfrac{6}{x}$ **16.** $f(x) = \sqrt[3]{x - 1}$

B   **17.** $f(x) = 3^{-x}$ **18.** $f(x) = 2\log_4 x$

     19. $f(x) = \sqrt{x + 1}$ **20.** $f(x) = \sqrt{1 - x}$

     21. $f(x) = -\sqrt{4 - x}$ **22.** $f(x) = -\sqrt{x - 4}$

     23. $f(x) = 1 - x^2$, $x \geq 0$ **24.** $f(x) = x^2 - 4$, $x \leq 0$

C   **25.** Let $f(x) = ax + b$. Under what conditions on a and b will $f(x) = f^{-1}(x)$ for all x?

26. Prove that the graphs of a linear function and its inverse are never perpendicular.

Composition of Functions

Recall that applying one function after another is called the composition of functions. This operation is denoted by a small circle, as $f \circ g$. The expression $f \circ g$ means "the composition of f with g. It is defined as follows:

$$[f \circ g](x) = f(g(x))$$

Similarly, $g \circ f$, the composition of g with f, is stated:

$$[g \circ f](x) = g(f(x))$$

Note that $f \circ g$ is not the same as $f(x)g(x)$, and, as shown in the following example, $f \circ g$ does not always equal $g \circ f$.

EXAMPLE If $f(x) = 2x + 1$ and $g(x) = x^2 - 1$,

$$\begin{aligned} \text{then } [f \circ g](x) &= f(g(x)) \\ &= f(x^2 - 1) \\ &= 2(x^2 - 1) + 1 \\ &= 2x^2 - 1 \end{aligned}$$

$$\begin{aligned} \text{but } [g \circ f](x) &= g(f(x)) \\ &= g(2x + 1) \\ &= (2x + 1)^2 - 1 \\ &= 4x^2 + 4x \end{aligned}$$

It is interesting to observe the composition of a function f with its inverse f^{-1} when the function is one-to-one.

$$[f^{-1} \circ f](x) = f^{-1}(f(x)) = x$$
$$[f \circ f^{-1}](x) = f(f^{-1}(x)) = x$$

Exercises

1. If $f(x) = x^2$ and $g(x) = x + 1$, find $f \circ g$ and $g \circ f$.

2. If $f(x) = 2x$ and $g(x) = x^2 + 4$, find $f \circ g$ and $g \circ f$.

3. Given $f(x) = 2x - 6$ and $f^{-1}(x) = \frac{1}{2}x + 3$, find $f \circ f^{-1}$ and $f^{-1} \circ f$.

10-5 *Laws of Logarithms*

OBJECTIVE   To learn the basic properties of logarithms.

By using the law of exponents

$$a^m \cdot a^n = a^{m+n}$$

you can prove that the logarithm of the *product* of two positive numbers equals the *sum* of the logarithms:

Let $\log_a p = m$, and $\log_a q = n$.
Then $p = a^m$, and $q = a^n$.
Thus, $pq = a^m \cdot a^n = a^{m+n}$.
By the definition of logarithm,

$$\log_a pq = m + n,$$

or

$$\log_a pq = \log_a p + \log_a q.$$

This proves the first of the *laws of logarithms* stated below.

LAWS OF LOGARITHMS

Let a be a positive number not equal to 1, let p and q be positive numbers, and let n be any real number.

1. $\log_a pq = \log_a p + \log_a q$

2. $\log_a \dfrac{p}{q} = \log_a p - \log_a q$

3. $\log_a p^n = n \log_a p$

The proofs of the second and third laws of logarithms use the laws of exponents $a^m \div a^n = a^{m-n}$ and $(a^m)^n = a^{mn}$, respectively. These laws are proved in Exercises 31 and 32. Figure 10-11 illustrates the first law of logarithms.

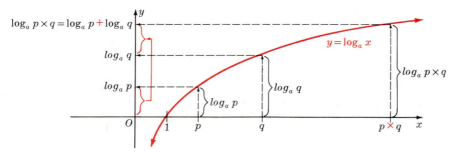

Figure 10-11

EXAMPLE 1   Given that $\log_3 2 = 0.631$ and $\log_3 5 = 1.465$, evaluate each expression.

a. $\log_3 10$ **b.** $\log_3 0.4$ **c.** $\log_3 32$ **d.** $\log_3 15$

SOLUTION   **a.** $\log_3 10 = \log_3(2 \cdot 5)$

$$= \log_3 2 + \log_3 5$$
$$= 0.631 + 1.465$$
$$= 2.096$$

b. $\log_3 0.4 = \log_3 \dfrac{2}{5}$

$$= \log_3 2 - \log_3 5$$
$$= 0.631 - 1.465$$
$$= -0.834$$

c. $\log_3 32 = \log_3 2^5$

$$= 5\log_3 2$$
$$= 5(0.631)$$
$$= 3.155$$

d. $\log_3 15 = \log_3(3 \cdot 5)$

$$= \log_3 3 + \log_3 5$$
$$= 1 + 1.465$$
$$= 2.465$$

EXAMPLE 2   Evaluate $36^{\log_6 5}$.

SOLUTION $36^{\log_6 5} = (6^2)^{\log_6 5}$

$$= 6^{2\log_6 5}$$
$$= 6^{\log_6 5^2}$$
$$= 5^2 = 25. \quad \textbf{\textit{Answer}}$$

EXAMPLE 3   Solve: $\log_2 x = 2\log_2 3 + \log_2 5$.

SOLUTION $\log_2 x = 2\log_2 3 + \log_2 5$

$$= \log_2 3^2 + \log_2 5$$
$$= \log_2(3^2 \cdot 5)$$

$\therefore \log_2 x = \log_2 45$

$x = 45$ **\textit{Answer}**

Oral Exercises

Express as a linear combination of logarithms of single variables or numbers. All variables denote positive real numbers.

SAMPLE $\log_3 \dfrac{5x^2}{y}$ **SOLUTION** $\log_3 \dfrac{5x^2}{y} = \log_3 5x^2 - \log_3 y$

$$= \log_3 5 + \log_3 x^2 - \log_3 y$$
$$= \log_3 5 + 2\log_3 x - \log_3 y \quad \textbf{\textit{Answer}}$$

1. $\log_2 \dfrac{t}{6}$

2. $\log_{10} 7x^2$

3. $\log_4 x^3 y^2$

4. $\log_5 \dfrac{2x}{yz}$

5. $\log_5 2\left(\dfrac{v}{u}\right)^3$

6. $\log_3 2\sqrt{r}$

Express as a single logarithm.

7. $\log_2 x + \log_2 y + \log_2 z$

8. $\log_3 u - \log_3 v + \log_3 w$

9. $2\log_{10} x + 3\log_{10} y$

10. $2\log_2 3x - \log_2 y$

11. $\log_a \dfrac{u}{v} - \log_a u$

12. $\log_a x^2 - \log_a xy + \log_a y^2$

13. $1 - \log_2 x$

14. $2 + \log_3 t$

Written Exercises

Solve for x.

A

1. $\log_{10} x = 3 \log_{10} 2$

2. $\log_5 x = \log_5 3 + \log_5 7$

3. $x = 2 \log_2 6 - \log_2 9$

4. $\log_{12} x = \frac{2}{3} \log_{12} 64$

5. $\log_3 x = 3 \log_3 5 - \frac{1}{2} \log_3 25$

6. $\log_7 x = \frac{1}{3} \log_7 27 + \frac{2}{3} \log_7 8$

7. $\log_2 x^2 = \log_2 9 + \log_2 16$

8. $\log_{10} x^3 = 3 \log_{10} 12 - 2 \log_{10} 8$

9. $\log_a 6x = 2(\log_a 2 + \log_a 3)$

10. $\log_a 2x^2 = 2 \log_a 6 - \log_a 2$

Given that $\log_{10} 3 = 0.477$ and $\log_{10} 5 = 0.699$, evaluate each logarithm.

11. $\log_{10} 15$ **12.** $\log_{10} 0.6$ **13.** $\log_{10} 25$ **14.** $\log_{10} 27$

B   **15.** $\log_{10} 0.0003$ **16.** $\log_{10} 500{,}000$ **17.** $\log_{10} 0.25$ **18.** $\log_{10} 2.7$

19. $\log_{10} 4.5$ **20.** $\log_{10} 1.8$ **21.** $\log_{0.1} 3$ **22.** $\log_{0.001} 5$

Find the value of each expression.

23. $9^{\log_3 2}$ **24.** $8^{\log_2 3}$ **25.** $10^{6 \log_{10} \sqrt{3}}$ **26.** $2^{\log_2 3 + \log_2 5}$

Solve for x.

SAMPLE $\log_6 x + \log_6(x - 5) = 2$

SOLUTION $\log_6 x + \log_6(x - 5) = 2$

$\log_6 x(x - 5) = 2$

$\log_6(x^2 - 5x) = 2$

Use exponential form: $x^2 - 5x = 6^2$

$x^2 - 5x - 36 = 0$

$(x + 4)(x - 9) = 0$

$x = -4 \text{ or } x = 9.$

Check: If $x = -4$, $\log_6 x$ is not defined; -4 is not a root.

If $x = 9$, $\log_6 x + \log_6(x - 5) = \log_6 9 + \log_6 4$

$= \log_6(9 \cdot 4)$

$= \log_6 36$

$= 2 \checkmark$

$\therefore$ 9 is the only solution.   ***Answer***

27. $\log_2(x + 3) + \log_2(x - 3) = 4$

28. $\log_7(x + 1) + \log_7(x - 5) = 1$

C   **29.** $\log_5(x - 1) + \log_5(x - 2) - \log_5(x + 6) = 0$

30. $2 \log_3 x - \log_3(x - 2) = 2$

31. Prove the second law of logarithms.

32. Prove the third law of logarithms.

33. Evaluate $4^{\log_2(2^{\log_2 5})}$.

Self-Test 2

VOCABULARY   logarithm (p. 380)   composition of functions (p. 385)
                   logarithmic function (p. 382)   inverse functions (p. 385)

1. Express in logarithmic form: $9^{\frac{3}{2}} = 27$.   Obj. 10-3, p. 380

2. Evaluate $\log_8 4$.   3. Solve: $\log_9 x = -\frac{3}{2}$.

4. Show that $f(x) = \sqrt[3]{1-x}$ and $g(x) = 1 - x^3$ are inverses of   Obj. 10-4, p. 385
   each other.

5. If $f(x) = 4x - 3$, find $f^{-1}(x)$.

6. Express $2 \log_2 u - 3 \log_2 v$ as a single logarithm.   Obj. 10-5, p. 390

7. Evaluate $\log_{10} 0.04$, given that $\log_{10} 5 = 0.699$.

Check your answers with those at the back of the book.

EXTRA

The Number e and Natural Logarithms

In more advanced courses you will find the letter e used to represent a very important irrational number. To five decimal places, that number is 2.71828.

The idea for this special number originated with the Swiss mathematician Leonhard Euler. He proved that when larger and larger numbers are substituted for n in the expression

$$\left(1 + \frac{1}{n}\right)^n$$

the results approach as a limit the number 2.718 . . . . This number is called e in honor of Euler.

The number e is so useful in applications that, to save the drudgery of computations, logarithms to the base e, called *natural logarithms*, were computed and arranged in tables. Often the abbreviation "ln" is used in referring to logarithms to the base e; that is, ln 5 means $\log_e 5$. Modern calculators may contain a key labeled "ln," so that by the mere touch of a finger you can obtain ln 5, for instance.

Exercises

Use the following information together with the laws of logarithms on page 390 to find the specified natural logarithms.

ln 1.5 = 0.405   ln 2.0 = 0.693   ln 3.0 = 1.099
ln 7.5 = 2.015   ln 10.0 = 2.303

1. ln 30   2. ln 5   3. ln $\frac{1}{2}$ 4. ln 4.5   5. ln $\frac{1}{3}$ 6. ln 2.5

APPLICATIONS

10-6 *Applications of Logarithms*

OBJECTIVE   To use common logarithms in solving equations involving powers and in evaluating logarithms with any given base.

The laws of logarithms can be used to simplify difficult computations. For example, since $\log_a pq = \log_a p + \log_a q$, the problem of multiplying two numbers can be solved by adding their logarithms.

In this section you will work largely with **common logarithms,** which are logarithms to the base 10. When writing common logarithms, the subscript 10 is omitted. Thus, instead of $\log_{10} 5$, you write $\log 5$. Because of the decimal nature of our number system, common logarithms have been used widely in the application of logarithms to computation. A full treatment of this usage of common logarithms is included in Appendix A of this book.

Although most of the computational functions of logarithms have been taken over by calculators, which are more versatile, more precise, and faster, logarithms continue to be of basic mathematical significance. In fact there are important types of problems for which logarithms provide the best, or even the only, method of solution. Before examining some of these problems, you need some familiarity with the use of a table of common logarithms. A complete table of common logarithms is found in Table 3 on page 640. Part of Table 3 is shown below.

N	0	1	2	3	4	5	6	7	8	9
20	3010	3032	3054	3075	3096	3118	3139	3160	3181	3201
21	3222	3243	3263	3284	3304	3324	3345	3365	3385	3404
22	3424	3444	3464	3483	3502	3522	3541	3560	3579	3598
23	3617	3636	3655	3674	3692	3711	3729	3747	3766	3784
24	3802	3820	3838	3856	3874	3892	3909	3927	3945	3962

In the table, the logarithms are rounded to four decimal places, and the decimal point is omitted. To find an approximation for $\log x$ for $1 < x < 10$, find the first two digits of x in the column headed N and the third digit in the row to the right of N. For example, to find $\log 2.36$, look for 23 under N and move along row 23 to the column headed 6, where you find 3729. Thus $\log 2.36 \approx 0.3729$.

To find an approximation for the logarithm of a number greater than 10 or less than 1, you can use Law 1 (page 390). For example,

$$\log 236 = \log (2.36 \times 10^2)$$
$$= \log 2.36 + \log 10^2 \longleftarrow \text{By Law 1}$$
$$= \log 2.36 + 2$$
$$\approx 0.3729 + 2 \longleftarrow \text{Using Table 3}$$
$$= 2.3729$$

Thus, you can see that the common logarithm of a number can be written as the sum of an integer, called the **characteristic,** and a nonnegative number less than 1, called the **mantissa,** which is found in a table of logarithms.

EXAMPLE 1 Find the following logarithms.

a. log 3.8 b. log 97,500 c. log 0.000542

SOLUTION

a. Find 38 under N; then read across to the column headed 0.
$\therefore$ log 3.8 = 0.5798 *Answer*

b. Write 97,500 in scientific notation and use laws of logarithms.
log 97,500 = log (9.75×10^4)
The mantissa (from the table) corresponding to 9.75 is 0.9890. The characteristic is 4.
$\therefore$ log 97,500 = 0.9890 + 4 = 4.9890 *Answer*

c. Write 0.000542 in scientific notation and use laws of logarithms.
log 0.000542 = log (5.42×10^{-4})
The mantissa corresponding to 5.42 is 0.7340. The characteristic is -4.
$\therefore$ log 0.000542 = 0.7340 + (-4) = -3.2660 *Answer*

For convenience, the symbol = was used in the preceding solutions. You should be aware that the logarithms in the table, and therefore the answers, are approximations.

EXAMPLE 2 Solve each equation.

a. log x = 2.1139 b. log x = -3.3851

SOLUTION Express each logarithm as the sum of its mantissa and characteristic. Then use the table and laws of logarithms.

a. log x = 2.1139
  = 0.1139 + 2
  = log 1.3 + log 10^2
  = log (1.3×10^2)
  = log 130
$\therefore$ x = 130

b. log x = -3.3851
  = 0.6149 + (-4)
  = log 4.12 + log 10^{-4}
  = log (4.12×10^{-4})
  = log 0.000412
$\therefore$ x = 0.000412

If log x = a, then x is called the **antilogarithm** of a. You can write the results of Example 2 as follows:

antilog 2.1139 = 130 and antilog -3.3851 = 0.000412.

When using a table to find antilogarithms, it is sometimes necessary to use inverse interpolation (Section 8-9). When using a calculator you need merely raise to a power of ten. For example,

antilog 2.1139 = $10^{2.1139}$ = 130.

Logarithms can sometimes be used to put the solution to a problem into **calculation-ready** form, where the next step is to obtain a decimal approximation using a table or a calculator.

EXAMPLE 3   Solve: $3^{2t} = 5$.

     a. Give the solution in calculation-ready form.
     b. Give the solution as a decimal with three significant digits.

SOLUTION   **a.** 1. Take logarithms of both sides. $3^{2t} = 5$

$$\log 3^{2t} = \log 5$$

            2. Use laws of logarithms to simplify. $2t \log 3 = \log 5$

            3. Solve for t. $t = \dfrac{\log 5}{2 \log 3}$

         $\therefore$ the solution in calculation-ready form is $\dfrac{\log 5}{2 \log 3}$.   ***Answer***

         b. Find $\log 5$ and $\log 3$ with a calculator or table.

$$t = \frac{0.6990}{2(0.4771)} = 0.733$$

         $\therefore$ the solution is 0.733 to three significant digits.   ***Answer***

EXAMPLE 4   Solve: $120x^{\frac{7}{3}} = 953$

SOLUTION $120x^{\frac{7}{3}} = 953$

$$x^{\frac{7}{3}} = \frac{953}{120}$$

$$\frac{7}{3} \log x = \log \frac{953}{120}$$

$$\log x = \frac{3}{7} \log \frac{953}{120}$$

$\therefore x = \text{antilog} \left[\dfrac{3}{7} (\log 953 - \log 120) \right]$ $\left\{ \begin{array}{l} \text{This expression can be} \\ \text{evaluated directly} \\ \text{with a calculator.} \end{array} \right.$

$ = \text{antilog} \left[\dfrac{3}{7} (\log 9.53 \times 10^2 - \log 1.2 \times 10^2) \right]$

$ = \text{antilog} \left[\dfrac{3}{7} (2.9791 - 2.0792) \right]$

$ = \text{antilog} \left[\dfrac{3}{7} (0.8999) \right]$

$ = \text{antilog} \left[0.3857 \right] \approx 2.43$

$\therefore$ the solution is 2.43 to three significant digits.   ***Answer***

Although tables and calculators usually give common logarithms, it may be necessary for you to evaluate logarithms in other bases. This problem is simplified by the **change of base formula** on the next page.

$$\log_a x = \frac{\log_b x}{\log_b a}$$

EXAMPLE 5 Evaluate $\log_2 7$.

SOLUTION Use the change of base formula, letting $a = 2$, $x = 7$, and $b = 10$.

$$\log_2 7 = \frac{\log 7}{\log 2}$$

$$= \frac{0.8451}{0.3010}$$

$\log_2 7 = 2.808$ to four significant digits. ***Answer***

In the previous example the quotient was rounded to four significant digits because both the dividend and the divisor were four-significant-digit approximations from a table. Numbers that are derived from measurements are also approximations. You can use the following rules to determine how to round computational results.

1. Give *products, quotients,* and *powers* to the same number of *significant digits* as appear in the least accurate approximation involved.

2. Give *sums* and *differences* to the same number of *decimal places* as appear in the approximation with the least number of decimal places.

Oral Exercises

Express x in terms of common logarithms.

1. $3^x = 6$ **2.** $(1.5)^x = 8.7$ **3.** $7^{2x} = 10$ **4.** $5^{\frac{x}{3}} = 12$

Express $\log x$ in terms of common logarithms.

5. $x^3 = 12$ **6.** $x^5 = 8$ **7.** $x^{\frac{2}{3}} = 23$ **8.** $x^{\frac{5}{3}} = 75$

9. Use the change of base formula to find $(\log_2 5) \cdot (\log_5 2)$.

10. Are the fractions $\dfrac{\log_2 7}{\log_2 5}$ and $\dfrac{\log_3 7}{\log_3 5}$ equal? If not, which is greater?

Written Exercises

Use Table 3 to find each logarithm.

A **1.** $\log 7.52$ **2.** $\log 29.7$ **3.** $\log 13.7$ **4.** $\log 0.61$

5. $\log 0.0408$ **6.** $\log 2590$ **7.** $\log 6.3 \times 10^3$ **8.** $\log 7.15 \times 10^{-3}$

Use Table 3 to find each antilogarithm to three significant digits.

9. antilog 0.6542   **10.** antilog 3.0414   **11.** antilog 4.9445

12. antilog 2.8406   **13.** antilog (6.9100 − 10)   **14.** antilog (9.4712 − 10)

Solve each equation.

a. Give the solution in calculation-ready form.
b. Give the solution to three significant digits.

15. $3^x = 30$ **16.** $5^t = 10$ **17.** $10^v = 3800$

18. $5.6^x = 56$ **19.** $z^{1.8} = 3.6$ **20.** $x^{3.6} = 1.8$

21. $x^\pi = 10$ **22.** $(1.1)^m = 2$ **23.** $3^{2t} = 25$

24. $6^{\frac{y}{5}} = 4$ **25.** $x = \log_2 5$ **26.** $x = \log_5 2$

B **27.** $5x^{\frac{2}{3}} = 16$ **28.** $12^{\frac{3x}{5}} = 100$ **29.** $10^{2x} = 5^{x+2}$

30. Evaluate $(\log_a b)(\log_b a)$.

C **31.** Evaluate $(\log_a b)(\log_b c)(\log_c a)$.

32. Prove the change of base formula. (*Hint:* Let $\log_a x = y$, so that $x = a^y$.)

Calculator Key-In _____

If you have a calculator that has both common logarithms and natural logarithms (see the Extra on page 393), you can verify that solution methods using logarithms are independent of the base of the logarithms used.

The example below shows a solution using natural logarithms of the equation in Example 4 on page 396. Notice in the example below that if x is a natural logarithm, the antilogarithm of x will be e^x.

EXAMPLE   Solve $120x^{\frac{7}{3}} = 953$ using natural logarithms.

SOLUTION $x^{\frac{7}{3}} = \dfrac{953}{120}$

$$\frac{7}{3} \ln x = \ln 953 - \ln 120$$

$$\ln x = \frac{3}{7}(\ln 953 - \ln 120)$$

$$\therefore x = e^{\frac{3}{7}(\ln 953 - \ln 120)} = e^{0.8880528} = 2.4303925$$

∴ the solution is 2.4303925 to eight significant digits. Notice that it agrees with the solution on page 396.

1. Use natural logarithms to solve Exercise 16 on this page. Compare your solution to the one you obtained previously.

2. Use natural logarithms to solve Exercise 19 on this page. Compare your solution to the one you obtained previously.

10-7 *Exponential Growth and Decay*

OBJECTIVE   To use exponential and logarithmic functions to study growth and decay.

A radioactive substance decays at a rate proportional to the amount present. After any given time period, some of the original substance, because of changes in its nuclei, will have changed to a different element. The **half-life,** h, is the time it takes until only half of the original remains unchanged. The amount x of the original substance remaining at time t is given by

$$x = x_0 \cdot 2^{-\frac{t}{h}},$$

where x_0 is the amount present when $t = 0$. This kind of behavior is called **exponential decay.**

EXAMPLE 1   The half-life of carbon-14 is 5730 y. How much of a 10.0 mg sample will remain after 4500 y?

SOLUTION   Let $x_0 = 10.0$, $h = 5730$, and $t = 4500$ in the exponential decay formula.

$$x = 10.0 \cdot 2^{-\frac{4500}{5730}}$$

If a calculator is used, the solution can now be found directly. Otherwise, continue as follows:

$$x = 10.0 \cdot 2^{-0.7853}$$
$$\log x = \log(10.0 \cdot 2^{-0.7853})$$
$$= \log 10.0 - 0.7853 \log 2$$
$$= 1 - (0.7853)(0.3010)$$
$$= 0.7636$$
$$x = \text{antilog } 0.7636 = 5.80$$

After 4500 y, 5.80 mg of the original carbon-14 remains.   **Answer**

Under ideal conditions, the population of a colony of individuals (bacteria, whales, or humans, for example) experiences **exponential growth.** That is, it obeys a law of the form

$$n = n_0 \cdot 2^{kt} \quad (k > 0)$$

where n is the population at time t and n_0 is the population when $t = 0$. The constant k depends on the characteristics of the particular population being studied.

EXAMPLE 2   At noon a culture of bacteria had 2.5×10^6 members, and at 3 P.M. the population was 4.5×10^6. Assuming exponential growth, find when the population will be 8.0×10^6.

(*The solution is given on page 400.*)

EXPONENTIAL AND LOGARITHMIC FUNCTIONS   **399**

SOLUTION Let n be the population *in millions* t hours after noon. Then $n_0 = 2.5$, and

$$n = 2.5 \cdot 2^{kt}.$$

To find k, set $n = 4.5$ and $t = 3$:

$$4.5 = 2.5 \cdot 2^{k \cdot 3}, \quad \text{or} \quad 2^{3k} = \frac{4.5}{2.5} = 1.8.$$

Take common logarithms:

$$\log 2^{3k} = \log 1.8$$
$$3k \log 2 = \log 1.8$$
$$k = \frac{\log 1.8}{3 \log 2}$$

Now set $n = 8.0$ and $k = \dfrac{\log 1.8}{3 \log 2}$ in the original equation and solve for t:

$$8.0 = 2.5 \cdot 2^{kt}$$
$$2^{kt} = \frac{8.0}{2.5} = 3.2$$
$$\log 2^{kt} = \log 3.2$$
$$kt \log 2 = \log 3.2$$
$$t = \frac{1}{k} \cdot \frac{\log 3.2}{\log 2}$$
$$t = \frac{3 \log 2}{\log 1.8} \cdot \frac{\log 3.2}{\log 2}$$
$$t = \frac{3 \log 3.2}{\log 1.8}$$
$$\therefore t = 5.94$$

The population will be 8.0×10^6 after 5.94 h, or at about 5:56 P.M. **Answer**

If an amount P is invested at an interest rate r (expressed as a decimal) compounded n times a year, the investment will increase to a value A, given by

$$A = P\left(1 + \frac{r}{n}\right)^{nt},$$

at the end of t years. This is the **compound interest formula.**

EXAMPLE 3 How long does it take an investment to triple in value if it is invested at 12% compounded quarterly?

SOLUTION In the compound interest formula, let $A = 3P$, $r = 0.12$, and $n = 4$.

Sheimae

Substitute these values in the formula.

$$3P = P\left(1 + \frac{0.12}{4}\right)^{4t}$$

$$3 = (1.03)^{4t}$$

$$\log 3 = 4t \log 1.03$$

$$t = \frac{\log 3}{4 \log 1.03}$$

$$t = \frac{0.4771}{4(0.0128)}$$

$$\therefore t = 9.3$$

At 12% interest compounded quarterly, an investment will triple in 9.3 y. **Answer**

Problems

Solve.
a. Give the solution in calculation-ready form.
b. Give the solution to three significant digits.

A **1.** The radioactive gas radon has a half-life of 3.8 days. How long would it take 1.0 gram of the gas to decay to 0.2 gram?

2. How long does it take $1000 to amount to $1500 if it is invested at 8% compounded quarterly?

3. Some years ago Ms. Lopez invested $5000 at 12% compounded monthly, and the account now contains $20,000. How long ago did she start the account?

4. The population of a colony of bacteria grew from 2×10^5 to 3×10^5 during the period from noon until 2 P.M. At what time will the population be 5×10^5?

B **5.** If the population of a city doubles every 20 years, how long does it take to triple?

6. If 10 g of tritium decays to 8.50 g in 2.93 y, what is the half-life of tritium?

7. Until recently Series E savings bonds paid $4 after 5 y for every $3 initially invested. To the nearest percent, to what annual interest rate, compounded quarterly, is this equivalent?

8. Sugar is put into a large quantity of water and the mixture is stirred. After 2 minutes 50% of the sugar has dissolved. How much longer will it take until 90% of the sugar has dissolved? (Use the exponential decay formula.)

9. Savings institutions sometimes use the term "effective yield" to describe the interest rate compounded *annually* (once a year) that is equivalent to a given rate. The effective yield can be found by computing the value of $1 at the end of a year at the given rate. For example, at 8% compounded quarterly, the value A of $1 at the end of a year is

$$A = 1\left(1 + \frac{0.08}{4}\right)^4 = (1.02)^4.$$

Evaluating A directly (without using logs), you find that, to four decimal places: $A = 1.0824$. Thus, the original $1 has grown in value by $0.0824, an increase of 8.24%. The effective yield is 8.24%.

Find the effective yield of 12% compounded quarterly.

C 10. Carbon-14 dating is based on the following scientific facts. All living organisms contain nonradioactive carbon, C-12, and radioactive carbon, C-14, in the same ratio, about 10^{12} parts of C-12 to 1 part of C-14. When an organism dies, the amount of C-12 remains the same, but the C-14 decays exponentially with a half-life of 5730 y, thereby changing the ratio. Thus, if a piece of wood contains C-12 and C-14 in the ratio 10^{12} to 0.5, the wood must be about one half-life, or 5730 y, old.

A cave in southern France contained firewood indicating that it had been inhabited in the past. The ratio of C-12 to C-14 in the wood was found to be 10^{12} to 0.08. How long ago was the cave inhabited?

Self-Test 3

VOCABULARY
common logarithms (p. 394)
characteristic (p. 395)
mantissa (p. 395)
antilogarithm (p. 395)
calculation-ready form
  (p. 396)
change of base (p. 396)
half-life (p. 399)
exponential decay (p. 399)
exponential growth (p. 399)
compound interest formula
  (p. 400)

Solve each equation.

1. $10^x = 20$ 2. $5 = 2^{4t}$ Obj. 10-6, p. 394

3. The population of a city was 50,000 in 1950 and 70,000 in 1960. Assuming exponential growth, when did the population reach 100,000?   Obj. 10-7, p. 399

4. Find the value of $1000 if it is invested for 5 y at 10% annual interest compounded semiannually.

Check your answers with those at the back of the book.

Chapter Summary

1. The meaning of rational exponents is defined as follows:
$$a^{\frac{p}{q}} = (\sqrt[q]{a})^p = \sqrt[q]{a^p}$$
   The meaning of exponents is further extended to define real exponents as in, for example, $2^{\sqrt{3}}$.

2. The equation $y = a^x$ defines the *exponential function* with base a, where $a > 0$ and $a \neq 1$.

3. *Logarithms* are defined by the relationship
$$\log_a u = v \text{ if and only if } u = a^v,$$
   where a and u are positive numbers ($a \neq 1$).

4. The equation $y = \log_a x$ defines the *logarithmic function* with base a, where $a > 0$ and $a \neq 1$.

5. *Inverse functions* are functions that "undo" one another . Exponential and logarithmic functions with the same base are inverses of each other.

6. The *laws of logarithms* are often useful:
$$\log_a pq = \log_a p + \log_a q;$$
$$\log_a \frac{p}{q} = \log_a p - \log_a q;$$
$$\log_a p^n = n \log_a p.$$

7. There are certain types of equations for which logarithms provide the best, or the only, method of solution. Logarithms are used in studying exponential equations and their applications to such phenomena as radioactive decay, population growth, and compound interest.

Chapter Review

Give the letter of the correct answer.

1. Which expression is equivalent to $(x^{\frac{1}{2}} - y^{\frac{1}{2}})^2$? **10-1**
   a. $x - y$ **b.** $x + 2\sqrt{xy} + y$ **c.** $x - 2\sqrt{xy} + y$

2. Simplify $\dfrac{2}{\sqrt[6]{8}}$.

   a. $\sqrt{2}$ **b.** $\dfrac{1}{\sqrt{2}}$ **c.** $\dfrac{1}{2}$ **d.** $\sqrt[3]{4}$

3. Solve $9^{x+2} = 3^{3x-3}$. **10-2**
   a. 2   **b.** 3   **c.** 4   **d.** 7

4. Simplify $\left(\frac{2^{1+\sqrt{2}}}{2^{1-\sqrt{2}}}\right)^{\sqrt{2}}$.

a. $2^{\sqrt{2}}$ **b.** 16   **c.** 8   **d.** 4

5. If f is any exponential function, then

a. $f(x + y) = f(x) \cdot f(y)$ **b.** $f(x + y) = f(x) + f(y)$
c. $f(xy) = f(x) \cdot f(y)$ **d.** $f(xy) = f(x) + f(y)$

6. Which of the following could be the graph of $y = 3^{-x}$?

a.   **b.**   **c.**   **d.**

7. Evaluate $\log_2 64$.   10-3

a. $\frac{1}{6}$ **b.** 6   **c.** 8   **d.** 32

8. Between which numbers is $\log_5 130$?

a. 0 and 1   **b.** 1 and 2   **c.** 2 and 3   **d.** 3 and 4

9. Are the functions f and g inverses of one another if $f(x) = \frac{3}{4}x - 1$ 10-4

and $g(x) = \frac{4(x + 1)}{3}$?

a. Yes   **b.** No

10. If $f(x) = 5x - 2$, find the function g that is the inverse of f.

a. $g(x) = \frac{1}{5}x + 2$ **b.** $g(x) = \frac{(x + 2)}{5}$ **c.** $g(x) = 2x + 5$

11. Evaluate $\log_6(36 \times 6^{-7})$.

a. -14 **b.** -5 **c.** $-\frac{7}{2}$ **d.** 9

12. If $\log_a w = \frac{1}{2}\log_a x + \log_a y$, express w in terms of x and y.   10-5

a. $(xy)^{\frac{1}{2}}$ **b.** $(x + y)^{\frac{1}{2}}$ **c.** $y\sqrt{x}$ **d.** $\frac{x}{2} + y$

13. Evaluate $4^{2+\log_4(\frac{1}{2})}$.

a. 2   **b.** 4   **c.** 8   **d.** 16

14. Which of the following could be the graph of $y = \log_3 x$?

a.   **b.**   **c.**   **d.**

15. Solve: $10^{5t} = 2$.   10-6

   a. $\dfrac{2}{5}$ **b.** $\dfrac{\log_{10} 2}{\log_{10} 5}$ **c.** $\dfrac{1}{5} \log_{10} 2$ **d.** $5 \log_{10} 2$

16. If 40 mg of a radioactive substance decays to 5 mg in 12 min, find   10-7
the half-life, in minutes, of the substance.

   a. 2 min   **b.** 4 min   **c.** 6 min   **d.** 8 min

Chapter Test

1. Find the value of x: **a.** $\left(\dfrac{1}{16}\right)^{-\frac{3}{4}} = x$ **b.** $9^x = 27$ 10-1

2. Simplify: **a.** $\sqrt[3]{\sqrt{27x^6}}$ **b.** $(125^{\frac{2}{3}} - 64^{\frac{2}{3}})^{\frac{3}{2}}$

3. Solve: $4^{x-2} = 8^{\pi+1} \div 8^{\pi-1}$.

4. a. Express in logarithmic form: $32^{\frac{6}{5}} = 64$.   10-2

   b. Express in exponential form: $\log_9 \left(\dfrac{1}{27}\right) = -\dfrac{3}{2}$.   10-3

5. Simplify: **a.** $4^{\log_4 3}$ **b.** $\log_3 9^{\sqrt{2}}$

6. Solve: **a.** $\log_9 x = \dfrac{3}{2}$ **b.** $\log_x \left(\dfrac{1}{4}\right) = -\dfrac{2}{3}$

7. Given that $f(x) = \sqrt[3]{x-1}$ and $g(x) = x^3 + 1$. Show that f and g are   10-4
inverses of each other.

8. If $f(x) = 3x - 2$, find $f^{-1}(x)$.

9. Solve: **a.** $\log_3 x = \log_3 12 + \log_3 2 - \log_3 6$.   10-5
          b. $\log_7 x^3 = \dfrac{3}{4} \log_7 64$.

10. Evaluate: **a.** $5^{\log_5 6 - 2 \log_5 3}$ **b.** $4^{\log_2 3}$

11. Given that $\log_{10} 2 = 0.301$ and $\log_{10} 3 = 0.477$, find

   a. $\log_{10} 8$ **b.** $\log_{10} 12$ **c.** $\log_{10} 15$

12. a. Find $\log_9 2$ given that $\log_2 9 = 3.17$.   10-6
   b. Express $\log_{\frac{1}{a}} x$ in terms of $\log_a x$.

13. Express t in terms of common logarithms: $2^{t+2} = 3^{t-1}$.

14. The population of a colony of bacteria doubles every 5 hours. How   10-7
long does it take for the population to triple? Give the answer to
two significant digits using the facts that $\log 2 = 0.301$ and
$\log 3 = 0.477$.

This top view of a grand piano with its lid removed gives a clear view of the piano's hammers, strings, and dampers. See problem 13 on page 416 for a discussion of the frequencies of the notes in the chromatic scale that is used in tuning pianos.

11

SEQUENCES
AND SERIES

SEQUENCES

11-1 *Arithmetic Sequences*

OBJECTIVE   **To find specified term(s) of an arithmetic sequence.**

Sequences of numbers are commonly found. Here are some examples:

(A) Average temperatures in Chicago for successive days

(A) $15°C$, $18°C$, $17°C$, $14°C$, $20°C$, . . .

(B) Number of atoms at each stage of a nuclear fission

(B) $1, 2, 4, 8, 16,$ . . .

(C) Value in dollars of an investment at six-month intervals

(C) $5000, 5300, 5600, 5900,$ . . .

The values of any function whose domain is composed of consecutive natural numbers is called a **sequence.** Each value is called a **term** of the sequence. A sequence is **finite** if it has a last term and **infinite** if it does not.

The nth term of a sequence can be denoted t_n. Thus, you can write the following for sequence (C) above:

$$t_1 = 5000, \quad t_2 = 5300, \quad t_3 = 5600, \ldots$$

Notice that the difference between each term and the term before it is 300. The number 300 is called the *common difference* of the sequence, and the sequence is called an *arithmetic sequence.*

If the difference between any two successive terms in a sequence is a constant, d, then the sequence is called an **arithmetic sequence,** or **arithmetic progression,** and d is called the **common difference.**

Consider an arithmetic sequence with first term a and common difference d. In the table below, compare each term, t_n, with its position, n.

n	1	2	3	4	$\cdots$	n
t_n	$a + 0d$	$a + 1d$	$a + 2d$	$a + 3d$	$\cdots$	$a + (n - 1)d$

In general, the nth term of an arithmetic sequence is given by

$$t_n = a + (n - 1)d.$$

The letter a is used to denote the first term of the sequence. In this formula and the others that follow, it is always possible to use t_1 for a. You can use this formula to find a specified term of an arithmetic sequence. The general term of sequence (C) is given by

$$t_n = 5000 + (n - 1)300.$$

look for a common difference

EXAMPLE 1 Find the fiftieth term of the arithmetic sequence 15, 9, 3, -3, . . .

SOLUTION First find the common difference.

$$d = t_2 - t_1$$
$$d = 9 - 15 = -6$$

Substitute $a = 15$, $n = 50$, and $d = -6$ in the formula:

$$t_n = a + (n - 1)d$$
$$t_{50} = 15 + (50 - 1)(-6) = 15 + 49(-6) = 15 - 294$$
$$= -279 \quad \textbf{\textit{Answer}}$$

EXAMPLE 2 On the first day of each month, Mrs. Burnham deposits a fixed amount in a mutual fund. On June 1 her account balance was $500, and on December 1 her account balance will be $2000.

a. How much does she deposit each month?
b. Find the balance in her account after each monthly deposit.

SOLUTION **a.** The balance in her account, after the first day of each month, forms an arithmetic sequence that looks like this:

June 1	July 1	Aug. 1	Sept. 1	Oct. 1	Nov. 1	Dec. 1
500	?	?	?	?	?	2000

Substitute $a = 500$, $n = 7$, and $t_7 = 2000$ in the formula:
$$t_n = a + (n - 1)d$$
$$2000 = 500 + (7 - 1)d$$
$$1500 = 6d$$
$$250 = d$$
$\therefore$ Mrs. Burnham deposits $250 per month.   *Answer*

b. The balance in her account after each monthly deposit is given by the sequence

$500, $750, $1000, $1250, $1500, $1750, $2000. *Answer*

The terms between two given terms of an arithmetic sequence are called **arithmetic means** between the two terms. In Example 2 there are five arithmetic means between $500 and $2000, namely $750, $1000, $1250, $1500, $1750. A single arithmetic mean between two numbers is called *the* **arithmetic mean,** or **average,** of the two numbers. The arithmetic mean (average) of a and b is $\frac{a+b}{2}$. For example, the arithmetic mean of 500 and 2000 is $\frac{500 + 2000}{2}$, or 1250.

EXAMPLE 3   Insert four arithmetic means between 1 and 11.

SOLUTION   Outline the sequence

$$1, \underline{\ ?\ }, \underline{\ ?\ }, \underline{\ ?\ }, \underline{\ ?\ }, 11$$

Substitute 11 for t_n, 1 for a, and 6 for n in $t_n = a + (n-1)d$, and solve for d.

$$11 = 1 + (6-1)d$$
$$11 = 1 + 5d$$
$$d = 2$$

The required means are obtained by adding 2: $1, 3, 5, 7, 9, 11$. *Answer*

Oral Exercises

Tell which of the following sequences are arithmetic.

1. 9, 7, 5, 3, . . . NO
2. 32, 16, 8, 4, . . . NO
3. 3, 4.5, 6, 7.5, . . . YES
4. 1, 5, 10, 16, . . . NO

State the next two terms in each arithmetic sequence.

5. 2, 5, 8, . . 11, 14
6. 20, 15, 10, . 5, 0
7. −10, −7, −4, . −1, 2
8. 24, 35, 46, . 57, 68

Give the first three terms of the arithmetic sequence whose first term and common difference are given.

9. $a = 7, d = 4$ 11, 15, 19
10. $a = 8, d = 5$ 13, 18, 23
11. $a = 20, d = 6$ 26, 32, 38
12. $a = -8, d = -2$ −6, −4, −2

State the arithmetic mean for each pair of numbers.   find avg.

13. 6, 14   10
14. 5, 25   15
15. 11, −1   5
16. −5, −11   −8

SEQUENCES AND SERIES   409

Written Exercises

State the next three terms of each arithmetic sequence.

A **1.** $3, 5, 7, \ldots$ **2.** $11, 17, 23, \ldots$ **3.** $12, 21, 30, \ldots$

4. $7, 18, 29, \ldots$ **5.** $-8, -5, -2, \ldots$ **6.** $19, 12, 5, \ldots$

7. $-3, -12, -21, \ldots$ **8.** $4, -4, -12, \ldots$ **9.** $6.7, 7.8, 8.9, \ldots$

10. $4\frac{1}{4}, 2\frac{3}{4}, 1\frac{1}{4}, \ldots$ **11.** $2x, 4x, 6x, \ldots$ **12.** $7a, 10a, 13a, \ldots$

13. Find the arithmetic mean between 17 and 53.

14. Find the arithmetic mean between -32 and 18.

Find the specified term of each arithmetic sequence.

15. $25, 33, 41, \ldots; t_{10}$ **16.** $62, 58, 54, \ldots; t_{25}$

17. $-17, -9, -1, \ldots; t_{100}$ **18.** $2.3, 4.5, \ldots; t_{1000}$

19. $t_1 = 12; t_3 = 18; t_{20}$ **20.** $t_2 = 5; t_3 = 9; t_{50}$

21. $t_6 = 38; t_{12} = 50; t_{18}$ **22.** $t_1 = k + 3b; t_2 = 5k - b; t_{11}$

Give a formula for the nth term of each arithmetic sequence.

23. The sequence of positive even integers

24. The sequence of positive odd integers

25. The sequence with $t_1 = 7$ and each term 10 greater than the one before

26. The sequence with $t_2 = -8$ and each term 6 less than the one before

27. The sequence of positive integers ending with the digit 5

28. The sequence of positive integers divisible by 6

29. The sequence of positive integers that give a remainder of 1 when divided by 5

30. The sequence of negative integers starting with the number -1

Find the position n of the term in red in each arithmetic sequence:

B **31.** $18, 24, 30, \ldots, 96, \ldots$ **32.** $-5, -1, 3, \ldots, 87, \ldots$

33. $81, 75, 69, \ldots, -33, \ldots$ **34.** $-101, -112, -123, \ldots, -321, \ldots$

Insert the specified number of arithmetic means between the given numbers.

35. a. One, between 18 and 54   **36. a.** One, between 7 and -53

     b. Two, between 18 and 54   **b.** Three, between 7 and -53

     c. Three, between 18 and 54   **c.** Five, between 7 and -53

37. Two, between $2x - 4y$ and $5x + 5y$ **38.** Four, between $5a - 3b$ and $15a + 2b$

C **39.** How many multiples of 7 are there between 100 and 1000?

40. How many three-digit numbers are divisible by 8?

41. The arithmetic mean of $5x - 7$ and $3x - 11$ is x. Find x.

42. Is it possible to have an arithmetic sequence of three positive integers whose sum is a prime number? Explain.

43. Is it possible to have three different numbers in an arithmetic sequence and their squares also in an arithmetic sequence? Explain.

Problems

A **1.** Sarah gets a job with a starting salary of $14,600 and annual raises of $700. What will her salary be after 5 years?

To solve Problems 2 and 3 use the information about Job A and Job B. Job A pays $1500 per month with a raise of $200 per month at the end of each year. Job B pays $1400 per month with a raise of $140 per month at the end of each half year.

2. Which job will pay more after one year?

3. Which job will pay more after two years?

4. A carpenter is building a staircase from the first floor to the second floor. The second floor is 3.3 m above the first floor. Each step rises 22 cm. Not counting the second floor itself, how many stairs will there be?

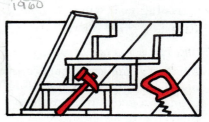

5. A pile of bricks has 85 bricks in the bottom row, 79 bricks in the second row, 73 in the third row, and so on until there is only 1 brick in the top row.
   a. How many bricks are in the 12th row?
   b. How many rows are there in all?

6. Twenty-five light poles are to be installed at equal intervals along a city street and at each end. If the street is 1800 m long, how far apart should the poles be placed?

The number h is called the harmonic mean of the numbers a and b if $\frac{1}{a}, \frac{1}{h}, \frac{1}{b}$ form an arithmetic sequence. Use this definition in Exercises 7 and 8.

B **7.** Show that $h = \dfrac{2ab}{a + b}$.

8. If you travel at a km/h for 100 km and then at b km/h for the next 100 km, show that your average speed is the harmonic mean of a and b. (Recall that average speed is defined to be the total distance divided by the total time.)

11-2 *Geometric Sequences*

OBJECTIVE   To find specified terms of geometric sequences.

The Singletons have just purchased a house for $80,000. They expect the value of the house to appreciate (increase) by 10% each year. In other words, they expect the house's value in any given year to be 110% of (or 1.1 times) its value in the preceding year. The following chart shows the expected values of the house in the future:

Year	1	2	3	4	...
Value	80,000	80,000(1.1)	$80,000(1.1)^2$	$80,000(1.1)^3$	...

If you let t_n represent the value of the house in the Singletons' nth year of ownership, you can see that

$$t_n = 80,000(1.1)^{n-1}.$$

Do you also see that the ratio of the value of the house to its value in the preceding year will always be 1.1? The sequence t_n is an example of a *geometric sequence.*

If the ratio r of every pair of two successive terms in a sequence is a constant, then the sequence is called a **geometric sequence,** or **geometric progression,** and r is called the **common ratio.** If a is the first term of a geometric progression, and r is the common ratio, then the following table shows an expression for each term, t_n.

n	1	2	3	4	...	n
t_n	ar^0	ar^1	ar^2	ar^3	...	ar^{n-1}

In general, the nth term of a geometric sequence is given by

$$t_n = ar^{n-1}.$$

look for a common ratio.

EXAMPLE 1   Find the twenty-fifth term of the geometric sequence $4, 6, 9, \ldots$; express the answer in exponential form.

SOLUTION   First find the common ratio.

$$r = \frac{t_2}{t_1} = \frac{6}{4} = 1.5$$

Then use the formula for t_n. Let $a = 4$, $r = 1.5$, and $n = 25$.

$$t_n = ar^{n-1}$$
$$t_{25} = 4(1.5)^{25-1}$$
$$= 4(1.5)^{24} \quad \textit{Answer}$$

The terms between two given terms of a geometric sequence are called **geometric means** between the given terms.

EXAMPLE 2 Insert three geometric means between 3 and 48.

SOLUTION 3, __?__ , __?__ , __?__ , 48

Thus, there are $n = 5$ terms with $a = 3$ and $t_5 = 48$.

$$t_n = ar^{n-1}$$
$$48 = 3r^{5-1}$$
$$16 = r^4$$
$$\pm 2 = r$$

If $r = 2$, the sequence is 3, 6, 12, 24, 48, and the geometric means are 6, 12, 24. If $r = -2$, the sequence is 3, -6, 12, -24, 48, and the geometric means are -6, 12, -24. **Answer**

A single geometric mean between two terms is called *the* **geometric mean,** or *the* **mean proportional,** of the numbers. If m is the geometric mean between p and q, then p, m, q is a geometric sequence, and

$$\frac{m}{p} = \frac{q}{m}.$$
$$\therefore \ m^2 = pq \text{ and } m = \pm\sqrt{pq}.$$

Since m^2 is positive, p and q are either both positive or both negative. If p and q are both positive, the positive root $\sqrt{pq}$ is usually considered to be the geometric mean. If p and q are both negative, the negative root $-\sqrt{pq}$ is considered to be the geometric mean.

Oral Exercises

a. State whether the sequence is arithmetic, geometric, or neither.
b. If the sequence is arithmetic, state the common difference and the next two terms.
c. If the sequence is geometric, state the common ratio and the next two terms.

1. 3, 6, 12, 24, . . .

2. 2, 4, 6, 8, . . .

3. 40, 20, 10, 5, . . .

4. 3, 9, 18, 30, . . .

5. 8, -4, 2, -1, . . .

6. -12, -4, 4, 12, . . .

7. c^6, c^4, c^2, c^0, . . .

8. a, a^2b, a^3b^2, a^4b^3, . . .

9. $\frac{1}{2}$, $\frac{2}{3}$, $\frac{3}{4}$, $\frac{4}{5}$, . . .

10. $\sqrt{5}$, $\sqrt{6}$, $\sqrt{7}$, $\sqrt{8}$, . . .

11. $6^{\frac{1}{3}}$, $6^{\frac{2}{3}}$, 6, $6^{\frac{4}{3}}$, . . .

12. $\log 2$, $2 \log 2$, $3 \log 2$, $4 \log 2$, . . .

Give the geometric mean of the given numbers.

13. 1 and 9

14. 2 and 18

15. $\frac{3}{5}$ and $\frac{5}{3}$

Written Exercises

Give the next three terms of each geometric sequence. Then write a formula for the nth term.

A **1.** $5, 10, 20, \ldots$ **2.** $8, 24, 72, \ldots$

    3. $64, -32, 16, \ldots$ **4.** $27, 18, 12, \ldots$

    5. $\dfrac{8}{27}, \dfrac{4}{9}, \dfrac{2}{3}, \ldots$ **6.** $1, \sqrt{2}, 2, \ldots$

    7. $0.1, -0.01, 0.001, \ldots$ **8.** $\dfrac{a}{b}, \dfrac{ac}{b^2}, \dfrac{ac^2}{b^3}, \ldots$

    9. $a^5b^3, a^7, a^9b^{-3}, \ldots$ **10.** $\dfrac{p}{q}, \dfrac{q}{p}, \dfrac{q^3}{p^3}, \ldots$

    11. $\log m, 2\log m, 4\log m, \ldots$ **12.** $e^x, e^{2x}, e^{3x}, \ldots$

For each pair of numbers, find **(a)** the arithmetic mean and **(b)** the geometric mean.

    13. $4, 9$ **14.** $2, 32$ **15.** $\dfrac{1}{2}, 50$

    16. $1.6, 0.4$ **17.** $\dfrac{5}{2}, \dfrac{8}{45}$ **18.** $\sqrt{2}, 2\sqrt{2}$

Find the specified term of the geometric sequence described.

    19. $a = 3; r = 2; t_8$ **20.** $a = 96; t_2 = 48; t_5$

    21. $a = 10; t_2 = -30; t_6$ **22.** $a = 16; t_{18} = 36; t_{20}$

    23. $a = k^2b^3; t_2 = k^3b^6; t_{10}$ **24.** $a = xy; t_3 = \dfrac{x}{y}; t_{15}$

The sequences in Exercises 25 and 26 are geometric.

B **25. a.** If $a = 8$ and $t_3 = 16$, show that $r = \pm\sqrt{2}$.

        b. If $a = 8$ and $t_4 = 16$, find r.

    26. a. If $a = 5^{\frac{1}{3}}$ and $t_2 = 15^{\frac{1}{3}}$, show that $r = 3^{\frac{1}{3}}$.

        b. If $a = 5^{\frac{1}{3}}$ and $t_4 = 15^{\frac{1}{3}}$, find r.

Insert the given number of geometric means and write the resulting geometric sequence(s).

    27. Two, between 9 and 72   **28.** Three, between 2 and 162

    29. Four, between 96 and 3   **30.** One, between x^2y^{-3} and x^8y

    31. Two, between $4x^{-1}y^5$ and $108x^8y^2$ **32.** One, between a^{2x} and a^{8x}

C **33.** Prove: The logarithms of numbers in a geometric sequence form an arithmetic sequence. (*Hint:* Consider $\log a$, $\log ar$, $\log ar^2$, $\log ar^3, \ldots$)

34. The first three numbers of the sequence $8, x, y, 36$ form an arithmetic sequence, but the last three numbers form a geometric sequence. Find all possible values for x and y.

In Exercises 35–37 refer to $\triangle ABC$ at the right. $\triangle ABC$ is a right triangle and $\overline{CD}$ is perpendicular to hypotenuse $\overline{AB}$.

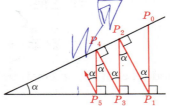

35. Given that $\triangle ACD$ is similar to $\triangle CBD$, prove that h is the *geometric mean* (or *mean proportional*) of x and y.

36. Given that $\triangle ABC$ is similar to $\triangle ACD$, prove that b is the geometric mean of x and c.

37. Given that $\triangle ABC$ is similar to $\triangle CBD$, prove that a is the geometric mean of y and c.

38. Is the arithmetic mean of two different positive numbers *always* greater than the geometric mean of the two numbers? Prove your answer. (*Hint:* $(a - b)^2 \geq 0$.)

39. Let P_0 be any point on one side of an acute angle. Construct the perpendicular $\overline{P_0P_1}$ to the other side, then construct the perpendicular $\overline{P_1P_2}$ to the first side, and so on, as shown. Show that the lengths

$$P_0P_1, P_1P_2, P_2P_3, \dots$$

form a geometric sequence. (It is this property that accounts for the name "geometric sequence.")

Problems

Let P_1 be the price of an item before a price increase or decrease, and P_2, the price after the change. Express each of the following price changes by an equation in the form $P_2 = P_1 \cdot r$, where r is a constant.

A **1.** An increase of 8%   **2.** A decrease of 8%

3. An increase of 50%   **4.** An increase of 100%

5. A decrease of 2%   **6.** An increase of 150%

7. A price increases 10% and the new price is later increased by 10%. Show that the two increases are equivalent to a single price increase of 21%.

8. A discount store reduces its price each week by 10% of the previous week's price. A coat priced at $120 during the first week was sold during the fourth week. At what price was the coat sold?

B 9. A house purchased last year for $50,000 is now worth $60,000. Assuming that the value of the house continues to appreciate at the same rate each year, find the value two years from now.

10. The value of a certain sports car depreciates (decreases) at about 20% per year. Find the value of the car five years after it was purchased for $16,000.

11. Job A has a starting salary of $12,000 with annual increases of $800. Job B has a starting salary of $11,000 with annual increases of 10%. Which job will pay more after 3 years? after 5 years?

12. How many great, great, great-grandparents did you have? Assume there are no duplications.

C 13. There are 13 notes in the chromatic scale from the A below middle C to the next higher A if both A's are included. This scale can be played by playing the notes in order. (See the diagram.) The frequencies of notes are usually given in hertz (Hz), which correspond to vibrations per second. The frequencies of notes in the chromatic scale form a geometric sequence. Show that the common ratio of this sequence is $2^{\frac{1}{12}}$, using the facts that the standard frequency for the A below middle C is 220 Hz and the standard frequency for the next higher A is 440 Hz.

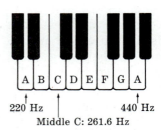

220 Hz 440 Hz

Middle C: 261.6 Hz

Self-Test 1

1. Find the twentieth term of the arithmetic sequence with $t_1 = 22$ and $d = -1.5$. **Obj. 11-1, p. 407**

2. Insert three arithmetic means between 15 and -13.

3. Find the fifth term of the geometric sequence with $t_1 = 36$ and $t_2 = -18$. **Obj. 11-2, p. 412**

4. Find the geometric mean of 15 and 45.

Check your answers with those at the back of the book.

11-3 *Arithmetic Series*

OBJECTIVE   **To find the sums of arithmetic series and to use summation notation.**

A **series** is the indicated sum of the terms in a sequence. Associated with the sequence $3, 5, 7, 9, 11$ is the series $3 + 5 + 7 + 9 + 11$. The sum of the first n terms of a sequence is denoted by S_n. Thus, in the example above, $S_2 = 3 + 5$ and $S_5 = 3 + 5 + 7 + 9 + 11$. An **arithmetic series** is a series whose associated sequence is arithmetic. The series $3 + 5 + 7 + 9 + 11$ is an arithmetic series in which the common difference is 2.

Consider an arithmetic sequence with first term a and common difference d. Then

$$S_n = a + (a + d) + (a + 2d) + \cdots + [a + (n - 1)d].$$

Also,

$$S_n = t_n + (t_n - d) + (t_n - 2d) + \cdots + [t_n - (n - 1)d].$$

If you add the corresponding sides of these two equations, you find that the sum of the terms involving d is 0, and you have

$$2S_n = (a + t_n) + (a + t_n) + \cdots + (a + t_n) \quad (n \text{ terms})$$
$$2S_n = n(a + t_n)$$
$$\therefore S_n = \frac{n}{2}(a + t_n)$$

The expression above for S_n is convenient to use when the last term (t_n) is known. A more general expression for S_n can be developed as follows:

$$S_n = \frac{n}{2}(a + t_n) = \frac{n}{2}[a + a + (n - 1)d] = \frac{n}{2}[2a + (n - 1)d]$$

The sum of the first n terms of an arithmetic series is given by the formula:

$$S_n = \frac{n}{2}[2a + (n - 1)d]$$

EXAMPLE 1   Find the sum of the first 15 terms of the arithmetic series $11 + 5 + (-1) + (-7) + \cdots$.

(*Solution on page 418.*)

SOLUTION   Here $n = 15$, $a = 11$ and $d = 5 - 11 = -6$.

$$S_n = \frac{n}{2}[2a + (n-1)d]$$

$$S_{15} = \frac{15}{2}[2 \cdot 11 + (15-1)(-6)] = \frac{15}{2}(22 - 84)$$

$$= \frac{15}{2}(-62) = -465 \quad \textit{Answer}$$

You can use the Greek letter Σ (sigma) to abbreviate the writing of a series. For instance, to abbreviate the writing of the series

$$3 + 6 + 9 + 12 + 15 + 18 + 21 + 24, \text{ or}$$
$$3(1) + 3(2) + 3(3) + 3(4) + \cdots + 3(8)$$

first observe that the general term is $3n$; then write $\sum_{n=1}^{8} 3n$ (read "the summation from 1 to 8 of $3n$"), where it is understood that you are to add all terms obtained from $3n$ by replacing n with the consecutive integers from 1 to 8 inclusive. The symbol $\sum$ is called the **summation sign,** the expression $3n$ is called the **summand,** and the letter n the **index.**

EXAMPLE 2   Write $\sum_{j=6}^{10} (3j - 2)$ in expanded form.

SOLUTION   Replace j with the integers 6 to 10 in turn:

$$\sum_{j=6}^{10} (3j - 2) = (3 \cdot 6 - 2) + (3 \cdot 7 - 2) + (3 \cdot 8 - 2) + (3 \cdot 9 - 2) + (3 \cdot 10 - 2)$$

$$= 16 + 19 + 22 + 25 + 28 \quad \textit{Answer}$$

EXAMPLE 3   Write the arithmetic series $2 + 5 + 8 + \cdots + 299$ using summation notation.

SOLUTION   First find the general term for t_n. Here $a = 2$ and $d = 3$.

$$t_n = t_1 + (n-1)d$$
$$= 2 + (n-1)3 = 3n - 1$$

Thus, the summand is $3n - 1$. Next, find the limits of summation. Since $t_1 = 2$, the lower limit is 1. To find the upper limit, n, substitute 299 for t_n and solve:

$$t_n = 3n - 1$$
$$299 = 3n - 1$$
$$100 = n$$

$$\therefore 2 + 5 + 8 + \cdots + 299 = \sum_{n=1}^{100} 3n - 1. \quad \textit{Answer}$$

Note that other answers are possible for Example 3. For example,

$$\sum_{n=0}^{99} 3n + 2 \text{ is also correct.}$$

Oral Exercises

Exercises 1–4 refer to $\displaystyle\sum_{i=4}^{10} 3i^2$.

1. State the index. **2.** State the summand.

3. State the limits of summation.

4. State the first and last terms of the series.

Read each symbol aloud and give the expanded form.

5. $\displaystyle\sum_{k=1}^{4} 3k$ **6.** $\displaystyle\sum_{k=2}^{5} k^2$ **7.** $\displaystyle\sum_{i=0}^{3} 2^i$ **8.** $\displaystyle\sum_{n=1}^{5} \frac{1}{n}$

9. $\displaystyle\sum_{i=5}^{10} (i+2)$ **10.** $\displaystyle\sum_{j=0}^{4} (2j-3)$ **11.** $\displaystyle\sum_{m=3}^{6} (10m-1)$ **12.** $\displaystyle\sum_{k=0}^{5} (k^2+1)$

Written Exercises

Use the given data to find the sum, S_n, of the following arithmetic series.

A **1.** $n = 100; t_1 = 7; t_{100} = 205$ **2.** $n = 50; t_1 = 120; t_{50} = 22$ *55 50*

3. $t_1 = 2; d = 3; n = 10$ **4.** $t_1 = 7; d = -5; n = 20$

5. $n = 20; t_{20} = 35, d = 2$ *320* **6.** $n = 40; t_1 = 8; t_3 = 22$

7. $3x + 5x + 7x + \cdots + t_n; n = 25$ **8.** $4a + 7a + 10a + \cdots + t_n; n = 10$

Find the sum of each arithmetic series.

9. $\displaystyle\sum_{k=1}^{5} 4k$ **10.** $\displaystyle\sum_{j=1}^{10} \frac{3}{2}j$ *165 82.5 /2* **11.** $\displaystyle\sum_{n=0}^{50} 2n + 1$ **12.** $\displaystyle\sum_{i=1}^{20} 7 - 5i$

13. $\displaystyle\sum_{k=1}^{60} 8 - 3k$ *-5010* **14.** $\displaystyle\sum_{m=0}^{15} 5m + 2$ **15.** $\displaystyle\sum_{i=1}^{50} 20 - i$ **16.** $\displaystyle\sum_{j=1}^{12} 3j - 2$ *210*

$\frac{3}{2} \cdot \frac{10}{1}$

Use summation notation to write each series.

17. $2 + 4 + 6 + 8 + 10$ **18.** $1 + 3 + 5 + 7 + 9 + 11 + 13$ *$\sum_{N=1}^{19}$ 55-5N*

$\frac{3}{2} = 1\frac{1}{2}$ **19.** $5 + 8 + 11 + \cdots + 98$ **20.** $50 + 45 + 40 + \cdots + 5$

21. $10 + 7 + 4 + \cdots + (-50)$ **22.** $1.5 + 2 + 2.5 + \cdots + 6.5$

In Exercises 23–27 find the sum of the elements of the given set of integers.

B **23.** The positive two-digit integers ending in 3

24. The positive three-digit integers ending in 7

25. The positive two-digit multiples of 3

26. The positive three-digit even integers   *247,050*

27. The positive three-digit odd integers

28. The average of 20 terms of an arithmetic series is 83. What is the sum of these 20 terms?

29. a. Show that the sum of the first n positive integers is $\dfrac{n^2 + n}{2}$.

   b. If $1 + 2 + 3 + \cdots + n = 210$, find n.

30. Derive a formula for the sum of the first n positive even integers.

31. In an arithmetic series, if $S_n = 2n^2 + 3n$, find t_1 and t_2.

32. In an arithmetic series, if $S_{10} = 155$ and $t_{10} = 29$, find t_1.

33. In an arithmetic series, if $S_{20} = 720$ and $S_{19} = 665$, find t_1.

use arithmetic formula to find summand

34. Show that $\log (1 \cdot 2 \cdot 3 \cdot 4 \cdot 5) = \displaystyle\sum_{k=1}^{5} \log k$.

C **35.** Show that $\displaystyle\sum_{k=1}^{3} k \log 3 = \log 3^6$

36. Evaluate $\displaystyle\sum_{k=1}^{n} \dfrac{1}{(3k - 2)(3k + 1)}$ in terms of n.

   (*Hint:* Observe the pattern of answers when $n = 1, 2, 3,$ and 4.)

Solve for x.

37. $\displaystyle\sum_{k=1}^{8} (kx - 1) = 64$ **38.** $\displaystyle\sum_{i=1}^{9} (2xi + 1) = 144$

Problems

Solve.

A **1.** Every hour a cuckoo clock sounds as many times as the hour. How many times does it sound starting with the first sound at 1 P.M. and continuing on through the last sound at midnight?

2. The front row of a lecture hall has 27 seats. There are two more seats in each following row. How many seats are there in the first 20 rows?

3. Some bricks are stacked so that there are 5 bricks in the top row and 3 more bricks in each successive row down to the ground. If there are 33 rows in all, how many bricks are there in the whole stack?

4. Verna is going to build a photography darkroom beneath her cellar stairs by nailing boards on both sides of the staircase. If each of the 12 stairs is 20 cm high, find the total length of the boards needed to enclose both sides. $5,120$

5. In a match game in which the object is to avoid picking up the last match, four rows of matches are placed on the table. If the numbers of matches in each row are consecutive integers and the second largest row has six matches, how many matches are there in all?

6. A student taking a test consisting of ten questions is told that each question after the first is worth two credits more than the preceding question. If the third question on the test is worth five credits, what is the maximum score that the student can obtain?

7. John repays the $630 he owes his sister by making monthly payments. If the first payment is $25 and each other payment is $5 more than that of the preceding month, how long does it take him to pay the debt?

8. Over a number of weeks May saved $66.60 from money earned on an after-school job. She saved $5.70 the first week and 75¢ more than the preceding week for every week following. For how many weeks did she save?

B 9. Find the sum of the first 25 odd positive integers.

10. Find the sum of the positive integers less than 100 and divisible by 6.

11. Two students are reading an 1100-page historical novel. One reads 50 pages a day and the other reads 10 pages the first day, 20 the second, 30 the third, and so on. After how many days will they be on the same page?

12. The largest integer in an arithmetic progression of consecutive even integers is nine times the smallest integer. The sum of the arithmetic progression is 90. Find the numbers.

13. On a test consisting of 12 questions, each question after the first is worth 2 credits more than the preceding one. If the fifth question is worth 20 credits, how much is the last question worth?

14. From two towns 363 km apart, Jack and Jill set out to meet each other. If Jill travels 1 km the first day, 3 the second, 5 the third, and so on in arithmetic progression, and Jack travels 2 km the first day, 6 the second, 10 the third, and so on in arithmetic progression, when will they meet?

11-4 *Geometric Series*

OBJECTIVE   **To find sums of geometric series.**

A **geometric series** is the indicated sum of a geometric sequence. For example,

$$1 + 6 + 36 + 216 + 1296$$

is a geometric series with a ratio of 6.

You can find an expression for the sum of a geometric series by writing the general geometric series in expanded form, and, directly beneath this, writing the results of multiplying each term in the series by $-r$.

$$S_n = \quad a \ + ar \ + ar^2 + \cdots + ar^{n-2} + ar^{n-1}$$
$$-rS_n = -ar - ar^2 - ar^3 - \cdots - ar^{n-1} - ar^n.$$

Adding the corresponding sides of each equation, you have

$$S_n - rS_n = a + (ar - ar) + (ar^2 - ar^2) + \cdots + (ar^{n-1} - ar^{n-1}) - ar^n$$
$$S_n - rS_n = a - ar^n,$$

since the sum of the terms in the right side between a and $-ar^n$ is 0. Factoring the left side, you have:

$$(1 - r)S_n = a - ar^n$$

$$S_n = \frac{a - ar^n}{1 - r} \quad \text{(provided } r \neq 1)$$

The sum of the first n terms of a geometric series with first term a and common ratio r is

$$S_n = \frac{a - ar^n}{1 - r}, r \neq 1.$$

EXAMPLE 1   Find the sum of the first eight terms in the geometric series whose first term is 1 and whose common ratio is 2.

SOLUTION   Substitute 1 for a, 2 for r, and 8 for n in

$$S_n = \frac{a - ar^n}{1 - r}.$$

$$S_8 = \frac{1 - 1(2)^8}{1 - 2}$$

$$S_8 = \frac{1 - 256}{-1} = 255 \quad \textbf{\textit{Answer}}$$

Another formula for S_n can be developed using the fact that $t_n = ar^{n-1}$.

$$S_n = \frac{a - ar^n}{1 - r} = \frac{a - r(ar^{n-1})}{1 - r} = \frac{a - rt_n}{1 - r} \qquad (r \neq 1)$$

EXAMPLE 2 Find the sum of a geometric series whose first term is 5, whose last term is 405, and whose common ratio is 3.

SOLUTION Substitute 5 for a, 3 for r, and 405 for t_n in

$$S_n = \frac{a - rt_n}{1 - r}.$$

$$S_n = \frac{5 - 3(405)}{1 - 3} = \frac{5 - 1215}{-2} = 605 \quad \textbf{\textit{Answer}}$$

Oral Exercises

Identify each series as arithmetic, geometric, or neither. If the series is arithmetic, state the common difference. If the series is geometric, state the common ratio.

1. $9 + 3 + 1 + \frac{1}{3} + \frac{1}{9}$

2. $1 + 4 + 9 + 16 + 25$

3. $2^{-1} + 2^{-2} + 2^{-3} + \cdots + 2^{-10}$

4. $1 + 10 + 100 + \cdots + 1{,}000{,}000$

5. $\log 2 + \log 6 + \log 18 + \log 54$

Written Exercises

Find the sum of each geometric series.

A

1. $t_1 = 2, r = 3, n = 5$

2. $t_1 = 5, r = 2, n = 6$

3. $t_1 = 16, r = \frac{1}{2}, n = 6$

4. $t_1 = 243, r = \frac{1}{3}, n = 7$

5. $t_1 = 27, r = -\frac{2}{3}, n = 4$

6. $t_1 = 1, r = -5, n = 4$

7. $\frac{1}{2} + \frac{1}{4} + \frac{1}{8} + \cdots + \left(\frac{1}{2}\right)^{10}$

8. $\frac{1}{2} - \frac{1}{4} + \frac{1}{8} - \cdots - \left(-\frac{1}{2}\right)^{10}$

9. $2 + 6 + \cdots + 13122$

10. $4800 + 2400 + \cdots + 75$

11. Show that the sum of the first 10 terms of the geometric series $1 + \frac{1}{3} + \frac{1}{9} + \frac{1}{27} + \cdots$ is twice the sum of the first 10 terms of the geometric series $1 - \frac{1}{3} + \frac{1}{9} - \frac{1}{27} + \cdots$.

12. Find S_{10} if the series $24 + 12 + \cdots$ is **(a)** arithmetic; **(b)** geometric.

13. Find S_{20} if the series $1 + 1.1 + \cdots$ is **(a)** arithmetic; **(b)** geometric.

14. Let $t_1 = 2$. Find the sum of
    a. the first 20 powers of 2;
    b. the first 20 multiples of 2.

B 15. a. Show that $\sum_{k=1}^{n} 2^{k-1} = 2^n - 1$.

   b. How many terms are needed before the sum exceeds one million?

16. a. Show that $\sum_{k=1}^{n} 2 \cdot 3^{k-1} = 3^n - 1$ for $n > 1$.

   b. How many terms are needed before the sum exceeds one billion?

17. If n is an even number, show that the sum of series (A) is three times the sum of series (B).

$$(A)\ 1 + \frac{1}{2} + \frac{1}{4} + \cdots + \left(\frac{1}{2}\right)^{n-1} \quad (B)\ 1 - \frac{1}{2} + \frac{1}{4} - \cdots + \left(-\frac{1}{2}\right)^{n-1}$$

In Exercises 18–20, you are given S_n of a series. Find the first three terms of the associated sequence, and identify the series as arithmetic, geometric, or neither. (*Hint:* $S_1 = t_1$)

18. $S_n = 2n^2 + 5n$ 19. $S_n = 8(n^2 - 1)$ 20. $S_n = 8(3^n - 1)$

Use the results of Exercise 21 to estimate the answers for Exercise 22.

C 21. Guess the *approximate* value of the following expressions. Check your guess with a calculator or with logarithms.

   a. $\left(\frac{1}{2}\right)^{20}$ b. $(0.9)^{100}$ c. $(-0.8)^{50}$

22. If $|r| < 1$ and n is a very large integer, estimate the approximate value of:

   a. r^n b. $S_n\ \left(Recall:\ S_n = \dfrac{t_1(1 - r^n)}{1 - r}\right)$

Problems

A 1. Sarah can trace her ancestors back through 10 generations. She counts her parents as the first generation back and her four grandparents as the second generation back, and so on. Assuming no duplications, how many ancestors has she in these 10 generations?

2. Every February for the last four years the Samuelsons have vacationed in the Rocky Mountains. Each year their vacation costs about 5% more than the year before. They spent $800 for their vacation 4 years ago. Find the total amount they have spent for their vacations in the past four years.

3. The Allisons have been renting a house for the past 5 years. During the first year of rental, they paid $400 a month, and each year thereafter their rent was increased by 10%. Find the total amount they have paid for rent over the last 5 years.

29304.48

4. The management of a large bank consists of a president, 3 vice-presidents, 9 managers, and so on, down through 6 levels of management. How many people are involved in the 6 levels?

B 5. The first blow of a pile driver drives a post 100 cm into the ground. Each succeeding blow drives the post only $\frac{4}{5}$ as far as the preceding blow. How far has the post been driven after 5 blows?

6. Gertrude Heitmiller received a 5% salary increase at the end of each of 8 years. If her starting salary was $8000, how much did she earn in all during the 8 years?

7. On the first day of each year, Mr. Daniel invests $1000 at 6% interest compounded annually. What will be the value of his investment after 10 years?

8. While Frances Chang worked for the Acme Company, she received a 20% salary increase at the end of each year. If she earned $74,416 during the five years she worked there, what was her first year's salary?

9. The 1560 members of the Western Environmental Society have a method of quickly notifying members about important developments. The president and treasurer each call 3 members (round 1), each of whom then calls 3 other members (round 2), each of whom then calls 3 more members (round 3), and so on. How many rounds of calls are needed before everyone is contacted?

C 10. Suppose that a certain female insect hatches $2x$ eggs, half of them female, and that one week later these x females each hatch $2x$ eggs, half of them females. If this process continues for n weeks and no insects die, find the number of insects descended from a single female. Give the answer in terms of x and n.

11. A large record company makes a 50% profit on each record that it sells to its regional distributors. These distributors sell the records at a 50% profit to district wholesalers, who in turn make a 50% profit selling to local retailers. Finally, the retailer makes a 50% profit selling records to you.
   a. If a record company produces a hit record for 80 cents, how much will it cost you?
   b. If sales of this hit record reach 1 million, what is the total of all the profits that are made?

12. The sum of the first two terms of a seven-term geometric progression is 20, and the sum of the last two terms is $-\frac{5}{8}$. Find the sum of all seven terms.

11-5 *Infinite Geometric Series*

OBJECTIVE **To find sums of infinite geometric series having ratios with absolute value less than one.**

Consider the sums $S_1, S_2, S_3, S_4, \ldots, S_n$ of the geometric series with $a = 1$ and $r = 0.5$.

$$S_1 = 1 \qquad\qquad S_2 = 1.5 \qquad\qquad S_3 = 1.75 \qquad\qquad S_4 = 1.875$$

In general:

$$S_n = \frac{1 - (0.5)^n}{1 - (0.5)} = \frac{1 - (0.5)^n}{0.5} = \frac{1}{0.5} - \frac{(0.5)^n}{0.5} = 2 - (0.5)^{n-1}$$

Two patterns can be observed in this example:

1. Since $S_n = 2 - (0.5)^{n-1}$, S_n is always less than 2 for any n.
2. As n increases in this series, the sum S_n comes closer and closer to a value of 2. If enough terms are added, the sum will approximate 2 as closely as you may require.

You can use a calculator to check these conclusions for very large n. Recall that the sum, S_n, of n terms of a geometric series is given by

$$S_n = \frac{a - ar^n}{1 - r},$$

which can be rewritten in the form

$$S_n = \frac{a(1 - r^n)}{1 - r} = \frac{a}{1 - r} - \frac{r^n}{1 - r}.$$

If $|r| < 1$, it can be shown that r^n gets closer and closer to 0 as n increases, so that the term $\frac{r^n}{1 - r}$ approaches $\frac{0}{1 - r}$, or 0. Therefore, the sum S of this geometric series is given by

$$S = \frac{a}{1 - r} - \frac{0}{1 - r} = \frac{a}{1 - r}.$$

The discussion above suggests several conclusions that are presented here without proof.

If an **infinite geometric series** has a common ratio r such that $|r| < 1$, then as n increases without limit:

1. t_n approaches 0.
2. S_n approaches a finite number S given by

$$S = \frac{a}{1 - r}.$$

EXAMPLE Find the sum of the infinite geometric series
$$8 - 4 + 2 - 1 + \cdots.$$

SOLUTION Since $r = -\frac{1}{2}$, and $|r| < 1$, the series has a sum.

$$S = \frac{a}{1-r} = \frac{8}{1-(-\frac{1}{2})} = \frac{8}{\frac{3}{2}} = \frac{16}{3} \quad \textbf{\textit{Answer}}$$

Oral Exercises

Find the common ratio of each infinite geometric series and tell whether the series has a sum.

1. $9 + 3 + 1 + \cdots$ **2.** $9 - 3 + 1 - \cdots$

3. $4 + 6 + 9 + \cdots$ **4.** $9 + 6 + 4 + \cdots$

5. $1 + \sqrt{2} + 2 + 2\sqrt{2} + \cdots$ **6.** $4^{-1} - 4^{-2} + 4^{-3} - \cdots$

Written Exercises

For each infinite geometric series, find the sum if the series has one. If not, so state.

A   **1.** $4 + 2 + 1 + \cdots$ 8   **2.** $4 - 2 + 1 - \cdots$

     3. $18 - 12 + 8 - \cdots$ 10.8   **4.** $10 + 8 + 6.4 + \cdots$

     5. $20 + 30 + 45 + \cdots$ no sum   **6.** $45 + 30 + 20 + \cdots$

     7. $3 - 2 + \frac{4}{3} - \cdots$ 1.8   **8.** $\frac{1}{5} + \frac{1}{7} + \frac{5}{49} + \cdots$

     9. $8 + 9 + 10\frac{1}{8} + \cdots$ no sum   **10.** $3 + 3\sqrt{5} + 15 + \cdots$

     11. $2\sqrt{2} + 2 + \sqrt{2} + \cdots$ $4\sqrt{2} + 4$ **12.** $4^{-\frac{1}{2}} + 4^{-\frac{3}{2}} + 4^{-\frac{5}{2}} + \cdots$

For each geometric series find S_1, S_2, S_3, S_4, and S_5. Use these sums to approximate S. Then use the formula to find S. Compare your approximation with the value found using the formula.

13. $8 + 2 + \frac{1}{2} + \cdots$ $4 \div \frac{1}{2}$ **14.** $\frac{9}{10} + \frac{9}{100} + \frac{9}{1000} + \cdots$

15. $\frac{3}{4} - \frac{3}{8} + \frac{3}{16} - \cdots$ 4   **16.** $\frac{1}{3} + \frac{1}{9} + \frac{1}{27} + \cdots$

Write the first three terms of the infinite geometric series satisfying the given conditions:

B   **17.** $a = 2, S = 6$ **18.** $a = 80, S = \frac{320}{7}$

     19. $r = -0.8, S = \frac{125}{9}$ **20.** $r = 0.01, S = \frac{5}{9}$

Express each repeating decimal as a common fraction by rewriting each as an infinite series.

SAMPLE $0.\overline{8} = 0.888\ldots = 0.8 + 0.08 + 0.008 + 0.0008 + \cdots$

SOLUTION Substitute 0.8 for a and 0.1 for r.

$$0.\overline{8} = \frac{0.8}{1 - 0.1}$$
$$= \frac{0.8}{0.9} = \frac{8}{9} \quad \textbf{\textit{Answer}}$$

21. $0.\overline{4}$ **22.** $0.\overline{7}$ **23.** $0.\overline{36}$ **24.** $2.\overline{45}$ **25.** $0.3\overline{18}$

In Exercises 26–28, a and b are digits. Express each repeating decimal as a common fraction.

C 26. $0.\overline{ab}$ **27.** $0.\overline{aab}$ **28.** $0.a\overline{b}$

Problems

A 1. Each year a certain type of tree grows vertically $\frac{14}{15}$ as much as it did the year before. If the tree grows 1.5 m during the first year, how tall will it ultimately grow? $A = 1.5$

2. In the first back-and-forth swing of a pendulum the bob traveled 16 cm. In each subsequent swing the bob travels 95% as far as in the preceding one. How far does the bob travel before coming to rest?

3. A side of a square is 12 cm. The midpoints of its sides are joined to form an inscribed square, and this process is continued as shown in the diagram. Find the sum of the perimeters of the squares if this process is continued without end.

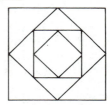

4. A side of an equilateral triangle is 10 cm. The midpoints of its sides are joined to form an inscribed equilateral triangle and the process is continued. Find the sum of the perimeters of the triangles if the process is continued without end.

5. Find the sum of the areas of the squares in Problem 3.

6. Find the sum of the areas of the triangles in Problem 4.

B 7. A rubber ball dropped from a height of 40 cm rebounds on each bounce to a height which is $\frac{2}{5}$ of its height on the previous bounce. How far will it travel before coming to rest?

8. A rubber ball dropped from a height of 30 cm rebounds on each bounce to a height which is $\frac{3}{8}$ of its height on the previous bounce. How far will it travel before coming to rest?

9. In its first month of operation, an oil well produced 250,000 barrels of oil. After that, its production each month was 95% of the previous month's production.
   a. Show that the oil well can never produce more than 5,000,000 barrels of oil no matter how long it operates.
   b. How many months of production, starting with the first month, are required for the well to produce more than 2,000,000 barrels?

10. Consider the following series, which is *not* a geometric series:

$$\frac{1}{1 \cdot 2} + \frac{1}{2 \cdot 3} + \frac{1}{3 \cdot 4} + \cdots + \frac{1}{n(n+1)} + \cdots$$

   a. Calculate S_1, S_2, and S_3 by adding the terms.
   b. Guess a value for S_n.
   c. Use the fact that $\frac{1}{k(k+1)} = \frac{1}{k} - \frac{1}{k+1}$ to verify your answer to part (b).

11. Consider the following series, which is *not* a geometric series:

$$\frac{1}{1 \cdot 3} + \frac{1}{3 \cdot 5} + \frac{1}{5 \cdot 7} + \cdots + \frac{1}{(2n-1)(2n+1)} + \cdots$$

   a. Calculate S_1, S_2, and S_3 by adding terms.
   b. Guess a value for S_n.
   c. Verify your answer to part (b). (*Hint:* Use a procedure similar to that used in Exercise 10(c).)

C 12. A "snowflake" curve is constructed as follows: The sides of an equilateral triangle are trisected, and the middle third of the trisection serves as a base for a new equilateral triangle, following which this segment is deleted from the figure. The process is continued. If the side of the initial equilateral triangle is of length 1, what is the area enclosed by the snowflake curve if the process is continued without end?

13. Show that the figure described in Problem 12 has no perimeter, that is, the perimeter is of unbounded length.

14. If $|x| < 1$, find the sum S of the series $1 + 3x + 5x^2 + 7x^3 + \cdots$. (*Hint:* Consider $S - xS$.)

15. Find the fallacy in the following argument.

Let $S = 1 + 2 + 2^2 + 2^3 + \cdots$

$$= 1 + 2(1 + 2 + 2^2 + \cdots)$$

$$= 1 + 2 \cdot \frac{1}{1-2} = 1 - 2$$

$$\therefore S = -1$$

Self-Test 2

Find the sum of the following arithmetic series.

1. $a = 48$; $d = -4$; $n = 20$ **2.** $a = -7$; $t_{50} = 91$; $n = 34$ **Obj. 11-3, p. 417**

Find the sum of the following geometric series.

3. $a = 5$; $r = -\dfrac{3}{2}$; $n = 6$ **4.** $a = 18$; $t_2 = 12$; $n = 4$ **Obj. 11-4, p. 422**

5. $\displaystyle\sum_{j=1}^{5} 3^j$

Each of the following is an infinite geometric series. Find the sum of the series if it has one. If not, so state.

6. $6 - 3 + \dfrac{3}{2} - \cdots$ **7.** $\dfrac{2}{3} + 2 + 6 + \cdots$ **Obj. 11-5, p. 426**

Check your answers with those at the back of the book.

Application The Annuity Formula

An annuity is a form of savings in which a fixed amount of money is deposited regularly in an account earning compound interest. Consider an annuity in which one dollar is deposited at the beginning of each of n time periods, and for which compound interest at the rate i (expressed as a decimal) is calculated at the end of each time period.

a. Show that the expression below gives the amount of money in the annuity at the beginning of the nth time period:

$$\frac{(1 + i)^n - 1}{i}$$

(*Hint*: The expression $(1 + i)^{n-1}$ gives the amount of money that will accumulate from the first dollar deposited. Form a geometric series of such terms.)

b. Find the value of an annuity where $500 is deposited at the beginning of each year for 20 years at 6%.

BINOMIAL EXPANSIONS

11-6 *Powers of Binomials*

OBJECTIVE   To expand powers of binomials.

An interesting pattern is formed by the coefficients of the expansion of $(a + b)^n$ where n is a nonnegative integer.

$$(a + b)^0 = 1$$

$$(a + b)^1 = 1a^1 + 1b^1$$

$$(a + b)^2 = 1a^2 + 2ab + 1b^2$$

$$(a + b)^3 = 1a^3 + 3a^2b + 3ab^2 + 1b^3$$

$$(a + b)^4 = 1a^4 + 4a^3b + 6a^2b^2 + 4ab^3 + 1b^4$$

$$(a + b)^5 = 1a^5 + 5a^4b + 10a^3b^2 + 10a^2b^3 + 5ab^4 + 1b^5$$

The pattern of coefficients suggests the triangular array of numbers shown at the right, called **Pascal's triangle.** The triangle has 1's at the beginning and end of each row. Each of the other numbers is the sum of the two numbers above it. For example, $15 = 10 + 5$.

```
              1
           1     1
        1     2     1
     1     3     3     1
   1     4     6     4     1
 1    5    10    10    5    1
1   6   15   20   15   6   1
```

When n is a positive integer, the coefficients of the expansion of $(a + b)^n$ are the elements of the $(n + 1)$th row of Pascal's triangle. The kth term of the expansion will be the product

$$C_k a^{n-(k-1)}b^{k-1},$$

where C_k is the kth entry in the $(n + 1)$th row of Pascal's triangle.

EXAMPLE 1   Find the fourth term of $(a + b)^6$.

SOLUTION   Substitute as follows: $k = 4$, $n = 6$, and $n + 1 = 7$.
The fourth term of the seventh row of Pascal's triangle is 20. Thus, $C_4 = 20$.
∴ the fourth term in the expansion is

$$20a^{6-(4-1)}b^{(4-1)}, \text{ or } 20a^3b^3. \quad \textit{Answer}$$

The expansion of $(a + b)^n$, for n a positive integer, is the sum of $n + 1$ terms in the form $C_k a^{n-(k-1)}b^{k-1}$ where k represents the position of the term in the sum, and the coefficient, C_k, is the kth term of the $(n + 1)$th row of Pascal's triangle.

EXAMPLE 2 Expand $(x^2 - 3y)^4$.

SOLUTION The numbers shown in red are the fifth row of Pascal's triangle.

$(x^2 + (-3y))^4 = 1(x^2)^4 + 4(x^2)^3(-3y) + 6(x^2)^2(-3y)^2 + 4(x^2)(-3y)^3 + 1(-3y)^4$

$\therefore (x^2 - 3y)^4 = x^8 - 12x^6y + 54x^4y^2 - 108x^2y^3 + 81y^4$ *Answer*

In Example 2 notice that every other term of the simplified expansion has a negative coefficient.

Another method of finding the coefficients is more convenient when n is large or when only a particular term, rather than the entire expansion, of $(a + b)^n$ is needed. In general,

$$C_{k+1} = \frac{[n - (k - 1)] \cdot C_k}{k}.$$

Note that $[n - (k - 1)]$ is the exponent of a in the kth term. This result provides a means of finding a given term when the previous term is known.

EXAMPLE 3 The seventh term in the expansion of $(x + y)^{10}$ is $210x^4y^6$. Find the eighth term.

SOLUTION Substitute as follows $k = 7$ and $n = 10$.

Term: $\qquad 210x^4y^6 \qquad \frac{4 \cdot 210}{7} x^{4-1}y^{6+1}$

Term number: $\qquad 7 \qquad\qquad 8$

$\therefore$ the eighth term is $120x^3y^7$. *Answer*

It is often useful to know that the coefficients of $(a + b)^n$ are symmetric. For example, in

$$(a + b)^5 = a^5 + 5a^4b + 10a^3b^2 + 10a^2b^3 + 5ab^4 + b^5$$

the coefficients of the last three terms are the same as the coefficients of the first three terms in reverse order.

Oral Exercises

The eighth row of Pascal's triangle is 1, 7, 21, 35, 35, 21, 7, 1. Use this to answer Exercises 1 and 2.

1. What is the ninth row?

2. State the first four terms of $(a + b)^7$.

3. State the number of terms in each of the following expansions.

   a. $(2x - 3)^{10}$ **b.** $(5m - n)^7$ **c.** $(3a + 6)^9$

4. State the first term of each of the following expansions.

    a. $(a - 1)^{12}$ **b.** $(2x + y)^3$ **c.** $(p^2 + q)^5$

5. State the last term of the following expansions.

    a. $(x - y)^6$ **b.** $(r^2 - 1)^5$ **c.** $(z + 2)^4$

Written Exercises

A   **1.** Given that 1, 7, 21, 35, 35, 21, 7, 1 is the eighth row of Pascal's triangle, write the ninth and tenth rows.

Write the binomial expansion of each expression.

2. a. $(a + b)^5$ **3. a.** $(a + b)^6$ **4. a.** $(x + y)^7$ **5. a.** $(p + 1)^8$
    b. $(a - b)^5$ **b.** $(a - b)^6$ **b.** $(x - y)^7$ **b.** $(p - 1)^8$

Write the binomial expansion of each expression, and simplify.

6. $(3r - s)^3$ **7.** $(x^2 + 1)^5$ **8.** $(n^2 - 2)^4$ **9.** $(2h + 3)^6$

10. $\left(t^2 - \dfrac{2}{t}\right)^6$ **11.** $\left(3c - \dfrac{d}{3}\right)^3$ **12.** $(y^3 - y^{\frac{1}{2}})^5$ **13.** $(5m - m^{\frac{1}{2}})^4$

Write the first three terms of each expansion.

14. $(m + n)^{20}$ **15.** $(p - 2)^{50}$ **16.** $(x - 1)^{100}$ **17.** $(1 + a^2)^{100}$

Find and simplify the specified term of the given expansion.

18. Third, $(x + m)^4$ **19.** Fifth, $(3d^2 - 2)^5$

20. Fourth $(2x - 6)^8$ **21.** Fifth, $(3x - y^2)^6$

22. Second $(4x - 9)^7$ **23.** Sixth, $(4xy - 7x^3)^5$

In Exercises 24–28, use the symmetry of the coefficients.

SAMPLE   The first three terms of $(a + b)^{20}$ are $a^{20} + 20a^{19}b + 190a^{18}b^2$. Write the last three terms.

SOLUTION $190a^2b^{18} + 20ab^{19} + b^{20}$ *Answer*

24. The first three terms of $(x + y)^{17}$ are $x^{17} + 17x^{16}y + 136x^{15}y^2$. Write the last three terms.

25. The first three terms of $(p - q)^{22}$ are $p^{22} - 22p^{21}q + 231p^{20}q^2$. Write the last three terms.

B   **26.** The tenth term of $(x + 1)^{20}$ is $167{,}960x^{11}$. Write the twelfth term. (*Hint:* The eleventh term is the middle term.)

27. The sixth term of $(x - y)^{12}$ is $-792x^7y^5$. Write the eighth term.

28. The eighth term of $(p - q)^{15}$ is $-6435p^8q^7$. Write the ninth term.

C   **29.** Write the first four terms of the general expansion of $(a + b)^n$.

11-7 *The General Binomial Expansion*

OBJECTIVE   **To use the binomial theorem to find a particular term of a binomial expansion.**

The patterns learned in the preceding section can be applied to the general expansion of $(a + b)^n$. This general expansion is called the **binomial theorem.**

THE BINOMIAL THEOREM

If n is a positive integer, then

$$(a + b)^n = a^n + \frac{n}{1} \cdot a^{n-1}b + \frac{n}{1} \cdot \frac{n-1}{2} a^{n-2}b^2 + \frac{n}{1} \cdot \frac{n-1}{2} \cdot \frac{n-2}{3} a^{n-3}b^3 + \cdots$$

$$+ \frac{n}{1} \cdot \frac{n-1}{2} \cdot \frac{n-2}{3} \cdots \frac{n-[k-2]}{k-1} a^{n-(k-1)}b^{k-1} + \cdots + b^n,$$

where k represents the number of the term in the expansion.

Factorial notation is used to abbreviate the product of consecutive integers beginning with 1. The symbol $r!$ (read "r factorial" or "factorial r") is defined as follows:

$$0! = 1 \text{ and}$$
$$r! = 1 \cdot 2 \cdot 3 \cdot 4 \cdots r, \text{ for } r \text{ a positive integer.}$$

Thus,

$$3! = 1 \cdot 2 \cdot 3 = 6$$
$$4! = 1 \cdot 2 \cdot 3 \cdot 4 = 24$$
$$6! = 1 \cdot 2 \cdot 3 \cdot 4 \cdot 5 \cdot 6 = 720$$
$$7! = 1 \cdot 2 \cdot 3 \cdot 4 \cdot 5 \cdot 6 \cdot 7 = 7(6!) = 5040$$

Factorial notation can be used to write the kth term of the binomial theorem.

If n is a positive integer, the kth term of the expansion $(a + b)^n$ is

$$\frac{n(n-1)(n-2) \cdots (n-[k-2])}{(k-1)!} a^{n-(k-1)}b^{k-1}$$

There are $k - 1$ factors in both the numerator and the denominator of the coefficient of the kth term.

EXAMPLE   Find the seventh term in the expansion of $(2x - y^2)^{10}$.

SOLUTION   Substitute as follows: $a = 2x$, $b = -y^2$, $n = 10$, and $k = 7$.

1. The coefficient of the seventh term is

$$\frac{n(n-1)(n-2)\cdots(n-[k-2])}{(k-1)!} = \frac{10(10-1)(10-2)\cdots(10-[7-2])}{(7-1)!}$$

$$= \frac{10\cdot9\cdot8\cdot7\cdot6\cdot5}{1\cdot2\cdot3\cdot4\cdot5\cdot6} = 210$$

Note that the numerator of the coefficient of the seventh term is the product of 6 factors descending from 10. The denominator is 6!.

2. The factor $a^{n-(k-1)}$ is $(2x)^{10-(7-1)} = (2x)^4 = 16x^4$
3. The factor b^{k-1} is $(-y^2)^{7-1} = (-y^2)^6 = y^{12}$
∴ the seventh term is $210(16x^4)(y^{12})$, or $3360x^4y^{12}$.   *Answer*

Written Exercises

Simplify each expression.

SAMPLE $\dfrac{10!}{3!7!}$ **SOLUTION** $\dfrac{10!}{3!7!} = \dfrac{10\cdot9\cdot8\cdot7!}{3\cdot2\cdot7!} = 120$ *Answer*

A **1.** $\dfrac{4!0!}{2!}$ **2.** $\dfrac{1!6!}{3!}$ **3.** $5\cdot4!$ **4.** $(2\cdot3)!$

   5. $\dfrac{(n+1)!}{n!}$ **6.** $\dfrac{n!}{(n-1)!}$ **7.** $\dfrac{(n+1)!}{(n-1)!}$ **8.** $\dfrac{(n-1)!}{(n+2)!}$

Write the first four terms in the expansion of each binomial.

   9. $(a+b)^{20}$ **10.** $(a+b)^{12}$ **11.** $(x-y)^{18}$ **12.** $(t^2+1)^{11}$

Find and simplify the specified term in each expansion.

   13. Term with x^3 in $(a+x)^8$ *x in b position, so x^3 would be looking for 4th term*   **14.** Term with y^4 in $(a-y)^9$
   15. Term with v^5 in $(u^2-v)^{12}$ **16.** Term with t^6 in $(s^3-t)^{10}$
   17. Sixth term of $(2a-b)^9$ **18.** Sixth term of $(3a+b)^8$
   19. Middle term of $(x^2+y^2)^6$ **20.** Middle term of $(c^2-2d)^8$

B **21.** The constant term of $\left(x+\dfrac{1}{x}\right)^{14}$ **22.** The constant term of $\left(y-\dfrac{1}{y^2}\right)^{15}$

C **23.** Show that $n(n-1)\cdots(n-[r-1]) = \dfrac{n!}{(n-r)!}$ for r and n positive integers and $r < n$.

24. Show that the binomial theorem can be written

$$(a + b)^n = \sum_{r=0}^{n} \frac{n!}{r!(n-r)!} a^{n-r} b^r.$$

(*Hint:* Use the results of Exercise 23 and let $r = k - 1$ in the binomial theorem.)

Assume that the binomial theorem is true for n any positive *rational* number (and the expansion is an infinite series). Write the first three terms of each expansion.

25. $(p + q)^{\frac{1}{2}}$ **26.** $(1 - x)^{\frac{3}{2}}$ **27.** $(a^2 - 1)^{\frac{1}{2}}$ **28.** $(r^3 + 1)^{\frac{2}{3}}$

Self-Test 3

VOCABULARY   Pascal's triangle (p. 431)
binomial theorem (p. 434)
factorial notation (p. 434)

Expand and simplify.

1. $(x - 1)^5$ **2.** $(a^2 + 2b)^6$ **Obj. 11-6, p. 431**

Find and simplify the specified term in each expansion.

3. Fifth term of $(p^3 - 0.2)^8$ **Obj. 11-7, p. 434**
4. Middle term of $(3 + h^2)^6$

Check your answers with those at the back of the book.

Chapter Summary

1. The nth term of an *arithmetic sequence* with first term t_1 and *common difference d* is given by $t_n = a + (n - 1)d$. The arithmetic mean (average) of a and b is $\dfrac{a + b}{2}$.

2. The nth term of a *geometric sequence* with first term a and *common ratio r*, is given by $t_n = ar^{n-1}$. The geometric mean of two positive numbers a and b is $\sqrt{ab}$.

3. The sum S_n of the first n terms of an *arithmetic series* is

$$S_n = \frac{n}{2}[2a + (n - 1)d].$$

4. The sum S_n of the first n terms of a *geometric series* is

$$S_n = \frac{a - ar^n}{1 - r} \ (r \neq 1).$$

5. An *infinite geometric series* has a sum $S = \dfrac{a}{1 - r}$, if $|r| < 1$.

6. The expansion of $(a + b)^n$, for n a positive integer, is the sum of $n + 1$ terms of the form $C_k A^{n-(k-1)}b^{k-1}$, where k is the position of the term in the series, and the coefficient, C_k, is the kth term of the $(n + 1)$th row of *Pascal's triangle*.

7. The *binomial theorem* gives the complete expansion of $(a + b)^n$. (See page 434.)

Chapter Review

Give the letter of the correct answer.

1. Find the tenth term of the arithmetic sequence with $a = 51$ and $t_2 = 41.5$.   **11-1**

   a. 136.5   **b.** 34.5   **c.** -43.5 **d.** -34.5

2. Find the arithmetic mean between $x - y$ and $x + y$.

   a. $\dfrac{x - y}{2}$ **b.** x **c.** $2x + y$ **d.** $2x$

3. Find the eighth term of the geometric sequence with $a = 3$ and $r = \sqrt{2}$.   **11-2**

   a. $24\sqrt{2}$ **b.** 48   **c.** $48\sqrt{2}$ **d.** $12\sqrt{2}$

4. Find the geometric mean of 0.4 and 10.

   a. 0.2   **b.** 0.40   **c.** 4   **d.** 2

5. Find the sum of the first twenty terms of an arithmetic series with $a = -13$ and $d = 2.5$.   **11-3**

   a. 215   **b.** 21.5   **c.** 34.5   **d.** 430

6. Evaluate $\displaystyle\sum_{i=0}^{6} (2i - 3)^2$.

   a. 165   **b.** 171   **c.** 175   **d.** 155

7. In a geometric series, $a = -18$ and $r = \frac{1}{3}$. Find S_4.   **11-4**

   a. $\frac{80}{3}$ **b.** $-\frac{80}{3}$ **c.** $-\frac{40}{3}$ **d.** $\frac{40}{3}$

8. Find the sum of the infinite geometric series 36, 30, 25, ...   **11-5**

   a. 216   **b.** 0   **c.** 46,656   **d.** 180

9. Find the third term of the expansion of $(2a^3 - b^2)^8$.   **11-6**

   a. $28a^6b^4$ **b.** $3584a^{18}b^4$ **c.** $1792a^6b^4$ **d.** $1792a^{18}b^4$

10. In the expansion of $(x - 2y)^9$, find the term with y^5.   **11-7**

   a. $-4032x^4y^5$ **b.** $-126x^4y^5$ **c.** $126x^4y^5$ **d.** $4032x^4y^5$

Chapter Test

1. Find the twelfth term of the arithmetic sequence with $a = -13$ and $d = 1.2$. 11-1
2. Find the arithmetic mean between 46 and -8.
3. Find the fifth term of the geometric sequence with $a = 2\pi$ and $r = \frac{3}{2}$. 11-2
4. Find the geometric mean of -36 and $-2\frac{1}{2}$.
5. In an arithmetic series $a = 13$ and $d = 5$. Find S_{15}. 11-3
6. Evaluate $\displaystyle\sum_{k=1}^{5} (10 - 2k)$.
7. In a geometric series, $a = 3$ and $t_6 = 96$. Find S_6. 11-4
8. Find the sum of the infinite geometric series in which $a = 10$ and $t_2 = 5$. 11-5
9. Write the first three terms of the expansion of $(a - 2b)^{10}$. 11-6
10. Write the middle term of the expansion of $(5 - x^2)^8$. 11-7

Calculator Key-In

1. Evaluate (a) 25!   (b) 50!
2. What is the smallest positive integer n for which
   a. $n!$ exceeds one million   b. $n!$ exceeds one billion
   c. $n!$ exceeds 10^{50} d. $n!$ cannot be calculated on your calculator
3. Which is greater, $5^{5!}$ or $5!^5$?
4. Find $\displaystyle\sum_{n=1}^{10} n!$

Cumulative Review   (Chapters 8–11)

Solve each system of equations.

1. $2m - 4n = 3$
   $3m - n = 11$

2. $x - y + 3z = -2$
   $2x + y + z = 7$
   $3x - 2y + 4z = -4$

3. $y^2 - 4x^2 = 9$
   $y = 4x - 3$

Graph the solution set of each inequality or system of inequalities.

4. $2x - y \geq 4$

5. $y \geq \frac{1}{2}x + 2$
   $y < -x - 1$

6. $2x + 3y > 6$
   $4x < 2$

7. Use the factor theorem or synthetic division to determine whether $z - 3$ is a factor of $z^4 + 4z^2 - 23z - 48$.

8. Two of the roots of a cubic equation with real coefficients are 2 and $3i$.
   a. What must the third root be?   **b.** Find the equation.

Find **(a)** the distance between and **(b)** the midpoint of each pair of points.

   9. $(-6, 4), (2, 1)$ **10.** $(a, -b), (a + b, b)$

11. Find the equation of the line that contains $(-1, 2)$ and is perpendicular to $x + 3y = 6$.

12. Find the center and radius of the circle
   $x^2 + y^2 - 4x + 6y - 12 = 0$.

13. Write the equation of the parabola with focus $(0, 5)$ and directrix $y = 1$.

14. Graph the ellipse with equation $\dfrac{x^2}{49} + \dfrac{y^2}{20} = 1$ and find its foci.

15. Write the equation of a hyperbola with asymptotes $y = 2x$ and $y = -2x$ and intercepts $(3, 0)$ and $(-3, 0)$.

16. The speed of a train is inversely proportional to the time the train takes to cover a fixed distance. If a train going 81 km/h takes 6 h to go from A to B, how long would it take a train going 108 km/h to make the same trip?

Simplify.

   17. $(9)^{-\frac{3}{2}}$ **18.** $\log_4 1$ **19.** $4^{\log_4 6}$ **20.** $\log_2 \dfrac{4}{\sqrt[3]{2}}$

Solve.

   21. $5^{2x-7} = \dfrac{1}{5}$ **22.** $\log_{\frac{1}{2}} x = -5$ **23.** $\log_2 6 = \log_2 x + \log_2 48$

24. Find $f^{-1}(x)$ if $f(x) = \frac{1}{2}x - 7$.

25. Use Table 3 to evaluate $\dfrac{\sqrt{238}}{0.715}$.

26. Find the 35th term of the arithmetic sequence 10, 7, 4, ...

27. Find the first term of a geometric series if $r = -3$ and $t_6 = 162$.

28. Find the sum of the arithmetic series $\sum\limits_{k=1}^{26} 5k - 3$.

29. Find the sum of the geometric series $\sqrt{2} - 2 + 2\sqrt{2} - \cdots - t_{20}$.

30. Find the sum of the infinite geometric series $12 - 2 + \frac{1}{3} - \cdots$.

31. Find and simplify the third term in the expansion $(p - q)^8$.

Shown above is a wheat field near Fargo, North Dakota. See page 481 for a discussion of how the sine function can be used to estimate the number of hours between sunrise and sunset on a given day in this vicinity.

12

THE TRIGONOMETRIC FUNCTIONS

MEASURING ANGLES

12-1 *Degree Measure of Angles*

OBJECTIVE To use degrees to measure angles in standard position.

The word trigonometry comes from two Greek words, *trigonon* and *metria*, meaning "triangle measurement." The earliest use of trigonometry was for surveying. Today, trigonometry is used in navigation, electronics, music, and meteorology.

The most common unit for measuring angles is the **degree.** One degree is subdivided into 60 equal parts called **minutes,** and one minute is subdivided into 60 equal parts called **seconds.** The angle measure

63 degrees, 10 minutes, and 24 seconds

is written

63°10′24″.

Decimal degrees can be used instead of minutes and seconds to express part of a degree. For example, $42°30' = 42.5°$. Many calculators will convert decimal degrees to degrees, minutes, and seconds, and conversely. If you do not use a calculator, you can use the methods shown in Example 1 on the following page.

EXAMPLE 1 **a.** Express $64°9'$ in decimal degrees.

b. Express $53.721°$ in degrees, minutes, and seconds.

SOLUTION **a.** Since $1' = \dfrac{1°}{60}$:

$$64°9' = 64° + \frac{9°}{60} = (64 + 0.15)° = 64.15°. \quad \textbf{\textit{Answer}}$$

b. Let $x =$ the number of minutes equivalent to $0.721°$. Then

$$\frac{x}{60} = \frac{0.721}{1}$$

$$x = 60(0.721) = 43.26$$

$$\therefore 53.721° = 53°43.26'$$

Let $y =$ the number of seconds equivalent to $0.26'$.

Since $60'' = 1'$: $\dfrac{y}{60} = \dfrac{0.26}{1}$

$$y = 16$$

$$53.721° = 53°43'16'' \quad \textbf{\textit{Answer}}$$

In trigonometry, an angle represents a rotation about a point, and the measure of the rotation is equal to the measure of the angle. Therefore, you can speak of angles of more than $180°$ or less than $0°$. (See Figures 12-1 and 12-2.)

In each diagram the angle has an **initial ray,** the positive x-axis, and a **terminal ray.** You can think of rotating the initial ray about the origin to the terminal ray. Counterclockwise rotations are considered positive and clockwise rotations are negative.

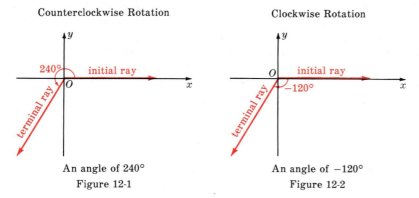

Counterclockwise Rotation

An angle of $240°$

Figure 12-1

Clockwise Rotation

An angle of $-120°$

Figure 12-2

Figures 12-1 and 12-2 show that two different angles, one of $240°$ and the other of $-120°$, can have the same initial and terminal rays. Such angles are called **coterminal angles.** Figure 12-3 shows a $90°$ angle and several others coterminal with it. Do you see that there are an infinite number of angles coterminal with the $90°$ angle?

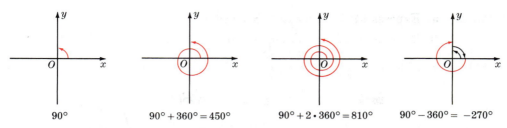

$90°$ $90° + 360° = 450°$ $90° + 2 \cdot 360° = 810°$ $90° - 360° = -270°$

Figure 12-3

Each of the angles coterminal with a 90° angle has a measure of 90° plus or minus a multiple of 360°. These measures are given by the formula $(90 + 360n)°$ where n is an integer (positive, negative, or zero). In Figure 12-3 n takes on the values 0, 1, 2, and -1.

EXAMPLE 2 **a.** Name three angles coterminal with a 30° angle.

b. State a general formula for all such angles.

SOLUTION **a.** $30° + 360° = 390°$
$30° + 360° \cdot 3 = 30° + 1080° = 1110°$
$30° + 360° \cdot (-2) = 30° - 720° = -690°$

b. $(30 + 360n)°$ (It is understood that n is an integer.)

Each angle pictured thus far has been in *standard position*. An angle is said to be in **standard position** if the angle's vertex is at the origin and its initial ray lies on the positive x-axis. If the terminal ray lies in the second quadrant, an angle can be referred to as a *second-quadrant* angle. Thus, a 120° angle is a second-quadrant angle. Similarly, a 200° angle is a third-quadrant angle.

If the terminal ray of an angle in standard position lies on the x-axis or y-axis, the angle is called a **quadrantal angle.** Examples of quadrantal angles include angles of 0°, 90°, 180°, 270°, and $-90°$. In general, an angle of $(90n)°$ where n is an integer is a quadrantal angle.

In trigonometry an angle is often denoted by a Greek letter, such as θ (theta) or ϕ (phi).

Oral Exercises

Name two angles, one positive and one negative, that are coterminal with the given angle.

1. 10°   **2.** 40°   **3.** 100°   **4.** 180°

5. $-50°$ **6.** $-120°$ **7.** 500°   **8.** 0°

9–16. State the quadrant of each angle in Exercises 1–8, or state that the angle is a quadrantal angle.

In each diagram estimate the measure of angle θ.

17.
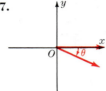

18.
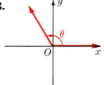

19.
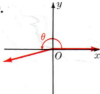

20.
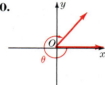

21.
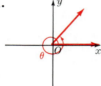

22.
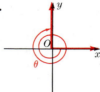

Written Exercises

Sketch each angle in standard position. Indicate the number of revolutions and the direction of rotation by a curved arrow. Also classify each angle by its quadrant.

A **1. a.** 30°   **b.** −30°   **2. a.** 100°   **b.** −100°

3. a. 225°   **b.** −225°   **4. a.** 300°   **b.** −300°

5. 60°   **6.** −135°   **7.** 210°   **8.** −315°

9. 370°   **10.** −400°   **11.** −720°   **12.** 1000°

Express each angle in degrees and minutes to the nearest minute.

13. 35.75°   **14.** 12.25°   **15.** 14.10°   **16.** 13.20°

Express each angle in degrees, minutes, and seconds to the nearest second.

17. 6.505°   **18.** 17.1515°   **19.** 18.3°   **20.** 7.16°

Express each angle in decimal degrees.

To the nearest 0.1°:   **21.** 128°40′   **22.** 37°55′

To the nearest 0.01°:   **23.** 7°35′40″   **24.** 8°47′2″

Sketch, in standard position, the angle determined by the given information. Find the degree measure of the angle.

SAMPLE $\frac{1}{5}$ of a clockwise revolution

SOLUTION $\frac{1}{5}(-360) = -72$

∴ the angle measures $-72°$. **Answer**

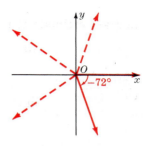

25. $\frac{1}{3}$ of a counterclockwise revolution

26. $\frac{3}{4}$ of a counterclockwise revolution

27. $\frac{2}{5}$ of a clockwise revolution

28. $\frac{5}{8}$ of a clockwise revolution

29. $1\frac{4}{5}$ counterclockwise revolutions

30. $3\frac{1}{6}$ counterclockwise revolutions

Name two angles, one positive and one negative, that are coterminal with the given angle.

31. $75°$ **32.** $150°$ **33.** $-180°$ **34.** $450°$

35. $515°$ **36.** $-642°$ **37.** $3601°$ **38.** One million degrees

39. a. Evaluate $(48 + 360n)°$ for $n = -1, 0, 1,$ and 2.

    b. With what first-quadrant angle whose measure is less than $360°$ are these four angles coterminal?

40. Repeat Exercise 39 for $(72 + 360n)°$ with $n = -2, -1, 0,$ and 1.

Suppose O is the origin and X is a point on the positive x-axis.

a. Write an equation of the circle with center O and that passes through the given point P.

b. Make a sketch and measure $\angle POX$ with a protractor.

SAMPLE $P(-2, 3)$

SOLUTION   **a.** $(-2)^2 + 3^2 = r^2$

                 $13 = r^2$

          $x^2 + y^2 = 13$

      b. $\angle POX \approx 124°$

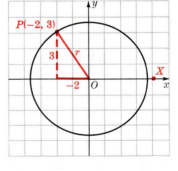

B **41.** $P(-4, 4)$ **42.** $P(3, 4)$ **43.** $P(-1, -1)$

44. $P(8, -6)$ **45.** $P\left(\frac{\sqrt{2}}{2}, \frac{\sqrt{2}}{2}\right)$ **46.** $P(-1, \sqrt{3})$

C **47. a.** The line $y = x$ intersects the circle $x^2 + y^2 = 4$ in points P and Q. Find the coordinates of P and Q.

      b. Find the measures of $\angle POX$ and $\angle QOX$. (O is the origin and X is a point on the positive x-axis.)

48. Repeat Exercise 47 but replace the line $y = x$ with the line $y = 1$.

12-2 *Radian Measure of Angles*

There are other units for measuring angles of rotation besides the degree. By far the most useful unit for measuring angles in advanced mathematics is the radian. Consider a circle and an angle in standard position as shown in Figure 12-4. If the rotation of the angle is counterclockwise and corresponds to an arc whose length is equal to the radius, the angle has measure one **radian,** denoted 1^R (see Figure 12-4). An angle with counterclockwise rotation corresponding to an arc length equal to twice the radius has measure 2^R (see Figure 12-5). An angle with clockwise rotation corresponding to seven times the radius has measure -7^R (Figure 12-6).

arc length = radius	arc length = 2 × radius	arc length = 7 × radius
Figure 12-4	Figure 12-5	Figure 12-6

In general, an angle of k^R will intercept an arc that is k times as long as the radius.

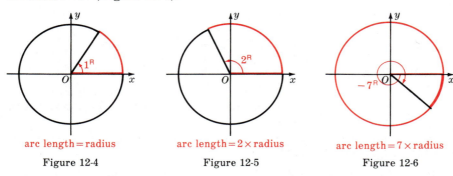

If s is the arc length and
θ^R is the measure of an angle in radians, then

$$s = \theta^R r \quad \text{or} \quad \theta^R = \frac{s}{r}.$$

Since an angle for a complete revolution is also measured by 360°, you have $360° = 2\pi^R$, or $180° = \pi^R$.

Thus, $1° = \frac{\pi}{180}^R$ and $1^R = \frac{180°}{\pi} \approx 57.3°.$

To change from degrees to radians, or from radians to degrees, we use the equations above to get the *conversion equations* on the next page.

$$\theta° = \frac{180}{\pi} \cdot \theta^R \quad \text{and} \quad \theta^R = \frac{\pi}{180} \cdot \theta°$$

(Note that we have used $\theta°$ to stand for the measure of θ in degrees and θ^R to stand for the measure of θ in radians.)

EXAMPLE 1 **a.** Express $\frac{\pi}{18}^R$ in degrees.   **b.** Express $-144°$ in radians.

SOLUTION **a.** $\theta° = \frac{180}{\pi} \cdot \theta^R = \frac{180}{\pi} \cdot \frac{\pi}{18}^R = 10°$

b. $\theta^R = \frac{\pi}{180} \cdot \theta° = \frac{\pi}{180}(-144)° = -\frac{4\pi}{5}^R$

You can also use tables or calculators to make degree-radian conversions. Table 4 on pages 642–649 and Table 6 on pages 655–658 give conversions for first-quadrant angles.

EXAMPLE 2 **a.** Express 49.5° in radians. Give your answer to the nearest ten-thousandth of a radian.

b. Express 1.45^R in degrees. Give your answer to the nearest hundredth of a degree.

SOLUTION **a.** Since 49.5° is greater than 45°, read up the right-hand column of Table 4 to the ".5" above "49.0."
49.5° = 0.8639^R

b. Table 6 gives $1.45^R \approx 83.08°$.

Figures 12-7, 12-8, and 12-9 show some angles that are studied frequently in trigonometry. The measure of each angle is given in degrees and radians. Study these diagrams carefully. You may want to refer to them later.

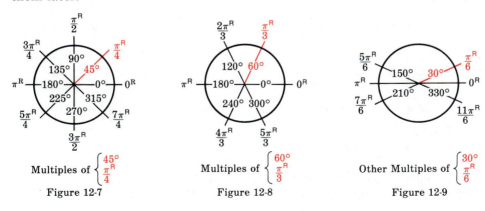

Figure 12-7   Figure 12-8   Figure 12-9

You have now learned three ways to express the measure of an angle: degrees, minutes, and seconds; decimal degrees; radians. Whichever system you use, the properties of the angle remain the same. The choice of which type of measure to use is really a matter of convenience. Degrees, minutes, and seconds, the traditional system, is preferred in surveying, for example. Decimal degrees are more compatible with computers and calculators; they are used in a wide variety of applications. Radians are preferred in advanced mathematics and a wide variety of scientific applications (see the Extra, Applications of the Sine and Cosine, on pages 480–482).

Oral Exercises

Give the radian measure of θ in each diagram.

1.
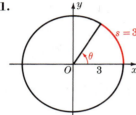

2.
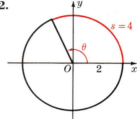

3.
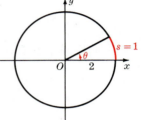

Written Exercises

Express in radians, leaving your answers in terms of π.

A 1. 90°   2. 30°   3. 120°   4. 150°

   5. 45°   6. 135°   7. 225°   8. 315°

   9. 60°   10. 240°   11. 180°   12. 210°

Express in degrees.

13. π^R 14. $\dfrac{\pi^R}{3}$ 15. $\dfrac{5\pi^R}{3}$ 16. $\dfrac{3\pi^R}{4}$

17. $\dfrac{4\pi^R}{3}$ 18. $\dfrac{\pi^R}{6}$ 19. $\dfrac{5\pi^R}{6}$ 20. $\dfrac{7\pi^R}{6}$

21. $\dfrac{\pi^R}{2}$ 22. $\dfrac{3\pi^R}{2}$ 23. $\dfrac{2\pi^R}{3}$ 24. $\dfrac{11\pi^R}{6}$

Express in radians. Use the conversion equation and leave your answer in terms of π.

25. 72°   26. 80°   27. 110°   28. 290°

29. 380°   30. 435°   31. −75°   32. −25°

Express in degrees using the conversion equation.

33. $\dfrac{2\pi^{\text{R}}}{5}$ **34.** $\dfrac{\pi^{\text{R}}}{9}$ **35.** $\dfrac{11\pi^{\text{R}}}{9}$ **36.** $\dfrac{8\pi^{\text{R}}}{5}$

37. $\dfrac{34\pi^{\text{R}}}{15}$ **38.** $\dfrac{37\pi^{\text{R}}}{18}$ **39.** $-\dfrac{5\pi^{\text{R}}}{18}$ **40.** $-\dfrac{22\pi^{\text{R}}}{15}$

Express in radians to the nearest ten-thousandth of a radian. (You will need to use Table 4 or a calculator.)

41. 38° **42.** 2° **43.** 0.5° **44.** 68°

Express in degrees to the nearest hundredth of a degree. (You will need to use Table 6 or a calculator.)

45. 1.13^{R} **46.** 0.5^{R} **47.** $\dfrac{3^{\text{R}}}{2}$ **48.** $\dfrac{5^{\text{R}}}{4}$

Give the degree measure to the nearest 10′ and radian measure to the nearest ten-thousandth of a radian of the angle between the hands of a clock at the given time.

B 49. 3 A.M. **50.** 4 P.M. **51.** 1 P.M.

52. 5 A.M. **53.** 1:30 P.M. **54.** 5:30 A.M.

Problems

A 1. A ferris wheel is 50 m in diameter. How far would a person riding the ferris wheel travel if the ferris wheel makes 38 revolutions per ride?

2. A wheel on a stationary exercise bicycle is 66 cm in diameter. How far does a point on the rim of the wheel travel if the wheel makes 100 revolutions?

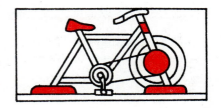

B 3. A cart wheel is 150 cm in diameter. How many revolutions does the wheel make if the cart travels 1 km? (*Hint:* 1 km = 100,000 cm)

C 4. A satellite travels in a circular orbit 1600 km above Earth's surface. If it completes 1 orbit every 2 h, find its approximate speed in kilometers per second (km/s). (Use 6400 km for Earth's radius.)

5. When you look at the moon, 3.86×10^8 m away, the angle illustrated in the diagram is about 0.0090^{R}. Find the approximate diameter of the moon. (You may assume that the diameter of the moon is approximately equal to the length of arc *AB*.)

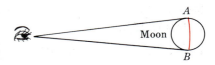

12-3 *The Sine and Cosine Functions*

OBJECTIVE   **To find the sine and cosine of an angle that is in standard position.**

In Figure 12-10, the terminal ray of the angle θ intersects the two concentric circles at P and Q. The radii of the circles are $\overline{OP}$ and $\overline{OQ}$, respectively. By constructing perpendiculars from P and Q to the x-axis, you can create two right triangles, $\triangle OPA$ and $\triangle OQB$. From your study of geometry, you may remember that $\triangle OPA$ and $\triangle OQB$ are similar triangles. (Why?) Thus,

$$\frac{AP}{OP} = \frac{BQ}{OQ}.$$

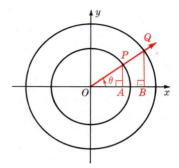

Figure 12-10

Note that the equivalent ratios, $\dfrac{AP}{OP}$ and $\dfrac{BQ}{OQ}$, depend only on the size of θ, not on the size of the circles. This ratio,

$$\frac{\text{the } y\text{-coordinate of the point}}{\text{radius of the circle}}, \quad \text{or} \quad \frac{y}{r},$$

(see Figure 12-11), is so important in mathematics that it is given a special name, *the sine of θ*. The *sine* and the *cosine*, the most common trigonometric functions, are defined as follows:

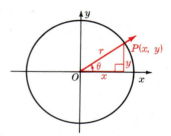

Figure 12-11

If the terminal ray of any angle θ in standard position intersects the circle $x^2 + y^2 = r^2$ at point P, then:

$$\text{the } \mathbf{sine} \text{ of } \theta = \frac{y\text{-coordinate of } P}{\text{radius}}$$

$$\text{the } \mathbf{cosine} \text{ of } \theta = \frac{x\text{-coordinate of } P}{\text{radius}}$$

These facts can be written in abbreviated form as

$$\sin \theta = \frac{y}{r} \quad \text{and} \quad \cos \theta = \frac{x}{r}.$$

EXAMPLE 1   If the terminal side of θ passes through $(3, -2)$, find $\sin \theta$ and $\cos \theta$.

SOLUTION Since $\quad r^2 = 3^2 + (-2)^2 = 13,$
$$r = \sqrt{13}.$$

Thus, $\sin \theta = \dfrac{y}{r} = \dfrac{-2}{\sqrt{13}} = -\dfrac{2}{\sqrt{13}}\quad$ and

$$\cos \theta = \dfrac{x}{r} = \dfrac{3}{\sqrt{13}}.$$

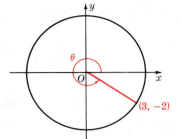

If you know the sine of an angle and the quadrant the angle is in, you can determine the cosine.

EXAMPLE 2 If θ is a second-quadrant angle and $\sin \theta = \dfrac{5}{13}$, find $\cos \theta$.

SOLUTION
1. Since $\sin \theta = \dfrac{y}{r} = \dfrac{5}{13}$, make a diagram of a circle with radius 13 as shown.
2. Use the equation of the circle to find x.

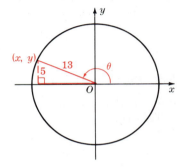

$$x^2 + y^2 = r^2$$
$$x^2 + 5^2 = 13^2$$
$$x^2 + 25 = 169$$
$$x^2 = 144$$
$$x = \pm 12$$

Choose -12 because θ is a second-quadrant angle.

3. $\cos \theta = \dfrac{x}{r} = \dfrac{-12}{13} = -\dfrac{12}{13}$ **Answer**

It is useful to consider the special circle $x^2 + y^2 = 1$, called the unit circle. Using the unit circle, the definitions of the sine and cosine are even simpler. If θ passes through (x, y) on the unit circle:

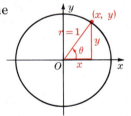

$$\sin \theta = \frac{y}{r} = \frac{y}{1} = y$$

$$\cos \theta = \frac{x}{r} = \frac{x}{1} = x$$

The unit circle and these definitions will help you to remember in which quadrants the sine and cosine are positive and in which they are negative. Since $\sin \theta = y$, $\sin \theta$ is positive when y is positive (first and second quadrants). Likewise, the sign of x determines the sign of $\cos \theta$.

Function Value	Quadrant of the terminal ray of θ			
	First	Second	Third	Fourth
$\sin \theta$	+	+	−	−
$\cos \theta$	+	−	−	+

EXAMPLE 3 Find **a.** $\sin 90°$ **b.** $\cos \pi^R$

SOLUTION   **a.**

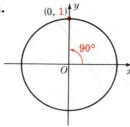

$$\sin 90° = y\text{-coordinate} = 1$$

b.

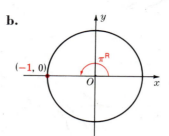

$$\cos \pi^R = x\text{-coordinate} = -1$$

Since the x- and y-coordinates of points on the unit circle vary from -1 to 1, the cosine and the sine do the same. Thus, for any angle θ,

$$-1 \le \cos \theta \le 1$$

and

$$-1 \le \sin \theta \le 1.$$

To find the sine and cosine of $30°$, $45°$, and $60°$, the following two facts are useful.

1. In a $30°$–$60°$–$90°$ triangle, the sides are in the ratio $1 : \sqrt{3} : 2$.

2. In a $45°$–$45°$–$90°$ triangle, the sides are in the ratio $\sqrt{2} : \sqrt{2} : 2$.

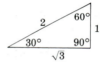

The two triangles above can be used to find the coordinates of points on a circle of radius 2 for angles of $30°$, $45°$, and $60°$. (See Figure 12-12.) Using the definitions of sine and cosine, you can now determine the sines and cosines of $30°$, $45°$, and $60°$. Because these particular sines and cosines appear so frequently in trigonometry, you may wish to remember them.

$$\sin 30° = \frac{1}{2}, \quad \cos 30° = \frac{\sqrt{3}}{2}$$

$$\sin 45° = \frac{\sqrt{2}}{2}, \quad \cos 45° = \frac{\sqrt{2}}{2}$$

$$\sin 60° = \frac{\sqrt{3}}{2}, \quad \cos 60° = \frac{1}{2}$$

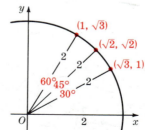

Figure 12-12

Oral Exercises

Find $\sin \theta$ and $\cos \theta$.

1.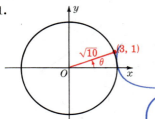

2.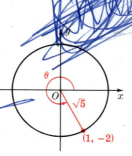

3.

Complete the statement by replacing the ? with one of the symbols $<$, $>$, or $=$. A sketch of a unit circle will be helpful.

SAMPLE **a.** $\sin 120°$? $\sin 130°$

b. $\cos 120°$? $\cos 130°$

SOLUTION **a.** The y-coordinate of the point where the terminal ray of the $130°$ angle intersects the unit circle is *greater* than the corresponding y-coordinate for the $120°$ angle. Thus:

$$\sin 120° > \sin 130° \quad \textbf{Answer}$$

b. By comparing the two x-coordinates:

$$\cos 120° > \cos 130° \quad \textbf{Answer}$$

4. a. $\sin 20°$? $\sin 10°$ **b.** $\cos 20°$? $\cos 10°$

5. a. $\sin 170°$? $\sin 160°$ **b.** $\cos 170°$? $\cos 160°$

6. a. $\sin 25°$? $\sin (-25)°$ **b.** $\cos 25°$? $\cos (-25)°$

Written Exercises

Find the sine and cosine of the given angle.

A **1.** $90°$ **2.** $360°$ **3.** $-180°$ **4.** $270°$

5. π^R **6.** 0^R **7.** $\dfrac{3\pi^R}{2}$ **8.** $-\dfrac{3\pi^R}{2}$

In each exercise, the coordinates of point P are given. If the terminal side of θ passes through P, find $\sin \theta$ and $\cos \theta$.

9. $(4, 3)$ **10.** $(1, 1)$ **11.** $(-8, 6)$ **12.** $(-2, -3)$

13. $(0, 5)$ **14.** $(-4, 0)$ **15.** $(\sqrt{3}, -1)$ **16.** $(-\sqrt{2}, \sqrt{2})$

17. $(8, -15)$ **18.** $(1, 0)$ **19.** $(-1, -\sqrt{3})$ **20.** $(\sqrt{5}, -2\sqrt{5})$

Complete the table. A sketch of a circle will be helpful.

	21.	22.	23.	24.	25.	26.	27.	28.
Quadrant	1st	1st	2nd	2nd	3rd	3rd	4th	4th
$\sin \theta$	$\dfrac{3}{5}$	?	$\dfrac{24}{25}$	?	$-\dfrac{\sqrt{10}}{10}$	?	$-\dfrac{\sqrt{2}}{2}$	?
$\cos \theta$	?	$\dfrac{12}{13}$	?	$-\dfrac{1}{2}$	?	$-\dfrac{15}{17}$	?	$\dfrac{\sqrt{3}}{2}$

Complete the statement by replacing the ? with one of the symbols $<$, $>$, or $=$.

29. $\sin 50° \; ? \; \sin 40°$ **30.** $\cos 50° \; ? \; \cos 40°$ **31.** $\sin 179° \; ? \; \sin 1°$

32. $\sin 181° \; ? \; \sin 359°$ **33.** $\sin 150° \; ? \; \sin 30°$ **34.** $\cos 40° \; ? \; \cos (-40)°$

B **35.** $\sin 179° \; ? \; \sin 178°$ **36.** $\cos \dfrac{\pi}{3}^{R} \; ? \; \cos \dfrac{\pi}{6}^{R}$ **37.** $\sin 4^{R} \; ? \; \sin (-4)^{R}$

Name all angles θ, $0° \le \theta < 360°$, that make the statement true.

38. $\sin \theta = 1$ **39.** $\cos \theta = 1$ **40.** $\sin \theta = -1$

41. $\cos \theta = -1$ **42.** $\sin \theta = 0$ **43.** $\cos \theta = 0$

44. $\sin 150° = \sin \theta$ **45.** $\sin 45° = \sin \theta$ **46.** $\cos 12° = \cos \theta$

Self-Test 1

VOCABULARY   degree (p. 441)   second-quadrant angle (p. 443)
minute (p. 441)   quadrantal angle (p. 443)
second (p. 441)   1 radian (p. 446)
initial ray (p. 442)   conversion equations (p. 446)
terminal ray (p. 442)   the sine of θ (p. 450)
coterminal angles (p. 442)   the cosine of θ (p. 450)
standard position (p. 443)

1. An angle θ between 0° and 360° is coterminal with an angle of   Obj. 12-1, p. 441
$(-74)°$. Find the measure of angle θ.

2. What fraction of a revolution is 144°?

3. a. Convert 80° to radians. Leave your answer in terms of π.   Obj. 12-2, p. 446
b. Convert $\dfrac{3\pi}{10}^{R}$ to degrees.

4. State: **a.** $\cos 180°$ **b.** $\sin \dfrac{\pi}{2}^{R}$ Obj. 12-3, p. 450

5. Find $\cos \theta$ if $\sin \theta = \dfrac{24}{25}$ and θ is a second-quadrant angle.

Check your answers with those at the back of the book.

VALUES OF TRIGONOMETRIC FUNCTIONS

12-4 *Finding Values of sin θ and cos θ*

OBJECTIVE   **To find the sine and cosine of first-quadrant angles.**

To find the sine and cosine of θ, you use Table 4 on page 644 if θ is in decimal degrees, Table 5 on page 652 if θ is in degrees and minutes, and Table 6 on page 657 if θ is in radians. If θ is a first-quadrant angle, you can read sin θ and cos θ directly from the tables. For example, using Table 4, sin 25.6° = 0.4321. When using Tables 4 and 5 to find the sines and cosines of angles between 45° and 90°, read *up* the *right-hand column* to find the desired angle, and use the headings at the *bottom* of the page to determine the proper column.

The sine and cosine values in the tables are four-significant-digit approximations. Even so, it is customary to write sin $0.7^R = 0.6442$ rather than sin $0.7^R \approx 0.6442$.

You can also find the sine or cosine of any angle in degrees or radians using a calculator.

EXAMPLE 1   Find sin 61°10′.

SOLUTION   In the right-hand column of Table 5 you find "61°10′." In the row opposite this, *above* the label "sin θ" at the bottom of the page, you find "0.8760."

∴ sin 61°10′ = 0.8760   *Answer*

If you wish to find the approximate value of a given function for an angle measure that is not a multiple of 10′, you may use the process of *linear interpolation* (Section 8-9). In so doing, you must be careful to take into account whether the values of the given function increase or decrease when the angle increases from 0° to 90°.

EXAMPLE 2   Find cos 37°18′.

SOLUTION   cos 37°10′ > cos 37°18′ > cos 37°20′. Using a convenient vertical arrangement for the linear interpolation, you can write:

$$10'\left[8'\begin{bmatrix}37°10' & 0.7969 \\ 37°18' & \underline{\ ?\ } \\ 37°20' & 0.7951\end{bmatrix}d\right]-0.0018\left\{\begin{array}{l}\text{A negative number} \\ \text{because} \\ \cos 37°20' < \cos 37°10'\end{array}\right.$$

$$\frac{8}{10} = \frac{d}{-0.0018}; \quad d = \frac{8}{10}(-0.0018) = -0.0014$$

cos 37°18′ = 0.7969 + (−0.0014), or 0.7955   *Answer*

You can also use Table 5 to approximate to the nearest minute the measure of an angle θ with measure between $0°$ and $90°$ when you are given the value for a trigonometric function of θ.

EXAMPLE 3 Find θ if θ is between $0°$ and $90°$ and $\sin \theta = 0.3891$.

SOLUTION You first locate the nearest values given for $\sin \theta$ that are above and below 0.3891. Then you arrange the values as follows:

$$
\begin{array}{c}
\quad\quad\quad\quad \theta \quad\quad\quad \sin\theta \\
\hline
10'\left[d\begin{bmatrix} 22°50' & 0.3881 \\ \quad? & 0.3891 \\ 23°00' & 0.3907 \end{bmatrix}\!0.0010\right]0.0026
\end{array}
\left\{\begin{array}{l}\text{Positive numbers}\\ \text{because}\\ \sin 23°0' > \sin 22°50'\end{array}\right.
$$

$$\frac{d}{10} = \frac{0.0010}{0.0026} = \frac{10}{26}; \quad d = \frac{10}{26}(10) = 4$$

$$\theta = 22°50' + 4', \text{ or } 22°54' \quad \textbf{\textit{Answer}}$$

Symbols such as $\sin 35°$ and $\cos 0.42^R$ are frequently written; they denote, respectively, the sine of any $35°$ angle and the cosine of any angle with radian measure 0.42. You can use Table 6 to find trigonometric values of a first-quadrant angle whose measure is given in radians.

EXAMPLE 4 Find $\cos 0.42^R$.

SOLUTION Locate "0.42" in the left-hand column on page 655. In the row opposite this, below the label "$\cos \theta$," you find "0.9131."

$$\therefore \cos 0.42^R = 0.9131 \quad \textbf{\textit{Answer}}$$

By using linear interpolation in Table 6, you can find approximate function values for x given as multiples of 0.001.

Oral Exercises

State each function value from Tables 4, 5, and 6 at the back of the book.

1. $\sin 15.5°$ **2.** $\cos 24.2°$ **3.** $\cos 56.3°$ **4.** $\sin 73.7°$

5. $\cos 42°$ **6.** $\sin 42°20'$ **7.** $\sin 75°30'$ **8.** $\cos 80°20'$

9. $\sin 1.08^R$ **10.** $\cos 1^R$ **11.** $\sin 1.46^R$ **12.** $\cos 0.07^R$

Use Table 5 to state the value of θ in degrees and minutes for which the given function has the given value.

13. $\sin \theta = 0.1937$ **14.** $\cos \theta = 0.7735$ **15.** $\sin \theta = 0.8746$

16. $\cos \theta = 0.2334$ **17.** $\sin \theta = 0.9996$ **18.** $\cos \theta = 0.6494$

Written Exercises

In Exercises 1–12 find a four-significant-digit approximation of the given function value. Use Tables 4, 5, and 6 at the back of the book and linear interpolation as necessary.

A 1. $\cos 28.2°$ 2. $\sin 46.8°$ 3. $\sin 29°26'$ 4. $\cos 45°59'$

5. $\sin 40°3'$ 6. $\sin 68°21'$ 7. $\cos 58°18'$ 8. $\cos 87°42'$

9. $\sin 1.057^R$ 10. $\cos 0.844^R$ 11. $\cos 1.429^R$ 12. $\sin 1.516^R$

Find the measure of θ in decimal degrees to the nearest tenth of a degree for the first-quadrant angle with the given function value.

13. $\sin \theta = 0.7660$ 14. $\cos \theta = 0.8090$ 15. $\cos \theta = 0.9781$

16. $\sin \theta = 0.5000$ 17. $\sin \theta = 0.7431$ 18. $\cos \theta = 0.9063$

Find the measure of θ in degrees and minutes, to the nearest minute, for the first-quadrant angle with the given function value.

19. $\sin \theta = 0.5040$ 20. $\sin \theta = 0.3807$ 21. $\cos \theta = 0.9670$

22. $\cos \theta = 0.6663$ 23. $\sin \theta = 0.8799$ 24. $\cos \theta = 0.5609$

Find the measure of θ in radians, to the nearest thousandth of a radian, for the first-quadrant angle with the given function value.

25. $\sin \theta = 0.5826$ 26. $\sin \theta = 0.9377$ 27. $\cos \theta = 0.9529$

28. $\cos \theta = 0.4740$ 29. $\sin \theta = 0.1663$ 30. $\cos \theta = 0.0498$

Find the first-quadrant angle (to the nearest ten minutes) whose terminal side in standard position passes through the given point.

B 31. $(3, 4)$ 32. $(12, 5)$ 33. $(8, 15)$ 34. $(21, 20)$

35. $(1, 2\sqrt{2})$ 36. $(\sqrt{5}, 2)$ 37. $(3\sqrt{5}, 2)$ 38. $(2, 2\sqrt{3})$

C 39. For what acute angle θ does $\sin \theta = 3 \cos \theta$?

Calculator Key-In _____

In Exercises 1–3, use a calculator to evaluate the given expression to the nearest ten thousandth.

1. $(\sin 40°)^2 + (\cos 40°)^2$
2. $(\sin 132°)^2 + (\cos 132°)^2$
3. $(\sin(-14°))^2 + (\cos(-14°))^2$

4. a. What generalization can you make from your results in Exercises 1–3?
   b. Explain why your generalization is true.

12-5 *Reference Angles*

OBJECTIVE To find sines and cosines of angles in all quadrants.

Notice how you can use the sine and cosine of 20° to find the sine and cosine of 160°. You can determine that $\cos 20° = 0.9397$ and $\sin 20° = 0.3420$. These values are the coordinates of the point P on the unit circle in Figure 12-13. The reflection of point P in the y-axis is the point Q that lies on the terminal ray of a 160° angle in standard position. By symmetry about the y-axis:

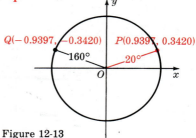

Figure 12-13

$\sin 160° = y$-coordinate of $Q = y$-coordinate of $P = \sin 20° = 0.3420$ and
$\cos 160° = x$-coordinate of $Q = -x$-coordinate of $P = -\cos 20° = -0.9397$.

In the following discussion you will learn why 20° is called the *reference angle* of 160° and how a reference angle can be used to find the sine and cosine of any angle.

Let $T(u, v)$ be any point other than the origin on the terminal side of θ, and let S be the point whose coordinates are $(|u|, |v|)$. The angle in standard position with $\overrightarrow{OS}$ as terminal side and measure between 0° and 90°, inclusive, is called a **reference angle** of θ and is labeled α (the Greek letter *alpha*) in each part of Figure 12-14.

Figure 12-14

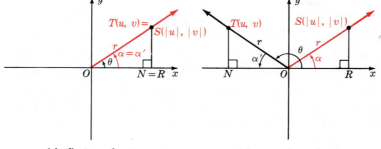

θ in first quadrant

θ in second quadrant

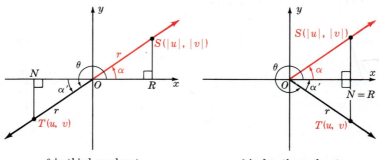

θ in third quadrant

θ in fourth quadrant

To determine the relationship between the values of the trigonometric functions of θ and α, you examine the relationship between u and $|u|$, and v and $|v|$, for each quadrant. Note that in all quadrants $r = \sqrt{u^2 + v^2} = \sqrt{|u|^2 + |v|^2}$.

θ in first quadrant: $u = |u|$ and $v = |v|$.
  This means $\sin\theta = \sin\alpha$ and $\cos\theta = \cos\alpha$.

θ in second quadrant: $u = -|u|$ and $v = |v|$.

$$\sin\theta = \frac{v}{r} = \frac{|v|}{r} = \sin\alpha$$

$$\cos\theta = \frac{u}{r} = \frac{-|u|}{r} = -\cos\alpha$$

By considering θ in the other quadrants, you can verify the other entries in the table below. Notice that you can obtain the value of any function of θ by multiplying the value of the corresponding function of α by 1 or -1 according as the value of the function of θ is positive or negative. (See the chart on page 451).

FUNCTIONS OF θ IN TERMS
OF ITS REFERENCE ANGLE α

Value	Quadrant in which θ terminates			
	First	Second	Third	Fourth
$\sin\theta$	$\sin\alpha$	$\sin\alpha$	$-\sin\alpha$	$-\sin\alpha$
$\cos\theta$	$\cos\alpha$	$-\cos\alpha$	$-\cos\alpha$	$\cos\alpha$

In Figure 12-14, consider angle α' in right triangle TON. In each quadrant, α' has the same measure as α, because α and α' are corresponding angles in two congruent right triangles: $\triangle TON$ and $\triangle SOR$. (Why?) This means that α', the nonnegative acute angle formed by the terminal side of θ and the x-axis, is also a reference angle of θ.

EXAMPLE 1 Find $\sin 210°$ and $\cos 210°$.

SOLUTION

1. Sketch angle θ in standard position.
2. α' measures $210° - 180° = 30°$.
3. Since θ is a third-quadrant angle, the table above gives

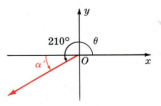

$$\sin 210° = -\sin 30° = -\frac{1}{2} = -0.5000;$$

$$\cos 210° = -\cos 30° = -\frac{\sqrt{3}}{2} = -0.8660$$

To determine the measure of a reference angle when the measure of θ is greater than 360° or less than 0°, you use the fact that *angles in standard position whose degree measures differ by an integral multiple of 360° are coterminal.*

EXAMPLE 2 Find four-significant-digit approximations of cos 856°40′ and sin 856°40′.

SOLUTION

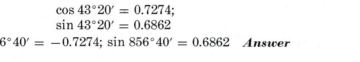

1. $856°40′ - 2(360°) = 856°40′ - 720° = 136°40′$
   Thus $\cos 856°40′ = \cos 136°40′$ and $\sin 856°40′ = \sin 136°40′$.

2. Sketch an angle of 136°40′ in standard position.

3. α' measures $180° - 136°40′$, or $43°20′$.

4. From the chart on page 459,
$$\cos 136°40′ = -\cos 43°20′;$$
$$\sin 136°40′ = \sin 43°20′.$$

5. From Table 5,
$$\cos 43°20′ = 0.7274;$$
$$\sin 43°20′ = 0.6862$$

$\therefore \cos 856°40′ = -0.7274; \sin 856°40′ = 0.6862$ **Answer**

When angle measures are given in radians, measures for reference angles can be approximated by using

$$\frac{\pi}{2} = 1.57, \ \pi = 3.14, \ \frac{3\pi}{2} = 4.71, \text{ and } 2\pi = 6.28.$$

For example: $\cos 4^R = -\cos (4 - \pi)^R = -\cos (4.00 - 3.14)^R = -\cos 0.86^R$

Then, using Table 6: $\cos 4^R = -(\cos 0.86^R) = -0.6524$

Reference angles are also useful in finding the measure of an angle when its quadrant and one of its trigonometric functions are known.

EXAMPLE 3 If θ is a second-quadrant angle with measure between 0° and 360° such that $\cos \theta = -0.8141$, find θ to the nearest tenth of a degree.

SOLUTION

1. Sketch θ and its reference angle α.

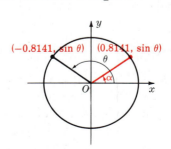

2. From the chart on page 459:
$$\cos \theta = -\cos \alpha$$
$$\therefore \cos \alpha = 0.8141$$

3. From Table 4:
$$\alpha = 35.4°$$
$$\theta = 180° - 35.4° = 144.6°$$ **Answer**

Oral Exercises

State the measure of the reference angle α you would use to evaluate the given function.

1. $\cos 144°$ **2.** $\sin 108°$ **3.** $\sin 215.6°$ **4.** $\cos 255.2°$

5. $\sin 302° 10'$ **6.** $\cos 351° 40'$ **7.** $\sin (-200)°$ **8.** $\cos 500°$

9. $\cos 100° 15'$ **10.** $\sin 172° 19'$ **11.** $\cos 3^R$ **12.** $\sin 2.6^R$

13. $\sin 4.213^R$ **14.** $\cos 5.476^R$ **15.** $\sin 7^R$ **16.** $\cos 8^R$

Written Exercises

A 1–16. For each of the function values in Oral Exercises 1–16, **(a)** find the reference angle of the given angle, **(b)** make a sketch showing the given angle (labeled θ) and the reference angle (labeled α), and **(c)** find the function value to the nearest ten-thousandth. Use Tables 4, 5, and 6 and interpolate when necessary.

Evaluate the function using Tables 4, 5, and 6. Interpolate when necessary.

17. $\sin (-132°)$ **18.** $\cos (-245°)$ **19.** $\cos 381°$ **20.** $\sin 673°$

21. $\cos 816°$ **22.** $\sin 536°$ **23.** $\sin 955°$ **24.** $\cos 1014°$

25. $\cos (-3.5)^R$ **26.** $\sin (-2.6)^R$ **27.** $\sin 8.5^R$ **28.** $\cos 11.7^R$

In Exercises 29–36, θ is an angle between $0°$ and $360°$ that has the given function value and lies in the given quadrant. Find θ to the nearest tenth of a degree using Table 4 as necessary.

29. $\sin \theta = -0.2924$; third quadrant   **30.** $\cos \theta = 0.9774$; fourth quadrant

31. $\cos \theta = -0.3206$; third quadrant   **32.** $\sin \theta = 0.6833$; second quadrant

33. $\cos \theta = -0.9426$; second quadrant   **34.** $\sin \theta = -0.7934$; third quadrant

35. $\sin \theta = 0.8545$; second quadrant   **36.** $\cos \theta = -0.0750$; third quadrant

Find the angle θ in degrees and minutes (to the nearest $10'$) such that the terminal side of θ in standard position passes through the given point and such that θ is between $0°$ and $360°$.

B 37. $(-3, -4)$ **38.** $(12, -5)$ **39.** $(-8, 15)$ **40.** $(24, -7)$

41. $(-2, \sqrt{5})$ **42.** $(-21, -20)$ **43.** $(2\sqrt{10}, -4)$ **44.** $(-5, 2\sqrt{6})$

45. a. The line $x = 1$ intersects the circle $x^2 + y^2 = 4$ in points P and Q. Make a sketch and find the coordinates of P and Q

b. If O is the origin and X is on the positive x-axis, find the measures of $\angle POX$ and $\angle QOX$ between $0°$ and $360°$.

c. State the sine and cosine of $\angle POX$ and $\angle QOX$.

12-6 *Graphs of the Sine and Cosine*

OBJECTIVE   To graph the sine and cosine and related functions.

The sine and cosine were introduced as functions of angles measured in degrees or radians. In order to discuss applications of the sine and cosine and draw their graphs in the coordinate plane, we will define them as functions of real numbers as follows:

If x is any real number:

$\sin x$ denotes the sine of any angle having radian measure x;

$\cos x$ denotes the cosine of any angle having radian measure x.

Therefore, to evaluate an expression such as $\sin x$ where $x = 1.2$, you proceed as if x were an angle of 1.2 radians. Also, you may write

$$\sin 1.2 = 0.9320 \quad \text{instead of} \quad \sin 1.2^{\text{R}} = 0.9320.$$

The real-number functions just defined are often called **circular functions** to distinguish them from trigonometric functions of angles. Expressions with Greek letters or angle measures, such as $\sin \alpha$, $\sin 30°$, and $\cos \frac{\pi^{\text{R}}}{2}$, refer to trigonometric functions. Expressions with roman letters or real numbers, such as $\sin x$ and $\cos 1.2$, refer to the circular functions.

The table and graph in Figure 12-15 show some ordered pairs for the sine function for $0 \le x \le \frac{\pi}{2}$. Note that the general ordered pair for the function is $(x, \sin x)$.

x	$\sin x$	$(x, \sin x)$
0	0	$(0, 0)$
$\dfrac{\pi}{6}$	0.5	$\left(\dfrac{\pi}{6}, 0.5\right)$
$\dfrac{\pi}{4}$	$\dfrac{\sqrt{2}}{2} \approx 0.71$	$\left(\dfrac{\pi}{4}, 0.71\right)$
$\dfrac{\pi}{3}$	$\dfrac{\sqrt{3}}{2} \approx 0.87$	$\left(\dfrac{\pi}{3}, 0.87\right)$
$\dfrac{\pi}{2}$	1	$\left(\dfrac{\pi}{2}, 1\right)$

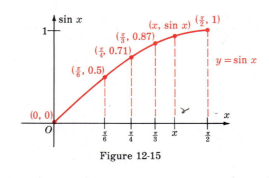

Figure 12-15

The graphs of the sine and cosine defined over the set of real numbers are shown in Figure 12-16. These graphs are often called **sinusoidal,** or **sine waves.** Because the values of the sine and cosine repeat every 2π units, these functions are said to have a **period** of 2π.

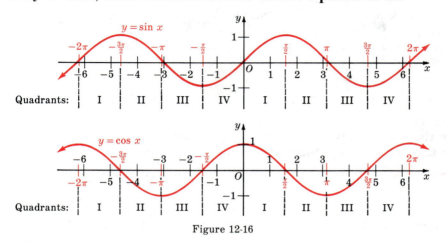

Figure 12-16

Whenever f is a function such that for a nonzero constant p,

$$f(x + p) = f(x)$$

for each x in the domain of f, then f is called a **periodic function.** The smallest such *positive* constant p is called the **period** of f. Thus, the sine and cosine functions are periodic with period 2π.

Since the sine and cosine functions have period 2π,

$$\sin (x + 2\pi) = \sin x$$

and

$$\cos (x + 2\pi) = \cos x.$$

Figure 12-17 illustrates this fact for the sine function.

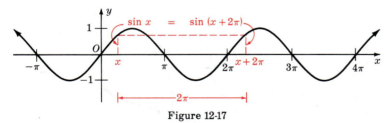

Figure 12-17

To draw the graph of

$$y = 2 \sin x,$$

notice that the ordinate of each point on the graph will be 2 times the corresponding ordinate of the graph of $y = \sin x$. As shown in Figure 12-18, both functions have period 2π.

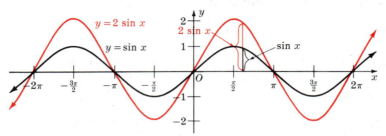

Figure 12-18

In general, the values of $y = A \sin x$ and $y = A \cos x$ vary from $-A$ to A. The number $|A|$ is called the **amplitude** of the function. The graph of $y = 2 \sin x$ shown in Figure 12-18 varies from -2 to 2. Therefore, its amplitude is 2.

The amplitude can also be determined by an algebraic formula.

> When a periodic function has a maximum value M and a minimum value m, the amplitude of the function is
> $$\frac{M - m}{2}.$$

Figure 12-18 showed that the graph of $y = 2 \sin x$ results from vertically stretching the graph of $y = \sin x$ by a factor of 2. Figure 12-19 compares the graphs of $y = \sin x$ and $y = \sin 2x$.

x	0	$\frac{\pi}{4}$	$\frac{\pi}{2}$	$\frac{3\pi}{4}$	π	$\frac{5\pi}{4}$	$\frac{3\pi}{2}$	$\frac{7\pi}{4}$	2π
$2x$	0	$\frac{\pi}{2}$	π	$\frac{3\pi}{2}$	2π	$\frac{5\pi}{2}$	3π	$\frac{7\pi}{2}$	4π
$y = \sin x$	0	$\frac{\sqrt{2}}{2}$	1	$\frac{\sqrt{2}}{2}$	0	$-\frac{\sqrt{2}}{2}$	-1	$-\frac{\sqrt{2}}{2}$	0
$y = \sin 2x$	0	1	0	-1	0	1	0	-1	0

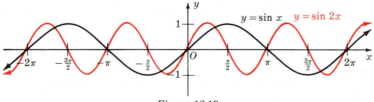

Figure 12-19

As you can see from the figure and the accompanying table, one period of the graph of $y = \sin 2x$ is half as long as one period of the graph of $y = \sin x$. Therefore, the function $y = \sin 2x$ has

$$\text{amplitude} = 1 \quad \text{and} \quad \text{period} = \frac{2\pi}{2}, \text{ or } \pi.$$

Thus, the graph of $y = \sin x$ has been compressed horizontally by a factor of 2 to form the graph of $y = \sin 2x$.

The graph of $y = \sin 4x$, below, shows that its period is $\frac{2\pi}{4}$, or $\frac{\pi}{2}$. The graph has been formed by compressing the graph of $y = \sin x$ horizontally by a factor of 4.

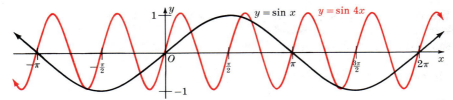

Figure 12-20

The functions $y = A \sin kx$ and $y = A \cos kx$ $(A > 0,\ k > 0)$ have

$$\text{amplitude} = A \quad \text{and} \quad \text{period} = \frac{2\pi}{k}.$$

Thus, if the graph of $y = \sin x$ (or $y = \cos x$) is vertically stretched by a factor of A and horizontally compressed by a factor of k, you obtain the graph of $y = A \sin kx$ (or $y = A \cos kx$).

EXAMPLE 1   The equation of a cosine graph is $y = \frac{2}{3} \cos \frac{1}{2} x$.

      a. Find the amplitude of the wave.
      b. Find the period.
      c. Sketch the graph in the interval $-2\pi \le x \le 4\pi$.

SOLUTION   **a.** $A = \frac{2}{3}$; $\therefore$ the amplitude is $\frac{2}{3}$.

      b. Since $k = \frac{1}{2}$, the period is $\frac{2\pi}{\frac{1}{2}}$, or 4π.

      c.

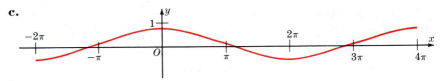

Note that in the graph in part (c) of Example 1, the function repeats every 4π units *regardless of where you begin measuring*. Thus, -2π to 2π constitutes one period as does $-\pi$ to 3π, $-\frac{\pi}{2}$ to $\frac{7\pi}{2}$, 0 to 4π, and so on.

EXAMPLE 2 The graph of $y = A\cos kx$ is shown at the right.

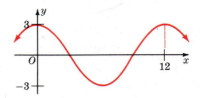

a. Find the values of A and k.
b. State the equation of the graph.

SOLUTION **a.** The amplitude A is 3 because the function varies from -3 to 3. The period is $\frac{2\pi}{k}$. The graph shows that the period is 12. Thus,

$$\frac{2\pi}{k} = 12 \quad \text{and} \quad k = \frac{\pi}{6}.$$

$\therefore A = 3$ and $k = \frac{\pi}{6}$. ***Answer***

b. The equation of the graph is $y = 3\cos\frac{\pi}{6}x$. ***Answer***

EXAMPLE 3 The graph of $y = c + A\cos kx$ is shown at the right.

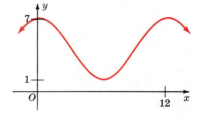

a. Find the values of A, k, and c.
b. State the equation of the graph.

SOLUTION **a.** The graph is the same as the graph in Example 2 except that it has been shifted 4 units upward. The amplitude and the period are unaffected.

$\therefore A = 3$, $k = \frac{\pi}{6}$, and $c = 4$. ***Answer***

b. The equation of the graph is $y = 4 + 3\cos\frac{\pi}{6}x$. ***Answer***

Oral Exercises

1. State the maximum and minimum values and the amplitude of each function.
    a. $y = 4\sin x$ **b.** $y = \cos 2x$ **c.** $y = 3\sin 2x$

2. State the period of each function in Exercise 1.

3. Find an equation of a sine wave with amplitude $\frac{1}{2}$ and period π.

4. Find an equation of a cosine wave with amplitude 2 and period 4π.

5. State the period of the function $y = 3\sin\frac{2\pi}{5}x$.

Written Exercises

A   **1.** Draw the graph of $y = \sin x$ for $-\frac{\pi}{2} \le x \le \frac{3\pi}{2}$.

     2. Draw the graph of $y = \cos x$ for $-\pi \le x \le \pi$.

In Exercises 3–8:
a. State the maximum and minimum values of each function.
b. State the period.
c. Sketch the graph. (Include at least two periods of the function.)

     3. $y = 3 \sin x$ **4.** $y = 2 \cos x$ **5.** $y = \cos 2x$

     6. $y = \cos 4x$ **7.** $y = 5 \sin 2x$ **8.** $y = \sin 3x$

State an equation for each sine wave or cosine wave.

9.

10.

11.
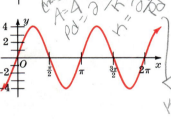

12.
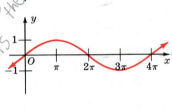

In Exercises 13–21:
a. State the maximum and minimum values of each function.
b. State the period.
c. Sketch the graph. (Include at least two periods of the function.)

B   **13.** $y = \cos \frac{1}{2} x$ **14.** $y = \sin \frac{1}{3} x$ **15.** $y = 4 \sin \frac{1}{2} x$

     16. $y = \cos \frac{\pi}{10} x$ **17.** $y = \cos \frac{2\pi}{365} x$ **18.** $y = 3 \sin 2\pi x$

     19. $y = 3 + \sin x$ **20.** $y = -1 + 2 \sin x$ **21.** $y = 2 + \frac{1}{2} \cos 3x$

State an equation for each sine wave or cosine wave.

22.
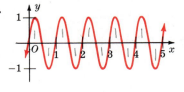

23.
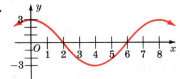

State an equation for each sine wave or cosine wave.

24.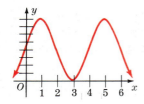

25.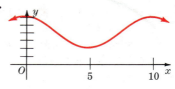

26. A sine wave varies from -5 to 5 with a period of 365. What is its equation?

27. A cosine wave varies from -32 to 32 with a period of 52. What is its equation?

28. A cosine wave has period 12. Its maximum and minimum values are 10 and 2. What is its equation?

29. A sine wave has period $\frac{1}{10}$. Its maximum and minimum values are 7 and -3. What is its equation?

C **30. a.** Sketch the graphs of $y = 2 \cos 2x$ and $y = -2 \cos 2x$ on the same set of axes.
  b. How are the graphs in part (a) related?

31. Repeat Exercise 30 for $y = \frac{1}{2} \sin \frac{1}{2} x$ and $y = -\frac{1}{2} \sin \frac{1}{2} x$.

Self-Test 2

VOCABULARY   reference angle (p. 458)   periodic function (p. 463)
                  circular functions (p. 462)   period (p. 463)
                  sinusoidal (p. 463)   amplitude (p. 464)
                  sine wave (p. 463)

Evaluate using tables.

1. $\cos 26° 10'$ **2.** $\sin 1.38^R$ **3.** $\cos 67.4°$ **Obj. 12-4, p. 455**

Evaluate using reference angles and tables.

4. $\sin 120° 20'$ **5.** $\cos 3.65^R$ **6.** $\sin 294.8°$ **Obj. 12-5, p. 458**

7. Solve $\sin \theta = 0.7683$ if θ is between $0°$ and $360°$. Give your answer in decimal degrees.

Sketch the graph of each function for $0 \le x \le 2\pi$.

8. $y = \cos x$ **9.** $y = \frac{1}{2} \sin x$ **Obj. 12-6, p. 462**

Check your answers with those at the back of the book.

TRIGONOMETRIC IDENTITIES

12-7 *The Trigonometric Functions*

OBJECTIVE   **To define and use the tangent, cotangent, secant, and co-secant.**

Besides the sine and cosine, there are four other basic trigonometric functions. The definitions of all six are given below. Assume that θ is an angle in standard position.

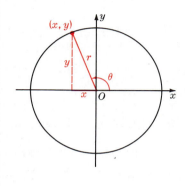

Function	Definition and Notation
sine	$\sin \theta = \dfrac{y}{r}$
cosine	$\cos \theta = \dfrac{x}{r}$
tangent	$\tan \theta = \dfrac{\sin \theta}{\cos \theta} = \dfrac{y}{x} \quad (x \neq 0)$
cotangent	$\cot \theta = \dfrac{\cos \theta}{\sin \theta} = \dfrac{x}{y} \quad (y \neq 0)$
secant	$\sec \theta = \dfrac{1}{\cos \theta} = \dfrac{r}{x} \quad (x \neq 0)$
cosecant	$\csc \theta = \dfrac{1}{\sin \theta} = \dfrac{r}{y} \quad (y \neq 0)$

As you can see from the definitions, the six trigonometric functions can be paired as reciprocal functions.

RECIPROCAL RELATIONSHIPS

$$\cot \theta = \frac{1}{\tan \theta} \qquad \sec \theta = \frac{1}{\cos \theta} \qquad \csc \theta = \frac{1}{\sin \theta}$$

You can also see from the definitions that the signs of the six trigono-metric functions in the various quadrants are as follows:

Function	Quadrant			
	First	Second	Third	Fourth
sine and cosecant	+	+	−	−
cosine and secant	+	−	−	+
tangent and cotangent	+	−	+	−

The use of reference angles can be extended to include all six trigonometric functions. For example, if θ is a third-quadrant angle:

$$\sec \theta = \frac{1}{\cos \theta} = \frac{1}{-\cos \alpha} = -\sec \alpha$$

The chart below shows all such relationships.

FUNCTIONS OF θ IN TERMS
OF ITS REFERENCE ANGLE α

Value	Quadrant in which θ terminates			
	First	Second	Third	Fourth
$\sin \theta$	$\sin \alpha$	$\sin \alpha$	$-\sin \alpha$	$-\sin \alpha$
$\cos \theta$	$\cos \alpha$	$-\cos \alpha$	$-\cos \alpha$	$\cos \alpha$
$\tan \theta$	$\tan \alpha$	$-\tan \alpha$	$\tan \alpha$	$-\tan \alpha$
$\csc \theta$	$\csc \alpha$	$\csc \alpha$	$-\csc \alpha$	$-\csc \alpha$
$\sec \theta$	$\sec \alpha$	$-\sec \alpha$	$-\sec \alpha$	$\sec \alpha$
$\cot \theta$	$\cot \alpha$	$-\cot \alpha$	$\cot \alpha$	$-\cot \alpha$

The related circular functions $\tan x$, $\cot x$, $\sec x$, and $\csc x$ are defined in the usual manner. For example tangent $= \{(x, y): y = \tan x^{\mathrm{R}}\}$.

EXAMPLE 1 Find $\sec 143°$.

SOLUTION The reference angle is $37°$.
From the chart:
$$\sec 143° = -\sec 37°$$
$$\sec 37° = 1.252 \quad \text{(from Table 5)}$$
$$\therefore \sec 143° = -1.252$$

EXAMPLE 2 Without using tables or a calculator, evaluate
a. $\sec 30°$ **b.** $\cot 0°$

SOLUTION **a.** Since $\sec \theta = \dfrac{1}{\cos \theta}$,

$$\sec 30° = \frac{1}{\cos 30°}$$

$$= \frac{1}{\frac{\sqrt{3}}{2}} = \frac{2}{\sqrt{3}} = \frac{2\sqrt{3}}{3}.$$

$$\therefore \sec 30° = \frac{2\sqrt{3}}{3} \quad \textbf{\textit{Answer}}$$

b. Since $\cot \theta = \dfrac{\cos \theta}{\sin \theta}$,

$$\cot 0° = \frac{\cos 0°}{\sin 0°}.$$

Since $\sin 0° = 0$, $\cot 0°$ is undefined. **Answer**

The following table will help you evaluate trigonometric functions of angles whose reference angles are 30°, 45°, or 60°. You may find it helpful to memorize the table.

θ Degrees	θ Radians	$\sin\theta$	$\cos\theta$	$\tan\theta$	$\cot\theta$	$\sec\theta$	$\csc\theta$
30°	$\dfrac{\pi}{6}$	$\dfrac{1}{2}$	$\dfrac{\sqrt{3}}{2}$	$\dfrac{\sqrt{3}}{3}$	$\sqrt{3}$	$\dfrac{2\sqrt{3}}{3}$	2
45°	$\dfrac{\pi}{4}$	$\dfrac{\sqrt{2}}{2}$	$\dfrac{\sqrt{2}}{2}$	1	1	$\sqrt{2}$	$\sqrt{2}$
60°	$\dfrac{\pi}{3}$	$\dfrac{\sqrt{3}}{2}$	$\dfrac{1}{2}$	$\sqrt{3}$	$\dfrac{\sqrt{3}}{3}$	2	$\dfrac{2\sqrt{3}}{3}$

EXAMPLE 3 Solve $\csc\theta = \dfrac{2\sqrt{3}}{3}$ for $0° \le \theta < 360°$.

SOLUTION Since $\sin\theta$ and $\csc\theta$ are reciprocals, $\csc\theta = \dfrac{1}{\sin\theta}$.

Thus, since $\csc\theta = \dfrac{2\sqrt{3}}{3}$, $\sin\theta = \dfrac{3}{2\sqrt{3}}$.

By rationalizing the denominator, you get
$$\sin\theta = \frac{3}{2\sqrt{3}} \cdot \frac{\sqrt{3}}{\sqrt{3}} = \frac{\sqrt{3}}{2}.$$

$\therefore$ The reference angle for θ is 60°.

Since $\csc\theta$ is positive, there are solutions in the first and second quadrants.
In the first quadrant, $\theta = 60°$.
In the second quadrant, $\theta = 180° - 60°$, or 120°.

$\therefore$ the solution set is $\{60°, 120°\}$. **Answer**

EXAMPLE 4 Solve $\cot\theta = 1.8$ to the nearest tenth of a degree for $0° \le \theta < 360°$.

SOLUTION Use Table 4. Locate the entry nearest 1.8 in the "cot" column. This is 1.797, which gives a reference angle of 29.1°.
Since $\cot\theta$ is positive, there are solutions in the first and third quadrants. Thus:

In the first quadrant, $\theta = 29.1°$.
In the third quadrant, $\theta = 180° + 29.1° = 209.1°$.

$\therefore$ the solution set is $\{29.1°, 209.1°\}$. **Answer**

The final example shows that if you know just one trigonometric function of θ and the quadrant θ is in, you can determine any of the other five trigonometric functions of θ.

EXAMPLE 5 If $\sec \theta = -\frac{13}{5}$ and θ is in the third quadrant, find $\tan \theta$.

SOLUTION Make a diagram to reflect the fact that $\sec \theta = -\frac{13}{5} = \frac{r}{x}$.

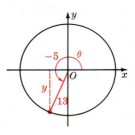

Find y:
$$y^2 + (-5)^2 = 13^2$$
$$y^2 = 144$$
$$y = -12$$

(Recall that θ is in the third quadrant.)

$$\tan \theta = \frac{y}{x} = \frac{-12}{-5} = \frac{12}{5} \quad \textit{Answer}$$

Besides their reciprocal relationships, the six trigonometric functions are related in other ways. In Figure 12-21, complementary acute angles, θ and $90° - \theta$, are drawn in standard position and perpendiculars are constructed from P and Q to the x-axis. The two triangles thus formed are congruent. (Why?) Since congruent triangles have equal corresponding sides, the x- and y-coordinates of P and Q are reversed, as shown in the figure. Therefore,

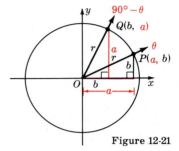

Figure 12-21

$$\sin \theta = \frac{y\text{-coordinate of } P}{\text{radius}} = \frac{b}{r} = \frac{x\text{-coordinate of } Q}{\text{radius}} = \cos (90° - \theta).$$

Because $\sin \theta = \cos (90° - \theta)$, the cosine is called the *cofunction* of the sine. Restated, the sine of an angle θ is the *cofunction* (*co*sine) of the complement $(90° - \theta)$ of θ. Likewise, the sine is the cofunction of the cosine because, as Figure 12-21 shows,

$$\cos \theta = \frac{a}{r} = \sin (90° - \theta).$$

Figure 12-21 can also be used to show that the tangent and cotangent are cofunctions as are the secant and cosecant. The cofunction relationships are summarized as follows:

COFUNCTION RELATIONSHIPS

$\sin \theta = \cos (90° - \theta)$ and $\cos \theta = \sin (90° - \theta)$

$\tan \theta = \cot (90° - \theta)$ and $\cot \theta = \tan (90° - \theta)$

$\sec \theta = \csc (90° - \theta)$ and $\csc \theta = \sec (90° - \theta)$

Note that the table of trigonometric functions of special angles on page 471 illustrates the cofunction relationships.

Oral Exercises

1. **a.** Use the diagram to find r.
   b. Find the values of the six trigonometric functions of θ.

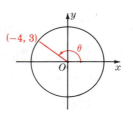

Name two possible quadrants for θ.

2. $\sin \theta < 0$

3. $\cos \theta > 0$

4. $\tan \theta < 0$

5. $\csc \theta < 0$

6. $\cot \theta > 0$

7. $\sec \theta < 0$

Simplify. Express as a single trigonometric function of θ.

8. $\dfrac{1}{\csc \theta}$

9. $\dfrac{1}{\cos \theta}$

10. $\dfrac{1}{\tan \theta}$

11. $\dfrac{1}{\sin \theta}$

12. $\sin (90° - \theta)$

13. $\cos (90° - \theta)$

Written Exercises

Simplify. Express as a single trigonometric function of θ.

A **1.** $\dfrac{1}{\sec \theta}$

2. $\dfrac{1}{\cot \theta}$

3. $\tan (90° - \theta)$

4. $\sec \left(\dfrac{\pi}{2} - \theta\right)$

5. $\sin \left(\dfrac{\pi}{2} - \theta\right)$

6. $\dfrac{1}{\cot (90° - \theta)}$

7. $\dfrac{\cos A}{\sin A}$

8. $\dfrac{\cos \theta}{\cot \theta}$

9. $\cos B \csc B$

10. $\cos B \sec B$

11. $\sin \theta \csc \theta$

12. $\sin A \sec A$

13. $\dfrac{\cot \theta}{\tan \theta}$

14. $\cot \theta \sin \theta$

15. $\dfrac{\sin \left(\dfrac{\pi}{2} - \theta\right)}{\cos \left(\dfrac{\pi}{2} - \theta\right)}$

16. $\dfrac{\sec \left(\dfrac{\pi}{2} - \theta\right)}{\csc \left(\dfrac{\pi}{2} - \theta\right)}$

Use Tables 4 and 6 or a calculator. Round calculator answers to the nearest thousandth.

17. $\tan 200°$

18. $\sec (-21)°$

19. $\cot 95.2°$

20. $\csc 600°$

21. $\csc 2.38$

22. $\tan 5.14$

23. $\sec 3$

24. $\cot 7.53$

Evaluate using Table 5.

25. $\tan 125°30'$

26. $\csc 307°40'$

27. $\cot 269°10'$

28. $\csc (-16°50')$

Evaluate without using tables or a calculator.

29. $\tan 135°$

30. $\cot 300°$

31. $\sec \pi$

32. $\csc \pi$

33. $\cot 315°$

34. $\csc (-60)°$

35. $\tan \dfrac{7\pi}{6}$

36. $\sec \dfrac{2\pi}{3}$

In Exercises 37-46:

a. Draw a positive angle θ in standard position that terminates in the given quadrant.

b. Use the given function of θ to find the other five trigonometric functions of θ.

37. $\sin \theta = \frac{3}{5}$; first quadrant

38. $\cos \theta = -\frac{1}{3}$; second quadrant

39. $\tan \theta = \frac{4}{3}$; first quadrant

40. $\cot \theta = \frac{5}{12}$; third quadrant

41. $\sec \theta = -\frac{3}{2}$; second quadrant

42. $\csc \theta = -\frac{15}{8}$; fourth quadrant

B 43. $\tan \theta = -\sqrt{3}$; fourth quadrant

44. $\csc \theta = \sqrt{2}$; second quadrant

45. $\sec \theta = -\frac{\sqrt{5}}{2}$; third quadrant

46. $\cot \theta = \frac{1}{\sqrt{3}}$; third quadrant

Solve for $0° \leq \theta < 360°$. Use Table 4 or 5 or a calculator. Interpolate where necessary. Give answers to the nearest hundredth of a degree or to the nearest minute.

47. $\sec \theta = 2.2$

48. $\tan \theta = \frac{3}{4}$

49. $\csc \theta = -\frac{5}{4}$

50. $\cot \theta = -1$

51. $\sec \theta = -1.72$

52. $\csc \theta = 1.43$

53. Recall that $\tan \theta = \frac{\sin \theta}{\cos \theta} = \frac{y}{x}$ when $x \neq 0$ (See the definition and diagram on page 469). Thus, $\tan \theta$ is not defined for $\theta = \frac{\pi}{2}, \frac{3\pi}{2}$, $\frac{5\pi}{2}, \ldots$ because $x = 0$ for these values of θ. Give the radian values of θ for which $\cot \theta$ is not defined.

54. Let n be an integer. Write a single expression, in terms of n, that represents all values of θ for which $\tan \theta$ is not defined.

55. For what radian values of θ is $\sec \theta$ not defined?

56. For what radian values of θ is $\csc \theta$ not defined?

57. a. Give a justification for each equals sign below.

$$\tan (90° - \theta) = \frac{\sin (90° - \theta)}{\cos (90° - \theta)} = \frac{\cos \theta}{\sin \theta} = \cot \theta$$

b. Prove $\sec (90° - \theta) = \csc \theta$.

Solve for $0° \leq \theta < 360°$ without tables or a calculator.

58. $\tan \theta = -1$

59. $\csc \theta = 2$

60. $\sec \theta = -2$

61. $\cot \theta = \sqrt{3}$

Draw the graph of the function.

C 62. $y = \tan \theta$

63. $y = \cot \theta$

64. $y = \sec \theta$

65. $y = \csc \theta$

12-8 *Trigonometric Identities*

OBJECTIVE To simplify trigonometric expressions and prove trigonometric identities.

A **trigonometric identity** is an equation, such as $\tan \theta = \cot (90° - \theta)$, that holds for all values of θ except those for which either side of the equation is undefined. You are already familiar with most of the identities shown below.

THE RECIPROCAL IDENTITIES

$$\csc \theta = \frac{1}{\sin \theta} \qquad\qquad \sin \theta = \frac{1}{\csc \theta}$$

$$\sec \theta = \frac{1}{\cos \theta} \qquad\qquad \cos \theta = \frac{1}{\sec \theta}$$

$$\tan \theta = \begin{cases} \dfrac{\sin \theta}{\cos \theta} \\[2mm] \dfrac{1}{\cot \theta} \end{cases} \qquad\qquad \cot \theta = \begin{cases} \dfrac{\cos \theta}{\sin \theta} \\[2mm] \dfrac{1}{\tan \theta} \end{cases}$$

THE COFUNCTION IDENTITIES

$$\sin \theta = \cos (90° - \theta) \qquad\qquad \cos \theta = \sin (90° - \theta)$$
$$\tan \theta = \cot (90° - \theta) \qquad\qquad \cot \theta = \tan (90° - \theta)$$
$$\sec \theta = \csc (90° - \theta) \qquad\qquad \csc \theta = \sec (90° - \theta)$$

THE PYTHAGOREAN IDENTITIES

$$\sin^2 \theta + \cos^2 \theta = 1 \quad \text{(Note: } \sin^2 \theta \text{ means } (\sin \theta)^2.\text{)}$$
$$1 + \tan^2 \theta = \sec^2 \theta.$$
$$1 + \cot^2 \theta = \csc^2 \theta.$$

The unit circle provides the basis for the proof of the first Pythagorean identity. The equation of the circle is $x^2 + y^2 = 1$. Substituting $\cos \theta$ for x and $\sin \theta$ for y, you get

$$(\cos \theta)^2 + (\sin \theta)^2 = 1.$$

This is usually written

$$\sin^2 \theta + \cos^2 \theta = 1.$$

(Proofs of the other two Pythagorean identities are called for in Exercises 54 and 55 on page 479.)

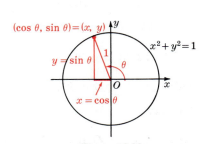

Figure 12-22

The identities on page 475 can be used to prove other identities and simplify trigonometric expressions.

EXAMPLE 1   Simplify $\csc\theta - \cos\theta\cot\theta$.

SOLUTION   It is often a good strategy to express each function in terms of $\sin\theta$ and $\cos\theta$.

$$\csc\theta - \cos\theta\cot\theta$$

$$\frac{1}{\sin\theta} - \cos\theta\,\frac{\cos\theta}{\sin\theta} = \frac{1-\cos^2\theta}{\sin\theta} = \frac{\sin^2\theta}{\sin\theta} = \sin\theta \quad \textbf{\textit{Answer}}$$

Csc θ and cot θ are not defined for $\theta = (180n)°$, where θ is an integer. Therefore, $\csc\theta - \cos\theta\cot\theta$ is equal to $\sin\theta$ only for $\theta \neq (180n)°$. You should assume that simplifications of expressions and proofs of identities are valid only where the variable is defined.

Using the Pythagorean and reciprocal identities, you can express any of the six basic trigonometric functions in terms of any other.

EXAMPLE 2   Express $\sec\phi$ in terms of $\sin\phi$.

SOLUTION   By the reciprocal identity for secant,

$$\sec\phi = \frac{1}{\cos\phi}.$$

Use the Pythagorean identity, $\sin^2\phi + \cos^2\phi = 1$, to express $\cos\phi$ in terms of $\sin\phi$.

$$\cos^2\phi = 1 - \sin^2\phi$$
$$\cos\phi = \pm\sqrt{1-\sin^2\phi}$$

By substitution,

$$\sec\phi = \frac{1}{\pm\sqrt{1-\sin^2\phi}}. \quad \textbf{\textit{Answer}}$$

The quadrant that ϕ is in determines whether the $+$ or the $-$ is used in front of the radical in Example 2. If ϕ is in the first or the fourth quadrant, $\sec\phi$ is positive. Thus, $\sec\phi = \dfrac{1}{\sqrt{1-\sin^2\phi}}$. If ϕ is in the second or the third quadrant, $\sec\phi$ is negative, and $\sec\phi = \dfrac{1}{-\sqrt{1-\sin^2\phi}}$ or $-\dfrac{1}{\sqrt{1-\sin^2\phi}}$.

In proving an identity, as in Example 3, simplify each side separately until the two sides are identical.

EXAMPLE 3   Prove that $\tan^2\theta + \cos^2\theta + \dfrac{1}{\csc^2\theta} = \sec^2\theta$.

SOLUTION Simplify the more complex side of the identity (in this case the left side) until it is identical to the other side.

$$\tan^2\theta + \cos^2\theta + \frac{1}{\csc^2\theta} \stackrel{?}{=} \sec^2\theta$$

$$\tan^2\theta + \underbrace{\cos^2\theta + \sin^2\theta}\ \Big|\ \sec^2\theta$$

$$\underbrace{\tan^2\theta + \qquad 1}\ \Big|\ \sec^2\theta$$

$$\sec^2\theta \qquad\qquad = \sec^2\theta$$

The following suggestions should be helpful in proving identities.

1. Simplify the more complex side of the identity if there is one.
2. Express each function in terms of sine and cosine. (Example 3 is an exception.)
3. Combine the terms on each side into a single fraction.
4. Make the denominators on each side the same.
5. Use the fact that the Pythagorean identities can be expressed as the difference of two squares.

$$\sin^2\theta = 1 - \cos^2\theta = (1 + \cos\theta)(1 - \cos\theta)$$
$$\cos^2\theta = 1 - \sin^2\theta = (1 + \sin\theta)(1 - \sin\theta)$$
$$\tan^2\theta = \sec^2\theta - 1 = (\sec\theta + 1)(\sec\theta - 1)$$
$$\cot^2\theta = \csc^2\theta - 1 = (\csc\theta + 1)(\csc\theta - 1)$$

EXAMPLE 4 Prove that $\csc\theta(\csc\theta + \cot\theta) = \dfrac{1}{1 - \cos\theta}$.

SOLUTION

$$\csc\theta(\csc\theta + \cot\theta) \quad \stackrel{?}{=}\quad \frac{1}{1 - \cos\theta}$$

$$\frac{1}{\sin\theta}\left(\frac{1}{\sin\theta} + \frac{\cos\theta}{\sin\theta}\right)\ \Big|\ \frac{1}{1 - \cos\theta}\ \left\{\text{Suggestions (1) and (2)}\right.$$

$$\frac{1}{\sin\theta}\left(\frac{1 + \cos\theta}{\sin\theta}\right)\ \Big|\ \frac{1}{1 - \cos\theta}$$

$$\frac{1 + \cos\theta}{\sin^2\theta}\ \Big|\ \frac{1}{1 - \cos\theta}\ \left\}\text{Suggestion (3)}\right.$$

$$\frac{1 + \cos\theta}{1 - \cos^2\theta}\ \Big|\ \frac{1}{1 - \cos\theta}$$

$$\frac{1 + \cos\theta}{(1 - \cos\theta)(1 + \cos\theta)}\ \Big|\quad\ \left\}\text{Suggestion (5)}\right.$$

$$\frac{1}{1 - \cos\theta} \quad = \quad \frac{1}{1 - \cos\theta}\ \left\{\text{Suggestion (4)}\right.$$

An alternate approach would be to multiply the right side by $\dfrac{1 + \cos\theta}{1 + \cos\theta}$ instead of converting $\sin^2\theta$ into $1 - \cos^2\theta$ on the left side.

Oral Exercises

1. Since $\sin^2 \theta + \cos^2 \theta = 1$, then:
    a. $1 - \cos^2 \theta = ?$ **b.** $1 - \sin^2 \theta = ?$ **c.** $\sin^2 \theta - 1 = ?$

2. Since $1 + \tan^2 \theta = \sec^2 \theta$, then:
    a. $\sec^2 \theta - 1 = ?$ **b.** $\sec^2 \theta - \tan^2 \theta = ?$ **c.** $\tan^2 \theta - \sec^2 \theta = ?$

Express the first function in terms of the second function.

3. $\sin \theta$; $\cos \theta$ **4.** $\cos \alpha$; $\sin \alpha$ **5.** $\tan \phi$; $\sin \phi$

Written Exercises

Simplify. (*Note:* The symbol β is the Greek letter "beta.")

A   **1.** $\cos^2 a + \sin^2 a$ **2.** $1 + \cot^2 \alpha$ **3.** $1 + \tan^2 x$

       4. $\csc^2 A - 1$ **5.** $\csc y \cos y \sin y$ **6.** $\tan \beta \sec \beta \sin \beta$

       7. $(1 - \cos^2 x) \csc^2 x$ **8.** $\cos^2 \theta + \sin^2 \theta + \cot^2 \theta$ **9.** $\cos \alpha \sec \alpha - \cos^2 \alpha$

10. $\dfrac{\sec^2 y - \tan^2 y}{\csc y}$ **11.** $\dfrac{\tan x}{\csc (90° - x)}$ **12.** $\dfrac{\sin A}{\cot \left(\dfrac{\pi}{2} - A \right)}$

13. $\sin^2 \theta (\cot^2 \theta + 1)$ **14.** $\cos \alpha \csc \alpha \tan \alpha$ **15.** $\sec^2 \beta - \tan^2 \beta + \cot^2 \beta$

16. $\csc x - \cos x \cot x$ **17.** $\csc \left(\dfrac{\pi}{2} - x \right) \cot x$ **18.** $\cos A (\sec A - \cos A)$

19. $1 - \dfrac{\sin^2 A}{\tan^2 A}$ **20.** $\dfrac{1}{\cos^2 \theta} - \dfrac{1}{\cot^2 \theta}$ **21.** $\sec^2 217° - \tan^2 217°$

22. $\cos^2 \dfrac{\pi^R}{3} + \sin^2 \dfrac{\pi^R}{3}$ **23.** $\cos^2 \left(\dfrac{\pi}{2} - \theta \right) - 1$ **24.** $\dfrac{\sin x \cos x}{1 - \cos^2 x}$

Express the first function in terms of the second function.

25. $\cot \theta$; $\sin \theta$ **26.** $\csc \phi$; $\cos \phi$ **27.** $\tan x \sec x$; $\cos x$ **28.** $\tan \theta \sec \theta$; $\sin \theta$

Prove each identity.

29. $\tan A (\tan A + \cot A) = \sec^2 A$ **30.** $\tan^2 \theta = \sin^2 \theta (1 + \tan^2 \theta)$

31. $\cos^2 \theta - \sin^2 \theta = 1 - 2 \sin^2 \theta$ **32.** $\cos^2 \theta - \sin^2 \theta = 2 \cos^2 \theta - 1$

33. $\sin x + \cos x \cot x = \csc x$ **34.** $\cos x + \sin x \tan x = \sec x$

35. $\dfrac{\sin \theta}{\csc \theta} + \dfrac{\cos \theta}{\sec \theta} = \sin \theta \csc \theta$ **36.** $\dfrac{1}{1 + \tan^2 A} + \dfrac{1}{1 + \cot^2 A} = 1$

37. $\cos^4 \theta - \sin^4 \theta = \cos^2 \theta - \sin^2 \theta$ **38.** $\tan^2 x - \sin^2 x = \tan^2 x \sin^2 x$

Simplify.

B   **39.** $\dfrac{\tan \beta + \cot \beta}{\sec^2 \beta}$ **40.** $\dfrac{1 + \tan^2 x}{1 + \cot^2 x}$ **41.** $\dfrac{\csc \theta - \sin \theta}{\cot^2 \theta}$

42. $\tan x (\sin x \cot x + \cos x)$ **43.** $\cos x + \sin x \tan x$

44. $\sin \beta + \cos \beta \cot \beta$

45. $\dfrac{\cos \alpha - \cot \alpha}{1 - \sin \alpha}$

46. $\dfrac{\sec x + \csc x}{1 + \tan x}$

47. $\dfrac{\sin \beta}{1 + \cos \beta} + \dfrac{1 + \cos \beta}{\sin \beta}$

48. $\sin^3 y + \sin y \cos^2 y$

49. $(1 - \cos \alpha)(\csc \alpha + \cot \alpha)$

50. $(\csc x - \cot x)(\sec x + 1)$

51. $(1 - \cos \theta)(1 + \sec \theta) \cos \theta$

52. $(\sin \alpha + \cos \alpha)^2 + (\sin \alpha - \cos \alpha)^2$

53. $(\tan A + 1)^2 + (\tan A - 1)^2$

54. Prove the Pythagorean identity $1 + \tan^2 \theta = \sec^2 \theta$.

55. Prove the Pythagorean identity $1 + \cot^2 \theta = \csc^2 \theta$.

Prove each identity.

56. $\dfrac{\tan x}{1 + \sec x} + \dfrac{1 + \sec x}{\tan x} = 2 \csc x$

57. $\dfrac{\sec \theta - 1}{\sin^2 \theta} = \dfrac{\sec^2 \theta}{1 + \sec \theta}$

58. $\dfrac{1 - \sin \alpha}{\cos \alpha} = \dfrac{\cos \alpha}{1 + \sin \alpha}$ $\left(\textit{Hint:} \text{ Multiply the right side by } \dfrac{1 - \sin \alpha}{1 - \sin \alpha}. \right)$

59. $\dfrac{1}{1 + \cos \beta} + \dfrac{1}{1 - \cos \beta} = 2 \csc^2 \beta$

60. $\dfrac{1}{\sec y - \tan y} - \dfrac{1}{\sec y + \tan y} = 2 \tan y$

61. $\dfrac{\tan A + \tan B}{\cot A + \cot B} = \tan A \tan B$

62. $\dfrac{1 + \csc \theta}{1 - \csc \theta} = \dfrac{\tan \theta + \sec \theta}{\tan \theta - \sec \theta}$

C 63. $\dfrac{\cos^2 \theta + 3 \sin \theta - 1}{3 + 2 \sin \theta - \sin^2 \theta} = \dfrac{1}{1 + \csc \theta}$

64. $\sqrt{\dfrac{1 - \sin x}{1 + \sin x}} = \left| \sec x - \tan x \right|$

Self-Test 3

VOCABULARY   the tangent of θ (p. 469)   reciprocal identities (p. 475)
the cotangent of θ (p. 469)   cofunction identities (p. 475)
the secant of θ (p. 469)   Pythagorean identities
the cosecant of θ (p. 469)   (p. 475)
trigonometric identity
(p. 475)

Evaluate without using tables or a calculator.

1. $\tan 60°$ **2.** $\sec 135°$ **3.** $\csc (-30)°$ Obj. 12-7, p. 469

Simplify.

4. $\cot (90° - \theta)$ **5.** $\sec (\pi + \theta)$ **6.** $\csc (90° - \theta)$

7. $(1 + \cos \theta)(1 - \cos \theta)$ **8.** $(\csc \theta + \cot \theta)(\csc \theta - \cot \theta)$ Obj. 12-8, p. 475

Check your answers with those at the back of the book.

Applications of the Sine and Cosine

In the discussion and exercises that follow, you will study applications of the sine and cosine related to tides and sunrise and sunset. These phenomena have a repetitive pattern, or period, just like the sine and cosine functions.

Mean high water is the average *height of tide* (depth of the water) at high tide. *Mean low water* is the average height of tide at low tide. The *tidal range* is the difference between mean high water and mean low water.

In the waters near Philadelphia, Pennsylvania, the tidal range is about 2 m. That is, mean high water is 2 m greater than mean low water. Figure 12-23 shows the graph of height of tide with mean low water arbitrarily given the value of 0.

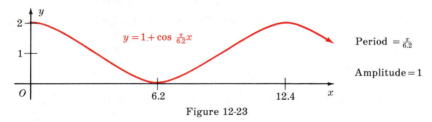

Figure 12-23

This curve approximates a cosine wave with equation

$$y = c + A \cos kx.$$

Since the tides make a full cycle every 12.4 h, the period of the curve is 12.4 and

$$k = \frac{2\pi}{12.4} = \frac{\pi}{6.2}.$$

The amplitude A is 1, which is one half the tidal range.

The letter c is the distance that the graph of $y = A \cos kx$ has been translated upward to give the graph of $y = c + A \cos kx$. You can find c by averaging mean high water and mean low water. Thus,

$$c = \frac{2 + 0}{2} = 1.$$

Therefore, the equation for height of tide near Philadelphia x hours after high tide is

$$y = 1 + \cos \frac{\pi}{6.2} x.$$

To find the height of tide 2 h after high tide, substitute 2 for x and calculate the expression as if x were an angle of 2^R. Thus,

$$y = 1 + \cos \frac{\pi}{6.2}(2)$$

$$= 1 + \cos \frac{\pi}{3.1} \approx 1 + \cos 1.01$$

$$= 1.53 \text{ m}$$

Therefore, 2 h after high tide, the height of tide is 1.53 m. (Remember that mean low tide was arbitrarily set equal to 0. Thus if mean low tide is j, the actual height of tide is $(1.53 + j)$ m.)

The mean number of hours between sunrise and sunset is 12. Twice a year, on or about March 21 and September 22, there are approximately 12 h between sunrise and sunset everywhere on Earth. Figure 12-24 gives the approximate amount of time between sunrise and sunset for any day of the year in Fargo, North Dakota. As shown in the figure, the graph is a sine wave.

Since there are 365 days in a year, the graph has period 365. The amplitude is 4 because the number of hours between sunrise and sunset varies from 8 to 16 $\left(\frac{16 - 8}{2} = 4 \right)$. Thus, the equation of this daylight graph is

$$y = 12 + 4 \sin \frac{2\pi}{365} x,$$

where x is the number of days after March 21, the first day of spring.

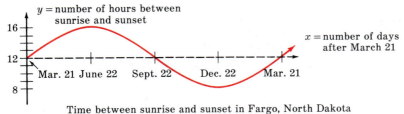

Time between sunrise and sunset in Fargo, North Dakota

Figure 12-24

EXAMPLE   Find the approximate amount of time between sunrise and sunset on April 1 in Fargo.

SOLUTION   April 1 is 11 days after March 21. Thus,

$$y = 12 + 4 \sin \frac{2\pi}{365} x$$

$$= 12 + 4 \sin \frac{2\pi}{365} \cdot 11 = 12 + 4 \sin 0.189$$

$$= 12.75 \qquad\qquad 12.75 \text{ h} = 12 \text{ h } 45 \text{ min}$$

∴ There are approximately 12 h 45 min between sunrise and sunset on April 1 in Fargo, North Dakota. *Answer*

Written Exercises

On page 480, an equation and graph are given for height of tide in the waters near Philadelphia. Modify this equation and graph for each location given.

A

	Location	Tidal Range	Period
1.	Boston, MA	3 m	12.4 h
2.	Eastport, ME	5.5 m	12.4 h
3.	Galveston, TX	0.4 m	12.4 h
4.	Vancouver, B.C.	3.2 m	12.4 h

5. The average depth of the water at the end of a pier is 2 m at low tide and 12 m at high tide. Find the depth of the water 3 h after high tide.

6. The average depth of the water at a certain anchorage site is 5 m at low tide and 9 m at high tide. How long after high tide is the depth of the water 7 m? 8 m?

7. Study the daylight graph for Fargo, North Dakota, on page 481.

   a. Is there a greater change in the amount of daylight between June 1 and June 22 or between Sept. 1 and Sept. 22?

   b. At what times of the year is the amount of daylight *changing* most rapidly?

8. The typical daylight curve shown on page 481 has the equation $y = 12 + A \sin x$. For Fargo, North Dakota, the value of A is 4. In general, the value of A depends on the latitude of the particular location.

   a. Find the value A for the town where your school is located by finding the amount of time between sunrise and sunset on December 21 and June 22. A is one half the difference of these times.

   b. Make a daylight curve for your latitude.

Chapter Summary

1. The measure of an angle in *standard position* is positive if its terminal ray is rotated counterclockwise, and negative if its terminal ray is rotated clockwise. The terminal ray can rotate through more than one revolution. Thus, the same terminal ray can be used to represent an infinite number of angles in standard position.

2. You can measure angles in decimal degrees; degrees, minutes, and seconds; or radians. A central angle of a circle of radius r has a measure of *1 radian* if it intercepts an arc of length r. Therefore, $180° = \pi^R$. The central angle θ measured in radians intercepts an arc of length $r\theta$.

3. If the terminal ray of an angle θ in standard position intersects the circle $x^2 + y^2 = r^2$ at point $P(x, y)$, then:

$$\sin \theta = \frac{y}{r} \qquad \tan \theta = \frac{y}{x}, x \neq 0 \qquad \sec \theta = \frac{r}{x}, x \neq 0$$

$$\cos \theta = \frac{x}{r} \qquad \cot \theta = \frac{x}{y}, y \neq 0 \qquad \csc \theta = \frac{r}{y}, y \neq 0$$

If the circle is a *unit circle* ($r = 1$), then $(x, y) = (\cos \theta, \sin \theta)$.

4. You can express the value of a trigonometric function of an angle in terms of the value of a trigonometric function of its *reference angle*. You can then use tables or a calculator to find the value of the trigonometric function of the reference angle. You can evaluate trigonometric functions of *quadrantal angles* (when defined) and angles with reference angles of 30°, 45°, or 60° without using tables or a calculator.

5. Because the sine and cosine are *periodic functions*, their graphs consist of a basic repetitive pattern. The length of one repetition of the pattern is one *period*. The sine and cosine have period 2π.

6. You can use basic *trigonometric identities* to simplify trigonometric expressions or prove more complicated identities.

Chapter Review

Give the letter of the correct answer.

12-1
1. Which angle in standard position is coterminal with an angle in standard position of $(-172)°$?

   a. 208° **b.** 172° **c.** 188° **d.** 542°

12-2
2. Find the length of the arc intercepted by an angle with measure 4^R in a circle of radius 2 cm.

   a. 8 cm **b.** 2 cm **c.** 0.5 cm **d.** 16 cm

3. Convert 240° to radians.

   a. $\frac{2\pi^R}{3}$ **b.** $\frac{7\pi^R}{6}$ **c.** $\frac{3\pi^R}{2}$ **d.** $\frac{4\pi^R}{3}$

4. Convert $\frac{7\pi^R}{9}$ to degrees.

   a. 140° **b.** 100° **c.** 165° **d.** 160°

5. If the terminal ray of an angle θ in standard position contains the point $(-2, 1)$, find $\sin \theta$. 12-3

    a. $-\dfrac{1}{2}$ **b.** $\dfrac{\sqrt{3}}{3}$ **c.** $-\dfrac{2\sqrt{5}}{5}$ **d.** $\dfrac{\sqrt{5}}{5}$

6. Which of the following is not true?

    a. $\sin 130° = \sin 50°$ **b.** $\cos 40° > \cos 30°$

    c. $\cos (-70)° = \cos 70°$ **d.** $\sin 170° < \sin 20°$

7. Find $\cos \theta$ if $\sin \theta = -\dfrac{1}{3}$ and θ is in the fourth quadrant.

    a. $-\dfrac{2\sqrt{2}}{3}$ **b.** $\dfrac{3\sqrt{10}}{10}$ **c.** $\dfrac{2\sqrt{2}}{3}$ **d.** $-\dfrac{3\sqrt{10}}{10}$

8. Evaluate $\cos 57°40'$ using tables. 12-4

    a. 0.8450   **b.** 0.5495   **c.** 0.5348   **d.** 0.8355

9. The reference angle for an angle of 2.5^R is approximately: 12-5

    a. 0.5^R **b.** 2.5^R **c.** 0.64^R **d.** 3.78^R

10. Use tables to find $\sin 236.4°$.

    a. 0.8329   **b.** -0.8329 **c.** 0.5534   **d.** -0.5534

11. Solve $\cos \theta = -1$ for $0^R \leq \theta < 2\pi^R$.

    a. 0^R **b.** $\dfrac{\pi^R}{2}$ **c.** π^R **d.** $\dfrac{3\pi^R}{2}$

12. Which of the following is an equation for the sine wave graphed at the right? 12-6

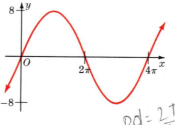
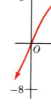

    a. $y = 8 \sin \dfrac{1}{2}x$

    b. $y = 8 \sin 2x$

    c. $y = 8 \sin x$

    d. $y = 8 \sin 4x$

13. State the period of the function defined by $y = \dfrac{2}{3} \cos \pi x$.

    a. $\dfrac{2}{3}$ **b.** π **c.** 2   **d.** 2π

14. Which of the following is not equal to 2? 12-7

    a. $\csc \dfrac{\pi^R}{6}$ **b.** $\csc 150°$ **c.** $\sec 30°$ **d.** $\sec (-420)°$

15. Solve $\tan \theta = -2.633$ for $0° \leq \theta < 360°$.

    a. $\{20°, 8°\}$ **b.** $\{69.2°\}$

    c. $\{159.2°, 339.2°\}$ **d.** $\{110.8°, 290.8°\}$

16. Simplify $\cot\left(\dfrac{\pi}{2} - \theta\right)\csc\theta$.

    a. $\sec\theta$ **b.** $\csc\theta$ **c.** $\dfrac{\cos\theta}{\sin^2\theta}$ **d.** $\dfrac{\sin\theta}{\cos^2\theta}$

17. Simplify $\sec^2\theta - \tan^2\theta - \cos^2\theta$.

    a. $\sin^2\theta$ **b.** 1 **c.** $\csc^2\theta$ **d.** 0

Chapter Test

1. Find the measure of an angle in standard position determined by $\frac{3}{5}$ of a clockwise revolution.

2. a. Convert $75°$ to radians. Leave your answer in terms of π.

    b. Convert $\dfrac{11\pi^{\text{R}}}{4}$ to degrees.

3. If $\cos\theta = \frac{2}{7}$ and θ is in the fourth quadrant, find $\sin\theta$.

4. Evaluate using tables.

    a. $\sin 39.2°$ **b.** $\cos 0.94^{\text{R}}$

5. Find the reference angle for the angle in standard position with the given measure. (Leave your answer to part (c) in terms of π.)

    a. $162°$ **b.** $(-114)°$ **c.** $\dfrac{5\pi^{\text{R}}}{7}$

6. Evaluate:

    a. $\cos\dfrac{7\pi^{\text{R}}}{4}$ **b.** $\sin 330°$ **c.** $\cos(-225)°$

7. Solve for $0° \le \theta < 360°$.

    a. $\cos\theta = 1$ **b.** $\sin\theta = -\dfrac{\sqrt{2}}{2}$

8. Sketch two periods of the graph of $y = \sin 3x$.

9. State an equation for the graph below.

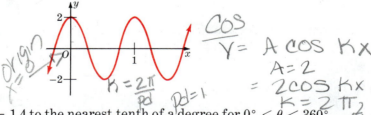

10. Solve $\sec\theta = 1.4$ to the nearest tenth of a degree for $0° \le \theta < 360°$.

11. Evaluate.

    a. $\tan 135°$ **b.** $\csc\dfrac{\pi^{\text{R}}}{6}$ **c.** $\sec 90°$

12. Simplify $\tan\theta \sin\theta \cos\theta \csc\theta$.

Although a low cloud cover can be quite appealing, this meteorological phenomenon can be of concern to airplane pilots. See problem 9 on page 492 for a method of estimating the height of a cloud cover.

13

TRIANGLE TRIGONOMETRY; VECTORS

Hi roomie

13-1 *Right-Triangle Trigonometry*

OBJECTIVE To find the sides and angles of a right triangle.

When some of the sides and angles of a triangle are known, you can use trigonometry to determine the remaining sides and angles of the triangle. This process, called solving a triangle, was applied to land surveying problems in Egypt more than 2000 years ago, and is the first known application of trigonometry. For simplicity, right triangles are considered first.

The longest side of a right triangle is called the **hypotenuse.** The leg opposite an acute angle θ is called the **opposite side,** and the leg adjacent to θ is called the **adjacent side.** Both of the two right triangles in Figure 13-1 have acute angles θ and are, therefore, similar triangles. Since corresponding sides of similar triangles are proportional, the following equations can be written:

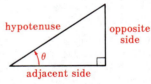

$$\frac{\sin \theta}{1} = \frac{\text{opposite side}}{\text{hypotenuse}} \qquad \frac{\cos \theta}{1} = \frac{\text{adjacent side}}{\text{hypotenuse}}$$

Also, since $\tan \theta = \dfrac{\sin \theta}{\cos \theta}$, you have

$$\tan \theta = \frac{\dfrac{\text{opposite side}}{\text{hypotenuse}}}{\dfrac{\text{adjacent side}}{\text{hypotenuse}}}.$$

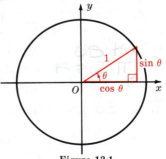

Figure 13-1

487

Simplifying these equations produces the following definitions for an acute angle θ in a right. triangle.

$$\sin \theta = \frac{\text{opposite side}}{\text{hypotenuse}} \qquad \cos \theta = \frac{\text{adjacent side}}{\text{hypotenuse}} \qquad \tan \theta = \frac{\text{opposite side}}{\text{adjacent side}}$$

EXAMPLE 1 Solve the right triangle shown in Figure 13-2. Express results to three significant digits.

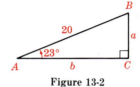

Figure 13-2

SOLUTION 1. $\sin 23° = \dfrac{\text{opposite side}}{\text{hypotenuse}}$

$0.3907 = \dfrac{a}{20}$

$a = 20(0.3907)$

$a = 7.81$

2. $\cos 23° = \dfrac{\text{adjacent side}}{\text{hypotenuse}}$

$0.9205 = \dfrac{b}{20}$

$b = 20(0.9205)$

$b = 18.4$

3. $\angle B = 180° - \angle A - \angle C = 180° - 23° - 90° = 67°$

$\therefore a = 7.81,\ b = 18.4,\ \angle B = 67°$. ***Answer***

In theoretical examples it is usual to assume that the measurements given are exact. In the previous example note that using a four-significant-digit approximation to sin 23° limits the accuracy of the final result. When working problems and exercises to a given number of significant digits, you can use the following as a guide to angle measures:
1. Two significant digits: give angles to the nearest 1°.
2. Three significant digits: give angles to the nearest 0.1° or 10′.
3. Four significant digits: give angles to the nearest 0.01° or 1′.

EXAMPLE 2 Find $\angle A$ to the nearest tenth of a degree.

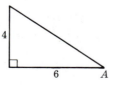

SOLUTION $\tan A = \dfrac{\text{opposite side}}{\text{adjacent side}}$

$\tan A = \dfrac{4}{6} \approx 0.6667$

$\therefore \angle A = 33.7°$. ***Answer***

In Figure 13-3 a pedestrian is looking at a passing airplane. Since the pedestrian's line of sight must be elevated from the horizontal, θ_1 is called the **angle of elevation** of the airplane. Similarly, the pilot's line of sight must be lowered, or depressed, to see the pedestrian, and θ_2 is called the **angle of depression** of the pedestrian.

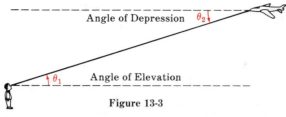

Angle of Depression θ_2

Angle of Elevation

θ_1

Figure 13-3

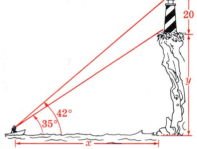

EXAMPLE 3 A sailor sights both the bottom and the top of a lighthouse that is 20 m high and stands on the edge of a cliff. The two angles of elevation are 35° and 42°. To the nearest meter, how far is the boat from the cliff?

SOLUTION

$$\tan 35° = \frac{y}{x} \qquad \text{and} \qquad \tan 42° = \frac{20 + y}{x}$$

$$0.7002 = \frac{y}{x} \qquad\qquad\qquad 0.9004 = \frac{20 + y}{x}$$

$$y = 0.7002x \qquad\qquad 0.9004x = 20 + y$$

Substitute $0.7002x$ for y in the second equation.

$$0.9004x = 20 + 0.7002x$$
$$0.2002x = 20$$
$$x = 100$$

∴ the boat is 100 m from the cliff. ***Answer***

The reciprocal trigonometric functions can also be used to solve triangles. Recall the basic definitions:

$$\cot \theta = \frac{1}{\tan \theta}, \quad \sec \theta = \frac{1}{\cos \theta}, \quad \csc \theta = \frac{1}{\sin \theta}.$$

Using the definitions on page 488, you have the following definitions for an acute angle θ in a right triangle.

$$\cot \theta = \frac{\text{adjacent side}}{\text{opposite side}} \qquad \sec \theta = \frac{\text{hypotenuse}}{\text{adjacent side}} \qquad \csc \theta = \frac{\text{hypotenuse}}{\text{opposite side}}$$

In some problems, you may notice that a careful choice of the function used can make your computations easier.

Oral Exercises

Use the diagram to evaluate the following.

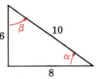

1. $\sin \alpha$ 2. $\cos \alpha$ 3. $\tan \alpha$

4. $\sin \beta$ 5. $\cos \beta$ 6. $\tan \beta$

7. $\cot \alpha$ 8. $\sec \alpha$ 9. $\csc \beta$

State an equation involving a trigonometric function that you would use to find x.

10.    11.   12.

Written Exercises

Draw a triangle with the given parts. Then solve the triangle (find all missing sides and angles). Give all answers to three significant digits. A lower-case letter denotes the side opposite the angle represented by the corresponding capital letter. For example, a is the side opposite angle A, and so on.

A
1. $\triangle ABC$, $\angle C = 90°$, $\angle A = 25°$, $c = 10$ 2. $\triangle ABC$, $\angle C = 90°$, $\angle B = 48°$, $c = 20$
3. $\triangle RST$, $\angle T = 90°$, $\angle R = 13°$, $r = 8$ 4. $\triangle RST$, $\angle T = 90°$, $\angle S = 37°$, $r = 5$
5. $\triangle XYZ$, $\angle Z = 90°$, $\angle X = 27°$, $x = 2$ 6. $\triangle XYZ$, $\angle X = 90°$, $\angle Y = 32°$, $z = 10$
7. $\triangle DEF$, $\angle D = 90°$, $d = 10$, $e = 3$ 8. $\triangle JKL$, $\angle L = 90°$, $j = 4$, $l = 5$
9. $\triangle MNP$, $\angle N = 90°$, $m = 7$, $p = 14$ 10. $\triangle NBA$, $\angle B = 90°$, $b = 12$, $a = 10$

Each triangle ABC is isosceles with $b = c$. Solve each triangle ABC, giving all answers to three significant digits.

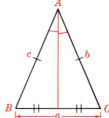

B 11. $\triangle ABC$, $b = 10$, $\angle B = 70°$
12. $\triangle ABC$, $c = 20$, $\angle A = 20°$
13. $\triangle ABC$, $c = 10$, $a = 4$
14. $\triangle ABC$, $b = 5$, $a = 6$
15. $\triangle ABC$, $\angle A = 40°$, $a = 20$
16. $\triangle ABC$, $\angle C = 64°$, $a = 12$

In Exercises 17–22, give all answers to three significant digits.

17. A rectangle is 8 cm long and 6 cm wide. Find the acute angle between its two diagonals.

PQRS is an isosceles trapezoid with *PS = RQ*.

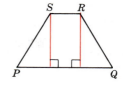

18. If $\angle P = 56°$, $SR = 10$, and $PQ = 18$, find *PS*.
19. If $SP = 8$, $SR = 9$, and $PQ = 19$, find $\angle P$.

$\overline{TA}$ and $\overline{TB}$ are tangents to circle O.

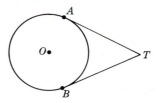

20. If $OA = 5$ and $OT = 10$, find $\angle ATB$.
(*Hint:* What do you know about $\angle OAT$?)

21. If $OA = 6$ and $\angle T = 50°$, find *AT*.

C 22. If $OT = 10$ and $AB = 6$, find $\angle ATB$.

Problems

Express results to three significant digits.

A 1. A person is standing 100 m from the base of a tower. The angle of elevation of the top of the tower is 40°. How tall is the tower?

2. A ladder 6 m long leans against a house so that its lower end is 1.5 m from the house. What angle does the ladder make with the ground?

3. A vertical pole 3 m tall casts a shadow 1.8 m long. What is the angle of elevation of the sun?

4. A pilot is required to approach the Elm City airport at a 10° angle of descent toward the runway. If the plane is at an altitude of 6000 m, at what distance (measured on the ground) from the airport should the descent begin?

5. The pitch of a roof is defined to be the ratio of its rise to its run. A carpenter would say that the pitch of the roof shown is "5 in 12." Find the angle that the roof makes with the horizontal.

6. What is the acute angle between the line $y = 2x$ and the x-axis?

7. To estimate the width of a river, Sally first stood directly opposite a large pine tree. Then she walked 35 m along the river bank and estimated that the angle between her line of sight to the pine tree and the river bank was 25°. Find the approximate width of the river.

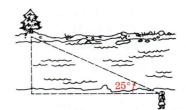

8. The angle of depression of a buoy from the top of a lighthouse is 5°. If the lighthouse stands at the edge of the ocean and is 20 m tall, find how far out in the ocean the buoy is located.

9. At night, the height of the cloud cover at an airport is found by shining a searchlight vertically upward. From a point on the ground 500 m from the searchlight, the angle of elevation of the illuminated clouds is found to be 65°. How high is the cloud cover? (*Note:* This height is often called the "ceiling.")

B 10. The latitude of a point P on the Earth equals the degree measure of $\angle POE$ where O is the center of the Earth and E is the point on the equator due south (or north) of P. If the radius of the Earth is 6400 km, find the radius of the Arctic Circle (latitude 62.5° N) to the nearest hundred kilometers.

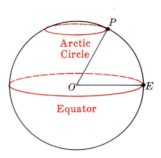

11. The latitude of Rangoon is 17° N. Find the radius of the circle of latitude through Rangoon. (See Exercise 10.)

12. When viewed from Earth, the angular separation of the sun and the planet Mercury varies between 0° and 23°. Assume that the orbits of Mercury and Earth are concentric circles, and that the greatest angular separation occurs when β is a right angle. If the distance from Earth to the sun is approximately 1.5×10^8 km, what is the radius of Mercury's orbit? Express the radius with two significant digits.

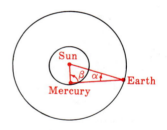

In Exercises 13–15 consider a ventilation tower that sits on top of a tall building.

13. If $CD = 100$ m and the angles of elevation of points B and A are 62° and 68°, find the height of the tower.

14. Assume that $CD = 60$ m, the building is 180 m tall, and the tower is 42 m high. Find $\angle ACB$.

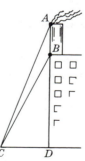

C 15. Assume the tower is 30 m high and that from point C the angles of elevation of the bottom and the top of the tower are 52° and 60°. Find CD and the height of the building.

16. Find the angle between a diagonal of a cube and a diagonal of a face of the cube that start from a common vertex.

13-2 *Areas of Triangles*

OBJECTIVE   **To find the area of a triangle, given two sides and the included angle.**

A basic formula for the area of a triangle is Area $= \frac{1}{2} \times$ base $\times$ height.

It is not always convenient, however, to find the height. It would be useful to have a formula expressed in terms of the sides and angles of the triangle.

For the triangle shown, suppose that you are given sides a and b and the included angle C. A formula for the area K of the triangle can be derived in terms of a, b, and angle C.

1. $K = \frac{1}{2}bh$

2. $\sin C = \frac{h}{a}$

   $\therefore h = a \sin C$

3. $K = \frac{1}{2}b(a \sin C)$ by substitution

   $K = \frac{1}{2}ab \sin C$

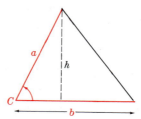

By letting another side be the base of the triangle and drawing the altitude to that base, two more formulas can be derived:

$$K = \frac{1}{2}bc \sin A \quad \text{and} \quad K = \frac{1}{2}ac \sin B$$

> **THEOREM**   The area of a triangle equals one-half the product of the lengths of two sides and the sine of their included angle.

EXAMPLE 1   Find the area of $\triangle PQR$ to three significant digits.

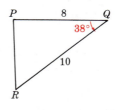

SOLUTION $K = \frac{1}{2}pr \sin Q$

$\qquad\qquad = \frac{1}{2} \cdot 10 \cdot 8 \cdot \sin 38°$

$\therefore K = 24.6.$ ***Answer***

EXAMPLE 2   Find the area, to three significant digits, of a regular pentagon inscribed in a circle of radius 10.

(*Solution is on page 494.*)

SOLUTION   Find the area of $\triangle OAB$ and multiply it by 5. Recall from geometry that $\angle AOB = 360° \div 5 = 72°$.

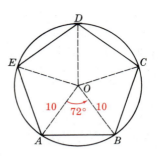

Area of $\triangle OAB = \frac{1}{2} \cdot 10 \cdot 10 \sin 72°$

$$= 50 \sin 72°$$

Area of $ABCDE = 5(50 \sin 72°)$
$$= 250 \sin 72°$$

$\therefore$ the area of $ABCDE$ is 238.   **Answer**

Oral Exercises

In Example 1, the area of $\triangle PQR$ was found to be $\frac{1}{2} \cdot 10 \cdot 8 \cdot \sin 38°$. In the same way, give an expression for the area of each triangle below.

1.

2.

3.

4.

5.

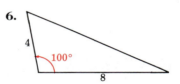

6.

7. Compare the areas of the triangles in Exercises 5 and 6. Which is greater? Explain.

Written Exercises

Three parts of triangle ABC are given. Find the area of the triangle. Express all answers to three significant digits.

A   **1.** $a = 2, b = 3, \angle C = 30°$

2. $a = 5, b = 4, \angle C = 40°$

3. $b = 7, c = 6, \angle A = 52°$

4. $a = 9, c = 20, \angle B = 110°$

5. a. $a = 4, b = 5, \angle C = 60°$
   b. $a = 4, b = 5, \angle C = 120°$

6. a. $b = 2, c = 9, \angle A = 32°$
   b. $b = 2, c = 9, \angle A = 148°$

Express all answers to three significant digits.

7. Find the area of an isosceles triangle with legs of length 12 and vertex angle 35°.

8. Find the area of an equilateral triangle with sides of length 8.

9. The area of $\triangle ABC$ is 50. If $\angle B = 30°$ and $c = 10$, find a.

10. The area of $\triangle XYZ$ is 18. If $\angle Z = 150°$ and $x = 8$, find y.

B 11. The area of $\triangle PQR$ is 15. If $p = 6$, and $q = 10$, find the two possible measures of $\angle R$.

12. The area of $\triangle XYZ$ is 24. If $y = 12$ and $z = 5$, find the two possible measures of $\angle X$.

13. Find the area of a parallelogram with sides of length 16 and 20 and one angle 120°.

14. Find the area of a rhombus with perimeter 24 and one angle 70°.

15. Find the area of a regular octagon inscribed in a circle of radius 20.

16. Find the area of a regular decagon (10 sides) inscribed in a circle of radius 10.

17. In $\triangle ABC$, $a = b = 5$ and $c = 6$. Find $\angle A$ and then find the area of $\triangle ABC$.

18. Find the area of a regular pentagon whose sides are 20 cm long.

C 19. A regular polygon with n sides is inscribed in a circle with radius r. If $\overline{AB}$ is a side of the polygon and O is the center of the circle, then $\angle AOB = \left(\frac{360}{n}\right)^\circ$. Find the area of the polygon in terms of n and r.

Self-Test 1

VOCABULARY
hypotenuse (p. 487)
opposite side (p. 487)
adjacent side (p. 487)
angle of elevation (p. 489)
angle of depression (p. 489)

1. Use the diagram at the right to evaluate each function.

   a. $\sin \phi$ b. $\tan \phi$
   c. $\cos \theta$ d. $\tan \theta$
   e. $\sec \theta$ f. $\cot \phi$

Obj. 13-1, p. 487

2. In $\triangle ABC$, $a = 3$, $b = 7$, and $\angle C = 90°$. Find $\angle B$ to the nearest tenth of a degree.

3. A ramp from the ground to the back of a truck is 3 m long. If the angle the ramp makes with the ground is 26°, how high off the ground is the floor of the truck? Give your answer to three significant digits.

4. Find the area of $\triangle ABC$ if $a = 5$, $b = 7$, and $\angle C = 62°$. Give your answer to three significant digits.

Obj. 13-2, p. 493

Check your answers with those at the back of the book.

GENERAL TRIANGLES

13-3 *The Law of Sines*

OBJECTIVE   **To use the law of sines to find sides or angles of triangles.**

In this section and the following sections, triangles are labeled so that lower-case letters represent the sides opposite angles denoted by the corresponding capital letters. For example, a, b, and c are the sides opposite angles A, B, and C, respectively.

The area of $\triangle ABC$ is given by the three equivalent expressions

$$\frac{1}{2}bc \sin A = \frac{1}{2}ac \sin B = \frac{1}{2}ab \sin C,$$

which were developed in Section 13-2. If each of these expressions is divided by $\frac{1}{2}abc$, the following result, known as the **law of sines,** is obtained.

LAW OF SINES

$$\frac{\sin A}{a} = \frac{\sin B}{b} = \frac{\sin C}{c}$$

According to the law of sines, in any triangle the sines of the angles are proportional to the lengths of the sides opposite the respective angles.

EXAMPLE 1   In $\triangle ABC$, $\angle A = 40°$, $a = 3$, and $b = 2$. Find $\angle B$ to the nearest degree.

SOLUTION

$$\frac{\sin A}{a} = \frac{\sin B}{b}$$

$$\frac{\sin 40°}{3} = \frac{\sin B}{2}$$

$$2 \sin 40° = 3 \sin B$$

$$\sin B = \frac{2 \sin 40°}{3}$$

$$= \frac{2(0.6428)}{3}$$

$$\sin B \approx 0.4285$$

$$\angle B = 25° \text{ or } \angle B = 155°$$

Note that $\angle B = 155°$ is not a solution because the sum of the angles of a triangle must be $180°$.

$\therefore$ $\angle B = 25°$.   *Answer*

EXAMPLE 2 The captain of a ship sighted a reef located so that the angle between the line of sight to the reef and the ship's course was 20°. After sailing 8 km, this angle was observed to be 70°. At that point, how far was the ship from the reef, to the nearest tenth of a kilometer?

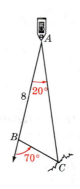

SOLUTION $\angle ABC = 110°$ and $\angle ACB = 50°$.

$$\frac{\sin A}{a} = \frac{\sin C}{c}$$

$$\frac{\sin 20°}{a} = \frac{\sin 50°}{8}$$

$$a = \frac{8 \sin 20°}{\sin 50°}$$

$$a = \frac{8(0.3420)}{0.7660}$$

$$a = 3.6$$

∴ the ship was about 3.6 km from the reef. *Answer*

Oral Exercises

Use the law of sines to state an expression equivalent to the given ratio.

1. $\dfrac{\sin A}{\sin C}$ **2.** $\dfrac{\sin B}{\sin C}$ **3.** $\dfrac{b}{a}$

4. $\dfrac{b}{\sin B}$ **5.** $\dfrac{\sin A}{\cos A}$, if $\angle C = 90°$ **6.** $\dfrac{a \sin B}{b \sin A}$

Written Exercises

Find the indicated part of $\triangle ABC$. Give all answers to three significant digits.

A   **1.** $a = 5$, $b = 3$, $\angle A = 35°$, $\angle B = ?$ **2.** $b = 4$, $c = 2$, $\angle B = 48°$, $\angle C = ?$

     3. $a = 15$, $c = 10$, $\angle A = 150°$, $\angle C = ?$ **4.** $b = 10$, $c = 8$, $\angle B = 122°$, $\angle C = ?$

     5. $b = 12$, $a = 6$, $\angle A = 30°$, $\angle B = ?$ **6.** $b = 10$, $c = 4$, $\angle B = 98.6°$, $\angle C = ?$

     7. $a = 10$, $\angle A = 45°$, $\angle B = 60°$, $b = ?$ **8.** $a = 3$, $\angle A = 120°$, $\angle B = 20°$, $b = ?$

     9. $b = 20$, $\angle A = 32°$, $\angle C = 103°$, $a = ?$ **10.** $c = 10$, $\angle A = 42°$, $\angle B = 27°$, $b = ?$

B   **11.** In $\triangle PQR$, $\angle P = 58°$, $\angle R = 74°$, and $q = 5$. Find p and the area of $\triangle PQR$ to three significant digits.

     12. In $\triangle ABC$, $\tan A = \dfrac{3}{4}$ and $\tan B = \dfrac{12}{5}$. Find the value of $\dfrac{a}{b}$.

13. In $\triangle PQR$, $\sin P = \frac{1}{3}$, $\cos Q = \frac{12}{13}$, and $p = 26$. Find the exact length of q without using tables or a calculator.

14. In $\triangle RST$, $\angle S = 30°$, $s = 3\sqrt{2}$, and $t = 6$. Find the exact measure of $\angle T$ without using tables or a calculator.

15. In $\triangle ABC$, $\angle A = 120°$, $\angle B = 45°$, $b = \sqrt{6}$. Find the exact length of a without using tables or a calculator.

C 16. Prove that the area K of $\triangle ABC$ is given by the formula

$$K = \frac{a^2}{2} \cdot \frac{\sin B \sin C}{\sin A}.$$

Problems

Give all answers to three significant digits.

A 1. Two points, X and Y, are separated by a swamp. To find the distance between them, Kelly walked 150 m from X to another point Z. Then she estimated $\angle ZXY = 35°$ and $\angle XZY = 60°$. Find the approximate distance from X to Y.

2. Two angles of a triangle are 20° and 65° and the longest side is 34 m. Find the length of the shortest side.

3. How long is the base of an isosceles triangle, if each leg is 35 cm long and each base angle measures 24°?

4. A balloon is released at a point on a straight runway. Lena, standing at one end of the runway, sights the balloon when it is 1.6 km away from her at an angle of elevation of 22°. Toru, standing at the other end of the runway, determines that at the same time the balloon is 3 km away from him. What is the angle of elevation of the balloon from Toru?

B 5. ABC is an equilateral triangle whose sides are 18 cm long. Lines AD and AE are drawn trisecting angle A and intersecting side $\overline{BC}$ in points D and E. Find the lengths of segments $\overline{BD}$, $\overline{DE}$, and $\overline{EC}$.

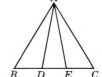

6. While on opposite ends of a beach 7.4 km long, two people noticed a ship on fire. If lines of sight from the ship to the people made a greater angle with each other than either of the angles of 59° and 40° which they made with the beach, how far was the ship from the nearer person?

7. Prove that in triangle ABC, $\dfrac{a - b}{b} = \dfrac{\sin A - \sin B}{\sin B}$.

C 8. In $\triangle ABC$, $\angle A = 50°$, $a = 12$, $b = 10$. The bisector of $\angle C$ meets $\overline{AB}$ at D. Find the length of $\overline{CD}$.

13-4 *The Law of Cosines*

Any triangle ABC can be placed in a coordinate system with $\angle C$ in standard position, as in Figure 13-4. Recall from Section 12-10 that the coordinates (r, s) of A are given by

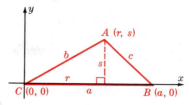

$$r = b \cos C \quad \text{and} \quad s = b \sin C.$$

Recall, also, that by the Pythagorean theorem

$$r^2 + s^2 = b^2.$$

Figure 13-4

According to the distance formula,

$$
\begin{aligned}
c^2 &= (r - a)^2 + (s - 0)^2 \\
&= r^2 - 2ar + a^2 + s^2 \\
&= a^2 + (r^2 + s^2) - 2ar \\
&= a^2 + b^2 - 2ar \\
&= a^2 + b^2 - 2ab \cos C \\
\therefore c^2 &= a^2 + b^2 - 2ab \cos C.
\end{aligned}
$$

If this process were to be repeated with $\angle A$ and $\angle B$ in turn put into standard position, similar results would be obtained. These equations are known as the **law of cosines.**

LAW OF COSINES

$$a^2 = b^2 + c^2 - 2bc \cos A$$

$$b^2 = a^2 + c^2 - 2ac \cos B$$

$$c^2 = a^2 + b^2 - 2ab \cos C$$

If $\angle C = 90°$, then $\cos C = 0$, and you have $c^2 = a^2 + b^2$. Thus, the Pythagorean theorem may be considered a special case of the law of cosines. If $\angle C$ is acute, then $\cos C > 0$ and $c^2 < a^2 + b^2$; if $\angle C$ is obtuse, then $\cos C < 0$ and $c^2 > a^2 + b^2$.

EXAMPLE 1   In $\triangle ABC, a = 20, b = 30,$ and $\angle C = 63°$. Find c to three significant digits.

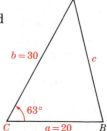

SOLUTION

$$
\begin{aligned}
c^2 &= a^2 + b^2 - 2ab \cos C \\
c^2 &= (20)^2 + (30)^2 - 2(20)(30) \cos 63° \\
&= 400 + 900 - 1200(0.4540) \\
&= 1300 - 544.8 = 755.2 \\
\therefore c &= \sqrt{755.2} = 27.5 \quad \textbf{\textit{Answer}}
\end{aligned}
$$

In Example 1 the law of cosines was used to find the length of a side of a triangle. The next example shows how the law of cosines can be used to find an angle.

EXAMPLE 2 Two planes, one flying at 600 km/h and the other at 900 km/h, left Capital Airport at the same time. Two hours later they were 2500 km apart. To the nearest degree, what was the measure of the angle between their flight paths?

SOLUTION Since the speeds of the airplanes were 600 km/h and 900 km/h respectively, in two hours one had flown 1200 km and the other 1800 km.

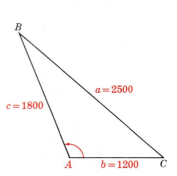

$$a^2 = b^2 + c^2 - 2bc \cos A$$

$$\cos A = \frac{b^2 + c^2 - a^2}{2bc}$$

$$= \frac{(1200)^2 + (1800)^2 - (2500)^2}{2 \cdot 1200 \cdot 1800}$$

$$= \frac{(144 \cdot 100^2) + (324 \cdot 100^2) - (625 \cdot 100^2)}{432 \cdot 100^2}$$

$$= \frac{144 + 324 - 625}{432}$$

$$= -\frac{157}{432} = -0.3634$$

$$\therefore \angle A = 111°. \quad \textbf{\textit{Answer}}$$

Oral Exercises

Use the law of cosines to state an equation involving the side or angle labeled x.

1.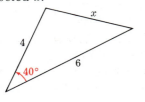

2.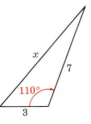

3.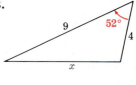

4.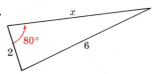

5.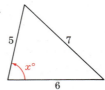

6.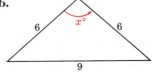

Written Exercises

In each exercise find the part indicated. Give answers to three significant digits.

A 1. $a = 6$, $b = 10$, $\angle C = 60°$, $c = ?$
    3. $b = 4$, $c = 6$, $\angle A = 55°$, $a = ?$
    5. $x = 7$, $y = 4$, $\angle Z = 120°$, $z = ?$
    7. $e = 2$, $f = 4$, $\angle D = 90°$, $d = ?$
    9. $r = 5$, $s = 6$, $t = 7$, $\angle T = ?$
    11. $y = 5$, $x = 12$, $z = 10$, $\angle X = ?$

2. $a = 3$, $b = 5$, $\angle C = 120°$, $c = ?$
4. $c = 2$, $a = 1$, $\angle B = 42°$, $b = ?$
6. $p = 10$, $r = 8$, $\angle Q = 100°$, $q = ?$
8. $y = 8$, $z = 5$, $\angle X = 60°$, $x = ?$
10. $c = 6$, $b = 10$, $a = 14$, $\angle A = ?$
12. $p = 5$, $q = 7$, $r = 8$, $\angle Q = ?$

Find all answers to three significant digits.

13. A triangle has sides $a = 9$, $b = 40$, and $c = 41$.
    a. Use the law of cosines to find $\angle C$.
    b. Use the converse of the Pythagorean theorem to verify your answer to part (a).

14. Find the smallest angle of a triangle with sides 2, 3, and 4.

B 15. In parallelogram $ABCD$, $AB = 6$, $AD = 3$, and $\angle A = 80°$. Find the length of each diagonal.

16. Find the length of each diagonal of a rhombus that has perimeter 40 and one angle 52°.

17. In $\triangle ABC$, $a = 10$, $b = 17$, and $c = 21$.
    a. Express $\cos C$ as a fraction in lowest terms.
    b. Find $\sin C$ without tables or a calculator.
    c. Find the area of $\triangle ABC$.

18. Repeat Exercise 17 if $a = 10$, $b = 11$, and $c = 3\sqrt{5}$.

19. The area of $\triangle ABC$ is 12; $a = 5$ and $b = 6$.
    a. Find $\sin C$.
    b. Find two possible values for $\cos C$.
    c. Find the value of c corresponding to each of the values of $\cos C$ found in part (b).

C 20. In $\triangle ABC$, $a = 2$, $b = 4$, and $c = 3$. Find the length of the median from A to $\overline{BC}$. (A median of a triangle is a segment from a vertex to the midpoint of the opposite side.)

Problems

Give all answers to three significant digits.

A 1. A plane flew 1500 km north. It then changed course by turning clockwise through an angle of 14° and flew 1000 km farther. How far was it then from its starting point?

2. Balston is 8 km east of Candia and Deerfield is 10 km northwest of Candia. How far is Balston from Deerfield?

3. A surveyor at point X sights points Y and Z on opposite sides of a pond. If $XY = 600$ m, $XZ = 400$ m, and $\angle YXZ = 108°$, find the distance across the pond from Y to Z.

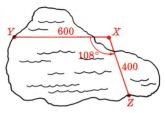

4. Kathy runs at 5 m/s and Lucy at 3 m/s. They start from the same point at the same time and run along paths that diverge at an angle of 120°. How far apart are they after 1 minute?

B 5. Two ships, one sailing at 30 km/h and the other at 45 km/h, left port at the same time. Three hours later they were 120 km apart. Find the angle between their courses.

6. The diagonals of a parallelogram are 12 cm and 20 cm long and they meet at a 60° angle. Find the perimeter and the area of the parallelogram.

C 7. The sides of a parallelogram have lengths a and b and the diagonals have lengths x and y. Prove that
$$x^2 + y^2 = 2a^2 + 2b^2.$$

8. Show that the law of cosines implies that $c = a + b$ if $\angle C = 180°$.

ʰistorical note Trigonometry

Among the first historical appearances of trigonometry is a "table of chords," recognizable as a sine table. It was composed by Hipparchus, a Greek astronomer who lived around 140 B.C.

The first diagram shows that the sine of an angle α is one half the length of the chord determined by the central angle 2α. (The use of the word "sine" resulted from a mistranslation of the Arabic word for "chord.")

Similar geometric ways of finding values of other trigonometric functions are shown here. Considering the definitions of the tangent and secant that you learned when you studied geometry, why are these functions named as they are? The use of cosine, cotangent, and cosecant follows from the fact that they represent the values of the sine, tangent, and secant of the complementary angle.

13-5 *Solving Triangles*

OBJECTIVE   **To solve any given triangle.**

In Section 13-1 you studied methods for solving *right* triangles. Now, with the law of sines and the law of cosines, you have the tools needed to be able to solve *any* triangle, given an appropriate combination of three of its sides and angles.

EXAMPLE 1   Solve $\triangle ABC$ if $\angle A = 20°$, $\angle B = 60°$, and $c = 10$. Give answers to three significant digits.

SOLUTION

1. Sketch $\triangle ABC$ and label the given parts.

2. $\angle A + \angle B + \angle C = 180°$.

   $\therefore \angle C = 100°$

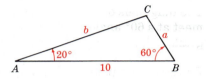

3. Use the law of sines to find a and b.

$$\frac{\sin C}{c} = \frac{\sin A}{a} \qquad\qquad \frac{\sin C}{c} = \frac{\sin B}{b}$$

$$\frac{\sin 100°}{10} = \frac{\sin 20°}{a} \qquad\qquad \frac{\sin 100°}{10} = \frac{\sin 60°}{b}$$

$$a \sin 100° = 10 \sin 20° \qquad\qquad b \sin 100° = 10 \sin 60°$$

$$a = \frac{10 \sin 20°}{\sin 100°} \qquad\qquad b = \frac{10 \sin 60°}{\sin 100°}$$

$$a = \frac{10(0.3420)}{0.9848} \qquad\qquad b = \frac{10(0.8660)}{0.9848}$$

$$a = 3.47 \qquad\qquad\qquad b = 8.79$$

$\therefore \angle C = 100°$, $a = 3.47$, and $b = 8.79$.   ***Answer***

EXAMPLE 2   Solve $\triangle ABC$ if $a = 17$, $c = 8$, and $\angle B = 52°$. Give answers to three significant digits.

SOLUTION

1. Sketch the triangle and label the given parts.

2. Use the law of cosines to find b.

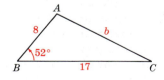

$$b^2 = a^2 + c^2 - 2ac \cos B$$
$$= (17)^2 + (8)^2 - 2(17)(8) \cos 52°$$
$$= 289 + 64 - 167.5$$
$$= 185.5$$
$$\therefore b = 13.6$$

(*Solution continued on page 504.*)

3. Use the law of sines to find $\angle C$, which must be acute since it is the smallest angle.

$$\frac{\sin C}{c} = \frac{\sin B}{b}$$

$$\frac{\sin C}{8} = \frac{\sin 52°}{13.6}$$

$$\sin C = \frac{8 \sin 52°}{13.6}$$

$$\sin C = 0.4635$$

$$\therefore \angle C = 27.6°$$

4. $\angle A = 180° - \angle B - \angle C$
   $= 180° - 52° - 27.6°$
   $= 100.4°$

$\therefore b = 13.6$, $\angle C = 27.6°$, and $\angle A = 100.4°$.   ***Answer***

The law of sines is used in solving a triangle when the lengths of two of its sides and the measure of an angle opposite one of them are known. In this case there may be no, one, or two solutions. Suppose, for example, that $\angle A$, a, and b are known. By sketching $\angle A$ and measuring the distance b on one of its sides, you have the possibilities suggested in Figures 13-5 and 13-6 ($\angle A < 90°$) and Figure 13-7 ($\angle A \geq 90°$).

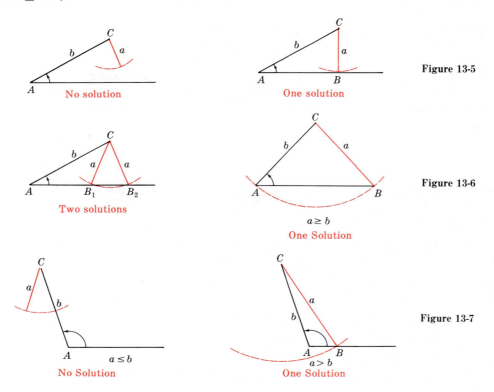

Figure 13-5

Figure 13-6

Figure 13-7

EXAMPLE 3   Solve $\triangle ABC$, if $a = 36$, $b = 24$, and $\angle B = 25°$. Give answers to three significant digits.

SOLUTION

1. Sketching the triangle suggests that there are two solutions.

2. Use the law of sines to find $\angle A$.

$$\frac{\sin A}{a} = \frac{\sin B}{b}$$

$$\sin A = \frac{a \sin B}{b} = \frac{36 \sin 25°}{24} = \frac{36(0.4226)}{24} = 0.6339$$

$\therefore$ $\angle A = 39.3°$ or $\angle A = 140.7°$

3. $\angle C = 180° - \angle A - \angle B$
   $\angle C = 180° - 39.3° - 25°$ or $\angle C = 180° - 140.7° - 25°$
$\therefore$ $\angle C = 115.7°$ or $\angle C = 14.3°$

4. Use the law of sines to find c.

$$\frac{\sin C}{c} = \frac{\sin A}{a}$$

$$c = \frac{a \sin C}{\sin A}$$

$$c = \frac{36 \sin 115.7°}{\sin 39.3°} = 51.2 \quad \text{or} \quad c = \frac{36 \sin 14.3°}{\sin 140.7°} = 14.0$$

$\therefore$ $\angle A = 39.3°$, $\angle C = 115.7°$, and $c = 51.2$;
or $\angle A = 140.7°$, $\angle C = 14.3°$, and $c = 14.0$.   ***Answer***

   In Example 3 there were two solutions. When an angle is found using the law of cosines there are never two solutions, because for a given cosine value, there is only one angle between 0° and 180° having that cosine.

Oral Exercises

Determine whether you would first use the law of sines, the law of cosines, or neither in solving the given triangle. Be alert for right or isosceles triangles.

1. $\triangle ABC$ with $a = 5$, $b = 6$, and $\angle C = 80°$

2. $\triangle RST$ with $r = 2$, $\angle S = 40°$, and $\angle T = 100°$

3. $\triangle XYZ$ with $\angle X = 24°$, $\angle Y = 62°$, and $x = 10$

4. $\triangle DEF$ with $d = 5$, $e = 6$, $f = 7$

5. $\triangle JKL$ with $\angle J = 40°$, $\angle K = 50°$, and $l = 4$

6. $\triangle NUT$ with $n = 6$, $u = 10$, and $\angle N = 30°$

7. $\triangle SIK$ with $\angle I = 100°$, $s = 5$, $k = 6$

8. $\triangle TAN$ with $\angle T = 40°$, $\angle A = 60°$, and $\angle N = 80°$

Written Exercises

Express all results to three significant digits.

A **1–8.** Solve the triangles given in Oral Exercises 1–8 on page 505.

B **9.** In $\triangle ABC$, $a = 6$, $b = 10$, and $\angle C = 120°$. Find the length of the median to the longest side. (A median is the segment from a vertex to the midpoint of the opposite side.)

10. Find the area of $\triangle RST$ if $r = 10$, $s = 14$, and $t = 16$.

11. In $\triangle XYZ$, $\angle X = \angle Y = 42°$ and $z = 20$. Find the length of the median to $\overline{ZY}$.

12. Find the area of $\triangle PQR$ if $\angle P = 20°$, $\angle Q = 100°$, and $p = 4$.

13. In rhombus $PQRS$, $PQ = 10$ and $\angle R = 140°$. Find the length of each diagonal.

14. In trapezoid $WXYZ$, $XY = YZ = ZW = 8$ and $\angle W = 50°$. Find the length of each diagonal.

C **15.** In quadrilateral $EFGH$, $\angle E = \angle G = 90°$, $HE = 6$, $EF = 8$, and $FG = 4$. Find the length of each diagonal.

16. Prove: In $\triangle ABC$, $\dfrac{\sin(A + C)}{\sin(B + C)} = \dfrac{b}{a}$.

17. Show that one angle of a triangle with sides of lengths 5, 7, and 8 is equal to one angle of a triangle whose sides have lengths 3, 5, and 7.

18. $WXYZ$ is a quadrilateral with $WX = 10$, $XY = 8$, $YZ = 6$, and $ZW = 7$. If diagonal $\overline{WY}$ is 9 units long, how long is diagonal $\overline{XZ}$?

Problems

Express all answers to three significant digits.

A **1.** Lee hears the 4:00 P.M. whistle of Archer Industries at 4:00:20 P.M.; he hears the 4:00 P.M. whistle of Gomez Manufacturing at 4:00:40 P.M. If the angle between Lee's lines of sight to the plants is 52°, and if sound travels at about 0.340 km/s, how far apart are the plants?

2. A baseball diamond is a square 90 feet on a side, and the pitcher's mound is 60 feet 6 inches from home plate on the diagonal from home to second base. How far is the pitcher's mound from third base?

3. Aurora is 150 km from Bruceton, Bruceton is 80 km from Cranesville, and Cranesville is 100 km from Aurora. A new road will join Cranesville to the Aurora-Bruceton Turnpike, which runs roughly in a straight line. What is the shortest possible length for the new road?

4. A water molecule consists of two hydrogen atoms and one oxygen atom joined as in the diagram. The distance from the nucleus of each hydrogen atom to the nucleus of the oxygen atom is 9.58×10^{-9} cm, and the bond angle θ is $104.8°$. How far are the nuclei of the hydrogen atoms from each other?

5. From the top of a house 10 m high, the angle of elevation of the top of a pole is $11°$. At the base of the house, the angle of elevation is $39°$. Find the height of the pole.

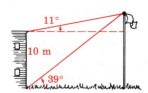

B 6. From the top of a mountain, a skier can see two base lodges on opposite sides of the mountain $180°$ apart. During separate runs down the mountain, the skier determines that the straight-line distances from the lodges to the summit are 8 km and 5.6 km respectively. If the lodges are at the same elevation and the angle of elevation of the summit along the 8 km trail is $9°$, what is the straight-line distance between the lodges?

7. A farmer sketched the diagram of an alfalfa field shown. How much fencing is required to enclose the field?

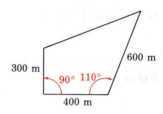

8. Sue Philips wants to know the distance between two points A and B on the opposite side of a river from her position. She finds that $CD = 91$ m, $\angle ADC = 60°$, $\angle ACD = 54°$, and $\angle ACB = 68°$. What is the distance from A to B if $A, B, C,$ and D are the vertices of a trapezoid?

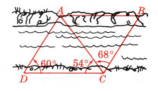

C 9. From the top of a lighthouse 45 m above the sea, the angle of depression of one buoy is $34°$ and the angle of depression of another buoy is $22°$. From the base of the lighthouse, which is at sea level, the angle between lines of sight to the buoys is $52°$. How far apart are the buoys?

Self-Test 2

VOCABULARY   law of sines (p. 496)   law of cosines (p. 499)

Give all answers to three significant digits.

1. In $\triangle ABC$, $\angle A = 52°$, $\angle B = 21°$, and $c = 8.6$. Find a.   Obj. 13-3, p. 496

2. In $\triangle DEF$, $d = 9$, $e = 5$, and $f = 8$. Find $\angle E$.   Obj. 13-4, p. 499

3. Solve $\triangle RST$ if $r = 12$, $s = 15$, and $\angle T = 78°$.   Obj. 13-5, p. 503

Check your answers with those at the back of the book.

13-6 *Resultants of Vectors*

OBJECTIVE   **To find the resultant of two vectors.**

The velocity of an airplane is given by telling *both* its speed *and* its direction. For example, you might say its velocity is 800 km/h due east. Any quantity, such as a velocity or a force, that is specified by giving both its magnitude and direction is called a vector quantity and is represented by a *vector*. **Vectors** are directed line segments, or arrows. The length of the arrow indicates the magnitude of the vector quantity, and the direction of the arrow indicates the direction of the vector quantity.

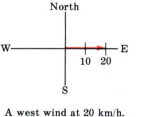

A west wind at 20 km/h.
(A west wind blows *from* the west to the east.)

A force of 5 N acting at a 30° angle with the ground.

Figure 13-8

The symbol $\overrightarrow{AB}$ (read "vector AB") refers to the vector *from A to B*. Point A is called the **initial point,** and B is called the **terminal point.** Vectors are sometimes also designated by lower-case letters in boldface type, such as **u** and **v**. Two vectors that have the same magnitude and direction, such as $\overrightarrow{AB}$ and $\overrightarrow{CD}$ in Figure 13-9, are called **equivalent vectors,** and you write $\overrightarrow{AB} = \overrightarrow{CD}$.

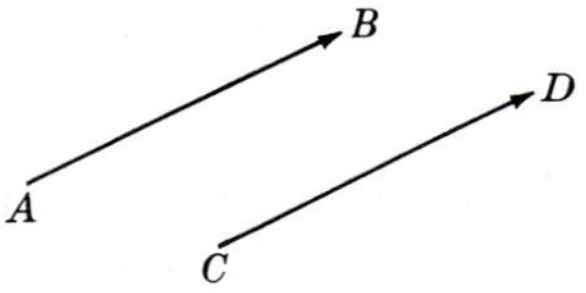

Figure 13-9

The vector diagram in Figure 13-10 illustrates a boat that sailed 8 km east from A to B and then 5 km northeast from B to C. Since the boat could get to the same final position by going directly from A to C, $\overrightarrow{AC}$ is called the *sum,* or *resultant,* of $\overrightarrow{AB}$ and $\overrightarrow{BC}$:

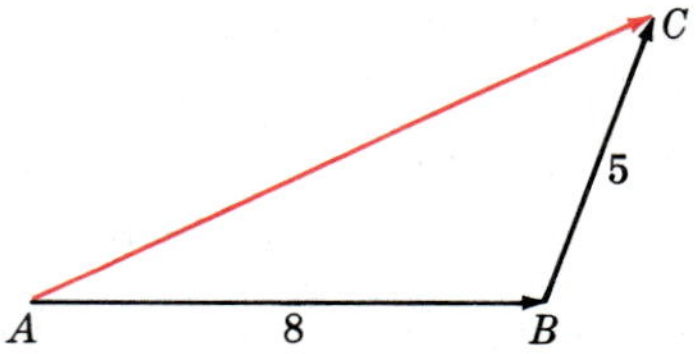

Figure 13-10

$$\overrightarrow{AB} + \overrightarrow{BC} = \overrightarrow{AC}$$

To define the resultant of any two vectors, you use the fact that given a vector $\overrightarrow{CD}$ and a point B, then there is a unique vector $\overrightarrow{BR}$ at B equivalent to $\overrightarrow{CD}$ (Figure 13-11 on page 509). If $\overrightarrow{AB}$ and $\overrightarrow{CD}$ are any two vectors and if $\overrightarrow{BR}$ is the vector at B equivalent to $\overrightarrow{CD}$, then the **sum,** or **resultant,** of $\overrightarrow{AB}$ and $\overrightarrow{CD}$ is $\overrightarrow{AR}$; that is, $\overrightarrow{AB} + \overrightarrow{CD} = \overrightarrow{AR}$ (Figure 13-12 on page 509).

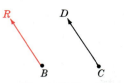

Figure 13-11

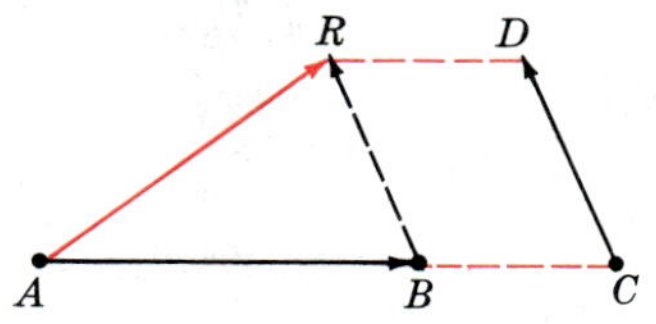

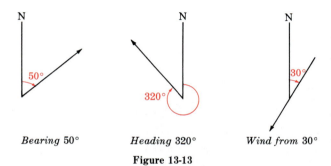

Figure 13-12

In working with vectors, it is convenient to have a standard method for expressing directions. The illustrations in Figure 13-13 show the use of the north-south line as reference in specifying direction angles in navigation and surveying. Each direction is given as an angle measured clockwise from due north.

Bearing 50°   *Heading* 320°   *Wind from* 30°

Figure 13-13

EXAMPLE   An object is pulled by a force of 10 N to the east and a force of 5 N to the northwest. Find the resultant of these forces, giving the magnitude and direction to three significant digits.

SOLUTION

1. Draw a diagram of the force vectors. Construct $\overrightarrow{AC}$ equivalent to $\overrightarrow{OB}$. $\overrightarrow{OC}$ is the resultant of $\overrightarrow{OB}$ and $\overrightarrow{OA}$.

2. Use the law of cosines to find x, the length of $\overrightarrow{OC}$.

$$x^2 = 5^2 + 10^2 - 2 \cdot 5 \cdot 10 \cos 45°$$
$$= 125 - 100(0.7071) = 54.29$$
$$x = \sqrt{54.29} = 7.37$$

3. Use the law of sines to find θ.

$$\frac{\sin \theta}{5} = \frac{\sin 45°}{7.37}$$

$$\sin \theta = \frac{5 \sin 45°}{7.37} = \frac{5(0.7071)}{7.37} = 0.4797$$

$$\therefore \theta = 28.7°$$

4. The direction of $\overrightarrow{OC}$ is $90° - 28.7° = 61.3°$.

$\therefore$ the resultant is a force of 7.37 N with a direction angle of 61.3°.   *Answer*

A point can be thought of as a vector of length 0, called a *zero vector*, and denoted **0.** The **opposite** of a vector $\overrightarrow{OA}$ is a vector $\overrightarrow{OB}$ with the same magnitude as $\overrightarrow{OA}$ but the opposite direction. Since $\overrightarrow{OA}$ and $\overrightarrow{OB}$ are opposites, you can write

$$\overrightarrow{OB} = -\overrightarrow{OA} \quad \text{and} \quad \overrightarrow{OA} = -\overrightarrow{OB}.$$

You can see that the sum of a pair of opposite vectors is the zero vector.

Oral Exercises

In Exercises 1-6, *PQRS* is a parallelogram. Determine whether each statement is true or false.

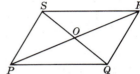

1. $\overrightarrow{PS} + \overrightarrow{SR} = \overrightarrow{PR}$
2. $\overrightarrow{OP} + \overrightarrow{OR} = \mathbf{0}$
3. $\overrightarrow{PS} + \overrightarrow{SR} = \overrightarrow{PQ} + \overrightarrow{QR}$
4. $\overrightarrow{OP} + \overrightarrow{OS} = PS$
5. $(\overrightarrow{PS} + \overrightarrow{SR}) + \overrightarrow{RQ} = \overrightarrow{PQ}$
6. $\overrightarrow{PS} = \overrightarrow{RQ}$

Written Exercises

In each exercise, two vector quantities are given. Make a scale diagram showing the vectors and their sum.

A 1. A 5 km trip north followed by a 3 km trip southeast

2. A 7 km trip northwest followed by a 2 km trip northeast

3. A 12 km trip southwest followed by a 12 km trip northeast

4. An airplane velocity of 600 km/h south and a wind blowing at 50 km/h from west to east

5. The velocity of a swimmer is 6 km/h north and the velocity of a river current is 2 km/h west.

6. A force of 10 N up and a force of 15 N down

7. A force of 8 N up and a force of 6 N to the right

8. A force of 12 N at 60° and a force of 8 N at 140°

Use the vectors **u, v,** and **w** shown to sketch the vector given in each exercise.

9. **u + u**
10. **u + v**
11. **−v**
12. **w + (−v)**
13. **(u + v) + w**
14. **(−u) + (−v)**

For each pair of vector quantities, find the magnitude and direction of the resultant. Express answers to three significant digits.

B 15. Forces of 10 N south and 6 N at a heading of 60°

16. An airplane velocity of 500 km/h at 40° and a wind velocity of 50 km/h from the north

17. An airplane velocity of 640 km/h at 130° and a wind velocity of 80 km/h from the west

18. Two forces of 100 N each pulling on an object, with the force vectors making an angle of 150° with each other

Problems

Give answers to three significant digits.

A 1. Florence can swim at 4 km/h in still water. She sets out to swim across a river with a current of 1 km/h. What is her actual speed relative to the surface of the earth?

2. A ship heads south at 28 km/h when there is a current of 8 km/h from 325°. By how many degrees does the ship's actual course differ from its intended course to the south?

3. At what bearing and speed should a ship head if it is to travel due north at 15 km/h when there is a 5 km/h current from the west?

4. Bill wants to swim across a river 200 m wide that has a current of 2 km/h to the east. He knows he can swim at the rate of 5 km/h when there is no current. What should his course be if he wants to land directly across the river from where he is now?

B 5. A mirror is hung from the middle of a wire so that each half of the wire pulls with a force of 100 N. The two halves of the wire make an angle of 130° with each other. What is the weight of the mirror?

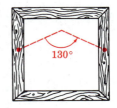

6. A plane was flying due west at 500 km/h toward Jamestown, which was 400 km away, when it encountered a wind of 70 km/h from the northeast. If the pilot had not corrected the course, the plane would have passed due south of Jamestown. At that time, how far would the plane have been from Jamestown?

C 7. Forces of 20 N, 10 N, and 25 N act on an object, making the angles shown with each other. In what direction will the object move?

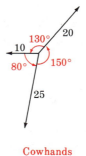

8. Two cowhands pull a wagon which resists with a force of 2000 N. If the ropes make the angles shown with the direction of the wagon's resistance, and the cowhands both pull with the same force, what is the maximum force that each can exert so that their combined efforts will still be unable to move the wagon?

13-7 *Components of Vectors*

OBJECTIVE **To find the horizontal and vertical components of a vector.**

If $\vec{AB} + \vec{BC} = \vec{AC}$, as in Figure 13-14, vectors $\vec{AB}$ and $\vec{BC}$ are called **components** of vector $\vec{AC}$. Of particular interest are components that are horizontal and vertical.

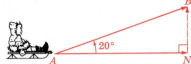

Figure 13-14

The vector $\vec{AB}$ shown in Figure 13-15 represents the force exerted by a person pulling on the rope of a sled. The vector $\vec{AN}$ is called the **horizontal component** of $\vec{AB}$. It represents the horizontal force that is pulling the sled along the ground. The **vertical component** of $\vec{AB}$ is $\vec{NB}$.

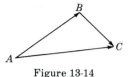

Figure 13-15

In a coordinate plane the horizontal and vertical components of a vector are called its *x*- and *y*-components. Often a vector is designated by giving its *x*- and *y*-components. In Figure 13-16, since $\vec{AB}$ has *x*- and *y*-components of 3 and -4 respectively, you can write $\vec{AB} = (3, -4)$. You can see, also, that $\vec{MN} = (3, -4)$, $\vec{PQ} = (5, 1)$, and $\vec{RS} = (-2, -3)$.

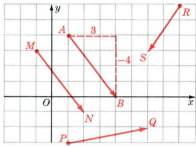

Figure 13-16

One advantage of expressing vectors in component form is that this simplifies addition of vectors. To add two vectors in component form, simply add the *x*-components, and then separately add the *y*-components. For example, if $\mathbf{u} = (5, 2)$ and $\mathbf{v} = (1, 3)$, as shown in Figure 13-17, then

$$\mathbf{u} + \mathbf{v} = (5, 2) + (1, 3)$$
$$= (5 + 1, 2 + 3)$$
$$= (6, 5).$$

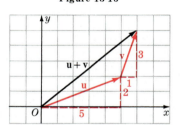

Figure 13-17

In a coordinate plane the direction of a vector is the angle θ that the vector makes with a ray directed parallel to, and in the direction of, the positive *x*-axis, where

$$0° \leq \theta < 360°$$

(see Figure 13-18). If the magnitude and direction of a vector are given, you can find its *x*- and *y*-components by using trigonometry.

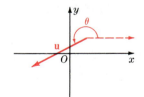

Figure 13-18

EXAMPLE 1 Find the *x*- and *y*-components, to three significant digits, of a vector 10 units long that has a direction angle of 140°.

SOLUTION Draw an equivalent vector with its initial point at the origin. Let x = the x-component, and y = the y-component.

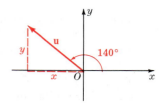

$$x = 10 \cos 140° \qquad\qquad y = 10 \sin 140°$$
$$= -7.66 \qquad\qquad\qquad = 6.43$$
$$\therefore x = -7.66 \text{ and } y = 6.43. \quad \textbf{\textit{Answer}}$$

EXAMPLE 2 A plane has an airspeed of 600 km/h on a heading of 40°, and a wind of 120 km/h is blowing from 150°. In one hour how far *north* will the plane fly, to three significant digits?

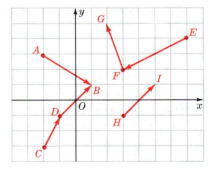

SOLUTION Let $\overrightarrow{DE}$ = the north component of wind velocity;

$\overrightarrow{CB}$ = the north component of airspeed;

$\overrightarrow{AN}$ = the component of the resultant velocity *due north*.

Then: $\overrightarrow{AN} = \overrightarrow{DE} + \overrightarrow{CB}$

In $\triangle ADE$: $\sin 60° = \dfrac{DE}{120}$ $\qquad$ In $\triangle ABC$: $\sin 50° = \dfrac{CB}{600}$

$$DE = 120 \sin 60° \qquad\qquad CB = 600 \sin 50°$$
$$= 103.9 \qquad\qquad\qquad\quad = 459.6$$

$$AN = 103.9 + 459.6 = 563.5$$

$\therefore$ the plane will fly about 564 km north. $\quad$ **\textit{Answer}**

Oral Exercises

Refer to the graph at the right, and give each vector in component form.

1. $\overrightarrow{CD}$
2. $\overrightarrow{EF}$
3. $\overrightarrow{FG}$
4. $\overrightarrow{HI}$
5. $\overrightarrow{DB}$
6. $\overrightarrow{AB}$

If $\mathbf{u} = (2, 1)$ and $\mathbf{v} = (3, 5)$, find the following.

7. $\mathbf{u} + (-\mathbf{v})$
8. $\mathbf{u} + \mathbf{u}$
9. $\mathbf{u} + \mathbf{v}$
10. $\mathbf{v} + (-\mathbf{u})$

Written Exercises

In each exercise, a vector has the given magnitude and direction. Find its x- and y-components. Give answers to three significant digits.

A 1. magnitude 10; $\theta = 52°$ $\quad$ 2. magnitude 7; $\theta = 270°$ $\quad$ 3. magnitude 5; $\theta = 150°$

 $\quad$ 1. magnitude 12; $\theta = 180°$ $\quad$ 5. magnitude 4; $\theta = 125°$ $\quad$ 6. magnitude 1; $\theta = 319°$

A vector is given in component form. Find its magnitude and direction. Give answers to three significant digits.

7. $(6, 8)$ **8.** $(3, -6)$ **9.** $(-2, 6)$

10. $(5, -12)$ **11.** $(-5, 5)$ **12.** $(-8, -20)$

If $\mathbf{u} = (3, 1)$ and $\mathbf{v} = (-4, 3)$, find a vector $\mathbf{w}$, in component form, that satisfies each equation.

13. $\mathbf{u} + \mathbf{w} = \mathbf{v}$ **14.** $\mathbf{w} + (-\mathbf{v}) = \mathbf{u}$ **15.** $\mathbf{v} + \mathbf{w} = \mathbf{u}$

16. $\mathbf{u} + \mathbf{v} + \mathbf{w} = 0$ **17.** $\mathbf{w} = (-\mathbf{u}) + (-\mathbf{v})$ **18.** $\mathbf{w} + (-\mathbf{u}) = -\mathbf{v}$

A pair of vectors is given in each exercise.
a. Find $\mathbf{u} + \mathbf{v}$ in component form.
b. Find the magnitude and direction of $\mathbf{u} + \mathbf{v}$, expressing them to three significant digits.

B   **19.** $\mathbf{u} = (2, 3), \mathbf{v} = (1, 1)$ **20.** $\mathbf{u} = (2, 0), \mathbf{v} = (0, 3)$

      21. $\mathbf{u} = (-2, 1), \mathbf{v} = (3, 3)$ **22.** $\mathbf{u} = (-2, -4), \mathbf{v} = (-2, 6)$

C   **23.** For two vectors $\mathbf{u}$ and $\mathbf{v}$, θ is the direction of $\mathbf{u} + \mathbf{v}$. If $\mathbf{u} = (x_1, y_1)$ and $\mathbf{v} = (x_2, y_2)$, show that

$$\tan \theta = \frac{y_1 + y_2}{x_1 + x_2}.$$

Problems

Give all answers to three significant digits.

A   **1.** Suppose Heather pulls with a force of 200 N on the rope of a sled. If the rope makes a 25° angle with the horizontal, what force is being exerted on the sled to pull it forward?

     2. The handle of a lawn mower makes an angle of 30° with the ground. If Bill pushes with a force of 100 N in the direction of the handle, how much force is acting to move the mower forward?

     3. Sally is opening a tall window by pulling down on the top with a window pole inclined at a 20° angle with the window. If she pulls with a force of 130 N, what is the force acting to lower the window?

     4. A kite string makes a 48° angle with the horizontal. If the string is going out at the rate of 2 m/s, how fast is the kite rising?

B   **5.** A wind is exerting a horizontal force of 30 N on a kite. Will the kite string break if it makes a 55° angle with the ground and if it can withstand a force of 50 N?

     6. A picture weighing 90 N is supported at the top corners by a taut wire which passes over a nail in the wall. If the corners and the nail form a 120° angle, what is the total pull on the wires?

7. Suppose the two signs shown each have the same length and weight and are each supported by cables of the same strength. Which sign is better supported? Explain.

8. A person pulls in the direction of a wagon's handle when the handle makes an angle of 40° with the horizontal. Express the force acting to move the wagon forward as a percent of the force of the pull.

C **9.** Gravity exerts a force of 18,000 N on a car parked on a hill that makes an angle of 10° with the horizontal. What is the minimum braking force that must be applied to keep the car from rolling down the hill?

Self-Test 3

VOCABULARY   vector (p. 508)
initial point (p. 508)
terminal point (p. 508)
equivalent vectors (p. 508)
sum (of vectors) (p. 508)
resultant (p. 508)
opposite (of a vector) (p. 510)
component (p. 512)
horizontal component (p. 512)
vertical component (p. 512)
x- and y-components (p. 512)

Give answers to three significant digits.

1. On a barge traveling north at 20 km/h a worker walks from the west side to the east side at 7 km/h. What are the worker's speed and direction of motion relative to the earth's surface?

Obj. 13-6, p. 508

2. Two forces of 50 N each, acting at an angle of 70° with each other, pull on an object. Find the magnitude of the resultant of the forces.

3. Find the x- and y-components of a vector with a magnitude of 10 and a direction of 160°.

Obj. 13-7, p. 512

4. A boat sails at 35 km/h on a heading of 155°. How far east of its starting place will the boat be in an hour?

Check your answers with those at the back of the book.

Chapter Summary

1. By using the definitions of the trigonometric functions for acute angles in a right triangle, the sides and angles of the right triangle can be determined. The basic definitions are

$$\sin \theta = \frac{\text{opposite side}}{\text{hypotenuse}} \qquad \cos \theta = \frac{\text{adjacent side}}{\text{hypotenuse}} \qquad \tan \theta = \frac{\text{opposite side}}{\text{adjacent side}}$$

2. The area of $\triangle ABC$ is given by the formula $K = \frac{1}{2} ab \sin C$.

3. *Law of Sines:* In any triangle ABC,
$$\frac{\sin A}{a} = \frac{\sin B}{b} = \frac{\sin C}{c}.$$

4. *Law of Cosines* (page 499): In any triangle ABC,
$$c^2 = a^2 + b^2 - 2ab \cos C.$$

5. The law of sines and the law of cosines can be used to solve any triangle. Depending on the information given, there may be no, one, or two solutions.

6. A *vector* is a directed line segment. Vectors are used to represent quantities such as forces and velocities that have both *magnitude* and *direction*. If $\mathbf{u} + \mathbf{v} = \mathbf{w}$, then $\mathbf{w}$ is the *sum*, or *resultant*, of $\mathbf{u}$ and $\mathbf{v}$; $\mathbf{u}$ and $\mathbf{v}$ are the *components* of $\mathbf{w}$.

Chapter Review

Give the letter of the correct answer.

1. In right triangle ABC, $\angle C = 90°$, $a = 3$, and $c = 4$. Find $\angle B$. **13-1**
   a. 48.6° b. 36.9° c. 41.4° d. 53.1°

2. In right triangle DEF, $\angle E = 90°$, $e = 10$, and $\angle D = 22°$. Find d.
   a. 3.75 b. 9.27 c. 4.04 d. 26.69

3. Find the area of an equilateral triangle with sides of length 12. **13-2**
   a. 36 b. $72\sqrt{3}$ c. 72 d. $36\sqrt{3}$

4. The area of $\triangle ABC$ is 40. If $\angle B = 40°$ and $a = 8$, find c.
   a. 7.8 b. 10.0 c. 15.6 d. 3.9

5. In $\triangle ABC$, which expression is equal to a? **13-3**
   a. $\dfrac{b \sin B}{\sin A}$ b. $\dfrac{c \sin A}{\sin C}$ c. $\dfrac{b \sin C}{\sin B}$ d. $\dfrac{\sin C}{c \sin A}$

6. In $\triangle MNP$, $\angle M = 68°$, $\angle N = 23°$, and $n = 13$. Find m.
   a. 30.8 b. 5.48 c. 12.0 d. 26

7. Which equation is *not* a statement of the law of cosines? **13-4**
   a. $a^2 = b^2 + c^2 - 2bc \cos B$ b. $c^2 = a^2 + b^2 - 2ab \cos C$
   c. $b^2 = c^2 + a^2 - 2ca \cos B$

8. In $\triangle ABC$, $\angle A = 163°$, $b = 8$, and $c = 12$. Find a.

    a. 4.94   **b.** 17.3   **c.** 19.8   **d.** 391.6

9. In $\triangle PQR$, $p = 6$, $q = 4$, and $r = 3$. Find $\angle P$.

    a. 117.3°   **b.** 62.7°   **c.** 142.3°   **d.** 156.4°

10. In $\triangle DEF$, $d = 14$, $e = 18$, and $\angle D = 35°$. How many solutions are there for $\triangle DEF$?   **13-5**

    a. 0   **b.** 1   **c.** 2   **d.** 3

11. Tanya swims at 6 km/h in still water. She decides to swim across a stream with a current of 3 km/h. What is her actual speed of travel?   **13-6**

    a. 9.00 km/h   **b.** 6.71 km/h   **c.** 5.20 km/h   **d.** 3 km/h

12. Forces of 6 N and 10 N pull on an object, making an angle of 20° with each other. What is the magnitude of the resultant of these forces?

    a. 15.8 N   **b.** 4.82 N   **c.** 13.9 N   **d.** 2.7 N

13. A vector has magnitude 12 and direction 285°. Find its y-component.   **13-7**

    a. 3.11   **b.** -3.11 **c.** 11.6   **d.** -11.6

14. If $\mathbf{u} = (-3, 8)$, find the direction of $\mathbf{u}$.

    a. 69°   **b.** 111°   **c.** 291°   **d.** 249°

Chapter Test

Give each answer to three significant digits.

1. Solve $\triangle ABC$ if $\angle A = 29°$, $\angle C = 90°$, and $c = 14$.   **13-1**

2. A satellite is being launched into orbit. An observer 25 km from the launch pad watches the rocket until it is too high to see. If the angle of elevation of the rocket at that time is 68°, what is the altitude of the rocket?

3. Find the area of $\triangle XYZ$ if $x = 5$, $y = 8$, and $\angle Z = 34°$.   **13-2**

4. Find $\angle C$ in $\triangle ABC$ if $\angle B = 27°$, $b = 16$, and $c = 9$.   **13-3**

5. Find r in $\triangle RST$ if $\angle R = 33°$, $s = 20$, and $t = 14$.   **13-4**

6. Solve $\triangle ABC$ if $\angle A = 74°$, $b = 8$, and $c = 11$.   **13-5**

7. Earl and Zona went out in two boats to place markers for a boat race. The angle formed by their paths was 110°. If Earl rowed 85 m and Zona rowed 102 m, how far apart were the markers?

8. An object is pushed to the west by a force of 20 N. At the same time the object is pushed south by a force of 12 N. Find the magnitude and direction of the resultant of these forces.   **13-6**

9. Find the x- and y-components of a vector 18 units long that has a direction angle of 70°.   **13-7**

Notice the spiral pattern in the arrangement of the seeds of the sunflower shown above. Equations of the many different spirals found in nature can be written conveniently using complex numbers in trigonometric, or polar, form (see the Extra on pages 551–553).

14

IDENTITIES, INVERSES, AND EQUATIONS

IDENTITIES

14-1 *Sine and Cosine of a Sum or Difference*

OBJECTIVE **To develop and use formulas for the sine and cosine of a sum or difference.**

If asked to find $\cos 75°$, you could use tables or a calculator to find an approximate answer. Table 6 gives $\cos 75° = 0.2588$. But in mathematics, an exact answer is generally preferred. Note that $\cos 75°$ can be expressed as follows:

$$\cos 75° = \cos (45° + 30°)$$

Thus, if $\cos (45° + 30°)$ can be evaluated in terms of trigonometric functions of $45°$ and $30°$, you can find an exact expression for $\cos 75°$.

The more general problem is to find a formula for $\cos (\alpha + \beta)$.

On a unit circle, let ray OP and ray OR be the terminal rays for angles α and $-\beta$ as shown in Figure 14-1. By the definition of the sine and cosine,

the coordinates of P are $(\cos \alpha, \sin \alpha)$, and
the coordinates of R are $(\cos (-\beta), \sin (-\beta))$,
or $(\cos \beta, -\sin \beta)$.

(Recall that $\cos (-\beta) = \cos \beta$ and $\sin (-\beta) = -\sin \beta$.)

The distance PR can be found by using the distance formula or by using the law of cosines, as shown on the next page.

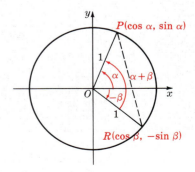

Figure 14-1

519

By the distance formula:

$$(PR)^2 = (\cos\alpha - \cos\beta)^2 + (\sin\alpha - (-\sin\beta))^2$$
$$= \cos^2\alpha - 2\cos\alpha\cos\beta + \cos^2\beta + \sin^2\alpha + 2\sin\alpha\sin\beta + \sin^2\beta$$
$$= (\cos^2\alpha + \sin^2\alpha) + (\cos^2\beta + \sin^2\beta) - 2[\cos\alpha\cos\beta - \sin\alpha\sin\beta]$$
$$= 1 + 1 - 2[\cos\alpha\cos\beta - \sin\alpha\sin\beta]$$
$$= 2 - 2[\cos\alpha\cos\beta - \sin\alpha\sin\beta]$$

By the law of cosines:

$$(PR)^2 = 1^2 + 1^2 - 2\cdot 1\cdot 1\cdot\cos(\alpha+\beta)$$
$$= 2 - 2\cos(\alpha+\beta)$$

If you equate the two expressions for $(PR)^2$, you get:

$$2 - 2\cos(\alpha+\beta) = 2 - 2(\cos\alpha\cos\beta - \sin\alpha\sin\beta)$$
$$\cos(\alpha+\beta) = \cos\alpha\cos\beta - \sin\alpha\sin\beta$$

This formula is called a **trigonometric addition formula.** Because it uses the law of cosines, the proof above is valid only for angles α and β such that $0° < \alpha + \beta < 180°$. It can be shown that the formula is true for all values of α and β.

The derivation of the formula for $\cos(\alpha - \beta)$ also uses the fact that $\cos(-\beta) = \cos\beta$ and $\sin(-\beta) = -\sin\beta$.

$$\cos(\alpha - \beta) = \cos[\alpha + (-\beta)]$$
$$= \cos\alpha\cos(-\beta) - \sin\alpha\sin(-\beta) \quad \left\{ \begin{array}{l} \text{by formula for} \\ \cos(\alpha+\beta) \end{array} \right.$$
$$= \cos\alpha\cos\beta - \sin\alpha(-\sin\beta)$$
$$= \cos\alpha\cos\beta + \sin\alpha\sin\beta$$
$$\therefore\ \cos(\alpha - \beta) = \cos\alpha\cos\beta + \sin\alpha\sin\beta$$

You can also derive formulas for the sine of the sum and difference of two angles. Because the sine of an angle equals the cosine of its complement:

$$\sin(\alpha + \beta) = \cos[90° - (\alpha+\beta)]$$
$$= \cos[(90° - \alpha) - \beta]$$
$$= \cos(90° - \alpha)\cos\beta + \sin(90° - \alpha)\sin\beta \quad \left\{ \begin{array}{l} \text{by formula for} \\ \cos(\alpha+\beta) \end{array} \right.$$
$$= \sin\alpha\cos\beta + \cos\alpha\sin\beta$$
$$\therefore\ \sin(\alpha + \beta) = \sin\alpha\cos\beta + \cos\alpha\sin\beta$$

By replacing β with $-\beta$ in the formula for $\sin(\alpha + \beta)$, you obtain a formula for $\sin(\alpha - \beta)$.

$$\sin(\alpha - \beta) = \sin[\alpha + (-\beta)]$$
$$= \sin\alpha\cos(-\beta) + \cos\alpha\sin(-\beta) \quad \left\{ \begin{array}{l} \text{by formula for} \\ \sin(\alpha+\beta) \end{array} \right.$$
$$= \sin\alpha\cos\beta + \cos\alpha(-\sin\beta)$$
$$= \sin\alpha\cos\beta - \cos\alpha\sin\beta$$

The trigonometric addition formulas for sine and cosine are summarized as follows:

$$\sin (\alpha + \beta) = \sin \alpha \cos \beta + \cos \alpha \sin \beta$$
$$\sin (\alpha - \beta) = \sin \alpha \cos \beta - \cos \alpha \sin \beta$$
$$\cos (\alpha + \beta) = \cos \alpha \cos \beta - \sin \alpha \sin \beta$$
$$\cos (\alpha - \beta) = \cos \alpha \cos \beta + \sin \alpha \sin \beta$$

EXAMPLE 1 Find: **a.** $\cos 75°$ **b.** $\sin 15°$

SOLUTION Let $\alpha = 45°$ and $\beta = 30°$.
Thus:

a.
$$\cos 75° = \cos (45° + 30°)$$
$$= \cos 45° \cos 30° - \sin 45° \sin 30°$$
$$= \frac{\sqrt{2}}{2} \cdot \frac{\sqrt{3}}{2} - \frac{\sqrt{2}}{2} \cdot \frac{1}{2}$$
$$= \frac{\sqrt{6} - \sqrt{2}}{4}$$
$$\therefore \cos 75° = \frac{\sqrt{6} - \sqrt{2}}{4} \quad \textbf{\textit{Answer}}$$

b.
$$\sin 15° = \sin (45° - 30°)$$
$$= \sin 45° \cos 30° - \cos 45° \sin 30°$$
$$= \frac{\sqrt{2}}{2} \cdot \frac{\sqrt{3}}{2} - \frac{\sqrt{2}}{2} \cdot \frac{1}{2}$$
$$= \frac{\sqrt{6} - \sqrt{2}}{4}$$
$$\therefore \sin 15° = \frac{\sqrt{6} - \sqrt{2}}{4} \quad \textbf{\textit{Answer}}$$

Notice that the answers to parts (a) and (b) are the same.

EXAMPLE 2 Express $\cos 100° \cos 80° + \sin 100° \sin 80°$ as a trigonometric function of a single angle.

SOLUTION The expression is in the pattern of the right-hand side of the trigonometric addition formula for $\cos (\alpha - \beta)$. If you let $\alpha = 100°$ and $\beta = 80°$, the formula
$$\cos \alpha \cos \beta + \sin \alpha \sin \beta = \cos (\alpha - \beta)$$
becomes
$$\cos 100° \cos 80° + \sin 100° \sin 80° = \cos (100° - 80°)$$
$$\therefore \cos 100° \cos 80° + \sin 100° \sin 80° = \cos 20°. \quad \textbf{\textit{Answer}}$$

EXAMPLE 3   Verify the cofunction identity $\sin\left(\frac{\pi}{2} - x\right) = \cos x$.

SOLUTION

$$\sin\left(\frac{\pi}{2} - x\right) \stackrel{?}{=} \cos x$$

$$
\begin{array}{c|c}
\sin\frac{\pi}{2}\cos x - \cos\frac{\pi}{2}\sin x & \cos x \\
1\cdot\cos x - 0\cdot\sin x & \cos x \\
\end{array}
$$
$$\cos x = \cos x$$

Oral Exercises

Use the trigonometric addition formulas to expand the given expression in terms of the angles named.

SAMPLE $\sin(60° + 45°) = \sin 60° \cos 45° + \cos 60° \sin 45°$

1. $\sin(30° + 45°)$
2. $\cos(45° + 30°)$
3. $\sin(120° - 45°)$
4. $\cos(90° - 25°)$
5. $\sin(80° - 60°)$
6. $\cos(45° - 20°)$

Express as a trigonometric function of a single angle and simplify where possible.

7. $\cos 35° \cos 25° + \sin 35° \sin 25°$
8. $\sin 50° \cos 20° - \cos 50° \sin 20°$
9. $\cos 50° \cos 40° - \sin 50° \sin 40°$
10. $\sin 2^R \cos 1^R + \cos 2^R \sin 1^R$
11. $\cos 3^R \cos 4^R + \sin 3^R \sin 4^R$
12. $\sin 3\alpha \cos 2\beta + \cos 3\alpha \sin 2\beta$
13. $\cos 2x \cos y + \sin 2x \sin y$
14. $\sin(x + y)\cos y - \cos(x + y)\sin y$

Written Exercises

Evaluate using trigonometric addition formulas. Leave your answers in simplest radical form.

A
1. $\cos 15°$
2. $\cos 105°$
3. $\sin 165°$
4. $\sin 75°$

Express as a trigonometric function of a single angle and simplify where possible. Do not use tables to approximate.

5. $\sin 70° \cos 20° + \cos 70° \sin 20°$
6. $\cos 45° \cos 15° - \sin 45° \sin 15°$
7. $\cos 140° \cos 80° + \sin 140° \sin 80°$
8. $\sin 210° \cos 30° - \cos 210° \sin 30°$
9. $\cos 160° \cos 120° - \sin 160° \sin 120°$
10. $\sin 310° \cos 200° - \cos 310° \sin 200°$
11. $\cos 1.2^R \cos 3.4^R + \sin 1.2^R \sin 3.4^R$
12. $\sin\frac{\pi}{12} \cos\frac{\pi}{4} + \cos\frac{\pi}{12} \sin\frac{\pi}{4}$
13. $\sin 3\alpha \cos 2\beta - \cos 3\alpha \sin 2\beta$
14. $\cos 2\alpha \cos \alpha + \sin 2\alpha \sin \alpha$

Use the addition formulas to prove the following identities.

15. $\cos\left(\frac{\pi}{2} + x\right) = -\sin x$ **16.** $\sin\left(\frac{\pi}{2} + x\right) = \cos x$

17. $\sin(\pi - x) = \sin x$ **18.** $\cos(\pi + x) = -\cos x$

19. $\cos\left(\frac{3\pi}{2} - x\right) = -\sin x$ **20.** $\sin\left(\frac{3\pi}{2} - x\right) = -\cos x$

B 21. $\cos\left(\frac{\pi}{3} + x\right) + \cos\left(\frac{\pi}{3} - x\right) = \cos x$

22. $\sin\left(\frac{\pi}{6} + x\right) + \sin\left(\frac{\pi}{6} - x\right) = \cos x$

23. $\cos\alpha\cos\beta\,(\tan\alpha + \tan\beta) = \sin(\alpha + \beta)$

24. $\sin\alpha\sin\beta\,(\cot\alpha\cot\beta + 1) = \cos(\alpha - \beta)$

25. $\dfrac{\sin(\alpha + \beta) + \sin(\alpha - \beta)}{\cos\alpha\cos\beta} = 2\tan\alpha$

26. $\dfrac{\cos(\alpha + \beta) + \cos(\alpha - \beta)}{\cot\alpha\cot\beta} = 2\sin\alpha\sin\beta$

Simplify.

27. $\cos(\alpha - \beta)\cos\beta - \sin(\alpha - \beta)\sin\beta$

28. $\sin(\alpha + \beta)\cos(\alpha - \beta) + \cos(\alpha + \beta)\sin(\alpha - \beta)$

29. a. If α is a first-quadrant angle and $\sin\alpha = \frac{3}{5}$, show that $\cos\alpha = \frac{4}{5}$.

  b. If β is a second-quadrant angle and $\sin\beta = \frac{5}{13}$, show that $\cos\beta = -\frac{12}{13}$.

  c. Use parts (a) and (b) to show that $\sin(\alpha + \beta) = -\frac{16}{65}$.

30. If α and β are second-quadrant angles and $\sin\alpha = \frac{1}{3}$ and $\sin\beta = \frac{2}{3}$, find $\cos\alpha$, $\cos\beta$, and $\cos(\alpha + \beta)$. (See Exercise 29.)

31. If α and β are fourth-quadrant angles and $\cos\alpha = \frac{1}{5}$ and $\cos\beta = \frac{3}{5}$, find $\sin\alpha$, $\sin\beta$, and $\sin(\alpha + \beta)$. (See Exercise 29.)

C 32. By squaring both sides of the formulas for $\sin(\alpha + \beta)$ and $\cos(\alpha + \beta)$, simplify $\sin^2(\alpha + \beta) + \cos^2(\alpha + \beta)$.

33. a. Find values for α and β that show that $\tan(\alpha + \beta) = \tan\alpha + \tan\beta$ is not an identity.

  b. Derive a formula that gives $\tan(\alpha + \beta)$ in terms of $\tan\alpha$ and $\tan\beta$. $\left[Hint: \tan(\alpha + \beta) = \dfrac{\sin(\alpha + \beta)}{\cos(\alpha + \beta)}\right]$

14-2 *The Tangent of a Sum or Difference*

OBJECTIVE   To develop and use formulas for the tangent of a sum or difference.

Since $\tan(\alpha + \beta) = \dfrac{\sin(\alpha + \beta)}{\cos(\alpha + \beta)}$, you can use the formulas for $\sin(\alpha + \beta)$ and $\cos(\alpha + \beta)$ to derive a formula for $\tan(\alpha + \beta)$.

$$\tan(\alpha + \beta) = \frac{\sin(\alpha + \beta)}{\cos(\alpha + \beta)} \qquad \{\text{Assume } \cos(\alpha + \beta) \neq 0$$

$$= \frac{\sin\alpha\cos\beta + \cos\alpha\sin\beta}{\cos\alpha\cos\beta - \sin\alpha\sin\beta} \qquad \{\text{Assume } \sin\alpha \neq 0, \cos\beta \neq 0$$

$$= \frac{\dfrac{\sin\alpha\cos\beta}{\cos\alpha\cos\beta} + \dfrac{\cos\alpha\sin\beta}{\cos\alpha\cos\beta}}{\dfrac{\cos\alpha\cos\beta}{\cos\alpha\cos\beta} - \dfrac{\sin\alpha\sin\beta}{\cos\alpha\cos\beta}} \qquad \begin{cases}\text{Divide numerator and}\\ \text{denominator by}\\ \cos\alpha\cos\beta\end{cases}$$

$$= \frac{\tan\alpha + \tan\beta}{1 - \tan\alpha\tan\beta}$$

$$\therefore \ \tan(\alpha + \beta) = \frac{\tan\alpha + \tan\beta}{1 - \tan\alpha\tan\beta}$$

To find $\tan(\alpha - \beta)$, use the formula for $\tan(\alpha + \beta)$ and the fact that $\tan(-\beta) = -\tan\beta$.

$$\tan(\alpha - \beta) = \tan(\alpha + (-\beta))$$

$$= \frac{\tan\alpha + \tan(-\beta)}{1 - \tan\alpha\tan(-\beta)}$$

$$= \frac{\tan\alpha - \tan\beta}{1 + \tan\alpha\tan\beta}$$

$$\therefore \ \tan(\alpha - \beta) = \frac{\tan\alpha - \tan\beta}{1 + \tan\alpha\tan\beta}$$

In summary:

$$\tan(\alpha + \beta) = \frac{\tan\alpha + \tan\beta}{1 - \tan\alpha\tan\beta}$$

$$\tan(\alpha - \beta) = \frac{\tan\alpha - \tan\beta}{1 + \tan\alpha\tan\beta}$$

EXAMPLE   If $\tan\alpha = 0.5$ and $\tan\beta = 0.2$, find $\tan(\alpha + \beta)$ and $\tan(\alpha - \beta)$.

SOLUTION $\tan(\alpha + \beta) = \dfrac{\tan\alpha + \tan\beta}{1 - \tan\alpha\tan\beta}$

$$= \frac{0.5 + 0.2}{1 - (0.5)(0.2)} = \frac{0.7}{0.9} = \frac{7}{9}$$

$$\tan (\alpha - \beta) = \frac{\tan \alpha - \tan \beta}{1 + \tan \alpha \tan \beta}$$

$$= \frac{0.5 - 0.2}{1 + 0.5(0.2)} = \frac{0.3}{1.1} = \frac{3}{11}$$

Oral Exercises

Simplify.

1. $\dfrac{\tan 50° + \tan 5°}{1 - \tan 50° \tan 5°}$

2. $\dfrac{\tan 25° - \tan 15°}{1 + \tan 25° \tan 15°}$

3. $\dfrac{\tan 130° - \tan 15°}{1 + \tan 130° \tan 15°}$

4. $\dfrac{\tan 320° + \tan 80°}{1 - \tan 320° \tan 80°}$

Written Exercises

Simplify to a trigonometric function of a single angle. Then evaluate if possible. Do not use tables or a calculator.

A **1.** $\dfrac{\tan 20° + \tan 40°}{1 - \tan 20° \tan 40°}$

2. $\dfrac{\tan 75° - \tan 45°}{1 + \tan 75° \tan 45°}$

3. $\dfrac{\tan 195° - \tan 15°}{1 + \tan 195° \tan 15°}$

4. $\dfrac{\tan \frac{\pi}{6} + \tan \frac{\pi}{12}}{1 - \tan \frac{\pi}{6} \tan \frac{\pi}{12}}$

5. $\dfrac{\tan 97° + \tan 38°}{1 - \tan 97° \tan 38°}$

6. $\dfrac{\tan 1° - \tan 61°}{1 + \tan 1° \tan 61°}$

7. $\dfrac{\tan 3 - \tan 2}{1 + \tan 3 \tan 2}$

8. $\dfrac{\tan 2 - \tan 3}{1 + \tan 2 \tan 3}$

9. $\dfrac{\tan 5\alpha - \tan 2\alpha}{1 + \tan 5\alpha \tan 2\alpha}$

10. $\dfrac{\tan 2\alpha - \tan 5\alpha}{1 + \tan 2\alpha \tan 5\alpha}$

Evaluate without using tables or a calculator. (See Example 1 in Section 14-1.)

11. $\tan 75°$ **12.** $\tan 15°$ **13.** $\tan 105°$ **14.** $\tan 165°$

15. If $\tan x = 0.5$, find $\tan \left(\frac{\pi}{4} + x\right)$ and $\tan \left(\frac{\pi}{4} - x\right)$.

16. If $\tan y = 3$, find $\tan \left(\frac{\pi}{4} + y\right)$ and $\tan \left(\frac{\pi}{4} - y\right)$.

17. If $\tan z = \frac{1}{3}$, find $\tan \left(\frac{3\pi}{4} + z\right)$ and $\tan \left(\frac{3\pi}{4} - z\right)$.

18. If θ is acute and $\sin \theta = \frac{3}{5}$, find $\tan \theta$ and $\tan (45° + \theta)$.

B **19. a.** If α is a first-quadrant angle and $\cos \alpha = \frac{3}{5}$, show that $\tan \alpha = \frac{4}{3}$.

 b. If β is a second-quadrant angle and $\sin \beta = \frac{12}{13}$, show that $\tan \beta = -\frac{12}{5}$.

 c. Use parts (a) and (b) to find $\tan (\alpha + \beta)$.

20. If α and β are second-quadrant angles and $\sin \alpha = \frac{1}{\sqrt{5}}$ and $\cos \beta = \frac{-3}{\sqrt{10}}$, find $\tan \alpha$, $\tan \beta$, and $\tan (\alpha - \beta)$. (See Exercise 19.)

C **21.** Prove that $\tan 3\alpha = \frac{3 \tan \alpha - \tan^3 \alpha}{1 - 3 \tan^2 \alpha}$.

22. a. Find a formula for $\cot (\alpha + \beta)$ in terms of $\cot \alpha$ and $\cot \beta$.

$$\left(Hint: \quad \cot (\alpha + \beta) = \frac{1}{\tan (\alpha + \beta)} \right)$$

 b. Use the formula derived in part (a) to find $\cot 75°$.

23. a. Find a formula for $\cot (\alpha - \beta)$ in terms of $\cot \alpha$ and $\cot \beta$.

 b. Use the formula derived in part (a) to find $\cot 15°$.

24. Compare the answer to Exercise 7 with the answer to Exercise 8. Do the same with Exercises 9 and 10. Of what formula do these pairs of exercises remind you?

Calculator Key-In

Suppose you had a calculator that had no trigonometric functions. Here is how you could make a table of sines and cosines for multiples of 10° given only that $\sin 10° = 0.17364818$.

1. a. Since $\sin^2 10° + \cos^2 10° = 1$, then $\cos 10° = \sqrt{1 - (0.17364818)^2} = \underline{\quad ? \quad}$.

 b. You now know $\sin 80°$ and $\cos 80°$ without any extra work. How?

2. a. Use an addition formula to find $\sin 20°$ as follows:
$$\sin 20° = \sin (10° + 10°) = \sin 10° \cos 10° + \cos 10° \sin 10°$$

 b. Find $\cos 20°$ using an addition formula or by the idea used in step 1.

 c. Use parts 2(a) and 2(b) to find $\cos 70°$ and $\sin 70°$.

3. Complete the table of sines and cosines for 10°, 20°, 30°, . . . , 90°.

14-3 Double-Angle Formulas

OBJECTIVE   To develop and use the double-angle formulas.

The formula for the sine of twice an angle α (or $\sin 2\alpha$) is derived from the formula for $\sin(\alpha + \beta)$ by substituting α for β.

$$\sin 2\alpha = \sin(\alpha + \alpha) = \sin\alpha\cos\alpha + \cos\alpha\sin\alpha$$
$$\therefore \sin 2\alpha = 2\sin\alpha\cos\alpha.$$

This formula is called a **double-angle formula.** By making similar substitutions, you can derive the double-angle formulas for cosine and tangent.

$$\cos 2\alpha = \cos(\alpha + \alpha) = \cos\alpha\cos\alpha - \sin\alpha\sin\alpha$$
$$\therefore \cos 2\alpha = \cos^2\alpha - \sin^2\alpha.$$

$$\tan 2\alpha = \tan(\alpha + \alpha) = \frac{\tan\alpha + \tan\alpha}{1 - \tan\alpha\tan\alpha}$$

$$\therefore \tan 2\alpha = \frac{2\tan\alpha}{1 - \tan^2\alpha}.$$

In summary:

$$\sin 2\alpha = 2\sin\alpha\cos\alpha$$
$$\cos 2\alpha = \cos^2\alpha - \sin^2\alpha$$
$$\tan 2\alpha = \frac{2\tan\alpha}{1 - \tan^2\alpha}$$

There are two other formulas for $\cos 2\alpha$. You can derive each from the formula for $\cos 2\alpha$ above by substituting $1 - \sin^2\alpha$ for $\cos^2\alpha$ or $1 - \cos^2\alpha$ for $\sin^2\alpha$.

$$\cos 2\alpha = \cos^2\alpha - \sin^2\alpha \qquad\qquad \cos 2\alpha = \cos^2\alpha - \sin^2\alpha$$
$$= (1 - \sin^2\alpha) - \sin^2\alpha \qquad\qquad = \cos^2\alpha - (1 - \cos^2\alpha)$$
$$= 1 - 2\sin^2\alpha \qquad\qquad = 2\cos^2\alpha - 1$$

$$\cos 2\alpha = 1 - 2\sin^2\alpha \qquad\qquad \cos 2\alpha = 2\cos^2\alpha - 1$$

EXAMPLE 1   Simplify: **a.** $2\sin 5°\cos 5°$ **b.** $1 - 2\sin^2\frac{\pi}{8}$

SOLUTION   **a.** Use the formula $2\sin\alpha\cos\alpha = \sin 2\alpha$.

$$2\sin 5°\cos 5° = \sin(2\cdot 5°) = \sin 10°$$

b. Use the formula $1 - 2\sin^2 \alpha = \cos 2\alpha$.

$$1 - 2\sin^2 \frac{\pi}{8} = \cos\left(2 \cdot \frac{\pi}{8}\right) = \cos \frac{\pi}{4} = \frac{\sqrt{2}}{2}$$

EXAMPLE 2 If $\sin \alpha = \frac{3}{5}$ and α is in the first quadrant, find $\sin 2\alpha$, $\cos 2\alpha$, and $\tan 2\alpha$.

SOLUTION The diagram shows that if $\sin \alpha = \frac{3}{5}$, then $\cos \alpha = \frac{4}{5}$ and $\tan \alpha = \frac{3}{4}$.

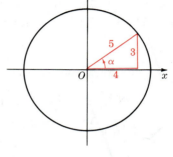

$$\sin 2\alpha = 2 \sin \alpha \cos \alpha$$
$$= 2\left(\frac{3}{5}\right)\left(\frac{4}{5}\right) = \frac{24}{25}$$
$$\cos 2\alpha = \cos^2 \alpha - \sin^2 \alpha$$
$$= \left(\frac{4}{5}\right)^2 - \left(\frac{3}{5}\right)^2 = \frac{7}{25}$$
$$\tan 2\alpha = \frac{2 \tan \alpha}{1 - \tan^2 \alpha}$$
$$= \frac{2\left(\frac{3}{4}\right)}{1 - \left(\frac{3}{4}\right)^2} = \frac{24}{7}$$

$$\therefore \sin 2\alpha = \frac{24}{25}, \cos 2\alpha = \frac{7}{25}, \text{ and } \tan 2\alpha = \frac{24}{7}. \quad \textit{Answer}$$

Oral Exercises

Simplify.

1. $2\cos^2 \alpha - 1$

2. $\dfrac{2 \tan \beta}{1 - \tan^2 \beta}$

3. $1 - 2\sin^2 \beta$

4. $2\sin \beta \cos \beta$

5. $\cos^2 \theta - \sin^2 \theta$

6. $\cos^2 \theta + \sin^2 \theta$

Written Exercises

Simplify.

A **1.** $1 - 2\sin^2 10°$

2. $2\sin 4° \cos 4°$

3. $\dfrac{2 \tan 80°}{1 - \tan^2 80°}$

4. $2\cos^2 50° - 1$

5. $\cos^2 70° + \sin^2 70°$

6. $\cos^2 70° - \sin^2 70°$

7. $2\sin 3\alpha \cos 3\alpha$

8. $1 - 2\sin^2 2\beta$

9. $\cos^2 5\alpha - \sin^2 5\alpha$

10. $\dfrac{2 \tan 4\alpha}{1 - \tan^2 4\alpha}$

11. $2\cos^2 \dfrac{\beta}{4} - 1$

12. $2\sin \dfrac{\alpha}{2} \cos \dfrac{\alpha}{2}$

Simplify each expression. Then evaluate without using tables or a calculator.

13. $\cos^2 15° - \sin^2 15°$

14. $2\sin 15° \cos 15°$

15. $1 - 2\sin^2 105°$

16. $\dfrac{2 \tan \frac{\pi}{8}}{1 - \tan^2 \frac{\pi}{8}}$

17. $\dfrac{2 \tan \frac{3\pi}{8}}{1 - \tan^2 \frac{3\pi}{8}}$

18. $2 \cos^2 \frac{5\pi}{8} - 1$

B **19.** $\sin 75° \cos 75°$

20. $\dfrac{4 \tan 22\frac{1}{2}°}{1 - \tan^2 22\frac{1}{2}°}$

21. $6 \sin 165° \cos 165°$

22. If $\sin \alpha = \frac{4}{5}$ and α is a first-quadrant angle, find:

   a. $\cos \alpha$ **b.** $\sin 2\alpha$ **c.** $\cos 2\alpha$ **d.** $\sin 4\alpha$
   e. Use your answers to parts (b) and (c) to verify that $\sin^2 2\alpha + \cos^2 2\alpha = 1$.

23. Repeat Exercise 22 if α is a second-quadrant angle.

24. If $\tan \beta = \frac{2}{3}$ and β is a first-quadrant angle, find:

   a. $\tan 2\beta$ **b.** $\tan 4\beta$ **c.** $\cos \beta$ **d.** $\cos 2\beta$

25. If $\cos \alpha = -\frac{1}{3}$ and α is a second-quadrant angle, find:

   a. $\cos 2\alpha$ **b.** $\cos 4\alpha$ **c.** $\csc \alpha$ **d.** $\csc 2\alpha$

26. **a.** Sketch the graph of $f(x) = \cos^2 x - \sin^2 x$ for $0 \le x \le 2\pi$.
   b. Give the period and the amplitude of this function.

27. **a.** Sketch the graph of $g(x) = \sin x \cos x$ for $0 \le x \le 2\pi$.
   b. Give the period and the amplitude of this function.

28. In the formula $\cos 2\alpha = 1 - 2 \sin^2 \alpha$, substitute $\frac{\theta}{2}$ for α and prove that

$$\sin \frac{\theta}{2} = \pm \sqrt{\frac{1 - \cos \theta}{2}}.$$

29. In the formula $\cos 2\alpha = 2 \cos^2 \alpha - 1$, substitute $\frac{\theta}{2}$ for α and prove that

$$\cos \frac{\theta}{2} = \pm \sqrt{\frac{1 + \cos \theta}{2}}.$$

Prove each identity.

30. $\csc 2\alpha = \dfrac{\sec \alpha \csc \alpha}{2}$

31. $\cot 2\beta = \dfrac{\cot \beta (1 - \tan^2 \beta)}{2}$

32. $\left(\sin \frac{\alpha}{2} + \cos \frac{\alpha}{2} \right)^2 = 1 + \sin \alpha$

33. $\dfrac{\sin 2\alpha}{1 - \cos 2\alpha} = \cot \alpha$

34. $\dfrac{1 - \tan^2 \alpha}{1 + \tan^2 \alpha} = \cos 2\alpha$

35. $2 \cos^2 \left(\frac{\pi}{4} - x \right) - 1 = 2 \sin x \cos x$

36. $\log \cos 2\theta = \log (\cos \theta + \sin \theta) + \log (\cos \theta - \sin \theta)$

C **37.** Express $\sin 3\theta$ in terms of $\sin \theta$ and $\cos \theta$.

38. Express $\cos 3\theta$ in terms of $\cos \theta$.

39. Find a formula for $\cot 2\alpha$ in terms of $\cot \alpha$.

14-4 *Half-Angle Formulas*

OBJECTIVE   **To develop and use the half-angle formulas.**

The sine and cosine **half-angle formulas** are derived from two of the cosine double-angle formulas by substituting $\frac{\theta}{2}$ for α.

$$\cos 2\alpha = 1 - 2 \sin^2 \alpha \qquad\qquad \cos 2\alpha = 2 \cos^2 \alpha - 1$$

$$\cos 2\left(\frac{\theta}{2}\right) = 1 - 2 \sin^2 \left(\frac{\theta}{2}\right) \qquad\qquad \cos 2\left(\frac{\theta}{2}\right) = 2 \cos^2 \left(\frac{\theta}{2}\right) - 1$$

$$\cos \theta = 1 - 2 \sin^2 \frac{\theta}{2} \qquad\qquad \cos \theta = 2 \cos^2 \frac{\theta}{2} - 1$$

$$2 \sin^2 \frac{\theta}{2} = 1 - \cos \theta \qquad\qquad 2 \cos^2 \frac{\theta}{2} = 1 + \cos \theta$$

$$\sin \frac{\theta}{2} = \pm \sqrt{\frac{1 - \cos \theta}{2}} \qquad\qquad \cos \frac{\theta}{2} = \pm \sqrt{\frac{1 + \cos \theta}{2}}$$

Notice that the half-angle formulas above involve a plus-or-minus sign. As illustrated in Example 1, you must decide which sign to use by determining which quadrant $\frac{\theta}{2}$ is in.

EXAMPLE 1   Find the exact values of $\sin \frac{5\pi}{8}$ and $\cos \frac{5\pi}{8}$.

SOLUTION   Since $\frac{5\pi}{8} = \frac{1}{2}\left(\frac{5\pi}{4}\right)$ the two half-angle formulas above can be applied. Since $\frac{5\pi}{8}$ is a second-quadrant angle, its sine is positive and its cosine is negative.

$$\sin \frac{5\pi}{8} = + \sqrt{\frac{1 - \cos \frac{5\pi}{4}}{2}} \qquad\qquad \cos \frac{5\pi}{8} = - \sqrt{\frac{1 + \cos \frac{5\pi}{4}}{2}}$$

$$= \sqrt{\frac{1 - \left(-\frac{\sqrt{2}}{2}\right)}{2}} \qquad\qquad = - \sqrt{\frac{1 + \left(-\frac{\sqrt{2}}{2}\right)}{2}}$$

$$= \sqrt{\frac{2 + \sqrt{2}}{4}} \qquad\qquad = - \sqrt{\frac{2 - \sqrt{2}}{4}}$$

$$= \frac{\sqrt{2 + \sqrt{2}}}{2} \qquad\qquad = - \frac{\sqrt{2 - \sqrt{2}}}{2}$$

$$\therefore \sin \frac{5\pi}{8} = \frac{\sqrt{2 + \sqrt{2}}}{2} \quad \text{and} \quad \cos \frac{5\pi}{8} = - \frac{\sqrt{2 - \sqrt{2}}}{2}. \quad \textit{Answer}$$

In Example 2 the values of θ and $\frac{\theta}{2}$ are not given. Part (a) describes a method for determining the proper quadrant for $\frac{\theta}{2}$ in such cases.

EXAMPLE 2 $\cos\theta = \frac{1}{3}$ and θ is a fourth-quadrant angle in the first counterclockwise revolution. Find:

a. the quadrant $\frac{\theta}{2}$ is in.   **b.** $\cos\frac{\theta}{2}$.

SOLUTION   **a.** Since θ is a fourth-quadrant angle and between $0°$ and $360°$,
$$270° < \theta < 360°.$$
Dividing by 2, you get
$$135° < \frac{\theta}{2} < 180°.$$

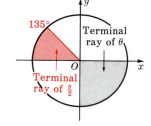

$\therefore \frac{\theta}{2}$ lies in the second quadrant. *Answer*

b. Since $\frac{\theta}{2}$ is a second-quadrant angle, $\cos\frac{\theta}{2}$ is negative. Therefore,
$$\cos\frac{\theta}{2} = -\sqrt{\frac{1+\frac{1}{3}}{2}} = -\sqrt{\frac{3+1}{6}} = -\sqrt{\frac{2}{3}}.$$
$\therefore \cos\frac{\theta}{2} = -\frac{\sqrt{6}}{3}.$ *Answer*

A half-angle formula for $\tan\frac{\theta}{2}$ is obtained from the half-angle formulas for sine and cosine as follows:

$$\tan\frac{\theta}{2} = \frac{\sin\frac{\theta}{2}}{\cos\frac{\theta}{2}} = \frac{\pm\sqrt{\frac{1-\cos\theta}{2}}}{\pm\sqrt{\frac{1+\cos\theta}{2}}} = \pm\sqrt{\frac{\frac{1-\cos\theta}{2}}{\frac{1+\cos\theta}{2}}}$$

$$\tan\frac{\theta}{2} = \pm\sqrt{\frac{1-\cos\theta}{1+\cos\theta}}$$

Another formula for $\tan\frac{\theta}{2}$ can be derived as follows:

$$\tan\alpha = \frac{\sin\alpha}{\cos\alpha} = \frac{2\sin\alpha\cos\alpha}{2\cos\alpha\cos\alpha} = \frac{2\sin\alpha\cos\alpha}{2\cos^2\alpha} = \frac{\sin 2\alpha}{1+\cos 2\alpha}.$$

Substituting $\frac{\theta}{2}$ for α and θ for 2α you obtain:

$$\tan\frac{\theta}{2} = \frac{\sin\theta}{1 + \cos\theta}$$

Since this formula for $\tan\frac{\theta}{2}$ involves no ambiguity in sign, it is often easier to use than the previous formula. A third version is proved in Exercise 18.

Oral Exercises

Simplify. Do not evaluate.

1. $\sqrt{\dfrac{1 + \cos 20°}{2}}$

2. $\sqrt{\dfrac{1 - \cos 70°}{2}}$

3. $-\sqrt{\dfrac{1 - \cos 200°}{1 + \cos 200°}}$

4. $\dfrac{\sin 130°}{1 + \cos 130°}$

5. $-\sqrt{\dfrac{1 + \cos 400°}{2}}$

6. $\dfrac{\sin 2}{1 + \cos 2}$

Written Exercises

Use the half-angle formulas to find the sine, cosine, and tangent of each angle.

A **1.** 15°   **2.** 22.5°   **3.** $(-67.5)°$ **4.** 105°

Use the given information to find $\sin\frac{\theta}{2}$, $\cos\frac{\theta}{2}$, and $\tan\frac{\theta}{2}$. Assume $0° \le \theta < 360°$. Give your answers in simplest radical form.

5. $\cos\theta = \dfrac{1}{4}$, θ a first-quadrant angle

6. $\cos\theta = \dfrac{1}{5}$, θ a first-quadrant angle

7. $\cos\theta = -\dfrac{2}{3}$, θ a second-quadrant angle

8. $\cos\theta = 0.4$, θ a fourth-quadrant angle

9. $\sin\theta = \dfrac{3}{5}$, θ a first-quadrant angle

10. $\tan\theta = \dfrac{12}{5}$, θ a third-quadrant angle

11. $\sec\theta = 2.5$, θ a fourth-quadrant angle

12. $\sec\theta = -3$, θ a second-quadrant angle

In Exercises 13–15, assume that all angles are between $0°$ and $360°$.

B 13. If α is acute and $\cos \alpha = \dfrac{7}{25}$, find $\cos \dfrac{\alpha}{2}$ and $\cos \dfrac{\alpha}{4}$.

14. If β is obtuse and $\cos \beta = -\dfrac{119}{169}$, find $\sin \dfrac{\beta}{2}$ and $\sin \dfrac{\beta}{4}$.

15. If θ is a third-quadrant angle and $\sin \theta = -\dfrac{4}{5}$, find $\tan \dfrac{\theta}{2}$ and $\tan \dfrac{\theta}{4}$.

16. If α is a first-quadrant angle in the second counterclockwise revolution, and $\cos \alpha = \dfrac{1}{3}$, find $\cos \dfrac{\alpha}{2}$ and $\cos 2\alpha$.

17. If β is a second-quadrant angle in the second counterclockwise revolution, and $\sin \beta = \dfrac{24}{25}$, find $\sin \dfrac{\beta}{2}$ and $\sin 2\beta$.

18. Derive the formula $\tan \dfrac{\theta}{2} = \dfrac{1 - \cos \theta}{\sin \theta}$ by modifying the right side of the formula $\tan \dfrac{\theta}{2} = \dfrac{\sin \theta}{1 + \cos \theta}$.

C 19. In Exercise 1, you found $\sin 15°$ using the formula for $\sin \dfrac{\theta}{2}$. In Example 1 of Section 14-1, the formula for $\sin(\alpha - \beta)$ was used to find $\sin 15°$. Prove that the answers obtained by these two methods are algebraically equivalent.

Self-Test 1

VOCABULARY   trigonometric addition   double-angle formula (p. 527)
                  formula (p. 520)   half-angle formula (p. 530)

1. Express as a trigonometric function of a single angle.   Obj. 14-1, p. 519
    a. $\sin 26° \cos 17° + \cos 26° \sin 17°$
    b. $\cos 78° \cos 32° + \sin 78° \sin 32°$

2. Evaluate $\cos 75°$ without tables or a calculator.

3. If $\tan \alpha = 0.4$ and $\tan \beta = -1.5$, find $\tan(\alpha + \beta)$.   Obj. 14-2, p. 524

4. Simplify.   Obj. 14-3, p. 527

    a. $2 \cos^2 31° - 1$ **b.** $\dfrac{4 \tan 4\alpha}{1 - \tan^2 4\alpha}$

5. If $\sin \alpha = -\dfrac{1}{2}$ and α is a fourth-quadrant angle, find:
    a. $\sin 2\alpha$ **b.** $\cos 2\alpha$

6. If $\cos \theta = 0.3$ and θ is a first-quadrant angle, find $\sin \dfrac{\theta}{2}$, $\cos \dfrac{\theta}{2}$,   Obj. 14-4, p. 530
and $\tan \dfrac{\theta}{2}$.

Check your answers with those at the back of the book.

14-5 *Graphs of the Remaining Trigonometric Functions*

In this section the graphs of the tangent, cotangent, secant, and cosecant functions will be discussed.

If $P(x, y)$ is a point on the unit circle as shown, then $\tan \theta = \dfrac{\sin \theta}{\cos \theta} = \dfrac{y}{x}$. Think of P starting at the point $(1, 0)$ where $\theta = 0$ and moving counterclockwise around the circle.

1. When $\theta = 0$, $(x, y) = (1, 0)$ and $\tan \theta = 0$.

2. As θ increases from 0 to $\dfrac{\pi^{\text{R}}}{2}$, y increases and x decreases, so $\dfrac{y}{x}$ increases. Therefore, $\tan \theta$ increases as θ increases from 0 to $\dfrac{\pi^{\text{R}}}{2}$.

3. When $\theta = \dfrac{\pi^{\text{R}}}{4}$, the x- and y-coordinates of P are equal, so $\tan \dfrac{\pi^{\text{R}}}{4} = 1$.

4. When $\theta = \dfrac{\pi^{\text{R}}}{2}$, $(x, y) = (0, 1)$ so $\dfrac{y}{x}$ and thus $\tan \theta$ are not defined.

5. Using the tangent sum formula on page 524, you can show that $\tan(\theta + \pi^{\text{R}}) = \tan \theta$. Therefore, the tangent function has period π.

As in the graphs of the sine and cosine functions, it is more convenient to graph the circular function. Thus, in the equation $y = \tan x$, y refers to the value of the tangent of the real number x. A table of values of $y = \tan x$ for $0 \le x < \dfrac{\pi}{2}$ is given below. The graph is shown on the next page.

x	$\tan x$
0	0
$\dfrac{\pi}{6}$	$\dfrac{\sqrt{3}}{3} \approx 0.58$
$\dfrac{\pi}{4}$	1
$\dfrac{\pi}{3}$	$\sqrt{3} \approx 1.73$
$\dfrac{\pi}{2}$	undefined

Figure 14-2

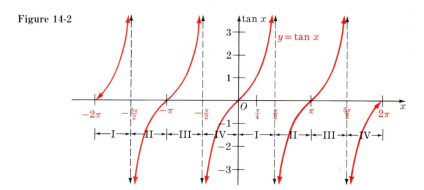

Since tan x does not exist when x is an odd multiple of $\frac{\pi}{2}$ $\left(\ldots, -\frac{\pi}{2}, \frac{\pi}{2}, \frac{3\pi}{2}, \frac{5\pi}{2}, \ldots\right)$, the graph of the tangent function is separated into branches by the asymptotes (recall Section 9-6) shown as dashed lines. The equations of the asymptotes are all of the form

$$x = (2n + 1)\frac{\pi}{2}, \text{ where } n \text{ is an integer.}$$

Do you see how the graph of $y = \tan x$ reflects the following facts about the tangent function?

1. The domain of the tangent is the set of all real numbers x, $x \neq (2n + 1)\frac{\pi}{2}$.

2. The range of the tangent is the set of all real numbers.

3. $\left.\begin{array}{l}\tan x > 0 \\ \tan x < 0\end{array}\right\}$ where x corresponds to an angle in $\left\{\begin{array}{l}\text{the first or third quadrant.} \\ \text{the second or fourth quadrant.}\end{array}\right.$

4. The tangent is periodic with period π.

The graphs of the cotangent, secant, and cosecant functions, with their reciprocal functions, are shown in Figures 14-3, 14-4, and 14-5.

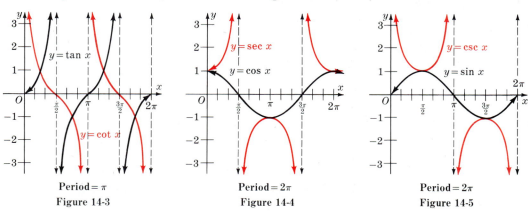

Period $= \pi$ Period $= 2\pi$ Period $= 2\pi$

Figure 14-3   Figure 14-4   Figure 14-5

Oral Exercises

State the period of each function.

1. $y = \tan x$ **2.** $y = \cot x$ **3.** $y = \sec x$ **4.** $y = \csc x$

5. $y = \tan 2x$ **6.** $y = \sec 3x$ **7.** $y = \csc \frac{1}{2}x$ **8.** $y = 3 \tan 2\pi x$

Written Exercises

Sketch the graph of each function over the interval $0 \le x < 2\pi$ or the given interval.

A

1. $y = \tan 2x$ **2.** $y = \sec 2x$ **3.** $y = \frac{1}{2} \sec x$ **4.** $y = 3 \csc x$

5. $y = -\csc x$ **6.** $y = -\tan x$ **7.** $y = -\cot x$ **8.** $y = -\sec x$

9. $y = \csc \frac{1}{2}x$ **10.** $y = \tan \frac{1}{3}x$ **11.** $y = \tan \pi x;$ $0 \le x < 1$ **12.** $y = \sec 2\pi x;$ $0 \le x < 1$

B **13.** $y = -\cot 2\pi x;$ $0 \le x < 1$ **14.** $y = -2 \csc \pi x$ **15.** $y = -\tan \frac{2}{3}x$ **16.** $y = -\frac{3}{2} \sec \frac{3}{2}x$

Use the following fact to graph each of the following over the interval $0 \le x \le 2\pi$: The graph of $y = f(x - a) + b$ is obtained by translating the graph of $y = f(x)$ a units horizontally and b units vertically.

17. $y = \sin\left(x - \frac{\pi}{6}\right)$ **18.** $y = \tan\left(x - \frac{\pi}{4}\right)$ **19.** $y = 2 \cos\left(x + \frac{\pi}{3}\right)$

20. $y = \sin x + 1$ **21.** $y = \cos\left(x - \frac{\pi}{4}\right) + 1$ **22.** $y = \tan\left(x + \frac{\pi}{4}\right) + 1$

Biography Joseph Fourier

Jean-Baptiste-Joseph Fourier (1768–1830) showed evidence of extraordinary intellectual ability at an early age. Despite difficult circumstances, he was able to obtain a number of years of formal education before the French Revolution put an end to his school years in 1789. At that time he returned to his birthplace, Auxerre, France, to teach at the local school.

Fourier made many contributions to the fields of mathematics and physics. His book on the conduction of heat was a landmark. He did significant work in the theory of equations and developed fundamental mathematical methods and notations. His most famous contribution is the Fourier Series, the representation of a given function by a trigonometric series.

14-6 *Inverse Sines and Inverse Cosines*

OBJECTIVE To evaluate expressions involving the inverse sine and inverse cosine functions.

In this section you will see how the *inverse sine* and *inverse cosine* functions can be defined. When working with inverses it is preferable to work with the circular functions since their ranges and domains are sets of real numbers.

The equation

$$\cos x = \frac{1}{2}$$

has infinitely many solutions, namely, $\frac{\pi}{3}$, $-\frac{\pi}{3}$, and all the numbers that differ from either of these by an integral multiple of 2π (see Figure 14-6).

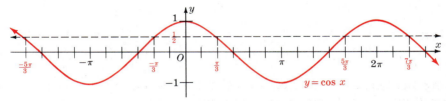

Figure 14-6

If, however, you require that a solution of

$$\cos x = \frac{1}{2}$$

also satisfies the condition

$$0 \le x \le \pi,$$

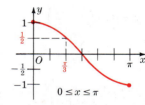

Figure 14-7

then there is *only one* solution, $\frac{\pi}{3}$ (see Figure 14-7).

If you restrict the domain of the cosine function to the interval $0 \le x \le \pi$, you obtain a new function, **Cosine,** whose graph is shown in Figures 14-7 and 14-8. By examining the graph of Cosine, you can see that for any u such that $-1 \le u \le 1$, there is a unique number v that satisfies

$$\text{Cos } v = u.$$

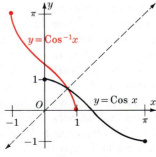

Figure 14-8

The number v is denoted by **Cos^{-1} u,** called "the **inverse cosine** of u." The inverse cosine is also called the **Arc cosine,** denoted **"Arccos."** $\Big($Note that $\text{Cos}^{-1} u$ does *not* mean $\dfrac{1}{\cos u}$.$\Big)$

EXAMPLE 1   Find: **a.** $\text{Cos}^{-1} 0$ **b.** $\text{Cos}^{-1} 1$ **c.** $\text{Cos}^{-1}\left(-\dfrac{\sqrt{2}}{2}\right)$

SOLUTION   **a.** If $v = \text{Cos}^{-1} 0$, then $\cos v = 0$ and $0 \le v \le \pi$.

$\therefore v = \dfrac{\pi}{2}$ and $\text{Cos}^{-1} 0 = \dfrac{\pi}{2}$.   **Answer**

b. Similarly, $\text{Cos}^{-1} 1 = 0$.   **Answer**

c. $\text{Cos}^{-1}\left(-\dfrac{\sqrt{2}}{2}\right) = \dfrac{3\pi}{4}$.   **Answer**

Note that the following statements are equivalent:

$$y = \text{Cos}^{-1} x \qquad \text{Cos}\, y = x$$

Thus, Cos^{-1} and Cos are inverse functions (recall Section 10-4). You can obtain the graph of

$$y = \text{Cos}^{-1} x$$

(shown in red in Figure 14-8) by reflecting the graph of

$$y = \text{Cos}\, x$$

in the line $y = x$.

In defining the **inverse sine function,** denoted **Sin^{-1},** you proceed as above, except that in order to obtain a unique solution of

$$\sin x = a \quad (-1 \le a \le 1),$$

you restrict the sine function to the interval

$$-\dfrac{\pi}{2} \le x \le \dfrac{\pi}{2}$$

instead of $0 \le x \le \pi$. (See Figure 14-9). The inverse sine function is also called the **Arc sine,** denoted **"Arcsin."**

Thus, you have

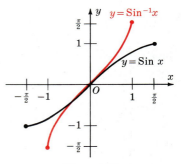

Figure 14-9

$$y = \text{Sin}^{-1} x \quad \text{if and only if} \quad \sin y = x \text{ and } -\dfrac{\pi}{2} \le y \le \dfrac{\pi}{2}.$$

EXAMPLE 2   Find: **a.** $\text{Sin}^{-1}\left(\cos\dfrac{\pi}{3}\right)$ **b.** $\sin\left[\text{Cos}^{-1}\left(-\dfrac{5}{13}\right)\right]$

SOLUTION   **a.** Since $\cos\dfrac{\pi}{3} = \dfrac{1}{2}$, you are to find $\text{Sin}^{-1}\dfrac{1}{2}$.

Since $\sin\dfrac{\pi}{6} = \dfrac{1}{2}$ and $-\dfrac{\pi}{2} \le \dfrac{\pi}{6} \le \dfrac{\pi}{2}$,

$\text{Sin}^{-1}\left(\cos\dfrac{\pi}{3}\right) = \dfrac{\pi}{6}$.   **Answer**

b. Let $v = \text{Cos}^{-1}\left(-\frac{5}{13}\right)$.

Then $\cos v = -\frac{5}{13}$ and $0 \leq v \leq \pi$.

$$\therefore \ \sin v = \sqrt{1 - \cos^2 v}$$
$$= \sqrt{1 - \left(-\frac{5}{13}\right)^2} = \frac{12}{13}. \quad \textbf{\textit{Answer}}$$

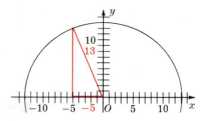

A sketch can be helpful in solving problems of this type.

Oral Exercises

State the value of each of the following expressions.

1. $\text{Cos}^{-1} 1$ **2.** $\text{Cos}^{-1} 0$ **3.** $\text{Cos}^{-1}(-1)$ **4.** $\text{Sin}^{-1}(-1)$

5. $\text{Cos}^{-1}\frac{1}{2}$ **6.** $\text{Sin}^{-1}\left(-\frac{1}{2}\right)$ **7.** $\text{Sin}^{-1}\frac{\sqrt{2}}{2}$ **8.** $\text{Cos}^{-1}\frac{\sqrt{2}}{2}$

State **a.** the domain and **b.** the range of the functions defined by the following formulas.

9. $f(x) = \text{Cos}^{-1} x$ **10.** $f(x) = \text{Sin}^{-1} x$ **11.** $f(x) = \text{Sin}^{-1}(\sin x)$

Written Exercises

Evaluate each of the following expressions.

A   **1.** $\text{Sin}^{-1}\left(\sin \frac{3\pi}{2}\right)$ **2.** $\text{Cos}^{-1}\left[\cos\left(-\frac{\pi}{4}\right)\right]$ **3.** $\text{Cos}^{-1}[\cos(-\pi)]$

    4. $\text{Sin}^{-1}\left(\sin \frac{7\pi}{6}\right)$ **5.** $\text{Sin}^{-1}\left(\sin \frac{3\pi}{4}\right)$ **6.** $\text{Cos}^{-1}\left(\cos \frac{5\pi}{3}\right)$

    7. $\text{Cos}^{-1}\left[\sin\left(-\frac{\pi}{6}\right)\right]$ **8.** $\text{Sin}^{-1}\left[\cos\left(-\frac{\pi}{6}\right)\right]$ **9.** $\sin\left[\text{Cos}^{-1}\left(-\frac{3}{5}\right)\right]$

  10. $\cos\left[\text{Sin}^{-1}\left(-\frac{8}{17}\right)\right]$ **11.** $\cos\left(\text{Sin}^{-1}\frac{12}{13}\right)$ **12.** $\sin\left[\text{Cos}^{-1}\left(-\frac{4}{5}\right)\right]$

  13. $\sin\left(\text{Sin}^{-1}\frac{\sqrt{3}}{2} + \text{Cos}^{-1}\frac{1}{2}\right)$ **14.** $\cos\left[\text{Cos}^{-1}\left(-\frac{\sqrt{3}}{2}\right) + \text{Sin}^{-1}\frac{1}{2}\right]$

  15. $\cos\left(2\,\text{Cos}^{-1}\frac{\sqrt{2}}{2}\right)$ **16.** $\sin\left[2\,\text{Cos}^{-1}\left(-\frac{1}{2}\right)\right]$

For each exercise, **a.** express without using trigonometric or inverse trigonometric functions and **b.** draw the graph.

B   **17.** $y = \cos(\text{Cos}^{-1} x)$ **18.** $y = \sin(\text{Cos}^{-1} x)$ **19.** $y = \cos(-\text{Sin}^{-1} x)$

Prove the following statements.

C   **20.** $\text{Sin}^{-1}\frac{3}{5} + \text{Sin}^{-1}\frac{12}{13} = \text{Cos}^{-1}\left(-\frac{16}{65}\right)$ **21.** $\text{Cos}^{-1}\left(-\frac{2}{3}\right) - \text{Cos}^{-1}\frac{2}{3} = \text{Cos}^{-1}\frac{1}{9}$

14-7 *More on Inverse Functions*

OBJECTIVE   To evaluate expressions involving inverse sine, cosine, tangent, cotangent, secant, and cosecant functions.

In this section you will see that an inverse function can be defined for the other four circular functions.

The **inverse tangent function** (denoted **Tan⁻¹**), or **Arc tangent function,** is defined as follows:

$$y = \text{Tan}^{-1}\, x \text{ if and only if } \tan y = x$$

$$\text{and } -\frac{\pi}{2} < y < \frac{\pi}{2}.$$

The notation Arctan x is often used in place of Tan⁻¹ x.

Notice that:

$$\text{Tan}^{-1}\, 1 = \frac{\pi}{4}$$

$$\text{Tan}^{-1}\, (-1) = -\frac{\pi}{4}$$

$$\text{Tan}^{-1}\, \sqrt{3} = \frac{\pi}{3}$$

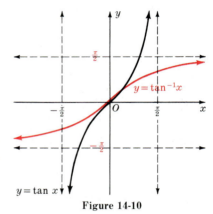

Figure 14-10

These and similar values can be used to draw the graph of the inverse tangent function, as shown in Figure 14-10.

The **inverse cotangent function** (denoted **Cot⁻¹**), or **Arc cotangent function,** is defined as follows:

$$y = \text{Cot}^{-1}\, x \quad \text{if and only if} \quad \cot y = x \text{ and } 0 < y < \pi.$$

The notation Arccot x is often used in place of Cot⁻¹ x.

The remaining inverse circular functions, **inverse secant** and **inverse cosecant,** can be defined in terms of those already discussed.

$$\text{If } |x| \geq 1,\ \text{Sec}^{-1}\, x = \text{Cos}^{-1}\frac{1}{x}, \quad \text{and} \quad \text{Csc}^{-1}\, x = \text{Sin}^{-1}\frac{1}{x}.$$

EXAMPLE 1   Evaluate $\tan\left[\text{Sin}^{-1}\left(-\frac{4}{5}\right) + \text{Tan}^{-1}\frac{1}{3}\right]$.

SOLUTION   Let $a = \text{Sin}^{-1}\left(-\frac{4}{5}\right)$ and $b = \text{Tan}^{-1}\frac{1}{3}$. Since

$$\tan(a + b) = \frac{\tan a + \tan b}{1 - \tan a \tan b},$$

you need to find $\tan a$ and $\tan b$.

Since $b = \text{Tan}^{-1} \frac{1}{3}$, you have $\tan b = \frac{1}{3}$.

Since $a = \text{Sin}^{-1} \left(-\frac{4}{5} \right)$, you have $\sin a = -\frac{4}{5}$.

Since a is restricted to the interval $-\frac{\pi}{2} \le a \le \frac{\pi}{2}$

and $\sin a$ is negative, you have $-\frac{\pi}{2} < a < 0$.

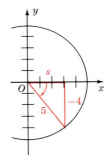

Sketch an appropriate right triangle, as shown, and use the Pythagorean theorem to determine s. You find $s = 3$, and hence,

$$\tan a = -\frac{4}{3}.$$

$$\therefore \tan\left[\text{Sin}^{-1}\left(-\frac{4}{5}\right) + \text{Tan}^{-1}\frac{1}{3}\right] = \frac{-\frac{4}{3} + \frac{1}{3}}{1 - \left(-\frac{4}{3}\right)\frac{1}{3}} = -\frac{9}{13}. \quad \textbf{\textit{Answer}}$$

EXAMPLE 2 Find an expression for $\sin(2\,\text{Cot}^{-1} x)$ that does not involve circular or inverse circular functions.

SOLUTION Plan: Use the formula $\sin 2y = 2 \sin y \cos y$ with $y = \text{Cot}^{-1} x$. Then $\cot y = x$ and $0 < y < \pi$.

$$\csc^2 y = 1 + \cot^2 y = 1 + x^2,$$

and so

$$\sin^2 y = \frac{1}{1 + x^2} \text{ and } \sin y = \frac{1}{\sqrt{1 + x^2}}.$$

From

$$\cos^2 y = 1 - \sin^2 y = 1 - \frac{1}{1 + x^2} = \frac{x^2}{1 + x^2},$$

you find

$$\cos y = \frac{x}{\sqrt{1 + x^2}}.$$

$$\therefore \sin(2\,\text{Cot}^{-1} x) = \sin 2y = 2 \sin y \cos y$$

$$= 2 \cdot \frac{1}{\sqrt{1 + x^2}} \cdot \frac{x}{\sqrt{1 + x^2}} = \frac{2x}{1 + x^2}. \quad \textbf{\textit{Answer}}$$

The material in this section and the preceding one can be restated to define the inverse *trigonometric* functions. For example, $\text{Tan}^{-1} \sqrt{3}$ can be interpreted as the *angle* whose tangent is $\sqrt{3}$ and which lies between $-90°$ and $90°$, that is, $\text{Tan}^{-1} \sqrt{3} = 60°$.

Oral Exercises

State the domain and range of each function as **(a)** an inverse circular function and **(b)** an inverse trigonometric function.

1. Tan^{-1} 2. Cot^{-1} 3. Sin^{-1}

4. Cos^{-1} 5. Sec^{-1} 6. Csc^{-1}

State the value of each of the following expressions as **(a)** a real number and **(b)** an angle.

7. $\text{Tan}^{-1}(-1)$ 8. $\text{Cos}^{-1}\left(\frac{\sqrt{3}}{2}\right)$ 9. $\text{Sin}^{-1}\left(-\frac{1}{2}\right)$

10. $\text{Cot}^{-1} 0$ 11. $\text{Tan}^{-1}\left(-\frac{\sqrt{3}}{3}\right)$ 12. $\text{Tan}^{-1} 0$

Written Exercises

Evaluate each of the following expressions.

A
1. $\sec\left(\text{Cos}^{-1}\frac{4}{7}\right)$ 2. $\tan\left(\text{Cot}^{-1} 5\right)$

3. $\csc\left(\text{Tan}^{-1}\frac{8}{15}\right)$ 4. $\cot\left(\text{Sin}^{-1}\frac{12}{13}\right)$

5. $2\tan\left[\text{Sin}^{-1}\left(-\frac{5}{13}\right)\right]$ 6. $2\csc\left[\text{Cos}^{-1}\left(-\frac{15}{17}\right)\right]$

7. $\tan\left(\text{Sec}^{-1}\frac{3}{2}\right)$ 8. $\cot\left(\text{Sin}^{-1}\frac{1}{3}\right)$

9. $\sin\left(\text{Cot}^{-1}(-2)\right)$ 10. $\cos\left(\text{Csc}^{-1}(-3)\right)$

11. $\sin\left[2\,\text{Cos}^{-1}\left(-\frac{3}{5}\right)\right]$ 12. $\cos\left[2\,\text{Tan}^{-1}\left(-\frac{4}{3}\right)\right]$

13. $\sin\left(\text{Cos}^{-1}\frac{3\sqrt{10}}{10} + \text{Sin}^{-1}\frac{\sqrt{5}}{5}\right)$ 14. $\tan\left(\text{Sin}^{-1}\frac{3}{5} + \text{Tan}^{-1}\frac{3}{5}\right)$

15. $\cot\left[\text{Tan}^{-1}\left(-\frac{4}{3}\right) - \text{Tan}^{-1}\left(-\frac{1}{7}\right)\right]$ 16. $\cos\left[\text{Sin}^{-1}\left(-\frac{16}{65}\right) + \text{Tan}^{-1}\left(-\frac{3}{4}\right)\right]$

Write without using circular or inverse circular functions.

B
17. $\tan\left(\text{Sin}^{-1} 2x\right)$ 18. $\sin\left(\text{Cos}^{-1}\frac{x}{2}\right)$ 19. $\cos\left(2\,\text{Tan}^{-1} x\right)$

20. $\cot\left(2\,\text{Cos}^{-1} x\right)$ 21. $\sin\left(\text{Cos}^{-1} x + \text{Cos}^{-1} y\right)$ 22. $\tan\left(\text{Cot}^{-1} x - \text{Cot}^{-1} y\right)$

Prove each statement.

23. $\text{Tan}^{-1}\frac{3}{4} + \text{Tan}^{-1}\frac{1}{7} = \frac{\pi}{4}$ 24. $\text{Cos}^{-1}\frac{3}{5} + \text{Sin}^{-1}\left(-\frac{5}{13}\right) = \frac{\pi}{2} - \text{Sin}^{-1}\frac{56}{65}$

25. $\text{Tan}^{-1}\frac{5}{3} - \text{Tan}^{-1}\frac{1}{4} = \frac{\pi}{4}$ 26. $\text{Sin}^{-1}\frac{3}{5} + \text{Cos}^{-1}\left(-\frac{5}{13}\right) = \text{Cos}^{-1}\left(-\frac{56}{65}\right)$

Self-Test 2

VOCABULARY Cosine (p. 537)
inverse cosine function,
    Cos^{-1} (p. 537)
Arc cosine (p. 537)
inverse sine function, Sin^{-1}
    (p. 538)
Arc sine (p. 538)
inverse tangent function,
    Tan^{-1} (p. 540)

Arc tangent (p. 540)
inverse cotangent function,
    Cot^{-1} (p. 540)
Arc cotangent (p. 540)
inverse secant function,
    Sec^{-1} (p. 540)
inverse cosecant function,
    Csc^{-1} (p. 540)

1. State the period of each function.   **Obj. 14-5, p. 534**

   a. $y = \cot x$ **b.** $y = \tan 4x$ **c.** $y = \sec 2x$

2. Sketch the graph of $y = \tan x$ over the interval $-\pi \le x \le \pi$.

3. Evaluate: **Obj. 14-6, p. 537**

   a. $\mathrm{Sin}^{-1}\left(-\frac{\sqrt{3}}{2}\right)$ **b.** $\mathrm{Sin}^{-1}\left(\sin\frac{\pi}{3}\right)$ **c.** $\mathrm{Cos}^{-1}\left(\cos\frac{5\pi}{6}\right)$

4. Sketch the graph of $y = \mathrm{Sin}^{-1} x$.

5. Evaluate: **Obj. 14-7, p. 540**

   a. $\mathrm{Cot}^{-1} 1$ **b.** $\mathrm{Tan}^{-1}\left(-\sqrt{3}\right)$ **c.** $\sec\left(\mathrm{Sin}^{-1}\frac{1}{3}\right)$

Check your answers with those at the back of the book.

Computer Key-In

BASIC does not have inverse sine or inverse cosine functions. When solving triangles, therefore, you may need to use the inverse tangent function to find one or more angles.

When two sides and the included angle (a, b, C) are given, a second angle can be found using the law of cosines and the law of sines. First, c is found: $c = \sqrt{a^2 + b^2 - 2ab \cos C}$.

Then: $\cos A = (b^2 + c^2 - a^2)/2bc$, $\sin A = (a \sin C)/c$,

     $\tan A = \sin A/\cos A$, $\angle A = \mathrm{ATN}(\tan A)$, $\angle B = 180 - \angle A - \angle C$

When three sides of a triangle are given, two angles may be found by the preceding method. Alternatively, these special formulas may be used:

$$\tan\frac{A}{2} = \sqrt{\frac{(s-b)(s-c)}{s(s-a)}}, \qquad \tan\frac{B}{2} = \sqrt{\frac{(s-c)(s-a)}{s(s-b)}}$$

where $s = (a + b + c)/2$. Then $\angle C = 180 - \angle A - \angle B$.

Write a program to solve a triangle:

1. When two sides and the included angle are given.

2. When three sides are given.

14-8 *Trigonometric Equations*

OBJECTIVE   To solve trigonometric equations.

To solve equations involving trigonometric functions, you can use algebraic transformations, trigonometric identities, and properties of inverse functions. The strategy used in the first two examples below is to transform the equation so it contains only one trigonometric function.

EXAMPLE 1   Solve $\sin \alpha = 3 \cos \alpha$ for α, $0° \le \alpha < 360°$.

SOLUTION   By dividing both sides of the equation by $\cos \alpha$, you get

$$\frac{\sin \alpha}{\cos \alpha} = 3, \quad \text{or} \quad \tan \alpha = 3.$$

By Table 4, the reference angle is approximately $71.6°$.
In the first quadrant, the solution is $71.6°$.
In the third quadrant, the solution is $251.6°$.
$\therefore$ the solution set is $\{71.6°, 251.6°\}$.   *Answer*

You are often asked for the solution set in a particular interval, usually the interval $0° \le \alpha < 360°$ or $0 \le x < 2\pi$. This solution set is called the **particular solution.** The set $\{71.6°, 251.6°\}$ is the particular solution of the equation $\sin \alpha = 3 \cos \alpha$ in the interval $0° \le \alpha < 360°$. The remaining solutions of the equation $\sin \alpha = 3 \cos \alpha$ differ from these two solutions by integral multiples of $180°$, the period of the tangent function. Thus, all solutions are of the form

$$\alpha = 71.6° + \text{multiples of } 180°$$
$$= 71.6° + n \cdot 180°, \ n \text{ an integer.}$$

Therefore, the **general solution** is

$$\{\alpha: \alpha = (71.6 + 180n)°\}.$$

EXAMPLE 2   **a.** Find the particular solution of $\cos 2x = 3 \cos x + 1$ in the interval $0 \le x < 2\pi$.

b. Find the general solution of the equation in part (a).

SOLUTION   **a.** There are three formulas for $\cos 2x$. By choosing $\cos 2x = 2 \cos^2 x - 1$, you can transform the equation so that $\cos x$ is the only trigonometric function the equation contains:

$$\cos 2x = 3 \cos x + 1$$
$$2 \cos^2 x - 1 = 3 \cos x + 1$$

The preceding equation is a quadratic equation in $\cos x$. Treat $\cos x$ as a quantity and solve first for $\cos x$, then for x:

$$2\cos^2 x - 3\cos x - 2 = 0$$
$$(2\cos x + 1)(\cos x - 2) = 0$$

$2\cos x + 1 = 0$	$\cos x - 2 = 0$
$\cos x = -\dfrac{1}{2}$	$\cos x = 2$
$x = \dfrac{2\pi}{3}, \dfrac{4\pi}{3}$	No solution since $-1 \le \cos x \le 1$.

$\therefore$ the particular solution is $\left\{\dfrac{2\pi}{3}, \dfrac{4\pi}{3}\right\}$. ***Answer***

b. Since the cosine function has period 2π, the general solution is

$$\left\{x: x = \frac{2\pi}{3} + n \cdot 2\pi \text{ or } x = \frac{4\pi}{3} + n \cdot 2\pi, n \text{ an integer}\right\}.$$

As illustrated in Example 3, it is not always necessary to transform the equation into one involving a single trigonometric function.

EXAMPLE 3   Solve $3\sin 2x = 4\cos x$ for x, $0 \le x < 2\pi$.

SOLUTION   Substituting $2\sin x \cos x$ for $\sin 2x$, you obtain

$$6\sin x \cos x = 4\cos x.$$

If you succumb to the temptation to divide both sides by $\cos x$ at this point, you will lose those solutions for which $\cos x = 0$. Rather, divide by 2, set the equation equal to 0, and factor:

$$3\sin x \cos x - 2\cos x = 0$$
$$\cos x\,(3\sin x - 2) = 0$$

$\cos x = 0$	$3\sin x - 2 = 0$
$x = \dfrac{\pi}{2}, \dfrac{3\pi}{2}$	$\sin x = \dfrac{2}{3} \approx 0.6667$
	From Table 6, reference angle $= 0.73$
	In the first quadrant, $x = 0.73$
	In the second quadrant, $x = \pi - 0.73 \approx 2.41$

$\therefore$ the solution set is $\left\{0.73, \dfrac{\pi}{2}, 2.41, \dfrac{3\pi}{2}\right\}$. ***Answer***

To solve the next type of trigonometric equation, you must first solve for a function of α such as $(\alpha + 50°)$ or (3α). This intermediate step involves shifting or stretching the interval asked for in the particular solution.

EXAMPLE 4   **a.** Solve $\sin(\theta + 40°) = \dfrac{1}{2}$ for θ, $0° \le \theta < 360°$.

                b. Solve $\tan 3x = 1$ for $0 \le x < 2\pi$.

(See page 546 for the solution.)

SOLUTION   **a.** Do not use the formula for $\sin(\alpha + \beta)$ to expand $\sin(\theta + 40°)$. Rather, solve directly for the quantity $\theta + 40°$. Since you are solving for θ in the interval $0° \le \theta < 360°$, you must look for $\theta + 40°$ in the interval $40° \le \theta + 40° < 400°$.

Since $\sin(\theta + 40°) = \frac{1}{2}$,

$$\theta + 40° = 150°, 390°.$$

Therefore,

$$\theta = 110°, 350°.$$

Notice that both solutions for θ are in the interval $0° \le \theta < 360°$.

$\therefore$ the solution set is $\{110°, 350°\}$.   **Answer**

b. Since you are solving for x in the interval $0 \le x < 2\pi$, you must look for $3x$ in the interval $0 \le 3x < 6\pi$.

Since $\tan 3x = 1$:

$$3x = \frac{\pi}{4}, \frac{5\pi}{4}, \frac{9\pi}{4}, \frac{13\pi}{4}, \frac{17\pi}{4}, \frac{21\pi}{4}$$

$$x = \frac{\pi}{12}, \frac{5\pi}{12}, \frac{3\pi}{4}, \frac{13\pi}{12}, \frac{17\pi}{12}, \frac{7\pi}{4}$$

Notice that all solutions are in the interval $0 \le x < 2\pi$.

$\therefore$ the solution set is $\left\{\frac{\pi}{12}, \frac{5\pi}{12}, \frac{3\pi}{4}, \frac{13\pi}{12}, \frac{17\pi}{12}, \frac{7\pi}{4}\right\}$.   **Answer**

Oral Exercises

How many solutions will each equation have in the interval $0 \le x < 2\pi$?

1. $\cos x = \frac{3}{5}$

2. $\sin x = 1$

3. $\sin x (\tan x + 1) = 0$

4. $\sin 2x = \frac{1}{2}$

5. $\csc x = \frac{1}{2}$

6. $\cos \frac{1}{2}x = \frac{\sqrt{3}}{2}$

7. When solving $5 \tan(\alpha + 10°) = 2$, would you use the formula for $\tan(\alpha + \beta)$ or would you solve for the quantity $\alpha + 10°$?

8. When solving $\cos 2x = \cos x$, which formula for $\cos 2x$ would you use?

9. When solving $2 \cos 2x = 1$, would you use the double-angle formula for $\cos 2x$ or would you solve for $\cos 2x$?

Describe the method you would use to solve each equation for θ, $0° \le \theta < 360°$.

10. $\sin \theta = \cos \theta$

11. $\tan \theta = \sin \theta$

12. $\cos(\theta - 40°) = 1$

13. $\sin 2\theta = \sin \theta$

14. $\tan^2 \theta - 3 \tan \theta = 0$

15. $\sin 4\theta = \sin 2\theta$

Written Exercises

Solve for α, $0° \le \alpha < 360°$. Give your answers to the nearest tenth of a degree. Use tables or a calculator when necessary.

A 1. $4 \sin \alpha = 3$

2. $5 \cos \alpha = -2$

3. $\sin \alpha = 5 \cos \alpha$

4. $3 \sin \alpha = \cos \alpha$

5. $\tan \alpha = \cot \alpha$

6. $1 + \csc \alpha = 4$

7. $\sin^2 \alpha = \dfrac{1}{4}$

8. $5 \sin \alpha = \csc \alpha$

9. $\cos \alpha = \sec \alpha$

10. $5 \cos \alpha = 2 \sin \alpha$

11. $\tan (\alpha + 15°) = 1$

12. $\sec (\alpha - 5°) = 2$

Solve for x, $0 \le x < 2\pi$. Give your answers to the nearest hundredth of a radian unless the answer can be expressed exactly in terms of π. Use tables or a calculator when necessary.

13. $3 \csc x = 8$

14. $2 \cot x = 3$

15. $4 \sin x - 3 \cos x = 0$

16. $3 \sin x + 2 \cos x = 0$

17. $\sec x + 9 \cos x = 0$

18. $\sec x = \csc x$

19. $5 \tan x - 2 \cot x = 0$

20. $3 \sec x = 4 \cos x$

21. $2 \sin x = \dfrac{1}{2 \sec x}$

22. $\dfrac{3}{1 + 5 \sin x} = 2$

23. $\sin 2x = 1$

24. $\cos 3x = \dfrac{\sqrt{3}}{2}$

Solve for θ, $0° \le \theta < 360°$.

B 25. $5 \tan^2 \theta - \tan \theta = 0$

26. $\sec^2 \theta + 2 \sec \theta = 0$

27. $3 \sin^2 \theta - 2 \sin \theta - 1 = 0$

28. $2 \cos^2 \theta - 3 \cos \theta + 1 = 0$

29. $\tan^2 \theta - 3 \tan \theta + 2 = 0$

30. $2 \sin^2 \theta - \sin \theta = 0$

31. $2 \tan^2 \theta - 3 \tan \theta + 1 = 0$

32. $\sec^2 \theta - 5 \sec \theta + 6 = 0$

33. $\sec^2 \theta - 4 = 0$

34. $3 \sin^2 \theta = 2 \cos \theta \sin \theta$

35. $2 \cos^2 \theta - \cos \theta - 1 = 0$

36. $6 \sin^2 \theta - 7 \sin \theta + 2 = 0$

37. $\sec \theta - 2 \cos \theta = 1$

38. $2 \sin \theta + 2 \csc \theta = 5$

39. $\cos^2 \theta - 3 \sin \theta = 3$

40. $\sec^2 \theta = 3 \tan \theta - 1$

41. $\cot^2 \theta = 1 + \csc \theta$

42. $2 \sin \theta \cos \theta = \tan \theta$

43. $\sin 2\theta = \sin \theta$

44. $\cos 2\theta = 2 \sin^2 \theta$

45. $\cos^2 \theta + \sin 2\theta = 0$

46. $\cos 2\theta + \cos \theta + 1 = 0$

47. $2 \sin (\theta + 75°) = 1$

48. $2 \cos (\theta - 60°) = \sqrt{2}$

49. $3 \cos 4\theta + 1 = 0$

50. $\tan 2\theta = -\sqrt{3}$

51. $\sin \left(\dfrac{\theta}{2} \right) = 4 \cos \left(\dfrac{\theta}{2} \right)$

52. $\sec 3\theta = \csc 3\theta$

53. $4 \cos 3\theta = \sec 3\theta$

54. $\tan (\theta - 15°) = 3 \cot (\theta - 15°)$

55. $\cos 6\theta = \cos^2 3\theta$

56. $\sin 4\theta = \cos 2\theta$

C 57. $2(\sin \theta + \cos \theta) = \sec \theta$

58. $\tan^2 \theta - \sin^2 \theta = \tan^2 \theta \sin^2 \theta$

59. $\tan^2 \theta - 4 \tan \theta + 2 = 0$

60. $\sin^2 \theta - \sin \theta - 1 = 0$

14-9 *Trigonometric Form of Complex Numbers*

OBJECTIVE **To plot complex numbers in the complex plane and to express a given complex number in both the $a + bi$ form and the trigonometric form.**

Like the ordered pair (a, b), the complex number $a + bi$ is uniquely determined by two numbers, a and b. Thus, you can graph complex numbers on a rectangular coordinate system much as you do ordered pairs of real numbers.

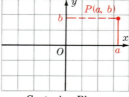 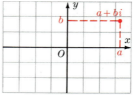

Figure 14-11   Cartesian Plane   Complex Plane

When points in a rectangular coordinate system are used to represent complex numbers, the coordinate system is called the **complex plane** rather than the Cartesian plane. As shown in Figure 14-11 above, the point that represents $a + bi$ in the complex plane corresponds to the point that represents (a, b) in the Cartesian plane. In the Cartesian plane, the x- and y-axes are real number lines. In the complex plane, the horizontal axis is called the **axis of reals** (or **real axis**) and the vertical axis is called the **axis of imaginaries** (or **imaginary axis**). Figure 14-12 illustrates the graph of five complex numbers.

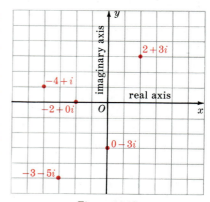

Figure 14-12

The point corresponding to $a + bi$ in the complex plane is often represented by an arrow drawn from the origin to the point (Figure 14-13). Such diagrams are called **Argand diagrams.** By the Pythagorean theorem, the length of the arrow (r) is $\sqrt{a^2 + b^2}$. This expression is called the **absolute value** of a + bi.* In general,

$$|a + bi| = \sqrt{a^2 + b^2}.$$

Therefore, the *absolute value* of a complex number is equal to its distance from the origin in an Argand diagram.

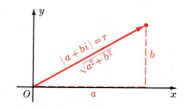

Figure 14-13

---

*If you studied the material on pages 242-244 in the Extra section at the end of Chapter 6, you should be familiar with the absolute value of a complex number.

An angle θ in standard position, whose terminal ray is the arrow from the origin to $a + bi$, is called the **amplitude** of $a + bi$ (Figure 14-14). Since

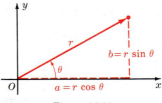

$$r = \sqrt{a^2 + b^2}, \cos \theta = \frac{a}{r}, \text{ and } \sin \theta = \frac{b}{r},$$

it follows that

$$a = r \cos \theta \text{ and } b = r \sin \theta.$$

Figure 14-14

Therefore,

$$a + bi = r \cos \theta + i r \sin \theta = r (\cos \theta + i \sin \theta).$$

In general:

The **trigonometric form** for the complex number $a + bi$ $(a^2 + b^2 \neq 0)$ is given by

$$a + bi = r (\cos \theta + i \sin \theta),$$

where $r = \sqrt{a^2 + b^2}$, $\cos \theta = \frac{a}{r}$, and $\sin \theta = \frac{b}{r}$.

In this book, θ will be chosen as the angle of *least nonnegative measure*. That is, $0° \leq \theta < 360°$.

EXAMPLE   Express: **a.** $-3 + 2i$ in trigonometric form.

b. $\sqrt{2} (\cos 315° + i \sin 315°)$ in the form $a + bi$.

SOLUTION

a. First, plot $-3 + 2i$ in the complex plane. Next, compute r.

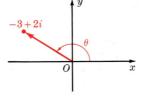

$$r = \sqrt{a^2 + b^2} = \sqrt{(-3)^2 + 2^2} = \sqrt{13}.$$

Using the definition of $\sin \theta$, you obtain

$$\sin \theta = \frac{b}{r} = \frac{2}{\sqrt{13}} = \frac{2\sqrt{13}}{13} \approx 0.5547.$$

From Table 4 or a calculator, the reference angle $\alpha = 33.7°$. Since θ is a second-quadrant angle,

$$\theta = 180° - 33.7° = 146.3°.$$

$$\therefore \ -3 + 2i \approx \sqrt{13} (\cos 146.3° + i \sin 146.3°) \quad \textbf{\textit{Answer}}$$

b. Since $\cos 315° = \cos 45° = \frac{\sqrt{2}}{2}$ and $\sin 315° = -\sin 45° = -\frac{\sqrt{2}}{2}$,

$$\sqrt{2} (\cos 315° + i \sin 315°) = \sqrt{2}\left(\frac{\sqrt{2}}{2} - i\frac{\sqrt{2}}{2}\right) = 1 - i. \quad \textbf{\textit{Answer}}$$

Oral Exercises

State the quadrant containing the graph of each complex number or state that the point lies on the real or on the imaginary axis.

1. $3 + 4i$ **2.** $5 - 2i$ **3.** $-1 - 7i$ **4.** 5

5. $-3 + 6i$ **6.** $-3i$ **7.** $2 - i$ **8.** $-3 - 3i$

9–16. Find the absolute value of each complex number in Exercises 1–8.

Written Exercises

Plot each set of numbers in the complex plane.

A **1.** $\{5 + 3i, -4 + 2i, 2i\}$ **2.** $\{3 - 6i, 1 + i, -4i\}$

   3. $\{2 - 5i, 5, -3 - 3i\}$ **4.** $\{-2, -4 + 3i, -1 - 6i\}$

   5. $\{0, 3 + i, 3 - i\}$ **6.** $\{-3 - 5i, -3 + 5i, 3 + 5i, 3 - 5i\}$

Express each complex number in the form $a + bi$. Leave a and b in simplest radical form when necessary.

7. $4(\cos 30° + i \sin 30°)$ **8.** $\sqrt{2}(\cos 45° + i \sin 45°)$

9. $3\sqrt{2}(\cos 135° + i \sin 135°)$ **10.** $2(\cos 240° + i \sin 240°)$

11. $5(\cos 0° + i \sin 0°)$ **12.** $3(\cos 90° + i \sin 90°)$

13. $\sqrt{3}(\cos 300° + i \sin 300°)$ **14.** $\dfrac{\sqrt{3}}{2}(\cos 330° + i \sin 330°)$

Express each complex number in the form $a + bi$. Give a and b to the nearest ten-thousandth, using Table 4 or a calculator.

15. $4(\cos 126° + i \sin 126°)$ **16.** $4(\cos 244° + i \sin 244°)$

17. $10(\cos 352.4° + i \sin 352.4°)$ **18.** $100(\cos 179.3° + i \sin 179.3°)$

Express each complex number in trigonometric form. When necessary, leave r in simplest radical form. Use Table 4 or a calculator only when necessary. Give your answers to the nearest tenth of a degree.

B **19.** $2 + 2i$ **20.** $1 + i\sqrt{3}$ **21.** $2\sqrt{3} - 2i$ **22.** $-5\sqrt{2} + i5\sqrt{2}$

   23. $3 - 4i$ **24.** $15 + 8i$ **25.** $2 + i$ **26.** $-5 - 12i$

   27. 3 **28.** -3 **29.** $3i$ **30.** $-3i$

In Exercises 31–32, z_1 and z_2 denote complex numbers.
a. Find $z_1 z_2$.
b. Find $|z_1|$, $|z_2|$, and $|z_1 z_2|$. How do these quantities compare?
c. Graph z_1, z_2 and $z_1 z_2$ in an Argand diagram.
d. Use a protractor to compare the amplitudes of z_1, z_2, and $z_1 z_2$.

C **31.** $z_1 = 3 + 3i, z_2 = \sqrt{3} + i$ **32.** $z_1 = 6 + 8i, z_2 = \frac{1}{2}i$

Self-Test 3

VOCABULARY particular solution (p. 544)   Argand diagram (p. 548)
general solution (p. 544)   amplitude of a complex
complex plane (p. 548)   number (p. 549)
real axis (p. 548)   trigonometric form of a
imaginary axis (p. 548)   complex number (p. 549)

Solve for θ, $0° \le \theta < 360°$. Give your answers to the nearest tenth of a degree.

1. $5 \cos \theta = 4$ **2.** $\cos \theta = 10 \sin \theta$ **Obj. 14-8, p. 544**

3. $2 \sin^2 \theta + 3 \sin \theta + 1 = 0$ **4.** $\sin 3\theta = -\frac{1}{2}$

5. Write $2 \left(\cos \frac{\pi}{6} + i \sin \frac{\pi}{6} \right)$ in the form $a + bi$.   **Obj. 14-9, p. 548**

6. Write $2 - 2i$ in trigonometric form.

Check your answers with those at the back of the book.

EXTRA

Products and Powers of Complex Numbers

The following theorem shows how to multiply two complex numbers that are expressed in trigonometric form.

> **THEOREM** If $z_1 = r(\cos \alpha + i \sin \alpha)$ and $z_2 = s(\cos \beta + i \sin \beta)$,
> then $z_1 z_2 = rs[\cos (\alpha + \beta) + i \sin (\alpha + \beta)]$.

PROOF

$$
\begin{aligned}
z_1 z_2 &= r(\cos \alpha + i \sin \alpha) \cdot s(\cos \beta + i \sin \beta) \\
&= rs(\cos \alpha \cos \beta + i \cos \alpha \sin \beta + i \sin \alpha \cos \beta - \sin \alpha \sin \beta) \\
&= rs[(\cos \alpha \cos \beta - \sin \alpha \sin \beta) + i(\sin \alpha \cos \beta + \cos \alpha \sin \beta)] \\
&= rs[\cos (\alpha + \beta) + i \sin (\alpha + \beta)]
\end{aligned}
$$

If you think of $z_1 z_2$ as a vector in the complex plane, its length is rs and it makes an angle of $\alpha + \beta$ with the positive x-axis. Thus, you can multiply two complex numbers in trigonometric form by (1) multiplying their lengths (absolute values), and (2) adding their angles.

EXAMPLE 1 Find $z_1 z_2$ if $z_1 = 2(\cos 20° + i \sin 20°)$ and
$z_2 = 3(\cos 50° + i \sin 50°)$.

(*The solution is on page 552.*)

SOLUTION

1. $r = 2$ and $s = 3$
   $\therefore rs = 3 \cdot 2 = 6$
2. $\alpha = 20°$ and $\beta = 50°$
   $\therefore \alpha + \beta = 70°$
   $\therefore z_1 z_2 = 6(\cos 70° + i \sin 70°)$ *Answer*

By successive applications of the previous theorem, you can obtain the following theorem, named after the French mathematician Abraham De Moivre.

DE MOIVRE'S THEOREM

If $z = r(\cos \theta + i \sin \theta)$ and n is a positive integer, then $z^n = r^n(\cos n\theta + i \sin n\theta)$.

EXAMPLE 2   If $z = 1 + i\sqrt{3}$, find z^5.

SOLUTION

1. Convert z to trigonometric form.
   $$|z| = |1 + i\sqrt{3}| = \sqrt{1 + 3} = 2$$
   $$\therefore z = 2\left(\frac{1}{2} + i\frac{\sqrt{3}}{2}\right) = 2(\cos 60° + i \sin 60°)$$

2. By De Moivre's theorem:
   $$z^5 = 2^5(\cos 5 \cdot 60° + i \sin 5 \cdot 60°)$$
   $$= 32(\cos 300° + i \sin 300°)$$
   $$= 32\left(\frac{1}{2} - \frac{\sqrt{3}}{2}\right)$$
   $$\therefore z^5 = 16 - 16i\sqrt{3}$$ *Answer*

The theorem on page 551 can be extended to cover division of complex numbers. (See Exercise 24.)

THEOREM   If $z_1 = r(\cos \alpha + i \sin \alpha)$ and $z_2 = s(\cos \beta + i \sin \beta)$, then $\dfrac{z_1}{z_2} = \dfrac{r}{s}[\cos(\alpha - \beta) + i \sin(\alpha - \beta)]$.

Exercises

Let $z_1 = 2(\cos 10° + i \sin 10°)$, $z_2 = 3(\cos 40° + i \sin 40°)$, and $z_3 = 4(\cos 60° + i \sin 60°)$. Find the following in trigonometric form.

A 1. $z_1 z_2$ 2. $z_2 z_3$ 3. $z_1 z_3$ 4. $z_1{}^2$

   5. $z_1{}^3$ 6. $z_2{}^3$ 7. $z_3{}^2$ 8. $z_1 z_2 z_3$

In Exercises 9–14:

a. Find $z_1 z_2$ algebraically.

b. Express z_1 and z_2 in trigonometric form. Use tables or a calculator when necessary.

c. Use the theorem on page 551 to find $z_1 z_2$ in trigonometric form. Verify that your answer agrees with your answer to part (a).

d. Illustrate the exercise with an Argand diagram.

9. $z_1 = i$, $z_2 = 1 + i$

10. $z_1 = -2 + 2i$, $z_2 = -2 - 2i$

11. $z_1 = 2 + 3i$, $z_2 = 2 + 3i$

12. $z_1 = 2 + i$, $z_2 = 2 - i$

13. $z_1 = 3 + i$, $z_2 = -2$

14. $z_1 = 3 - 4i$, $z_2 = -i$

15. a. If $z_1 = -1 + i\sqrt{3}$ and $z_2 = i$, find $\dfrac{z_1}{z_2}$.

   b. Make an Argand diagram of the result in part (a) to illustrate the theorem on quotients on page 552.

16. If $z = \cos 72° + i \sin 72°$, write z^2, z^3, z^4, and z^5 in trigonometric form. Represent these five numbers in an Argand diagram.

17. If $z = 2(\cos 60° + i \sin 60°)$, write z^2, z^3, and z^4 in trigonometric form. Represent these four numbers in an Argand diagram.

18. If $z = 1 - i$, find z, z^4, and z^8 in trigonometric form and simplify.

B 19. a. If $z = -\dfrac{1}{2} + \dfrac{\sqrt{3}}{2}i$, find z, z^3, and z^4 in trigonometric form.

   b. Verify that z is a cube root of 1.

   c. Show that $z^4 = z$.

   d. Show that $z^{100} = z$.

20. Square the complex number $\cos \theta + i \sin \theta$ without using the theorems of this section. Show that your result equals $\cos 2\theta + i \sin 2\theta$.

21. Show that De Moivre's theorem is true for $n = 0$.

22. a. If $z = r(\cos \theta + i \sin \theta)$, then $z^{-1} = \dfrac{1}{r(\cos \theta + i \sin \theta)}$. Multiply the numerator and denominator of this fraction by $\cos \theta - i \sin \theta$ and prove that $z^{-1} = r^{-1}[\cos(-\theta) + i \sin(-\theta)]$. (Recall that $\sin(-\theta) = -\sin \theta$ and $\cos(-\theta) = \cos \theta$.)

   b. Does your result agree with De Moivre's theorem for $n = -1$?

C 23. Use Exercises 21 and 22 to show that De Moivre's theorem holds for $n = -2$.

24. Let $z_1 = r(\cos \alpha + i \sin \alpha)$ and $z_2 = s(\cos \beta + i \sin \beta)$. Prove that $\dfrac{z_1}{z_2} = \dfrac{r}{s}[\cos(\alpha - \beta) + i \sin(\alpha - \beta)]$.

   a. *Method 1:* Multiply the numerator and denominator of $\dfrac{z_1}{z_2}$ by $\cos \beta - i \sin \beta$.

   b. *Method 2:* Write $\dfrac{z_1}{z_2}$ as $z_1 \cdot z_2^{-1}$.

Chapter Summary

1. *Trigonometric addition formulas, double-angle formulas,* and *half-angle formulas* are used to simplify and evaluate expressions, prove identities, and solve equations.

2. Like the graphs of the sine and cosine functions, the graphs of the tangent, cotangent, secant, and cosecant functions have a basic repetitive pattern. The tangent and cotangent have period π. The secant and cosecant have period 2π. The concept of reciprocal functions is useful in illustrating the relationship between the graphs of the cotangent, secant, and cosecant and the graphs of the tangent, cosine, and sine, respectively.

3. The *inverse circular* (or *trigonometric*) *functions* are the inverses of the corresponding circular (or trigonometric) functions restricted to an appropriate interval.

4. You can use algebraic transformations, trigonometric identities, and inverse circular (or trigonometric) functions to solve equations involving circular (or trigonometric) functions.

5. Complex numbers can be represented by points in the complex plane. The trigonometric form of $a + bi$ $(a + bi \neq 0)$ is given by

$$a + bi = r\,(\cos\theta + i\sin\theta),$$

where $r = \sqrt{a^2 + b^2}$, $\cos\theta = \dfrac{a}{r}$, and $\sin\theta = \dfrac{b}{r}$.

Chapter Review

Give the letter of the correct answer.

1. Simplify $\cos 41° \cos 1° + \sin 41° \sin 1°$.   **14-1**

   a. $\sin 40°$ **b.** $\sin 42°$ **c.** $\cos 40°$ **d.** $\cos 42°$

2. Which of the following is an expression for $\sin 105°$?

   a. $\dfrac{\sqrt{6} + \sqrt{2}}{4}$ **b.** $\dfrac{\sqrt{6} - \sqrt{2}}{4}$ **c.** $\dfrac{\sqrt{2} - \sqrt{6}}{4}$ **d.** $\dfrac{\sqrt{3} + \sqrt{2}}{2}$

3. Simplify $\dfrac{\tan 38° - \tan 49°}{1 + \tan 38° \tan 49°}$.   **14-2**

   a. $\tan 87°$ **b.** $-\tan 87°$ **c.** $\tan 11°$ **d.** $-\tan 11°$

4. If $\tan\phi = 2.2$ and $\tan\theta = 0.5$, find $\tan(\phi - \theta)$.

   a. $\dfrac{17}{10}$ **b.** $\dfrac{17}{21}$ **c.** $-\dfrac{17}{21}$ **d.** -27

5. Simplify $1 - 2\sin^2 18°$.   **14-3**

   a. $\sin 9°$ **b.** $\cos 9°$ **c.** $\sin 36°$ **d.** $\cos 36°$

6. Which of the following is *not* identical to $\cos 2x$?

    a. $\cos^2 x - \sin^2 x$ **b.** $\dfrac{1}{\sec 2x}$

    c. $1 - 2\sin^2 x$ **d.** $1 - 2\cos^2 x$

7. If α is a fourth-quadrant angle, and $\cos \alpha = \frac{4}{5}$, find $\cos \frac{\alpha}{2}$.   14-4

    a. $-\dfrac{3\sqrt{10}}{10}$ **b.** $\dfrac{3\sqrt{10}}{10}$ **c.** $-\dfrac{\sqrt{10}}{10}$ **d.** $\dfrac{\sqrt{10}}{10}$

8. If α is a first-quadrant angle, and $\sin \alpha = \frac{8}{17}$, find $\tan \frac{\alpha}{2}$.

    a. $\dfrac{8}{15}$ **b.** 4 **c.** $\dfrac{1}{4}$ **d.** $\dfrac{240}{161}$

9. What is the period of the function $y = \frac{1}{2} \sec \frac{1}{2} x$?   14-5

    a. 2π **b.** 4π **c.** π **d.** 2

10. Evaluate $\operatorname{Sin}^{-1}\left(-\dfrac{\sqrt{3}}{2}\right)$.   14-6

    a. $\dfrac{5\pi}{3}$ **b.** $\dfrac{11\pi}{3}$ **c.** $-\dfrac{\pi}{3}$ **d.** $\dfrac{7\pi}{3}$

11. Evaluate $\operatorname{Cos}^{-1}\left(\cos\left(-\dfrac{\pi}{3}\right)\right)$.

    a. $-\dfrac{\pi}{3}$ **b.** $\dfrac{\pi}{3}$ **c.** $\dfrac{2\pi}{3}$ **d.** $\dfrac{5\pi}{3}$

12. Evaluate $\cos\left(\operatorname{Csc}^{-1}\dfrac{5}{3}\right)$.   14-7

    a. $\dfrac{3}{5}$ **b.** $\dfrac{5}{3}$ **c.** $\dfrac{4}{5}$ **d.** $\dfrac{3}{4}$

13. Find $\cos\left(\operatorname{Tan}^{-1} x\right)$.

    a. $\dfrac{1}{\sqrt{x^2 + 1}}$ **b.** $\sqrt{1 - x^2}$ **c.** $\operatorname{Sin}^{-1} x$ **d.** $\dfrac{1}{x}$

14. How many solutions does the equation $2 \sin 2x = 1$ have in the interval $0 \le x < 2\pi$?   14-8

    a. 1 **b.** 2 **c.** 3 **d.** 4

15. The set $\left\{\dfrac{3\pi}{2}, \dfrac{2\pi}{3}, \dfrac{5\pi}{3}\right\}$ is the particular solution of which of the following equations in the interval $0 \le x < 2\pi$?

    a. $\cos x \left(\tan x + \sqrt{3}\right) = 0$
    b. $\cos x \left(3 \tan x + \sqrt{3}\right) = 0$
    c. $(\sin x + 1)(3 \tan x + \sqrt{3}) = 0$
    d. $(\sin x + 1)(\tan x + \sqrt{3}) = 0$

16. Find the general solution of $\tan x \left(2 \sin x - \sqrt{2}\right) = 0$. Assume n is an integer.

    a. $\left\{0, \dfrac{\pi}{4}, \dfrac{3\pi}{4}\right\}$ **b.** $\left\{n\pi, \dfrac{\pi}{4} + n\pi\right\}$

    c. $\left\{n\pi, \dfrac{\pi}{4} + 2n\pi, \dfrac{3\pi}{4} + 2n\pi\right\}$

17. Express $2\sqrt{3}\left(\cos 210° + i \sin 210°\right)$ in the form $a + bi$.   14-9

    a. $-3 - \sqrt{3}i$ **b.** $-\sqrt{3} - 3i$ **c.** $2\sqrt{3} + 2\sqrt{3}i$ **d.** $-\sqrt{6} - \sqrt{6}i$

18. Express $-4\sqrt{2} + 4\sqrt{2}i$ in trigonometric form.

    a. $8\left(\cos \dfrac{7\pi}{4} + i \sin \dfrac{7\pi}{4}\right)$ **b.** $8\left(\cos \dfrac{3\pi}{4} + i \sin \dfrac{3\pi}{4}\right)$

    c. $8\sqrt{2}\left(\cos \dfrac{7\pi}{4} + i \sin \dfrac{7\pi}{4}\right)$ **d.** $8\sqrt{2}\left(\cos \dfrac{3\pi}{4} + i \sin \dfrac{3\pi}{4}\right)$

Chapter Test

1. Simplify $\sin\left(\dfrac{3\pi}{2} + \theta\right)$.   14-1

2. Evaluate $\dfrac{\tan \dfrac{\pi}{4} - \tan \dfrac{\pi}{12}}{1 + \tan \dfrac{\pi}{4} \tan \dfrac{\pi}{12}}$.   14-2

3. If $\sin \theta = -\dfrac{3}{5}$ and θ is a third-quadrant angle, find: 14-3

    a. $\sin 2\theta$ **b.** $\cos 2\theta$

4. If $\cos \theta = -\dfrac{12}{13}$ and θ is a second-quadrant angle, find: 14-4

    a. $\sin \dfrac{\theta}{2}$ **b.** $\cos \dfrac{\theta}{2}$ **c.** $\tan \dfrac{\theta}{2}$

5. Sketch the graph of $y = \csc 2x$.   14-5

6. Evaluate: 14-6

    a. $\mathrm{Cos}^{-1} \dfrac{\sqrt{3}}{2}$ **b.** $\sin\left(\mathrm{Sin}^{-1} x\right)$ **c.** $\sin\left(\mathrm{Cos}^{-1} \dfrac{1}{2}\right)$

7. Evaluate: 14-7

    a. $\mathrm{Tan}^{-1} \sqrt{3}$ **b.** $\cot\left(\mathrm{Tan}^{-1} \dfrac{3}{2}\right)$ **c.** $\tan\left(\mathrm{Sec}^{-1} 4\right)$

Solve for x, $0° \le x < 360°$.

8. $\sin x \sec x = \sqrt{2} \sin x$ 14-8

9. $4 \cos^2 x - 1 = 0$

10. $\tan 3x = 1$

11. Express $3 + 3\sqrt{3}i$ in trigonometric form.   14-9

Cumulative Review (Chapters 12–14)

1. What angle in degrees equals $1\frac{1}{5}$ clockwise revolutions?

2. Express $54°$ in radians, leaving your answer in terms of π.

3. Express $\frac{5\pi}{8}^{R}$ in degrees.

4. The terminal side of the angle θ in standard position passes through $P(1, -3)$. Find the value of the six trigonometric functions of θ.

5. A sine wave varies from -3 to 3 with a period of 6. What is its equation?

6. If $\tan \theta = \frac{5}{2}$ and θ is in the third quadrant, find $\sec \theta$.

State the period and draw the graph of each function.

7. $y = \frac{1}{2} \sin x$
8. $y = \tan \frac{1}{2} x$
9. $y = 2 \cos 4x$

Evaluate without tables or a calculator.

10. $\cos 30°$
11. $\csc \frac{5\pi}{4}$
12. $\tan 150°$
13. $\sin \frac{5\pi}{2}$

Simplify and express as a single function of θ.

14. $\csc\left(\frac{\pi}{2} - \theta\right)$
15. $\dfrac{\sin x}{\tan x}$
16. $\dfrac{(1 - \sin y)(1 + \sin y)}{\cos y}$

17. Prove the identity $\dfrac{\cos \theta}{1 + \sin \theta} + \tan \theta = \sec \theta$.

18. Find the area of $\triangle XYZ$ if $x = 7$, $y = 10$, and $\angle Z = 120°$. Give your answer in simplest radical form.

Solve $\triangle XYZ$. Give all answers to three significant digits.

19. $x = 8$, $y = 13$, $\angle Y = 90°$
20. $x = 11$, $z = 8$, $\angle Y = 60°$

21. Find the magnitude and direction of $\mathbf{u} + \mathbf{v}$ to three significant digits if $\mathbf{u} = (4, -1)$ and $\mathbf{v} = (7, 3)$.

22. Simplify $\sin 81° \cos 39° - \cos 81° \sin 39°$.

23. If $\sin \beta = -\frac{4}{5}$ and β is a fourth-quadrant angle, find:
    a. $\cos \beta$
    b. $\sin 2\beta$
    c. $\cos 2\beta$
    d. $\tan 2\beta$
    e. $\sin 3\beta$

24. Evaluate:
    a. $\text{Sin}^{-1}\left(-\frac{\sqrt{2}}{2}\right)$
    b. $\text{Cos}^{-1}\left(\cos \frac{7\pi}{8}\right)$
    c. $\tan\left(\text{Sin}^{-1} \frac{3}{5}\right)$

25. Solve the equation $6 \cos^2 x - \cos x - 2 = 0$ for x, $0 \le x < 360°$.

26. Express $-\sqrt{3} + i$ in trigonometric form.

Shown above is a coaxial cable (left) and the new cable used in lightwave communication systems (right). The new cable can carry more than 46,300 telephone conversations. See pages 571–577 for a discussion of the matrices used to study communication networks.

15

MATRICES AND DETERMINANTS

MATRICES

15-1 *Terminology*

OBJECTIVE   **To learn and apply matrix terminology.**

A **matrix** is a rectangular array of numbers enclosed by brackets. For example,

$$\begin{bmatrix} 4 & 3 \\ -9 & 1\frac{1}{2} \\ 0 & 10 \end{bmatrix}, \quad \begin{bmatrix} 0 & 1 & -8 \\ -2 & 0 & 0 \end{bmatrix}, \quad \begin{bmatrix} 9 \\ \sqrt{3} \end{bmatrix}, \quad \text{and} \quad \begin{bmatrix} 8 & -16 & 2.1 \end{bmatrix}$$

are matrices. The numbers that make up a matrix are called the **elements,** or **entries,** of the matrix. The number of **rows** (horizontal) and **columns** (vertical) determine the **dimensions** of the matrix. The examples above are a 3×2 (read "three by two") matrix, a 2×3 matrix, a 2×1 matrix, and a 1×3 matrix. Notice that the number of rows is always given first.

A matrix having only one row is called a **row matrix.** For example,

$$\begin{bmatrix} 8 & -16 & 2.1 \end{bmatrix}$$

is a row matrix. A matrix having only one column is called a **column matrix.** Thus,

$$\begin{bmatrix} 9 \\ \sqrt{3} \end{bmatrix}$$

is a column matrix. An $n \times n$ matrix is called a **square matrix** of order n.

Capital letters are used to denote matrices, and subscripts are used to indicate dimensions. Thus, $A_{3\times4}$ denotes a 3×4 matrix. If all the entries in a matrix are zeros, the matrix is called a **zero matrix.** Thus,

$$\begin{bmatrix} 0 & 0 \\ 0 & 0 \\ 0 & 0 \end{bmatrix}$$

is a 3×2 zero matrix, symbolized by $O_{3\times2}$.

Two matrices are equal if and only if they have the same dimensions and the elements in all corresponding positions are equal. The examples below should help you understand the definition of matrix equality.

$$\begin{bmatrix} \frac{1}{2} & 4 & 1 \\ 2 & \frac{9}{6} & 5 \end{bmatrix} = \begin{bmatrix} \frac{2}{4} & 4 & \frac{2}{2} \\ 2 & \frac{3}{2} & 5 \end{bmatrix} \qquad \begin{bmatrix} 3 & 1 \\ 2 & 7 \end{bmatrix} \neq \begin{bmatrix} 3 & 1 \\ 7 & 2 \end{bmatrix}$$

Oral Exercises

State the dimensions of each matrix.

1. $\begin{bmatrix} 2 & 9 \\ 3 & -\sqrt{2} \\ 4 & 0 \end{bmatrix}$ 3×2

2. $\begin{bmatrix} -4 & 5 & -3 & 6 \\ 1 & 0 & 0 & 0 \end{bmatrix}$ 2 × 4

3. $[15]$ 1×1

4. $\begin{bmatrix} 6 \\ 3 \\ -1 \\ 0 \end{bmatrix}$ 4×1

5. $\begin{bmatrix} a_1 & b_1 \\ a_2 & b_2 \end{bmatrix}$ 2×2

6. $[8 \ \ 0 \ \ -4 \ \ 3 \ \ 7]$ 1×5

7. $\begin{bmatrix} 9 \\ 18 \\ 27 \\ \frac{1}{3} \\ 7 \end{bmatrix}$ 5×1

8. $\begin{bmatrix} 0 & 0 & 0 \\ 0 & 0 & 0 \\ 0 & 0 & 0 \\ 0 & 0 & 0 \end{bmatrix}$ 4×3

Let $A = \begin{bmatrix} 5 & 3 & -1 & 0 \\ 3 & 8 & 2 & -2 \\ -1 & 4 & 0 & 1 \end{bmatrix}$. State each of the following.

9. The dimensions of A 3×4

10. The elements in the third row   -1, 4, 0, 1

11. The elements in the second column   3, 8, 4

12. The element in row two, column three   2

13. The element in row one, column two   3

14. The element in row two, column four   -2

Written Exercises

Write the zero matrix of the dimensions specified.

A   1. $O_{2\times1}$ 2. $O_{3\times2}$ 3. $O_{1\times3}$ 4. $O_{5\times2}$

Find the value of each variable.

5. $O_{2\times2} = \begin{bmatrix} x & y \\ z & 0 \end{bmatrix}$

6. $O_{3\times2} = \begin{bmatrix} x-2 & 0 \\ 5y & 0 \\ 3-z & 0 \end{bmatrix}$

7. $\begin{bmatrix} 1-x \\ 2y+8 \\ z-7 \end{bmatrix} = O_{3\times1}$

8. $\begin{bmatrix} 1 \\ 0 \\ x \end{bmatrix} = \begin{bmatrix} 1 \\ 0 \\ -1 \end{bmatrix}$

9. $\begin{bmatrix} 3 & 2 \\ -1 & 0 \\ x & y \end{bmatrix} = \begin{bmatrix} 3 & 2 \\ -1 & 0 \\ 5 & -3 \end{bmatrix}$

10. $\begin{bmatrix} x-3 \\ 2 \\ 0 \end{bmatrix} = \begin{bmatrix} 5 \\ y \\ z+2 \end{bmatrix}$

11. $\begin{bmatrix} 2x & 4 \\ -5 & 8 \end{bmatrix} = \begin{bmatrix} -4 & y+1 \\ z & 8 \end{bmatrix}$

B 12. $\begin{bmatrix} x+y & 1 \\ 0 & x-y \end{bmatrix} = \begin{bmatrix} 2 & 1 \\ 0 & 8 \end{bmatrix}$

13. $\begin{bmatrix} 8-y & 0 \\ x+2z & x+z \end{bmatrix} = \begin{bmatrix} -3y & 0 \\ -5 & -1 \end{bmatrix}$

Let a, b, c, and d be nonzero real numbers. Find the values of x and y in the matrix equations below.

14. $\begin{bmatrix} ax \\ by \end{bmatrix} = \begin{bmatrix} 1 \\ 0 \end{bmatrix}$

15. $[ax+b \quad cy+d] = [1 \quad 0]$

16. $\begin{bmatrix} ax+y \\ bx+y \end{bmatrix} = \begin{bmatrix} 1 \\ 0 \end{bmatrix}$

17. $[ax+by \quad cx+dy] = [1 \quad 1]$

Historical Note Matrices

Matrices are a relatively new concept in mathematics. They were not devised until 1857 when the British mathematician Arthur Cayley (1821–1895) invented them while studying linear transformations.

Cayley was working on linear transformations of the type

$$x_1 = ax + by$$
$$y_1 = cx + dy$$

which map an ordered pair (x, y) onto another ordered pair (x_1, y_1). In this transformation a, b, c, and d are real numbers. Cayley found that the entire transformation could be determined by these real numbers when arranged in the square array

$$\begin{bmatrix} a & b \\ c & d \end{bmatrix}.$$

Further analysis led Cayley to formulate most of the general rules for the algebra of matrices.

15-2 *Addition and Scalar Multiplication*

OBJECTIVE   **To find sums and differences of matrices and products of a scalar and a matrix.**

The sum of two matrices of the same dimensions is the matrix whose elements are the sums of the corresponding elements of the matrices being added. For example,

$$\begin{bmatrix} 3 & 1 & -2 \\ 0 & 5 & -1 \end{bmatrix} + \begin{bmatrix} 2 & -1 & 3 \\ -2 & 0 & -3 \end{bmatrix} = \begin{bmatrix} 3+2 & 1-1 & -2+3 \\ 0-2 & 5+0 & -1-3 \end{bmatrix} = \begin{bmatrix} 5 & 0 & 1 \\ -2 & 5 & -4 \end{bmatrix}.$$

Note that matrices with different dimensions do not have corresponding elements and, therefore, addition of matrices of different dimensions is not defined. You can show that in each set of $m \times n$ matrices, addition is both commutative and associative. (See Exercises 21 and 22 on page 565.)

For each set of $m \times n$ matrices, $O_{m \times n}$ act as an additive identity. For example, let $A_{2 \times 3} = \begin{bmatrix} a & b & c \\ d & e & f \end{bmatrix}$.

$$A_{2 \times 3} + O_{2 \times 3} = \begin{bmatrix} a & b & c \\ d & e & f \end{bmatrix} + \begin{bmatrix} 0 & 0 & 0 \\ 0 & 0 & 0 \end{bmatrix} = \begin{bmatrix} a+0 & b+0 & c+0 \\ d+0 & e+0 & f+0 \end{bmatrix} = \begin{bmatrix} a & b & c \\ d & e & f \end{bmatrix} = A_{2 \times 3}$$

In general, for each set of $m \times n$ matrices,

$$A_{m \times n} + O_{m \times n} = O_{m \times n} + A_{m \times n} = A_{m \times n}.$$

The **additive inverse of matrix** A is the matrix $-A$, each of whose elements is the opposite of the corresponding element in A. Thus,

if $A = \begin{bmatrix} 4 & 2 \\ 0 & -3 \end{bmatrix}$, then $-A = \begin{bmatrix} -4 & -2 \\ 0 & 3 \end{bmatrix}$.

Moreover, $A + (-A) = \begin{bmatrix} 4 & 2 \\ 0 & -3 \end{bmatrix} + \begin{bmatrix} -4 & -2 \\ 0 & 3 \end{bmatrix} = \begin{bmatrix} 0 & 0 \\ 0 & 0 \end{bmatrix} = O_{2 \times 2}.$

In general,

$$A_{m \times n} + (-A_{m \times n}) = -A_{m \times n} + A_{m \times n} = O_{m \times n}.$$

Subtraction of matrices is defined to be the inverse of addition. Let A and B be $m \times n$ matrices. The **difference** $A - B$ is the matrix X whose sum with B is A. Thus, the equations

$$A - B = X \quad \text{and} \quad X + B = A$$

have the same solution and are equivalent. Solve the second equation for X.

$$X + B = A$$
$$X + B + (-B) = A + (-B)$$
$$X = A + (-B)$$

In general, $A_{m \times n} - B_{m \times n} = A_{m \times n} + (-B_{m \times n})$.

EXAMPLE 1 Let $A = \begin{bmatrix} 8 & -1 \\ 5 & 3 \end{bmatrix}$ and $B = \begin{bmatrix} 3 & 8 \\ 6 & -2 \end{bmatrix}$. Find $A - B$.

SOLUTION $A - B = A + (-B)$

$$\begin{bmatrix} 8 & -1 \\ 5 & 3 \end{bmatrix} - \begin{bmatrix} 3 & 8 \\ 6 & -2 \end{bmatrix} = \begin{bmatrix} 8 & -1 \\ 5 & 3 \end{bmatrix} + \begin{bmatrix} -3 & -8 \\ -6 & 2 \end{bmatrix}$$

$$= \begin{bmatrix} 5 & -9 \\ -1 & 5 \end{bmatrix} \quad \textit{Answer}$$

The properties of addition of matrices are summarized below.

PROPERTIES OF ADDITION OF MATRICES

Let A, B, C be $m \times n$ matrices. Let O be the $m \times n$ zero matrix.

1. CLOSURE PROPERTY $\qquad\qquad$ $\boldsymbol{A + B}$ is an $m \times n$ matrix
2. COMMUTATIVE PROPERTY $\qquad$ $\boldsymbol{A + B = B + A}$
3. ASSOCIATIVE PROPERTY $\qquad$ $\boldsymbol{(A + B) + C = A + (B + C)}$
4. ADDITIVE-IDENTITY PROPERTY $\;$ $\boldsymbol{A + O = O + A = A}$
5. ADDITIVE-INVERSE PROPERTY $\;$ $\boldsymbol{A + (-A) = -A + A = O}$

In matrix algebra a real number is called a **scalar.** The **scalar product** of a real number r and a matrix A is the matrix rA each of whose elements is r times the corresponding element of A. In the expression $2A$, 2 is a scalar and $2A$ is another matrix.

EXAMPLE 2 Let $A = \begin{bmatrix} 3 & 0 \\ -1 & 4 \end{bmatrix}$. Find the matrix:

$\qquad$ **a.** $2A$; $\quad$ **b.** rA.

SOLUTION **a.** $2A = 2\begin{bmatrix} 3 & 0 \\ -1 & 4 \end{bmatrix} = \begin{bmatrix} 2 \cdot 3 & 2 \cdot 0 \\ 2(-1) & 2 \cdot 4 \end{bmatrix} = \begin{bmatrix} 6 & 0 \\ -2 & 8 \end{bmatrix} \quad \textit{Answer}$

$\qquad\qquad$ **b.** $rA = r\begin{bmatrix} 3 & 0 \\ -1 & 4 \end{bmatrix} = \begin{bmatrix} r \cdot 3 & r \cdot 0 \\ r(-1) & r \cdot 4 \end{bmatrix} = \begin{bmatrix} 3r & 0 \\ -r & 4r \end{bmatrix} \quad \textit{Answer}$

Scalar multiplication, that is, the product of a scalar and a matrix, is both commutative and associative. Thus in Part (b) of Example 2, $rA = Ar$. (See Exercises 25 and 26 on page 565.)

$\qquad$ The properties of scalar multiplication are summarized on the following page.

PROPERTIES OF SCALAR MULTIPLICATION

Let A and B be $m \times n$ matrices; let O be the $m \times n$ zero matrix; and let p and q be scalars.

1. CLOSURE PROPERTY pA is an $m \times n$ matrix.
2. COMMUTATIVE PROPERTY $pA = Ap$
3. ASSOCIATIVE PROPERTY $p(qA) = (pq)A$
4. DISTRIBUTIVE PROPERTIES $(p + q)A = pA + qA$
      $p(A + B) = pA + pB$
5. MULTIPLICATIVE-IDENTITY
 PROPERTY $1 \cdot A = A$
6. MULTIPLICATION PROPERTY $(-1)A = -A$
 OF NEGATIVE ONE
7. ZERO PROPERTIES $0 \cdot A = O$
      $p \cdot O = O$

Oral Exercises

State the specified element in the sum.

$$\begin{bmatrix} 0 & 2 \\ 1 & 0 \end{bmatrix} + \begin{bmatrix} 3 & 1 \\ 1 & 0.5 \end{bmatrix} = \begin{bmatrix} a & b \\ c & d \end{bmatrix}$$

1. a **2.** b **3.** c **4.** d

State the specified element in the scalar product.

$$-1[2 \quad 0 \quad -3 \quad 15] = [p \quad q \quad r \quad s]$$

5. p **6.** q **7.** r **8.** s

Written Exercises

Perform the indicated operations. Express each result as a single matrix.

A

1. $\begin{bmatrix} 5 & 0 \\ 1 & 4 \end{bmatrix} + \begin{bmatrix} 2 & 3 \\ 0 & -3 \end{bmatrix}$ **2.** $\begin{bmatrix} 4 & -3 \\ -2 & 0 \end{bmatrix} + \begin{bmatrix} -2 & 6 \\ 2 & 0 \end{bmatrix}$

3. $\begin{bmatrix} 8 & 3 \\ 5 & 12 \end{bmatrix} - \begin{bmatrix} 3 & 0 \\ 4 & 8 \end{bmatrix}$ **4.** $\begin{bmatrix} 10 & 3 \\ -4 & 6 \end{bmatrix} - \begin{bmatrix} 4 & -2 \\ 9 & -2 \end{bmatrix}$

5. $\begin{bmatrix} 4 & 9 \\ 3 & -1 \\ 0 & 6 \end{bmatrix} + \begin{bmatrix} 0 & 2 \\ 6 & 1 \\ 3 & -8 \end{bmatrix}$ **6.** $\begin{bmatrix} 3 & 7 \\ -4 & 12 \\ 0 & -5 \end{bmatrix} - \begin{bmatrix} 3 & 4 \\ 6 & -1 \\ -5 & -5 \end{bmatrix}$

7. $\begin{bmatrix} 0 & -4 & 3 \\ 6 & -5 & -2 \end{bmatrix} + \begin{bmatrix} 14 & 7 & 0 \\ 2 & 8 & -9 \end{bmatrix}$ **8.** $12 \begin{bmatrix} 6 & 0 \\ -7 & 4 \end{bmatrix}$

9. $2\begin{bmatrix} 6 & -1 \\ -2 & 5 \\ 0 & 8 \end{bmatrix} + \begin{bmatrix} 1 & 8 \\ 0 & -1 \\ 6 & 3 \end{bmatrix}$

10. $\begin{bmatrix} 3 & 0 \\ 8 & -4 \\ 0 & -5 \end{bmatrix} - 4\begin{bmatrix} 0 & -3 \\ 2 & 1 \\ -1 & 2 \end{bmatrix}$

11. $\begin{bmatrix} 3 & -1 & 4 \\ 5 & 7 & 0 \end{bmatrix} + (-2)\begin{bmatrix} 2 & 0 & 1 \\ -1 & -2 & 4 \end{bmatrix}$

12. $\begin{bmatrix} 17 & -6 \\ -2 & 19 \end{bmatrix} - \begin{bmatrix} 17 & -6 \\ -2 & 19 \end{bmatrix}$

13. $O_{2\times3} + \begin{bmatrix} 6 & 2 & 5 \\ -2 & 7 & 0 \end{bmatrix}$

14. $\begin{bmatrix} 4 & 2 \\ 1 & 3 \end{bmatrix} + \begin{bmatrix} -4 & -2 \\ -1 & -3 \end{bmatrix}$

15. $3\begin{bmatrix} 6 \\ 2 \\ 8 \end{bmatrix} + 5\begin{bmatrix} 0 \\ 7 \\ 2 \end{bmatrix}$

16. $O_{2\times3} - 5\begin{bmatrix} 8 & 0 & 2 \\ 2 & 5 & 1 \end{bmatrix}$

Solve each equation for the matrix $X_{2\times2}$.

SAMPLE $2X + 2\begin{bmatrix} 1 & -2 \\ 0 & 3 \end{bmatrix} = 8\begin{bmatrix} \frac{1}{2} & 0 \\ -1 & \frac{1}{4} \end{bmatrix}$

SOLUTION   Find the scalar products:

$$2X + \begin{bmatrix} 2 & -4 \\ 0 & 6 \end{bmatrix} = \begin{bmatrix} 4 & 0 \\ -8 & 2 \end{bmatrix}$$

Add $\begin{bmatrix} -2 & 4 \\ 0 & -6 \end{bmatrix}$, the inverse of $\begin{bmatrix} 2 & -4 \\ 0 & 6 \end{bmatrix}$, to each side.

$$2X + \begin{bmatrix} 2 & -4 \\ 0 & 6 \end{bmatrix} + \begin{bmatrix} -2 & 4 \\ 0 & -6 \end{bmatrix} = \begin{bmatrix} 4 & 0 \\ -8 & 2 \end{bmatrix} + \begin{bmatrix} -2 & 4 \\ 0 & -6 \end{bmatrix}$$

$$2X + O_{2\times2} = \begin{bmatrix} 2 & 4 \\ -8 & -4 \end{bmatrix}$$

$$X = \tfrac{1}{2}\begin{bmatrix} 2 & 4 \\ -8 & -4 \end{bmatrix} = \begin{bmatrix} 1 & 2 \\ -4 & -2 \end{bmatrix} \quad \textbf{\textit{Answer}}$$

B 17. $X + \begin{bmatrix} 3 & 2 \\ 0 & 4 \end{bmatrix} = \begin{bmatrix} 7 & -2 \\ -5 & 0 \end{bmatrix}$

18. $X + \begin{bmatrix} 1 & 0 \\ 0 & 6 \end{bmatrix} = \begin{bmatrix} 5 & -4 \\ 3 & 0 \end{bmatrix}$

19. $X + 2\begin{bmatrix} -3 & 1 \\ 0 & 2 \end{bmatrix} = \begin{bmatrix} 5 & 10 \\ 0 & 4 \end{bmatrix}$

20. $X - \begin{bmatrix} 1 & -3 \\ 2 & 5 \end{bmatrix} = 3\begin{bmatrix} -2 & 1 \\ 0 & 5 \end{bmatrix}$

Let p and q be scalars and let A, B, and C be 2×2 matrices. Prove these properties for the set of 2×2 matrices.

C 21. $A + B = B + A$ 22. $(A + B) + C = A + (B + C)$

23. $(-1)A = -A$ 24. $p(A + B) = pA + pB$

25. $pC = Cp$ 26. $(pq)B = p(qB)$

27. $0 \cdot A = O$ 28. $p \cdot O = O$

15-3 *Matrix Multiplication*

OBJECTIVE   **To find the product of two matrices.**

Before you study the product of two matrices in general, consider this example.

A department store sells ten-speed, five-speed, and three-speed bicycles. The profit on the sale of each ten-speed bicycle is $30, the profit on each five-speed bicycle is $32, and the profit on each three-speed bicycle is $25. This information is shown in the 1×3 matrix, A, below.

$$\begin{matrix} \text{10-speed} & \text{5-speed} & \text{3-speed} \\ A = \quad [30 & 32 & 25] \end{matrix}$$

In April, sales of ten-speed, five-speed, and three-speed bicycles numbered 60, 50, and 20 bikes, respectively. In May, sales were 45, 40, and 55. Sales are displayed in the 3×2 matrix B, below.

$$B = \begin{matrix} \text{April} & \text{May} \\ \begin{bmatrix} 60 & 45 \\ 50 & 40 \\ 20 & 55 \end{bmatrix} \end{matrix}$$

In April, profits from sales of ten-speed bikes were $30 \cdot 60$; profits from sales of five-speed bikes were $32 \cdot 50$; and profits from sales of three-speed bikes were $25 \cdot 20$. The total profit from bicycle sales in April and May were:

April: $30 \cdot 60 + 32 \cdot 50 + 25 \cdot 20 = 1800 + 1600 + 500$
May: $30 \cdot 45 + 32 \cdot 40 + 25 \cdot 55 = 1350 + 1280 + 1375$

The monthly profits can be represented by the matrix P.

$$\begin{matrix} \text{April} & \text{May} \\ P = [(1800 + 1600 + 500) & (1350 + 1280 + 1375)] = [3900 \quad 4005] \end{matrix}$$

Matrix P is the **product** of matrices A and B.

$$P = A \times B = [30 \quad 32 \quad 25] \begin{bmatrix} 60 & 45 \\ 50 & 40 \\ 20 & 55 \end{bmatrix}$$

$$= [(30 \cdot 60 + 32 \cdot 50 + 25 \cdot 20) \quad (30 \cdot 45 + 32 \cdot 40 + 25 \cdot 55)]$$
$$= [(1800 + 1600 + 500) \quad (1350 + 1280 + 1375)]$$
$$= [3900 \quad 4005]$$

Note that each element in P is obtained by multiplying elements of the *row* in A by elements of a *column* in B.

The procedure above suggests the following definition of the product of two matrices. The **product** of a matrix $A_{m \times n}$ and $B_{n \times p}$ is the $m \times p$ matrix whose element in the ath row and bth column is the sum of the products of corresponding elements of the ath row of A and the bth column of B. Notice that the second dimension of the first matrix must equal the first dimension of the second matrix. Otherwise, matrices cannot be multiplied. For example, if

$$A_{1\times2} = [1 \quad -2] \text{ and } B_{2\times3} = \begin{bmatrix} 1 & 0 & 2 \\ 0 & 1 & -1 \end{bmatrix},$$

then $A_{1\times2} \times B_{2\times3} = [1 \quad -2]\begin{bmatrix} 1 & 0 & 2 \\ 0 & 1 & -1 \end{bmatrix} = [1 \quad -2 \quad 4];$

but $B_{2\times3} \times A_{1\times2} = \begin{bmatrix} 1 & 0 & 2 \\ 0 & 1 & -1 \end{bmatrix}[1 \quad -2]$ is not defined.

In the last attempted multiplication, there are more elements in each row of B (three elements) than there are in each column of A (one element).

EXAMPLE

Multiply: $\begin{bmatrix} 0 & 1 & 2 \\ 3 & 1 & 1 \\ -1 & 1 & 2 \end{bmatrix}\begin{bmatrix} 1 & 0 & 1 \\ -1 & 3 & 2 \\ 2 & 0 & -1 \end{bmatrix}$

SOLUTION

$\begin{bmatrix} 0 & 1 & 2 \\ 3 & 1 & 1 \\ -1 & 1 & 2 \end{bmatrix}\begin{bmatrix} 1 & 0 & 1 \\ -1 & 3 & 2 \\ 2 & 0 & -1 \end{bmatrix} = \begin{bmatrix} 3 & & \\ & & \\ & & \end{bmatrix}$ $\qquad 0 \cdot 1 + 1(-1) + 2 \cdot 2 = 3$

$\begin{bmatrix} 0 & 1 & 2 \\ 3 & 1 & 1 \\ -1 & 1 & 2 \end{bmatrix}\begin{bmatrix} 1 & 0 & 1 \\ -1 & 3 & 2 \\ 2 & 0 & -1 \end{bmatrix} = \begin{bmatrix} 3 & 3 & \\ & & \\ & & \end{bmatrix}$ $\qquad 0 \cdot 0 + 1 \cdot 3 + 2 \cdot 0 = 3$

$\begin{bmatrix} 0 & 1 & 2 \\ 3 & 1 & 1 \\ -1 & 1 & 2 \end{bmatrix}\begin{bmatrix} 1 & 0 & 1 \\ -1 & 3 & 2 \\ 2 & 0 & -1 \end{bmatrix} = \begin{bmatrix} 3 & 3 & 0 \\ & & \\ & & \end{bmatrix}$ $\qquad 0 \cdot 1 + 1 \cdot 2 + 2(-1) = 0$

$\begin{bmatrix} 0 & 1 & 2 \\ 3 & 1 & 1 \\ -1 & 1 & 2 \end{bmatrix}\begin{bmatrix} 1 & 0 & 1 \\ -1 & 3 & 2 \\ 2 & 0 & -1 \end{bmatrix} = \begin{bmatrix} 3 & 3 & 0 \\ 4 & 3 & 4 \\ & & \end{bmatrix}$ $\qquad \begin{aligned} 3 \cdot 1 + 1(-1) + 1 \cdot 2 &= 4 \\ 3 \cdot 0 + 1 \cdot 3 + 1 \cdot 0 &= 3 \\ 3 \cdot 1 + 1 \cdot 2 + 1(-1) &= 4 \end{aligned}$

$\begin{bmatrix} 0 & 1 & 2 \\ 3 & 1 & 1 \\ -1 & 1 & 2 \end{bmatrix}\begin{bmatrix} 1 & 0 & 1 \\ -1 & 3 & 2 \\ 2 & 0 & -1 \end{bmatrix} = \begin{bmatrix} 3 & 3 & 0 \\ 4 & 3 & 4 \\ 2 & 3 & -1 \end{bmatrix}$ $\qquad \begin{aligned} -1 \cdot 1 + 1(-1) + 2 \cdot 2 &= 2 \\ -1 \cdot 0 + 1 \cdot 3 + 2 \cdot 0 &= 3 \\ -1 \cdot 1 + 1 \cdot 2 + 2(-1) &= -1 \end{aligned}$

$\therefore$ the product equals $\begin{bmatrix} 3 & 3 & 0 \\ 4 & 3 & 4 \\ 2 & 3 & -1 \end{bmatrix}$. **Answer**

Powers of square matrices are defined as for real numbers. That is, $A^2 = A \times A$, and $A^3 = A \times A \times A$. In general,

$$A^n = \underline{A \times A \times A \times \ldots \times A}$$
$$n \text{ factors}$$

An $n \times n$ matrix whose **main diagonal** (from upper left to lower right) has all elements 1 while all the other elements are 0 is called an **identity matrix,** and is denoted by $I_{n \times n}$. For example,

$$I_{2 \times 2} = \begin{bmatrix} 1 & 0 \\ 0 & 1 \end{bmatrix} \text{ and } I_{3 \times 3} = \begin{bmatrix} 1 & 0 & 0 \\ 0 & 1 & 0 \\ 0 & 0 & 1 \end{bmatrix}$$

are the identity matrices for multiplication of 2×2 and 3×3 matrices, respectively. It can be shown that for a square matrix of order n,

$$I \times A = A \times I = A.$$

Multiplication of a matrix by the zero matrix yields the zero matrix. That is, if A is any square matrix of order n,

$$O \times A = A \times O = O.$$

A major difference between multiplication of real numbers and multiplication of matrices is the fact that $CD = O$ does *not* imply that either C or D is O. This is illustrated in the following example.

Let $C = \begin{bmatrix} -2 & 1 \\ -4 & 2 \end{bmatrix}$ and $D = \begin{bmatrix} 2 & 3 \\ 4 & 6 \end{bmatrix}$.

Then $CD = \begin{bmatrix} -2 & 1 \\ -4 & 2 \end{bmatrix}\begin{bmatrix} 2 & 3 \\ 4 & 6 \end{bmatrix}$

$$= \begin{bmatrix} 0 & 0 \\ 0 & 0 \end{bmatrix} = O.$$

Unlike multiplication with real numbers, matrix multiplication is not commutative. For example,

if $A = \begin{bmatrix} 3 & 1 \\ 0 & -2 \end{bmatrix}$ and $B = \begin{bmatrix} 1 & -2 \\ 2 & 0 \end{bmatrix}$,

then $AB = \begin{bmatrix} 3 & 1 \\ 0 & -2 \end{bmatrix}\begin{bmatrix} 1 & -2 \\ 2 & 0 \end{bmatrix} = \begin{bmatrix} 5 & -6 \\ -4 & 0 \end{bmatrix}$,

but $BA = \begin{bmatrix} 1 & -2 \\ 2 & 0 \end{bmatrix}\begin{bmatrix} 3 & 1 \\ 0 & -2 \end{bmatrix} = \begin{bmatrix} 3 & 5 \\ 6 & 2 \end{bmatrix}$.

Thus, $AB \neq BA$. Clearly, it is necessary to compute a product in the order it is written.

The associative and distributive properties, however, are valid for matrix multiplication. The properties for multiplication of square matrices are summarized below.

PROPERTIES OF MATRIX MULTIPLICATION

Let A, B, and C be $n \times n$ matrices.

1. ASSOCIATIVE PROPERTY $\quad\quad (AB)C = A(BC)$
2. DISTRIBUTIVE PROPERTIES $\quad AB + AC = A(B + C)$
   $\quad\quad\quad\quad\quad\quad\quad\quad\quad\quad\quad BA + CA = (B + C)A$
3. MULTIPLICATIVE-IDENTITY
   PROPERTY $\quad\quad\quad\quad\quad\quad I_{n \times n}A = AI_{n \times n} = A$
4. ZERO PROPERTY $\quad\quad\quad\quad O_{n \times n}A = AO_{n \times n} = O_{n \times n}$

Oral Exercises

State whether each pair of matrices can be multiplied.

1. $\begin{bmatrix} 2 & 3 \\ 1 & 0 \end{bmatrix}\begin{bmatrix} 3 & 4 \\ -1 & 0 \end{bmatrix}$

2. $\begin{bmatrix} 6 \\ 2 \\ 1 \end{bmatrix}\begin{bmatrix} 0 & 1 \end{bmatrix}$

3. $\begin{bmatrix} 2 & 1 & 6 \end{bmatrix}\begin{bmatrix} 6 & 0 & 2 \\ 8 & 1 & 3 \end{bmatrix}$

4. $\begin{bmatrix} 0 & 1 & 6 \\ 3 & 6 & 8 \\ -2 & 5 & \frac{1}{2} \end{bmatrix}\begin{bmatrix} 4 & 3 \\ 0 & 1 \\ -1 & 0 \end{bmatrix}$

5. $\begin{bmatrix} 1 & 0 & 0 \\ 0 & 1 & 0 \\ 0 & 0 & 0 \end{bmatrix}\begin{bmatrix} 16 & 3 & 9 & 4 \end{bmatrix}$

6. $\begin{bmatrix} 0 & 0 \\ 0 & 0 \\ 0 & 0 \\ 0 & 0 \end{bmatrix}\begin{bmatrix} 2 & 0 & 1 & 7 \end{bmatrix}$

State the value of the specified variable in the computation of the product.

$$\begin{bmatrix} -1 & 0 & 5 \\ 3 & 2 & -2 \end{bmatrix}\begin{bmatrix} -1 \\ 3 \\ 1 \end{bmatrix} = \begin{bmatrix} -1(-1) + 0 \cdot 3 + 5 \cdot a \\ 3(-1) + b \cdot 3 + -2 \cdot c \end{bmatrix} = \begin{bmatrix} d \\ e \end{bmatrix}$$

7. a **8.** b **9.** c **10.** d **11.** e

Written Exercises

Multiply.

A 1. $[3 \quad 4]\begin{bmatrix} 6 \\ 5 \end{bmatrix}$

2. $[-2 \quad 0 \quad 1]\begin{bmatrix} 3 \\ -1 \\ 0 \end{bmatrix}$

3. $\begin{bmatrix} 5 \\ -1 \end{bmatrix}[3 \quad 0 \quad 1 \quad 5]$

4. $\begin{bmatrix} -1 & 0 \\ 1 & 2 \end{bmatrix}\begin{bmatrix} 3 \\ 2 \end{bmatrix}$

5. $\begin{bmatrix} 3 & -1 \\ 4 & 0 \end{bmatrix}\begin{bmatrix} 1 & 3 \\ 0 & -2 \end{bmatrix}$

6. $\begin{bmatrix} 1 & 0 \\ 2 & -1 \\ 6 & 3 \end{bmatrix}\begin{bmatrix} 3 & 1 & 0 \\ -1 & 0 & -2 \end{bmatrix}$

7. $\begin{bmatrix} 3 & 1 & 0 \\ 0 & -1 & 2 \\ 4 & -2 & 0 \end{bmatrix}\begin{bmatrix} -1 & 0 & 0 \\ 0 & 1 & 2 \\ 0 & -2 & -1 \end{bmatrix}$

8. $\begin{bmatrix} 0 & 1 & 0 \\ 2 & -1 & 0 \\ 0 & 0 & 1 \end{bmatrix}\begin{bmatrix} 2 & -3 & 1 \\ -1 & 0 & -2 \\ 0 & 1 & 0 \end{bmatrix}$

9. $\begin{bmatrix} 2 & 0 \\ 0 & -1 \\ 1 & 2 \end{bmatrix}\begin{bmatrix} 1 & 0 & -1 & 1 \\ 0 & 1 & 3 & -1 \end{bmatrix}$

10. $\begin{bmatrix} 1 & 0 & 2 \\ -2 & 1 & 0 \\ 1 & 0 & 0 \end{bmatrix}\begin{bmatrix} a & b & c \\ d & e & f \\ g & h & i \end{bmatrix}$

11. $\begin{bmatrix} 1 & 0 & 3 \\ 2 & -1 & 0 \\ 0 & -3 & 2 \end{bmatrix}\begin{bmatrix} r & s & t \\ u & v & w \\ x & y & z \end{bmatrix}$

12. $\begin{bmatrix} a & b & c \\ d & e & f \\ g & h & i \end{bmatrix}\begin{bmatrix} 3 & 1 & 2 \\ -2 & 0 & -1 \\ -1 & 2 & -3 \end{bmatrix}$

In Exercises 13–20, let $A = \begin{bmatrix} 0 & 1 \\ -1 & 2 \end{bmatrix}$, $B = \begin{bmatrix} 2 & 1 \\ 1 & 0 \end{bmatrix}$, and $C = \begin{bmatrix} 0 & -2 \\ 1 & 0 \end{bmatrix}$.

B 13. Find AB and BA.
14. Find BC and CB.
15. Find $(AB)C$ and $A(BC)$.
16. Find $AC + BC$ and $(A + B)C$.
17. Find $(A + B)(A - B)$ and $A^2 - B^2$.
18. Find $(A + B)^2$ and $A^2 + 2AB + B^2$.
19. Find $O_{2 \times 2} \cdot A$ and $A \cdot O_{2 \times 2}$.
20. Find $I_{2 \times 2} \cdot C$ and $C \cdot I_{2 \times 2}$.

In Exercises 21–22, let $A = \begin{bmatrix} 1 & 2 \\ 2 & 1 \end{bmatrix}$ and $B = \begin{bmatrix} -\frac{1}{3} & \frac{2}{3} \\ \frac{2}{3} & -\frac{1}{3} \end{bmatrix}$.

21. Find AB.
22. Find BA.

23. If $D = \begin{bmatrix} 1 & 0 & 2 \\ 0 & -1 & 1 \\ 1 & -1 & 0 \end{bmatrix}$, find: **a.** D^2 **b.** D^3 **c.** $(-D)^2$

Prove the following properties for all 2×2 matrices.

C 24. $AI = IA = A$
25. $AO = OA = O$
26. $(AB)C = A(BC)$
27. $A(B + C) = AB + AC$

15-4 *Applications of Matrices*

OBJECTIVE   **To solve problems using matrices.**

Matrices are used to solve a large variety of problems in the social and physical sciences. In this section two applications of matrices are considered, *communication networks* and *transition problems.*

Communication Networks

Consider four ships at sea linked by communication lines as shown in Figure 15-1. The arrows indicate the directions in which radio messages can be transmitted and received.

A Communication Network

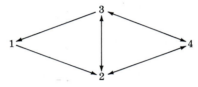

Figure 15-1

Ship 2, for example, can transmit messages to Ships 3 and 4, but it cannot send messages to Ship 1. Ship 2 can receive messages from Ships 1, 3, and 4. Matrix A below can be used to characterize this network.

$$
\text{From Ship}
\begin{array}{c}
\\
1 \\ 2 \\ 3 \\ 4
\end{array}
\overset{\displaystyle \text{To Ship}}{\overset{\displaystyle 1 \ \ 2 \ \ 3 \ \ 4}{
\begin{bmatrix}
0 & 1 & 0 & 0 \\
0 & 0 & 1 & 1 \\
1 & 1 & 0 & 1 \\
0 & 1 & 1 & 0
\end{bmatrix}}} = A
$$

The element "1" indicates that direct communication *to* another point is possible. The element "0" indicates that direct communication *to* another point is not possible. For example, the "0" in row one, column three of matrix A indicates that Ship 1 cannot send a message directly *to* Ship 3. The "1" written in row four, column two indicates that Ship 4 can send a message directly *to* Ship 2. Rows, therefore, represent the possible directions in which a ship can transmit messages. On the other hand, columns represent the possible sources from which a ship can receive messages. Ship 3 can receive messages from two sources, Ships 2 and 4 (column three). Compare each row and column of matrix A with the corresponding point of Figure 15-1. Matrix A is called a **communication matrix.**

In addition to sending a message directly, it is possible to send a message from one point to another via a relay point. For example, Ship 1 can send a message to Ship 3 via Ship 2. It can be proved that matrix A^2 represents the number of ways one point can send a message to a second point using exactly one relay point.

$$\text{From Ship} \begin{array}{c} \\ 1 \\ 2 \\ 3 \\ 4 \end{array} \overset{\displaystyle\begin{array}{cccc} \text{To Ship} \\ 1 \ \ 2 \ \ 3 \ \ 4 \end{array}}{\begin{bmatrix} 0 & 0 & 1 & 1 \\ 1 & 2 & 1 & 1 \\ 0 & 2 & 2 & 1 \\ 1 & 1 & 1 & 2 \end{bmatrix}} = A^2$$

Compare A^2 with Figure 15-1. Trace the possible routes for sending a message from Ship 3 to Ship 2 via one relay point. There are two possible routes:

   (1) from Ship 3 to Ship 1, then to Ship 2,
   (2) from Ship 3 to Ship 4, and then to Ship 2.

The element in row three, column two of A^2 is 2, the number of ways a message can go from Ship 3 to Ship 2 using exactly one relay. The "1" written in row two, column one of A^2 indicates that there is exactly 1 route from Ship 2 to Ship 1 using one relay. Verify this by checking Figure 15-1.

   Thus, matrix A represents direct communication and matrix A^2 represents communication using one relay. Furthermore, it can be shown that A^3 represents the number of ways a message can be sent using exactly two relay points. The matrix $A + A^2$ shows the total number of ways a message can be sent from one point to another using no more than one relay point; $A + A^2 + A^3$ shows the total number of ways a message can be sent using no more than two relay points.

EXAMPLE 1   Use matrices to find the number of ways a message can be sent from Ship 4 (p. 571) to Ship 3 using no more than one relay point.

SOLUTION $A + A^2$ shows the number of ways a message can be sent from one ship to another using at most one relay.

$$A + A^2 = \begin{bmatrix} 0 & 1 & 0 & 0 \\ 0 & 0 & 1 & 1 \\ 1 & 1 & 0 & 1 \\ 0 & 1 & 1 & 0 \end{bmatrix} + \begin{bmatrix} 0 & 0 & 1 & 1 \\ 1 & 2 & 1 & 1 \\ 0 & 2 & 2 & 1 \\ 1 & 1 & 1 & 2 \end{bmatrix} = \begin{bmatrix} 0 & 1 & 1 & 1 \\ 1 & 2 & 2 & 2 \\ 1 & 3 & 2 & 2 \\ 1 & 2 & 2 & 2 \end{bmatrix}$$

The element of $A + A^2$ in row four, column three is 2. Thus there are 2 ways a message can travel from Ship 4 to Ship 3 using at most one relay.   *Answer*

Transition Problems

Business and governments must predict shifts in population distributions to plan for future needs.

EXAMPLE 2 Suppose a region has a population of 25 million people, with 10 million currently living in cities, 8 million living in suburbs, and 7 million living in rural areas. Assume that the table below describes the predicted population shift for one year. Persons who do not move are included in the shift from city to city, suburb to suburb, or rural area to rural area. Find the population distribution at the end of one year.

Predicted Population Shift

From	To		
	City	Suburb	Rural Area
City	65%	31%	4%
Suburb	18%	70%	12%
Rural Area	17%	8%	75%

SOLUTION The row matrix, P, represents the original locations of the 25 million people.

$$\begin{array}{ccc} \text{City} & \text{Suburb} & \text{Rural Area} \end{array}$$
$$P = [10 \quad\quad 8 \quad\quad\quad 7]$$

The data in the table above are summarized in matrix T below.

$$\begin{array}{c} \\ \text{City} \\ \text{Suburb} \\ \text{Rural Area} \end{array} \begin{array}{ccc} \text{City} & \text{Suburb} & \text{Rural Area} \end{array}$$

$$\begin{array}{c} \text{City} \\ \text{Suburb} \\ \text{Rural Area} \end{array} \begin{bmatrix} 0.65 & 0.31 & 0.04 \\ 0.18 & 0.70 & 0.12 \\ 0.17 & 0.08 & 0.75 \end{bmatrix} = T$$

Matrix T is called a **transition matrix;** it describes a transition from one *state* (condition) to another. The product, $P \times T$, gives the population distribution at the end of one year.

$$P \times T = [10 \quad 8 \quad 7] \begin{bmatrix} 0.65 & 0.31 & 0.04 \\ 0.18 & 0.70 & 0.12 \\ 0.17 & 0.08 & 0.75 \end{bmatrix}$$

The product of the two matrices, $P \times T$, is computed in the usual fashion:

$$P \times T = [6.5 + 1.44 + 1.19 \quad 3.1 + 5.6 + 0.56 \quad 0.40 + 0.96 + 5.25]$$
$$= [9.13 \quad 9.26 \quad 6.61]$$

Thus, after one year, 9.13 million people live in cities, 9.26 million people live in suburbs, and 6.61 million people live in rural areas. ***Answer***

Assuming that matrix T in Example 2 also describes the population shift for the second year, it is possible to predict the population distribution after two years. One way to do this is to multiply the one year population prediction,

$$[9.13 \quad 9.26 \quad 6.61]$$

by the transition matrix, T. An alternate method is to multiply the original row matrix for the population by T^2. That is, $P \times T^2$ will give the population distribution after two years.

Oral Exercises

Matrix A below describes a communication network.

$$\text{From Point} \begin{array}{c} \\ 1 \\ 2 \\ 3 \\ 4 \end{array} \overset{\begin{array}{cccc} 1 & 2 & 3 & 4 \end{array}}{\begin{bmatrix} 0 & 1 & 1 & 1 \\ 1 & 0 & 0 & 1 \\ 0 & 0 & 0 & 1 \\ 0 & 1 & 0 & 0 \end{bmatrix}} = A$$

To Point

Use matrix A to answer these questions.

1. Name the destinations to which each point can send messages.
   a. Point 1   **b.** Point 2   **c.** Point 3   **d.** Point 4

2. Which point can send messages to the greatest number of destinations?

3. Name the sources from which each point can receive messages.
   a. Point 1   **b.** Point 2   **c.** Point 3   **d.** Point 4

4. Which point can receive messages from the greatest number of sources?

Written Exercises

Use the situation below for Exercises 1–3.

Situation: All existing routes of communication in a five-person work situation are described as follows. Person 1 sends messages to Person 2. Person 2 sends messages to and receives messages from Persons 1, 3, and 4. Person 5 receives messages from Persons 3 and 4.

A   1. Draw the communication network that describes this situation.

2. Write the communication matrix that describes this situation.

3. Find the matrix that shows the number of ways a message can be sent from one person to another using exactly one relay.

Use the situation below for Exercises 4–6.

Situation: A tennis club plans to add a swimming pool. A survey of present members reveals that all will continue to play tennis, and that 55% will also use the pool. Of new members expected to join after the pool is completed, it is predicted that 82% will use the pool, and 40% will play tennis. There are at present 460 members. After the pool is in use, it is hoped that 250 new members will join.

4. Write the transition matrix that describes the expected shift of activity when the pool is completed.

5. Write the matrix that shows the distribution of old and new members.

6. Find the matrix that shows the expected number of members who will use each facility (tennis courts and pool) after the pool is completed.

Use the communication network at the right for Exercises 7–9.

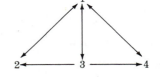

B 7. Write the communication matrix for the network shown and find the matrix that shows the number of ways a message can be sent from one point to another via one relay.

8. Find the matrix that shows the number of ways a message can be sent from one point to another using no more than one relay.

9. Find the matrix that shows the number of ways a message can be sent from one point to another using two relays.

10. A student taking a foreign language course has a 70% chance of continuing the foreign language next semester and a 30% chance of switching to another course. A student not taking a foreign language has a 10% chance of switching to a foreign language and a 90% chance of not switching. During the first semester, 210 students studied a foreign language, and 350 students did not. Find the distribution for next semester.

11. In the communication network at the right, a "hook" indicates that two lines do not intersect. Find the number of ways each point can send a message back to itself using no more than two relays.

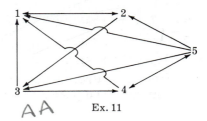

Ex. 11

12. Over a two-year period people living in cities have a 30% chance of moving to the suburbs, and people living in the suburbs have a 20% chance of moving to a city. Of all those who live in either cities or suburbs there are currently 60% in the cities and 40% in the suburbs. What is the predicted distribution four years from now?

13. Find the point(s) having the greatest number of incoming message routes allowing no more than two relay points.

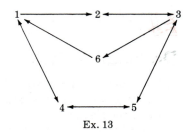

Ex. 13

Self-Test 1

1. Find the value of each variable.

Obj. 15-1, p. 559

$$O_{3\times2} = \begin{bmatrix} x+1 & 0 \\ y^2 & 0 \\ z-4 & 0 \end{bmatrix}$$

In Exercises 2–6,

let $A = \begin{bmatrix} -1 & 2 \\ 3 & 7 \end{bmatrix}$ and $B = \begin{bmatrix} 6 & -4 \\ -3 & 1 \end{bmatrix}$.

Find the following:

2. $A + B$ **3.** $A - B$ **4.** $5A$ **Obj. 15-2, p. 562**

5. AB **6.** B^2 **Obj. 15-3, p. 566**

7. a. Write the communication matrix for the network shown.

   b. Then use matrices to find the number of ways a message can be sent from point 1 to point 3 using at most one relay point.

Obj. 15-4, p. 571

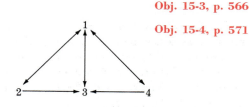

Check your answers with those at the back of the book.

Dominance Relations

A *dominance relation* exists between the members of a group when, between any two members one dominates the other.

Consider a tournament with four teams participating. The Aces beat the Bolts and the Cobras but lost to the Darts. The Bolts beat the Cobras and the Darts, and the Cobras beat the Darts.

One-stage dominances are displayed in the dominance matrix M. A "1" indicates that the team named in the corresponding row beat the team in the corresponding column.

		Aces	Bolts	Cobras	Darts	Row Sum
	Aces	0	1	1	0	2
M =	Bolts	0	0	1	1	2
	Cobras	0	0	0	1	1
	Darts	1	0	0	0	1
Column Sum:		1	1	2	2	

The first row shows that the Aces have one-stage dominances over the Bolts and Cobras. The number of wins for each team is indicated by the row sums. The number of losses for each team is indicated by the column sums. Notice that both the Aces and the Bolts have won two and lost one.

A member x is said to have a two-stage dominance over a member z when x dominates y and y dominates z. Two-stage dominances are shown in M^2.

		Aces	Bolts	Cobras	Darts	Row Sum
	Aces	0	0	1	2	3
$M^2 =$	Bolts	1	0	0	1	2
	Cobras	1	0	0	0	1
	Darts	0	1	1	0	2

The first row indicates that the Aces exert a two-stage dominance over the Cobras and a pair of two-stage dominances over the Darts. The Aces did not beat the Darts, but the Aces beat two other teams that, in turn, beat the Darts. By adding M and M^2, the winner of the tournament can be determined. The row sums of $M + M^2$ show that the Aces, with a total of 5 one- or two-stage dominances, win the tournament.

Notice that the matrix operations used in the study of dominance relations are similar to those used in the study of communication networks.

15-5 *Determinants*

OBJECTIVE   To find the determinant of a 2 × 2 or 3 × 3 matrix.

Associated with each square matrix is a real number called the *determinant* of the matrix. Each entry is called an **element** of the determinant and the number of elements in any row or column is called the **order** of the determinant. The determinant of a matrix is often displayed in the same form as the matrix, but with vertical bars rather than brackets enclosing the entries. For example,

Let $A = \begin{bmatrix} a & b \\ c & d \end{bmatrix}$. The **determinant** of A, denoted by det A, is defined as follows:

$$\det A = \begin{vmatrix} a & b \\ c & d \end{vmatrix} = ad - bc$$

EXAMPLE 1   Evaluate $\begin{vmatrix} 5 & 3 \\ -4 & 2 \end{vmatrix}$.

SOLUTION $\begin{vmatrix} 5 & 3 \\ -4 & 2 \end{vmatrix} = 5(2) - (-4)3 = 22$ *Answer*

The determinant of a 3 × 3 matrix is defined as follows:

Let $B = \begin{bmatrix} a_1 & b_1 & c_1 \\ a_2 & b_2 & c_2 \\ a_3 & b_3 & c_3 \end{bmatrix}$.

$$\det B = \begin{vmatrix} a_1 & b_1 & c_1 \\ a_2 & b_2 & c_2 \\ a_3 & b_3 & c_3 \end{vmatrix} = a_1b_2c_3 + a_2b_3c_1 + a_3b_1c_2 - a_1b_3c_2 - a_2b_1c_3 - a_3b_2c_1$$

A convenient device for finding the six terms needed to evaluate a 3 × 3 determinant is shown below.

1. Copy the first two columns of the matrix in order to the right of the third column.

    $\begin{vmatrix} a_1 & b_1 & c_1 \\ a_2 & b_2 & c_2 \\ a_3 & b_3 & c_3 \end{vmatrix} \begin{matrix} a_1 & b_1 \\ a_2 & b_2 \\ a_3 & b_3 \end{matrix}$

2. Multiply each entry in the first row of the original matrix by the other two entries on the left to right diagonal. The products are the first three terms of the determinant.

    $\begin{vmatrix} a_1 & b_1 & c_1 \\ a_2 & b_2 & c_2 \\ a_3 & b_3 & c_3 \end{vmatrix} \begin{matrix} a_1 & b_1 \\ a_2 & b_2 \\ a_3 & b_3 \end{matrix}$

    $+ \quad + \quad +$

3. Multiply each entry in the first row of the original matrix, starting from the right, by the other two entries on the diagonal going from right to left. The opposites of these products are the last three terms of the determinant.

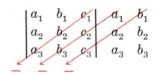

Note that this device is valid only for 3×3 matrices.

EXAMPLE 2   Evaluate det $A = \begin{vmatrix} 3 & 1 & 2 \\ 4 & -2 & 3 \\ 1 & 0 & 1 \end{vmatrix}$.

SOLUTION

$$\begin{vmatrix} 3 & 1 & 2 \\ 4 & -2 & 3 \\ 1 & 0 & 1 \end{vmatrix} \begin{matrix} 3 & 1 \\ 4 & -2 \\ 1 & 0 \end{matrix}$$

$$\det A = (-6) + (3) + (0) - (-4) - (0) - (4) = -3 \quad \textit{Answer}$$

Oral Exercises

Evaluate.

1. $\begin{vmatrix} 1 & 0 \\ 0 & 1 \end{vmatrix}$ **2.** $\begin{vmatrix} 0 & 0 \\ 0 & 0 \end{vmatrix}$ **3.** $\begin{vmatrix} 3 & 1 \\ 1 & 2 \end{vmatrix}$ **4.** $\begin{vmatrix} -2 & 2 \\ -1 & 1 \end{vmatrix}$

5. $\begin{vmatrix} 2 & 0 \\ 0 & 1 \end{vmatrix} + \begin{vmatrix} 0 & 1 \\ -1 & 0 \end{vmatrix}$ **6.** $\begin{vmatrix} 8 & 0 \\ 0 & -1 \end{vmatrix} - \begin{vmatrix} -3 & 0 \\ 0 & 1 \end{vmatrix}$ **7.** $\begin{vmatrix} 4 & 0 \\ 0 & -3 \end{vmatrix} \div \begin{vmatrix} 1 & 0 \\ 0 & 1 \end{vmatrix}$

Written Exercises

Evaluate each determinant.

A **1.** $\begin{vmatrix} 2 & 3 \\ 1 & 4 \end{vmatrix}$ **2.** $\begin{vmatrix} 6 & 5 \\ 0 & 3 \end{vmatrix}$ **3.** $\begin{vmatrix} 4 & -3 \\ 5 & 1 \end{vmatrix}$ **4.** $\begin{vmatrix} 0 & 8 \\ 1 & 10 \end{vmatrix}$

5. $\begin{vmatrix} 2 & -5 & 3 \\ 0 & 8 & 1 \\ -5 & 4 & 0 \end{vmatrix}$ **6.** $\begin{vmatrix} 4 & 0 & -7 \\ 6 & 1 & 11 \\ -6 & 0 & 3 \end{vmatrix}$ **7.** $\begin{vmatrix} 12 & -7 & 19 \\ 0 & 0 & 5 \\ -9 & 3 & 43 \end{vmatrix}$ **8.** $\begin{vmatrix} 2 & 5 & 1 \\ -3 & 7 & -8 \\ 11 & -4 & 15 \end{vmatrix}$

B **9.** Show that for any 2×2 matrix, A, if all of the elements in one row or one column are zeros, then the determinant of A is 0.

10. Show that for any 3×3 matrix, B, if all the elements in one row or one column are zeros, then the determinant of B is 0.

C **11.** Let A be any 2×2 matrix. Show that if any row or column of A is multiplied by the scalar r, then det A is multiplied by r.

12. Let r be a scalar, and A be any 2×2 matrix. Show that det $(rA) = r^2$ det A.

15-6 *Inverses of Matrices*

OBJECTIVE   To solve systems of equations using inverses of matrices.

The product of the two matrices

$$\begin{bmatrix} 2 & 3 \\ 1 & 2 \end{bmatrix} \begin{bmatrix} 2 & -3 \\ -1 & 2 \end{bmatrix} = \begin{bmatrix} 4-3 & -6+6 \\ 2-2 & -3+4 \end{bmatrix} = \begin{bmatrix} 1 & 0 \\ 0 & 1 \end{bmatrix}$$

is the identity matrix, $I_{2 \times 2}$. For any two matrices A and B, if $AB = BA = I$, then A and B are called **inverses.** The symbol A^{-1} denotes the inverse of matrix A. Thus, $B = A^{-1}$.

Does every nonzero 2×2 matrix, A, have an inverse, A^{-1}?

Let $A = \begin{bmatrix} a & b \\ c & d \end{bmatrix}$. Find $A^{-1} = \begin{bmatrix} x & u \\ y & v \end{bmatrix}$ such that $AA^{-1} = I_{2 \times 2}$.

$$\begin{bmatrix} a & b \\ c & d \end{bmatrix} \begin{bmatrix} x & u \\ y & v \end{bmatrix} = \begin{bmatrix} ax+by & au+bv \\ cx+dy & cu+dv \end{bmatrix} = \begin{bmatrix} 1 & 0 \\ 0 & 1 \end{bmatrix}$$

The equation above is true if and only if

$$\begin{array}{ccc} ax + by = 1 & & au + bv = 0 \\ cx + dy = 0 & \text{and} & cu + dv = 1. \end{array}$$

If $ad - bc \neq 0$, these systems may be solved to yield the following:

$$x = \frac{d}{ad-bc} \qquad u = \frac{-b}{ad-bc}$$

$$y = \frac{-c}{ad-bc} \qquad v = \frac{a}{ad-bc}$$

Substitute these values in the matrix A^{-1}.

Then $A^{-1} = \begin{bmatrix} \dfrac{d}{ad-bc} & \dfrac{-b}{ad-bc} \\ \dfrac{-c}{ad-bc} & \dfrac{a}{ad-bc} \end{bmatrix} = \dfrac{1}{ad-bc} \begin{bmatrix} d & -b \\ -c & a \end{bmatrix}, \; ad - bc \neq 0.$

You can verify that $AA^{-1} = A^{-1}A = I_{2 \times 2}$. Since $ad - bc$ is the determinant of A, you have the following general result.

If $A = \begin{bmatrix} a & b \\ c & d \end{bmatrix}$ and $\det A \neq 0$,

$$A^{-1} = \frac{1}{\det A} \begin{bmatrix} d & -b \\ -c & a \end{bmatrix}.$$

Thus, you can find the inverse of any 2×2 matrix *provided its determinant is not 0*. If det $A = 0$, A has no inverse. Notice what the equation says to do to find A^{-1}: interchange a and d, replace b and c with their respective negatives, and multiply the resulting matrix by $\dfrac{1}{\det A}$.

You can use the inverse of a matrix to solve a system of linear equations. Consider the system

$$ax + by = e$$
$$cx + dy = f$$

where a, b, c, d, e, f are real numbers, and e and f are not both zero. First write this system using the definitions of matrix multiplication and equality of matrices.

$$\begin{bmatrix} a & b \\ c & d \end{bmatrix} \begin{bmatrix} x \\ y \end{bmatrix} = \begin{bmatrix} e \\ f \end{bmatrix}$$

This equation is in the form

$$AX = B$$

where $A = \begin{bmatrix} a & b \\ c & d \end{bmatrix}$, $X = \begin{bmatrix} x \\ y \end{bmatrix}$, and $B = \begin{bmatrix} e \\ f \end{bmatrix}$.

Then, if A^{-1} exists:

$$A^{-1}(AX) = A^{-1}(B)$$
$$(A^{-1}A)X = A^{-1}B$$
$$IX = A^{-1}B$$
$$X = A^{-1}B$$

Thus if A^{-1} exists, the system of equations has a unique solution, namely, $X = A^{-1}B$. But A^{-1} exists if and only if det $A \neq 0$. It follows that the system of equations above has a unique solution if and only if det $A \neq 0$.

EXAMPLE Find the solution of the system: $2x - 3y = 1$
$\qquad\qquad\qquad\qquad\qquad\qquad\qquad\qquad\quad x + 4y = 6$

SOLUTION Write the matrix equation:

$$\begin{bmatrix} 2 & -3 \\ 1 & 4 \end{bmatrix} \begin{bmatrix} x \\ y \end{bmatrix} = \begin{bmatrix} 1 \\ 6 \end{bmatrix}$$

Recall that the solution of matrix equation $AX = B$ is $X = A^{-1}B$. Find the inverse of the matrix of coefficients.

$$\begin{bmatrix} 2 & -3 \\ 1 & 4 \end{bmatrix}^{-1} = \frac{1}{11} \begin{bmatrix} 4 & 3 \\ -1 & 2 \end{bmatrix}$$

(*solution is continued on page 582.*)

$$\begin{bmatrix} x \\ y \end{bmatrix} = \frac{1}{11}\begin{bmatrix} 4 & 3 \\ -1 & 2 \end{bmatrix}\begin{bmatrix} 1 \\ 6 \end{bmatrix}$$

$$\begin{bmatrix} x \\ y \end{bmatrix} = \frac{1}{11}\begin{bmatrix} 22 \\ 11 \end{bmatrix}$$

$$\begin{bmatrix} x \\ y \end{bmatrix} = \begin{bmatrix} 2 \\ 1 \end{bmatrix}$$

∴ the solution is (2, 1). *Answer*

Oral Exercises

Determine which of these systems have unique solutions.

1. $4x + y = 1$
$6x + 2y = 3$

2. $4x + 2y = -6$
$6x + 3y = -9$

3. $5x - y = 2$
$3x + 2y = -8$

Written Exercises

Find the inverse for each matrix. If the matrix has no inverse, so state.

A 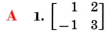 **1.** $\begin{bmatrix} 1 & 2 \\ -1 & 3 \end{bmatrix}$
2. $\begin{bmatrix} 4 & 5 \\ 0 & 1 \end{bmatrix}$
3. $\begin{bmatrix} 3 & -1 \\ 4 & 2 \end{bmatrix}$
4. $\begin{bmatrix} 1 & 0 \\ 0 & 1 \end{bmatrix}$

5. $\begin{bmatrix} -1 & 3 \\ -2 & 4 \end{bmatrix}$
6. $\begin{bmatrix} 3 & -1 \\ 6 & -2 \end{bmatrix}$
7. $\begin{bmatrix} 1 & -3 \\ 1 & 5 \end{bmatrix}$
8. $\begin{bmatrix} 1 & -2 \\ -1 & 5 \end{bmatrix}$

Use matrices to find the solution of each system of equations. If a system has no unique solution, so state.

9. $4x - y = 1$
$3x + y = 13$

10. $x + y = 9$
$x - 3y = 13$

11. $2x + y = 1$
$3x - y = 9$

12. $2x - y = 10$
$x - 3y = 0$

13. $4x + 3y = 1$
$4x + y = -5$

14. $3x + 5y = 1$
$x + 6y = 9$

15. $x + y = 1$
$2x + 2y = 5$

16. $x = 3$
$-x + y = 2$

Solve each matrix equation for A.

B **17.** $\begin{bmatrix} 1 & 3 \\ 2 & 7 \end{bmatrix}A = \begin{bmatrix} 4 & 1 \\ -2 & 3 \end{bmatrix}$

18. $\begin{bmatrix} 3 & 2 \\ 2 & 2 \end{bmatrix}A = \begin{bmatrix} 5 & 0 \\ -1 & -1 \end{bmatrix}$

19. $\begin{bmatrix} 4 & 2 \\ 1 & 1 \end{bmatrix}A = \begin{bmatrix} 2 & 3 \\ 0 & 1 \end{bmatrix}$

20. $\begin{bmatrix} 5 & 3 \\ 3 & 2 \end{bmatrix}A - \begin{bmatrix} 1 & 3 \\ 2 & 1 \end{bmatrix} = \begin{bmatrix} 1 & 2 \\ -1 & 3 \end{bmatrix}$

Self-Test 2

113
4/52

VOCABULARY   determinant (p. 578)
order of a determinant (p. 578)
inverse of a matrix (p. 580)

Evaluate each determinant.   **Obj. 15-5, p. 578**

1. $\begin{vmatrix} 6 & -2 \\ 8 & 3 \end{vmatrix}$ 2. $\begin{vmatrix} 2 & -1 & 0 \\ 1 & 5 & -3 \\ 0 & -2 & 1 \end{vmatrix}$ $-9/5$

3. Find A^{-1} if $A = \begin{bmatrix} 2 & -1 \\ 0 & 4 \end{bmatrix}$.   **Obj. 15-6, p. 580**

4. Solve for B: $\begin{bmatrix} -1 & 6 \\ 2 & 5 \end{bmatrix} B = \begin{bmatrix} -9 & -4 \\ 1 & 8 \end{bmatrix}$

Check your answers with those at the back of the book.

$-1/5 + -9/5$

$-19/5 = -2$

fashion
service
quality

$-3/5 + 18/5$

$\dfrac{-15}{8} + \dfrac{-1}{8} = \dfrac{-16}{8}$

Computer Key-In

In Section 15-6, it was shown that the solution of $AX = B$, where $A = \begin{bmatrix} a & b \\ c & d \end{bmatrix}$, $X = \begin{bmatrix} x \\ y \end{bmatrix}$, and $B = \begin{bmatrix} e \\ f \end{bmatrix}$, is $X = A^{-1}B$, where A^{-1} is the inverse of A. The same formula holds when A, X, B, and A^{-1} are larger than 2×2.

$\dfrac{10}{2}$

The program beginning on the bottom of the page can be used to solve systems of linear equations with up to 10 variables.

```
10   PRINT "TO SOLVE N EQUATIONS IN N VARIABLES (N<=10),"
20   PRINT "INPUT N";
30   INPUT N
40   PRINT
50   PRINT "INPUT COEF. MATRIX";
60   MAT INPUT A[N,N]
70   PRINT "INPUT CONSTANTS";
80   MAT INPUT B[N]
90   MAT V=ZER[N,N]
100  MAT V=INV(A)
110  MAT X=ZER[N]
120  MAT X=V*B
130  PRINT "SOLUTION:     (";
140  FOR I=1 TO N-1
```

$-2-3$

```
150  PRINT INT(X[I]*1000+.5)/1000;",";
160  NEXT I
170  PRINT INT(X[I]*1000+.5)/1000;")"
180  PRINT
190  PRINT "DO YOU WISH TO DO ANOTHER (Y/N)";
200  INPUT A$
210  IF A$="Y" THEN 20
220  END

END
```

Exercises

Copy and RUN the preceding program to solve the following.

1. Example 1, page 592

2. Example 2, page 593

3. Exercise 13, page 596

4. Exercise 14, page 596

In Section 15-9, it will be shown that the solution of $\begin{aligned} ax + by = e \\ cx + dy = f \end{aligned}$ is $\left(\dfrac{de - bf}{ad - bc}, \dfrac{af - ce}{ad - bc}\right)$, provided $ad - bc \neq 0$. Similarly, the real solutions of $\begin{aligned} ax^2 + by^2 = e \\ cx^2 + dy^2 = f \end{aligned}$ are $\left(\pm\sqrt{\dfrac{de - bf}{ad - bc}}, \pm\sqrt{\dfrac{af - ce}{ad - bc}}\right)$, provided $ad - bc \neq 0$ and the radicands are not zero.

Here is the nucleus of a program to solve such systems.

```
100  PRINT "INPUT A, B, E";
110  INPUT A,B,E
120  PRINT "INPUT C, D, F";
130  INPUT C,D,F
140  LET M=A*D-B*C
150  IF M=0 THEN 250
160  LET R1=(D*E-B*F)/M
170  IF R1<0 THEN 250
180  LET R2=(A*F-C*E)/M
190  IF R2<0 THEN 250
200  LET X=SQR(R1)
210  LET Y=SQR(R2)
220  PRINT "THE SOLUTIONS ARE:"
230  PRINT "(";X;",";Y;"),    (";-X;",";Y;")"
240  PRINT "(";X;",";-Y;"),    (";-X;",";-Y;")"
250  END
```

5. Write some introductory steps for the preceding program to explain what the variables A, B, C, D, E, and F represent.

Use the program to solve the following.

6. Example 3, page 362

7. Exercise 14, page 364

8. Exercise 15, page 364

DETERMINANTS

15-7 *Expansion of Determinants by Minors*

OBJECTIVE   To evaluate third-order determinants using expansion by minors.

It is important to distinguish between matrices and determinants. A matrix is an array of numbers; a determinant is a real number associated with a square matrix. The process of evaluating a determinant is called "expanding the determinant." This section considers "expansion by minors," which is a method applicable to determinants of order n when $n \geq 3$.

The **minor** of an element in a determinant is the determinant resulting from the deletion of the row and column containing the element. Thus in the determinant

$$\begin{vmatrix} 0 & 4 & -2 \\ 3 & 8 & 0 \\ -1 & 2 & 1 \end{vmatrix}$$

the minor of the element -2 is

$$\begin{vmatrix} 0 & 4 & -2 \\ 3 & 8 & 0 \\ -1 & 2 & 1 \end{vmatrix}, \text{ or } \begin{vmatrix} 3 & 8 \\ -1 & 2 \end{vmatrix}.$$

The minor of the element 8 is

$$\begin{vmatrix} 0 & 4 & -2 \\ 3 & 8 & 0 \\ -1 & 2 & 1 \end{vmatrix}, \text{ or } \begin{vmatrix} 0 & -2 \\ -1 & 1 \end{vmatrix}.$$

Recall that, by definition, the value of a third-order determinant is given by

$$\begin{vmatrix} a_1 & b_1 & c_1 \\ a_2 & b_2 & c_2 \\ a_3 & b_3 & c_3 \end{vmatrix} = a_1 b_2 c_3 + a_2 b_3 c_1 + a_3 b_1 c_2 - a_1 b_3 c_2 - a_2 b_1 c_3 - a_3 b_2 c_1$$

$$= a_1(b_2 c_3 - b_3 c_2) - b_1(a_2 c_3 - a_3 c_2) + c_1(a_2 b_3 - a_3 b_2) \quad \begin{cases} \text{Rearranging} \\ \text{terms and} \\ \text{factoring} \end{cases}$$

$$= a_1 \begin{vmatrix} b_2 & c_2 \\ b_3 & c_3 \end{vmatrix} - b_1 \begin{vmatrix} a_2 & c_2 \\ a_3 & c_3 \end{vmatrix} + c_1 \begin{vmatrix} a_2 & b_2 \\ a_3 & b_3 \end{vmatrix}.$$

That is, the three expressions in parentheses are the minors of a_1, b_1, and c_1, denoted below by A_1, B_1, and C_1, respectively. Thus,

$$\begin{vmatrix} a_1 & b_1 & c_1 \\ a_2 & b_2 & c_2 \\ a_3 & b_3 & c_3 \end{vmatrix} = a_1 A_1 - b_1 B_1 + c_1 C_1$$

The right-hand expression is the expansion of this determinant by minors *about the first row*.

A determinant may be expanded by minors about any row or column.

TO EXPAND A DETERMINANT BY MINORS

1. Find the product of each element of that row or column with its minor.
2. Add the number of the row and the number of the column for each element. If that sum is odd, multiply the product obtained in step 1 by -1.
3. Add the products to obtain the value of the determinant.

EXAMPLE   Expand $\begin{vmatrix} 3 & -1 & 2 \\ -1 & 2 & 5 \\ 0 & -4 & 6 \end{vmatrix}$ by the minors of the first row.

SOLUTION   Multiply each element of the first row by its minor. Multiply the product for the element in the first row, second column by -1 since the sum $1 + 2 = 3$ is odd. Then add the products.

$$3\begin{vmatrix} 2 & 5 \\ 4 & 6 \end{vmatrix} + 1(-1)\begin{vmatrix} -1 & 5 \\ 0 & 6 \end{vmatrix} + 2\begin{vmatrix} -1 & 2 \\ 0 & 4 \end{vmatrix}$$

$$= 3(12 - 20) - 1(-6 - 0) + 2(-4 - 0)$$
$$= 3(-8) - 1(-6) + 2(-4)$$
$$= -24 + 6 - 8 = -26 \quad \textit{Answer}$$

The method of expansion by minors is used to define determinants of order $n \geq 3$. For example, consider the matrix

$$M = \begin{bmatrix} a_1 & b_1 & c_1 & d_1 \\ a_2 & b_2 & c_2 & d_2 \\ a_3 & b_3 & c_3 & d_3 \\ a_4 & b_4 & c_4 & d_4 \end{bmatrix}.$$

Let $A_1 = \begin{vmatrix} b_2 & c_2 & d_2 \\ b_3 & c_3 & d_3 \\ b_4 & c_4 & d_4 \end{vmatrix}$ $B_1 = \begin{vmatrix} a_2 & c_2 & d_2 \\ a_3 & c_3 & d_3 \\ a_4 & c_4 & d_4 \end{vmatrix}$

$$C_1 = \begin{vmatrix} a_2 & b_2 & d_2 \\ a_3 & b_3 & d_3 \\ a_4 & b_4 & d_4 \end{vmatrix} \qquad D_1 = \begin{vmatrix} a_2 & b_2 & c_2 \\ a_3 & b_3 & c_3 \\ a_4 & b_4 & c_4 \end{vmatrix}$$

The determinant of M is defined as

$$\det M = a_1A_1 - b_1B_1 + c_1C_1 - d_1D_1.$$

Note that A_1, B_1, C_1, and D_1 are the minors of a_1, b_1, c_1, and d_1, respectively. In short, they are minors with respect to row one of this 4×4 matrix. As with third-order determinants, determinants of order four may be expanded by minors about any row or any column. The minors of a fourth-order determinant are each third-order determinants. In general, minors of a determinant of order n are determinants of order $n - 1$. Since the expansion of determinants of order greater than four can be tedious, computers are often used to evaluate higher-order determinants.

Oral Exercises

Give the requested element or determinant using the given expansion by minors.

$$\begin{vmatrix} 2 & 1 & -1 \\ 5 & 3 & -3 \\ -1 & 10 & 5 \end{vmatrix} = a_1 \begin{vmatrix} 3 & -3 \\ 10 & 5 \end{vmatrix} - a_2 \begin{vmatrix} 1 & -1 \\ 10 & 5 \end{vmatrix} + (-1)A_3$$

1. a_1 **2.** a_2 **3.** Det A_3

Find the value of the following.

4. $\begin{vmatrix} 1 & 0 \\ 0 & 1 \end{vmatrix}$

5. $\begin{vmatrix} 1 & 0 & 0 \\ 0 & 1 & 0 \\ 0 & 0 & 1 \end{vmatrix}$

6. $\begin{vmatrix} 1 & 0 & 0 & 0 \\ 0 & 1 & 0 & 0 \\ 0 & 0 & 1 & 0 \\ 0 & 0 & 0 & 1 \end{vmatrix}$

Written Exercises

Expand the given determinant about the given row or column.

A **1.** $\begin{vmatrix} 1 & 4 & 2 \\ 2 & 3 & 1 \\ 6 & 2 & 4 \end{vmatrix}$; row one

2. $\begin{vmatrix} 3 & 0 & -1 \\ 2 & 3 & 4 \\ -1 & 5 & -3 \end{vmatrix}$; column two

3. $\begin{vmatrix} 2 & -1 & 0 \\ 0 & 2 & 8 \\ 1 & -3 & 1 \end{vmatrix}$; column one

4. $\begin{vmatrix} 2 & 3 & -1 \\ 8 & 0 & -3 \\ 1 & 1 & 5 \end{vmatrix}$; row three

5. $\begin{vmatrix} 0 & -1 & -2 \\ 2 & 4 & 1 \\ -5 & 1 & 0 \end{vmatrix}$; row two

6. $\begin{vmatrix} -1 & 3 & -4 \\ 2 & 1 & 0 \\ 1 & 6 & 10 \end{vmatrix}$; column three

7. $\begin{vmatrix} 4 & 0 & -7 \\ 9 & 1 & 11 \\ -6 & 0 & 3 \end{vmatrix}$; column one

8. $\begin{vmatrix} 4 & 0 & -7 \\ 9 & 1 & 11 \\ -6 & 0 & 3 \end{vmatrix}$; row two

Expand the given determinant about any row or column.

9. $\begin{vmatrix} 1 & 2 & 4 \\ 5 & 12 & 10 \\ -1 & -1 & 2 \end{vmatrix}$

10. $\begin{vmatrix} 0 & 2 & 5 \\ -2 & 1 & 3 \\ 1 & 0 & 8 \end{vmatrix}$

11. $\begin{vmatrix} 0 & -7 & -14 \\ 5 & 6 & -5 \\ 1 & 3 & 4 \end{vmatrix}$

Solve each equation for x.

B 12. $\begin{vmatrix} 0 & -35 & 63 \\ 3 & 95 & x \\ 1 & -35 & 63 \end{vmatrix} = 0$

13. $\begin{vmatrix} 1 & 3 & 4 \\ 5 & 15 & 10 \\ -1 & x & 2 \end{vmatrix} = 80$

14. $\begin{vmatrix} 12 & -7 & 19 \\ 0 & x & 5 \\ -9 & 3 & 43 \end{vmatrix} = 135$

15. $\begin{vmatrix} x & 2 & 3 \\ 1 & x & 3 \\ 1 & -1 & 1 \end{vmatrix} = 5$

Find the value of the determinant for each matrix.

16. $\begin{bmatrix} 4 & 0 & 3 & 7 \\ 5 & 2 & 4 & 9 \\ -6 & -1 & 5 & 8 \\ 3 & 0 & 8 & 2 \end{bmatrix}$

17. $\begin{bmatrix} 7 & 0 & 0 & 0 \\ 4 & -3 & 0 & 0 \\ 8 & 2 & 2 & 0 \\ -9 & 14 & 3 & 5 \end{bmatrix}$

Prove the following properties for third-order determinants.

C 18. A determinant with two rows alike is equal to zero.

19. If each element in one row is 0, then the determinant is equal to zero.

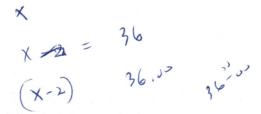

Challenge

A group of friends went to a restaurant for lunch. They had agreed to split the bill equally. However, when the bill arrived two of them discovered that they had left their money at home. The others in the group then agreed to make up the difference, resulting in each one having to pay an extra $1.50. If the total bill was $36.00, how many people were in the group that had lunch at the restaurant?

15-8 *Properties of Determinants*

OBJECTIVE   To use the properties of determinants to simplify the expansion of determinants by minors.

Determinants have properties that can simplify their evaluation. These properties are especially helpful for determinants of order greater than two. Although third-order determinants are used as examples, these properties apply to determinants of any order. Some of these properties were proved in earlier exercises.

PROPERTY 1: If each element in any row (or each element in any column) is 0, then the determinant is equal to 0.

$$\begin{vmatrix} 1 & 2 & -1 \\ 3 & -1 & 1 \\ 0 & 0 & 0 \end{vmatrix} = 0 \begin{vmatrix} 2 & -1 \\ -1 & 1 \end{vmatrix} - 0 \begin{vmatrix} 1 & -1 \\ 3 & 1 \end{vmatrix} + 0 \begin{vmatrix} 1 & 2 \\ 3 & -1 \end{vmatrix}$$

$$= 0 + 0 + 0 = 0$$

PROPERTY 2: If two rows (or two columns) of a determinant are interchanged, the resulting determinant is the negative of the original determinant.

$$\begin{vmatrix} 7 & 2 & -2 \\ 3 & 1 & -1 \\ 2 & 3 & 4 \end{vmatrix} = 7 \begin{vmatrix} 1 & -1 \\ 3 & 4 \end{vmatrix} - 3 \begin{vmatrix} 2 & -2 \\ 3 & 4 \end{vmatrix} + 2 \begin{vmatrix} 2 & -2 \\ 1 & -1 \end{vmatrix}$$

$$= 7(7) - 3(14) + 2(0)$$

$$= 7$$

$$\begin{vmatrix} 2 & 7 & -2 \\ 1 & 3 & -1 \\ 3 & 2 & 4 \end{vmatrix} = -7 \begin{vmatrix} 1 & -1 \\ 3 & 4 \end{vmatrix} + 3 \begin{vmatrix} 2 & -2 \\ 3 & 4 \end{vmatrix} - 2 \begin{vmatrix} 2 & -2 \\ 1 & -1 \end{vmatrix}$$

$$= -7(7) + 3(14) - 2(0)$$

$$= -7$$

PROPERTY 3: If two rows (or two columns) of a determinant have corresponding elements that are equal, then the determinant is equal to 0.

$$\begin{vmatrix} 3 & -1 & 2 \\ 1 & -2 & 4 \\ 1 & -2 & 4 \end{vmatrix} = 3 \begin{vmatrix} -2 & 4 \\ -2 & 4 \end{vmatrix} - (-1) \begin{vmatrix} 1 & 4 \\ 1 & 4 \end{vmatrix} + 2 \begin{vmatrix} 1 & -2 \\ 1 & -2 \end{vmatrix}$$

$$= 3(0) + 1(0) + 2(0)$$

$$= 0$$

PROPERTY 4: If each element in one row (or one column) of a determinant is multiplied by a real number k, then the determinant is multiplied by k.

$$\begin{vmatrix} 1 & 2 & 1 \\ -1 & 3 & -2 \\ 3 & -1 & 4 \end{vmatrix} = 1\begin{vmatrix} 3 & -2 \\ -1 & 4 \end{vmatrix} - 2\begin{vmatrix} -1 & -2 \\ 3 & 4 \end{vmatrix} + 1\begin{vmatrix} -1 & 3 \\ 3 & -1 \end{vmatrix} = -2$$

$$\begin{vmatrix} 5\cdot 1 & 5\cdot 2 & 5\cdot 1 \\ -1 & 3 & -2 \\ 3 & -1 & 4 \end{vmatrix} = 5\cdot 1\begin{vmatrix} 3 & -2 \\ -1 & 4 \end{vmatrix} - 5\cdot 2\begin{vmatrix} -1 & -2 \\ 3 & 4 \end{vmatrix} + 5\cdot 1\begin{vmatrix} -1 & 3 \\ 3 & -1 \end{vmatrix}$$

$$= 5\left(1\begin{vmatrix} 3 & -2 \\ -1 & 4 \end{vmatrix} - 2\begin{vmatrix} -1 & -2 \\ 3 & 4 \end{vmatrix} + 1\begin{vmatrix} -1 & 3 \\ 3 & -1 \end{vmatrix}\right)$$

$$= 5(-2) = -10$$

PROPERTY 5: If each element of one row (or one column) is multiplied by a real number k and if the resulting products are then added to the corresponding elements of another row (or another column), respectively, the resulting determinant equals the original one.

$$\begin{vmatrix} -4 & 5 & 1 \\ 6 & -3 & 2 \\ -6 & 3 & -1 \end{vmatrix} = -4\begin{vmatrix} -3 & 2 \\ 3 & -1 \end{vmatrix} - 6\begin{vmatrix} 5 & 1 \\ 3 & -1 \end{vmatrix} - 6\begin{vmatrix} 5 & 1 \\ -3 & 2 \end{vmatrix} = -18$$

$$\begin{vmatrix} -4+2(5) & 5 & 1 \\ 6+2(-3) & -3 & 2 \\ -6+2(3) & 3 & -1 \end{vmatrix} = \begin{vmatrix} 6 & 5 & 1 \\ 0 & -3 & 2 \\ 0 & 3 & -1 \end{vmatrix} = 6\begin{vmatrix} -3 & 2 \\ 3 & -1 \end{vmatrix} + 0 + 0 = -18$$

These properties may be used to simplify the computation of determinants. The strategy in the first example below is to reduce the first row to the form 1   0   0. Notice how this greatly simplifies the expansion of the determinant.

EXAMPLE   Evaluate $\begin{vmatrix} 15 & 0 & 2 \\ 45 & -1 & 3 \\ 30 & 2 & 8 \end{vmatrix}$.

SOLUTION   1. Factor column one; factor 15 from the matrix. (Property 4)

$$\begin{vmatrix} 15 & 0 & 2 \\ 45 & -1 & 3 \\ 30 & 2 & 8 \end{vmatrix} = \begin{vmatrix} 15(1) & 0 & 2 \\ 15(3) & -1 & 3 \\ 15(2) & 2 & 8 \end{vmatrix} = 15\begin{vmatrix} 1 & 0 & 2 \\ 3 & -1 & 3 \\ 2 & 2 & 8 \end{vmatrix}$$

2. Multiply the first column by -2 and add the results to column three. (Property 5)

$$15\begin{vmatrix} 1 & 0 & 2 \\ 3 & -1 & 3 \\ 2 & 2 & 8 \end{vmatrix} = 15\begin{vmatrix} 1 & 0 & 2+(-2) \\ 3 & -1 & 3+(-6) \\ 2 & 2 & 8+(-4) \end{vmatrix} = 15\begin{vmatrix} 1 & 0 & 0 \\ 3 & -1 & -3 \\ 2 & 2 & 4 \end{vmatrix}$$

3. Expand by minors about row one.

$$15\begin{vmatrix} 1 & 0 & 0 \\ 3 & -1 & -3 \\ 2 & 2 & 4 \end{vmatrix} = 15\left(1\begin{vmatrix} -1 & -3 \\ 2 & 4 \end{vmatrix} - 0\begin{vmatrix} 3 & -3 \\ 2 & 4 \end{vmatrix} + 0\begin{vmatrix} 3 & -1 \\ 2 & 2 \end{vmatrix}\right)$$

$$= 15(2 - 0 + 0)$$
$$= 15(2) = 30 \quad \textbf{\textit{Answer}}$$

Oral Exercises

Use the properties of determinants to find the value of each determinant below, given that

$$\begin{vmatrix} 1 & 3 & -5 \\ 0 & -1 & 2 \\ -3 & 7 & 3 \end{vmatrix} = -20.$$

1. $\begin{vmatrix} 0 & -1 & 2 \\ 1 & 3 & -5 \\ -3 & 7 & 3 \end{vmatrix}$ **2.** $\begin{vmatrix} 2 & 6 & -10 \\ 0 & -1 & 2 \\ -3 & 7 & 3 \end{vmatrix}$ **3.** $\begin{vmatrix} 1 & 3 & -5 \\ 0 & -1 & 2 \\ -3r & 7r & 3r \end{vmatrix}$

Written Exercises

Evaluate each of the given determinants. Use Properties 1–5 to simplify the work.

A **1.** $\begin{vmatrix} 6 & 2 & 4 \\ 5 & 15 & -10 \\ 9 & 3 & 6 \end{vmatrix}$ **2.** $\begin{vmatrix} -1 & 7 & 12 \\ 1 & -1 & -12 \\ 8 & 16 & -9 \end{vmatrix}$ **3.** $\begin{vmatrix} 5 & 0 & 0 \\ 0 & 5 & 0 \\ 0 & 0 & 5 \end{vmatrix}$

4. $\begin{vmatrix} 4 & 12 & 8 \\ 3 & -3 & 3 \\ 4 & 2 & 8 \end{vmatrix}$ **5.** $\begin{vmatrix} 16 & -1 & 4 \\ 8 & 9 & -7 \\ 16 & -1 & 4 \end{vmatrix}$ **6.** $\begin{vmatrix} 1 & 5 & 10 \\ -4 & -5 & -8 \\ 6 & 5 & -2 \end{vmatrix}$

7. $\begin{vmatrix} 12 & 9 & 13 \\ 11 & 8 & 12 \\ 6 & -2 & 1 \end{vmatrix}$ **8.** $\begin{vmatrix} 9 & -1 & 6 \\ 2 & 4 & 2 \\ 1 & 1 & 1 \end{vmatrix}$ **9.** $\begin{vmatrix} 3 & 1 & 1 \\ 1 & 3 & 1 \\ 1 & 1 & 3 \end{vmatrix}$

B **10.** $\begin{vmatrix} 1 & 2 & 2 & 0 \\ 1 & 4 & 1 & -1 \\ 1 & 3 & 1 & 3 \\ 1 & 5 & 1 & 2 \end{vmatrix}$ **11.** $\begin{vmatrix} 2 & 0 & 0 & 0 \\ 0 & 2 & 0 & 0 \\ 0 & 0 & 2 & 0 \\ 0 & 0 & 0 & 2 \end{vmatrix}$ **12.** $\begin{vmatrix} 1 & 2 & -3 & -4 \\ 1 & 2 & -3 & 4 \\ 1 & -2 & 3 & 4 \\ -1 & 2 & 3 & 4 \end{vmatrix}$

C **13.** Prove Property 2 for third-order determinants.

14. Prove Property 5 for second-order determinants.

15-9 *Cramer's Rule*

OBJECTIVE **To solve systems of equations using determinants.**

Determinants may be used to solve systems of linear equations. Consider this system of two linear equations in two variables:

$$ax + by = e$$
$$cx + dy = f$$

Using the linear-combination method of Section 8-1, you can verify that

$$x = \frac{de - bf}{ad - bc} \quad \text{and} \quad y = \frac{af - ce}{ad - bc}$$

provided that $ad - bc \neq 0$. Note that the denominators are equal to the determinant of coefficients,

$$D = \begin{vmatrix} a & b \\ c & d \end{vmatrix}.$$

The numerators are equal to the determinants D_x and D_y where

$$D_x = \begin{vmatrix} e & b \\ f & d \end{vmatrix} \quad \text{and} \quad D_y = \begin{vmatrix} a & e \\ c & f \end{vmatrix}.$$

By substitution,

$$x = \frac{\begin{vmatrix} e & b \\ f & d \end{vmatrix}}{\begin{vmatrix} a & b \\ c & d \end{vmatrix}} = \frac{D_x}{D} \quad \text{and} \quad y = \frac{\begin{vmatrix} a & e \\ c & f \end{vmatrix}}{\begin{vmatrix} a & b \\ c & d \end{vmatrix}} = \frac{D_y}{D}.$$

To find D_x, replace the coefficients of x in D with the constant terms e and f. Similarly, to find D_y, replace the coefficients of y in D with the constant terms e and f.

EXAMPLE 1 Use determinants to solve $\begin{aligned} 7x + 5y &= 4 \\ 2x - y &= -11 \end{aligned}$.

SOLUTION

$$x = \frac{\begin{vmatrix} 4 & 5 \\ -11 & -1 \end{vmatrix}}{\begin{vmatrix} 7 & 5 \\ 2 & -1 \end{vmatrix}} = \frac{-4 + 55}{-7 - 10} = -3$$

$$y = \frac{\begin{vmatrix} 7 & 4 \\ 2 & -11 \end{vmatrix}}{\begin{vmatrix} 7 & 5 \\ 2 & -1 \end{vmatrix}} = \frac{-77 - 8}{-7 - 10} = 5$$

Thus the solution is $(-3, 5)$. *Answer*

Similarly, determinants may be used to solve a system of three linear equations in three variables.

$$a_1x + b_1y + c_1z = d_1$$
$$a_2x + b_2y + c_2z = d_2$$
$$a_3x + b_3y + c_3z = d_3$$

Let $D = \begin{vmatrix} a_1 & b_1 & c_1 \\ a_2 & b_2 & c_2 \\ a_3 & b_3 & c_3 \end{vmatrix} \neq 0,$ $\qquad D_x = \begin{vmatrix} d_1 & b_1 & c_1 \\ d_2 & b_2 & c_2 \\ d_3 & b_3 & c_3 \end{vmatrix},$

$$D_y = \begin{vmatrix} a_1 & d_1 & c_1 \\ a_2 & d_2 & c_2 \\ a_3 & d_3 & c_3 \end{vmatrix}, \qquad \text{and} \qquad D_z = \begin{vmatrix} a_1 & b_1 & d_1 \\ a_2 & b_2 & d_2 \\ a_3 & b_3 & d_3 \end{vmatrix}.$$

Then $x = \dfrac{D_x}{D}$, $y = \dfrac{D_y}{D}$, and $z = \dfrac{D_z}{D}$.

This method is valid for systems of n linear equations in n variables and is summarized below in Cramer's Rule, which is named for Gabriel Cramer (1704-1752), a Swiss mathematician.

CRAMER'S RULE

The solution of a system of n linear equations in n variables can be found from

$$x = \frac{D_x}{D}, y = \frac{D_y}{D}, \ldots D \neq 0,$$

where D is the determinant of the matrix of coefficients of the variables and D_x, D_y, $\ldots$, are derived from D by replacing the coefficients of x, y, $\ldots$, respectively, by the constants.

EXAMPLE 2 Use Cramer's Rule to solve:

$$x - 3y - 2z = 9$$
$$3x + 2y + 6z = 20$$
$$4x - y + 3z = 25$$

SOLUTION

$$D = \begin{vmatrix} 1 & -3 & -2 \\ 3 & 2 & 6 \\ 4 & -1 & 3 \end{vmatrix} = 1(12) + (-1)(3)(-11) + 4(-14) = -11$$

$$D_x = \begin{vmatrix} 9 & -3 & -2 \\ 20 & 2 & 6 \\ 25 & -1 & 3 \end{vmatrix} = 9(12) + (-1)(20)(-11) + 25(-14) = -22$$

(solution continued)

$$D_y = \begin{vmatrix} 1 & 9 & -2 \\ 3 & 20 & 6 \\ 4 & 25 & 3 \end{vmatrix} = 1(-90) + (-1)(3)(77) + 4(94) = 55$$

$$D_z = \begin{vmatrix} 1 & -3 & 9 \\ 3 & 2 & 20 \\ 4 & -1 & 25 \end{vmatrix} = 1(70) + (-1)(3)(-66) + 4(-78) = -44$$

$$x = \frac{D_x}{D} = \frac{-22}{-11} = 2 \qquad y = \frac{D_y}{D} = \frac{55}{-11} = -5 \qquad z = \frac{D_z}{D} = \frac{-44}{-11} = 4$$

$\therefore$ the solution is $(2, -5, 4)$. ***Answer***

Cramer's Rule provides a method for finding a solution for a set of n linear equations in n variables. Recall that such a system has a unique solution if and only if $D \neq 0$.

If $D = 0$, the system is either dependent or inconsistent. Consider the system

$$ax + by = e$$
$$cx + dy = f$$

where either $e \neq 0$ or $f \neq 0$. If $D = 0$ and $D_y = 0$, the system is dependent and the graphs of the equations coincide. If $D = 0$ and $D_y \neq 0$, the system is inconsistent and the graphs of the equations are parallel lines. The examples below illustrate this point.

$x + y = 1$	$2x - y = -1$	$3x + 2y = 2$
$2x + y = 4$	$2x - y = \quad 4$	$6x + 4y = 4$

 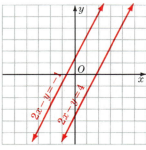 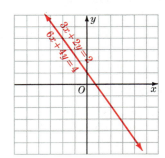

$D \neq 0$
Consistent equations—
graphs intersect.

$D = 0$
$D_y \neq 0$
Inconsistent equations
graphs are parallel.

$D = 0$
$D_y = 0$
Dependent equations—
graphs coincide.

EXAMPLE 3 Determine whether there is a unique solution to each system.

a. $\quad x - 2y = -9$ **b.** $2x - \quad y = 4$
$\quad\quad 3x + \quad y = 1$ $x - 0.5y = 2$

SOLUTION

a. $D = \begin{vmatrix} 1 & -2 \\ 3 & 1 \end{vmatrix} = 1 - (-6) = 7 \neq 0$

$\therefore$ there is a unique solution. **Answer**

b. $D = \begin{vmatrix} 2 & -1 \\ 1 & -0.5 \end{vmatrix} = -1.0 - (-1) = 0$

$\therefore$ there is no unique solution. **Answer**

Oral Exercises

For each system state the entries for columns one, two, and three of the determinant D.

1. $\begin{aligned} x - 3y + 2z &= 1 \\ x + y + z &= 6 \\ 2x - y + z &= -3 \end{aligned}$

2. $\begin{aligned} 4x - y + 3z &= 1 \\ 7x - 4y + 3z &= 33 \\ 2x + 3y - z &= 2 \end{aligned}$

3. $\begin{aligned} 2x + 3y + 4z &= 3 \\ x \qquad - 2z &= 0 \\ 3y - 8z &= -1 \end{aligned}$

4. $\begin{aligned} 3x \qquad - 4z &= 0 \\ 6x + 4y \qquad &= -1 \\ 8y + 2z &= 5 \end{aligned}$

State the elements in columns one, two, and three of the indicated determinants.

5. Exercise 1, D_x

6. Exercise 1, D_y

7. Exercise 1, D_z

8. Exercise 2, D_y

9. Exercise 2, D_z

10. Exercise 3, D_x

11. Exercise 3, D_y

12. Exercise 4, D_x

13. Exercise 4, D_y

14. Exercise 2, D_x

15. Exercise 3, D_z

16. Exercise 4, D_z

Written Exercises

Solve each system using Cramer's Rule.

A

1. $\begin{aligned} x - y + z &= 3 \\ x - 3y + 2z &= 1 \\ 2x - y - z &= -3 \end{aligned}$

2. $\begin{aligned} x - y - z &= 7 \\ x + 4y - 3z &= 0 \\ 2x + y - z &= -5 \end{aligned}$

3. $\begin{aligned} 2x - 3y + z &= 11 \\ 3x + 5y + 4z &= 0 \\ x + 2y - 3z &= -5 \end{aligned}$

4. $\begin{aligned} 2x - 3y + 5z &= 7 \\ x + 3y - 2z &= -1 \\ 3x + 5y - 4z &= 3 \end{aligned}$

5. $\begin{aligned} 3x - 2y - z &= -\tfrac{1}{2} \\ 2x + 3y - 4z &= 27 \\ 4x - y + z &= -1 \end{aligned}$

6. $\begin{aligned} a - 2b + 2c &= 1 \\ 2a - 3b + 4c &= 4 \\ 4a - 5b - 6c &= 3 \end{aligned}$

7. $\begin{aligned} 3x - 2y + z &= 6 \\ 2x + 3y + 2z &= -1 \\ 5y - 4z &= -3 \end{aligned}$

8. $\begin{aligned} x + z &= 2 \\ 2x + y &= 2 \\ y + 7z &= 11 \end{aligned}$

Tell whether each system has no solution, one solution, or more than one solution.

9. $3x + 2y = 9$
$6x + 4y = 18$

10. $-6a - b = 8$
$18a + 3b = 10$

11. $11m - 9n = 36$
$11m + 9n = 41$

12. $5p - 10q = 24$
$2p - 4q = 10$

Solve each system using Cramer's Rule.

B **13.** $2p - 3q + r - 3s = -1$
$p + 2q + 3r - s = 1$
$3p + 5q + 6r = 4$
$3p - q - 2s = 6$

14. $w - 2x + y = -4$
$2w - y + z = -3$
$x + 2y - 3z = -14$
$3w - 3x + 2y = -13$

Self-Test 3

VOCABULARY   minor of an element (p. 585)
expansion of a determinant (p. 586)

1. Expand by minors: $\begin{vmatrix} 1 & 0 & -2 \\ 3 & -1 & 0 \\ 2 & 1 & 0 \end{vmatrix}$

Obj. 15-7, p. 585

2. Evaluate: $\begin{vmatrix} 3 & 2 & 0 & -1 \\ -2 & 1 & 0 & 5 \\ 6 & 3 & -1 & 2 \\ 0 & 3 & 1 & 3 \end{vmatrix}$

Obj. 15-8, p. 589

3. Solve using Cramer's Rule:
$2x - y + 2z = 1$
$x + y - z = -2$
$3x + 2y - z = -3$

Obj. 15-9, p. 592

Check your answers with those at the back of the book.

Chapter Summary

1. Two *matrices* are equal if and only if they have the same *dimensions* and all corresponding *elements* are equal.

2. Matrices of the same dimension may be added (or subtracted) by adding (or subtracting) corresponding elements. See the properties for addition of matrices listed on page 563.

3. In dealing with matrices, a real number is often called a *scalar*. The scalar product of a real number, r, and a matrix, A, is the matrix rA each of whose elements is r times the corresponding element of A. See the properties of scalar multiplication listed on page 564.

4. The product of a matrix $A_{m \times n}$ and $B_{n \times p}$ is the $m \times p$ matrix whose element in row i and column j is the sum of the products of corresponding elements of row i in A and column j in B. Multiplication of matrices is not commutative. The fact that $A \times B = O$ does not imply that either $A = O$ or $B = O$. See the properties of matrix multiplication listed on page 569.

5. Associated with each $n \times n$ matrix A is a real number called the *determinant* of A. For 2×2 matrices of the form $\begin{bmatrix} a & b \\ c & d \end{bmatrix}$, the determinant is $ad - bc$. Higher order determinants can be defined and expanded by minors about the elements of any row or column. Determinants have properties that can simplify expansion by minors. See properties 1–5 listed on pages 589–590.

6. For any two matrices, A and B, if $AB = BA = I$, A and B are called inverses.

$$\text{If } A = \begin{bmatrix} a & b \\ c & d \end{bmatrix}, \text{ then } A^{-1} = \frac{1}{\det A} \begin{bmatrix} d & -b \\ -c & a \end{bmatrix}, \text{ if } \det A \neq 0.$$

7. The solution of a system of n linear equations in n variables can be found from

$$x = \frac{D_x}{D}, \, y = \frac{D_y}{D}, \, \ldots \, D \neq 0$$

where D is the determinant of the matrix of coefficients of the variables and D_x, D_y, $\ldots$, are derived from D by replacing the coefficients of x, y, $\ldots$, respectively, by the constants. This method of solution is called *Cramer's Rule*.

Chapter Review

Give the letter of the correct answer.

1. Solve for x: $[-2 + x \quad 0] = O_{1 \times 2}$. 15-1
    a. $x = -2$ **b.** $x = 0$ **c.** $x = 2$ **d.** $x = 1$

In Exercises 2 and 3, let $A = \begin{bmatrix} -3 & 5 \\ 8 & 1 \end{bmatrix}$ and $B = \begin{bmatrix} 4 & -2 \\ 3 & 1 \end{bmatrix}$.

2. Find $B - 2A$. 15-2
    a. $\begin{bmatrix} 10 & -12 \\ -13 & -1 \end{bmatrix}$ **b.** $\begin{bmatrix} 7 & -7 \\ -5 & 0 \end{bmatrix}$ **c.** $\begin{bmatrix} -6 & 10 \\ 16 & 2 \end{bmatrix}$

3. Find BA. 15-3
    a. $\begin{bmatrix} 3 & 11 \\ 35 & -15 \end{bmatrix}$ **b.** $\begin{bmatrix} -28 & 18 \\ -1 & 16 \end{bmatrix}$ **c.** $\begin{bmatrix} 3 & -1 \\ 29 & -17 \end{bmatrix}$

4. Find the matrix that shows the number of ways a message can be sent from one point to another using exactly one relay.

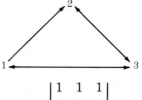

15-4

a. $\begin{vmatrix} 0 & 1 & 1 \\ 0 & 0 & 1 \\ 1 & 1 & 0 \end{vmatrix}$
b. $\begin{vmatrix} 0 & 2 & 2 \\ 0 & 0 & 2 \\ 2 & 2 & 0 \end{vmatrix}$
c. $\begin{vmatrix} 1 & 1 & 1 \\ 1 & 1 & 0 \\ 0 & 1 & 2 \end{vmatrix}$

5. Expand $\begin{vmatrix} -2 & 0 \\ 5 & 8 \end{vmatrix}$.
15-5

a. -21 **b.** -11 **c.** -16 **d.** -18

6. Expand $\begin{vmatrix} 3 & 0 & -5 \\ 1 & 2 & -1 \\ 1 & 5 & -2 \end{vmatrix}$.

a. -12 **b.** 38 **c.** 18 **d.** 36

7. Find the inverse of $A = \begin{bmatrix} -1 & 4 \\ -1 & 5 \end{bmatrix}$.
15-6

a. $\begin{bmatrix} 5 & 4 \\ -1 & -1 \end{bmatrix}$
b. $\begin{bmatrix} -5 & 4 \\ -1 & 1 \end{bmatrix}$
c. $\begin{bmatrix} 1 & 1 \\ -4 & -5 \end{bmatrix}$

8. Expand this determinant by minors about column 3.
15-7

$$\begin{vmatrix} 5 & -3 & -2 \\ 1 & -1 & -1 \\ 2 & 4 & 0 \end{vmatrix}$$

a. -38 **b.** -14 **c.** 14 **d.** 38

9. Evaluate the determinant $\begin{vmatrix} 15 & -12 & 32 \\ 29 & 14 & -21 \\ 30 & -24 & 64 \end{vmatrix}$.
15-8

a. 0 **b.** -112 **c.** 78 **d.** -78

10. Solve using Cramer's Rule.
15-9

$$\begin{aligned} x + y \quad\quad &= 1 \\ 2x \quad\quad - z &= 0 \\ x + y + z &= -1 \end{aligned}$$

a. $(2, -1, -2)$ **b.** $(1, -2, 2)$ **c.** $(-1, 2, -2)$ **d.** $(-1, 2, -2)$

Chapter Test

1. Find the value of x and y. $\begin{bmatrix} 2x + 3 \\ 4 - y \end{bmatrix} = O_{2 \times 1}$
15-1

In Exercises 2-7, let $A = \begin{bmatrix} 5 & -1 & 0 \\ -8 & 1 & 6 \\ 2 & 1 & -1 \end{bmatrix}$, and $B = \begin{bmatrix} -3 & 4 & 8 \\ 7 & -5 & 1 \\ 0 & 5 & 1 \end{bmatrix}$.

Express the following as a single matrix.

15-2

2. $A + B$

3. $A - B$

4. $3B$

5. $2A - B$

6. $A \times B$

7. B^2

15-3

8. A bus system is increasing its fares. Gasoline prices are also increasing. Public opinion polls indicate the following trends after fare increases. Of regular bus passengers, 65% will continue to ride the bus, while 35% will use cars instead. Of the persons who usually drive, 16% will start to use the bus, and the remainder will continue to drive. In the area served by this bus system, it is estimated that, before the fare increase, 19,000 used the bus and 26,000 drove. Find the number of bus passengers and drivers after the fare increase.

15-4

Expand these determinants.

9. $\begin{vmatrix} -1 & 4 \\ 8 & 5 \end{vmatrix}$

10. $\begin{vmatrix} 1 & -1 & 2 \\ 3 & -2 & 1 \\ 1 & 0 & 4 \end{vmatrix}$

15-5

11. Solve this equation for A.

$$\begin{bmatrix} 2 & 3 \\ -1 & 0 \end{bmatrix} A = \begin{bmatrix} 7 & 3 \\ 4 & 0 \end{bmatrix}$$

15-6

12. Expand this determinant by minors about row 2.

$$\begin{vmatrix} 1 & -1 & 0 \\ 3 & 0 & 2 \\ -2 & 1 & 4 \end{vmatrix}$$

15-7

Use the properties of determinants to evaluate these determinants.

15-8

13. $\begin{vmatrix} 2 & 1 & -1 \\ 10 & 5 & -5 \\ 5 & 0 & -1 \end{vmatrix}$

14. $\begin{vmatrix} 4 & 3 & -1 \\ -3 & -3 & 5 \\ 5 & 5 & 3 \end{vmatrix}$

15. Solve using Cramer's Rule.

15-9

$$\begin{aligned} 2x + 3y + 4z &= 3 \\ 3y - 8z &= -1 \\ x \qquad - 2z &= 0 \end{aligned}$$

Shown above is a herd of barren ground caribou grazing the high tundra of the Alaskan interior. The science of statistics is useful in the study of the distribution of characteristics such as height and life span among large populations of animals.

16

PROBABILITY AND STATISTICS

COUNTING

16-1 *Fundamental Counting Principles*

OBJECTIVE To apply fundamental counting principles.

A bicycle shop sells 4 different types of bicycles. Each type is available in 3 colors. If you first select the type, or "style," you can then select a color in one of 3 ways. Thus, there are

$$4 \times 3, \text{ or } 12$$

different combinations of style and color that can be ordered.

This example illustrates a *fundamental counting principle:*

> If one selection can be made in m ways, and for each of these a second selection can be made in n ways, then the number of ways the two selections can be made is $m \times n$.

EXAMPLE 1 How many odd 2-digit integers are there?

SOLUTION A diagram, such as ☐☐ or ___ ___ is useful to help analyze the problem. The *nine* possible integers, or selections, for the tens' digit are 1, 2, 3, 4, 5, 6, 7, 8, or 9. Write 9 in the first space: ⟨9⟩ . The *five* possible selections for the ones' digit are 1, 3, 5, 7, or 9. Write 5 in the second space: ⟨9 5⟩ . The fundamental counting principle tells you that there are 9×5, or 45, odd, 2-digit integers. *Answer*

To get to school, Cindy can (1) walk 2 blocks and take a local bus, (2) walk 5 blocks and take either an express bus or a subway train, or (3) either walk or ride her bicycle all the way (14 blocks). Thus, there are 5 different, or mutually exclusive, ways in which she can get to school.

Suppose you wanted to find the number of positive integers less than 100 that can be represented using the digits 1, 2, and 3. You would consider two mutually exclusive possibilities: (1) the 1-digit integers and (2) the 2-digit integers.

	T	U	
1-digit integers	—	3	3
2-digit integers	3	3	$3 \times 3 = $ 9

$$\text{total} = 12$$

Thus, there are 12 positive integers less than 100 that can be represented by the digits 1, 2, and 3. This example illustrates another *fundamental counting principle*, the additive rule for mutually exclusive possibilities:

> If one selection can be made in m ways, and another, mutually exclusive, selection can be made in n ways, the number of ways in which the two selections can be made is $m + n$.

EXAMPLE 2   How many positive even integers less than 1000 can be represented using the digits 2, 3, 4, and 5?

SOLUTION   Note first that there can be 1-, 2-, or 3-digit integers. Consider these cases separately. For each case the units digit can be 2 or 4, since the integer is to be even. The remaining digits can be any of the 4 given.

	H	T	U	
1-digit integers	—	—	2	2
2-digit integers	—	4	2	$4 \times 2 = 8$
3-digit integers	4	4	2	$4 \times 4 \times 2 = 32$

$$\text{total} = 42$$

There are 42 positive even integers less than 1000 that can be formed using the digits 2, 3, 4, and 5.   ***Answer***

EXAMPLE 3 How many positive integers less than 1000 can be represented using at least 2 digits? (Note that no 2- or 3-digit integer begins with 0.)

SOLUTION

	H	T	U	
2-digit integers	—	9	10	$9 \times 10 = 90$
3-digit integers	9	10	10	$9 \times 10 \times 10 = \underline{900}$

$$\text{total} = 990$$

A total of 990 positive integers less than 1000 can be represented using at least 2 digits. ***Answer***

Oral Exercises

1. Jeff must wear one of 4 shirts and one of 2 ties. How many possible shirt-tie combinations can he choose?

2. There are 4 roads from Oakton to Parkland and 5 roads from Parkland to Pine Hill. In how many ways can Susan drive from Oakton to Pine Hill?

3. Sam has some things to pick up on the way home from school. He can buy them in one of 2 variety stores or in one of 3 drug stores. In how many ways can he run his errand?

4. Martha can buy one of 9 different flavors of ice cream, 4 different flavors of sherbet, or 3 different flavors of frozen yogurt. In how many ways can she choose a single dessert?

Written Exercises

A 1. On a bookshelf there are 12 different algebra books, 8 different geometry books, and 3 different calculus books. In how many ways can you choose 3 books, one of each kind?

2. In how many different ways can a 10-question true-false test be answered if each question must be answered?

3. In how many ways can a 10-question true-false test be answered if it is permissible to leave blanks?

4. How many ways are there of selecting 3 cards, one after the other, from a deck of 52 cards if selected cards are not returned to the deck?

5. A student council has 8 seniors and 7 juniors as members. In how many ways can a 3-member council committee be formed if 2 of the members are to be juniors?

6. How many license plates of 5 symbols can be made using letters for the first 2 symbols and digits for the remaining 3 symbols?

B 7. How many license plates of 3 symbols (letters and digits) can be made using at least 2 letters for each?

8. How many license plates of 3 symbols (letters and digits) can be made using at least 1 letter for each?

9. How many 4-letter code words can be formed if at least 3 of the letters are to be chosen from the vowels a, e, i, o, and u?

10. How many positive even integers containing 3 digits can be formed using the digits 4, 5, 6, 7, 8, and 9?

11. How many positive even integers having at most 3 digits can be formed using the digits 4, 5, 6, 7, 8, and 9?

12. How many positive even integers less than 100 can be formed using the digits 4, 5, 6, 7, and 8?

13. How many positive odd integers less than 10,000 can be formed using the digits 2, 3, 4, 6, 8, and 0?

14. How many positive odd integers between 100 and 10,000 can be formed using the digits 1, 2, 3, 4, 5, and 6?

C 15. How many multiples of 3 less than 100 can be formed from the digits 1, 4, 5, 7, and 9?

(Hint: The sum of the digits of any multiple of 3 is also a multiple of 3.)

16. How many multiples of 3 less than 1000 can be formed from the digits 2, 5, and 9?

17. DNA (deoxyribonucleic acid) molecules include the base units adenine, thymine, cytosine, and guanine (A, T, C, and G). The linear sequence of base units along a strand of DNA encodes genetic information. In how many different sequences can the 4 base units A, T, C, and G be arranged along a short strand of DNA that includes only 10 base units?

18. Protein molecules are made up of many amino acid residues joined end-to-end. Proteins have different properties, depending on the sequence of amino acid residues in the molecules. If there are 20 naturally occurring amino acids, how many different sequences of amino acid residues can occur in a 4-residue-long fragment of a protein molecule?

16-2 *Permutations*

OBJECTIVE   **To find the permutations of a group of elements.**

The letters p, q, and r can be arranged in six different orders:

$$pqr \qquad qpr \qquad rpq$$
$$prq \qquad qrp \qquad rqp$$

Each of these arrangements is called a *permutation* of the letters p, q, and r. An arrangement of objects in a definite order is called a **permutation.**

    Any one of the 3 letters p, q, or r may be written first, as indicated in the following diagram:

3		

After the first letter has been chosen, the second must be selected from the remaining 2 letters:

3	2	

Only one selection remains for the last letter:

3	2	1

Using the first fundamental counting principle, you can find the number of permutations of p, q, and r:

$$3 \cdot 2 \cdot 1 = 6$$

EXAMPLE 1   Find the number of permutations of the four letters p, q, r, and s.

SOLUTION   Complete a diagram:

4	3	2	1

The number of permutations is

$$4 \cdot 3 \cdot 2 \cdot 1, \text{ or } 24. \quad \textbf{\textit{Answer}}$$

Six of these permutations are shown at the right. Can you write the remaining 18 permutations? (Hint: Make three similar columns starting with the letters q, r, and s.)

pqrs
pqsr
prqs
prsq
psqr
psrq

Recall from Section 11-7 that $4 \cdot 3 \cdot 2 \cdot 1 = 4!$ (read "four factorial"). In general:

> The number of permutations of n objects is $n!$.

EXAMPLE 2 How many permutations can be formed from the letters in the word JUNIOR using all 6 letters?

SOLUTION The number of permutations of 6 objects is:
$$6! = 6 \cdot 5 \cdot 4 \cdot 3 \cdot 2 \cdot 1 = 720 \quad \textbf{\textit{Answer}}$$

EXAMPLE 3 How many permutations can be formed from the letters in the word JUNIOR using only 4 letters at a time?

SOLUTION Use a diagram to record the number of possible choices for each letter. The first choice can be any one of 6 letters, the second can be any one of the 5 remaining letters, and so on:

6	5	4	3

Thus, there are $6 \cdot 5 \cdot 4 \cdot 3$, or 360, permutations of 6 letters taken 4 at a time. **\textit{Answer}**

The symbol $_nP_r$ is read, "the number of permutations of n things taken r at a time." In Example 3 a diagram was used to find $_6P_4$, the number of permutations of 6 things taken 4 at a time. In the general case the diagram has r spaces to be filled:

n	$n-1$	$n-2$	$\ldots$	$n-(r-1)$

Thus:
$$_nP_r = \underbrace{n(n-1)(n-2) \ldots [n-(r-1)]}_{r \text{ factors}}$$

Notice that when $r = n$, the final factor in the preceding equation, $n - (r - 1)$, becomes $n - (n - 1) = n - n + 1$. Thus,
$$_nP_n = n!$$
as you learned earlier.

EXAMPLE 4 From a group of 9 different books, 5 books are to be selected and arranged on a shelf. How many arrangements are possible?

SOLUTION The problem is to find the number of permutations of 9 books taken 5 at a time. $_9P_5 = 9 \cdot 8 \cdot 7 \cdot 6 \cdot 5 = 15{,}120$ **\textit{Answer}**

When the expression for $_nP_r$ is multiplied by $\frac{(n-r)(n-r-1)\,\cdots\,1}{(n-r)(n-r-1)\,\cdots\,1}$, it becomes

$$\frac{n(n-1)\,\cdots\,(n-r+1)(n-r)(n-r-1)\,\cdots\,1}{(n-r)(n-r-1)\,\cdots\,1}.$$

Thus:

$$_nP_r = \frac{n!}{(n-r)!}.$$

Written Exercises

Evaluate each of the following.

A   **1.** $7!$ **2.** $\frac{8!}{6!}$ **3.** $\frac{6!}{(6-3)!}$ **4.** $\frac{50!}{48!}$

     5. $\frac{5!}{2!3!}$ **6.** $(3!)(4!)$ **7.** $5(3!)$ **8.** $\frac{10!}{(10-7)!}$

Find $_nP_r$ for each pair of values of n and r.

     9. $n=4,\ r=2$ **10.** $n=8,\ r=8$ **11.** $n=6,\ r=2$ **12.** $n=6,\ r=4$

13. In how many ways can you arrange 4 different books on a shelf?

14. In how many ways can 3 people be lined up in a row for a photograph?

15. In how many ways can the letters of the word FRIDAY be arranged using all 6 letters?

16. In how many ways can the letters of the word COUNT be arranged using only 3 of the letters at a time?

B   **17.** How many positive integers between 999 and 4000 can be formed using the digits 2, 3, 4, 5, 6, 7, and 8 if no digit may be repeated?

18. How many positive integers less than 1000 can be formed using the digits 1, 2, 3, 4, 5, and 6 if no digit may be repeated?

19. Show that $_7P_4 = 7(_6P_3)$.   **20.** Show that $_6P_r = 6(_5P_{r-1})$.

21. Show that $_nP_5 = n(_{n-1}P_4)$.   **22.** Show that $_5P_3 - {}_5P_2 = 2(_5P_2)$.

23. Show that $_nP_5 - {}_nP_4 = (n-5)\,_nP_4$.

24. Show that $_nP_r - {}_nP_{r-1} = (n-r)\,_nP_{r-1}$.

C   **25.** Solve for n: $_nP_5 = 14(_nP_4)$.   **26.** Solve for n: $_nP_3 = 17(_nP_2)$.

16-3 *Permutations with Repeated Elements*

OBJECTIVE   **To find the permutations of a group of elements that are not all different.**

If you consider the letters a and a to be distinct, the letters a, a, and b, taken 3 at a time, can be arranged in 6 distinguishable ways:

$$\begin{array}{ccc}
aab & aba & baa \\
aab & aba & baa
\end{array}$$

This result is consistent with the relationship $_nP_n = n!$, since

$$_3P_3 = 3 \cdot 2 \cdot 1 = 6.$$

In contrast, the letters a, a, and b, taken 3 at a time, give only 3 distinguishable arrangements:

$$\begin{array}{ccc}
aab & aba & baa
\end{array}$$

The number of "permutations" of aa, taken 2 at a time, is $_2P_2$. And the number of "permutations" of aab, taken 3 at a time, is $_3P_3$, of which $_2P_2$ are indistinguishable. Since P normally stands for the number of *distinguishable* permutations,

$$2!P = 3!.$$

That is, there are 2! indistinguishable permutations of aa for each distinguishable permutation of aab.

In more general terms, for 3 elements taken 3 at a time, with 2 elements alike, the number of permutations, P, is $\frac{3!}{2!}$, or 3. In a similar way, it can be shown that for n elements taken n at a time, with n_1 elements alike, the number of permutations, P, is

$$\frac{n!}{n_1!}.$$

EXAMPLE 1   How many permutations can be formed from the letters, taken 5 at a time, in POPPY?

SOLUTION $P = \dfrac{n!}{n_1!} = \dfrac{5!}{3!} = 20$

A similar relationship exists when *two or more* repeated elements occur.

The number of permutations, P, of n elements taken n at a time, with n_1 elements alike, n_2 of another kind alike, and so on is

$$\frac{n!}{n_1!n_2! \cdots}.$$

EXAMPLE 2 How many permutations can be formed from the letters, taken 5 at a time, in TOOTH?

SOLUTION $P = \dfrac{n!}{n_1! n_2!} = \dfrac{5!}{2!2!} = 30$

Oral Exercises

Find the number of permutations of all the letters in each word.

1. TOT **2.** ALL **3.** COOK

4. CALL **5.** CLOCK **6.** TOOT

Written Exercises

Find the number of permutations of all the letters in each word.

A **1.** LITTLE **2.** PROPER **3.** WEEDED

4. DEEDED **5.** SASSAFRAS **6.** CINCINNATI

7. How many different signals can be made by displaying five pennants, all at a time, on a vertical flagpole? The pennants differ only in color; two are red, two are yellow, and one is blue.

8. How many different signals could be made if the pennants of Exercise 7 were of the following colors: three red, one yellow, and one blue?

B **9.** In how many ways can 3 field guides to birds, 4 field guides to plants, and 2 field guides to reptiles be distributed among 9 students seated in a row if each student receives one field guide?

10. In how many ways can 3 white tiles, 2 blue tiles, and 2 red tiles be arranged in a single row?

How many five-digit numerals can be made in each case?

11. 2, 5, and 8 may each be used once; 9 may be used twice.

12. 6 and 7 may each be used twice; 3 may be used once.

13. 4 may be used three times; 2 may be used twice.

C **14.** Find the number of 5-letter permutations that can be formed from the letters in the word COPPER. (*Hint:* (a) Find the number of distinguishable 5-letter sequences containing just one P. (b) Find the number of distinguishable 5-letter sequences containing 2 P's. (c) Add the results of steps a and b.)

16-4 *Combinations*

OBJECTIVE   **To find the number of ways in which combinations of elements can be formed.**

A set B is a **subset** of set A if each member of set B is also a member of set A. Thus, any set is a subset of itself. By agreement, the empty set, $\emptyset$, is a subset of every set.

EXAMPLE 1   For the 3-letter set $\{K, L, M\}$, specify:

a. all the subsets.   **b.** the 2-letter subsets.

SOLUTION   **a.** $\{K, L, M\}, \{K, L\}, \{K, M\}, \{L, M\}, \{K\}, \{L\}, \{M\}, \emptyset$

b. $\{K, L\}, \{K, M\}, \{L, M\}$

There are four 3-letter subsets of the 4-letter set $\{W, X, Y, Z\}$:

$$\{W, X, Y\}, \{W, X, Z\}, \{W, Y, Z\}, \{X, Y, Z\}$$

These subsets are also known as the "combinations" of the letters W, X, Y, and Z taken three at a time. An r-element subset of a set of n elements is called a **combination** of n elements taken r at a time.

The number of combinations of n elements taken r at a time can be expressed as $_nC_r$. For example, $_4C_3$ stands for the number of combinations of 4 letters taken 3 at a time.

There may be a number of different arrangements, or permutations, of a given combination. For example, there are $_3P_3$, or 3!, permutations possible for the letters X, Y, and Z:

$$XYZ, \ XZY, \ YXZ, \ YZX, \ ZXY, \ ZYX.$$

Similarly, there are 3! permutations possible for each of the other 3-letter combinations of the letters W, X, Y, and Z. The total number of permutations of the 4 letters taken 3 at a time is just the number of combinations multiplied by the number of permutations per combination: $_4P_3 = (_3P_3)(_4C_3)$. In general:

$$_nP_r = (_rP_r)(_nC_r).$$

Thus:

$$_nC_r = \frac{_nP_r}{_rP_r} = \frac{n(n-1)(n-2)\cdots[n-(r-1)]}{r!}.$$

EXAMPLE 2   Find the number of combinations of the letters A, B, C, D, and E, taking them: **a.** 5 at a time.   **b.** 2 at a time.
Specify each combination.

SOLUTION   **a.** $_5C_5 = \dfrac{5 \cdot 4 \cdot 3 \cdot 2 \cdot 1}{5 \cdot 4 \cdot 3 \cdot 2 \cdot 1} = 1$ $ABCDE$

b. $_5C_2 = \dfrac{5 \cdot \overset{2}{\cancel{4}}}{\cancel{2} \cdot 1} = 10$ $AB \;\; AC \;\; AD \;\; AE \;\; BC$
$BD \;\; BE \;\; CD \;\; CE \;\; DE$

EXAMPLE 3   In how many ways can a committee of 7 be chosen from 5 teachers and 5 students if:

a. all are equally eligible?

b. the committee must include 4 students and 3 teachers?

SOLUTION   **a.** $_{10}C_7 = \dfrac{10 \cdot \overset{3}{\cancel{9}} \cdot \overset{4}{\cancel{8}} \cdot 7 \cdot \cancel{6} \cdot \cancel{5} \cdot \cancel{4}}{\cancel{7} \cdot \cancel{6} \cdot \cancel{5} \cdot \cancel{4} \cdot \cancel{3} \cdot \cancel{2} \cdot 1} = 120$

b. The 4 students can be chosen in $_5C_4$ ways. The 3 teachers can be chosen in $_5C_3$ ways. Use a fundamental counting principle to find the number of ways of selecting the committee:

$$_5C_4 \cdot _5C_3 = \dfrac{5 \cdot \cancel{4} \cdot \cancel{3} \cdot \cancel{2}}{\cancel{4} \cdot \cancel{3} \cdot \cancel{2} \cdot 1} \cdot \dfrac{5 \cdot \overset{2}{\cancel{4}} \cdot \cancel{3}}{\cancel{3} \cdot \cancel{2} \cdot 1} = 50$$

EXAMPLE 4   A standard bridge deck of cards consists of 4 suits (diamonds, clubs, hearts, and spades) of 13 cards each. How many 5-card hands can be dealt that include exactly 4 cards from any one suit?

SOLUTION   There are 4 suits, and there are $_{13}C_4$ possible combinations of 4 cards from any one suit.

$$4(_{13}C_4) = 4\left(\dfrac{13 \cdot \overset{3}{\cancel{12}} \cdot 11 \cdot \overset{5}{\cancel{10}}}{\cancel{4} \cdot 3 \cdot \cancel{2} \cdot 1}\right) = 2860$$

The remaining card must come from the other 3 suits.

$$52 - 13 = 39 \text{ cards}$$
$$_{39}C_1 = 39$$

Thus, the number of 5-card hands that include 4 cards from any one suit is $2860 \cdot 39$, or 111,540.   *Answer*

The following relationship was given in Section 16-2:

$$_nP_r = \dfrac{n!}{(n-r)!}$$

This relationship can be used to give an alternative expression for $_nC_r$:

$$_nC_r = \dfrac{_nP_r}{_rP_r} = \dfrac{n!}{r!(n-r)!}$$

You can use the alternative expression to prove that $_nC_r = {_nC_{n-r}}$ (see Written Exercise 27, page 613). The expression $_nC_{n-r}$ can be useful in the solution of some problems.

Written Exercises

A **1.** For the 3-digit set $\{2, 6, 8\}$, specify:

   a. all the subsets.

   b. the subsets in which the sum of the digits ≤ 8.

2. For the 4-digit set $\{1, 2, 3, 4\}$, specify:

   a. the 2-digit subsets.

   b. the subsets in which the sum of the digits ≥ 4.

Evaluate.

3. $_8C_3$ **4.** $_6C_3$ **5.** $_7C_2$ **6.** $_9C_3$

7. $_{14}C_{11}$ **8.** $_{12}C_{10}$ **9.** $_{12}C_2$ **10.** $_{200}C_2$

11. How many combinations can be formed from the letters in the word STUDY, taking them:

   a. 4 at a time?   **b.** 3 at a time?   **c.** 2 at a time?

12. How many combinations can be formed from the letters in the word PELICAN, taking them:

   a. 6 at a time?   **b.** 4 at a time?   **c.** 2 at a time?

13. In a club having 20 members, how many different combinations of 6 members can be chosen to sit in the front row for the club picture?

14. A sample of 5 light bulbs taken from a batch of 50 light bulbs is to be inspected. How many different samples could be selected?

15. How many line segments can be drawn by joining two points, given seven points, no three of which are collinear?

16. At the Hamburger Hut you can order hamburgers with cheese, onion, pickle, relish, mustard, lettuce, or tomato. How many different combinations of the "extras" can you order, choosing any three of them?

B **17.** Six points lie on a circle. How many inscribed triangles can be constructed having any three of these points as vertices?

18. Students are required to answer any seven out of ten questions on a certain test. How many different combinations of seven questions can a student choose to answer?

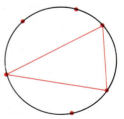

19. Nine points lie on the circumference of a circle. How many inscribed quadrilaterals can be drawn having these points as vertices? (Recall that the sides of a quadrilateral intersect only at the vertices.)

20. How many different 5-card hands can be dealt from a pack of 52 cards?

Exercises 21–24 deal with a standard bridge deck of cards as described in Example 4 on page 611.

21. How many 13-card hands having exactly 8 spades can be dealt? (*Hint*: The spades must come from the 13 spades in the deck. The other cards must come from the remaining 39 cards.)

22. How many 13-card hands having exactly 7 cards from any suit can be dealt?

23. How many 13-card hands having exactly 6 clubs, 5 hearts, and the other cards from the remaining suits can be dealt?

24. How many 13-card hands having exactly 4 diamonds, 3 hearts, 3 clubs, and 3 spades can be dealt?

C **25.** In how many ways can 4 or more students be selected from 7 students?

26. In how many ways can 3 balls be drawn from a bag containing 5 green and 6 red balls if:

　a. 2 must be green and 1 red?　　**b.** all must be the same color?

27. Prove that $_nC_r = {_nC_{n-r}}$ by using the formula $_nC_r = \dfrac{n!}{r!(n-r)!}$.

28. Show that the total number of subsets of a set having n elements is 2^n. (*Hint*: Each member of the set is or is not selected in forming a subset. Recall that the empty set is defined to be a subset of every set.)

Self-Test 1

VOCABULARY　　　fundamental counting　　　subset (p. 610)
　　　　　　　　　　　principles (pp. 601, 602)　　combination (p. 610)
　　　　　　　　　　permutation (p. 605)

1. In how many ways can 4 cards be selected, one after the other, from a deck of 10 cards, if selected cards are not returned to the deck?

Obj. 16-1, p. 601

2. In how many ways can 5 people line up in a ticket line?

Obj. 16-2, p. 605

3. How many different permutations can be formed using all the letters in the word PENNANT?

Obj. 16-3, p. 608

4. In how many ways can a 3-person committee be selected from a group of 9 people?

Obj. 16-4, p. 610

Check your answers with those at the back of the book.

16-5 *Sample Spaces and Events*

OBJECTIVE   To specify sample spaces and events for random experiments.

Suppose you toss a coin and it comes up heads. Then you repeat the "experiment" in as nearly the same way as possible, and you get tails. An experiment in which you do not necessarily get the same result when you repeat it under essentially the same conditions is called a **random experiment.**

Although you never know what the outcome will be when you toss a coin, you know that only two outcomes are possible. The set of all possible outcomes of a random experiment is known as the **sample space** for the experiment. For the tossing of a coin the sample space is $\{H, T\}$.

Any subset of possible outcomes for an experiment is known as an **event.** When an event involves a single element of the sample space, it is often called a **simple event.** There are two possible events when you toss a coin: $\{H\}$ and $\{T\}$. Both are, of course, simple events.

EXAMPLE 1   For the rolling of a single die, specify:
  a. the sample space for the experiment.
  b. the event that an even number results.
  c. the event that a number greater than 4 results.

SOLUTION   **a.** $\{1, 2, 3, 4, 5, 6\}$ **b.** $\{2, 4, 6\}$ **c.** $\{5, 6\}$

Suppose you roll two dice, one red and one green. A simple event in this experiment can be represented by the ordered pair (r, g). In this pair, r is the number up on the red die and g is the number up on the green die.

The sample space for the two-dice experiment is shown in graph form in Figure 16-1. Point A, with coordinates $(2, 3)$, denotes the simple event "red die shows 2 and green die shows 3." Point B $(6, 3)$ denotes the event "red die shows 6 and green die shows 3."

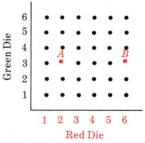

Figure 16-1

EXAMPLE 2   For the two-dice experiment, specify each event.

  a. The sum of the numbers turned up on the two dice is 7.
  b. The red die turns up 3.

SOLUTION   **a.** $\{(1, 6), (2, 5), (3, 4), (4, 3), (5, 2), (6, 1)\}$
  b. $\{(3, 1), (3, 2), (3, 3), (3, 4), (3, 5), (3, 6)\}$

Written Exercises

A **1.** Each of the letters A, B, C, D, E, F, G, H, I, and J is written on a separate card. The cards are then shuffled, and one card is drawn.
   a. Specify the sample space for the experiment.
   b. Specify the event that a vowel is drawn.

2. A penny and a dime are tossed. Let each simple event be represented by (p, d).
   a. Specify the sample space for the experiment.
   b. Specify the event that exactly one head is up.
   c. Specify the event that at least one tail is up.

For Exercises 3–7, refer to the two-dice experiment and its sample space in Figure 16-1.

3. How many simple events are there in the sample space?

4. Specify the event that both dice turn up the same number.

5. Specify the event that the numbers turned up on the two dice total eleven.

6. Specify the event that the number turned up on the red die is two more than the number turned up on the green die.

7. Specify the event that the sum of the numbers turned up on the two dice is greater than seven.

8. Specify the sample space for tossing a penny, a dime, and a quarter. Specify the event that at least two coins turn up heads.

B **9.** A coin is tossed and a die is rolled. Specify the sample space. Specify the event that the number turned up on the die is less than four.

10. Two bags contain marbles. The first bag contains one red marble and one white marble. The second bag contains one red marble, one white marble, and one blue marble. One marble is drawn from each bag. Specify the sample space. Specify the event that neither marble is white.

For Exercises 11–18, refer again to the two-dice experiment. The ordered pair (r, g) denotes a simple event, as before.

11. Specify the event that $r + g = 5$.

12. Specify the event that $r < g$.

13. Specify the event that r is a factor of g.

14. Specify the event that $r + g$ is an even number.

15. Specify the event that $g \geq 5$.

C **16.** Specify the event that $r > 3$ or $g \leq 2$.

17. Specify the event that r is an even number or g is an odd number.

18. Specify the event that $r + g = 3$ or $r - g = 2$.

16-6 Probability

OBJECTIVE To find the probability that an event will occur.

Consider the toss of a single coin. The sample space consists of two simple events, $\{H\}$ and $\{T\}$. If the coin is fair, the two simple events are **equally likely** to occur. That is, if you repeated the coin toss a great many times, you would expect heads about half of the time and tails about half of the time. Thus, the probability of simple event $\{H\}$ equals the probability of simple event $\{T\}$. If the probability of $\{H\}$ is denoted by $P(H)$ and the probability of $\{T\}$ is denoted by $P(T)$, then:

$$P(H) = P(T) = \frac{1}{2}$$

Consider the rolling of a die. The sample space consists of six simple events, $\{1, 2, 3, 4, 5, 6\}$. If the die is fair, the six simple events are equally likely to occur. Thus:

$$P(1) = P(2) = P(3) = P(4) = P(5) = P(6) = \frac{1}{6}$$

In general, if $\{a_1, a_2, a_3, \ldots, a_n\}$ is a sample space containing n equally likely simple events, then:

$$P(a_1) = P(a_2) = P(a_3) = \cdots = P(a_n) = \frac{1}{n}$$

In the roll of a die let A be the event that the outcome is an odd number. Event A is the subset $\{1, 3, 5\}$ of the sample space $\{1, 2, 3, 4, 5, 6\}$. The probability of A is defined as the sum of the probabilities of the simple events in A. Thus:

$$P(A) = P(1) + P(3) + P(5) = \frac{1}{6} + \frac{1}{6} + \frac{1}{6} = \frac{3}{6} = \frac{1}{2}$$

If there are n equally likely simple events, and j of them are in event E, then:

$$P(E) = \underbrace{\frac{1}{n} + \frac{1}{n} + \cdots + \frac{1}{n}}_{j \text{ addends}} = \frac{j}{n}$$

EXAMPLE 1 A die is rolled. Find the probability of each event.

Event A: The number turned up is less than 4.

Event B: The number turned up is between 1 and 4.

SOLUTION The sample space is $\{1, 2, 3, 4, 5, 6\}$. The six simple events are equally likely to occur. The probability of each simple event is $\frac{1}{6}$.

$$\text{Event } A = \{1, 2, 3\} \qquad \text{Event } B = \{2, 3\}$$

$$P(A) = \frac{3}{6} = \frac{1}{2} \quad \textit{Answer} \qquad P(B) = \frac{2}{6} = \frac{1}{3} \quad \textit{Answer}$$

EXAMPLE 2   Of the one dozen eggs in a carton, three are bad. If two eggs are selected at random, find the probability of each event.
Event Q: Both eggs are bad.
Event S: One egg is good and one is bad.

SOLUTION   *Event Q*: Since the eggs are selected at random, all possible pairs are equally likely to be selected. Thus:

$$P(Q) = \frac{\text{number of ways to pick a pair of bad eggs}}{\text{number of ways to pick any pair of eggs}}$$

There are 3 bad eggs. The number of ways of picking 2 of them is:

$$_3C_2 = \frac{3 \cdot 2}{2 \cdot 1} = 3$$

There are 12 eggs in all. The number of ways of picking 2 of them is:

$$_{12}C_2 = \frac{12 \cdot 11}{2 \cdot 1} = 66$$

Thus, $P(Q) = \frac{3}{66} = \frac{1}{22}$ *Answer*

Event S: The number of ways of picking one good egg and one bad egg is:

$$9 \cdot 3 = 27$$

Thus, $P(S) = \frac{27}{66} = \frac{9}{22}$ *Answer*

In the experiment of Example 1, the event, rolling a 9, is an impossible outcome; its probability is 0. In the experiment of Example 1 the event, rolling a 1, 2, 3, 4, 5, or 6, is certain to occur; its probability is 1. In general, the probability of an impossible event is 0, and the probability of a certain event is 1.

Written Exercises

A   **1.** One card is drawn at random from a 52-card bridge deck. Find the probability of each event.

     a. It is an ace.   **b.** It is a heart.

     c. It is the ace of hearts.   **d.** It is a red jack.

     e. It is a 9 or 10.   **f.** It is a red club.

   2. A letter is drawn at random from those in RHOMBUS. Find the probability of each event.

     a. It is a vowel.   **b.** It is a consonant.

     c. It comes from the first half of the alphabet.

3. One marble is drawn at random from a bag containing 3 white, 4 red, and 7 black marbles. Find the probability of each event.
   a. It is black.
   b. It is blue.
   c. It is not white.
   d. It is either red or white.

4. A box contains 25 slips of paper, numbered 1–25. A "number" is drawn from the box. Find the probability of each event.
   a. It is an 8.
   b. It is an even number.
   c. It is divisible by 3.
   d. It is > 15.
   e. It is < 0.
   f. It is a positive integer < 26.

5. Three coins are tossed. Find the probability of each event.
   a. All come up heads.
   b. All come up tails.
   c. Two come up tails and one comes up heads.
   d. At least one comes up tails.

6. At a class reunion, a television set is to be given as a door prize to the person whose ticket stub is drawn at random from a bowl. A total of 240 tickets, numbered 1–240, are sold. Find the probability that the winning number is:
   a. 125.
   b. between 99 and 199.
   c. divisible by 5.

7. Of 1,000,000 income tax returns received by a tax collector, all are checked for arithmetic and 8,000 returns are checked thoroughly. For a given return, find the probability of each event.
   a. It is checked for arithmetic accuracy.
   b. It is checked thoroughly.
   c. It is not checked thoroughly.

B 8. Mrs. Nake picked four kinds of apples: MacIntosh, Baldwin, Cortland, and Red Delicious. She picked twice as many MacIntosh apples as Baldwin apples, and twice as many Baldwin apples as Cortland or Red Delicious apples. If she chooses an apple at random from a basket containing all the apples, what is the probability she chooses:
   a. a MacIntosh apple?
   b. a Baldwin apple?
   c. either a Cortland apple or a Red Delicious apple?

9. A bag contains 2 red, 4 yellow, and 6 blue marbles. Two marbles are drawn at random. Find the probability of each event.
   a. Both are red.
   b. Both are yellow.
   c. Both are blue.
   d. Neither is blue.
   e. One is red and one is yellow.

10. Two cards are drawn at random from a 52-card bridge deck. Find the probability of each event.
    a. Both are diamonds.
    b. Both are red.
    c. Neither is a club.
    d. Both are kings.

C 11. A bridge hand consists of 13 cards drawn at random from a 52-card bridge deck. Find the probability of each event.
    a. A hand contains all four jacks.
    b. A hand contains no aces.

16-7 *Mutually Exclusive and Independent Events*

OBJECTIVE To identify mutually exclusive and independent events and find the probability of such events.

Consider the sets A and B, such that $A = \{1, 2, 3, 4\}$ and $B = \{3, 4, 5, 6\}$. Notice that these sets have two members, or elements, in common, namely 3 and 4. This fact can be indicated with the use of a diagram like the one in Figure 16-2. (Such diagrams are known as Venn diagrams.) In this diagram, sets A and B are shown as subsets of the set W of whole numbers. The shaded region represents the set of elements, $\{3, 4\}$, that belongs to both A and B. This set is called the *intersection* of sets A and B. Expressed in symbols, "the intersection of $\{1, 2, 3, 4\}$ and $\{3, 4, 5, 6\}$ equals $\{3, 4\}$" is written as follows:

$$\{1, 2, 3, 4\} \cap \{3, 4, 5, 6\} = \{3, 4\}$$

In general, if A and B are any sets, then the set whose members are the elements belonging to both A and B is called the **intersection** of A and B and is denoted by $A \cap B$.

The sets $\{1, 2, 3, 4\}$ and $\{5, 6, 7, 8\}$ have no members in common. That is:

$$\{1, 2, 3, 4\} \cap \{5, 6, 7, 8\} = \emptyset$$

Sets that have no members in common are called **disjoint** sets.

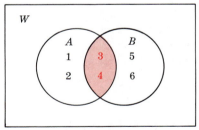

Figure 16-2

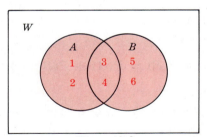

Figure 16-3

In Figure 16-3 the shaded region represents the set consisting of all the elements that belong to *at least one* of the sets A and B. That is, the set represented by the shaded region contains all the elements of A together with all the elements of B. This set is called the *union* of sets A and B. Expressed in symbols, "the union of $\{1, 2, 3, 4\}$ and $\{3, 4, 5, 6\}$ is $\{1, 2, 3, 4, 5, 6\}$" is written as follows:

$$\{1, 2, 3, 4\} \cup \{3, 4, 5, 6\} = \{1, 2, 3, 4, 5, 6\}$$

In general, if A and B are any sets, then the set whose members are the elements belonging to A or B (or to both A and B) is called the **union** of A and B and is denoted by $A \cup B$.

EXAMPLE 1 Specify each of the following sets by roster, referring to the Venn diagram at the right.

a. $A \cap B$ **b.** $A \cup B$
c. $B \cap C$ **d.** $B \cup C$
e. $A \cap D$ **f.** $(A \cup B) \cap C$

SOLUTION **a.** $\{7, 9\}$
b. $\{1, 2, 3, 4, 5, 7, 9, 10\}$
c. $\{9, 10\}$
d. $\{1, 2, 4, 7, 9, 10, 15, 20\}$
e. $\emptyset$ **f.** $\{1, 9, 10\}$

Figure 16-4 shows the sample space S for the experiment of drawing a number at random from $\{1, 2, 3, 4, 5, 6\}$. The figure also shows events A and B in S. Event A is the drawing of a number less than 3. Event B is the drawing of an odd number. Thus $A = \{1, 2\}$ and $B = \{1, 3, 5\}$. The probability of A, $P(A)$, is $\frac{2}{6}$, and $P(B)$ is $\frac{3}{6}$.

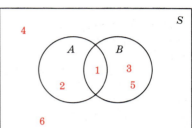

Figure 16-4

What is the probability that *either A or B* will occur? This is equivalent to $P(A \cup B)$. Since $A \cup B$ is $\{1, 2, 3, 5\}$, $P(A \cup B)$ is $\frac{4}{6}$.

To see how $P(A \cup B)$, $P(A)$, and $P(B)$ are related, notice that $A \cap B$ is $\{1\}$ and $P(A \cap B)$ is $\frac{1}{6}$:

$$P(A \cup B) = \frac{4}{6} = \frac{2 + 3 - 1}{6} = \frac{2}{6} + \frac{3}{6} - \frac{1}{6}$$

For any two events A and B in a sample space:

$$P(A \cup B) = P(A) + P(B) - P(A \cap B)$$

If two events have no simple events in common (that is, their intersection is empty), the events are said to be **mutually exclusive**. For mutually exclusive events, $P(A \cap B) = P(\emptyset) = 0$.

If A and B are mutually exclusive events:

$$P(A \cup B) = P(A) + P(B)$$

EXAMPLE 2 From a group of 10 men and 12 women, 3 people are to be selected at random as delegates to a national convention. What is the probability that at least 2 of the delegates will be women?

SOLUTION   The committee will include at least 2 women if *either* exactly 2 women and 1 man are selected (event M) *or* 3 women are selected (event N). Since the two events are mutually exclusive:

$$P(M \cup N) = P(M) + P(N).$$

$$P(M) = \frac{{}_{12}C_2 \cdot {}_{10}C_1}{{}_{22}C_3} = \frac{3}{7}$$

$$P(N) = \frac{{}_{12}C_3 \cdot {}_{10}C_0}{{}_{22}C_3} = \frac{1}{7}$$

$$P(M \cup N) = \frac{3}{7} + \frac{1}{7} = \frac{4}{7} \quad \textbf{Answer}$$

Consider the experiment of tossing a coin twice. What is the probability of getting a head on both tosses? The sample space for the experiment is $\{(H, H), (H, T), (T, H), (T, T)\}$. Let A be the event that a head is obtained on the first toss. Let B be the event that a head is obtained on the second toss. Then:

$$A = \{(H, H), (H, T)\} \text{ and } B = \{(H, H), (T, H)\}.$$

The two events are not mutually exclusive, since $A \cap B = \{(H, H)\}$. The probability of the events and of the intersection are: $P(A) = \frac{1}{2}$, $P(B) = \frac{1}{2}$, and $P(A \cap B) = \frac{1}{4}$. Notice the pattern:

$$P(A) \times P(B) = P(A \cap B)$$

$$\frac{1}{2} \times \frac{1}{2} = \frac{1}{4}$$

Note, further, that in this experiment the occurrence of A has no effect on the probability of the occurrence of B. Such events are called **independent** events.

Two events A and B are independent if and only if:

$$P(A \cap B) = P(A) \cdot P(B)$$

EXAMPLE 3   A bag contains 5 red and 5 blue marbles. Two marbles are drawn at random from the bag as follows:

a. The first marble drawn is put back into the bag before the second marble is drawn.

b. The first marble drawn is *not* put back into the bag before the second marble is drawn.

Let A be the event that the first marble drawn is red.

Let B be the event that the second marble drawn is red.

Are the events in each case dependent or independent?

(*Solution continued on page 622.*)

SOLUTION   **a.** $P(A) = \frac{5}{10} = \frac{1}{2}$

$$P(B) = \frac{5}{10} = \frac{1}{2}$$

$$P(A \cap B) = \frac{{}_5C_1 \cdot {}_5C_1}{{}_{10}C_1 \cdot {}_{10}C_1} = \frac{1}{4}$$

$$P(A) \cdot P(B) = \frac{1}{4} = P(A \cap B)$$

∴ events A and B are independent.   ***Answer***

b. $P(A) = \frac{5}{10} = \frac{1}{2}$

$P(B)$ can be found independently of the event A. Since any of the ten marbles is equally likely to be the second marble and 5 of the ten marbles are red,

$$P(B) = \frac{5}{10} = \frac{1}{2}.$$

The event $(A \cap B)$ is equivalent to drawing two red marbles. There are ${}_{10}C_2$ pairs of marbles that are equally likely to be chosen. Of these, ${}_5C_2$ are pairs of red marbles. Thus:

$$P(A \cap B) = \frac{{}_5C_2}{{}_{10}C_2} = \frac{10}{45} = \frac{2}{9}$$

$$P(A) \cdot P(B) = \frac{1}{4} \neq P(A \cap B)$$

∴ events A and B are dependent.   ***Answer***

    Suppose you have a problem involving event A in sample space S. It is sometimes useful to consider the elements of S that are not members of A, or the **complement** of A. The symbol for the complement of an event A is $\bar{A}$.

    If event A consists of h elements and S consists of n equally likely elements, then $\bar{A}$ consists of $n - h$ elements. The probability, $P(\bar{A})$, that A does not occur is $1 - P(A)$:

$$P(\bar{A}) = \frac{n - h}{n} = 1 - \frac{h}{n} = 1 - P(A).$$

EXAMPLE 4   Based on past performances, the probability that Tony will solve a certain problem is $\frac{2}{3}$, that Dolores will solve it is $\frac{3}{4}$, and that Mark will solve it is $\frac{1}{2}$. Find the probability of each of the following events.

    a. Tony and Dolores solve the problem, but Mark does not.

    b. At least one of the three solves the problem.

SOLUTION If the event that Tony solves the problem is A, that Dolores solves it is B, and that Mark solves it is C:

$P(A) = \frac{2}{3}$, $P(B) = \frac{3}{4}$, and $P(C) = \frac{1}{2}$.

a. The probability that Mark will not solve the problem is:

$P(\bar{C}) = 1 - P(C) = 1 - \frac{1}{2} = \frac{1}{2}$.

Thus:
$P(A) \cdot P(B) \cdot P(\bar{C}) = \frac{2}{3} \cdot \frac{3}{4} \cdot \frac{1}{2} = \frac{1}{4}$.   *Answer*

b. Call the event that at least one of them solves the problem D; call the event that none of them solves the problem E. It should be apparent that $D = \bar{E}$.

$$
\begin{aligned}
P(D) &= P(\bar{E}) \\
&= 1 - P(E) \\
&= 1 - P(\bar{A}) \cdot P(\bar{B}) \cdot P(\bar{C}) \quad \left\{ \begin{array}{l} E \text{ is equivalent to } \bar{A}, \bar{B}, \\ \text{and } \bar{C} \text{ occurring together.} \end{array} \right. \\
&= 1 - \frac{1}{3} \cdot \frac{1}{4} \cdot \frac{1}{2} \\
&= 1 - \frac{1}{24} = \frac{23}{24}
\end{aligned}
$$

$\therefore$ the probability that *at least one* of the three solves the problem is $\frac{23}{24}$.   *Answer*

Oral Exercises

1. Specify each of the following sets by roster, referring to the Venn diagram.

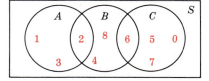

  a. $A \cap B$ **b.** $A \cap C$
  c. $B \cap C$ **d.** $A \cup B$
  e. $B \cup C$ **f.** $A \cup (B \cap C)$

2. Use the given probabilities to tell whether A and B are dependent or independent events.

  a. $P(A) = \frac{1}{4}$; $P(B) = \frac{1}{5}$; $P(A \cap B) = \frac{1}{20}$

  b. $P(A) = \frac{1}{2}$; $P(B) = \frac{1}{4}$; $P(A \cap B) = \frac{1}{6}$

  c. $P(A) = 0.25$; $P(B) = 0.20$; $P(A \cap B) = 0.050$
  d. $P(A) = 0.30$; $P(B) = 0.40$; $P(A \cap B) = 0.070$

Written Exercises

A **1.** Two dice are rolled. What is the probability that both come up 5?

  2. A single ball is drawn from a bag containing 5 red, 6 white, and 3 green balls. Find the probability of each event.
    a. A red or green ball is drawn.
    b. A white or red ball is drawn.

3. A die and a coin are tossed. Let A be the event that the die turns up even and B the event that the coin turns up tails.
   a. Specify the sample space for the experiment.
   b. Specify the simple events in A, B, $A \cup B$, and $A \cap B$.
   c. Find the probability of A, B, $A \cup B$, and $A \cap B$.
   d. Are A and B mutually exclusive? Are they independent?

4. A red and a green die are rolled. Let A be the event that the red die turns up 5 and B the event that the sum of the numbers is 7.
   a. Find the probability of A, B, $A \cup B$, and $A \cap B$.
   b. Are A and B independent events?

5. Two dice are rolled. Find the probability of each event.
   a. The sum of the numbers up is 3.
   b. Either the sum of the numbers up is 3 or both of the numbers up are 4.

6. Two cards are drawn from a 52-card bridge deck. Find the probability of each event.
   a. Both are 8's.   b. Both are jacks.
   c. Either both are 8's or both are jacks.

7. A coin is tossed three times. Find the probability of each event, then tell whether the events are independent.
   a. At least two tosses come up heads.
   b. At least one toss comes up tails.

8. A card is drawn from a 52-card bridge deck, replaced, the deck shuffled, and a second card is drawn. Find the probability of each event.
   a. Both cards are kings.   b. Both cards are diamonds.

B 9. If a set of eight books is placed randomly on a shelf, what is the probability that they will be arranged in either correct or reverse order?

10. Ten people attend a conference. Four are executives, five are sales representatives, and one is a lawyer. Three executives, one sales representative, and the lawyer are stockholders. A fly in the room lands at random on the hand of one of the ten. Find the probability of each event. Then tell whether the events are independent.
    a. The fly lands on an executive.
    b. The fly lands on a stockholder.

11. A card is drawn from a 52-card bridge deck. Let A be the event that the card is red, B the event that it is a 9, and C the event that it is either a 9 or a 10. Which of the following are independent events?
    a. A and B b. A and C c. B and C

12. When Carlos shoots a basketball, the probability that he will make a basket is 0.5. When Rudy shoots, the probability of a basket is 0.4. What is the probability that at least one basket is made if Carlos and Rudy take one shot each?

13. The probability that Jeff will ask Manny to be his bridge partner is $\frac{1}{3}$, that Rose will ask him is $\frac{1}{2}$, and that Art will ask him is $\frac{2}{3}$. Find the probability of each event.
 a. Rose and Jeff ask him.
 b. Art and Rose ask him, but Jeff does not.
 c. At least two of the three ask him.
 d. At least one of the three asks him.

14. According to the weather reports, the probability of rain on a certain day is 80% in Yellow Falls and 60% in Copper Creek. Find the probability of each of the following events.
 a. It will rain in Yellow Falls, but not in Copper Creek.
 b. It will rain in both cities.
 c. It will rain in neither city.
 d. It will rain in at least one of the cities.

C 15. Two cards are drawn from a 52-card bridge deck. Find the probability of each event.
 a. Both are black.   b. Both are aces.
 c. Either both are black or both are aces.

Self-Test 2

VOCABULARY   random experiment (p. 614)   intersection (p. 619)
             sample space (p. 614)   union (p. 619)
             event (p. 614)   mutually exclusive events
             simple event (p. 614)   (p. 620)
             equally likely events (p. 616) independent events (p. 621)
                                            complement (p. 622)

Solve.

1. Each of the letters in the word SQUARE is written on a different card, and the six cards are shuffled. Then one card is drawn.   **Obj. 16-5 (p. 614)**
 a. Specify the sample space for the drawing.
 b. Specify the event that a consonant is drawn.

2. One marble is drawn from a bag containing 7 green, 5 orange, and 4 yellow marbles. What is the probability that the marble is orange?   **Obj. 16-6 (p. 616)**

3. Two dice are rolled.   **Obj. 16-7 (p. 619)**
 a. Find the probability that either both numbers are 1's or their sum is less than 4.
 b. Are the two events independent?

Check your answers with those at the back of the book.

16-8 *Frequency Distributions*

OBJECTIVE   **To recognize and characterize frequency distributions.**

The results of a certain algebra test are shown at the right. This display shows what scores were attained and how many students attained each score.

   Another way of displaying such data is shown in Figure 16-5. This type of graph is known as a *histogram*. In this histogram, the scores have been grouped into convenient intervals (55-60, 60-65, and so on). A "boundary" score is included in the interval to its left. (For example, the two 75's are included in the 70-75 interval.)

Score	Number of Students
100	2
98	1
95	3
94	1
93	1
90	2
88	2
87	3
85	5
83	3
82	1
80	2
78	1
75	2
74	1
73	2
68	1
65	1
56	1

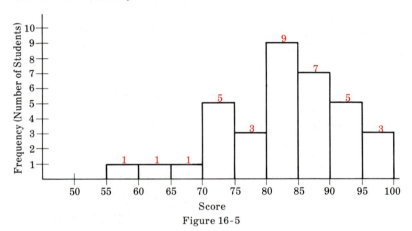

Figure 16-5

   Both types of display give information about the scores and the frequency of occurrence of the scores. Displays that give such information are known as **frequency distributions.**

   Frequency distributions are often discussed in terms of certain numbers. One number used to indicate the location of a distribution's center is called the *mean*. The **mean** of a collection of data is the arithmetic average of the data.

EXAMPLE 1   The scores attained on a certain test were 80, 80, 75, 75, 75, and 59. What is the mean (M) of the test scores?

SOLUTION $M = \dfrac{3(75) + 2(80) + 1(59)}{6} = \dfrac{444}{6} = 74$

Important numbers for describing the spread, or *dispersion*, of a set of data are the *range*, the *variance*, and the *standard deviation*.

The **range** of a frequency distribution is the difference between the highest and the lowest values. For example, the range of the data displayed in Figure 16-5 is the difference between 100 and 56, or 44.

Although the range of a frequency distribution gives some indication of the dispersion, a display of the distribution is much more informative. For example, suppose that 34 of the scores on an algebra test were 100 and one was 56. Clearly, this frequency distribution is significantly different from the one displayed in Figure 16-5, although the range is the same in each case.

Score	Deviation
84	$+20$
79	$+15$
78	$+14$
63	-1
60	-4
54	-10
51	-13
43	-21

Scores on a history test were 84, 79, 78, 63, 60, 54, 51, and 43. The mean score is 64. The display at the right shows how much each score differs from the mean. These differences are called *deviations* from the mean.

The **variance** of a distribution is computed by squaring each deviation from the mean, adding these squares, and dividing their sum by the number of entries in the distribution. Thus, the variance gives you an idea of how the data are scattered about the mean.

If x_j denotes the jth entry in a distribution of n entries, and M denotes the mean of the distribution, then:

$$\text{variance} = \frac{(x_1 - M)^2 + (x_2 - M)^2 + \cdots + (x_n - M)^2}{n}.$$

EXAMPLE 2 Find the variance for the distribution of the history test scores.

SOLUTION

$$\text{variance} = \frac{(+20)^2 + (+15)^2 + (+14)^2 + (-1)^2 + (-4)^2 + (-10)^2 + (-13)^2 + (-21)^2}{8}$$

$$= \frac{1548}{8} = 193.5 \quad \textbf{\textit{Answer}}$$

The principal square root of the variance is known as the **standard deviation.** The standard deviation is the number that is most commonly used in characterizing the dispersion of a distribution. It is denoted by the Greek letter sigma (σ). Thus,

$$\sigma = \sqrt{\frac{\text{sum of the squares of the deviations from the mean}}{\text{number of entries in the distribution}}} = \sqrt{\text{variance}}.$$

The mean provides a measure of the location of the center of a distribution. The standard deviation and the variance both provide a measure of the dispersion of the distribution. It is common practice to give both kinds of measures when describing a distribution with the use of numbers.

EXAMPLE 3   The frequency distribution of the heights of the members of a high school basketball team is shown at the right.
Find the mean and standard deviation for the distribution.

Height (cm)	Frequency
177	1
178	1
179	2
181	1
183	3
184	2
186	1
189	1

SOLUTION   Use a table to organize the data:

1. Complete the first 3 columns.
2. Find the mean.
3. Complete the rest of the table.
4. Find the standard deviation.

The final results are as follows:

Ht.	Freq.	Ht. × Freq.	Dev.	(Dev.)^2	(Dev.)^2 × Freq.
177	1	177	-5	25	25
178	1	178	-4	16	16
179	2	358	-3	9	18
181	1	181	-1	1	1
183	3	549	$+1$	1	3
184	2	368	$+2$	4	8
186	1	186	$+4$	16	16
189	1	189	$+7$	49	49
Sums	12	2186			136

$$M = \frac{2186}{12} = 182 \qquad \sigma = \sqrt{\frac{136}{12}} = 3.4$$

Oral Exercises

1. On a certain day the high temperature reading was 17°C, and on the next day it was 9°C. Find:
   a. the mean high temperature.   **b.** the high-temperature range.
2. Miguel's algebra test scores during one month were 80, 90, and 100. For his test scores that month, find:
   a. the mean score.   **b.** the range.

3. During the wettest month of the year in Mountainside the total precipitation was 40 cm. During the next month, it was 16 cm. For the two-month period, find the mean monthly precipitation and the range.

4. In five successive soccer games, Robin scored 2, 1, 0, 3, and 2 goals, respectively. For this goal distribution, find the mean score and the range.

Written Exercises

For the data given in Exercises 1–4, find the mean, variance, standard deviation, and range to the nearest integer.

A 1. 36, 42, 45, 66, 72, 75
2. 7, 25, 46, 66, 89, 103
3. 42, 46, 49, 50, 52, 55, 56
4. 49, 48, 45, 43, 42, 39, 35

5. Find the mean and the standard deviation for the average monthly temperatures, in °C, for Indianapolis: $-0.056, 2.00, 6.28, 12.72, 18.61, 24.33, 27.44, 26.39, 22.00, 15.89, 8.94,$ and 2.17.

6. In a golf tournament the 18-hole totals for the top nine golfers were: 68, 69, 70, 70, 72, 73, 73, 73, and 74. Find the mean, variance, standard deviation, and range of this set of scores to the nearest tenth of a stroke.

B 7. Sonja has quiz scores of 85, 75, 80, and 95. What must she score on the fifth quiz for the mean for the five quizzes to be 85?

8. The mean of 8 numbers is 15. What is the sum of the numbers?

9. If each score in a set of algebra test scores were increased by 8 points, how would this affect the mean, the range, and the standard deviation?

10. If each entry in a set of scores were multiplied by three, how would this affect the mean, the range, and the standard deviation?

C 11. At high school A, the mean score of 50 students on a mathematics test is 75. At high school B, the mean score of 40 students on the same test is 80. Use x_i to denote the score of the ith student at school A and y_i to denote the score of the ith student at school B.
a. What is the value of the sum of the x_i's?
b. What is the value of the sum of the y_i's?
c. What is the mean score for the 90 students?

12. The mean of n scores is M_1. The mean of m additional scores is M_2.
a. What is the mean of $n + m$ scores?
b. Under what conditions is the combined mean $\dfrac{M_1 + M_2}{2}$?

16-9 *The Normal Distribution*

OBJECTIVE   **To recognize and analyze normal distributions.**

The frequency distribution for the possible outcomes when coins are tossed can be shown by means of a histogram. A histogram for the tossing of three coins is shown at the right.

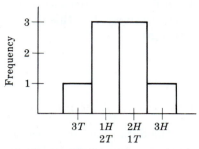

Result (3 coins are tossed)

EXAMPLE 1   Three coins are tossed. Find the probability of each outcome.

a. 3 heads

b. 2 heads and 1 tail

c. at least 2 tails

SOLUTION   **a.** The area of the bar corresponding to 3 heads is one square unit. The total area of all the bars in the histogram is $(1 + 3 + 3 + 1)$ square units, or 8 square units. Thus the probability of 3 heads turning up in a given toss is $\frac{1}{8}$.

b. $\frac{3}{8}$

c. $\frac{3 + 1}{8} = \frac{4}{8} = \frac{1}{2}$

If the midpoints at the tops of the bars in a histogram are connected, a smooth curve like the one shown below results. Such "bell-shaped" curves can result from the plotting of a wide variety of data. Among other things, a bell-shaped curve might represent the frequency distribution for the heights of high school seniors, the scores achieved on a given test, or the diameters of tennis balls.

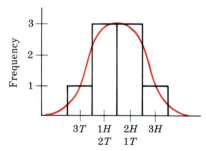

Result (3 coins are tossed)

Certain distributions represented by bell-shaped curves are known as *normal distributions.* A normal distribution with a mean equal to zero and a standard deviation equal to one is called the **standard normal distribution.** The bell-shaped curve that represents a standard normal distribution is known as the **standard normal curve.** Figure 16-6 shows a standard normal curve.

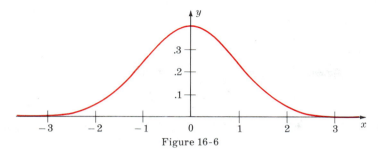

Figure 16-6

The standard normal curve has the following properties:

1. It is symmetric with respect to the y-axis.
2. It approaches the x-axis asymptotically as $|x|$ increases.
3. The total area under the curve and above the x-axis is equal to 1.

Property 3 makes it easy to find the probability represented by a given region under the standard normal curve. The probability an event will lie within a given region is the ratio of the area of the region to the area of the region representing all possible outcomes. Since the area under the curve and above the x-axis is 1, the probability that an event lies within a given region is simply the area of that region. For example, suppose you wanted to find the probability that an observation, X, lies between a and b in a standard normal distribution. The observation would lie within the area bounded by the standard normal curve, the x-axis, and the vertical lines $x = a$ and $x = b$. That is, it would lie in the shaded region in Figure 16-7. The probability is simply the area of the shaded region.

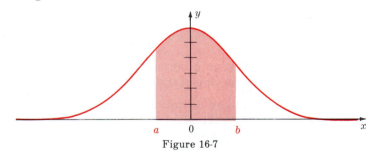

Figure 16-7

The area of the shaded region must be found in order to determine the probability that $a \leq X \leq b$. This area can be approximated by rectangles. The areas of the rectangles can then be added to give the total area, as in a histogram. To save the time and effort required to do this, extensive tables of area measures for the standard normal distributions have been produced. Area measures from 0 to x, at intervals of 0.2, are given in Table 16-1 for $0 \leq X \leq 4.0$.

Table 16-1

Area Under the Standard Normal Curve for $0 \leq X \leq 4.0$

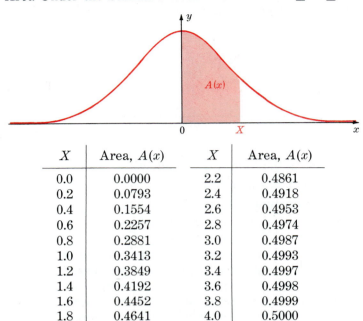

X	Area, $A(x)$	X	Area, $A(x)$
0.0	0.0000	2.2	0.4861
0.2	0.0793	2.4	0.4918
0.4	0.1554	2.6	0.4953
0.6	0.2257	2.8	0.4974
0.8	0.2881	3.0	0.4987
1.0	0.3413	3.2	0.4993
1.2	0.3849	3.4	0.4997
1.4	0.4192	3.6	0.4998
1.6	0.4452	3.8	0.4999
1.8	0.4641	4.0	0.5000
2.0	0.4772		

EXAMPLE 2   What is the probability that an observation, X, lies between $+2.6$ and $+2.8$ in a standard normal distribution?

SOLUTION   The required probability equals the area under the curve between 2.6 and 2.8. This is the area from 0 to 2.8 minus the area from 0 to 2.6. Thus:

$$P(2.6 < X < 2.8) = A(2.8) - A(2.6)$$
$$= 0.4974 - 0.4953 = 0.0021 \quad \textbf{\textit{Answer}}$$

EXAMPLE 3   What is the probability that an observation, X, lies within two standard deviations of the mean in a standard normal distribution?

SOLUTION   The mean is 0 and the standard deviation is 1. Since the normal curve is symmetric with respect to the y-axis, the area under the curve between -2 and 2 is twice the area between 0 and 2. Thus:

$$P(-2 < X < 2) = 2 \cdot A(2)$$
$$= 2(0.4772)$$
$$= 0.9544 \quad \textbf{\textit{Answer}}$$

Notice that slightly more than 95% of the observations in a standard normal distribution are within two standard deviations of the mean. It can be shown similarly that slightly more than 68% of the observations are within one standard deviation of the mean.

Written Exercises

For Exercises 1 and 2, refer to the histogram below. It shows the frequency distribution for the tossing of 10 coins.

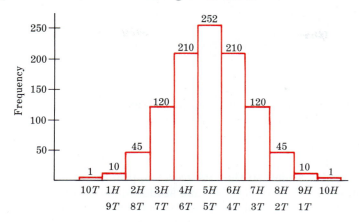

A 1. What is the total area of the bars in the histogram for tossing 10 coins?

2. For the tossing of 10 coins, find the probability of each outcome.
  a. 9 heads and 1 tail
  b. 5 heads and 5 tails
  c. at least 6 tails
  d. 2 heads or 2 tails
  e. at most 2 heads
  f. more than 3 tails

For Exercises 3–8, refer to Table 16-1.

3. In a standard normal distribution, what is the probability that an observation, X, lies between the mean and $+0.6$?

4. In a standard normal distribution, what is the probability that an observation, X, lies between -0.2 and $+0.2$?

5. In a standard normal distribution, find $P(-4 < X < -3)$ for observation X.

6. In a standard normal distribution, what is the probability that an observation, X, lies within 3 standard deviations of the mean?

7. The mean of the heights of a certain group of adults was found to be 180 cm, with a standard deviation of 8 cm. Assuming a normal distribution of heights, find the percentage of the adults studied in each category.
  a. height > 180 cm   **b.** height < 172 cm   **c.** height > 196 cm

8. The mean mass of a loaf of bread was found by sampling to be 455 g, with a standard deviation of 5 g. Assuming a normal distribution, find the percentage of loaves in each category.
  a. mass < 450 g   **b.** mass > 445 g   **c.** mass > 470 g

B 9. Find the variance of the standard normal distribution.

10. If X is an observation from a standard normal distribution, find k such that $P(X \leq k)$ is:

    a. 0.5000   **b.** 1.0

11. Explain why $P(X > k) = 1 - P(X < k)$.

12. Explain why $P(|X| > k) = 2[1 - P(X < k)]$, $k \geq 0$.

C 13. The equation of the standard normal curve is:

$$y = \frac{1}{\sqrt{2\pi}} e^{\frac{-x^2}{2}}$$

The base of the natural logarithms, e, is equal to 2.71828. . . . Use a table of logarithms to compute the ordinate, y, of the point on the normal curve for:

    a. $x = 0$ **b.** $x = 1$ **c.** $x = 2$

14. A college aptitude test is scaled so that its scores approximate a normal distribution with mean equal to 500 and standard deviation equal to 100. Find the probability that a student selected at random will score:

    a. 800 or more points.   **b.** less than 400 points.

15. Use the binomial expansion (Chapter 11) to compute the probabilities you found by comparing areas in Exercise 2.

Self-Test 3

Solve.

1. Find the mean, variance, standard deviation, and range, all to the nearest integer, for the following distribution.   **Obj. 16-8, p. 626**

Score	Frequency
30	2
35	6
40	5
50	5

2. In a standard normal distribution, what is the probability that an observation, X, lies between -2.0 and $+1.0$? (Refer to Table 16-1.)   **Obj. 16-9, p. 630**

Check your answers with those at the back of the book.

Chapter Summary

1. Using the first of the two fundamental counting principles (pages 601 and 602), you can derive the following expressions for the number of *permutations* of n things taken r at a time:

$$_nP_r = n(n-1)(n-2) \cdots [n - (r-1)] = \frac{n!}{(n-r)!}$$

2. The number of *combinations* of n things taken r at a time is given by:

$$_nC_r = \frac{n(n-1)(n-2) \cdots [n - (r-1)]}{r!}$$

3. Each possible outcome in a *random experiment* is called a *simple event*. The set of all simple events is called the *sample space* of the experiment. Any *subset* of the sample space is known as an *event*.

4. If the sample space for an experiment consists of n equally likely simple events and the event E consists of j simple events:

$$P(E) = \frac{1}{n} + \frac{1}{n} + \cdots + \frac{1}{n} = \frac{j}{n}$$

5. In general, for any two events A and B in a sample space:

$$P(A \cup B) = P(A) + P(B) - P(A \cap B).$$

If the events have no simple events in common (their intersection is empty), the events are said to be *mutually exclusive*. For mutually exclusive events:

$$P(A \cup B) = P(A) + P(B).$$

6. Two events, A and B, are *independent* if and only if:

$$P(A \cap B) = P(A) \cdot P(B).$$

7. The *mean* of a frequency distribution is the arithmetic average of the entries.

8. The *variance* of a distribution is defined as follows:

$$\text{variance} = \frac{(x_1 - M)^2 + (x_2 - M)^2 + \cdots + (x_n - M)^2}{n}.$$

In this expression x_j denotes the jth entry of n entries and M denotes the mean of the distribution.

9. The *standard deviation*, σ, is the principal square root of the variance:

$$\sigma = \sqrt{\text{variance}}.$$

10. The *standard normal curve* is symmetric with respect to the y-axis, and approaches the x-axis asymptotically as $|x|$ increases. The total area under the curve and above the x-axis equals 1.

Chapter Review

1. How many positive integers less than 50 can be formed by using the integers 1, 2, and 3?

     a. 9   **b.** 6   **c.** 12   **d.** 3

   16-1

2. In how many ways can 3 cards be selected, one after the other, from a deck of 12 cards, if selected cards are not returned to the deck?

     a. 1728   **b.** 360   **c.** 1320   **d.** 220

3. In how many ways can 5 books, taken 3 at a time, be arranged on a shelf?

     a. 15   **b.** 120   **c.** 20   **d.** 60

   16-2

4. How many different permutations can be made using all the letters in the word ICICLE?

     a. 180   **b.** 720   **c.** 30   **d.** 360

   16-3

5. In how many ways can 5 players be chosen from 11 players?

     a. 720   **b.** 55,440   **c.** 462   **d.** 11,088

   16-4

6. Two coins are tossed. What does $\{(H, H), (H, T), (T, H), (T, T)\}$ represent?

     a. the event that at least one head turns up
     b. the event that exactly one tail turns up
     c. the sample space for the experiment

   16-5

7. Three coins are tossed. What is the probability that at least two tails turn up?

     a. $\frac{7}{8}$ **b.** $\frac{1}{2}$ **c.** $\frac{3}{8}$ **d.** $\frac{1}{4}$

   16-6

8. A dime and a penny are tossed. Let A be the event that the dime turns up heads and B the event that the penny turns up tails. What is the probability of $A \cap B$?

     a. $\frac{1}{4}$ **b.** $\frac{1}{2}$ **c.** $\frac{3}{4}$ **d.** 1

   16-7

9. If A and B are mutually exclusive events, which of the following relationships applies?

     a. $P(A \cup B) = P(A) \cdot P(B)$ **b.** $P(A \cup B) = 0$
     c. $P(A \cup B) = P(A) + P(B)$ **d.** $P(A \cap B) = P(A) \cdot P(B)$

10. On 4 quizzes, Jean got the following scores: $100, 79, 86$, and 91. What is the variance for this distribution?

      a. 89   **b.** 58.5   **c.** 234   **d.** 15.3

    16-8

11. Under the standard normal curve, the area bounded by the x- and y-axes and the line $x = 3$ is 0.4987. For the observation X, what is $P(-3 < X < +3)$?

      a. 0.4987   **b.** 0.9974   **c.** 0.2494   **d.** 0

    16-9

Chapter Test

16-1

1. How many positive even integers less than 1000 can be formed using the integers 4, 5, 6, and 7?

16-2

2. In how many different ways can 7 potted plants be arranged in a row on a windowsill that holds only 3 plants at a time?

16-3

3. How many different signals can be made by displaying four pennants, all at one time, on a vertical flagpole? The pennants are identical except for color. Two are yellow and two are green.

16-4

4. How many 3-letter subsets can be formed from the letters in the set $\{L, M, N, O\}$? Specify the subsets.

5. How many combinations can be formed using the letters in the word CHEMISTRY, taken 8 at a time?

16-5

6. A coin and a die are tossed. Specify each of the following events.

   a. The number turned up on the die is less than 3.

   b. The coin turns up tails and the die turns up an even number.

16-6

7. One card is drawn at random from a 52-card bridge deck. Find the probability of each event.

   a. It is a king.   **b.** It is red.   **c.** It is a 1, 2, or 3.

16-7

8. There are 3 red, 3 white, and 3 green balls in a bag. Two are drawn at random. Let A be the event that at least one ball is red. Let B be the event that both balls are the same color.

   a. Find $P(A)$, $P(B)$, $P(A \cap B)$, and $P(A \cup B)$.

   b. Are events A and B mutually exclusive? independent?

9. On a certain day, the probability that it will snow in Anchorage is 70% and in Tokyo, 40%. What is the probability that it will snow in at least one of the two cities?

16-8

10. A panel of 12 tea tasters rates teas on a scale of 1–10, with 10 the top score. The frequency distribution of ratings for a certain sample of tea follows. Find the mean, range, variance, and standard deviation.

Score	Frequency	Score	Frequency
10	0	5	1
9	2	4	1
8	3	3	0
7	3	2	0
6	2	1	0

16-9

11. The scores on an algebra test gave a normal frequency distribution. The mean score was 74.3, and the standard deviation was 5.7. What is the probability that a student's score is greater than 80? (Refer to Table 16-1.)

Table 1   Squares and Square Roots

N	N^2	$\sqrt{N}$	$\sqrt{10N}$	N	N^2	$\sqrt{N}$	$\sqrt{10N}$
1.0	1.00	1.000	3.162	**5.5**	30.25	2.345	7.416
1.1	1.21	1.049	3.317	**5.6**	31.36	2.366	7.483
1.2	1.44	1.095	3.464	**5.7**	32.49	2.387	7.550
1.3	1.69	1.140	3.606	**5.8**	33.64	2.408	7.616
1.4	1.96	1.183	3.742	**5.9**	34.81	2.429	7.681
1.5	2.25	1.225	3.873	**6.0**	36.00	2.449	7.746
1.6	2.56	1.265	4.000	**6.1**	37.21	2.470	7.810
1.7	2.89	1.304	4.123	**6.2**	38.44	2.490	7.874
1.8	3.24	1.342	4.243	**6.3**	39.69	2.510	7.937
1.9	3.61	1.378	4.359	**6.4**	40.96	2.530	8.000
2.0	4.00	1.414	4.472	**6.5**	42.25	2.550	8.062
2.1	4.41	1.449	4.583	**6.6**	43.56	2.569	8.124
2.2	4.84	1.483	4.690	**6.7**	44.89	2.588	8.185
2.3	5.29	1.517	4.796	**6.8**	46.24	2.608	8.246
2.4	5.76	1.549	4.899	**6.9**	47.61	2.627	8.307
2.5	6.25	1.581	5.000	**7.0**	49.00	2.646	8.367
2.6	6.76	1.612	5.099	**7.1**	50.41	2.665	8.426
2.7	7.29	1.643	5.196	**7.2**	51.84	2.683	8.485
2.8	7.84	1.673	5.292	**7.3**	53.29	2.702	8.544
2.9	8.41	1.703	5.385	**7.4**	54.76	2.720	8.602
3.0	9.00	1.732	5.477	**7.5**	56.25	2.739	8.660
3.1	9.61	1.761	5.568	**7.6**	57.76	2.757	8.718
3.2	10.24	1.789	5.657	**7.7**	59.29	2.775	8.775
3.3	10.89	1.817	5.745	**7.8**	60.84	2.793	8.832
3.4	11.56	1.844	5.831	**7.9**	62.41	2.811	8.888
3.5	12.25	1.871	5.916	**8.0**	64.00	2.828	8.944
3.6	12.96	1.897	6.000	**8.1**	65.61	2.846	9.000
3.7	13.69	1.924	6.083	**8.2**	67.24	2.864	9.055
3.8	14.44	1.949	6.164	**8.3**	68.89	2.881	9.110
3.9	15.21	1.975	6.245	**8.4**	70.56	2.898	9.165
4.0	16.00	2.000	6.325	**8.5**	72.25	2.915	9.220
4.1	16.81	2.025	6.403	**8.6**	73.96	2.933	9.274
4.2	17.64	2.049	6.481	**8.7**	75.69	2.950	9.327
4.3	18.49	2.074	6.557	**8.8**	77.44	2.966	9.381
4.4	19.36	2.098	6.633	**8.9**	79.21	2.983	9.434
4.5	20.25	2.121	6.708	**9.0**	81.00	3.000	9.487
4.6	21.16	2.145	6.782	**9.1**	82.81	3.017	9.539
4.7	22.09	2.168	6.856	**9.2**	84.64	3.033	9.592
4.8	23.04	2.191	6.928	**9.3**	86.49	3.050	9.644
4.9	24.01	2.214	7.000	**9.4**	88.36	3.066	9.695
5.0	25.00	2.236	7.071	**9.5**	90.25	3.082	9.747
5.1	26.01	2.258	7.141	**9.6**	92.16	3.098	9.798
5.2	27.04	2.280	7.211	**9.7**	94.09	3.114	9.849
5.3	28.09	2.302	7.280	**9.8**	96.04	3.130	9.899
5.4	29.16	2.324	7.348	**9.9**	98.01	3.146	9.950
5.5	30.25	2.345	7.416	**10**	100.00	3.162	10.000

Table 2 Cubes and Cube Roots

N	N^3	$\sqrt[3]{N}$	$\sqrt[3]{10N}$	$\sqrt[3]{100N}$	N	N^3	$\sqrt[3]{N}$	$\sqrt[3]{10N}$	$\sqrt[3]{100N}$
1.0	1.000	1.000	2.154	4.642	5.5	166.375	1.765	3.803	8.193
1.1	1.331	1.032	2.224	4.791	5.6	175.616	1.776	3.826	8.243
1.2	1.728	1.063	2.289	4.932	5.7	185.193	1.786	3.849	8.291
1.3	2.197	1.091	2.351	5.066	5.8	195.112	1.797	3.871	8.340
1.4	2.744	1.119	2.410	5.192	5.9	205.379	1.807	3.893	8.387
1.5	3.375	1.145	2.466	5.313	6.0	216.000	1.817	3.915	8.434
1.6	4.096	1.170	2.520	5.429	6.1	226.981	1.827	3.936	8.481
1.7	4.913	1.193	2.571	5.540	6.2	238.328	1.837	3.958	8.527
1.8	5.832	1.216	2.621	5.646	6.3	250.047	1.847	3.979	8.573
1.9	6.859	1.239	2.668	5.749	6.4	262.144	1.857	4.000	8.618
2.0	8.000	1.260	2.714	5.848	6.5	274.625	1.866	4.021	8.662
2.1	9.261	1.281	2.759	5.944	6.6	287.496	1.876	4.041	8.707
2.2	10.648	1.301	2.802	6.037	6.7	300.763	1.885	4.062	8.750
2.3	12.167	1.320	2.844	6.127	6.8	314.432	1.895	4.082	8.794
2.4	13.824	1.339	2.884	6.214	6.9	328.509	1.904	4.102	8.837
2.5	15.625	1.357	2.924	6.300	7.0	343.000	1.913	4.121	8.879
2.6	17.576	1.375	2.962	6.383	7.1	357.911	1.922	4.141	8.921
2.7	19.683	1.392	3.000	6.463	7.2	373.248	1.931	4.160	8.963
2.8	21.952	1.409	3.037	6.542	7.3	389.017	1.940	4.179	9.004
2.9	24.389	1.426	3.072	6.619	7.4	405.224	1.949	4.198	9.045
3.0	27.000	1.442	3.107	6.694	7.5	421.875	1.957	4.217	9.086
3.1	29.791	1.458	3.141	6.768	7.6	438.976	1.966	4.236	9.126
3.2	32.768	1.474	3.175	6.840	7.7	456.533	1.975	4.254	9.166
3.3	35.937	1.489	3.208	6.910	7.8	474.552	1.983	4.273	9.205
3.4	39.304	1.504	3.240	6.980	7.9	493.039	1.992	4.291	9.244
3.5	42.875	1.518	3.271	7.047	8.0	512.000	2.000	4.309	9.283
3.6	46.656	1.533	3.302	7.114	8.1	531.441	2.008	4.327	9.322
3.7	50.653	1.547	3.332	7.179	8.2	551.368	2.017	4.344	9.360
3.8	54.872	1.560	3.362	7.243	8.3	571.787	2.025	4.362	9.398
3.9	59.319	1.574	3.391	7.306	8.4	592.704	2.033	4.380	9.435
4.0	64.000	1.587	3.420	7.368	8.5	614.125	2.041	4.397	9.473
4.1	68.921	1.601	3.448	7.429	8.6	636.056	2.049	4.414	9.510
4.2	74.088	1.613	3.476	7.489	8.7	658.503	2.057	4.431	9.546
4.3	79.507	1.626	3.503	7.548	8.8	681.472	2.065	4.448	9.583
4.4	85.184	1.639	3.530	7.606	8.9	704.969	2.072	4.465	9.619
4.5	91.125	1.651	3.557	7.663	9.0	729.000	2.080	4.481	9.655
4.6	97.336	1.663	3.583	7.719	9.1	753.571	2.088	4.498	9.691
4.7	103.823	1.675	3.609	7.775	9.2	778.688	2.095	4.514	9.726
4.8	110.592	1.687	3.634	7.830	9.3	804.357	2.103	4.531	9.761
4.9	117.649	1.698	3.659	7.884	9.4	830.584	2.110	4.547	9.796
5.0	125.000	1.710	3.684	7.937	9.5	857.375	2.118	4.563	9.830
5.1	132.651	1.721	3.708	7.990	9.6	884.736	2.125	4.579	9.865
5.2	140.608	1.732	3.733	8.041	9.7	912.673	2.133	4.595	9.899
5.3	148.877	1.744	3.756	8.093	9.8	941.192	2.140	4.610	9.933
5.4	157.464	1.754	3.780	8.143	9.9	970.299	2.147	4.626	9.967
5.5	166.375	1.765	3.803	8.193	10	1000.000	2.154	4.642	10.000

Table 3 Common Logarithms of Numbers

N	0	1	2	3	4	5	6	7	8	9
10	0000	0043	0086	0128	0170	0212	0253	0294	0334	0374
11	0414	0453	0492	0531	0569	0607	0645	0682	0719	0755
12	0792	0828	0864	0899	0934	0969	1004	1038	1072	1106
13	1139	1173	1206	1239	1271	1303	1335	1367	1399	1430
14	1461	1492	1523	1553	1584	1614	1644	1673	1703	1732
15	1761	1790	1818	1847	1875	1903	1931	1959	1987	2014
16	2041	2068	2095	2122	2148	2175	2201	2227	2253	2279
17	2304	2330	2355	2380	2405	2430	2455	2480	2504	2529
18	2553	2577	2601	2625	2648	2672	2695	2718	2742	2765
19	2788	2810	2833	2856	2878	2900	2923	2945	2967	2989
20	3010	3032	3054	3075	3096	3118	3139	3160	3181	3201
21	3222	3243	3263	3284	3304	3324	3345	3365	3385	3404
22	3424	3444	3464	3483	3502	3522	3541	3560	3579	3598
23	3617	3636	3655	3674	3692	3711	3729	3747	3766	3784
24	3802	3820	3838	3856	3874	3892	3909	3927	3945	3962
25	3979	3997	4014	4031	4048	4065	4082	4099	4116	4133
26	4150	4166	4183	4200	4216	4232	4249	4265	4281	4298
27	4314	4330	4346	4362	4378	4393	4409	4425	4440	4456
28	4472	4487	4502	4518	4533	4548	4564	4579	4594	4609
29	4624	4639	4654	4669	4683	4698	4713	4728	4742	4757
30	4771	4786	4800	4814	4829	4843	4857	4871	4886	4900
31	4914	4928	4942	4955	4969	4983	4997	5011	5024	5038
32	5051	5065	5079	5092	5105	5119	5132	5145	5159	5172
33	5185	5198	5211	5224	5237	5250	5263	5276	5289	5302
34	5315	5328	5340	5353	5366	5378	5391	5403	5416	5428
35	5441	5453	5465	5478	5490	5502	5514	5527	5539	5551
36	5563	5575	5587	5599	5611	5623	5635	5647	5658	5670
37	5682	5694	5705	5717	5729	5740	5752	5763	5775	5786
38	5798	5809	5821	5832	5843	5855	5866	5877	5888	5899
39	5911	5922	5933	5944	5955	5966	5977	5988	5999	6010
40	6021	6031	6042	6053	6064	6075	6085	6096	6107	6117
41	6128	6138	6149	6160	6170	6180	6191	6201	6212	6222
42	6232	6243	6253	6263	6274	6284	6294	6304	6314	6325
43	6335	6345	6355	6365	6375	6385	6395	6405	6415	6425
44	6435	6444	6454	6464	6474	6484	6493	6503	6513	6522
45	6532	6542	6551	6561	6571	6580	6590	6599	6609	6618
46	6628	6637	6646	6656	6665	6675	6684	6693	6702	6712
47	6721	6730	6739	6749	6758	6767	6776	6785	6794	6803
48	6812	6821	6830	6839	6848	6857	6866	6875	6884	6893
49	6902	6911	6920	6928	6937	6946	6955	6964	6972	6981
50	6990	6998	7007	7016	7024	7033	7042	7050	7059	7067
51	7076	7084	7093	7101	7110	7118	7126	7135	7143	7152
52	7160	7168	7177	7185	7193	7202	7210	7218	7226	7235
53	7243	7251	7259	7267	7275	7284	7292	7300	7308	7316
54	7324	7332	7340	7348	7356	7364	7372	7380	7388	7396

Table 3 Common Logarithms of Numbers

N	0	1	2	3	4	5	6	7	8	9
55	7404	7412	7419	7427	7435	7443	7451	7459	7466	7474
56	7482	7490	7497	7505	7513	7520	7528	7536	7543	7551
57	7559	7566	7574	7582	7589	7597	7604	7612	7619	7627
58	7634	7642	7649	7657	7664	7672	7679	7686	7694	7701
59	7709	7716	7723	7731	7738	7745	7752	7760	7767	7774
60	7782	7789	7796	7803	7810	7818	7825	7832	7839	7846
61	7853	7860	7868	7875	7882	7889	7896	7903	7910	7917
62	7924	7931	7938	7945	7952	7959	7966	7973	7980	7987
63	7993	8000	8007	8014	8021	8028	8035	8041	8048	8055
64	8062	8069	8075	8082	8089	8096	8102	8109	8116	8122
65	8129	8136	8142	8149	8156	8162	8169	8176	8182	8189
66	8195	8202	8209	8215	8222	8228	8235	8241	8248	8254
67	8261	8267	8274	8280	8287	8293	8299	8306	8312	8319
68	8325	8331	8338	8344	8351	8357	8363	8370	8376	8382
69	8388	8395	8401	8407	8414	8420	8426	8432	8439	8445
70	8451	8457	8463	8470	8476	8482	8488	8494	8500	8506
71	8513	8519	8525	8531	8537	8543	8549	8555	8561	8567
72	8573	8579	8585	8591	8597	8603	8609	8615	8621	8627
73	8633	8639	8645	8651	8657	8663	8669	8675	8681	8686
74	8692	8698	8704	8710	8716	8722	8727	8733	8739	8745
75	8751	8756	8762	8768	8774	8779	8785	8791	8797	8802
76	8808	8814	8820	8825	8831	8837	8842	8848	8854	8859
77	8865	8871	8876	8882	8887	8893	8899	8904	8910	8915
78	8921	8927	8932	8938	8943	8949	8954	8960	8965	8971
79	8976	8982	8987	8993	8998	9004	9009	9015	9020	9025
80	9031	9036	9042	9047	9053	9058	9063	9069	9074	9079
81	9085	9090	9096	9101	9106	9112	9117	9122	9128	9133
82	9138	9143	9149	9154	9159	9165	9170	9175	9180	9186
83	9191	9196	9201	9206	9212	9217	9222	9227	9232	9238
84	9243	9248	9253	9258	9263	9269	9274	9279	9284	9289
85	9294	9299	9304	9309	9315	9320	9325	9330	9335	9340
86	9345	9350	9355	9360	9365	9370	9375	9380	9385	9390
87	9395	9400	9405	9410	9415	9420	9425	9430	9435	9440
88	9445	9450	9455	9460	9465	9469	9474	9479	9484	9489
89	9494	9499	9504	9509	9513	9518	9523	9528	9533	9538
90	9542	9547	9552	9557	9562	9566	9571	9576	9581	9586
91	9590	9595	9600	9605	9609	9614	9619	9624	9628	9633
92	9638	9643	9647	9652	9657	9661	9666	9671	9675	9680
93	9685	9689	9694	9699	9703	9708	9713	9717	9722	9727
94	9731	9736	9741	9745	9750	9754	9759	9763	9768	9773
95	9777	9782	9786	9791	9795	9800	9805	9809	9814	9818
96	9823	9827	9832	9836	9841	9845	9850	9854	9859	9863
97	9868	9872	9877	9881	9886	9890	9894	9899	9903	9908
98	9912	9917	9921	9926	9930	9934	9939	9943	9948	9952
99	9956	9961	9965	9969	9974	9978	9983	9987	9991	9996

Table 4 Trigonometric Functions of θ (θ in decimal degrees)

θ Degrees	θ Radians	$\sin\theta$	$\cos\theta$	$\tan\theta$	$\cot\theta$	$\sec\theta$	$\csc\theta$		
0.0	.0000	.0000	1.0000	.0000	undefined	1.000	undefined	1.5708	**90.0**
0.1	.0017	.0017	1.0000	.0017	573.0	1.000	573.0	1.5691	89.9
0.2	.0035	.0035	1.0000	.0035	286.5	1.000	286.5	1.5673	89.8
0.3	.0052	.0052	1.0000	.0052	191.0	1.000	191.0	1.5656	89.7
0.4	.0070	.0070	1.0000	.0070	143.2	1.000	143.2	1.5638	89.6
0.5	.0087	.0087	1.0000	.0087	114.6	1.000	114.6	1.5621	89.5
0.6	.0105	.0105	.9999	.0105	95.49	1.000	95.49	1.5603	89.4
0.7	.0122	.0122	.9999	.0122	81.85	1.000	81.85	1.5586	89.3
0.8	.0140	.0140	.9999	.0140	71.62	1.000	71.62	1.5568	89.2
0.9	.0157	.0157	.9999	.0157	63.66	1.000	63.66	1.5551	89.1
1.0	.0175	.0175	.9998	.0175	57.29	1.000	57.30	1.5533	**89.0**
1.1	.0192	.0192	.9998	.0192	52.08	1.000	52.09	1.5516	88.9
1.2	.0209	.0209	.9998	.0209	47.74	1.000	47.75	1.5499	88.8
1.3	.0227	.0227	.9997	.0227	44.07	1.000	44.08	1.5481	88.7
1.4	.0244	.0244	.9997	.0244	40.92	1.000	40.93	1.5464	88.6
1.5	.0262	.0262	.9997	.0262	38.19	1.000	38.20	1.5446	88.5
1.6	.0279	.0279	.9996	.0279	35.80	1.000	35.81	1.5429	88.4
1.7	.0297	.0297	.9996	.0297	33.69	1.000	33.71	1.5411	88.3
1.8	.0314	.0314	.9995	.0314	31.82	1.000	31.84	1.5394	88.2
1.9	.0332	.0332	.9995	.0332	30.14	1.001	30.16	1.5376	88.1
2.0	.0349	.0349	.9994	.0349	28.64	1.001	28.65	1.5359	**88.0**
2.1	.0367	.0366	.9993	.0367	27.27	1.001	27.29	1.5341	87.9
2.2	.0384	.0384	.9993	.0384	26.03	1.001	26.05	1.5324	87.8
2.3	.0401	.0401	.9992	.0402	24.90	1.001	24.92	1.5307	87.7
2.4	.0419	.0419	.9991	.0419	23.86	1.001	23.88	1.5289	87.6
2.5	.0436	.0436	.9990	.0437	22.90	1.001	22.93	1.5272	87.5
2.6	.0454	.0454	.9990	.0454	22.02	1.001	22.04	1.5254	87.4
2.7	.0471	.0471	.9989	.0472	21.20	1.001	21.23	1.5237	87.3
2.8	.0489	.0488	.9988	.0489	20.45	1.001	20.47	1.5219	87.2
2.9	.0506	.0506	.9987	.0507	19.74	1.001	19.77	1.5202	87.1
3.0	.0524	.0523	.9986	.0524	19.08	1.001	19.11	1.5184	**87.0**
3.1	.0541	.0541	.9985	.0542	18.46	1.001	18.49	1.5167	86.9
3.2	.0559	.0558	.9984	.0559	17.89	1.002	17.91	1.5149	86.8
3.3	.0576	.0576	.9983	.0577	17.34	1.002	17.37	1.5132	86.7
3.4	.0593	.0593	.9982	.0594	16.83	1.002	16.86	1.5115	86.6
3.5	.0611	.0610	.9981	.0612	16.35	1.002	16.38	1.5097	86.5
3.6	.0628	.0628	.9980	.0629	15.89	1.002	15.93	1.5080	86.4
3.7	.0646	.0645	.9979	.0647	15.46	1.002	15.50	1.5062	86.3
3.8	.0663	.0663	.9978	.0664	15.06	1.002	15.09	1.5045	86.2
3.9	.0681	.0680	.9977	.0682	14.67	1.002	14.70	1.5027	86.1
4.0	.0698	.0698	.9976	.0699	14.30	1.002	14.34	1.5010	**86.0**
4.1	.0716	.0715	.9974	.0717	13.95	1.003	13.99	1.4992	85.9
4.2	.0733	.0732	.9973	.0734	13.62	1.003	13.65	1.4975	85.8
4.3	.0750	.0750	.9972	.0752	13.30	1.003	13.34	1.4957	85.7
4.4	.0768	.0767	.9971	.0769	13.00	1.003	13.03	1.4940	85.6
4.5	.0785	.0785	.9969	.0787	12.71	1.003	12.75	1.4923	85.5
4.6	.0803	.0802	.9968	.0805	12.43	1.003	12.47	1.4905	85.4
4.7	.0820	.0819	.9966	.0822	12.16	1.003	12.20	1.4888	85.3
4.8	.0838	.0837	.9965	.0840	11.91	1.004	11.95	1.4870	85.2
4.9	.0855	.0854	.9963	.0857	11.66	1.004	11.71	1.4853	85.1
5.0	.0873	.0872	.9962	.0875	11.43	1.004	11.47	1.4835	**85.0**
5.1	.0890	.0889	.9960	.0892	11.20	1.004	11.25	1.4818	84.9
5.2	.0908	.0906	.9959	.0910	10.99	1.004	11.03	1.4800	84.8
5.3	.0925	.0924	.9957	.0928	10.78	1.004	10.83	1.4783	84.7
5.4	.0942	.0941	.9956	.0945	10.58	1.004	10.63	1.4765	84.6
5.5	.0960	.0958	.9954	.0963	10.39	1.005	10.43	1.4748	84.5
5.6	.0977	.0976	.9952	.0981	10.20	1.005	10.25	1.4731	84.4
5.7	.0995	.0993	.9951	.0998	10.02	1.005	10.07	1.4713	84.3
5.8	.1012	.1011	.9949	.1016	9.845	1.005	9.895	1.4696	84.2
5.9	.1030	.1028	.9947	.1033	9.677	1.005	9.728	1.4678	84.1
6.0	.1047	.1045	.9945	.1051	9.514	1.006	9.567	1.4661	**84.0**
		$\cos\theta$	$\sin\theta$	$\cot\theta$	$\tan\theta$	$\csc\theta$	$\sec\theta$	θ Radians	θ Degrees

Table 4 Trigonometric Functions of θ (θ in decimal degrees)

θ Degrees	θ Radians	$\sin \theta$	$\cos \theta$	$\tan \theta$	$\cot \theta$	$\sec \theta$	$\csc \theta$		
6.0	.1047	.1045	.9945	.1051	9.514	1.006	9.567	1.4661	**84.0**
6.1	.1065	.1063	.9943	.1069	9.357	1.006	9.411	1.4643	83.9
6.2	.1082	.1080	.9942	.1086	9.205	1.006	9.259	1.4626	83.8
6.3	.1100	.1097	.9940	.1104	9.058	1.006	9.113	1.4608	83.7
6.4	.1117	.1115	.9938	.1122	8.915	1.006	8.971	1.4591	83.6
6.5	.1134	.1132	.9936	.1139	8.777	1.006	8.834	1.4574	83.5
6.6	.1152	.1149	.9934	.1157	8.643	1.007	8.700	1.4556	83.4
6.7	.1169	.1167	.9932	.1175	8.513	1.007	8.571	1.4539	83.3
6.8	.1187	.1184	.9930	.1192	8.386	1.007	8.446	1.4521	83.2
6.9	.1204	.1201	.9928	.1210	8.264	1.007	8.324	1.4504	83.1
7.0	.1222	.1219	.9925	.1228	8.144	1.008	8.206	1.4486	**83.0**
7.1	.1239	.1236	.9923	.1246	8.028	1.008	8.091	1.4469	82.9
7.2	.1257	.1253	.9921	.1263	7.916	1.008	7.979	1.4451	82.8
7.3	.1274	.1271	.9919	.1281	7.806	1.008	7.870	1.4434	82.7
7.4	.1292	.1288	.9917	.1299	7.700	1.008	7.764	1.4416	82.6
7.5	.1309	.1305	.9914	.1317	7.596	1.009	7.661	1.4399	82.5
7.6	.1326	.1323	.9912	.1334	7.495	1.009	7.561	1.4382	82.4
7.7	.1344	.1340	.9910	.1352	7.396	1.009	7.463	1.4364	82.3
7.8	.1361	.1357	.9907	.1370	7.300	1.009	7.368	1.4347	82.2
7.9	.1379	.1374	.9905	.1388	7.207	1.010	7.276	1.4329	82.1
8.0	.1396	.1392	.9903	.1405	7.115	1.010	7.185	1.4312	**82.0**
8.1	.1414	.1409	.9900	.1423	7.026	1.010	7.097	1.4294	81.9
8.2	.1431	.1426	.9898	.1441	6.940	1.010	7.011	1.4277	81.8
8.3	.1449	.1444	.9895	.1459	6.855	1.011	6.927	1.4259	81.7
8.4	.1466	.1461	.9893	.1477	6.772	1.011	6.845	1.4242	81.6
8.5	.1484	.1478	.9890	.1495	6.691	1.011	6.765	1.4224	81.5
8.6	.1501	.1495	.9888	.1512	6.612	1.011	6.687	1.4207	81.4
8.7	.1518	.1513	.9885	.1530	6.535	1.012	6.611	1.4190	81.3
8.8	.1536	.1530	.9882	.1548	6.460	1.012	6.537	1.4172	81.2
8.9	.1553	.1547	.9880	.1566	6.386	1.012	6.464	1.4155	81.1
9.0	.1571	.1564	.9877	.1584	6.314	1.012	6.392	1.4137	**81.0**
9.1	.1588	.1582	.9874	.1602	6.243	1.013	6.323	1.4120	80.9
9.2	.1606	.1599	.9871	.1620	6.174	1.013	6.255	1.4102	80.8
9.3	.1623	.1616	.9869	.1638	6.107	1.013	6.188	1.4085	80.7
9.4	.1641	.1633	.9866	.1655	6.041	1.014	6.123	1.4067	80.6
9.5	.1658	.1650	.9863	.1673	5.976	1.014	6.059	1.4050	80.5
9.6	.1676	.1668	.9860	.1691	5.912	1.014	5.996	1.4032	80.4
9.7	.1693	.1685	.9857	.1709	5.850	1.015	5.935	1.4015	80.3
9.8	.1710	.1702	.9854	.1727	5.789	1.015	5.875	1.3998	80.2
9.9	.1728	.1719	.9851	.1745	5.730	1.015	5.816	1.3980	80.1
10.0	.1745	.1736	.9848	.1763	5.671	1.015	5.759	1.3963	**80.0**
10.1	.1763	.1754	.9845	.1781	5.614	1.016	5.702	1.3945	79.9
10.2	.1780	.1771	.9842	.1799	5.558	1.016	5.647	1.3928	79.8
10.3	.1798	.1788	.9839	.1817	5.503	1.016	5.593	1.3910	79.7
10.4	.1815	.1805	.9836	.1835	5.449	1.017	5.540	1.3893	79.6
10.5	.1833	.1822	.9833	.1853	5.396	1.017	5.487	1.3875	79.5
10.6	.1850	.1840	.9829	.1871	5.343	1.017	5.436	1.3858	79.4
10.7	.1868	.1857	.9826	.1890	5.292	1.018	5.386	1.3840	79.3
10.8	.1885	.1874	.9823	.1908	5.242	1.018	5.337	1.3823	79.2
10.9	.1902	.1891	.9820	.1926	5.193	1.018	5.288	1.3806	79.1
11.0	.1920	.1908	.9816	.1944	5.145	1.019	5.241	1.3788	**79.0**
11.1	.1937	.1925	.9813	.1962	5.097	1.019	5.194	1.3771	78.9
11.2	.1955	.1942	.9810	.1980	5.050	1.019	5.148	1.3753	78.8
11.3	.1972	.1959	.9806	.1998	5.005	1.020	5.103	1.3736	78.7
11.4	.1990	.1977	.9803	.2016	4.959	1.020	5.059	1.3718	78.6
11.5	.2007	.1994	.9799	.2035	4.915	1.020	5.016	1.3701	78.5
11.6	.2025	.2011	.9796	.2053	4.872	1.021	4.973	1.3683	78.4
11.7	.2042	.2028	.9792	.2071	4.829	1.021	4.931	1.3666	78.3
11.8	.2059	.2045	.9789	.2089	4.787	1.022	4.890	1.3648	78.2
11.9	.2077	.2062	.9785	.2107	4.745	1.022	4.850	1.3631	78.1
12.0	.2094	.2079	.9781	.2126	4.705	1.022	4.810	1.3614	**78.0**
		$\cos \theta$	$\sin \theta$	$\cot \theta$	$\tan \theta$	$\csc \theta$	$\sec \theta$	θ Radians	θ Degrees

Table 4 Trigonometric Functions of θ (θ in decimal degrees)

θ Degrees	θ Radians	$\sin \theta$	$\cos \theta$	$\tan \theta$	$\cot \theta$	$\sec \theta$	$\csc \theta$		
12.0	.2094	.2079	.9781	.2126	4.705	1.022	4.810	1.3614	**78.0**
12.1	.2112	.2096	.9778	.2144	4.665	1.023	4.771	1.3596	77.9
12.2	.2129	.2113	.9774	.2162	4.625	1.023	4.732	1.3579	77.8
12.3	.2147	.2130	.9770	.2180	4.586	1.023	4.694	1.3561	77.7
12.4	.2164	.2147	.9767	.2199	4.548	1.024	4.657	1.3544	77.6
12.5	.2182	.2164	.9763	.2217	4.511	1.024	4.620	1.3526	77.5
12.6	.2199	.2181	.9759	.2235	4.474	1.025	4.584	1.3509	77.4
12.7	.2217	.2198	.9755	.2254	4.437	1.025	4.549	1.3491	77.3
12.8	.2234	.2215	.9751	.2272	4.402	1.025	4.514	1.3474	77.2
12.9	.2251	.2233	.9748	.2290	4.366	1.026	4.479	1.3456	77.1
13.0	.2269	.2250	.9744	.2309	4.331	1.026	4.445	1.3439	**77.0**
13.1	.2286	.2267	.9740	.2327	4.297	1.027	4.412	1.3422	76.9
13.2	.2304	.2284	.9736	.2345	4.264	1.027	4.379	1.3404	76.8
13.3	.2321	.2300	.9732	.2364	4.230	1.028	4.347	1.3387	76.7
13.4	.2339	.2317	.9728	.2382	4.198	1.028	4.315	1.3369	76.6
13.5	.2356	.2334	.9724	.2401	4.165	1.028	4.284	1.3352	76.5
13.6	.2374	.2351	.9720	.2419	4.134	1.029	4.253	1.3334	76.4
13.7	.2391	.2368	.9715	.2438	4.102	1.029	4.222	1.3317	76.3
13.8	.2409	.2385	.9711	.2456	4.071	1.030	4.192	1.3299	76.2
13.9	.2426	.2402	.9707	.2475	4.041	1.030	4.163	1.3282	76.1
14.0	.2443	.2419	.9703	.2493	4.011	1.031	4.134	1.3265	**76.0**
14.1	.2461	.2436	.9699	.2512	3.981	1.031	4.105	1.3247	75.9
14.2	.2478	.2453	.9694	.2530	3.952	1.032	4.077	1.3230	75.8
14.3	.2496	.2470	.9690	.2549	3.923	1.032	4.049	1.3212	75.7
14.4	.2513	.2487	.9686	.2568	3.895	1.032	4.021	1.3195	75.6
14.5	.2531	.2504	.9681	.2586	3.867	1.033	3.994	1.3177	75.5
14.6	.2548	.2521	.9677	.2605	3.839	1.033	3.967	1.3160	75.4
14.7	.2566	.2538	.9673	.2623	3.812	1.034	3.941	1.3142	75.3
14.8	.2583	.2554	.9668	.2642	3.785	1.034	3.915	1.3125	75.2
14.9	.2601	.2571	.9664	.2661	3.758	1.035	3.889	1.3107	75.1
15.0	.2618	.2588	.9659	.2679	3.732	1.035	3.864	1.3090	**75.0**
15.1	.2635	.2605	.9655	.2698	3.706	1.036	3.839	1.3073	74.9
15.2	.2653	.2622	.9650	.2717	3.681	1.036	3.814	1.3055	74.8
15.3	.2670	.2639	.9646	.2736	3.655	1.037	3.790	1.3038	74.7
15.4	.2688	.2656	.9641	.2754	3.630	1.037	3.766	1.3020	74.6
15.5	.2705	.2672	.9636	.2773	3.606	1.038	3.742	1.3003	74.5
15.6	.2723	.2689	.9632	.2792	3.582	1.038	3.719	1.2985	74.4
15.7	.2740	.2706	.9627	.2811	3.558	1.039	3.695	1.2968	74.3
15.8	.2758	.2723	.9622	.2830	3.534	1.039	3.673	1.2950	74.2
15.9	.2775	.2740	.9617	.2849	3.511	1.040	3.650	1.2933	74.1
16.0	.2793	.2756	.9613	.2867	3.487	1.040	3.628	1.2915	**74.0**
16.1	.2810	.2773	.9608	.2886	3.465	1.041	3.606	1.2898	73.9
16.2	.2827	.2790	.9603	.2905	3.442	1.041	3.584	1.2881	73.8
16.3	.2845	.2807	.9598	.2924	3.420	1.042	3.563	1.2863	73.7
16.4	.2862	.2823	.9593	.2943	3.398	1.042	3.542	1.2846	73.6
16.5	.2880	.2840	.9588	.2962	3.376	1.043	3.521	1.2828	73.5
16.6	.2897	.2857	.9583	.2981	3.354	1.043	3.500	1.2811	73.4
16.7	.2915	.2874	.9578	.3000	3.333	1.044	3.480	1.2793	73.3
16.8	.2932	.2890	.9573	.3019	3.312	1.045	3.460	1.2776	73.2
16.9	.2950	.2907	.9568	.3038	3.291	1.045	3.440	1.2758	73.1
17.0	.2967	.2924	.9563	.3057	3.271	1.046	3.420	1.2741	**73.0**
17.1	.2985	.2940	.9558	.3076	3.251	1.046	3.401	1.2723	72.9
17.2	.3002	.2957	.9553	.3096	3.230	1.047	3.382	1.2706	72.8
17.3	.3019	.2974	.9548	.3115	3.211	1.047	3.363	1.2689	72.7
17.4	.3037	.2990	.9542	.3134	3.191	1.048	3.344	1.2671	72.6
17.5	.3054	.3007	.9537	.3153	3.172	1.049	3.326	1.2654	72.5
17.6	.3072	.3024	.9532	.3172	3.152	1.049	3.307	1.2636	72.4
17.7	.3089	.3040	.9527	.3191	3.133	1.050	3.289	1.2619	72.3
17.8	.3107	.3057	.9521	.3211	3.115	1.050	3.271	1.2601	72.2
17.9	.3124	.3074	.9516	.3230	3.096	1.051	3.254	1.2584	72.1
18.0	.3142	.3090	.9511	.3249	3.078	1.051	3.236	1.2566	**72.0**
		$\cos \theta$	$\sin \theta$	$\cot \theta$	$\tan \theta$	$\csc \theta$	$\sec \theta$	θ Radians	θ Degrees

Table 4 Trigonometric Functions of θ (θ in decimal degrees)

θ Degrees	θ Radians	$\sin \theta$	$\cos \theta$	$\tan \theta$	$\cot \theta$	$\sec \theta$	$\csc \theta$		
18.0	.3142	.3090	.9511	.3249	3.078	1.051	3.236	1.2566	**72.0**
18.1	.3159	.3107	.9505	.3269	3.060	1.052	3.219	1.2549	71.9
18.2	.3177	.3123	.9500	.3288	3.042	1.053	3.202	1.2531	71.8
18.3	.3194	.3140	.9494	.3307	3.024	1.053	3.185	1.2514	71.7
18.4	.3211	.3156	.9489	.3327	3.006	1.054	3.168	1.2497	71.6
18.5	.3229	.3173	.9483	.3346	2.989	1.054	3.152	1.2479	71.5
18.6	.3246	.3190	.9478	.3365	2.971	1.055	3.135	1.2462	71.4
18.7	.3264	.3206	.9472	.3385	2.954	1.056	3.119	1.2444	71.3
18.8	.3281	.3223	.9466	.3404	2.937	1.056	3.103	1.2427	71.2
18.9	.3299	.3239	.9461	.3424	2.921	1.057	3.087	1.2409	71.1
19.0	.3316	.3256	.9455	.3443	2.904	1.058	3.072	1.2392	**71.0**
19.1	.3334	.3272	.9449	.3463	2.888	1.058	3.056	1.2374	70.9
19.2	.3351	.3289	.9444	.3482	2.872	1.059	3.041	1.2357	70.8
19.3	.3368	.3305	.9438	.3502	2.856	1.060	3.026	1.2339	70.7
19.4	.3386	.3322	.9432	.3522	2.840	1.060	3.011	1.2322	70.6
19.5	.3403	.3338	.9426	.3541	2.824	1.061	2.996	1.2305	70.5
19.6	.3421	.3355	.9421	.3561	2.808	1.062	2.981	1.2287	70.4
19.7	.3438	.3371	.9415	.3581	2.793	1.062	2.967	1.2270	70.3
19.8	.3456	.3387	.9409	.3600	2.778	1.063	2.952	1.2252	70.2
19.9	.3473	.3404	.9403	.3620	2.762	1.064	2.938	1.2235	70.1
20.0	.3491	.3420	.9397	.3640	2.747	1.064	2.924	1.2217	**70.0**
20.1	.3508	.3437	.9391	.3659	2.733	1.065	2.910	1.2200	69.9
20.2	.3526	.3453	.9385	.3679	2.718	1.066	2.896	1.2182	69.8
20.3	.3543	.3469	.9379	.3699	2.703	1.066	2.882	1.2165	69.7
20.4	.3560	.3486	.9373	.3719	2.689	1.067	2.869	1.2147	69.6
20.5	.3578	.3502	.9367	.3739	2.675	1.068	2.855	1.2130	69.5
20.6	.3595	.3518	.9361	.3759	2.660	1.068	2.842	1.2113	69.4
20.7	.3613	.3535	.9354	.3779	2.646	1.069	2.829	1.2095	69.3
20.8	.3630	.3551	.9348	.3799	2.633	1.070	2.816	1.2078	69.2
20.9	.3648	.3567	.9342	.3819	2.619	1.070	2.803	1.2060	69.1
21.0	.3665	.3584	.9336	.3839	2.605	1.071	2.790	1.2043	**69.0**
21.1	.3683	.3600	.9330	.3859	2.592	1.072	2.778	1.2025	68.9
21.2	.3700	.3616	.9323	.3879	2.578	1.073	2.765	1.2008	68.8
21.3	.3718	.3633	.9317	.3899	2.565	1.073	2.753	1.1991	68.7
21.4	.3735	.3649	.9311	.3919	2.552	1.074	2.741	1.1973	68.6
21.5	.3752	.3665	.9304	.3939	2.539	1.075	2.729	1.1956	68.5
21.6	.3770	.3681	.9298	.3959	2.526	1.076	2.716	1.1938	68.4
21.7	.3787	.3697	.9291	.3979	2.513	1.076	2.705	1.1921	68.3
21.8	.3805	.3714	.9285	.4000	2.500	1.077	2.693	1.1903	68.2
21.9	.3822	.3730	.9278	.4020	2.488	1.078	2.681	1.1886	68.1
22.0	.3840	.3746	.9272	.4040	2.475	1.079	2.669	1.1868	**68.0**
22.1	.3857	.3762	.9265	.4061	2.463	1.079	2.658	1.1851	67.9
22.2	.3875	.3778	.9259	.4081	2.450	1.080	2.647	1.1833	67.8
22.3	.3892	.3795	.9252	.4101	2.438	1.081	2.635	1.1816	67.7
22.4	.3910	.3811	.9245	.4122	2.426	1.082	2.624	1.1798	67.6
22.5	.3927	.3827	.9239	.4142	2.414	1.082	2.613	1.1781	67.5
22.6	.3944	.3843	.9232	.4163	2.402	1.083	2.602	1.1764	67.4
22.7	.3962	.3859	.9225	.4183	2.391	1.084	2.591	1.1746	67.3
22.8	.3979	.3875	.9219	.4204	2.379	1.085	2.581	1.1729	67.2
22.9	.3997	.3891	.9212	.4224	2.367	1.086	2.570	1.1711	67.1
23.0	.4014	.3907	.9205	.4245	2.356	1.086	2.559	1.1694	**67.0**
23.1	.4032	.3923	.9198	.4265	2.344	1.087	2.549	1.1676	66.9
23.2	.4049	.3939	.9191	.4286	2.333	1.088	2.538	1.1659	66.8
23.3	.4067	.3955	.9184	.4307	2.322	1.089	2.528	1.1641	66.7
23.4	.4084	.3971	.9178	.4327	2.311	1.090	2.518	1.1624	66.6
23.5	.4102	.3987	.9171	.4348	2.300	1.090	2.508	1.1606	66.5
23.6	.4119	.4003	.9164	.4369	2.289	1.091	2.498	1.1589	66.4
23.7	.4136	.4019	.9157	.4390	2.278	1.092	2.488	1.1572	66.3
23.8	.4154	.4035	.9150	.4411	2.267	1.093	2.478	1.1554	66.2
23.9	.4171	.4051	.9143	.4431	2.257	1.094	2.468	1.1537	66.1
24.0	.4189	.4067	.9135	.4452	2.246	1.095	2.459	1.1519	**66.0**
		$\cos \theta$	$\sin \theta$	$\cot \theta$	$\tan \theta$	$\csc \theta$	$\sec \theta$	θ Radians	θ Degrees

Table 4 Trigonometric Functions of θ (θ in decimal degrees)

θ Degrees	θ Radians	$\sin \theta$	$\cos \theta$	$\tan \theta$	$\cot \theta$	$\sec \theta$	$\csc \theta$		
24.0	.4189	.4067	.9135	.4452	2.246	1.095	2.459	1.1519	**66.0**
24.1	.4206	.4083	.9128	.4473	2.236	1.095	2.449	1.1502	65.9
24.2	.4224	.4099	.9121	.4494	2.225	1.096	2.439	1.1484	65.8
24.3	.4241	.4115	.9114	.4515	2.215	1.097	2.430	1.1467	65.7
24.4	.4259	.4131	.9107	.4536	2.204	1.098	2.421	1.1449	65.6
24.5	.4276	.4147	.9100	.4557	2.194	1.099	2.411	1.1432	65.5
24.6	.4294	.4163	.9092	.4578	2.184	1.100	2.402	1.1414	65.4
24.7	.4311	.4179	.9085	.4599	2.174	1.101	2.393	1.1397	65.3
24.8	.4328	.4195	.9078	.4621	2.164	1.102	2.384	1.1380	65.2
24.9	.4346	.4210	.9070	.4642	2.154	1.102	2.375	1.1362	65.1
25.0	.4363	.4226	.9063	.4663	2.145	1.103	2.366	1.1345	**65.0**
25.1	.4381	.4242	.9056	.4684	2.135	1.104	2.357	1.1327	64.9
25.2	.4398	.4258	.9048	.4706	2.125	1.105	2.349	1.1310	64.8
25.3	.4416	.4274	.9041	.4727	2.116	1.106	2.340	1.1292	64.7
25.4	.4433	.4289	.9033	.4748	2.106	1.107	2.331	1.1275	64.6
25.5	.4451	.4305	.9026	.4770	2.097	1.108	2.323	1.1257	64.5
25.6	.4468	.4321	.9018	.4791	2.087	1.109	2.314	1.1240	64.4
25.7	.4485	.4337	.9011	.4813	2.078	1.110	2.306	1.1222	64.3
25.8	.4503	.4352	.9003	.4834	2.069	1.111	2.298	1.1205	64.2
25.9	.4520	.4368	.8996	.4856	2.059	1.112	2.289	1.1188	64.1
26.0	.4538	.4384	.8988	.4877	2.050	1.113	2.281	1.1170	**64.0**
26.1	.4555	.4399	.8980	.4899	2.041	1.114	2.273	1.1153	63.9
26.2	.4573	.4415	.8973	.4921	2.032	1.115	2.265	1.1135	63.8
26.3	.4590	.4431	.8965	.4942	2.023	1.115	2.257	1.1118	63.7
26.4	.4608	.4446	.8957	.4964	2.014	1.116	2.249	1.1100	63.6
26.5	.4625	.4462	.8949	.4986	2.006	1.117	2.241	1.1083	63.5
26.6	.4643	.4478	.8942	.5008	1.997	1.118	2.233	1.1065	63.4
26.7	.4660	.4493	.8934	.5029	1.988	1.119	2.226	1.1048	63.3
26.8	.4677	.4509	.8926	.5051	1.980	1.120	2.218	1.1030	63.2
26.9	.4695	.4524	.8918	.5073	1.971	1.121	2.210	1.1013	63.1
27.0	.4712	.4540	.8910	.5095	1.963	1.122	2.203	1.0996	**63.0**
27.1	.4730	.4555	.8902	.5117	1.954	1.123	2.195	1.0978	62.9
27.2	.4747	.4571	.8894	.5139	1.946	1.124	2.188	1.0961	62.8
27.3	.4765	.4586	.8886	.5161	1.937	1.125	2.180	1.0943	62.7
27.4	.4782	.4602	.8878	.5184	1.929	1.126	2.173	1.0926	62.6
27.5	.4800	.4617	.8870	.5206	1.921	1.127	2.166	1.0908	62.5
27.6	.4817	.4633	.8862	.5228	1.913	1.128	2.158	1.0891	62.4
27.7	.4835	.4648	.8854	.5250	1.905	1.129	2.151	1.0873	62.3
27.8	.4852	.4664	.8846	.5272	1.897	1.130	2.144	1.0856	62.2
27.9	.4869	.4679	.8838	.5295	1.889	1.132	2.137	1.0838	62.1
28.0	.4887	.4695	.8829	.5317	1.881	1.133	2.130	1.0821	**62.0**
28.1	.4904	.4710	.8821	.5340	1.873	1.134	2.123	1.0804	61.9
28.2	.4922	.4726	.8813	.5362	1.865	1.135	2.116	1.0786	61.8
28.3	.4939	.4741	.8805	.5384	1.857	1.136	2.109	1.0769	61.7
28.4	.4957	.4756	.8796	.5407	1.849	1.137	2.103	1.0751	61.6
28.5	.4974	.4772	.8788	.5430	1.842	1.138	2.096	1.0734	61.5
28.6	.4992	.4787	.8780	.5452	1.834	1.139	2.089	1.0716	61.4
28.7	.5009	.4802	.8771	.5475	1.827	1.140	2.082	1.0699	61.3
28.8	.5027	.4818	.8763	.5498	1.819	1.141	2.076	1.0681	61.2
28.9	.5044	.4833	.8755	.5520	1.811	1.142	2.069	1.0664	61.1
29.0	.5061	.4848	.8746	.5543	1.804	1.143	2.063	1.0647	**61.0**
29.1	.5079	.4863	.8738	.5566	1.797	1.144	2.056	1.0629	60.9
29.2	.5096	.4879	.8729	.5589	1.789	1.146	2.050	1.0612	60.8
29.3	.5114	.4894	.8721	.5612	1.782	1.147	2.043	1.0594	60.7
29.4	.5131	.4909	.8712	.5635	1.775	1.148	2.037	1.0577	60.6
29.5	.5149	.4924	.8704	.5658	1.767	1.149	2.031	1.0559	60.5
29.6	.5166	.4939	.8695	.5681	1.760	1.150	2.025	1.0542	60.4
29.7	.5184	.4955	.8686	.5704	1.753	1.151	2.018	1.0524	60.3
29.8	.5201	.4970	.8678	.5727	1.746	1.152	2.012	1.0507	60.2
29.9	.5219	.4985	.8669	.5750	1.739	1.154	2.006	1.0489	60.1
30.0	.5236	.5000	.8660	.5774	1.732	1.155	2.000	1.0472	**60.0**
		$\cos \theta$	$\sin \theta$	$\cot \theta$	$\tan \theta$	$\csc \theta$	$\sec \theta$	θ Radians	θ Degrees

Table 4 Trigonometric Functions of θ (θ in decimal degrees)

θ Degrees	θ Radians	$\sin \theta$	$\cos \theta$	$\tan \theta$	$\cot \theta$	$\sec \theta$	$\csc \theta$		
30.0	.5236	.5000	.8660	.5774	1.732	1.155	2.000	1.0472	**60.0**
30.1	.5253	.5015	.8652	.5797	1.725	1.156	1.994	1.0455	59.9
30.2	.5271	.5030	.8643	.5820	1.718	1.157	1.988	1.0437	59.8
30.3	.5288	.5045	.8634	.5844	1.711	1.158	1.982	1.0420	59.7
30.4	.5306	.5060	.8625	.5867	1.704	1.159	1.976	1.0402	59.6
30.5	.5323	.5075	.8616	.5890	1.698	1.161	1.970	1.0385	59.5
30.6	.5341	.5090	.8607	.5914	1.691	1.162	1.964	1.0367	59.4
30.7	.5358	.5105	.8599	.5938	1.684	1.163	1.959	1.0350	59.3
30.8	.5376	.5120	.8590	.5961	1.678	1.164	1.953	1.0332	59.2
30.9	.5393	.5135	.8581	.5985	1.671	1.165	1.947	1.0315	59.1
31.0	.5411	.5150	.8572	.6009	1.664	1.167	1.942	1.0297	**59.0**
31.1	.5428	.5165	.8563	.6032	1.658	1.168	1.936	1.0280	58.9
31.2	.5445	.5180	.8554	.6056	1.651	1.169	1.930	1.0263	58.8
31.3	.5463	.5195	.8545	.6080	1.645	1.170	1.925	1.0245	58.7
31.4	.5480	.5210	.8535	.6104	1.638	1.172	1.919	1.0228	58.6
31.5	.5498	.5225	.8526	.6128	1.632	1.173	1.914	1.0210	58.5
31.6	.5515	.5240	.8517	.6152	1.625	1.174	1.908	1.0193	58.4
31.7	.5533	.5255	.8508	.6176	1.619	1.175	1.903	1.0175	58.3
31.8	.5550	.5270	.8499	.6200	1.613	1.177	1.898	1.0158	58.2
31.9	.5568	.5284	.8490	.6224	1.607	1.178	1.892	1.0140	58.1
32.0	.5585	.5299	.8480	.6249	1.600	1.179	1.887	1.0123	**58.0**
32.1	.5603	.5314	.8471	.6273	1.594	1.180	1.882	1.0105	57.9
32.2	.5620	.5329	.8462	.6297	1.588	1.182	1.877	1.0088	57.8
32.3	.5637	.5344	.8453	.6322	1.582	1.183	1.871	1.0071	57.7
32.4	.5655	.5358	.8443	.6346	1.576	1.184	1.866	1.0053	57.6
32.5	.5672	.5373	.8434	.6371	1.570	1.186	1.861	1.0036	57.5
32.6	.5690	.5388	.8425	.6395	1.564	1.187	1.856	1.0018	57.4
32.7	.5707	.5402	.8415	.6420	1.558	1.188	1.851	1.0001	57.3
32.8	.5725	.5417	.8406	.6445	1.552	1.190	1.846	.9983	57.2
32.9	.5742	.5432	.8396	.6469	1.546	1.191	1.841	.9966	57.1
33.0	.5760	.5446	.8387	.6494	1.540	1.192	1.836	.9948	**57.0**
33.1	.5777	.5461	.8377	.6519	1.534	1.194	1.831	.9931	56.9
33.2	.5794	.5476	.8368	.6544	1.528	1.195	1.826	.9913	56.8
33.3	.5812	.5490	.8358	.6569	1.522	1.196	1.821	.9896	56.7
33.4	.5829	.5505	.8348	.6594	1.517	1.198	1.817	.9879	56.6
33.5	.5847	.5519	.8339	.6619	1.511	1.199	1.812	.9861	56.5
33.6	.5864	.5534	.8329	.6644	1.505	1.201	1.807	.9844	56.4
33.7	.5882	.5548	.8320	.6669	1.499	1.202	1.802	.9826	56.3
33.8	.5899	.5563	.8310	.6694	1.494	1.203	1.798	.9809	56.2
33.9	.5917	.5577	.8300	.6720	1.488	1.205	1.793	.9791	56.1
34.0	.5934	.5592	.8290	.6745	1.483	1.206	1.788	.9774	**56.0**
34.1	.5952	.5606	.8281	.6771	1.477	1.208	1.784	.9756	55.9
34.2	.5969	.5621	.8271	.6796	1.471	1.209	1.779	.9739	55.8
34.3	.5986	.5635	.8261	.6822	1.466	1.211	1.775	.9721	55.7
34.4	.6004	.5650	.8251	.6847	1.460	1.212	1.770	.9704	55.6
34.5	.6021	.5664	.8241	.6873	1.455	1.213	1.766	.9687	55.5
34.6	.6039	.5678	.8231	.6899	1.450	1.215	1.761	.9669	55.4
34.7	.6056	.5693	.8221	.6924	1.444	1.216	1.757	.9652	55.3
34.8	.6074	.5707	.8211	.6950	1.439	1.218	1.752	.9634	55.2
34.9	.6091	.5721	.8202	.6976	1.433	1.219	1.748	.9617	55.1
35.0	.6109	.5736	.8192	.7002	1.428	1.221	1.743	.9599	**55.0**
35.1	.6126	.5750	.8181	.7028	1.423	1.222	1.739	.9582	54.9
35.2	.6144	.5764	.8171	.7054	1.418	1.224	1.735	.9564	54.8
35.3	.6161	.5779	.8161	.7080	1.412	1.225	1.731	.9547	54.7
35.4	.6178	.5793	.8151	.7107	1.407	1.227	1.726	.9529	54.6
35.5	.6196	.5807	.8141	.7133	1.402	1.228	1.722	.9512	54.5
35.6	.6213	.5821	.8131	.7159	1.397	1.230	1.718	.9495	54.4
35.7	.6231	.5835	.8121	.7186	1.392	1.231	1.714	.9477	54.3
35.8	.6248	.5850	.8111	.7212	1.387	1.233	1.710	.9460	54.2
35.9	.6266	.5864	.8100	.7239	1.381	1.235	1.705	.9442	54.1
36.0	.6283	.5878	.8090	.7265	1.376	1.236	1.701	.9425	**54.0**
		$\cos \theta$	$\sin \theta$	$\cot \theta$	$\tan \theta$	$\csc \theta$	$\sec \theta$	θ Radians	θ Degrees

Table 4 Trigonometric Functions of θ (θ in decimal degrees)

θ Degrees	θ Radians	$\sin\theta$	$\cos\theta$	$\tan\theta$	$\cot\theta$	$\sec\theta$	$\csc\theta$		
36.0	.6283	.5878	.8090	.7265	1.376	1.236	1.701	.9425	**54.0**
36.1	.6301	.5892	.8080	.7292	1.371	1.238	1.697	.9407	53.9
36.2	.6318	.5906	.8070	.7319	1.366	1.239	1.693	.9390	53.8
36.3	.6336	.5920	.8059	.7346	1.361	1.241	1.689	.9372	53.7
36.4	.6353	.5934	.8049	.7373	1.356	1.242	1.685	.9355	53.6
36.5	.6370	.5948	.8039	.7400	1.351	1.244	1.681	.9338	53.5
36.6	.6388	.5962	.8028	.7427	1.347	1.246	1.677	.9320	53.4
36.7	.6405	.5976	.8018	.7454	1.342	1.247	1.673	.9303	53.3
36.8	.6423	.5990	.8007	.7481	1.337	1.249	1.669	.9285	53.2
36.9	.6440	.6004	.7997	.7508	1.332	1.250	1.666	.9268	53.1
37.0	.6458	.6018	.7986	.7536	1.327	1.252	1.662	.9250	**53.0**
37.1	.6475	.6032	.7976	.7563	1.322	1.254	1.658	.9233	52.9
37.2	.6493	.6046	.7965	.7590	1.317	1.255	1.654	.9215	52.8
37.3	.6510	.6060	.7955	.7618	1.313	1.257	1.650	.9198	52.7
37.4	.6528	.6074	.7944	.7646	1.308	1.259	1.646	.9180	52.6
37.5	.6545	.6088	.7934	.7673	1.303	1.260	1.643	.9163	52.5
37.6	.6562	.6101	.7923	.7701	1.299	1.262	1.639	.9146	52.4
37.7	.6580	.6115	.7912	.7729	1.294	1.264	1.635	.9128	52.3
37.8	.6597	.6129	.7902	.7757	1.289	1.266	1.632	.9111	52.2
37.9	.6615	.6143	.7891	.7785	1.285	1.267	1.628	.9093	52.1
38.0	.6632	.6157	.7880	.7813	1.280	1.269	1.624	.9076	**52.0**
38.1	.6650	.6170	.7869	.7841	1.275	1.271	1.621	.9058	51.9
38.2	.6667	.6184	.7859	.7869	1.271	1.272	1.617	.9041	51.8
38.3	.6685	.6198	.7848	.7898	1.266	1.274	1.613	.9023	51.7
38.4	.6702	.6211	.7837	.7926	1.262	1.276	1.610	.9006	51.6
38.5	.6720	.6225	.7826	.7954	1.257	1.278	1.606	.8988	51.5
38.6	.6737	.6239	.7815	.7983	1.253	1.280	1.603	.8971	51.4
38.7	.6754	.6252	.7804	.8012	1.248	1.281	1.599	.8954	51.3
38.8	.6772	.6266	.7793	.8040	1.244	1.283	1.596	.8936	51.2
38.9	.6789	.6280	.7782	.8069	1.239	1.285	1.592	.8919	51.1
39.0	.6807	.6293	.7771	.8098	1.235	1.287	1.589	.8901	**51.0**
39.1	.6824	.6307	.7760	.8127	1.230	1.289	1.586	.8884	50.9
39.2	.6842	.6320	.7749	.8156	1.226	1.290	1.582	.8866	50.8
39.3	.6859	.6334	.7738	.8185	1.222	1.292	1.579	.8849	50.7
39.4	.6877	.6347	.7727	.8214	1.217	1.294	1.575	.8831	50.6
39.5	.6894	.6361	.7716	.8243	1.213	1.296	1.572	.8814	50.5
39.6	.6912	.6374	.7705	.8273	1.209	1.298	1.569	.8796	50.4
39.7	.6929	.6388	.7694	.8302	1.205	1.300	1.566	.8779	50.3
39.8	.6946	.6401	.7683	.8332	1.200	1.302	1.562	.8762	50.2
39.9	.6964	.6414	.7672	.8361	1.196	1.304	1.559	.8744	50.1
40.0	.6981	.6428	.7660	.8391	1.192	1.305	1.556	.8727	**50.0**
40.1	.6999	.6441	.7649	.8421	1.188	1.307	1.552	.8709	49.9
40.2	.7016	.6455	.7638	.8451	1.183	1.309	1.549	.8692	49.8
40.3	.7034	.6468	.7627	.8481	1.179	1.311	1.546	.8674	49.7
40.4	.7051	.6481	.7615	.8511	1.175	1.313	1.543	.8657	49.6
40.5	.7069	.6494	.7604	.8541	1.171	1.315	1.540	.8639	49.5
40.6	.7086	.6508	.7593	.8571	1.167	1.317	1.537	.8622	49.4
40.7	.7103	.6521	.7581	.8601	1.163	1.319	1.534	.8604	49.3
40.8	.7121	.6534	.7570	.8632	1.159	1.321	1.530	.8587	49.2
40.9	.7138	.6547	.7559	.8662	1.154	1.323	1.527	.8570	49.1
41.0	.7156	.6561	.7547	.8693	1.150	1.325	1.524	.8552	**49.0**
41.1	.7173	.6574	.7536	.8724	1.146	1.327	1.521	.8535	48.9
41.2	.7191	.6587	.7524	.8754	1.142	1.329	1.518	.8517	48.8
41.3	.7208	.6600	.7513	.8785	1.138	1.331	1.515	.8500	48.7
41.4	.7226	.6613	.7501	.8816	1.134	1.333	1.512	.8482	48.6
41.5	.7243	.6626	.7490	.8847	1.130	1.335	1.509	.8465	48.5
41.6	.7261	.6639	.7478	.8878	1.126	1.337	1.506	.8447	48.4
41.7	.7278	.6652	.7466	.8910	1.122	1.339	1.503	.8430	48.3
41.8	.7295	.6665	.7455	.8941	1.118	1.341	1.500	.8412	48.2
41.9	.7313	.6678	.7443	.8972	1.115	1.344	1.497	.8395	48.1
42.0	.7330	.6691	.7431	.9004	1.111	1.346	1.494	.8378	**48.0**
		$\cos\theta$	$\sin\theta$	$\cot\theta$	$\tan\theta$	$\csc\theta$	$\sec\theta$	θ Radians	θ Degrees

Table 4 Trigonometric Functions of θ (θ in decimal degrees)

θ Degrees	θ Radians	$\sin \theta$	$\cos \theta$	$\tan \theta$	$\cot \theta$	$\sec \theta$	$\csc \theta$		
42.0	.7330	.6691	.7431	.9004	1.111	1.346	1.494	.8378	**48.0**
42.1	.7348	.6704	.7420	.9036	1.107	1.348	1.492	.8360	47.9
42.2	.7365	.6717	.7408	.9067	1.103	1.350	1.489	.8343	47.8
42.3	.7383	.6730	.7396	.9099	1.099	1.352	1.486	.8325	47.7
42.4	.7400	.6743	.7385	.9131	1.095	1.354	1.483	.8308	47.6
42.5	.7418	.6756	.7373	.9163	1.091	1.356	1.480	.8290	47.5
42.6	.7435	.6769	.7361	.9195	1.087	1.359	1.477	.8273	47.4
42.7	.7453	.6782	.7349	.9228	1.084	1.361	1.475	.8255	47.3
42.8	.7470	.6794	.7337	.9260	1.080	1.363	1.472	.8238	47.2
42.9	.7487	.6807	.7325	.9293	1.076	1.365	1.469	.8221	47.1
43.0	.7505	.6820	.7314	.9325	1.072	1.367	1.466	.8203	**47.0**
43.1	.7522	.6833	.7302	.9358	1.069	1.370	1.464	.8186	46.9
43.2	.7540	.6845	.7290	.9391	1.065	1.372	1.461	.8168	46.8
43.3	.7557	.6858	.7278	.9424	1.061	1.374	1.458	.8151	46.7
43.4	.7575	.6871	.7266	.9457	1.057	1.376	1.455	.8133	46.6
43.5	.7592	.6884	.7254	.9490	1.054	1.379	1.453	.8116	46.5
43.6	.7610	.6896	.7242	.9523	1.050	1.381	1.450	.8098	46.4
43.7	.7627	.6909	.7230	.9556	1.046	1.383	1.447	.8081	46.3
43.8	.7645	.6921	.7218	.9590	1.043	1.386	1.445	.8063	46.2
43.9	.7662	.6934	.7206	.9623	1.039	1.388	1.442	.8046	46.1
44.0	.7679	.6947	.7193	.9657	1.036	1.390	1.440	.8029	**46.0**
44.1	.7697	.6959	.7181	.9691	1.032	1.393	1.437	.8011	45.9
44.2	.7714	.6972	.7169	.9725	1.028	1.395	1.434	.7994	45.8
44.3	.7732	.6984	.7157	.9759	1.025	1.397	1.432	.7976	45.7
44.4	.7749	.6997	.7145	.9793	1.021	1.400	1.429	.7959	45.6
44.5	.7767	.7009	.7133	.9827	1.018	1.402	1.427	.7941	45.5
44.6	.7784	.7022	.7120	.9861	1.014	1.404	1.424	.7924	45.4
44.7	.7802	.7034	.7108	.9896	1.011	1.407	1.422	.7906	45.3
44.8	.7819	.7046	.7096	.9930	1.007	1.409	1.419	.7889	45.2
44.9	.7837	.7059	.7083	.9965	1.003	1.412	1.417	.7871	45.1
45.0	.7854	.7071	.7071	1.0000	1.000	1.414	1.414	.7854	**45.0**
		$\cos \theta$	$\sin \theta$	$\cot \theta$	$\tan \theta$	$\csc \theta$	$\sec \theta$	θ Radians	θ Degrees

Table 5 Trigonometric Functions of θ (θ in degrees and minutes)

Angle	Sin	Cos	Tan	Cot	Sec	Csc	
0° 00′	.0000	1.0000	.0000	- - - -	1.000	- - - -	90° 00′
10′	.0029	1.0000	.0029	343.8	1.000	343.8	50′
20′	.0058	1.0000	.0058	171.9	1.000	171.9	40′
30′	.0087	1.0000	.0087	114.6	1.000	114.6	30′
40′	.0116	.9999	.0116	85.94	1.000	85.95	20′
50′	.0145	.9999	.0145	68.75	1.000	68.76	10′
1° 00′	.0175	.9998	.0175	57.29	1.000	57.30	89° 00′
10′	.0204	.9998	.0204	49.10	1.000	49.11	50′
20′	.0233	.9997	.0233	42.96	1.000	42.98	40′
30′	.0262	.9997	.0262	38.19	1.000	38.20	30′
40′	.0291	.9996	.0291	34.37	1.000	34.38	20′
50′	.0320	.9995	.0320	31.24	1.001	31.26	10′
2° 00′	.0349	.9994	.0349	28.64	1.001	28.65	88° 00′
10′	.0378	.9993	.0378	26.43	1.001	26.45	50′
20′	.0407	.9992	.0407	24.54	1.001	24.56	40′
30′	.0436	.9990	.0437	22.90	1.001	22.93	30′
40′	.0465	.9989	.0466	21.47	1.001	21.49	20′
50′	.0494	.9988	.0495	20.21	1.001	20.23	10′
3° 00′	.0523	.9986	.0524	19.08	1.001	19.11	87° 00′
10′	.0552	.9985	.0553	18.07	1.002	18.10	50′
20′	.0581	.9983	.0582	17.17	1.002	17.20	40′
30′	.0610	.9981	.0612	16.35	1.002	16.38	30′
40′	.0640	.9980	.0641	15.60	1.002	15.64	20′
50′	.0669	.9978	.0670	14.92	1.002	14.96	10′
4° 00′	.0698	.9976	.0699	14.30	1.002	14.34	86° 00′
10′	.0727	.9974	.0729	13.73	1.003	13.76	50′
20′	.0756	.9971	.0758	13.20	1.003	13.23	40′
30′	.0785	.9969	.0787	12.71	1.003	12.75	30′
40′	.0814	.9967	.0816	12.25	1.003	12.29	20′
50′	.0843	.9964	.0846	11.83	1.004	11.87	10′
5° 00′	.0872	.9962	.0875	11.43	1.004	11.47	85° 00′
10′	.0901	.9959	.0904	11.06	1.004	11.10	50′
20′	.0929	.9957	.0934	10.71	1.004	10.76	40′
30′	.0958	.9954	.0963	10.39	1.005	10.43	30′
40′	.0987	.9951	.0992	10.08	1.005	10.13	20′
50′	.1016	.9948	.1022	9.788	1.005	9.839	10′
6° 00′	.1045	.9945	.1051	9.514	1.006	9.567	84° 00′
10′	.1074	.9942	.1080	9.255	1.006	9.309	50′
20′	.1103	.9939	.1110	9.010	1.006	9.065	40′
30′	.1132	.9936	.1139	8.777	1.006	8.834	30′
40′	.1161	.9932	.1169	8.556	1.007	8.614	20′
50′	.1190	.9929	.1198	8.345	1.007	8.405	10′
7° 00′	.1219	.9925	.1228	8.144	1.008	8.206	83° 00′
10′	.1248	.9922	.1257	7.953	1.008	8.016	50′
20′	.1276	.9918	.1287	7.770	1.008	7.834	40′
30′	.1305	.9914	.1317	7.596	1.009	7.661	30′
40′	.1334	.9911	.1346	7.429	1.009	7.496	20′
50′	.1363	.9907	.1376	7.269	1.009	7.337	10′
8° 00′	.1392	.9903	.1405	7.115	1.010	7.185	82° 00′
10′	.1421	.9899	.1435	6.968	1.010	7.040	50′
20′	.1449	.9894	.1465	6.827	1.011	6.900	40′
30′	.1478	.9890	.1495	6.691	1.011	6.765	30′
40′	.1507	.9886	.1524	6.561	1.012	6.636	20′
50′	.1536	.9881	.1554	6.435	1.012	6.512	10′
9° 00′	.1564	.9877	.1584	6.314	1.012	6.392	81° 00′
	Cos	Sin	Cot	Tan	Csc	Sec	Angle

Table 5 Trigonometric Functions of θ (θ in degrees and minutes)

Angle	Sin	Cos	Tan	Cot	Sec	Csc	
9° 00′	.1564	.9877	.1584	6.314	1.012	6.392	81° 00′
10′	.1593	.9872	.1614	6.197	1.013	6.277	50′
20′	.1622	.9868	.1644	6.084	1.013	6.166	40′
30′	.1650	.9863	.1673	5.976	1.014	6.059	30′
40′	.1679	.9858	.1703	5.871	1.014	5.955	20′
50′	.1708	.9853	.1733	5.769	1.015	5.855	10′
10° 00′	.1736	.9848	.1763	5.671	1.015	5.759	80° 00′
10′	.1765	.9843	.1793	5.576	1.016	5.665	50′
20′	.1794	.9838	.1823	5.485	1.016	5.575	40′
30′	.1822	.9833	.1853	5.396	1.017	5.487	30′
40′	.1851	.9827	.1883	5.309	1.018	5.403	20′
50′	.1880	.9822	.1914	5.226	1.018	5.320	10′
11° 00′	.1908	.9816	.1944	5.145	1.019	5.241	79° 00′
10′	.1937	.9811	.1974	5.066	1.019	5.164	50′
20′	.1965	.9805	.2004	4.989	1.020	5.089	40′
30′	.1994	.9799	.2035	4.915	1.020	5.016	30′
40′	.2022	.9793	.2065	4.843	1.021	4.945	20′
50′	.2051	.9787	.2095	4.773	1.022	4.876	10′
12° 00′	.2079	.9781	.2126	4.705	1.022	4.810	78° 00′
10′	.2108	.9775	.2156	4.638	1.023	4.745	50′
20′	.2136	.9769	.2186	4.574	1.024	4.682	40′
30′	.2164	.9763	.2217	4.511	1.024	4.620	30′
40′	.2193	.9757	.2247	4.449	1.025	4.560	20′
50′	.2221	.9750	.2278	4.390	1.026	4.502	10′
13° 00′	.2250	.9744	.2309	4.331	1.026	4.445	77° 00′
10′	.2278	.9737	.2339	4.275	1.027	4.390	50′
20′	.2306	.9730	.2370	4.219	1.028	4.336	40′
30′	.2334	.9724	.2401	4.165	1.028	4.284	30′
40′	.2363	.9717	.2432	4.113	1.029	4.232	20′
50′	.2391	.9710	.2462	4.061	1.030	4.182	10′
14° 00′	.2419	.9703	.2493	4.011	1.031	4.134	76° 00′
10′	.2447	.9696	.2524	3.962	1.031	4.086	50′
20′	.2476	.9689	.2555	3.914	1.032	4.039	40′
30′	.2504	.9681	.2586	3.867	1.033	3.994	30′
40′	.2532	.9674	.2617	3.821	1.034	3.950	20′
50′	.2560	.9667	.2648	3.776	1.034	3.906	10′
15° 00′	.2588	.9659	.2679	3.732	1.035	3.864	75° 00′
10′	.2616	.9652	.2711	3.689	1.036	3.822	50′
20′	.2644	.9644	.2742	3.647	1.037	3.782	40′
30′	.2672	.9636	.2773	3.606	1.038	3.742	30′
40′	.2700	.9628	.2805	3.566	1.039	3.703	20′
50′	.2728	.9621	.2836	3.526	1.039	3.665	10′
16° 00′	.2756	.9613	.2867	3.487	1.040	3.628	74° 00′
10′	.2784	.9605	.2899	3.450	1.041	3.592	50′
20′	.2812	.9596	.2931	3.412	1.042	3.556	40′
30′	.2840	.9588	.2962	3.376	1.043	3.521	30′
40′	.2868	.9580	.2994	3.340	1.044	3.487	20′
50′	.2896	.9572	.3026	3.305	1.045	3.453	10′
17° 00′	.2924	.9563	.3057	3.271	1.046	3.420	73° 00′
10′	.2952	.9555	.3089	3.237	1.047	3.388	50′
20′	.2979	.9546	.3121	3.204	1.048	3.356	40′
30′	.3007	.9537	.3153	3.172	1.049	3.326	30′
40′	.3035	.9528	.3185	3.140	1.049	3.295	20′
50′	.3062	.9520	.3217	3.108	1.050	3.265	10′
18° 00′	.3090	.9511	.3249	3.078	1.051	3.236	72° 00′
	Cos	Sin	Cot	Tan	Csc	Sec	Angle

Table 5 Trigonometric Functions of θ (θ in degrees and minutes)

Angle	Sin	Cos	Tan	Cot	Sec	Csc	
18° 00′	.3090	.9511	.3249	3.078	1.051	3.236	72° 00′
10′	.3118	.9502	.3281	3.047	1.052	3.207	50′
20′	.3145	.9492	.3314	3.018	1.053	3.179	40′
30′	.3173	.9483	.3346	2.989	1.054	3.152	30′
40′	.3201	.9474	.3378	2.960	1.056	3.124	20′
50′	.3228	.9465	.3411	2.932	1.057	3.098	10′
19° 00′	.3256	.9455	.3443	2.904	1.058	3.072	71° 00′
10′	.3283	.9446	.3476	2.877	1.059	3.046	50′
20′	.3311	.9436	.3508	2.850	1.060	3.021	40′
30′	.3338	.9426	.3541	2.824	1.061	2.996	30′
40′	.3365	.9417	.3574	2.798	1.062	2.971	20′
50′	.3393	.9407	.3607	2.773	1.063	2.947	10′
20° 00′	.3420	.9397	.3640	2.747	1.064	2.924	70° 00′
10′	.3448	.9387	.3673	2.723	1.065	2.901	50′
20′	.3475	.9377	.3706	2.699	1.066	2.878	40′
30′	.3502	.9367	.3739	2.675	1.068	2.855	30′
40′	.3529	.9356	.3772	2.651	1.069	2.833	20′
50′	.3557	.9346	.3805	2.628	1.070	2.812	10′
21° 00′	.3584	.9336	.3839	2.605	1.071	2.790	69° 00′
10′	.3611	.9325	.3872	2.583	1.072	2.769	50′
20′	.3638	.9315	.3906	2.560	1.074	2.749	40′
30′	.3665	.9304	.3939	2.539	1.075	2.729	30′
40′	.3692	.9293	.3973	2.517	1.076	2.709	20′
50′	.3719	.9283	.4006	2.496	1.077	2.689	10′
22° 00′	.3746	.9272	.4040	2.475	1.079	2.669	68° 00′
10′	.3773	.9261	.4074	2.455	1.080	2.650	50′
20′	.3800	.9250	.4108	2.434	1.081	2.632	40′
30′	.3827	.9239	.4142	2.414	1.082	2.613	30′
40′	.3854	.9228	.4176	2.394	1.084	2.595	20′
50′	.3881	.9216	.4210	2.375	1.085	2.577	10′
23° 00′	.3907	.9205	.4245	2.356	1.086	2.559	67° 00′
10′	.3934	.9194	.4279	2.337	1.088	2.542	50′
20′	.3961	.9182	.4314	2.318	1.089	2.525	40′
30′	.3987	.9171	.4348	2.300	1.090	2.508	30′
40′	.4014	.9159	.4383	2.282	1.092	2.491	20′
50′	.4041	.9147	.4417	2.264	1.093	2.475	10′
24° 00′	.4067	.9135	.4452	2.246	1.095	2.459	66° 00′
10′	.4094	.9124	.4487	2.229	1.096	2.443	50′
20′	.4120	.9112	.4522	2.211	1.097	2.427	40′
30′	.4147	.9100	.4557	2.194	1.099	2.411	30′
40′	.4173	.9088	.4592	2.177	1.100	2.396	20′
50′	.4200	.9075	.4628	2.161	1.102	2.381	10′
25° 00′	.4226	.9063	.4663	2.145	1.103	2.366	65° 00′
10′	.4253	.9051	.4699	2.128	1.105	2.352	50′
20′	.4279	.9038	.4734	2.112	1.106	2.337	40′
30′	.4305	.9026	.4770	2.097	1.108	2.323	30′
40′	.4331	.9013	.4806	2.081	1.109	2.309	20′
50′	.4358	.9001	.4841	2.066	1.111	2.295	10′
26° 00′	.4384	.8988	.4877	2.050	1.113	2.281	64° 00′
10′	.4410	.8975	.4913	2.035	1.114	2.268	50′
20′	.4436	.8962	.4950	2.020	1.116	2.254	40′
30′	.4462	.8949	.4986	2.006	1.117	2.241	30′
40′	.4488	.8936	.5022	1.991	1.119	2.228	20′
50′	.4514	.8923	.5059	1.977	1.121	2.215	10′
27° 00′	.4540	.8910	.5095	1.963	1.122	2.203	63° 00′
	Cos	Sin	Cot	Tan	Csc	Sec	Angle

Table 5 Trigonometric Functions of θ (θ in degrees and minutes)

Angle	Sin	Cos	Tan	Cot	Sec	Csc	
27° 00'	.4540	.8910	.5095	1.963	1.122	2.203	63° 00'
10'	.4566	.8897	.5132	1.949	1.124	2.190	50'
20'	.4592	.8884	.5169	1.935	1.126	2.178	40'
30'	.4617	.8870	.5206	1.921	1.127	2.166	30'
40'	.4643	.8857	.5243	1.907	1.129	2.154	20'
50'	.4669	.8843	.5280	1.894	1.131	2.142	10'
28° 00'	.4695	.8829	.5317	1.881	1.133	2.130	62° 00'
10'	.4720	.8816	.5354	1.868	1.134	2.118	50'
20'	.4746	.8802	.5392	1.855	1.136	2.107	40'
30'	.4772	.8788	.5430	1.842	1.138	2.096	30'
40'	.4797	.8774	.5467	1.829	1.140	2.085	20'
50'	.4823	.8760	.5505	1.816	1.142	2.074	10'
29° 00'	.4848	.8746	.5543	1.804	1.143	2.063	61° 00'
10'	.4874	.8732	.5581	1.792	1.145	2.052	50'
20'	.4899	.8718	.5619	1.780	1.147	2.041	40'
30'	.4924	.8704	.5658	1.767	1.149	2.031	30'
40'	.4950	.8689	.5696	1.756	1.151	2.020	20'
50'	.4975	.8675	.5735	1.744	1.153	2.010	10'
30° 00'	.5000	.8660	.5774	1.732	1.155	2.000	60° 00'
10'	.5025	.8646	.5812	1.720	1.157	1.990	50'
20'	.5050	.8631	.5851	1.709	1.159	1.980	40'
30'	.5075	.8616	.5890	1.698	1.161	1.970	30'
40'	.5100	.8601	.5930	1.686	1.163	1.961	20'
50'	.5125	.8587	.5969	1.675	1.165	1.951	10'
31° 00'	.5150	.8572	.6009	1.664	1.167	1.942	59° 00'
10'	.5175	.8557	.6048	1.653	1.169	1.932	50'
20'	.5200	.8542	.6088	1.643	1.171	1.923	40'
30'	.5225	.8526	.6128	1.632	1.173	1.914	30'
40'	.5250	.8511	.6168	1.621	1.175	1.905	20'
50'	.5275	.8496	.6208	1.611	1.177	1.896	10'
32° 00'	.5299	.8480	.6249	1.600	1.179	1.887	58° 00'
10'	.5324	.8465	.6289	1.590	1.181	1.878	50'
20'	.5348	.8450	.6330	1.580	1.184	1.870	40'
30'	.5373	.8434	.6371	1.570	1.186	1.861	30'
40'	.5398	.8418	.6412	1.560	1.188	1.853	20'
50'	.5422	.8403	.6453	1.550	1.190	1.844	10'
33° 00'	.5446	.8387	.6494	1.540	1.192	1.836	57° 00'
10'	.5471	.8371	.6536	1.530	1.195	1.828	50'
20'	.5495	.8355	.6577	1.520	1.197	1.820	40'
30'	.5519	.8339	.6619	1.511	1.199	1.812	30'
40'	.5544	.8323	.6661	1.501	1.202	1.804	20'
50'	.5568	.8307	.6703	1.492	1.204	1.796	10'
34° 00'	.5592	.8290	.6745	1.483	1.206	1.788	56° 00'
10'	.5616	.8274	.6787	1.473	1.209	1.781	50'
20'	.5640	.8258	.6830	1.464	1.211	1.773	40'
30'	.5664	.8241	.6873	1.455	1.213	1.766	30'
40'	.5688	.8225	.6916	1.446	1.216	1.758	20'
50'	.5712	.8208	.6959	1.437	1.218	1.751	10'
35° 00'	.5736	.8192	.7002	1.428	1.221	1.743	55° 00'
10'	.5760	.8175	.7046	1.419	1.223	1.736	50'
20'	.5783	.8158	.7089	1.411	1.226	1.729	40'
30'	.5807	.8141	.7133	1.402	1.228	1.722	30'
40'	.5831	.8124	.7177	1.393	1.231	1.715	20'
50'	.5854	.8107	.7221	1.385	1.233	1.708	10'
36° 00'	.5878	.8090	.7265	1.376	1.236	1.701	54° 00'
	Cos	Sin	Cot	Tan	Csc	Sec	Angle

Table 5 Trigonometric Functions of θ (θ in degrees and minutes)

Angle	Sin	Cos	Tan	Cot	Sec	Csc	
36° 00′	.5878	.8090	.7265	1.376	1.236	1.701	54° 00′
10′	.5901	.8073	.7310	1.368	1.239	1.695	50′
20′	.5925	.8056	.7355	1.360	1.241	1.688	40′
30′	.5948	.8039	.7400	1.351	1.244	1.681	30′
40′	.5972	.8021	.7445	1.343	1.247	1.675	20′
50′	.5995	.8004	.7490	1.335	1.249	1.668	10′
37° 00′	.6018	.7986	.7536	1.327	1.252	1.662	53° 00′
10′	.6041	.7969	.7581	1.319	1.255	1.655	50′
20′	.6065	.7951	.7627	1.311	1.258	1.649	40′
30′	.6088	.7934	.7673	1.303	1.260	1.643	30′
40′	.6111	.7916	.7720	1.295	1.263	1.636	20′
50′	.6134	.7898	.7766	1.288	1.266	1.630	10′
38° 00′	.6157	.7880	.7813	1.280	1.269	1.624	52° 00′
10′	.6180	.7862	.7860	1.272	1.272	1.618	50′
20′	.6202	.7844	.7907	1.265	1.275	1.612	40′
30′	.6225	.7826	.7954	1.257	1.278	1.606	30′
40′	.6248	.7808	.8002	1.250	1.281	1.601	20′
50′	.6271	.7790	.8050	1.242	1.284	1.595	10′
39° 00′	.6293	.7771	.8098	1.235	1.287	1.589	51° 00′
10′	.6316	.7753	.8146	1.228	1.290	1.583	50′
20′	.6338	.7735	.8195	1.220	1.293	1.578	40′
30′	.6361	.7716	.8243	1.213	1.296	1.572	30′
40′	.6383	.7698	.8292	1.206	1.299	1.567	20′
50′	.6406	.7679	.8342	1.199	1.302	1.561	10′
40° 00′	.6428	.7660	.8391	1.192	1.305	1.556	50° 00′
10′	.6450	.7642	.8441	1.185	1.309	1.550	50′
20′	.6472	.7623	.8491	1.178	1.312	1.545	40′
30′	.6494	.7604	.8541	1.171	1.315	1.540	30′
40′	.6517	.7585	.8591	1.164	1.318	1.535	20′
50′	.6539	.7566	.8642	1.157	1.322	1.529	10′
41° 00′	.6561	.7547	.8693	1.150	1.325	1.524	49° 00′
10′	.6583	.7528	.8744	1.144	1.328	1.519	50′
20′	.6604	.7509	.8796	1.137	1.332	1.514	40′
30′	.6626	.7490	.8847	1.130	1.335	1.509	30′
40′	.6648	.7470	.8899	1.124	1.339	1.504	20′
50′	.6670	.7451	.8952	1.117	1.342	1.499	10′
42° 00′	.6691	.7431	.9004	1.111	1.346	1.494	48° 00′
10′	.6713	.7412	.9057	1.104	1.349	1.490	50′
20′	.6734	.7392	.9110	1.098	1.353	1.485	40′
30′	.6756	.7373	.9163	1.091	1.356	1.480	30′
40′	.6777	.7353	.9217	1.085	1.360	1.476	20′
50′	.6799	.7333	.9271	1.079	1.364	1.471	10′
43° 00′	.6820	.7314	.9325	1.072	1.367	1.466	47° 00′
10′	.6841	.7294	.9380	1.066	1.371	1.462	50′
20′	.6862	.7274	.9435	1.060	1.375	1.457	40′
30′	.6884	.7254	.9490	1.054	1.379	1.453	30′
40′	.6905	.7234	.9545	1.048	1.382	1.448	20′
50′	.6926	.7214	.9601	1.042	1.386	1.444	10′
44° 00′	.6947	.7193	.9657	1.036	1.390	1.440	46° 00′
10′	.6967	.7173	.9713	1.030	1.394	1.435	50′
20′	.6988	.7153	.9770	1.024	1.398	1.431	40′
30′	.7009	.7133	.9827	1.018	1.402	1.427	30′
40′	.7030	.7112	.9884	1.012	1.406	1.423	20′
50′	.7050	.7092	.9942	1.006	1.410	1.418	10′
45° 00′	.7071	.7071	1.000	1.000	1.414	1.414	45° 00′
	Cos	Sin	Cot	Tan	Csc	Sec	Angle

Table 6 Trigonometric Functions of θ (θ in radians)

θ Radians	θ Degrees	$\sin \theta$	$\cos \theta$	$\tan \theta$	$\cot \theta$	$\sec \theta$	$\csc \theta$
0.00	0° 00′	0.0000	1.000	0.0000	Undefined	1.000	Undefined
.01	0° 34′	.0100	1.000	.0100	100.0	1.000	100.0
.02	1° 09′	.0200	0.9998	.0200	49.99	1.000	50.00
.03	1° 43′	.0300	0.9996	.0300	33.32	1.000	33.34
.04	2° 18′	.0400	0.9992	.0400	24.99	1.001	25.01
0.05	2° 52′	0.0500	0.9988	0.0500	19.98	1.001	20.01
.06	3° 26′	.0600	.9982	.0601	16.65	1.002	16.68
.07	4° 01′	.0699	.9976	.0701	14.26	1.002	14.30
.08	4° 35′	.0799	.9968	.0802	12.47	1.003	12.51
.09	5° 09′	.0899	.9960	.0902	11.08	1.004	11.13
0.10	5° 44′	0.0998	0.9950	0.1003	9.967	1.005	10.02
.11	6° 18′	.1098	.9940	.1104	9.054	1.006	9.109
.12	6° 53′	.1197	.9928	.1206	8.293	1.007	8.353
.13	7° 27′	.1296	.9916	.1307	7.649	1.009	7.714
.14	8° 01′	.1395	.9902	.1409	7.096	1.010	7.166
0.15	8° 36′	0.1494	0.9888	0.1511	6.617	1.011	6.692
.16	9° 10′	.1593	.9872	.1614	6.197	1.013	6.277
.17	9° 44′	.1692	.9856	.1717	5.826	1.015	5.911
.18	10° 19′	.1790	.9838	.1820	5.495	1.016	5.586
.19	10° 53′	.1889	.9820	.1923	5.200	1.018	5.295
0.20	11° 28′	0.1987	0.9801	0.2027	4.933	1.020	5.033
.21	12° 02′	.2085	.9780	.2131	4.692	1.022	4.797
.22	12° 36′	.2182	.9759	.2236	4.472	1.025	4.582
.23	13° 11′	.2280	.9737	.2341	4.271	1.027	4.386
.24	13° 45′	.2377	.9713	.2447	4.086	1.030	4.207
0.25	14° 19′	0.2474	0.9689	0.2553	3.916	1.032	4.042
.26	14° 54′	.2571	.9664	.2660	3.759	1.035	3.890
.27	15° 28′	.2667	.9638	.2768	3.613	1.038	3.749
.28	16° 03′	.2764	.9611	.2876	3.478	1.041	3.619
.29	16° 37′	.2860	.9582	.2984	3.351	1.044	3.497
0.30	17° 11′	0.2955	0.9553	0.3093	3.233	1.047	3.384
.31	17° 46′	.3051	.9523	.3203	3.122	1.050	3.278
.32	18° 20′	.3146	.9492	.3314	3.018	1.053	3.179
.33	18° 55′	.3240	.9460	.3425	2.920	1.057	3.086
.34	19° 29′	.3335	.9428	.3537	2.827	1.061	2.999
0.35	20° 03′	0.3429	0.9394	0.3650	2.740	1.065	2.916
.36	20° 38′	.3523	.9359	.3764	2.657	1.068	2.839
.37	21° 12′	.3616	.9323	.3879	2.578	1.073	2.765
.38	21° 46′	.3709	.9287	.3994	2.504	1.077	2.696
.39	22° 21′	.3802	.9249	.4111	2.433	1.081	2.630
0.40	22° 55′	0.3894	0.9211	0.4228	2.365	1.086	2.568
.41	23° 30′	.3986	.9171	.4346	2.301	1.090	2.509
.42	24° 04′	.4078	.9131	.4466	2.239	1.095	2.452
.43	24° 38′	.4169	.9090	.4586	2.180	1.100	2.399
.44	25° 13′	.4259	.9048	.4708	2.124	1.105	2.348
0.45	25° 47′	0.4350	0.9004	0.4831	2.070	1.111	2.299
.46	26° 21′	.4439	.8961	.4954	2.018	1.116	2.253
.47	26° 56′	.4529	.8916	.5080	1.969	1.122	2.208
.48	27° 30′	.4618	.8870	.5206	1.921	1.127	2.166
.49	28° 05′	.4706	.8823	.5334	1.875	1.133	2.125

Table 6 Trigonometric Functions of θ (θ in radians)

θ Radians	θ Degrees	sin θ	cos θ	tan θ	cot θ	sec θ	csc θ
0.50	28° 39′	0.4794	0.8776	0.5463	1.830	1.139	2.086
.51	29° 13′	.4882	.8727	.5594	1.788	1.146	2.048
.52	29° 48′	.4969	.8678	.5726	1.747	1.152	2.013
.53	30° 22′	.5055	.8628	.5859	1.707	1.159	1.978
.54	30° 56′	.5141	.8577	.5994	1.668	1.166	1.945
0.55	31° 31′	0.5227	0.8525	0.6131	1.631	1.173	1.913
.56	32° 05′	.5312	.8473	.6269	1.595	1.180	1.883
.57	32° 40′	.5396	.8419	.6410	1.560	1.188	1.853
.58	33° 14′	.5480	.8365	.6552	1.526	1.196	1.825
.59	33° 48′	.5564	.8309	.6696	1.494	1.203	1.797
0.60	34° 23′	0.5646	0.8253	0.6841	1.462	1.212	1.771
.61	34° 57′	.5729	.8196	.6989	1.431	1.220	1.746
.62	35° 31′	.5810	.8139	.7139	1.401	1.229	1.721
.63	36° 06′	.5891	.8080	.7291	1.372	1.238	1.697
.64	36° 40′	.5972	.8021	.7445	1.343	1.247	1.674
0.65	37° 15′	0.6052	0.7961	0.7602	1.315	1.256	1.652
.66	37° 49′	.6131	.7900	.7761	1.288	1.266	1.631
.67	38° 23′	.6210	.7838	.7923	1.262	1.276	1.610
.68	38° 58′	.6288	.7776	.8087	1.237	1.286	1.590
.69	39° 32′	.6365	.7712	.8253	1.212	1.297	1.571
0.70	40° 06′	0.6442	0.7648	0.8423	1.187	1.307	1.552
.71	40° 41′	.6518	.7584	.8595	1.163	1.319	1.534
.72	41° 15′	.6594	.7518	.8771	1.140	1.330	1.517
.73	41° 50′	.6669	.7452	.8949	1.117	1.342	1.500
.74	42° 24′	.6743	.7385	.9131	1.095	1.354	1.483
0.75	42° 58′	0.6816	0.7317	0.9316	1.073	1.367	1.467
.76	43° 33′	.6889	.7248	.9505	1.052	1.380	1.452
.77	44° 07′	.6961	.7179	.9697	1.031	1.393	1.437
.78	44° 41′	.7033	.7109	.9893	1.011	1.407	1.422
.79	45° 16′	.7104	.7038	1.009	.9908	1.421	1.408
0.80	45° 50′	0.7174	0.6967	1.030	0.9712	1.435	1.394
.81	46° 25′	.7243	.6895	1.050	.9520	1.450	1.381
.82	46° 59′	.7311	.6822	1.072	.9331	1.466	1.368
.83	47° 33′	.7379	.6749	1.093	.9146	1.482	1.355
.84	48° 08′	.7446	.6675	1.116	.8964	1.498	1.343
0.85	48° 42′	0.7513	0.6600	1.138	0.8785	1.515	1.331
.86	49° 17′	.7578	.6524	1.162	.8609	1.533	1.320
.87	49° 51′	.7643	.6448	1.185	.8437	1.551	1.308
.88	50° 25′	.7707	.6372	1.210	.8267	1.569	1.297
.89	51° 00′	.7771	.6294	1.235	.8100	1.589	1.287
0.90	51° 34′	0.7833	0.6216	1.260	0.7936	1.609	1.277
.91	52° 08′	.7895	.6137	1.286	.7774	1.629	1.267
.92	52° 43′	.7956	.6058	1.313	.7615	1.651	1.257
.93	53° 17′	.8016	.5978	1.341	.7458	1.673	1.247
.94	53° 52′	.8076	.5898	1.369	.7303	1.696	1.238
0.95	54° 26′	0.8134	0.5817	1.398	0.7151	1.719	1.229
.96	55° 00′	.8192	.5735	1.428	.7001	1.744	1.221
.97	55° 35′	.8249	.5653	1.459	.6853	1.769	1.212
.98	56° 09′	.8305	.5570	1.491	.6707	1.795	1.204
.99	56° 43′	.8360	.5487	1.524	.6563	1.823	1.196

$\frac{\pi}{6}$ → (at .52)

$\frac{\pi}{4}$ → (at .78)

Table 6 Trigonometric Functions of θ (θ in radians)

θ Radians	θ Degrees	$\sin \theta$	$\cos \theta$	$\tan \theta$	$\cot \theta$	$\sec \theta$	$\csc \theta$
1.00	57° 18′	0.8415	0.5403	1.557	0.6421	1.851	1.188
1.01	57° 52′	.8468	.5319	1.592	.6281	1.880	1.181
1.02	58° 27′	.8521	.5234	1.628	.6142	1.911	1.174
1.03	59° 01′	.8573	.5148	1.665	.6005	1.942	1.166
1.04	59° 35′	.8624	.5062	1.704	.5870	1.975	1.160
1.05	60° 10′	0.8674	0.4976	1.743	0.5736	2.010	1.153
1.06	60° 44′	.8724	.4889	1.784	.5604	2.046	1.146
1.07	61° 18′	.8772	.4801	1.827	.5473	2.083	1.140
1.08	61° 53′	.8820	.4713	1.871	.5344	2.122	1.134
1.09	62° 27′	.8866	.4625	1.917	.5216	2.162	1.128
1.10	63° 02′	0.8912	0.4536	1.965	0.5090	2.205	1.122
1.11	63° 36′	.8957	.4447	2.014	.4964	2.249	1.116
1.12	64° 10′	.9001	.4357	2.066	.4840	2.295	1.111
1.13	64° 45′	.9044	.4267	2.120	.4718	2.344	1.106
1.14	65° 19′	.9086	.4176	2.176	.4596	2.395	1.101
1.15	65° 53′	0.9128	0.4085	2.234	0.4475	2.448	1.096
1.16	66° 28′	.9168	.3993	2.296	.4356	2.504	1.091
1.17	67° 02′	.9208	.3902	2.360	.4237	2.563	1.086
1.18	67° 37′	.9246	.3809	2.428	.4120	2.625	1.082
1.19	68° 11′	.9284	.3717	2.498	.4003	2.691	1.077
1.20	68° 45′	0.9320	0.3624	2.572	0.3888	2.760	1.073
1.21	69° 20′	.9356	.3530	2.650	.3773	2.833	1.069
1.22	69° 54′	.9391	.3436	2.733	.3659	2.910	1.065
1.23	70° 28′	.9425	.3342	2.820	.3546	2.992	1.061
1.24	71° 03′	.9458	.3248	2.912	.3434	3.079	1.057
1.25	71° 37′	0.9490	0.3153	3.010	0.3323	3.171	1.054
1.26	72° 12′	.9521	.3058	3.113	.3212	3.270	1.050
1.27	72° 46′	.9551	.2963	3.224	.3102	3.375	1.047
1.28	73° 20′	.9580	.2867	3.341	.2993	3.488	1.044
1.29	73° 55′	.9608	.2771	3.467	.2884	3.609	1.041
1.30	74° 29′	0.9636	0.2675	3.602	0.2776	3.738	1.038
1.31	75° 03′	.9662	.2579	3.747	.2669	3.878	1.035
1.32	75° 38′	.9687	.2482	3.903	.2562	4.029	1.032
1.33	76° 12′	.9711	.2385	4.072	.2456	4.193	1.030
1.34	76° 47′	.9735	.2288	4.256	.2350	4.372	1.027
1.35	77° 21′	0.9757	0.2190	4.455	0.2245	4.566	1.025
1.36	77° 55′	.9779	.2092	4.673	.2140	4.779	1.023
1.37	78° 30′	.9799	.1994	4.913	.2035	5.014	1.021
1.38	79° 04′	.9819	.1896	5.177	.1931	5.273	1.018
1.39	79° 39′	.9837	.1798	5.471	.1828	5.561	1.017
1.40	80° 13′	0.9854	0.1700	5.798	0.1725	5.883	1.015
1.41	80° 47′	.9871	.1601	6.165	.1622	6.246	1.013
1.42	81° 22′	.9887	.1502	6.581	.1519	6.657	1.011
1.43	81° 56′	.9901	.1403	7.055	.1417	7.126	1.010
1.44	82° 30′	.9915	.1304	7.602	.1315	7.667	1.009
1.45	83° 05′	0.9927	0.1205	8.238	0.1214	8.299	1.007
1.46	83° 39′	.9939	.1106	8.989	.1113	9.044	1.006
1.47	84° 14′	.9949	.1006	9.887	.1011	9.938	1.005
1.48	84° 48′	.9959	.0907	10.98	.0911	11.03	1.004
1.49	85° 22′	.9967	.0807	12.35	.0810	12.39	1.003

$\dfrac{\pi}{3}$ → (points to row 1.05)

Table 6 Trigonometric Functions of θ (θ in radians)

θ Radians	θ Degrees	sin θ	cos θ	tan θ	cot θ	sec θ	csc θ
1.50	85° 57′	0.9975	0.0707	14.10	0.0709	14.14	1.003
1.51	86° 31′	.9982	.0608	16.43	.0609	16.46	1.002
1.52	87° 05′	.9987	.0508	19.67	.0508	19.70	1.001
1.53	87° 40′	.9992	.0408	24.50	.0408	24.52	1.001
1.54	88° 14′	.9995	.0308	32.46	.0308	32.48	1.000
1.55	88° 49′	0.9998	0.0208	48.08	0.0208	48.09	1.000
1.56	89° 23′	.9999	.0108	92.62	.0108	92.63	1.000
1.57	89° 57′	1.000	.0008	1256	.0008	1256	1.000

$\dfrac{\pi}{2}$ →

Table 7 Geometry Formulas

A = area, P = perimeter, C = circumference, S = lateral surface area, T = total surface area, V = volume, $\pi \approx 3.1416$

Triangle

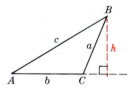

$$P = a + b + c$$
$$A = \frac{1}{2}bh$$

Rectangle

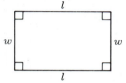

$$P = 2l + 2w$$
$$A = lw$$

Parallelogram

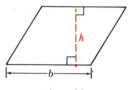

$$A = bh$$

Trapezoid

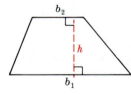

$$A = \frac{1}{2}h(b_1 + b_2)$$

Circle

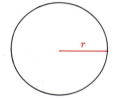

$$C = 2\pi r$$
$$A = \pi r^2$$

Rectangular Box

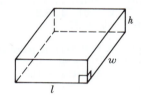

$$V = lwh$$
$$T = 2lw + 2lh + 2wh$$

Sphere

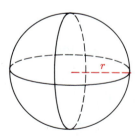

$$V = \frac{4}{3}\pi r^3$$
$$T = 4\pi r^2$$

Right Circular Cylinder

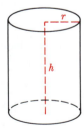

$$V = \pi r^2 h$$
$$S = 2\pi rh$$
$$T = 2\pi rh + 2\pi r^2$$

Right Circular Cone

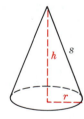

$$V = \frac{1}{3}\pi r^2 h$$
$$S = \pi rs$$
$$T = \pi rs + \pi r^2$$

ANSWERS TO SELF-TESTS

Chapter 1, Self-Test 1, page 13   **1.** 68   **2.** 7
3.

4. $-2 < 1 < 7$ **5.** false   **6.** true   **7.** true
8. false   **9.** 40   **10.** 24

Chapter 1, Self-Test 2, page 26
1. a. Assoc. ax. for add.
b. Inv. ax. for add.   **c.** Id. ax. for add.
d. Inv. ax. for mult.   **2. a.** Dist. ax.
b. Com. ax. for add.
c. Assoc. ax. for add.   **d.** Dist. ax.
3. 1. Hyp. (or Given)   2. Subst. prin.
3. Canc. rule for add.
4. 1. Hyp. (or Given)   2. Inv. ax. for mult.
3. Mult. prop. of =   4. Inv. ax. for mult.

Chapter 1, Self-Test 3, page 40   **1.** 15
2. -7 **3.** -61 **4.** 8.2   **5.** -45
6. $18 - 36z + 27z^2$ **7.** -1 **8.** 5   **9.** -13

Chapter 2, Self-Test 1, page 63   **1.** $5x + 6$
2. $15ab - 10a - 4b$ **3.** 9   **4.** -10
5. $3x + 3$, where x is the least integer.
6. $35°$

Chapter 2, Self-Test 2, pages 76–77
1. $\{d: d < 5\}$

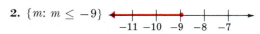

2. $\{m: m \le -9\}$

3. $\{x: -1 < x \le 2\}$

4. $\{n: 4 \le n \le 14\}$

5. $\{2\}$

6. $\{r: -9 \le r \le 3\}$

7. 1:00 P.M.

Chapter 3, Self-Test 1, pages 94–95
1.

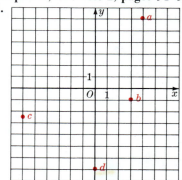

2. $x = 9,\ y = -2$ **3.** $y = -\dfrac{1}{2}x + 2$;
$\left\{(-6, 5),\ (0, 2),\ (2, 1),\ \left(7, -\dfrac{3}{2}\right)\right\}$ **4.** No
12 cm bricks and 6 16 cm bricks, 4 12 cm
bricks and 3 16 cm bricks, or 8 12 cm bricks
and no 16 cm bricks.   **5.** $x - 4y = 16$
6.   **7.** 3

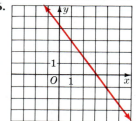

Chapter 3, Self-Test 2, page 106   **1. a.** 2
b. $\dfrac{1}{4}$ **2.** $\dfrac{5}{3}$
3.

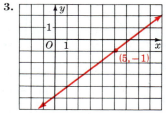

4. -6 **5.** $2x - 3y = -15$ **6.** $2x - y = 8$
7. $x = 3$ **8.** $x + y = 2$

Chapter 3, Self-Test 3, pages 123–124
1. $D = \{-5, 0, 4\}$, $R = \{0, 7\}$
2. $\{-13, -1, 7\}$ **3.** $f(x) = 2x + 1$
4. a. 15 **b.** $\dfrac{3}{2}$

5. function

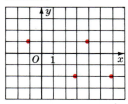

Chapter 4, Self-Test 1, page 136 **1.** $-21y^5$
2. $6c^5 - 15c^3 - 12c^2$ **3.** $9x^2 - y^2$
4. $15\,m^2 - m - 28$
5. $12n^3 + 23n^2 + 13n + 2$

Chapter 4, Self-Test 2, page 146
1. $2^2 \cdot 5 \cdot 13$ **2.** $2^2 \cdot 3 \cdot 5^2$ **3. a.** $3m^2$
b. $9m^3n$ **4. a.** $6xy^2$ **b.** $36x^2y^3$
5. $(2x - 1)(2x + 1)$ **6.** $(a - 2)^2$
7. $4x(x + 6)$ **8.** $(y - 2)(y^2 + 2y + 4)$
9. $(m - 5)(m - 4)$ **10.** $(3x + 4)(2x - 3)$

Chapter 4, Self-Test 3, pages 156–157
1. $\{-4, 2\}$ **2.** $\left\{-\dfrac{5}{3}, 2\right\}$ **3.** 10 cm
4. $\{y: y < 2 \text{ or } y > 3\}$

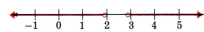

5. $\{x: -5 < x < 2\}$

Chapter 5, Self-Test 1, page 175 **1.** $\dfrac{4x^3}{3}$

2. $\dfrac{2a^3b^2}{3c}$ **3.** $-\dfrac{1}{8}$ **4.** $\dfrac{y^5}{2}$ **5.** $1 + 2x + 3x^2$
6. 4.7275×10^4 **7.** 2.54×10^{-5} **8.** 876,300
9. 0.004415 **10.** 1×10^2, or 100

Chapter 5, Self-Test 2, page 192 **1.** $a - x$
2. $-\dfrac{t + 3}{1 + 2t}$ **3.** quotient: $x^2 - 2x - 6$,

remainder: 0 **4.** $\dfrac{9s^2u}{t}$ **5.** $\dfrac{x + 3a}{x - a}$
6. $\dfrac{(a - b)^2}{2a^3b^2}$ **7.** $-\dfrac{1}{t(t - 2)}$ **8.** 14 **9.** $\dfrac{x + y}{xy}$

Chapter 5, Self-Test 3, page 204 **1.** $\left\{-3, \dfrac{2}{3}\right\}$

2. $\left\{-\dfrac{1}{2}, \dfrac{2}{5}\right\}$ **3.** 9 L **4.** $\{4\}$ **5.** $\{2\}$ **6.** 6 h

Chapter 6, Self-Test 1, page 223 **1. a.** 0.5

b. -5 **2.** $x \le 9$ **3.** $\dfrac{c\sqrt[3]{36abc}}{3b^2}$
4. $\dfrac{\sqrt{x(x + 1)}}{x + 1}$ **5.** $\dfrac{3\sqrt[3]{2}}{2}$ **6.** $x - a$
7. $-1 + \sqrt{3}$ **8.** $\{-10\}$ **9.** $\{4\}$

Chapter 6, Self-Test 2, page 233
1. $x^5 + 3 = 0$ **2.** The only possible rational
roots are -1, 1, -2, and 2, and none of
these satisfies the equation. **3.** $\sqrt[3]{2}$ is a
root of $x^3 - 2 = 0$. The only possible
rational roots of $x^3 - 2 = 0$ are -1, 1, -2,
and 2. $\therefore \sqrt[3]{2}$ is irrational. **4.** $0.38\overline{63}$ **5.** $\dfrac{549}{110}$
6. $1.7404004004\ldots$ (answers may vary)

Chapter 6, Self-Test 3, page 240 **1. a.** $\dfrac{\sqrt{6}}{4}i$

b. $i\sqrt{3}$ **2.** $\left\{-\dfrac{1}{3}i, \dfrac{1}{3}i\right\}$ **3.** $1 + i$
4. $5 - 12i$ **5.** 5 **6.** $\dfrac{4}{13} + \dfrac{7}{13}i$

Chapter 7, Self-Test 1, page 260
1. $\{2 + \sqrt{6}, 2 - \sqrt{6}\}$
2. $\left\{\dfrac{-5 + 3\sqrt{5}}{2}, \dfrac{-5 - 3\sqrt{5}}{2}\right\}$
3. $\left\{\dfrac{1 + \sqrt{5}}{2}, \dfrac{1 - \sqrt{5}}{2}\right\}$
4. $\left\{1 + \dfrac{3}{2}i, 1 - \dfrac{3}{2}i\right\}$ **5.** 0.6 cm by 3.4 cm
6. $\{-1, 1, -\sqrt{5}, \sqrt{5}\}$

Chapter 7, Self-Test 2, page 267 **1.** two
imaginary conjugate roots **2.** two real,
unequal, rational roots **3.** $k > \dfrac{4}{3}$ **4.** sum: $\dfrac{1}{2}$;

product: $-\dfrac{1}{3}$ **5.** sum: 3; product: -4
6. (Answers may vary) $x^2 + 4x + 7 = 0$

Chapter 7, Self-Test 3, page 277
1. Vertex: $(2, -4)$; axis: $x = 2$

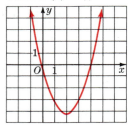

2. $y = -\dfrac{1}{2}(x + 2)^2 + 3$

3. 7 is the maximum value. **4.** -9

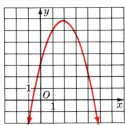

Chapter 8, Self-Test 1, page 302
1. $\{(-2, 7)\}$ **2.** 240 adult tickets and 160 student tickets

3.

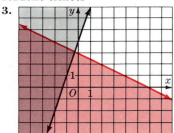

4. $\{2, 4, -3\}$

Chapter 8, Self-Test 2, page 314
1. $6x^3 + 15x^2 + 45x + 139; 409$
2. $\{-2, 2, 5\}$ **3.** $\{-\sqrt{2}, \sqrt{2}, 3 + i, 3 - i\}$

Chapter 8, Self-Test 3, page 321
1. zeros: $-2, 0, 2$

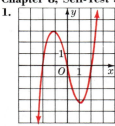

2. zeros: $-\dfrac{1}{2}, 2, 4$

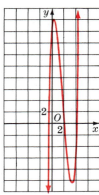

3. 1.740

Chapter 9, Self-Test 1, page 333 **1.** 13
2. $(-2, 2)$ **3.** $3x + 2y = 7$
4. $3x - 4y = -14$

Chapter 9, Self-Test 2, pages 356–357
1. $(x + 3)^2 + (y - 2)^2 = 9$
2. $C(3, -4), r = 5$ **3.** $(y - 3)^2 = 8x$
4.

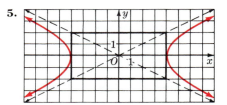

5.

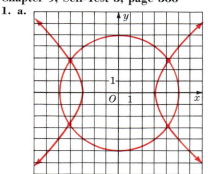

6. 484 W

Chapter 9, Self-Test 3, page 366
1. a.

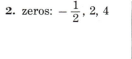

b. 4 solutions

c. $\{(4.1, 2.8), (4.1, -2.8), (-4.1, -2.8), (-4.1, 2.8)\}$

2. a.

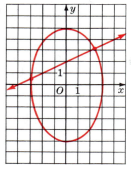

b. 2 solutions **c.** $\{(2.4, 3.2), (-3.0, 0.5)\}$

3. a.

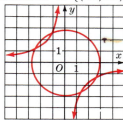

b. 4 solutions

c. $\{(2.6, -1.2), (1.2, -2.6), (-2.6, 1.2), (-1.2, 2.6)\}$

4. $\{(3, -4), (-3, -4), (-4, 3), (4, 3)\}$

5. $\{(6, 1)\}$ **6.** 1 and $\dfrac{1}{4}$

Chapter 10, Self-Test 1, page 379

1. a. $\sqrt[3]{3}$ **b.** $\sqrt[6]{a}$ **2. a.** $\dfrac{2x^{\frac{2}{3}}}{y^{\frac{1}{3}}}$

b. $\dfrac{1}{a} + \dfrac{2}{a^2} + \dfrac{1}{a^3}$ **3. a.** 343 **b.** 125 **4.** -3

Chapter 10, Self-Test 2, page 393

1. $\log_9 27 = \dfrac{3}{2}$ **2.** $\dfrac{2}{3}$ **3.** $\dfrac{1}{27}$

4. $f(g(x)) = f(1 - x^3) = \sqrt[3]{1 - (1 - x^3)} = \sqrt[3]{x^3} = x,$

$g(f(x)) = g(\sqrt[3]{1 - x}) = 1 - (\sqrt[3]{1 - x})^3 = 1 - (1 - x) = x$

5. $f^{-1}(x) = \dfrac{x + 3}{4}$ **6.** $\log_2 \dfrac{u^2}{v^3}$ **7.** -1.398

Chapter 10, Self-Test 3, page 402   **1.** 1.30

2. 0.581 **3.** 1971 **4.** \$1629

Chapter 11, Self-Test 1, page 416   **1.** -6.5

2. $-6, 1, 8$ **3.** 2.25 **4.** $15\sqrt{3}$

Chapter 11, Self-Test 2, page 430   **1.** 200

2. 884 **3.** $-\dfrac{665}{32}$ **4.** $43\dfrac{1}{3}$ **5.** 363 **6.** 4

7. no sum

Chapter 11, Self-Test 3, page 436

1. $x^5 - 5x^4 + 10x^3 - 10x^2 + 5x - 1$

2. $a^{12} + 12a^{10}b + 60a^8b^2 + 160a^6b^3 + 240a^4b^4 + 192a^2b^5 + 64b^6$

3. $0.112p^{12}$ **4.** $540h^6$

Chapter 12, Self-Test 1, page 454   **1.** $286°$

2. $\dfrac{2}{5}$ **3. a.** $\dfrac{4\pi^{\text{R}}}{9}$ **b.** $54°$ **4. a.** -1 **b.** 1

5. $-\dfrac{7}{25}$

Chapter 12, Self-Test 2, page 468

1. 0.8975 **2.** 0.9819 **3.** 0.3843 **4.** 0.8631

5. -0.8727 **6.** -0.9078 **7.** $\{50.2°, 129.8°\}$

8.

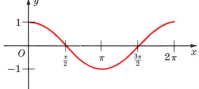

9.

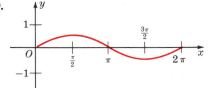

Chapter 12, Self-Test 3, page 479   **1.** $\sqrt{3}$

2. $-\sqrt{2}$ **3.** -2 **4.** $\tan \theta$ **5.** $-\sec \theta$

6. $\sec \theta$ **7.** $\sin^2 \theta$ **8.** 1

Chapter 13, Self-Test 1, page 495

1. a. $\dfrac{3\sqrt{13}}{13}$ **b.** $\dfrac{3}{2}$ **c.** $\dfrac{3\sqrt{13}}{13}$ **d.** $\dfrac{2}{3}$ **e.** $\dfrac{\sqrt{13}}{3}$

f. $\dfrac{2}{3}$ **2.** $66.8°$ **3.** 1.32 m **4.** 15.5

Chapter 13, Self-Test 2, page 507   **1.** 7.09

2. $33°30'$, or $33.6°$

3. $\angle R = 43°30'$, or $43.5°$;

$\angle S = 58°30'$, or $58.5°$; $t = 17.2$

Chapter 13, Self-Test 3, page 515
1. speed: 21.2 km; bearing: $19°20'$, or $19.3°$
2. 81.9 N   3. $x = -9.4, y = 3.42$
4. 14.8 km

Chapter 14, Self-Test 1, page 533
1. a. $\sin 43°$ b. $\cos 46°$ 2. $\dfrac{\sqrt{6}-1}{4}$

3. $-\dfrac{11}{16}$ 4. a. $\cos 62°$ b. $2 \tan 8\alpha$

5. a. $-\dfrac{\sqrt{3}}{2}$ b. $\dfrac{1}{2}$ 6. $\dfrac{1}{20}\sqrt{140}$; $\dfrac{1}{20}\sqrt{260}$;

$\dfrac{1}{13}\sqrt{910}$

Chapter 14, Self-Test 2, page 543   1. a. π
b. $\dfrac{\pi}{4}$ c. π

2.

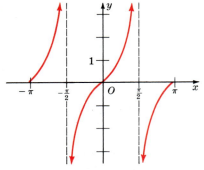

3. a. $-\dfrac{\pi}{3}$ b. $\dfrac{\pi}{3}$ c. $\dfrac{5\pi}{6}$

4.

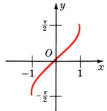

5. a. $\dfrac{\pi}{4}$ b. $-\dfrac{\pi}{3}$ c. $\dfrac{3\sqrt{2}}{2}$

Chapter 14, Self-Test 3, page 551
1. $\{36.9°, 323.1°\}$ 2. $\{5.8°, 185.8°\}$
3. $\{150°, 270°, 330°\}$
4. $\{50°, 110°, 170°, 230°, 290°, 350°\}$
5. $\sqrt{3} + i$ 6. $2\sqrt{2}\left(\cos\dfrac{3\pi}{4} + i \sin\dfrac{3\pi}{4}\right)$

Chapter 15, Self-Test 1, page 576
1. $x = -1, y = 0, z = 4$

2. $\begin{bmatrix} 5 & -2 \\ 0 & 8 \end{bmatrix}$ 3. $\begin{bmatrix} -7 & 6 \\ 6 & 6 \end{bmatrix}$

4. $\begin{bmatrix} -5 & 10 \\ 15 & 35 \end{bmatrix}$ 5. $\begin{bmatrix} -12 & 6 \\ -3 & -5 \end{bmatrix}$

6. $\begin{bmatrix} 48 & -28 \\ -21 & 13 \end{bmatrix}$

7. a. $\begin{bmatrix} 0 & 1 & 1 & 1 \\ 1 & 0 & 1 & 0 \\ 1 & 0 & 0 & 0 \\ 1 & 0 & 1 & 0 \end{bmatrix}$

b. 3

Chapter 15, Self-Test 2, page 583   1. 34
2. 1

3. $\begin{bmatrix} \dfrac{1}{2} & 0 \\ \dfrac{1}{8} & \dfrac{1}{4} \end{bmatrix}$

4. $\begin{bmatrix} -\dfrac{47}{7} & -\dfrac{36}{7} \\ -\dfrac{55}{7} & \dfrac{16}{7} \end{bmatrix}$

Chapter 15, Self-Test 3, page 596   1. -10
2. -23 3. $(-1, 1, 2)$

Chapter 16, Self-Test 1, page 613
1. $_{10}P_4 = 5040$ 2. $5! = 120$ 3. 840
4. $_9C_3 = 84$

Chapter 16, Self-Test 2, page 625
1. a. $\{S, Q, U, A, R, E\}$ b. $\{S, Q, R\}$ 2. $\dfrac{5}{16}$

3. a. $\dfrac{1}{12}$ b. no

Chapter 16, Self-Test 3, page 634
1. mean = 40; var. = 47; st. dev. = 7;
range = 20   2. 0.8185

APPENDIX: COMPUTATION WITH COMMON LOGARITHMS

A-1 *Notation and Interpolation*

OBJECTIVE   **To find logarithms and antilogarithms using interpolation.**

You can use common logarithms to find approximations for complex algebraic expressions such as

$$\frac{\sqrt{93.8}}{0.0592 \times 3.67}$$

You will recall from Section 10-6 that every common logarithm has two parts, a *characteristic* and a *mantissa* (see page 395). In order to use Table 3 as an aid in computation, the mantissa must remain positive. Consider

$$
\begin{aligned}
\log 0.0217 &= \log (2.17 \times 10^{-2}) \\
&= \log 2.17 + \log 10^{-2} \\
&= 0.3365 - 2.
\end{aligned}
$$

To retain the positive mantissa, the characteristic -2 is usually written as $8.0000 - 10$, giving

$$\log 0.0217 = 8.3365 - 10.$$

In some cases it may be more convenient to use other differences such as $28.0000 - 30$ or $98.0000 - 100$ to represent -2. Thus, $\log 0.0217$ might be written as $28.3365 - 30$ or as $98.3365 - 100$.

Table 3 gives logarithms of numbers with three significant digits. By interpolating (see Section 8-9) you can find better approximations for (1) the logarithms of numbers with four significant digits and (2) the antilogarithms of numbers that fall between entries in the body of the table.

EXAMPLE   Find: **a.** $\log 26.83$ **b.** antilog $(6.7382 - 10)$

SOLUTION   **a.** Since $\log 26.83 = \log 2.683 + 1$, interpolate using Table 3 to find $\log 2.683$.

x	$\log x$
2.690	0.4298
2.683	log 2.683
2.680	0.4281

$$0.010 \begin{bmatrix} 0.003 \begin{bmatrix} \\ \end{bmatrix} d \end{bmatrix} 0.0017$$

$$\frac{d}{0.0017} = \frac{0.003}{0.010}$$

$$d = \frac{3}{10} \times 0.0017 \approx 0.0005$$

(*The solution is continued on page 666.*)

The difference d is rounded to four decimal places because mantissas in Table 3 are accurate to only four places.

Thus, $\log 2.683 \approx 0.4281 + 0.0005$
$= 0.4286$

$\therefore \log 26.83 \approx 1.4286$ ***Answer***

b. To find antilog $(6.7382 - 10)$, locate in the body of Table 3 the consecutive entries 7380 and 7390, between which the mantissa 7382 lies. Make note of the corresponding four-digit sequences 5.470 and 5.480 and interpolate as follows:

x	$\log x$
5.480	0.7388
antilog 0.7382	0.7382
5.470	0.7380

$0.010 \left[c \begin{bmatrix} 5.480 \\ \text{antilog } 0.7382 \\ 5.470 \end{bmatrix} \begin{bmatrix} 0.7388 \\ 0.7382 \\ 0.7380 \end{bmatrix} 0.0002 \right] 0.0008$

$$\frac{c}{0.010} = \frac{0.0002}{0.0008}$$

$$c = 0.0025 \approx 0.003$$

$$\text{antilog } 0.7382 \approx 5.470 + 0.003$$
$$= 5.473$$

$\therefore$ antilog $(6.7382 - 10) \approx 5.473 \times 10^{-4}$
$$= 0.0005473 \quad \textbf{\textit{Answer}}$$

Note that the value of c was rounded to one significant figure because reverse interpolation in a four-place table yields at most four significant digits for the number whose logarithm is given. With practice, much of the interpolation can be performed mentally.

Written Exercises

Find each logarithm using interpolation.

A **1.** log 3.475   **2.** log 8.612   **3.** log 77.68   **4.** log 239.6

 5. log 0.5624   **6.** log 0.03857   **7.** log 68244   **8.** log 138760

 9. log 0.4962   **10.** log 0.001634   **11.** log 48560   **12.** log 79820

Find each antilogarithm to four significant digits using interpolation.

13. antilog 0.6968   **14.** antilog 0.7728   **15.** antilog 1.3843

16. antilog 3.8402   **17.** antilog 8.9531 − 10   **18.** antilog 5.1322 − 10

19. antilog 9.9296 − 10   **20.** antilog 7.2388 − 10   **21.** antilog 6.8041 − 10

A-2 *Multiplication and Division with Common Logarithms*

OBJECTIVE   **To use common logarithms to calculate products and quotients.**

For common logarithms, the first two laws stated on page 390 become

(1) $\log p \times q = \log p + \log q$ and
(2) $\log p \div q = \log p - \log q$.

When using logarithms in computation, you can use these laws to replace the operations of multiplication and division with addition and subtraction.

You can avoid making mistakes when computing with logarithms by arranging your work according to these rules:

1. Estimate the answer.
2. List numbers to be added or subtracted in vertical columns.
3. Align equality symbols and decimal points vertically.
4. Write all characteristics before looking up the mantissas.
5. Indicate the operations $(+, -, \times)$ to be performed.
6. Label each step so that if you must check back, you will know what you are checking.

The purpose of making a preliminary estimate of the answer is to avoid the common error of misplacing the decimal point.

Example 1 below does not require interpolation. In general, examples and exercises *do* require interpolation and will be worked to four-digit accuracy.

EXAMPLE 1   Evaluate 0.0192×4370.

SOLUTION
1. Let $N = 0.0192 \times 4370$.
2. Estimate the value of N.

   $0.0192 \approx 0.02$
   $4370 \approx 4000$

   $\therefore N \approx 0.02 \times 4000 = 80$ (estimate)

3. $\log N = \log (0.0192 \times 4370)$
                 $= \log 0.0192 + \log 4370$

   $\log 0.0192 = \quad 8.2833 - 10$
   $\underline{\log 4370 = \quad 3.6405 \qquad\qquad +}$
   $\log N = 11.9238 - 10$
   $\qquad\quad N = \text{antilog } 1.9238 = 83.9$

   $\therefore 0.0192 \times 4370 = 83.9$ ***Answer***

Note that the answer and the estimate agree to one significant digit.

Only common logarithms of numbers that are powers of 10 can be stated exactly. Thus, although 0.0192×4370 is only approximately equal to 83.9, the "=" sign will be used for simplicity.

EXAMPLE 2 Evaluate $\dfrac{-7.394}{91.47}$.

SOLUTION

1. Since you know the answer will be negative, let $N = \dfrac{7.394}{91.47}$ to facilitate computation by logarithms.

2. Estimate the value of N.

$$\frac{7.394}{91.47} \approx \frac{7}{9 \times 10^1} \approx 0.7 \times 10^{-1} = 0.07$$

3. $\log N = \log \dfrac{7.394}{91.47}$

$= \log 7.394 - \log 91.47$

$\log 7.394 = 0.8688$ (by interpolation)
$\underline{\log 91.47 = 1.9613}$ $-$ (by interpolation)

To obtain a difference in which the mantissa is positive, write 0.8688 as $10.8688 - 10$.

$\log 7.394 = 10.8688 - 10$
$\underline{\log 91.47 = 1.9613}$ $-$
$ \log N = 8.9075 - 10$
$ N = 0.08082$ (by interpolation)

$\therefore \dfrac{-7.394}{91.47} = -0.08082$ ***Answer***

Check the answer against the estimate.

Written Exercises

Given that $\log A = 3.6100$, $\log B = 8.1234 - 10$ and $\log C = 1.2000$, find the following.

A   **1.** $\log AC$

2. $\log BC$

3. $\log \dfrac{A}{B}$

4. $\log \dfrac{A}{C}$

5. $\log AB$

6. $\log ABC$

7. $\log \dfrac{C}{A}$

8. $\log \dfrac{C}{B}$

9. $\log 100B$

10. $\log 0.01A$

11. $\log \dfrac{1000}{C}$

12. $\log \dfrac{0.001}{B}$

Use Table 3 to evaluate each expression to four significant digits. Interpolate where necessary.

13. 281×0.94

14. 0.749×0.562

15. 943×804

16. 0.321×8.35

17. 36.9×7.71 **18.** 13.5×642 **19.** 8.26×545 **20.** 727×0.013

B **21.** $\dfrac{4.26}{1.32}$ **22.** $\dfrac{432}{27}$ **23.** $\dfrac{117}{3.26}$ **24.** $\dfrac{4960}{54600}$

25. $\dfrac{0.013}{427}$ **26.** $\dfrac{0.526}{0.049}$ **27.** $\dfrac{0.359}{1.28}$ **28.** $\dfrac{0.728}{0.0351}$

29. 0.572×6370 **30.** 23.64×1.47 **31.** 0.8215×0.051

32. $\dfrac{0.1496}{0.582}$ **33.** $\dfrac{137}{5242}$ **34.** $\dfrac{0.05274}{0.9412}$

35. $2.16 \times 46.73 \times 134.5$ **36.** $94 \times 0.05 \times 1.728$ **37.** $1.8 \times 32 \times 0.01347$

C **38.** $\dfrac{52.97 \times 0.1152}{3219}$ **39.** $\dfrac{36.21}{0.4892 \times 4.825}$ **40.** $(3.641)^7$

41. $(0.9327)^5$ **42.** $\sqrt{29.84}$ **43.** $\sqrt[3]{0.1396}$

A-3 *Finding Powers and Roots*

OBJECTIVE   **To use logarithms to evaluate powers, roots, and mixed expressions.**

You can use the third law of logarithms,

$$\log p^n = n \log p,$$

to compute powers and roots.

EXAMPLE 1   Evaluate $(0.239)^7$.

SOLUTION   1. Let $N = (0.239)^7$.

2. To estimate, round 3 factors up and 4 factors down.
$N \approx (0.2)^4(0.3)^3 = (0.0016)(0.027) = 0.0000432$ (estimate)

3. $\log N = 7 \log 0.239$

$$\log 0.239 = \begin{array}{r} 9.3784 - 10 \\ \underline{ 7} \end{array} \times$$

$$\log N = 65.6488 - 70$$
$$= 5.6488 - 10$$
$$N = \text{antilog}\,(5.6488 - 10) = 0.00004454$$

$\therefore (0.239)^7 = 0.00004454$ ***Answer***

EXAMPLE 2 Evaluate $\sqrt[3]{0.482}$

SOLUTION 1. Let $N = \sqrt[3]{0.482} = (0.482)^{\frac{1}{3}}$.

2. Estimate the value of N.

$(0.7)^3 = 0.343; \quad (0.8)^3 = 0.512$

$\therefore 0.7 < N < 0.8$

3. $\quad \log N = \frac{1}{3}(0.482)$

$\log 0.482 = 9.6830 - 10$

To ensure that the negative part of the characteristic remains an integer after it is multiplied by $\frac{1}{3}$, write $9.6830 - 10$ as $29.6830 - 30$.

$\log 0.482 = 29.6830 - 30$

$\frac{1}{3} \; \times$

$\overline{}$

$\log N = \quad 9.8943 - 10$

$N = \text{antilog } (9.8943 - 10) = 0.7841$

$\therefore \sqrt[3]{0.482} = 0.7841$ ***Answer***

You can apply the laws of logarithms to several operations at once as in Example 3.

EXAMPLE 3 Evaluate $\sqrt[5]{\dfrac{(81.2)^2}{0.59 \times 367}}$ to four significant digits.

SOLUTION 1. Estimate: $\sqrt[5]{\dfrac{(81.2)^2}{0.59 \times 367}} \approx \sqrt[5]{\dfrac{81^2}{6 \times 36}} = \sqrt[5]{\dfrac{3^8}{3^3 \cdot 2^3}}$

$\approx \sqrt[5]{\dfrac{3^5}{2^3}} \approx \sqrt[5]{\dfrac{243}{8}} \approx \sqrt[5]{30} \approx \sqrt[5]{32} = 2$

2. Let $H = (81.2)^2$, $K = 0.59 \times 367$, and $N = \left(\dfrac{H}{K}\right)^{\frac{1}{5}}$.

Then $\log N = \frac{1}{5}(\log H - \log K)$.

$\log H = 2 \log 81.2$ $\log K = \log 0.59 + \log 367$

$\log 81.2 = 1.9096$ $\log 0.59 = 9.7709 - 10$

$\qquad\qquad 2 \;\times$ $\log 367 = 2.5647$ $+$

$\overline{}$ $\overline{}$

$\log H = 3.8192$ $\log K = 2.3356$

$\log H = 3.8192$

$\log K = 2.3356 \quad -$

$\overline{}$

$\log H - \log K = 1.4836$

$\frac{1}{5} \; \times$

$\overline{}$

$\log N = 0.2967$

$\text{antilog } 0.2967 = 1.980$

$\therefore \sqrt[5]{\dfrac{(81.2)^2}{0.59 \times 367}} = 1.980$ ***Answer***

Written Exercises

Given that $\log A = 13.600$, $\log B = 8.1310 - 10$, and $\log C = 3.2148$, find the following.

A

1. $\log B^2$
2. $\log C^{10}$
3. $\log \sqrt{C}$
4. $\log \sqrt[3]{A}$
5. $\log C^{\frac{3}{4}}$
6. $\log B^{\frac{3}{2}}$
7. $\log \sqrt{A^3}$
8. $\log \sqrt[3]{B^2}$
9. $\log A^2 B$
10. $\log (BC^2)^3$
11. $\log \sqrt{ABC}$
12. $\log A\sqrt{B}$
13. $\log \dfrac{BC}{A}$
14. $\log \dfrac{C}{AB}$
15. $\log \dfrac{\sqrt{A}}{\sqrt[3]{C}}$
16. $\log \dfrac{B}{\sqrt{A}}$

Use Table 3 to evaluate each expression to three significant digits. Do not interpolate.

17. $(2.81)^{10}$
18. $(90.3)^5$
19. $(0.395)^7$
20. $(0.0431)^2$
21. $(21.4)^{\frac{1}{3}}$
22. $(8.26)^{\frac{2}{3}}$
23. $\sqrt{12.4}$
24. $\sqrt[3]{1.36}$

B

25. $(12.4)^3(3.86)^2$
26. $(37.4)^5(812)^2$
27. $(42.3)^4(0.0016)^2$
28. $\dfrac{57 \times 641}{8.5}$
29. $\dfrac{0.32 \times 756}{9.52}$
30. $\dfrac{(1.57)^8}{156 \times 2.15}$
31. $\sqrt{\dfrac{427}{0.592}}$
32. $\sqrt[3]{\dfrac{(2.37)^2}{1.15}}$
33. $\sqrt{\dfrac{(2.03)^3}{97.5 \times 1.98}}$

Use Table 3 to evaluate each expression to four significant digits. Interpolate where necessary.

C

34. $\sqrt[3]{\dfrac{94.61^2}{1.027^4}}$
35. $\dfrac{\sqrt{0.02563^3}}{\sqrt[3]{0.03159^2}}$
36. $\sqrt[5]{\dfrac{(527.4)^2}{1542 \times (0.2592)^2}}$
37. $\sqrt{\dfrac{12560^3}{79.21 \times 8004}}$
38. $92.37^{0.562}$
39. $0.3142^{1.273}$

40. Using $\pi \approx 3.142$, find V when $V = \frac{4}{3}\pi r^3$ and $r = 0.1526$.

41. Given that $\log 2 = 0.3010$ and $\log 3 = 0.4771$, find $\log 4$, $\log 5$, $\log 6$, $\log 8$, and $\log 9$ without using tables or a calculator.

42. Determine the number of digits in 3^{51} without using a calculator.

APPENDIX: MORE ABOUT CONIC SECTIONS

The circle, ellipse, and hyperbola are called **conic sections.** As described on page 366 when a plane intersects a double cone at various angles, the following plane figures are formed:

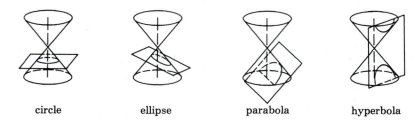

circle   ellipse   parabola   hyperbola

So far you have studied mostly **central conics,** that is, conics with centers at the origin. Let us consider what happens to the equations and corresponding graphs of a circle, ellipse, and hyperbola when the centers are not at the origin.

Circle

Recall that the equation of a circle with center (h, k) and radius r is

$$(x - h)^2 + (y - k)^2 = r^2 \qquad (1)$$

If the center $(h, k) = (0, 0)$, then the equation becomes

$$x^2 + y^2 = r^2 \qquad (2)$$

If we take the graph of equation (2) and move it *horizontally* h units and *vertically* k units, we will obtain the graph of equation (1).

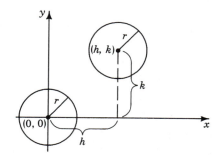

Ellipse

You have studied the equation for an ellipse having its center at the origin:

$$\frac{x^2}{a^2} + \frac{y^2}{b^2} = 1 \qquad \text{(foci are on } x\text{-axis)} \tag{3}$$

$$\frac{x^2}{b^2} + \frac{y^2}{a^2} = 1 \qquad \text{(foci are on } y\text{-axis)} \tag{4}$$

where $b^2 = a^2 - c^2$.

The segments that are cut off by the intersection of the ellipse with the x-axis and y-axis are also called axes. We call the longer segment the **major axis** and the shorter one the **minor axis.** In (3) the major axis is on the x-axis

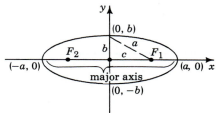

and in (4) the major axis is on the y-axis.

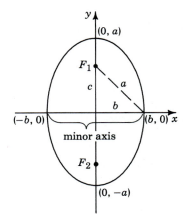

If the center (h, k) is not at the origin, the equations (when $a > b$) are:

$$\frac{(x - h)^2}{a^2} + \frac{(y - k)^2}{b^2} = 1 \qquad \begin{array}{l}\text{(major axis is} \\ \text{parallel to } x\text{-axis)}\end{array} \tag{5}$$

$$\frac{(x - h)^2}{b^2} + \frac{(y - k)^2}{a^2} = 1 \qquad \begin{array}{l}\text{(major axis is} \\ \text{parallel to } y\text{-axis)}\end{array} \tag{6}$$

The graph of equation (5) is easily obtained by moving every point on the graph of equation (3) horizontally h units and vertically k units.

EXAMPLE 1 Analyze the equation and sketch its graph. $\dfrac{(x-2)^2}{25} + \dfrac{(y+3)^2}{16} = 1$

SOLUTION

1. The major axis is parallel to the x-axis.

2. Since $h = 2$ and $k = -3$, every point on the graph of $\dfrac{x^2}{25} + \dfrac{y^2}{16} = 1$ is moved 2 units to the **right** and 3 units **down.**

3. $a = \pm 5$, $b = \pm 4$, and $c = \pm\sqrt{25-16} = \pm 3$. The center moves from $(0, 0)$ to $(2, -3)$. The x-intercepts move from $(5, 0)$ and $(-5, 0)$ to $(-3, -3)$ and $(7, -3)$. The y-intercepts move from $(0, 4)$ and $(0, -4)$ to $(2, 1)$ and $(2, -7)$. The foci move from $(-3, 0)$ and $(3, 0)$ to $(-1, -3)$ and $(5, -3)$.

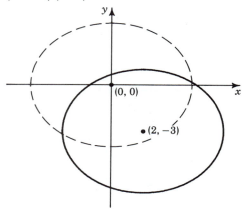

Hyperbola

The method used for graphing the hyperbola is very much like that for the ellipse.

When the center of a hyperbola is at the origin, the equations are:

$$\frac{x^2}{a^2} - \frac{y^2}{b^2} = 1 \qquad \text{(Vertices } (-a, 0) \text{ and } (a, 0) \qquad (7)$$
$$\text{are the } x\text{-intercepts.)}$$

$$\frac{y^2}{a^2} - \frac{x^2}{b^2} = 1 \qquad \text{(Vertices } (0, -a) \text{ and } (0, a) \qquad (8)$$
$$\text{are the } y\text{-intercepts.)}$$

where $b^2 = c^2 - a^2$.

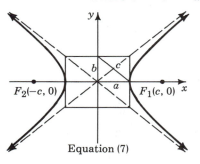

Equation (7)

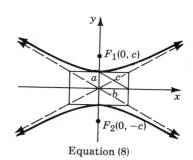

Equation (8)

When the center (h, k) is not at the origin the equations are:

$$\frac{(x - h)^2}{a^2} - \frac{(y - k)^2}{b^2} \qquad \text{(hyperbola ``opens} \qquad (9)$$
$$\text{outward'' parallel}$$
$$\text{to } y\text{-axis)}$$

$$\frac{(y - k)^2}{a^2} - \frac{(x - h)^2}{b^2} \qquad \text{(hyperbola ``opens} \qquad (10)$$
$$\text{outward'' parallel}$$
$$\text{to } x\text{-axis)}$$

Again, the graph of equation (9) is easily obtained by moving every point on the graph of equation (7), including the asymptotes, h units horizontally and k units vertically.

EXAMPLE 2   Analyze the equation and sketch its graph.
$$25y^2 - 4x^2 + 100y + 40x - 100 = 0.$$

SOLUTION   Complete the square twice:

$$25y^2 + 100y - 4x^2 + 40x = 100$$
$$25(y^2 + 4y + \quad) - 4(x^2 - 10x + \quad) = 100$$
$$25(y^2 + 4y + 4) - 4(x^2 - 10x + 25) = 100 + 100 - 100$$
$$25(y + 2)^2 - 4(x - 5)^2 = 100$$
$$\frac{(y + 2)^2}{4} - \frac{(x - 5)^2}{25} = 1$$

1. The hyperbola opens outward and parallel to the x-axis.

2. Since $h = -2$ and $k = 5$, every point on the graph of $\dfrac{y^2}{4} - \dfrac{x^2}{25} = 1$ is moved 2 units to the **left** and 5 units **up.** The asymptotes of $\dfrac{y^2}{4} - \dfrac{x^2}{25} = 1$ are the diagonals of the rectangle formed by the lines $y = 2$, $y = -2$, $x = 5$, and $x = -5$.

3. The y-intercepts move from $(0, -2)$ and $(0, 2)$ to $(-2, 3)$ and $(-2, 7)$. The asymptotes are the diagonals of the rectangle formed by the lines $y = 7$, $y = 3$, $x = 3$, and $x = -7$.

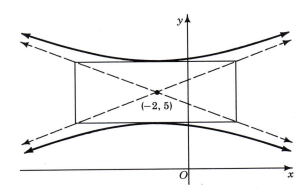

Written Exercises

Identify each conic section. Indicate the direction the corresponding central conic will be moved to obtain the graph of the given conic section.

$$\frac{(x - 10)^2}{4} + \frac{(y + 4)^2}{25} = 1$$

Given conic section is an ellipse. The corresponding conic section is moved to the right 10 units and down 4 units.

A

1. $\dfrac{(x + 1)^2}{16} - \dfrac{(y + 3)^2}{9} = 1$

2. $(x - 5)^2 + (y + 2)^2 = 49$

3. $4(x - 6)^2 + (y - 1)^2 = 100$

Graph each conic section.

4. $x^2 + 4y^2 + 6x - 64y + 249 = 0$

5. $16y^2 - 9x^2 + 64y + 54x - 593 = 0$

6. $x^2 + y^2 - 8x - 10y + 25 = 0$

7. $25(x - 5)^2 = 36(y + 1)^2 + 900$

8. $4x^2 - (y - 3)^2 = 36$

B

9. Graph the inequality $64(x + 7)^2 + 4y^2 > 64$

10. Solve the system and check by graphing.
$$(x + 2)^2 + 9(y - 1)^2 = 36$$
$$x - y = -5$$

APPENDIX: BOUNDS FOR ROOTS

In Section 8-7 you used Descartes' rule of signs to obtain the *number* of positive and negative roots of a polynomial equation $P(x) = 0$ with real coefficients. You can use the following theorem to find *bounds* for the real roots of a polynomial equation.

> THEOREM Let $P(x)$ be a polynomial with real coefficients and with positive leading coefficient. Let M be a nonnegative real number and L a nonpositive real number. If the coefficients of the quotient and remainder obtained on dividing $P(x)$ by $x - M$ are all positive numbers or zero, then $P(x) = 0$ has no roots greater than M. If the coefficients obtained on dividing $P(x)$ by $x - L$ are alternately nonnegative and nonpositive numbers, then $P(x) = 0$ has no roots less than L.

The numbers M and L are called **upper** and **lower bounds** for the real roots. To apply the theorem, you look at the numbers in the last line of the synthetic substitution of M or L for x in $P(x)$.

EXAMPLE Find the least nonnegative integral upper bound and the greatest nonpositive integral lower bound for the roots of
$$2x^3 - 3x^2 - 3x + 3 = 0.$$

SOLUTION Use synthetic substitution with $x = 1, 2, 3, \ldots$ until an upper bound is reached, and with $x = -1, -2, -3, \ldots$ until a lower bound is reached.

	2	−3	−3	3	
1	2	−1	−4	−1	
2	2	1	−1	1	
3	2	3	6	21	$\rightarrow$ all positive or zero
−1	2	−5	2	1	
−2	2	−7	11	−19	$\rightarrow$ alternating nonnegative and nonpositive

Thus, 3 is an upper bound and −2 is a lower bound. **Answer**

Written Exercises

Find the least nonnegative integral upper bound and the greatest nonpositive integral lower bound of the real roots for each equation.

A
    1. $2x^3 - 2x^2 + x + 8 = 0$

    2. $x^3 - 2x^2 + 3x + 5 = 0$

    3. $2y^3 + 3y^2 - 4y - 1 = 0$

    4. $m^5 + m^4 - 2m - 4 = 0$

    5. $2x^3 - 3x^2 - 3x + 3 = 0$

    6. $2t^4 - 7t^3 + 4t^2 + 7t - 6 = 0$

C
    7. Let $P(x) = (x - M)Q(x) + P(M)$. Prove that if the terms of $Q(x)$ all have nonnegative coefficients, and if M is a nonnegative real number such that $P(M) \geqslant 0$, then $P(x) = 0$ can have no roots greater than M. *Hint:* For all $x > M$, $(x - M) > 0$ and $Q(x) > 0$.

    8. Let $P(x) = (x - L)Q(x) + P(L)$. Prove that if L is a nonpositive real number, and if the coefficients of $Q(x)$ and $P(L)$ are alternately nonnegative and nonpositive numbers, then $P(x) = 0$ can have no roots less than L. *Hint:* Examine the value for $Q(x)$ under the circumstances described and observe that for all $x < L$, $(x - L) < 0$.

GLOSSARY

abscissa (p. 84). The first coordinate in an ordered pair of numbers associated with a point in a coordinate plane. Also called *x-coordinate*.

absolute value (p. 27). The positive number in any pair of nonzero additive inverses.

algebraic expressions (p. 11). Numerical expressions, variables, and indicated sums, products, differences, and quotients containing variables.

amplitude of a complex number (p. 549). The angle θ in standard position whose terminal ray is the arrow from the origin to $a + bi$.

amplitude of a periodic function (p. 464). When a periodic function has a maximum value M and a minimum value m, its amplitude is $\frac{M - m}{2}$.

angle (p. 54). A figure formed by two rays that have the same endpoint.

antilogarithm (p. 395). If $\log x = a$, then x is called the antilogarithm of a.

arithmetic means (p. 409). The terms between two given terms of an arithmetic sequence. A single arithmetic mean between two numbers is called *the arithmetic mean,* or *average,* of the two numbers.

arithmetic sequence (p. 408). A sequence in which the difference between any two successive terms is a constant, called the *common difference.* Also called *arithmetic progression.*

axiom (p. 14). A statement that is assumed to be true. Also called *postulate.*

axis (p. 83). A number line used for reference in locating points on a coordinate plane.

base (p. 2). The repeated factor in a power. In a^2, a is the base.

binomial (p. 46). A polynomial consisting of two terms.

characteristic (p. 395). The integral, or whole number, part of a logarithm.

circle (p. 334). The set of all points in a plane that are equidistant from a given point, called the *center.*

combination (p. 610). An r-element subset of a set of n elements is called a combination of n elements taken r at a time.

common logarithms (p. 394). Logarithms to the base 10.

complex fraction (p. 189). A fraction whose numerator or denominator (or both) contains one or more fractions or powers with negative exponents.

complex number (p. 234). A number of the form $a + bi$, in which a and b are real and i is the imaginary unit.

complex plane (p. 547). The rectangular coordinate system used to graph complex numbers.

components of a vector (p. 512). Two vectors whose sum is another vector, $\overrightarrow{RS}$, are called components of $\overrightarrow{RS}$.

conjugates (p. 238). Two complex numbers in the form $a + bi$ and $a - bi$ are called conjugates of each other.

consistent equations (p. 286). The equations in a system that has at least one solution.

constant of variation (pp. 115, 353). In an equation of the form $y = mx$ ($m \neq 0$), which specifies a direct variation, m is the constant of variation. In an equation of the form $xy = k$ ($k \neq 0$), which specifies an inverse variation, k is the constant of variation. Also called *constant of proportionality.*

converse (p. 20). A statement obtained by interchanging the hypothesis and conclusion in an if-then statement.

coordinate (p. 6). On a number line, the real number paired with a point. *See also* plane rectangular coordinate system.

coordinate plane (p. 83). A one-to-one pairing of all points of a plane with all ordered pairs of real numbers. Also called *Cartesian coordinate plane.*

corollary (p. 20). A theorem that follows easily from another.

cosecant of $\boldsymbol{\theta}$ (p. 469).
$$\csc \theta = \frac{1}{\sin \theta}, \ \sin \theta \neq 0$$

cosine (p. 450). If the terminal ray of any angle θ in standard position intersects the circle $x^2 + y^2 = r^2$ at point P, then the
$$\text{cosine of } \theta = \frac{x\text{-coordinate of } P}{\text{radius}}.$$

cotangent of $\boldsymbol{\theta}$ (p. 469).
$$\cot \theta = \frac{\cos \theta}{\sin \theta}, \ \sin \theta \neq 0$$

coterminal angles (p. 442). Angles that have the same initial and terminal rays.

degree of a monomial (p. 45). The total number of times the variables in a monomial occur as factors; the sum of the exponents of the variables.

degree of a polynomial (p. 46). The greatest of the degrees of the terms of the polynomial after it has been simplified.

dependent equations (p. 286). The equations in a system that has an infinite solution set.

discriminant (p. 262). The expression $b^2 - 4ac$ is called the discriminant of the quadratic equation $ax^2 + bx + c = 0$.

domain of a relation (pp. 107, 120). The set of all the first coordinates of the ordered pairs in the relation.

domain of a variable (p. 10). The set whose members may serve as replacements for a variable. The members of a domain are called the *values* of the variable.

ellipse (p. 343). The set of points in a plane such that for each point of the set, the sum of the distances to two fixed points (the *foci*) is a given constant.

equation (p. 1). A sentence formed by placing an equals sign ($=$) between two expressions.

equivalent equations (p. 49). Equations that have the same solution set over a given domain.

equivalent expressions (p. 47). Expressions that are equal for every value of the variable for which each expression makes sense.

event (p. 614). Any subset of possible outcomes for an experiment is known as an event.

exponent (p. 2). In a power, the number of times the base occurs as a factor. In the power 4^3, 3 is the exponent.

exponential function with base a (p. 377). If $a > 0$ and $a \neq 1$, the function defined by $y = a^x$.

extremes of a proportion (p. 116). In the proportion $\dfrac{y_1}{x_1} = \dfrac{y_2}{x_2}$, y_1 and x_2 are called the extremes.

factorial notation (p. 434). A notation used to abbreviate the product of consecutive integers beginning with 1. For example, 3! (3 factorial) is the product $3 \cdot 2 \cdot 1$.

finite sequence (p. 407). A sequence that has a last term.

formula (p. 51). An equation that states a relationship among quantities represented by variables.

fractional equation (p. 199). An equation in which a variable appears in the denominator of a fraction.

function (p. 107). A relation that assigns to each element in the domain a single element in the range.

geometric means (p. 413). The terms between two given terms of a geometric sequence. A single geometric mean between two terms is called *the geometric mean*, or the *mean proportional*.

geometric sequence (p. 412). A sequence in which the ratio r of every pair of successive terms is constant. The ratio r is called the *common ratio*. Also called *geometric progression*.

greatest common factor (pp. 137, 138). (1) The greatest integer that is a factor of two or more given integers. (2) The monomial with the greatest numerical coefficient and the greatest degree that is a factor of each of several monomials.

hyperbola (p. 348). A set of points in a plane such that for each point of the set, the difference of its distances to two fixed points (called *foci*) is a given constant.

hypotenuse (p. 487). The longest side of a right triangle.

identity (p. 47). An equation whose sides are equivalent expressions.

imaginary unit (p. 234). The number i with the property that $i^2 = -1$.

inconsistent equations (p. 286). The equations in a system that has no solution.

inequality (p. 7). A statement formed by placing an inequality symbol between two numerical or variable expressions.

infinite sequence (p. 407). A sequence that does not have a last term.

integer (p. 6). A member of the set $\{ \cdots, -3, -2, -1, 0, 1, 2, 3, \cdots \}$.

inverse functions (p. 385). Two functions f and g are inverse functions if $f(g(x)) = x$ for all x in the domain of g and $g(f(x)) = x$ for all x in the domain of f.

inverse matrices (p. 580). Any two matrices A and B such that $AB = BA = I$ (the identity matrix) are called inverse matrices, or *inverses*.

inverse variation (p. 353). Any function defined by an equation of the form $xy = k \, (k \neq 0)$.

irrational number (p. 6). A real number that is not rational, such as $\sqrt{2}, -\sqrt{5}, \pi$.

least common multiple (p. 138). The monomial with the least positive coefficient and least degree that is a multiple of each of several monomials.

linear direct variation (p. 115). Any linear function specified by an equation of the form $y = mx$, in which m is a nonzero constant.

linear equation (p. 91). An equation in which each term is either a constant or a monomial of degree 1.

linear function (p. 111). A function f is a linear function provided there exist real numbers b and m $(m \neq 0)$ such that for every x in the domain of f, $f(x) = mx + b$.

linear inequality (p. 294). An inequality whose associated equation is a linear equation.

linear interpolation (p. 318). A process based on the assumption that a small part of the graph of a function is a straight line, so that the value of the function at a given point (not given in an appropriate table) can be approximated.

logarithmic function with base a (p. 382). The function defined for $x > 0$ by the equation $y = \log_a x \, (a > 0, a \neq 1)$.

mantissa (p. 395). The decimal, or fractional, part of a logarithm.

matrix (p. 559). A rectangular array of numbers enclosed by brackets. Individual numbers that make up a matrix are called *elements*, or *entries*.

mean (p. 626). Of a collection of data, the arithmetic average of the data.

monomial (p. 45). A term that is either a numeral, a variable, or a product of a numeral and one or more variables. A *constant monomial*, or *constant*, contains no variable.

natural numbers (p. 6). Members of the set $\{1, 2, 3, 4, \cdots\}$.

numeral (p. 1). A symbol used to represent a number. Also called *numerical expression*.

open sentence (p. 49). A sentence that contains one or more variables.

ordered pair of numbers (p. 84). A pair of numbers in which the order is important.

ordinate (p. 84). The second coordinate in an ordered pair of numbers associated with a point in a coordinate plane. Also called *y-coordinate*.

origin (p. 7). On a number line, the graph of zero. In a plane rectangular coordinate system, the point at which the axes intersect.

parabola (pp. 268, 338). Any curve consisting of the set of points equidistant from a fixed line (the *directrix*) and a fixed point (the *focus*) not on the line.

periodic function (p. 463). A function f such that for a nonzero constant p, $f(x + p) = f(x)$ for each x in the domain of f. The constant, p, is called the *period* of f.

permutation (p. 605). An arrangement of objects in a definite order.

polynomial (p. 46). A monomial or a sum of monomials.

power (p. 2). A product of equal factors. The second power of a is a^2.

power function (p. 210). A function defined by an equation of the form $y = x^n$.

prime number (p. 137). An integer greater than 1 that has no positive integral factors other than itself and 1.

prime polynomial (p. 144). An irreducible polynomial whose greatest monomial factor is 1.

proof (p. 20). A form of logical reasoning from hypothesis to conclusion.

quadrant (p. 83). One of the four regions into which a plane rectangular coordinate system is divided by its axes.

quadratic equation (p. 249). An equation of the form $ax^2 + bx + c = 0$, in which a, b, and c are real numbers and $a \neq 0$.

quadratic formula (p. 253). Solutions of the quadratic equation $ax^2 + bx + c = 0$ $(a \neq 0)$ are given by the formula
$$x = \frac{-b \pm \sqrt{b^2 - 4ac}}{2a}.$$

quadratic function (p. 273). A function f of the form
$$f(x) = ax^2 + bx + c \, (a \neq 0).$$

radian (p. 446). An angular measure. The measure of 1 radian is assigned to an angle subtended by an arc of measure 1 on a circle of radius 1.

radical (p. 211). The symbol $\sqrt[n]{b}$, read "the principal nth root of b" or "the nth root of b."

radicand (p. 211). The expression under a radical sign.

range of a relation (pp. 107, 120). The set of all the second coordinates of the ordered pairs in the relation.

rational algebraic expression (p. 177). Any expression that is the quotient of two polynomials. Also called *rational expression*.

rational number (p. 6). Any number that can be expressed in the form $\frac{a}{b}$, in which a is an integer and b is a nonzero integer.

real numbers (p. 6). The rational numbers and the irrational numbers.

reciprocal (p. 15). Each nonzero real number has a reciprocal, or *multiplicative inverse*, such that the product of the number and its reciprocal is 1.

reference angle (p. 458). A reference angle α in the first quadrant is associated with each angle θ in standard position such that the absolute values of the trigonometric functions of α and θ are equal.

relation (p. 120). Any set of ordered pairs.

resultant (p. 508). The sum of two vectors.

sample space (p. 614). The set of all possible outcomes of a random experiment.

scalar (p. 563). In matrix algebra a real number is called a scalar.

scientific notation (p. 172). Expression of a number in the form $a \times 10^n$, in which a is a number between 1 and 10 and n is an integer.

secant of θ (p. 469).
$\sec \theta = \frac{1}{\cos \theta}$, $\cos \theta \neq 0$

sequence (p. 407). The values of any function whose domain is composed of consecutive natural numbers. Each value is called a *term* of the sequence.

series (p. 417). The indicated sum of the terms in a sequence. An *arithmetic series* is a series whose associated sequence is arithmetic. A *geometric series* is the indicated sum of a geometric sequence.

significant digit (p. 172). A significant digit of a decimal numeral is any nonzero digit or any zero whose purpose is not just to place the decimal point.

sine of θ (p. 450). If the terminal ray of any angle θ in standard position intersects the circle $x^2 + y^2 = r^2$ at point P, then the sine of $\theta = \frac{y\text{-coordinate of } P}{\text{radius}}$.

slope (p. 96). If (x_1, y_1) are the coordinates of a point P in a plane, and (x_2, y_2) are the coordinates of a different point Q, then the slope of line PQ is $\frac{y_2 - y_1}{x_2 - x_1}$.

solution (p. 49). Any value(s) of the variable(s) that make(s) an open sentence true. Also called *root*.

solution set (pp. 49, 87). For an open sentence in one variable, the set of all solutions over a given domain of the variable. For an open sentence in two variables, the set of ordered pairs of numbers that belong to the replacement sets of the variables for which the sentence is true.

standard deviation (p. 627). The number most commonly used in characterizing the *spread* of a frequency distribution.

standard position of an angle (p. 443). The angle's vertex is at the origin and its initial ray lies on the positive x-axis.

synthetic division (p. 303). A method using detached coefficients to display the process of dividing a polynomial in x by $x - r$. Also called *synthetic substitution*.

system of simultaneous equations (p. 284). Two or more equations in the same variables.

tangent of θ (p. 469).
$\tan \theta = \frac{\sin \theta}{\cos \theta}$, $\cos \theta \neq 0$.

theorem (p. 20). An assertion that has been proved or is to be proved.

trinomial (p. 46). A polynomial consisting of three terms.

value of f at x (p. 108). The second coordinate of the ordered pair of f whose first coordinate is x. Denoted $f(x)$.

variable (p. 10). A symbol used to represent any member of a given set.

vector (p. 508). Directed line segment, or arrow. The length of an arrow indicates the magnitude of the vector quantity, and the direction of the arrow indicates the direction of the vector.

vertex of a parabola (p. 268). The point where the parabola crosses its axis (of symmetry).

x-coordinate (p. 88). *See* abscissa.

x-intercept (p. 104). The x-coordinate of a point where a line or curve crosses the x-axis.

y-coordinate (p. 88). *See* ordinate.

y-intercept (p. 103). The y-coordinate of the point where a line or curve crosses the y-axis.

INDEX

ANSWERS TO SELECTED EXERCISES

CHAPTER 1   THE REAL NUMBERS

Written Exercises, pages 4–5   **1.** 8   **3.** 1
5. =   **7.** =   **9.** =   **11.** =   **13.** $\neq$
15. 14   **17.** 7   **19.** 0   **21.** 2   **23.** 6   **25.** 1
27. 5   **29.** 5   **31.** 3   **33.** 93   **35.** 23
37. $8(3 + 7) - 2$ **39.** $9(7 - 1) + 6 \cdot 8 + 6$
41. $(2 + 10)^2 \div (10 - 6)^2$
43. $(2 + 5)^2 - 4 \cdot 5 = 29$
45. $3^3 - (3 \div 3) - 3$

Calculator Key-In, page 5   **1.** 25.298   **3.** 33
5. 29.55

Written Exercises, pages 8–9   **1.** -2 **3.** 0
5. 6   **7.** 4.5   **9.** 1.25

11.

$-3 < 0 < 1$

13.

$-1 < 0 < \dfrac{1}{2}$

15.

$-3 < -0.5 < 1.5$

17.

$-\dfrac{5}{4} < -\dfrac{3}{4} < \dfrac{1}{4}$

19. $-1 < 2$ **21.** $0 > -7$ **23.** $5 > 4$
25. $7 < 10 < 50$ **27.** $-7, -5, -1, 1, 3$
29. $-3, -2\dfrac{1}{2}, 1, 2$

31. $-4.5, -3.5, -2, -1$ **33.** -3 **35.** 0
37. -1 **39.** 0   **41.** 0.2

Written Exercises, pages 12–13   **1.** 7
3–7. Answers may vary.   **3.** 0   **5.** 7

7. -1 **9.** 21   **11.** 85   **13.** 2   **15.** 5   **17.** $\dfrac{42}{13}$

19. 0   **21.** For all real numbers x,
$2x + 6 = 2(x + 3)$.   **23.** There exists a real
number y such that $2y > y + 4$.

Written Exercises, pages 17–19   **1. a.** Com.
ax. for add.   **b.** Assoc. ax. for add.
3. a. Com. ax. for add.   **b.** Assoc. ax. for
add.   **5. a.** Assoc. ax. for mult.   **b.** Com.
ax. for mult.   **c.** Assoc. ax. for mult.
d. Assoc. ax. for mult.   **7. a.** Dist. ax.
b. Assoc. ax. for mult.   **c.** Id. ax. for mult.
9. a. Com. ax. for add.   **b.** Assoc. ax. for
add.   **c.** Id. ax. for mult.   **d.** Dist. ax.
e. Id. ax. for mult.   **f.** Dist. ax.
11. a. Dist. ax.   **b.** Assoc. ax. for mult.
c. Inv. ax. for mult.   **d.** Id. ax. for mult.

Written Exercises, pages 23–25
1. (1) Assoc. ax. for add.   (2) Inv. ax. for
add.   (3) Id. ax. for add.   (4) Trans. prop.
of =   **3.** (1) Hyp. (or given)   (2) Add. prop.
of =   (3) Add. prop. of =   (4) Trans. prop.
of =   **5.** (1) Hyp. (or given)   (2) Inv. ax.
for mult.   (3) Mult. prop. of =   (4) Assoc.
ax. for mult.   (5) Trans. prop. of =   (6) Inv.
ax. for mult.   (7) Id. ax. for mult.
7. a. (1) Hyp. (or given)   (2) Inv. ax. for
mult.   (3) Mult. prop. of =   (4) Assoc. ax.
for mult.   (5) Inv. ax. for mult.   (6) Id. ax.
for mult.   **b.** (1) Hyp. (or given)   (2) Com.
ax. for mult.   (3) Exercise 7a   **9.** (1) Inv.
ax. for add.   (2) Exercise 8   (3) Id. ax. for
add.
11. 1. $x + b = 0$ Hyp. (or given)
    2. $x = 0 + (-b)$ Exercise 8
    3. $x = -b$ Id. ax. for add.
13. 1. $a \neq 0$ Hyp. (or given)

    2. $a \cdot \dfrac{1}{a} = 1$ Inv. ax. for mult.

    3. $a = \dfrac{1}{\frac{1}{a}}$ Exercise 12

    4. $\dfrac{1}{\frac{1}{a}} = a$ Sym. prop. of =

15. 1. $a \neq 0; ax + b = c$ Hyp. (or given)
    2. $ax = c + (-b)$ Exercise 8
    3. $xa = c + (-b)$ Com. ax. for mult.

    4. $x = [c + (-b)]\dfrac{1}{a}$ Exercise 10

    5. $x = \dfrac{1}{a}[c + (-b)]$ Com. ax. for mult.

17.

1. $a \neq 0$ and $b \neq 0$ — Hyp. (or given)

2. $\frac{1}{a}$ and $\frac{1}{b}$ are real numbers — Inv. ax. for mult.

3. $\left(\frac{1}{a} \cdot \frac{1}{b}\right)(ab) = \left(\frac{1}{a} \cdot \frac{1}{b}\right)(ba)$ — Com. ax. for mult.

4. $= \left[\left(\frac{1}{a} \cdot \frac{1}{b}\right)b\right]a$ — Assoc. ax. for mult.

5. $= \left[\frac{1}{a}\left(\frac{1}{b} \cdot b\right)\right]a$ — Assoc. ax. for mult.

6. $= \frac{1}{a}(1)a$ — Inv. ax. for mult.

7. $= \frac{1}{a} \cdot a$ — Id. ax. for mult.

8. $= 1$ — Inv. ax. for mult.

9. $\left(\frac{1}{a} \cdot \frac{1}{b}\right)(ab) = 1$ — Trans prop. of $=$

10. $\frac{1}{a} \cdot \frac{1}{b} = \frac{1}{ab}$ — Exercise 12

11. $\frac{1}{ab} = \frac{1}{a} \cdot \frac{1}{b}$ — Sym. prop. of $=$

Written Exercises, page 29 **1.** -90 **3.** -111 **5.** 0 **7.** -4 **9.** -37 **11.** -19 **13.** 4 **15.** -7 **17.** 0.6 **19.** -8 **21.** 47 **23. a.** 1 **b.** 3 **25. a.** -10 **b.** -4

27.
1. $r + [-(r + s)] = r + [(-r) + (-s)]$ — Prop. of the opp. of a sum
2. $= [r + (-r)] + (-s)$ — Assoc. ax. for add.
3. $= 0 + (-s)$ — Inv. ax. for add.
4. $= -s$ — Id. ax. for add.
5. $r + [-(r + s)] = -s$ — Trans. prop. of $=$

29.
1. $-[(-a) + (-b)] + (-b) = -(-a) + [-(-b)] + (-b)$ — Prop. of the opp. of a sum
2. $= a + b + (-b)$ — Exercise 9, p. 24
3. $= a + [b + (-b)]$ — Assoc. ax. for add.
4. $= a + 0$ — Inv. ax. for add.
5. $= a$ — Id. ax. for add.
6. $-[(-a) + (-b)] + (-b) = a$ — Trans. prop. of $=$

Written Exercises, pages 31–32 **1.** 44 **3.** -33 **5.** 9.6 **7.** 2 **9.** -8 **11.** 1 **13.** 11 **15.** -10 **17.** 8 **19.** -13 **21.** -16 **23.** $-\frac{11}{7}$ **25.** 2.9 **27.** 159 m **29.** -405 V

31. 1. Rule for subt. 2. Prop. of the opp. of a sum 3. Exercise 9, p. 24 4. Com. ax. for add. 5. Rule for subt.

33.
1. $a = b$ — Hyp. (or given)
2. $a + (-c) = b + (-c)$ — Add. prop. of $=$
3. $a - c = b - c$ — Rule for subt.

Written Exercises, pages 34–35 **1.** 0 **3.** -1320 **5.** -390 **7.** -580 **9.** -6480 **11.** -40 **13.** -507 **15.** -19 **17.** 0 **19.** $24x - 16$ **21.** $-49n - 77$ **23.** $-2x^2 + 6x + 2$ **25.** 1. Id. ax. for add. 2. Mult. prop. of $=$ 3. Dist. ax. 4. Trans. prop. of $=$ 5. Exercise 6, p. 24 6. Com. ax. for mult. **27.** Since $a \cdot 0 = 0$ is true for all real numbers, no value of a exists for which $a \cdot 0 = 1$. $\therefore$ 0 has no reciprocal.

Written Exercises, pages 38–39 **1.** -2 **3.** -3 **5.** 0 **7.** -2 **9.** 30 **11.** 4 **13.** -1 **15.** 0 **17.** $5 \div 3 \neq 3 \div 5$

19. 1. Rule for div. 2. Inv. ax. for mult. 3. Trans. prop. of = **21.** 1. Mult. prop. of -1 2. Exercise 9, p. 24 3. Trans. prop. of = 4. Inv. ax. for mult.

23.

1.	$c \neq 0$	Hyp.
2.	$\dfrac{a+b}{c} = \dfrac{1}{c}(a+b)$	Rule for div.
3.	$= \dfrac{1}{c}(a) + \dfrac{1}{c}(b)$	Dist. ax.
4.	$= \dfrac{a}{c} + \dfrac{b}{c}$	Rule for div.
5.	$\dfrac{a+b}{c} = \dfrac{a}{c} + \dfrac{b}{c}$	Trans. prop. of =

25.

1.	$b \neq 0$	Hyp.
2.	$(ab) \div b = (ab) \cdot \dfrac{1}{b}$	Rule for div.
3.	$= a\left(b \cdot \dfrac{1}{b}\right)$	Assoc. ax. for mult.
4.	$= a \cdot 1$	Inv. ax. for mult.
5.	$= a$	Id. ax. for mult.
6.	$(ab) \div b = a$	Trans prop. of =

Extra, pages 40–41 1. $\forall_x 2x = x + x$
3. $\exists!_x 4x + 3 = 17$ **5.** $\forall_x \forall_y x + y = y + x$

Chapter Review, pages 41–42 1. c **2.** b
3. d **4.** a **5.** a **6.** b **7.** b **8.** d **9.** d
10. a **11.** d **12.** b **13.** b

CHAPTER 2 EQUATIONS AND INEQUALITIES

Written Exercises, page 48
1. $(5x + 8) - (3x - 7) + 4x = 6x + 15$
3. $3(a + 4) + (a - 7) = 4a + 5$
5. $8\left(q - \dfrac{1}{2}\right) - (q - 4) = 7q$
7. $m^2 + 4(m^2 - 1) + 3 = 5m^2 - 1$
9. $a + 6(a + b) - 7(a - b) + b = 14b$
11. $5(x - y) - 2(x + y) + 10xy$
$\quad = 3x - 7y + 10xy$
13. $(6a^2 - 6a - 4) + (a^2 - a) =$
$\quad 7a^2 - 7a - 4$
15. $(1 - 4y + y^2) - (y + y^2 - 1) = -5y + 2$
17. $(6x^3 - 5x + 2x^2 - 1) + (3 - 7x - x^2 - x^3) = 5x^3 + x^2 - 12x + 2$
19. $(w^3 - 7w^2 - w + 4) - (w^3 - 8w^2 + 2w + 3) = w^2 - 3w + 1$
21. $(12x^2 - 5xy - y^2) + (-2y^2 + 4xy - x^2) = 11x^2 - xy - 3y^2$
23. $a = 3, b = 1, c = 13$

Calculator Key-In, page 48 1. 14
3. a. 1.01^2 is greater; increasing **b.** 0.99 is greater; decreasing **c.** Numbers greater than one increase when squared. Positive numbers less than one decrease when squared.

Written Exercises, pages 52–53 1. 1 **3.** 1
5. 0 **7.** 6 **9.** 48 **11.** 10 **13.** 9 **15.** 10
17. -18 **19.** 10 **21.** 6 **23.** 14 **25.** -6
27. $C = \dfrac{5}{9}(F - 32)$ **29.** $z = 0$ **31.** $y = \dfrac{1}{a}$
33. $z = 47$ **35.** $r = 0.075$ **37.** $d = 3$
39. $y_1 = 3$ **41.** $z = 3A - x - y$
43. $r = \dfrac{A - P}{Pt}$ **45.** $d = \dfrac{2(S - an)}{n(n - 1)}$
47. $y_1 = y_2 - m(x_2 - x_1)$

Written Exercises, pages 57–58
1. $(2x + 11)$ persons **3.** $(180 - 4r)°$
5. $\dfrac{300 - z}{2}$ cm **7.** $(2h + 83)$ cm **9.** The woman, $(2d - 20)$ y; the daughter, $(d - 20)$ y. **11.** $(5x - 24)$ m
13. $(5r - 27)$ km **15.** $\left(5 + \dfrac{d}{50}\right)$ h
17. $125n$¢, where n is the number of nickels. **19.** $(375 - 9x)°$, where $\angle D = x°$.

Problems, pages 62–63 1. Al, \$12; Mary, \$87 **3.** 21 and 63 **5.** Each leg, 40 cm; base, 18 cm **7.** 400 km **9.** 52, 54, and 56 **11.** 15 m, 16 m, 17 m, and 18 m **13.** 11:00 A.M. **15.** 4.5 and 23 **17.** 77 ppm **19.** Winner, 1280 votes; loser, 1220 votes

Written Exercises, pages 66–67

1. $\{x: x < 3\}$

3. $\{z: z > -14\}$

5. $\{K: K > -7\}$

7. $\{y: y > -3\}$

9. $\{n: n > -1\}$

11. $\{d: d < 7\}$

13. $\{h: h > 0\}$

15. $\left\{x: x > -\dfrac{1}{3}\right\}$

17. $\{z: z > 2\}$

19. $\{y: y > -6\}$

21. $\{x: x > -9\}$
23. $\{s: s < -3\}$ **25.** $1 > -3$, but
$(1)^2 \not> (-3)^2$

27. 1. $a < b$ and $c < d$ Hyp. (or given)
   2. $a + c < b + c$ Add. ax. of order
   3. $c + b < d + b$ Add. ax. of order
   4. $b + c < b + d$ Com. ax. for add.
   5. $a + c < b + d$ Trans. ax. of order

29. 1. $0 < a < b$ Hyp.
   2. $a^2 < ba$ Mult. prop. of order
   3. $a^2 < ab$ Com. prop. of mult.
   4. $ab < b^2$ Mult. prop. of order
   5. $a^2 < b^2$ Trans. prop. of order

Written Exercises, page 69

1. $\{x: x \le 3\}$

3. $\{z: -2 \le z < 4\}$

5. $\{y: 4 < y \le 5\}$

7. No solution
9. $\{n: -2 < n \le 8\}$

11. $\{K: -1 < K < 3\}$

13. $\{a: -2 < a < 3\}$

15. $\{p: p < -1 \text{ or } p > 3\}$

17. All real numbers

19. No solution
21. $\{r: r > 1\}$

23. $\{k: -4 \le k \le -1 \text{ or } 1 \le k \le 4\}$

25. $\{k: -4 < k \le -3 \text{ or } 3 \le k < 4\}$

Written Exercises, page 73

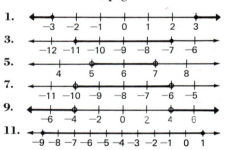

1.
3.
5.
7.
9.
11.

13. $\left\{3, \dfrac{11}{3}\right\}$

15. $\{4\}$

17. $\{r: r < 2 \text{ or } r > 10\}$

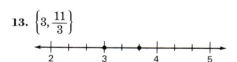

19. $\left\{n: 1 \le n \le \dfrac{5}{3}\right\}$

21. $\{1, 3\}$

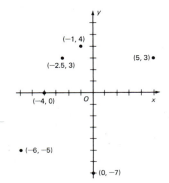

23. $\{x: x \le -10 \text{ or } x \ge -4\}$

25. $\{h: 0 < h < 2\}$

27. $\left\{1, \dfrac{11}{3}\right\}$

29. No solution

31. $|x + b| < a$ is equivalent to:
$$-a < x + b < a$$
$$-a < x + b \quad \text{and} \quad x + b < a$$
$$-a - b < x \qquad\qquad x < a - b$$
Thus $\quad -a - b < x < a - b$

Problems, pages 75–76   **1.** $\{2, 4, 6\}$ and $\{4, 6, 8\}$ **3.** 10 cm   **5.** 7 m   **7.** 19 cm by 114 cm   **9.** 3 min   **11.** $a = 7\,\text{cm}, b = 13\,\text{cm}, h = 7\,\text{cm}$

Chapter Review, pages 77–78   **1.** b   **2.** d   **3.** c   **4.** b   **5.** c   **6.** a   **7.** d   **8.** b   **9.** b   **10.** a   **11.** c   **12.** c

Extra, page 81   **1.** T   **3.** T   **5.** T   **7.** T   **9.** T

CHAPTER 3   GRAPHS AND FUNCTIONS

Written Exercises, pages 85–86

1–11.

13.

$PT = 5$

15. $PT = 9$

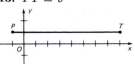

17. $PT = 7$

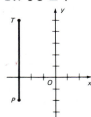

19. $x = -3, y = 4$ **21.** $x = 4, y = 0$
23. $x = 7, y = -3$ **25.** $x = 2$ or -2, $y = 5$ or -5
27.

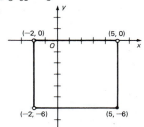

29.

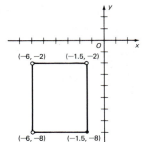

31.

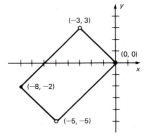

33. $(-3, 1), (5, 3), (-3, -7)$ **35.** $|c - b|$

Written Exercises, page 89
1. $y = -2x + 3$; $\{(-12, 27), (0, 3), (6, -9)\}$
3. $y = -\dfrac{1}{2}x$; $\{(-12, 6), (0, 0), (6, -3)\}$
5. $y = -\dfrac{3}{4}x + 4$; $\left\{(-12, 13), (0, 4), \left(6, -\dfrac{1}{2}\right)\right\}$

7. $y = \frac{4}{9}x - \frac{1}{3}$; $\left\{\left(-12, -\frac{17}{3}\right), \left(0, -\frac{1}{3}\right), \left(6, \frac{7}{3}\right)\right\}$ **9.** 2, 6, 16 **11.** $-1, -3, 2$
13. 2, -2, 14 **15.** 8, 2, 12 **17.** $\{(0, 8), (1, 7), (2, 6), (3, 5), (4, 4), (5, 3), (6, 2), (7, 1), (8, 0)\}$
19. $\{(0, 4), (2, 3), (4, 2), (6, 1), (8, 0)\}$
21. $\{(3, 0)\}$ **23.** $\{(0, 0), (0, 1), (0, 2), (0, 3), (0, 4), (1, 0), (1, 1), (1, 2), (2, 0), (2, 1)\}$
25. $\{(-1, 1), (-1, 2), (-1, 3), (-1, 4), (0, 1), (0, 2), (0, 3), (1, 1), (1, 2)\}$ **27.** $\{(-1, 1), (-1, 2), (-1, 3), (0, 1), (0, 2), (0, 3), (1, 1), (1, 2), (1, 3)\}$ **29.** $\{(-1, 1)\}$

Problems, page 90 1. a. Let the ordered pair (a, b) represent corresponding temperatures in Amber City and Bayville.
b. $b - a = 9$ **c.** $(-8°C, 1°C)$, $(-7°C, 2°C)$, $(-6°C, 3°C)$, $(-5°C, 4°C)$, $(-4°C, 5°C)$, $(-3°C, 6°C)$, $(-2°C, 7°C)$, $(-1°C, 8°C)$
3. a. Let f = number of 15¢ stamps and let t = number of 20¢ stamps.
b. $15f + 20t = 90$ **c.** 2 15¢ stamps and 3 20¢ stamps, 6 15¢ stamps and no 20¢ stamps. **5.** 40, 51, 62, 73, 84, 95 **7.** 4, 1, 10; 5, 2, 8; 6, 3, 6; 4, 7, 4 **9.** 60 and 75, 61 and 74, 62 and 73, 63 and 72, 64 and 71, 65 and 70, 66 and 69, 67 and 68.

Written Exercises, pages 93–94
1. $6x + y = 9$ **3.** $x = -14$
5. $3x - y = -6$ **7.** $3x + 4y = 4$
9. $3x - 4y = 24$

11.

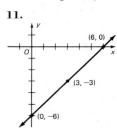

13.

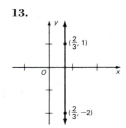

15.

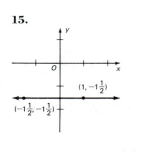

17.

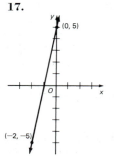

19.

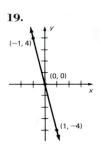

21.

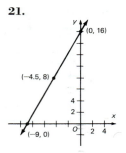

23.

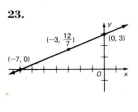

25.

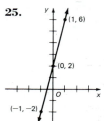

27. -1 **29.** 7
31. $(3, -1)$; $(3) + (-1) = 2$; $(3) - 3(-1) = 6$

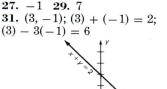

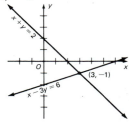

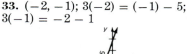

33. $(-2, -1)$; $3(-2) = (-1) - 5$; $3(-1) = -2 - 1$

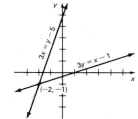

35.

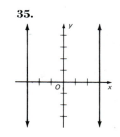

37.

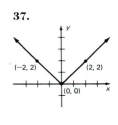

39.

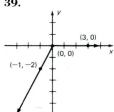

41.

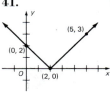

Written Exercises, pages 100–101   1. 1
3. 7 **5.** 0 **7.** No slope **9.** -6
11. $-a - 1$ **13.** $-\dfrac{3}{4}$ **15.** $\dfrac{5}{2}$ **17.** -1

19. 2 **21.** $-\dfrac{4}{5}$

23.

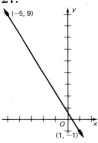

25.

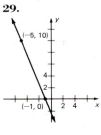

27.

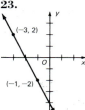

29.

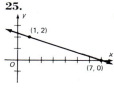

31.

33.

35. The points do not lie on a line.
37. 1. Theorem, p. 97 2. Subst.
3. Mult. prop. of = 4. Dist. ax.
5. Add. prop. of = 6. Since (x_1, y_1) is on
L 7. Trans. prop. of = 8. Since (x_2, y_2)
satisfies an equation of L **39. a.** -1
b. 0 **41.** -6 **43.** -2 **45.** -4 **47.** 9
49. $-\dfrac{1}{2}$

Written Exercises, pages 105–106
1. $3x - y = -8$ **3.** $x + y = -5$
5. $x - 2y = 0$ **7.** $y = -3$
9. $3x + 5y = 12$ **11.** $x = 9$ **13.** $x + y = 3$
15. $3x - 5y = 10$ **17.** $2x + 10y = 7$
19. $y = 9$ **21.** $3x + y = 0$
23. $x - 5y = -8$ **25.** $5x - 3y = 9$
27. $x - 4y = -8$ **29.** $x + 3y = 0$
31. $x - 4y = 3$ **33.** $x = -6$ **35.** $y = 7$
37. $x - y = -6$ **39.** $5x - y = -1$
41. $3x + 2y = -6$ **43.** $3x + 4y = 12$
45. $x = 2$ **47.** $7x + 2y = 17$

Written Exercises, pages 109–110
1. $\{-8, -2, 1\}$ **3.** $\{-1, 2\}$ **5.** $\{0, 1, 4\}$
7. $\{-1, 0, 1\}$
9.

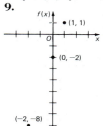

11.

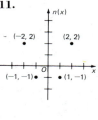

13.

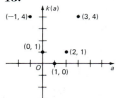

15.

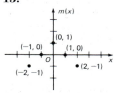

17. Not equal **19.** Equal **21.** 50 **23.** 26
25. 3 **27.** $4a^2 + 3$ **29.** $16a^2 - 40a + 26$
31. a. Let $x = 0$; $g(3 \cdot 0) = g(3) + g(0)$;
$g(0) = g(3) + g(0)$; $\therefore$ $0 = g(3)$
b. Let $x = 1$; $g(3 \cdot 1) = g(3) + g(1)$;
$g(3) = g(3) + g(1)$; $\therefore$ $g(1) = 0$
33. a. $E(0 + b) = E(0) \cdot E(b)$;
$E(b) = E(0) \cdot E(b)$; $\therefore$ $1 = E(0)$
b. $E(-b + b) = E(-b) \cdot E(b)$;
$E(0) = E(-b) \cdot E(b)$; $1 = E(-b) \cdot E(b)$;
$\therefore$ $\dfrac{1}{E(b)} = E(-b)$

Application, page 110   1. $8000 **2.** 18,800

Written Exercises, page 113
1. $f(x) = 3x - 7$ **3.** $k(x) = -5x + 21$

5. $t(x) = \frac{4}{3}x - 5$ **7.** $h(x) = \frac{1}{2}$ **9.** 21

11. 0 **13.** 3 **15.** -2 **17.** -2 **19.** $\frac{5}{2}$

21. m

Problems, pages 113–114 1. 72.75 cm
3. $194 **5.** $2.50 **7.** $838,333 **9.** 75V
11. a. $E = 4.756N + 525$
b. $E = 4.15N + 1070.4$

Written Exercises, page 118 1. 24 **3.** 52
5. 3 **7.** $\frac{3}{2}$

Problems, page 119 1. $6900 **3.** 75 g
5. 9 g **7.** 9 cm **9.** 98 m/s
11. Scudder's Restaurant **13.** 87,500

Written Exercises, pages 122–123

1. function **3.** not a function

5. function

7. $\{-7, -5, -3, -1, 1, 3, 5\}$; yes
9. $\{-1, 0, 3, 8\}$; yes
11. $\{-6, -5, -4, -3, -2, -1, 0, 1, 2, 3, 4,$
$5, 6\}$; no
13. $\{-2, -1, 0, 1, 2\}$; no
15. $\{-6, -5, -2, 3, 10\}$; yes
17. $\{y: y < 5\}$; no
19. $\{y: y > 0\}$; no
21. $\{y: y \leq 4\}$; no

Computer Key-In, page 125 1. The slope
of a straight line through points (x_1, y_1)
and (x_2, y_2) is $\frac{y_2 - y_1}{x_2 - x_1}$. Since the slope is
constant, $\frac{y - y_1}{x - x_1} = \frac{y_2 - y_1}{x_2 - x_1}$, or
$(x_2 - x_1)(y - y_1) = (x - x_1)(y_2 - y_1)$, which
simplifies to
$(y_2 - y_1)x + (x_1 - x_2)y = x_1 y_2 - x_2 y_1$. To
write the program, alter the program in
the text as follows:

```
20   PRINT "LINE IN STANDARD FORM,"
100  LET A=Y2-Y1
110  LET B=X1-X2
115  LET C=X1*Y2-X2*Y1
130  PRINT "(";A;")X + (";B;")Y = ";C
```

Chapter Review, pages 126–127 1. a **2.** c
3. c **4.** c **5.** c **6.** d **7.** a **8.** a **9.** c
10. d **11.** d **12.** a **13.** c **14.** a **15.** b
16. a **17.** a

Calculator Key-In, page 128 1. 8.804
3. 0.082 **5.** 0.027

**Cumulative Review (Chapters 1–3), page
129 1.** 17 **3.** -5 **5.** -5 **7.** 1 **9.** false
11. a. Dist. ax. **b.** Assoc. ax. for add.
c. Inv. ax. for add. **d.** Id. ax. for add.
13. 5

15. $\left\{z: z < \frac{1}{3}\right\}$

17. $\{3, 7\}$

19. $h = \dfrac{2A}{a + b}$

21. $y = \dfrac{7}{4}x - 2$ **23. a.** $f(x) = -2x + 5$
b.

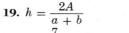

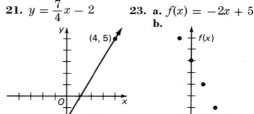

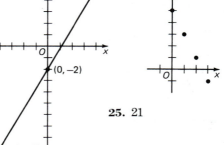

25. 21

**CHAPTER 4 POLYNOMIALS AND
FACTORING**

Written Exercises, page 133 1. $8a^5$ **3.** y^{16}
5. $16a^2$ **7.** $\frac{8c^4}{3}$ **9.** $-4x^3y - 4x^2y^2$ **11.** a^9
13. $-96x^6y^6$ **15.** $2x^3y - 8x^2y^2 + 8xy$

17. $\dfrac{5x^4}{7y^4}$ **19.** $-16a^7$ **21.** $4b^{6+a}$ **23.** $5x^{2t}$

25. $y^{4n} + 2y^{5n} + 4y^{3n}$

27. $-6m^{3n} + 12m^{2n} - 3m^n$

29. $x^{2+m}y + x^{2+m}y^{1+m} + x^2y^{1+m}$

31. $17m^3n^4$ **33.** $-28a^2b^2$ **35.** $\dfrac{3y^{2a+4c}}{7}$

37. $\dfrac{3}{5m^y}$ **39.** $(3x)^{8c-6d}$

Written Exercises, pages 135–136
1. $8x^2 + 10x - 3$ **3.** $49c^2 - 9$
5. $4r^2 - 20r + 25$ **7.** $2x^2 + 11x - 21$
9. $30m^2 + 61m + 30$ **11.** $24x^2 + x - 10$
13. $25a^2 - 4b^2$ **15.** $5x^2 - 68x - 28$
17. $121 - 25z^2$ **19.** $12n^4 + 11n^2 - 5$
21. $x^6 + 4x^3 + 4$
23. $a^2 + ab + 3a + 2b + 2$
25. $6ac - 4a + 21c - 14$
27. $18m^3 - 51m^2 + 21m + 5$
29. $16a^4c^2 - 25b^2$ **31.** $x^{2n} - 2x^ny^n + y^{2n}$
33. $a^2 + 2ab + 2ac + b^2 + 2bc + c^2$
35. $4a^8 - 4a^7 + a^6$
37. $x^4y^2 - x^3y^3 - 6x^2y^4$
39. $-3x^3 + 18x^2y - 27xy^2$ **41.** $x^4 - y^4$
43. $a^3 + 3a^2b + 3ab^2 + b^3$ **45.** $a^3 + b^3$
47. 4 **49.** -5

Written Exercises, page 139 **1.** $2 \cdot 3^4$ **3.** 41
5. $3^2 \cdot 7^2$ **7.** $3^2 \cdot 5 \cdot 7$ **9. a.** 13 **b.** 78
11. a. 12 **b.** 216 **13. a.** $7mn$ **b.** $84m^2n^2$
15. a. $18xy^2z^2$ **b.** $72x^2y^3z^5$
17. a. $19m^2nr^2$ **b.** $114m^3n^2r^4$ **19. a.** 8
b. $208x^3y^3$ **21.** GCF = 1; LCM = pq
23. 1, 2, 4, 8, 16, 31, 62, 124, 248;
$1 + 2 + 4 + 8 + 16 + 31 + 62 + 124 + 248$
25. $9v^7w^4$

Calculator Key-In, page 139 **1.** 59049
3. 0.0014349 **5.** 41.033867 **7.** 1616.04
9. 1.7958563

Written Exercises, page 142
1. $16x^2(2x - 3)$ **3.** $(x - 9)(x + 9)$
5. $x^2y^2z^2(xz - 2x + 4z^2)$ **7.** $(m - 4)^2$
9. $(x + 3)^2$ **11.** $3(x - 3)(x + 3)$
13. $-(x + 3)^2$ **15.** $(b + 5)(a - 4)$
17. $4(x + 2)(x^2 - 2x + 4)$ **19.** $-(n + 2)^2$
21. $(x + y)(a - b)$ **23.** $3(x - 4)^2$
25. $-(x - 25)^2$ **27.** $(5 - y)(25 + 5y + y^2)$
29. $4x^2(3y - 1)(3y + 1)$
31. $(y^2 + 3)(y^4 - 3y^2 + 9)$
33. $(n - 2y - 1)(n + 2y - 1)$
35. $(1 - 3y)(1 + 3y + 9y^2)$
37. $(x - y)(x + y - 7)$ **39.** $(n - 1)^2$
41. $(3 - r)(9 + 3r + r^2)$

43. $(1 + x + y)(1 - x - y)$
45. $(c - 2)^3(c - 1)(3 - c)$
47. $(x^n - y^n)(x^{2n} + x^ny^n + y^{2n})$
49. $(5y^n - 8)^2$
51. $(3s - r + 1)(9s^2 + 3rs - 3s + r^2 - 2r + 1)$ **53.** $(5 - x^n)(5 + x^n)$

Written Exercises, pages 145–146
1. $(x + 9)(x + 1)$ **3.** $(n + 7)(n + 3)$
5. $(x - 5)(x - 2)$ **7.** $(n + 3)(n - 1)$
9. $(x - 3)(x + 1)$ **11.** $(t + 4)(3 - t)$
13. $(2n - 3)(n + 1)$ **15.** irreducible
17. $(5y - 3)(2y + 7)$ **19.** $(5n - 3)(2n + 1)$
21. $(7n + 2)(2n + 3)$ **23.** $(2t - 5)(t + 1)$
25. $3(2n - 3)(n + 1)$ **27.** $x(4x + 1)(x - 3)$
29. $(5t^2 - 2)(t - 1)(t + 1)$
31. $2x(1 - 2x)(1 + 2x + 4x^2)$
33. $(2t^2 - 3)(t^2 - 3)$ **35.** $5n(n + 3)(n + 1)$
37. a. $x + 3$ **b.** $(x + 3)^2(x - 3)$
39. a. $3x - 1$ **b.** $(2x + 3)(3x - 1)(x + 9)$
41. a. $r(s - v)$ **b.** $r(s - v)^2$
43. $(x^{3n} - 4)(x^n - 1)(x^{2n} + x^n + 1)$
45. $2(n - 2)^2$ **47.** $(2x^{2n} - 3)(x^{2n} - 5)$
49. $x(x - 4)^2$

Written Exercises, pages 149–150

1. $\{-4, 4\}$ **3.** $\left\{-\dfrac{1}{2}, \dfrac{2}{5}\right\}$ **5.** $\{1, 3\}$

7. $\{0, 5\}$ **9.** $\left\{0, \dfrac{1}{2}\right\}$ **11.** $\{-7\}$;

double root: -7 **13.** $\{-5, -2\}$ **15.** $\left\{\dfrac{1}{2}, 2\right\}$

17. $\{-3, 0, 3\}$; double root: 0 **19.** $\{-4, 4\}$

21. $\left\{-1, \dfrac{2}{3}\right\}$ **23.** $\{1\}$; double root: 1

25. $\left\{-\dfrac{5}{2}, \dfrac{5}{2}\right\}$ **27.** $\{-1, 1, 3\}$ **29.** $\{-2, 2\}$;

double roots: -2 and 2 **31.** $\{-1, 1\}$
33. $\{0, 5\}$; double roots: 5 **35.** $-16, 2$
37. 3 **39. a.** True **b.** If $ac = bc$, then
$a = b$. False **41. a.** True **b.** If $m^2 = n^2$,
then $m = n$. False **43. a.** false **b.** If
$p^2 < 4$, then $p < 2$. True

Problems, pages 152–153 **1.** -6 or 5
3. 8, 9, 10 **5.** 20 m by 2 m
7. 50 m and 100 m **9.** $-20, -18, -16$ or
16, 18, 20 **11.** Archie: 8 km/h;
Claire: 11 km/h; Belinda: 15 km/h.
13. $x - 1 = 2$ or $x - 2 = 3$ does not follow
from the previous statement. **15.** 5 s
17. 3.5 s

Written Exercises, page 156

1. $\{x: 0 < x < 3\}$

$$\xleftarrow{\quad}\underset{-2\ -1\ \ 0\ \ 1\ \ 2\ \ 3\ \ 4}{\overline{\ \ |\ \ |\ \ \circ\ |\ \ |\ \ \circ\ |\ \ }}\xrightarrow{\quad}$$

3. $\{y: y \neq -2\}$

$$\xleftarrow{\quad}\underset{-5\ -4\ -3\ -2\ -1\ \ 0\ \ 1}{\overline{\ |\ \ |\ \ |\ \ \circ\ |\ \ |\ \ |\ }}\xrightarrow{\quad}$$

5. $\{m: -2 \leq m \leq 2\}$

$$\xleftarrow{\quad}\underset{-3\ -2\ -1\ \ 0\ \ 1\ \ 2\ \ 3}{\overline{\ |\ \ \bullet\ |\ \ |\ \ |\ \ \bullet\ |\ }}\xrightarrow{\quad}$$

7. $\{n: n < 1 \text{ or } n > 5\}$

$$\xleftarrow{\quad}\underset{-1\ \ 0\ \ 1\ \ 2\ \ 3\ \ 4\ \ 5\ \ 6\ \ 7}{\overline{\ |\ \ |\ \ \circ\ |\ \ |\ \ |\ \ \circ\ |\ \ |\ }}\xrightarrow{\quad}$$

9. $\{y: -4 < y < 1\}$

$$\xleftarrow{\quad}\underset{-5\ -4\ -3\ -2\ -1\ \ 0\ \ 1\ \ 2}{\overline{\ |\ \ \circ\ |\ \ |\ \ |\ \ |\ \ \circ\ |\ }}\xrightarrow{\quad}$$

11. No solution

13. $\left\{x: -4 < x < \dfrac{5}{2}\right\}$

$$\xleftarrow{\quad}\underset{-5\ -4\ -3\ -2\ -1\ \ 0\ \ 1\ \ 2\ \ 3\ \ 4}{\overline{\ |\ \ \circ\ |\ \ |\ \ |\ \ |\ \ |\ \ \circ\ |\ \ |\ }}\xrightarrow{\quad}$$

15. No solution

17. $\left\{x: -\dfrac{3}{2} \leq x \leq \dfrac{4}{5}\right\}$

$$\xleftarrow{\quad}\underset{-2\ \ -1\ \ 0\ \ 1\ \ 2}{\overline{\ |\ \ \bullet\ \ |\ \ \bullet\ |\ \ |\ }}\xrightarrow{\quad}$$

19. $\{x: x \leq -3 \text{ or } -1 \leq x \leq 1 \text{ or } x \geq 3\}$

$$\xleftarrow{\quad}\underset{-4\ -3\ -2\ -1\ \ 0\ \ 1\ \ 2\ \ 3\ \ 4}{\overline{\ |\ \ \bullet\ |\ \ \bullet\ |\ \ \bullet\ |\ \ \bullet\ |\ }}\xrightarrow{\quad}$$

Chapter Review, page 158 1. b **2.** c
3. a **4.** c **5.** d **6.** a **7.** c **8.** b **9.** b
10. a **11.** d **12.** a **13.** c **14.** d

Computer Key-In, pages 159–160 1. a. 1;
3; 37; 111 **b.** 1; 11; 101; 1111 **c.** 1; 41; 271;
11,111 **d.** 1; 3; 7; 11; 13; 21; 33; 37; 39; 77;
91; 111; 143; 231; 259; 273; 407; 429; 481; 777;
1001; 1221; 1443; 2849; 3003; 3367; 5291; 8547;
10,101; 15,873; 37,037; 111,111 **3. a.** 1; 3; 7;
21; 141; 329; 987 **b.** 1; 2; 3; 4; 6; 12; 823;
1646; 2469; 3292; 4938; 9876 **c.** 1; 5; 19,753;
98,765 **d.** 1; 2; 3; 6; 97; 194; 291; 582; 1697;
3394; 5091; 10,182; 164,609; 329,218; 493,827;
987,654 **5. 1. a.** 3; 37 **b.** 11; 101 **c.** 41;
271 **d.** 3; 7; 11; 13; 37 **5. 2. a.** 3; 41 **b.** 2;
617 **c.** 3; 5; 823 **d.** 2; 2; 2; 2; 2; 2; 3; 643
5. 3. a. 3; 7; 47 **b.** 2; 2; 3; 823 **c.** 5;
19,753 **d.** 2; 3; 97; 1697 **5. 4. a.** 3; 107
b. 29; 149 **c.** 3; 19; 953 **d.** 3; 218,107

CHAPTER 5 RATIONAL EXPRESSIONS

Written Exercises, pages 166–167 1. $\dfrac{2c^3}{3}$

3. b^2 **5.** $-\dfrac{6x}{5a}$ **7.** $\dfrac{1}{4p}$ **9.** $\dfrac{a^2 b}{2}$ **11.** $4a$

13. $\dfrac{y^4}{x^2}$ **15.** $\dfrac{4}{9c^2}$ **17.** $\dfrac{3}{8k^4}$ **19.** $-\dfrac{8x^8}{9}$

21. $\dfrac{x^7 y^9}{z^3}$ **23.** b^n **25.** $\dfrac{4b}{3}$ **27.** $-\dfrac{2xy}{9}$

29. a **31.** $\dfrac{y^2}{x^3}$ **33.** Yes

35. 1. Rule for div. 2. Com. ax. for mult.
and assoc. ax. for mult. 3. Prop. of the
recip. of a prod. 4. Rule for div.
5. Trans prop. of $=$

Written Exercises, pages 170–171 1. $\dfrac{2}{9}$

3. 9 **5.** $\dfrac{1}{9}$ **7.** $\dfrac{25}{2}$ **9.** 0.27 **11.** 0.00049

13. 0.16 **15.** -1.8 **17.** $\dfrac{3}{x^2 y}$ **19.** $ax^2 y^2 z$

21. x^6 **23.** $\dfrac{a}{b^2}$ **25.** $\dfrac{1}{t^3}$ **27.** $\dfrac{u^2}{3v^5}$ **29.** $\dfrac{5b}{a^2 c}$

31. $\dfrac{1}{x^4}$ **33.** $\dfrac{2}{x^5}$ **35.** $\dfrac{4}{9rs^2}$ **37.** $4a^4 b^2$

39. $(2 + 2)^{-1} = 4^{-1} = \dfrac{1}{4}$;

$2^{-1} + 2^{-1} = \dfrac{1}{2} + \dfrac{1}{2} = 1; \dfrac{1}{4} \neq 1$

41. $(2 \cdot 1)^{-2} = 2^{-2} = \dfrac{1}{2^2} = \dfrac{1}{4}$;

$2 \cdot 1^{-2} = 2 \cdot \dfrac{1}{1^2} = 2 \cdot 1 = 2; \dfrac{1}{4} \neq 2$

43. $1 + 2x + x^2$
45. $1 + 2z + 5z^2 + z^3 + 2z^4$
47. $2 + t - 4t^2 + 3t^3$ **49.** $3x + 1$
51. $x^2 + 4x$ **53.** 1. Def. of a neg. exp.
2. Prop. of quot. 3. Law 1 of exp. 4. Def.
of a neg. exp. 5. Prop. of the opp. of a
sum

Written Exercises, pages 173–174
1. 4.71×10^1 **3.** 4.906×10^3
5. 6.920×10^1 **7.** 2.5×10^{-2}
9. 4.0×10^{-4} **11.** 8.3×10^{-1}
13. 3.0507×10^6 **15.** 100,000 **17.** 0.001
19. 204 **21.** 0.000918 **23.** 4×10^2, or 400
25. 4.5, or 4.5×10^0 **27.** 50 **29.** 60,000

Problems, pages 174–175
1. 3.99×10^2 to 1, or 399 to 1
3. 6.31×10^4, or 63,100 **5.** 6.037×10^1 g, or
60.37 g **7.** The farthest apart that
components can be is 1.20×10^2 cm, or
120 cm.

Written Exercises, pages 178–179 1. $\dfrac{2x - 3}{x}$

3. $t^2 + at - 2a^2$ **5.** -1 **7.** $\dfrac{t - 1}{t + 1}$ **9.** $\dfrac{x + 3}{x - 3}$

11. $\dfrac{z(z + 1)}{z - 1}$ **13.** $\dfrac{u + 1}{u + 2}$ **15.** $-\dfrac{(x + 2)}{x(1 + 2x)}$

17. $\dfrac{t(t + 2)}{t^2 - 2t + 4}$ **19.** $\dfrac{3x - 1}{2x + 1}$

21. a. All real numbers **b.** $-2, 2$
23. a. All real numbers except 2 **b.** $-1, 1$
25. a. All real numbers except 2 and -2

b. $0, -\dfrac{1}{2}, \dfrac{1}{2}$ **27. a.** All real numbers

except 2 **b.** $-2, -1, 1$ **29.** $\dfrac{x^2 + y^2}{(x - y)(x + y)}$

31. $\dfrac{(u - v)(u^2 + v^2)}{u^2 - uv + v^2}$ **33.** $\dfrac{x - a + 1}{x + a}$

35. $\dfrac{t^2 + 1}{t - 1}$ **37.** $\dfrac{-x - 3}{x - 2}$

39. $\dfrac{(x - 2)(x + 2)^3}{x - 4}$ **41.** $\dfrac{(t^2 + 5)(t + 4)}{t - 4}$

43. $\dfrac{2(r^3 + 1)(r^2 + r + 1)}{3r}$

Written Exercises, page 182

1. $x + 5 + \dfrac{14}{x - 2}$ **3.** $u + 2 - \dfrac{4}{u + 3}$

5. $2u + 1 - \dfrac{2}{3u - 2}$ **7.** $2x + 5 + \dfrac{10}{2x - 5}$

9. $x^2 + 3x - 2 + \dfrac{6}{x + 2}$ **11.** $2x^2 + 1$

13. $3x + 2$ **15.** $x^3 - x^2 + 3x - 3 + \dfrac{3}{x + 3}$

17. $6c^3 + 4c^2 - 1 + \dfrac{4}{3c - 2}$

19. $4p - 3q - \dfrac{2q^2}{2p + q}$ **21.** $u + 2v$

23. $3p + q$ **25.** $x^2 - 2x + 2$
27. $x^2 - ax + a^2$
29. $x^5 - ax^4 + a^2x^3 - a^3x^2 + a^4x - a^5 +$
$\dfrac{2a^6}{x + a}$

31. $2x^2 - 3x + 3$ **33.** $a = 5, b = -3$
35. $3, -\dfrac{3}{2}$

Written Exercises, page 185 1. -1 **3.** $8a$

5. $\dfrac{t}{4}$ **7.** $\dfrac{2b^2}{3a}$ **9.** $\dfrac{5u}{wv}$ **11.** $\dfrac{x + 3}{(x + 2)(x + 1)}$

13. $\dfrac{(t + 3)(t - 1)}{(t + 2)^2}$ **15.** $\dfrac{(x + 1)^2}{(x - 1)^2}$

17. $\dfrac{x - a}{(x + a)^2}$ **19.** $\dfrac{v}{u}$ **21.** $\dfrac{x + 1}{3x + 1}$

23. $-\dfrac{(6v + u)}{(3v - u)^2}$

Written Exercises, pages 187–188 1. $\dfrac{5}{8}$

3. $-\dfrac{7}{12}$ **5.** $\dfrac{3a}{4}$ **7.** $\dfrac{3}{2c}$ **9.** $\dfrac{x + 2}{2x^2}$ **11.** $\dfrac{13}{6}$

13. $\dfrac{3x + 4y}{2x^2y^2}$ **15.** $\dfrac{x + 2}{x^3}$ **17.** $\dfrac{u^2 + v^2 + w^2}{uvw}$

19. $\dfrac{1}{t - 2}$ **21.** $\dfrac{2x}{(x - 2)(x + 2)}$ **23.** $\dfrac{1}{x^2(x + 1)}$

25. $\dfrac{1}{u(u + 1)}$ **27.** $\dfrac{x^2 + 1}{(x + 1)(x - 1)}$

29. $\dfrac{x^2 + 2x + 2}{x + 1}$

31. $\dfrac{x}{(x - 3a)(x - 2a)(x + 2a)}$

33. $\dfrac{4a}{(a - b)(a + b)}$ **35.** $-\dfrac{12}{(u + 1)(u - 1)}$

37. $A = 3, B = 1$

Written Exercises, pages 190–192 1. $\dfrac{7}{4}$

3. $\dfrac{3}{8}$ **5.** a **7.** $-ab$ **9.** $\dfrac{t - 1}{t}$ **11.** $\dfrac{v - u}{v + u}$

13. $\dfrac{xy}{y - x}$ **15.** $\dfrac{t^2 - t + 1}{t}$

17. $-\dfrac{1}{uv(u + v)}$ **19.** $\dfrac{a - 1}{a + 1}$ **21.** $\dfrac{x}{x + 1}$

23. $\dfrac{a + 1}{a}$ **25.** $\dfrac{8}{5}$ **27.** $-\dfrac{1}{x(x + h)}$

29. $-\dfrac{1}{(x + 1)(x + h + 1)}$

31. $\dfrac{(x^2 + y^2)(x + y)}{yx^2}$

Computer Key-In, pages 192–193 1. a. 60
b. 60 **c.** 60 **d.** 60

Written Exercises, page 196 1. $\left\{-1, \dfrac{7}{5}\right\}$

3. $\left\{-\dfrac{1}{2}, 4\right\}$ **5.** $\left\{-\dfrac{1}{3}, 2\right\}$ **7.** $\{-2, 8\}$

9. $\{-3, 1\}$ **11.** $\left\{\dfrac{5}{3}, \dfrac{5}{2}\right\}$ **13.** $\left\{x: x < -\dfrac{1}{2}\right\}$

15. $\{z: z < -6\}$ **17.** $\{x: x \le 5\}$

Problems, pages 197–198   **1.** $\frac{4}{5}$ **3.** 200

5. 800 women and 720 men   **7.** $30
9. Will spent $48, Myrna spent $72, and Jim spent $64.   **11.** $8,000 at 5% and $20,000 at 8%   **13.** 12 h   **15.** 24 mL
17. $34\frac{2}{7}$ h   **19.** 200 g of the 25% solution and 400 g of the 55% solution   **21.** $509\frac{1}{11}$ g of the 30 ¢/kg mixture and $254\frac{6}{11}$ g of the 50 ¢/kg mixture   **23.** 125 km   **25.** 3 L

Written Exercises, page 201   **1.** $\left\{\frac{1}{4}\right\}$

3. $\{2\}$ **5.** $\{6\}$ **7.** $\left\{\frac{1}{3}\right\}$ **9.** $\{0\}$ **11.** $\{1\}$
13. $\{2\}$ **15.** No solution   **17.** $\{3\}$
19. $\left\{-\frac{1}{2}, 2\right\}$ **21.** $\left\{\frac{1}{4}\right\}$ **23.** $\{-1, 3\}$
25. $\left\{\frac{5}{2}, 4\right\}$

Problems, page 202   **1.** 18   **3.** 6 d
5. 6 and 10   **7.** 60 km/h   **9.** 18.75 km/L
11. 15 km/h   **13.** 40 students   **15.** 6 h
17. 8 m/s   **19.** $53\frac{1}{3}$ km/h   **21.** $9000 at 8%
23. 0.6 m/s   **25. a.** 3   **b.** $x = \frac{2ab}{a+b}$

Chapter Review, page 205   **1.** c   **2.** b
3. d   **4.** b   **5.** a   **6.** c   **7.** d   **8.** a   **9.** b
10. b   **11.** d   **12.** c   **13.** a   **14.** c   **15.** d
16. a   **17.** b   **18.** d

CHAPTER 6 IRRATIONAL AND COMPLEX NUMBERS

Written Exercises, page 212   **1.** 5   **3.** 4
5. not a real number   **7.** -4 **9.** $\frac{1}{3}$ **11.** $\frac{3}{2}$
13. 0.4   **15.** 0.3   **17.** $|a|$ **19.** a^2
21. no real roots   **23.** $-\frac{4}{3}$ **25.** $-6, 6$
27. $x \le 2$ **29.** all real numbers   **31.** $x \ge 3$
33. all real numbers   **35.** $-2 \le x \le 2$
37.

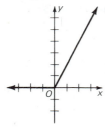

Written Exercises, pages 216–217

1. $-3\sqrt[3]{2}$ **3.** $\frac{2\sqrt[3]{5}}{5}$ **5.** $\frac{\sqrt{15}}{5}$ **7.** $2a\sqrt[5]{2a}$
9. $4|a|c^2\sqrt{2ac}$ **11.** $\frac{|b|\sqrt{2ac}}{2c^2}$ **13.** 6.856
15. 30.33   **17.** 4.243   **19.** 0.4807
21. $\frac{2\sqrt[3]{2x^2y}}{xyz}$ **23.** $2a$ **25.** $\frac{2|u|}{|v|}$ **27.** $a\sqrt{2}$
29. $\frac{\sqrt{xy^2 + yx^2}}{|xy|}$ **31.** $|a + 2|$
33. $|u + 1|\sqrt{u}$ **35.** $\frac{\sqrt{t-1}}{|t+1|}$ **37.** $\frac{\sqrt{x^2-1}}{|x+1|}$
39. $\frac{\sqrt[3]{(a+2)^2(a-1)}}{a+2}$
41. $\frac{\sqrt[3]{v^2(1-v)(v+1)^2}}{v(v+1)}$ **43.** $a\sqrt[3]{a}$
45. $x^{12}\sqrt{x^5}$ **47.** $\frac{\sqrt[10]{a^7}}{a}$

Written Exercises, pages 219–220   **1.** $\sqrt{3}$
3. $4\sqrt{3}$ **5.** $\sqrt[3]{3} + 4\sqrt[3]{2}$ **7.** $6a\sqrt{2a}$ **9.** $\frac{5\sqrt{6}}{6}$
11. $a - \sqrt{a}$ **13.** 1   **15.** $1 + \sqrt{3}$
17. $9 - 6\sqrt{2}$ **19.** 14   **21.** $\frac{4 - 3\sqrt{2}}{2}$
23. $\frac{\sqrt{15} + 3}{2}$ **25.** $\frac{\sqrt{x} + 2}{x - 4}$
27. $\frac{2\sqrt{x+1} - 2}{x}$ **29.** $\sqrt{a+2} + \sqrt{a}$
31. $\frac{(3x-2)(\sqrt{x}-1)}{2(x-1)}$ **33.** $\frac{\sqrt{1-t^2}}{t(1-t^2)}$
35. $(x - 3\sqrt{3})(x + 3\sqrt{3})$ **37.** $(x + \sqrt{3})^2$
39. $(u + 2\sqrt{3})(u - \sqrt{3})$ **41.** Let $a = 1$: $\sqrt{a} + \sqrt{4a} = \sqrt{1} + \sqrt{4} = 1 + 2 = 3$; $\sqrt{5a} = \sqrt{5}$; $3 \ne \sqrt{5}$ **43.** Let $a = 8$ and $b = 1$: $\sqrt[3]{a} - \sqrt[3]{b} = \sqrt[3]{8} - \sqrt[3]{1} = 2 - 1 = 1$; $\sqrt[3]{a - b} = \sqrt[3]{8 - 1} = \sqrt[3]{7}$; $1 \ne \sqrt[3]{7}$

Written Exercises, pages 222–223
1. $\{-64\}$ **3.** $\{26\}$ **5.** no solution   **7.** $\{2\}$
9. $\{4\}$ **11.** $\{3\}$ **13.** $\{-5, 5\}$ **15.** $\{2\}$
17. $\{3\}$ **19.** $\{3\}$ **21.** $\{1, 5\}$ **23.** $\{7\}$
25. $\{30\}$ **27.** $\{32\}$ **29.** $\{-4, 3\}$ **31.** $\{4\}$
33. no solution   **35.** $\{0, 4\}$ **37.** $\{4\}$
39. $\{-2\}$ **41.** $m = \frac{2k}{v^2}$ **43.** $t = \pm\frac{\sqrt{s^2-1}}{s}$

Written Exercises, pages 226–227   **1.** $\sqrt{5}$ is a root of $x^2 - 5 = 0$. The only possible rational roots of $x^2 - 5 = 0$ are $-1, 1, -5,$ and 5. Since none of these satisfies the equation, $\sqrt{5}$ is not rational.   **3.** $-2\sqrt{3}$ is a root of $x^2 - 12 = 0$. The only possible rational roots of $x^2 - 12 = 0$ are -1, 1, -2, 2, -3, 3, -4, 4, -6, 6, -12, and 12. Since none of these satisfies the equation, $-2\sqrt{3}$ is not rational. **5.** $\sqrt[3]{4}$ is a root of $x^3 - 4 = 0$. The only possible rational roots of $x^3 - 4 = 0$ are -1, 1, -2, 2, -4, and 4. Since none of these satisfies the equation, $\sqrt[3]{4}$ is not rational. **7.** $\sqrt[5]{-\dfrac{2}{3}}$ is a root of $3x^5 + 2 = 0$. The only possible rational roots of $3x^5 + 2 = 0$ are -1, 1, -2, 2, $-\dfrac{1}{3}$, $\dfrac{1}{3}$, $-\dfrac{2}{3}$, $\dfrac{2}{3}$. Since none of these satisfies the equation, $\sqrt[5]{-\dfrac{2}{3}}$ is not rational. **9.** -1, 2, 3 **11.** -1, 1 **13.** -1, 1, $\dfrac{1}{2}$ **15.** $\dfrac{2}{3}$

17. The only possible rational roots of $x^4 - 10x^2 + 1 = 0$ are 1 and -1. Thus, since $\sqrt{3} - \sqrt{2}$ is a root, but not a rational root, it is not a rational number.
19. Assume that $\sqrt{3} - 1 = r$ where r is a rational number. Then $\sqrt{3} = 1 + r$. Since both 1 and r are rational, their sum is rational. This is a contradiction since $\sqrt{3}$ is irrational. $\therefore$ $\sqrt{3} - 1$ must be irrational.
21. Assume that $\dfrac{4 + \sqrt{2}}{3} = r$ where r is a rational number. Then $\sqrt{2} = 3r - 4$. Since $3r$ and 4 are rational, their difference is rational. This is a contradiction since $\sqrt{2}$ is irrational. $\therefore$ $\dfrac{4 + \sqrt{2}}{3}$ is irrational.
23. $(3 + \sqrt{2}) + (3 - \sqrt{2}) = 6$, which is a rational number. $(3 + \sqrt{2})(3 - \sqrt{2}) = 7$, which is also a rational number. $\therefore$ The set of irrational numbers is not closed under addition or multiplication.

Calculator Key-In, page 227 1. 2.2894
3. 2.7784 **5.** 2.6550 **7.** 1.2254 **9.** 1.3325
11. 2.8284 **13.** 2.8738 **15.** 6.0675
17. 1.2490 **19.** 4.6564 **21.** 1.9129; 7
23. 2.1407; 21 **25.** 1.5034; 59

Written Exercises, page 231 1. 0.4375
3. $0.\overline{5}$ **5.** 3.275 **7.** $0.4\overline{09}$ **9.** $0.568\overline{1}$
11. $0.\overline{076923}$ **13.** $\dfrac{15}{8}$ **15.** $\dfrac{1}{9}$ **17.** $\dfrac{1}{99}$
19. $\dfrac{79}{111}$ **21.** $\dfrac{169}{330}$ **23.** $\dfrac{71}{3330}$
25–33. Answers may vary **25.** $\dfrac{9}{16}$;

0.5010010001... **27.** -1.62; $-1.601020304...$ **29.** 1.73; 1.7070070007... **31.** 3.142; 3.142020020002... **33.** 3.1415927; 3.1415927020020002...

Computer Key-In, page 232 1. $\dfrac{1}{2} = 0.5$, $\dfrac{1}{3} = 0.\overline{3}$, $\dfrac{1}{4} = 0.25$, $\dfrac{1}{5} = 0.2$, $\dfrac{1}{6} = 0.1\overline{6}$, $\dfrac{1}{7} = 0.\overline{142857}$, $\dfrac{1}{8} = 0.125$, $\dfrac{1}{9} = 0.\overline{1}$, $\dfrac{1}{10} = 0.1$, $\dfrac{1}{11} = 0.\overline{09}$, $\dfrac{1}{12} = 0.08\overline{3}$, $\dfrac{1}{13} = 0.\overline{076923}$, $\dfrac{1}{14} = 0.0\overline{714285}$, $\dfrac{1}{15} = 0.6\overline{6}$, $\dfrac{1}{16} = 0.0625$, $\dfrac{1}{17} = 0.\overline{0588235294117647}$, $\dfrac{1}{18} = 0.0\overline{5}$, $\dfrac{1}{19} = 0.\overline{052631578947368421}$, $\dfrac{1}{20} = 0.05$, $\dfrac{1}{21} = 0.\overline{047619}$, $\dfrac{1}{22} = 0.0\overline{45}$, $\dfrac{1}{23} = 0.\overline{0434782608695652173913}$, $\dfrac{1}{24} = 0.041\overline{6}$, $\dfrac{1}{25} = 0.04$ **3.** you get the repetends for $\dfrac{1}{14}$ and $\dfrac{1}{21}$ by dividing the repetend for $\dfrac{1}{7}$ by 2 and 3 respectively. **5.** 7, 17, 19, 23

Calculator Key-In, page 233 $\dfrac{2}{3}$, $\dfrac{1}{6}$, $\dfrac{4}{9}$; $\dfrac{2}{3} = 0.\overline{6}$, $\dfrac{1}{6} = 0.1\overline{6}$, $\dfrac{4}{9} = 0.\overline{4}$; $\dfrac{7}{24} = 0.291\overline{6}$

Written Exercises, page 236 1. $4i\sqrt{2}$ **3.** $\dfrac{1}{4}i$
5. $\dfrac{i\sqrt{3}}{3}$ **7.** 3 **9.** -3 **11.** $-\dfrac{i\sqrt{2}}{2}$
13. -18 **15.** $12i$ **17.** $-2i\sqrt{3}$ **19.** i
21. $-\sqrt{6}$ **23.** $13i\sqrt{2}$ **25.** $\{-2i\sqrt{2}, 2i\sqrt{2}\}$
27. $\{-4i, 4i\}$ **29.** $\left\{-\dfrac{1}{2}i, \dfrac{1}{2}i\right\}$ **31.** $-6a$
33. -2 **35.** $8ci$ **37.** 0 **39.** $x^2 i\sqrt{x}$
41. $-3i$ **43.** $3t^2$

Written Exercises, pages 239–240
1. $5 + 10i$ **3.** $2 + 3i$ **5.** $7 - 2i$ **7.** 10
9. $1 + 3i$ **11.** $11 - 13i$ **13.** $2i$
15. $-2 + 2i$ **17.** -4 **19.** 3 **21.** $\dfrac{2}{5} - \dfrac{1}{5}i$
23. $\dfrac{1}{10} - \dfrac{1}{5}i$ **25.** $\dfrac{2}{15} - \dfrac{1}{15}i$ **27.** $\dfrac{3}{2} - \dfrac{1}{2}i$
29. $\dfrac{2}{5} + \dfrac{4}{5}i$ **31.** $\dfrac{9}{2} + \dfrac{1}{2}i$

Extra: Part 1, Exercises, page 241 **1.** 1
3. -1 **5.** 0 **7.** -1 **9.** 0 **11.** 1 **13.** 1
15. $(1 - i\sqrt{3})^3 = (1 - i\sqrt{3})^2(1 - i\sqrt{3}) =$
$(-2 - 2i\sqrt{3})(1 - i\sqrt{3}) = -8$
17. $(-1 - i\sqrt{3})^3 = (-1 - i\sqrt{3})^2 \times$
$(-1 - i\sqrt{3}) = (-2 + 2i\sqrt{3})(-1 - i\sqrt{3})$
$= 8$ **19.** $\left(-\dfrac{\sqrt{3}}{2} + \dfrac{1}{2}i\right)^3 =$
$\left(-\dfrac{\sqrt{3}}{2} + \dfrac{1}{2}i\right)^2\left(-\dfrac{\sqrt{3}}{2} + \dfrac{1}{2}i\right) =$
$\left(\dfrac{1}{2} - \dfrac{i\sqrt{3}}{2}\right)\left(-\dfrac{\sqrt{3}}{2} + \dfrac{1}{2}i\right) = i$

Extra: Part 2, Exercises, pages 243–244
1. 3 **3.** 13 **5.** $\sqrt{2}$ **7.** 1 **9. a.** 10 **b.** 8
11. $|\bar{z}| = |a - bi| = \sqrt{(a)^2 + (-b)^2} =$
$\sqrt{a^2 + b^2} = |a + bi| = z$ **13.** $\dfrac{z - \bar{z}}{2}$

Chapter Review, pages 245–246 **1.** c **2.** b
3. a **4.** c **5.** c **6.** d **7.** a **8.** b **9.** d
10. d **11.** d **12.** c **13.** c **14.** b **15.** c
16. a **17.** c

CHAPTER 7 QUADRATIC EQUATIONS AND FUNCTIONS

Written Exercises, page 252
1. $\{2 + \sqrt{3}, 2 - \sqrt{3}\}$
3. $\{-2 + \sqrt{5}, -2 - \sqrt{5}\}$
5. $\{-3 + 2\sqrt{3}, -3 - 2\sqrt{3}\}$ **7.** $\{-1, 5\}$
9. $\{1 + \sqrt{11}, 1 - \sqrt{11}\}$
11. $\{-4 + 2\sqrt{2}, -4 - 2\sqrt{2}\}$
13. $\left\{\dfrac{-1 + \sqrt{5}}{2}, \dfrac{-1 - \sqrt{5}}{2}\right\}$
15. $\left\{\dfrac{3 + 3\sqrt{5}}{2}, \dfrac{3 - 3\sqrt{5}}{2}\right\}$
17. $\left\{\dfrac{-3 + \sqrt{15}}{3}, \dfrac{-3 - \sqrt{15}}{3}\right\}$
19. $\left\{-\dfrac{1}{2}, -1\right\}$ **21.** $\left\{\dfrac{1 + \sqrt{6}}{5}, \dfrac{1 - \sqrt{6}}{5}\right\}$
23. $\left\{\dfrac{1 + \sqrt{97}}{4}, \dfrac{1 - \sqrt{97}}{4}\right\}$
25. $\{-1 + i\sqrt{3}, -1 - i\sqrt{3}\}$

27. $\left\{\dfrac{-1 + i\sqrt{19}}{4}, \dfrac{-1 - i\sqrt{19}}{4}\right\}$
29. $\left\{\dfrac{-3 + i\sqrt{39}}{6}, \dfrac{-3 - i\sqrt{39}}{6}\right\}$
31. $\{1 + \sqrt{2}, 1 - \sqrt{2}\}$
33. $\left\{\dfrac{3 + \sqrt{57}}{4}, \dfrac{3 - \sqrt{57}}{4}\right\}$ **35.** $\{1\}$
37. $\{8\}$ **39.** $(x - 2)^2 + (y - 1)^2 = 9$
41. $(x + 5)^2 + (y - 5)^2 = 50$
43. $y = (x + 4)^2 - 13$
45. $y = \left(x + \dfrac{3}{2}\right)^2 - \dfrac{1}{4}$

Written Exercises, pages 255–256
1. $\{-3 + \sqrt{5}, -3 - \sqrt{5}\}$
3. $\{-2 + 2i, -2 - 2i\}$
5. $\left\{-\dfrac{1}{2} + \dfrac{\sqrt{3}}{2}i, -\dfrac{1}{2} - \dfrac{\sqrt{3}}{2}i\right\}$
7. $\{-3 + \sqrt{14}, -3 - \sqrt{14}\}$
9. $\left\{\dfrac{-4 + \sqrt{6}}{2}, \dfrac{-4 - \sqrt{6}}{2}\right\}$
11. $\left\{-\dfrac{6}{5} + \dfrac{2}{5}i, -\dfrac{6}{5} - \dfrac{2}{5}i\right\}$ **13.** $\left\{\dfrac{2}{3}, -\dfrac{8}{5}\right\}$
15. $\left\{-\dfrac{1}{5} + \dfrac{7}{5}i, -\dfrac{1}{5} - \dfrac{7}{5}i\right\}$ **17.** $\left\{2, -\dfrac{1}{3}\right\}$
19. $\left\{\dfrac{-7 + \sqrt{73}}{4}, \dfrac{-7 - \sqrt{73}}{4}\right\}$
21. $\{1 + \sqrt{5}, 1 - \sqrt{5}\}$
23. $\left\{\dfrac{3 + \sqrt{129}}{4}, \dfrac{3 - \sqrt{129}}{4}\right\}$
25. $\left\{\dfrac{-c + \sqrt{c^2 - 4ab}}{2b}, \dfrac{-c - \sqrt{c^2 - 4ab}}{2b}\right\}$
27. $\left\{\dfrac{\sqrt{2} + \sqrt{6}}{2}, \dfrac{\sqrt{2} - \sqrt{6}}{2}\right\}$
29. $\{\sqrt{2} + 1, \sqrt{2} - 1\}$
31. $\left\{-\dfrac{\sqrt{2}}{2}, -2\sqrt{2}\right\}$ **33.** $\{-2i, i\}$
35. $\{1 + i, 2 + i\}$ **37.** $\{-i, 7i\}$
39. a. $u = (2 \pm \sqrt{5})v$ **b.** $v = (-2 \pm \sqrt{5})u$
41. a. $u = -2v$ or $u = -\dfrac{v}{2}$ **b.** $v = -\dfrac{u}{2}$ or $v = -2u$

Problems, pages 256–257 **1.** 144.72 m by
55.28 m **3.** 20.49 mm
5. smaller pipe: 5.24 h; larger pipe: 3.24 h
7. 10.47 cm by 10.47 cm **9.** 1.91 cm deep or
13.09 cm deep **11.** 1.62

Written Exercises, page 259
1. $\{-1, 1, -2, 2\}$ **3.** $\left\{-\dfrac{1}{2}\sqrt[3]{2}, 1\right\}$
5. $\{4, 9\}$ **7.** $\left\{-\dfrac{1}{2}, 2\right\}$ **9.** $\{-\sqrt[3]{3}, -1\}$

11. $\{-1, 1\}$ **13.** $\{-1, 1, -i, i\}$
15. $\{0, -1, 1, -\sqrt{10}, \sqrt{10}\}$
17. $\{-2, 2, -2i, 2i, -1, 1, -i, i\}$ **19.** $\left\{\dfrac{1}{4}\right\}$
21. $\{4\}$ **23.** $\{-1, 1, 3\}$ **25.** $\left\{0, \dfrac{3}{2}\right\}$
27. $\{-3, -1, 2, 6\}$ **29.** $\{3\}$

Written Exercises, page 263 1. real, unequal, irrational **3.** imaginary conjugates **5.** imaginary conjugates **7.** real, unequal, rational **9.** real, unequal, rational **11.** real, unequal, irrational
13. $k > 3$ **15.** $k = \pm 4\sqrt{3}$ **17.** $k < \dfrac{1}{8}$
19. $k = -2$ or $k = 6$

Written Exercises, pages 266–267
1–21. Answers may vary
1. $x^2 + 2x - 3 = 0$ **3.** $2x^2 - 3x - 14 = 0$
5. $4x^2 - 4x - 3 = 0$ **7.** $x^2 + 7x = 0$
9. $x^2 - 4x + 2 = 0$ **11.** $x^2 - 3x + 1 = 0$
13. $x^2 - 6x + 10 = 0$ **15.** $x^2 + 5 = 0$
17. $3x^2 - 2x + 1 = 0$
19. $x^2 - 2\sqrt{3}x + 1 = 0$
21. $x^2 - 2x + 1 - \sqrt{2} = 0$ **23.** other root $= 3$; $c = 6$ **25.** other root: $1 + i$; $b = -2 - 2i$ **27.** roots: 4 and -1; $c = -8$

Written Exercises, pages 271–272
1.

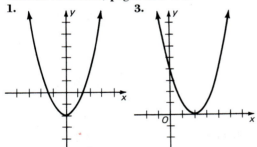

3.

5.

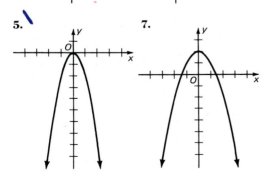

7.

9.

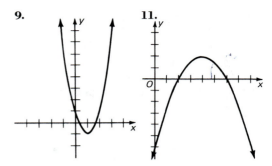

11.

13. $y = -\dfrac{1}{2}x^2 + 2$ **15.** $y = \dfrac{1}{2}(x - 2)^2$
17. $y = -2(x - 4)^2 + 5$ **19.** $k = 2$
21. $a = -\dfrac{2}{3}$ **23.** $h = 1$ or $h = 5$
25. $h = -4$ or $h = 8$ **27.** $a = 2$, $k = 3$
29. y-intercept: 8; x-intercepts: 2 and 4
31. y-intercept: 16; no x-intercepts **33.** y-intercept: $\dfrac{7}{3}$; x-intercepts: $\dfrac{2 + 3\sqrt{2}}{2}$ and $\dfrac{2 - 3\sqrt{2}}{2}$ **35.** $\dfrac{k}{a} > 0$

39.

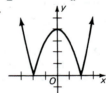

41. a.

x	y
-9	-3
-4	-2
-1	-1
0	0
-1	1
-4	2
-9	3

b.

x	y
11	-3
6	-2
3	-1
2	0
3	1
6	2
11	3

41. c.

x	y
9	-4
4	-3
1	-2
0	-1
1	0
4	1
9	2

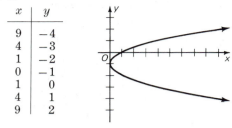

d.

x	y
11	-4
6	-3
3	-2
2	-1
3	0
6	1
11	2

e.

x	y
$-\dfrac{3}{2}$	-1
1	0
$\dfrac{5}{2}$	1
3	2
$\dfrac{5}{2}$	3
1	4
$-\dfrac{3}{2}$	5

43. a. $x = a(y - k)^2 + h$ **b.** 1; 0 , 1, or 2

Written Exercises, pages 275–276

1. 2 is the maximum value. (Graph below)

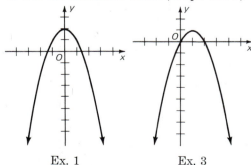

Ex. 1   Ex. 3

3. 1 is the maximum value. (Graph above)

5. 0 is the minimum value.

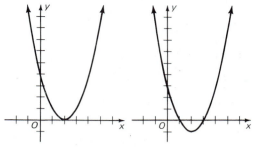

Ex. 5   Ex. 7

7. -1 is the minimum value.
9. 7 is the maximum value.

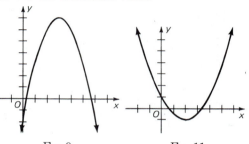

Ex. 9   Ex. 11

11. -1 is the minimum value.

13. $y = (x - 2)^2 - 9$
15. $y = 2\left(x + \dfrac{3}{2}\right)^2 - \dfrac{13}{2}$
17. $y = \left(x + \dfrac{b}{2}\right)^2 + \dfrac{4c - b^2}{4}$ **19.** none
21. 1 **23.** 2 **25.** none **27.** 2
29. domain: all real numbers; range:
$\{y : y \le -2\}$

Problems, pages 276–277
1. a. 5 cm by 5 cm **3.** 50 s **5.** 225 W
7. 78 m by 78 m **9.** 20 **11.** $\dfrac{a_1 + a_2 + a_3}{3}$;

$$\dfrac{a_1 + a_2 + \cdots + a_n}{n}$$

Chapter Review, pages 278–280 1. d
2. b **3.** b **4.** a **5.** b **6.** c **7.** a **8.** d
9. c **10.** b **11.** c **12.** a **13.** a **14.** d
15. b **16.** b **17.** c **18.** d

Cumulative Review, page 281 1. $-32a^{10}$
3. $18x^3 + 3x^2 - 105x$ **5. a.** p^2q
b. $21p^5q^4r^2$ **7.** width: 15 m; length: 20 m

9. $\dfrac{5y^2}{x^3}$ **11.** $\dfrac{s-2}{r^2-3r+9}$

13. $\dfrac{x+12}{x(x+3)(x-3)}$ **15.** $\{1\}$

17. $43 - 30\sqrt{2}$ **19.** $\{7\}$

21. $\{5 + 2\sqrt{2}, 5 - 2\sqrt{2}\}$

23. $\left\{\dfrac{3+\sqrt{21}}{6}, \dfrac{3-\sqrt{21}}{6}\right\}$ **25.** Two real,

unequal, irrational roots **27.** $\dfrac{33}{8}$, or $4\dfrac{1}{8}$

CHAPTER 8 EQUATIONS AND NUMERICAL METHODS

Written Exercises, pages 287–288
1–7. See below for art. **1.** consistent
3. consistent **5.** inconsistent **7.** consistent

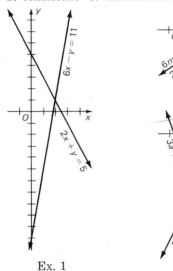

Ex. 1

Ex. 3

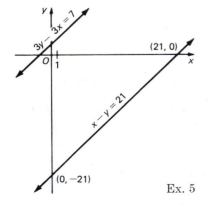

Ex. 5

Ex. 7

9. $\{(2,2)\}$ **11.** $\{(-2,8)\}$ **13.** $\{(4,2)\}$

15. $\left\{\left(\dfrac{5}{7}, \dfrac{17}{35}\right)\right\}$ **17.** inconsistent

19. $\{(x,y)\colon -4x + 9y = 7\}$ **21.** $\{(-4,6)\}$

23. $\left\{\left(\dfrac{1}{7}, \dfrac{1}{14}\right)\right\}$ **25.** $\left\{\left(-\dfrac{1}{3}, 0\right)\right\}$

27. $\{(3,7)\}$ **29.** $\left\{\left(-\dfrac{26}{45}, -\dfrac{4}{9}\right)\right\}$

31. $\left\{\left(-\dfrac{74}{133}, \dfrac{3}{38}\right)\right\}$ **33.** $\left\{\left(\dfrac{1}{5}, \dfrac{1}{2}\right)\right\}$

35. $\left\{\left(-\dfrac{7}{6}, -\dfrac{7}{4}\right)\right\}$ **37.** $\left\{\left(\dfrac{3}{2}, \dfrac{3}{11}\right)\right\}$

39. $\left\{\left(\dfrac{5}{7}, -\dfrac{5}{3}\right)\right\}$ **41.** $A = \dfrac{70}{31}, B = \dfrac{55}{31}$

43. $A = 3, B = -7$ **45.** $x = 1, y = 0$

Problems, pages 291–292 **1.** 28 and 36
3. 1.5 cm, 3.5 cm, 3.5 cm; 1.5 cm, 7 cm, 7 cm
5. 13 seniors, 15 juniors **7.** Martha: 26 h; Joan: 19 h **9.** a dozen eggs: $.95; a loaf of bread: $.65 **11.** $y = -\dfrac{4}{5}x + \dfrac{19}{5}$

13. $v_0 = 8.5, a = 6.5$ **15.** original number = 25 **17.** $16/d, 12 ¢/km **19.** 130 km/h

Written Exercises, pages 295–296
1. **3.**

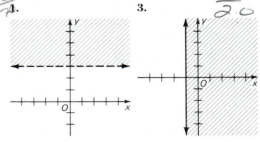

5. **7.**

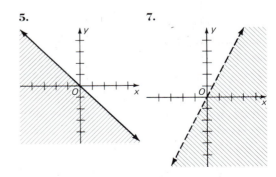

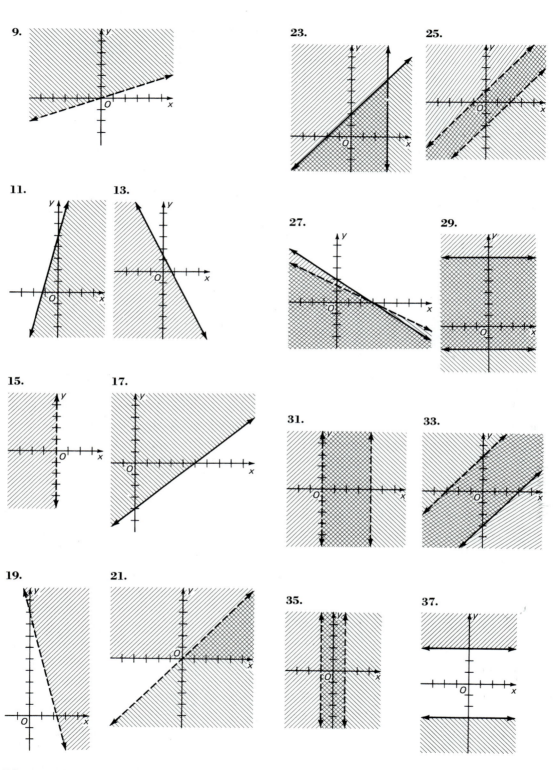

39.

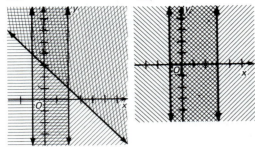

41.

43.

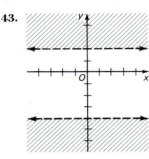

Written Exercises, pages 299–300
1. $\{(10, 2, 3)\}$ **3.** $\{(0, 2, -2)\}$
5. $\{(-1, -2, 1)\}$ **7.** $\{(-5, -5, 14)\}$
9. $\{(-2, 3, -1)\}$ **11.** $\{(3, -2, 0)\}$
13. $\{(1, -1, -2)\}$ **15.** $\left\{\left(-2, \frac{7}{5}, -\frac{1}{5}\right)\right\}$
17. $\left\{\left(-6, -\frac{1}{2}, 2\right)\right\}$ **19.** $A = -\frac{2}{7}, B = \frac{5}{7},$
$C = -\frac{1}{7}$

Problems, pages 300–302 **1.** 1, 5, 6
3. 11 \$1 bills, 7 \$5 bills, 5 \$10 bills
5. length = 50 cm, width = 10 cm,
height = 15 cm **7.** an avocado: 59¢; a
bunch of celery: 47¢; a bag of radishes: 53¢
9. regular washer: 50¢; large washer 75¢;
dryer: 60¢ **11.** 6, 8, 12

Written Exercises, page 304 **1.** $3x^2 - x$; 2
3. $y^2 - 4y + 6$; -15 **5.** $2a^3 + a^2 + 4a + 3$;
15 **7.** $2x^2 + 3x - 2$; 0
9. $2z^3 + (-1 + 6i)z^2 + (-18 - 3i)z + 11 - 54i$; $166 + 33i$ **11.** $3t^2 - 2t + 6$; 0
13. $2v^2 - 3v + \frac{7}{2}$; $\frac{27}{2}$
15. $2x^2 + 3x - 16$; 0
17. $3x^3 + (-6 + 6i)x^2 + (-12 - 12i)x + 27 - 24i$; $52 + 54i$ **19.** -6

Written Exercises, page 308 **1.** 5 **3.** 129
5. -717 **7.** no **9.** no **11.** no **13.** yes
15. $\left\{1, \frac{3}{2} + \frac{\sqrt{11}}{2}i, \frac{3}{2} - \frac{\sqrt{11}}{2}i\right\}$
17. $\left\{1, \frac{-5 - \sqrt{61}}{6}, \frac{-5 + \sqrt{61}}{6}\right\}$
19. $\left\{-2, -\frac{3}{2}, -1, 1\right\}$ **21.** $-\sqrt{3}, \sqrt{3}$

Computer Key-In, pages 309–310 **1.** The
polynomial has a real root between $x = 4$
and $x = 5$. **3.** Real roots: $-3, -2, -1$

Written Exercises, pages 313–314

	No. of pos. real roots	No. of neg. real roots	No. of imag. roots
1.	0	4	0
	0	2	2
	0	0	4
3.	1	1	2
5.	0	1	4
	2	1	2
7.	1	0	6

9. $i\sqrt{2}$; $(i\sqrt{2})^3 + (i\sqrt{2})^2 + 2(i\sqrt{2}) + 2 = -2i\sqrt{2} - 2 + 2i\sqrt{2} + 2 = 0$
11. $1 + 3i$; (answers may vary)
$x^3 - 4x^2 + 14x - 20 = 0$
13. $\left\{-\frac{1}{2}, 3 + 5i, 3 - 5i\right\}$
15. $\{-3, 2, -1 + 3i, -1 - 3i\}$

Written Exercises, pages 316–317

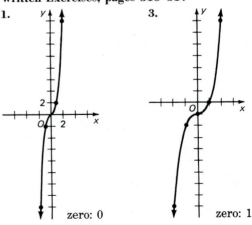

1. zero: 0   **3.** zero: 1

5.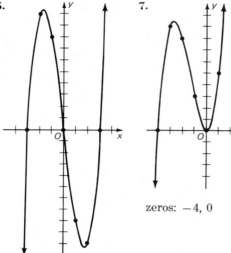

zeros: $-3, 0, 3$

7.

zeros: $-4, 0$

9.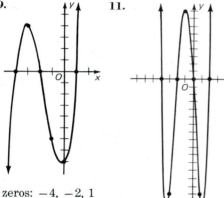

zeros: $-4, -2, 1$

11.

zeros: $-4, -2, 0, 2$

13. 1   **15.** $2 + 2\sqrt{3}$

Written Exercises, pages 320–321   1. 1.312
3. 2.163 **5.** 2.455 **7.** 3.023 **9.** 1.099
11. 1.727 **13.** 3.72 **15.** 1.28 **17. a.** 32.81
b. 8.39 **19. a.** 62.5 g **b.** 11.0 weeks

Chapter Review, pages 322–323   1. c **2.** b
3. b **4.** c **5.** d **6.** b **7.** c **8.** c **9.** a

CHAPTER 9   ANALYTIC GEOMETRY

Written Exercises, page 328   1. a. 5
b. $\left(0, -\dfrac{3}{2}\right)$ **3. a.** $6\sqrt{2}$ **b.** $(2, 2)$ **5. a.** $\dfrac{5}{2}$
b. $\left(-\dfrac{1}{4}, 2\right)$ **7. a.** 4 **b.** $(3, 0)$ **9. a.** $2\sqrt{2}$
b. $\left(\dfrac{\sqrt{3}+1}{2}, \dfrac{\sqrt{3}-1}{2}\right)$ **11. a.** $4\sqrt{a^2 + b^2}$
b. $(a, 0)$ **13.** $(2, 6)$ **15.** $(-1, -10)$
17. $(2a, 2b)$ **19. a.** isosceles **b.** right; 34
21. a. isosceles **b.** right; 9
23. a. not isosceles **b.** not right

Problems, page 328   1. The distance from
$(0, 0)$ to (a, b) is
$\sqrt{(a - 0)^2 + (b - 0)^2}$, or $\sqrt{a^2 + b^2}$.
3. a. $x - 3y = 5$ **b.** $x + 4y = 6$ **5.** 7, -1

Written Exercises, pages 331–332
1. $3x + 2y = 0$ **3.** $2x + y = -2$
5. $x + 3y = 7$ **7.** $x - 2y = -8$
9. $5x + 2y = 10$ **11.** $x + 2y = 6$ **19.** $\dfrac{8\sqrt{5}}{5}$
21. $2\sqrt{10}$ **23.** $L_1: m_1 x - y = m_1 r - s$;
$L_2: m_2 x - y = m_2 r - s$
25. $T_1 T_2 = |m_2 - m_1|$; $PT_1 = \sqrt{1 + m_1{}^2}$;
$PT_2 = \sqrt{1 + m_2{}^2}$

Written Exercises, pages 336–337
1. $x^2 + y^2 - 2y = 0$
3. $x^2 + y^2 - 4x + 4y = 0$ **5.** $C(0, 0)$, $r = 4$
7. $C(2, 0)$, $r = 2$ **9.** $C(-2, 0)$, $r = 2$
11. no graph **13.** $C\left(\dfrac{3}{2}, -\dfrac{1}{2}\right)$, $r = \dfrac{\sqrt{10}}{2}$
15. $C\left(\dfrac{3}{2}, \dfrac{1}{2}\right)$, $r = 1$ **17.** $(x - 2)^2 + y^2 = 4$
19. $(x - 3)^2 + (y - 1)^2 = 9$
21. $(x - 2)^2 + (y - 4)^2 = 16$
23. $(x + 1)^2 + (y + 1)^2 = 1$,
$(x - 1)^2 + (y + 1)^2 = 1$,
$(x - 1)^2 + (y - 1)^2 = 1$,
$(x + 1)^2 + (y - 1)^2 = 1$

25.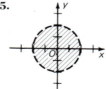

27.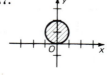

29.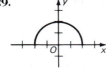

31.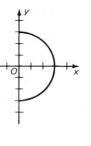

33.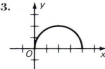

35. $x^2 + (y - 5\sqrt{2})^2 = 25$
37. $(x + 1)^2 + (y - 1)^2 = 100$
39. $a^2 + b^2 - 4c > 0$

Written Exercises, pages 340–341

1. $x = \dfrac{1}{4}y^2 - 1$

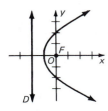

3. $y = \dfrac{1}{12}(x - 2)^2$

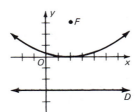

5. $y = -\dfrac{1}{8}(x - 2)^2 + 2$

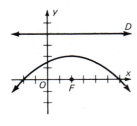

7. $y = -\dfrac{1}{8}(x - 3)^2$

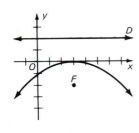

9. $V(0, 0)$;
  axis: $y = 0$

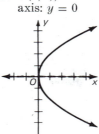

11. $V(-4, -2)$;
  axis: $y = -2$

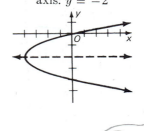

13. $V(1, 2)$;
  axis: $y = 2$

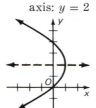

15. $V\left(1, -\dfrac{1}{2}\right)$;
  axis: $x = 1$

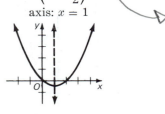

17.

19.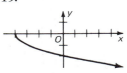

Extra, Exercises, page 342
1. focus: $(-2, 0)$; directrix: $x = 2$;
opens left **3.** focus: $(0, 1)$;
directrix: $y = -1$; opens up
5. $y^2 = -24x$ **7. a.** $y^2 = \dfrac{4}{5}x$ **b.** $x^2 = \dfrac{25}{2}y$
9. $c = \dfrac{1}{4a}$

Written Exercises, pages 346–347
1. foci: $(0, \sqrt{5})$,
$(0, -\sqrt{5})$

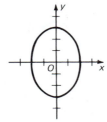

3. foci: $(\sqrt{5}, 0)$,
$(-\sqrt{5}, 0)$

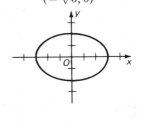

5. foci: $(8, 0), (-8, 0)$

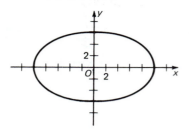

7. foci: $(0, 8), (0, -8)$

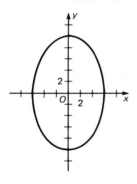

9. foci: $(10\sqrt{3}, 0), (-10\sqrt{3}, 0)$

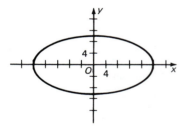

11. foci: $\left(\dfrac{\sqrt{3}}{2}, 0\right)$, $\left(-\dfrac{\sqrt{3}}{2}, 0\right)$

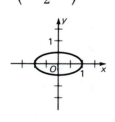

13. foci: $(0, 2\sqrt{2})$, $(0, -2\sqrt{2})$

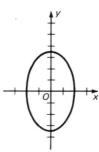

15. foci: $\left(0, \dfrac{\sqrt{3}}{2}\right)$, $\left(0, -\dfrac{\sqrt{3}}{2}\right)$

17. $\dfrac{x^2}{20} + \dfrac{y^2}{36} = 1$

19.

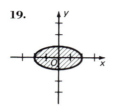

21.

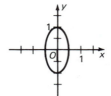

23. $\dfrac{x^2}{a^2} + \dfrac{y^2}{b^2} = 1$

25.

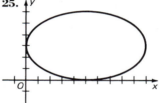

Written Exercises, pages 351–352

1. a.

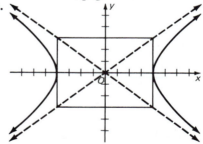

b. foci: $(5, 0), (-5, 0)$

3. a.

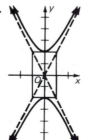

b. foci: $(0, \sqrt{5})$, $(0, -\sqrt{5})$

5. a.

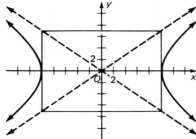

b. foci: $(\sqrt{149}, 0)$, $(-\sqrt{149}, 0)$

7. a.

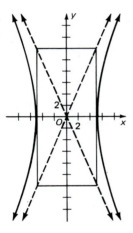

b. foci: $(13, 0)$, $(-13, 0)$

9. b. foci: $(0, 10\sqrt{2})$, $(0, -10\sqrt{2})$

11. b. foci: $\left(\dfrac{\sqrt{17}}{2}, 0\right)$, $\left(-\dfrac{\sqrt{17}}{2}, 0\right)$

15. $\dfrac{y^2}{9} - \dfrac{x^2}{16} = 1$ **17.** $\dfrac{x^2}{16} - \dfrac{y^2}{4} = 1$

19.

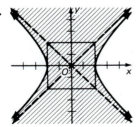

21.

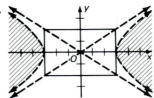

23. $\dfrac{y^2}{4} - \dfrac{x^2}{32} = 1$ **25.** $\dfrac{x^2}{a^2} - \dfrac{y^2}{b^2} = 1$

27. $xy = \dfrac{a^2}{2}$ **29.** x must be greater than 5.05. $\therefore$ the point $(6, \sqrt{35})$ satisfies the condition.

Problems, pages 355–356   **1.** \$15,000
3. 968 r/min   **5.** 36 cm   **7.** $5\sqrt{2}$ m
9. 3.6 Ω **11.** 840 kg

Written Exercises, pages 359–360
1. 2 real solutions

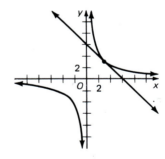

3. 1 real solution

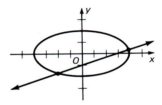

5. 4 real solutions

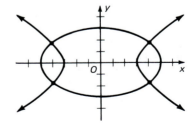

7. 4 real solutions

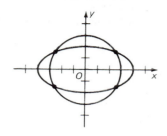

9. $\{(3.9, 0.3), (-2.1, -1.7)\}$ **11.** $\{(3, 3)\}$
13. $\{(4.0, 1.8), (4.0, -1.8), (-4.0, -1.8), (-4.0, 1.8)\}$ **15.** $\{(2.6, 1.5), (2.6, -1.5), (-2.6, -1.5), (-2.6, 1.5)\}$

17.

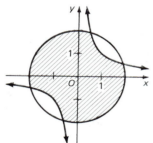

19.

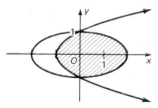

Written Exercises, page 364
1. $\{(4, 12), (-1, -3)\}$ **3.** $\{(1, -2), (2, -1)\}$
5. $\left\{\left(-\dfrac{2}{3}, \dfrac{10}{3}\right), (2, -2)\right\}$
7. $\{(-5, 0), (3, 4)\}$
9. $\{(\sqrt{5}, 0), (-\sqrt{5}, 0), (2, -1), (-2, -1)\}$
11. $\{(2, 0), (-2, 0)\}$ **13.** $\{(3, 2), (1, 2)\}$
15. $\{(2, \sqrt{5}), (2, -\sqrt{5}), (-2, \sqrt{5}), (-2, -\sqrt{5})\}$
17. $\{(3, 2), (-3, -2), (2, 3), (-2, -3)\}$
19. $2 - i, -2 + i$ **21.** $3 + 2i, -3 - 2i$

Problems, pages 364–365 **1.** 5 cm by 2 cm
3. 3.5 and 1.4 **5.** 60 m by 30 m
7. $\sqrt{6}$ and 2; $-\sqrt{6}$ and -2; $-\sqrt{6}$ and 2; $\sqrt{6}$ and -2 **9.** $(x - 3)^2 + y^2 = 25$
11. $\dfrac{x^2}{12} + \dfrac{y^2}{4} = 1$

Chapter Review, pages 368–370 **1.** c **2.** d
3. c **4.** b **5.** a **6.** a **7.** b **8.** c **9.** c
10. b **11.** b **12.** a **13.** c **14.** b **15.** c
16. d **17.** c **18.** b **19.** c **20.** b **21.** d

CHAPTER 10 EXPONENTIAL AND LOGARITHMIC FUNCTIONS

Written Exercises, page 375 **1.** $x^{\frac{2}{3}}y^2$ **3.** $\dfrac{b^{\frac{3}{2}}}{a^{\frac{1}{2}}}$
5. $\dfrac{2a^{\frac{1}{3}}}{b^{\frac{1}{3}}}$ **7.** 27 **9.** $\dfrac{4}{25}$ **11.** 49 **13.** 4 **15.** 9
17. $2\sqrt[4]{2}$ **19.** 3 **21.** $\sqrt[3]{3}$ **23.** $3^{\frac{1}{2}}$ **25.** 1
27. $\dfrac{7}{12}$ **29.** 5 **31.** $c^{\frac{1}{6}}$ **33.** $3^{\frac{1}{2}}$ **35.** $a^{\frac{9}{8}}$
37. $\dfrac{1}{27}$ **39.** 36 **41.** $\{1, 16\}$ **43.** $\sqrt{a} + \sqrt{b}$

Written Exercises, pages 378–379 **1.** $\dfrac{1}{49}$
3. 100 **5.** 0.00001 **7.** 27 **9.** 3 **11.** 8
13. 2 **15.** 2 **17.** 1 **19.** -2 **21.** $-\dfrac{1}{11}$

23.

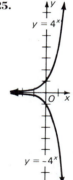

25.

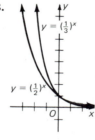

27.

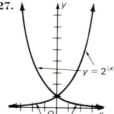

29. The solution is approximately 0.6.

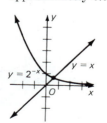

31. The solutions are -3 and approximately 0.7.

33. The solutions are 2, 4 and approximately -0.8.

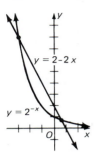

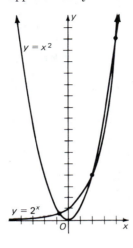

1. inverses **3.** not inverses
5. not inverses **7.** inverses **9.** inverses
11. $f^{-1}(x) = \dfrac{x+1}{3}$

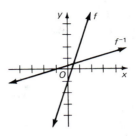

13. no inverse
15. $f^{-1}(x) = -\dfrac{6}{x}$

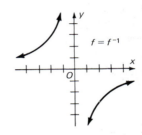

Written Exercises, pages 383–384 1. 3
3. 1 **5.** $\dfrac{1}{2}$ **7.** -3 **9.** -3 **11.** $\dfrac{3}{2}$ **13.** -2
15. $\dfrac{3}{2}$ **17.** 4 **19.** $3\sqrt[3]{3}$ **21.** 27 **23.** -3
25. 64 **27.** 3 **29.** 9 **31.** 27 **33.** 9
35. -4 **37.** $\{-2, 2\}$
39.

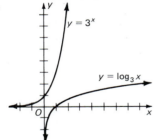

41.

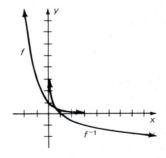

43. 1 **45.** 0 **47.** 1 **49.** 1

17. $f^{-1}(x) = \log_{\frac{1}{2}} x$, or $f^{-1}(x) = -\log_2 x$

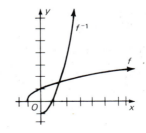

19. $f^{-1}(x) = x^2 - 1$ where $x \geq 0$

21. $f^{-1}(x) = 4 - x^2$
where $x \leq 0$ **23.** $f^{-1}(x) = \sqrt{1 - x}$
where $x \leq 1$

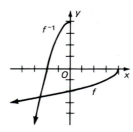
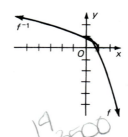

25. $(a = -1)$ or $(a = 1$ and $b = 0)$

Extra Exercises, page 389
1. $[f \circ g](x) = (x + 1)^2$, $[g \circ f](x) = x^2 + 1$
3. $[f \circ f^{-1}](x) = x$, $[f^{-1} \circ f](x) = x$

Written Exercises, page 392   **1.** 8   **3.** 2
5. 25   **7.** $\{-12, 12\}$ **9.** 6   **11.** 1.176
13. 1.398   **15.** -3.523 **17.** -0.602
19. 0.653   **21.** -0.477 **23.** 4   **25.** 27   **27.** 5
29. $2 + 2\sqrt{2}$ **33.** 25

Extra Exercises, page 393   **1.** 3.402
3. -0.693 **5.** -1.099

Written Exercises, pages 397–398
1. 0.8762   **3.** 1.1367   **5.** -1.3893 **7.** 3.7993
9. 4.51   **11.** 88,000   **13.** 0.000813
15. a. $\dfrac{\log 30}{\log 3}$ **b.** 3.10   **17. a.** $\dfrac{\log 3800}{\log 10}$
b. 3.58   **19. a.** antilog $\left(\dfrac{\log 3.6}{1.8}\right)$ **b.** 2.04
21. a. antilog $\left(\dfrac{1}{\pi}\right)$ **b.** 2.08   **23. a.** $\dfrac{\log 25}{\log 9}$
b. 1.46   **25. a.** $\dfrac{\log 5}{\log 2}$ **b.** 2.32
27. a. antilog $\left(\dfrac{3 \log 3.2}{2}\right)$ **b.** 5.72
29. a. $\dfrac{2 \log 5}{2 - \log 5}$ **b.** 1.07   **31.** 1

Calculator Key-In, page 398   **1.** 1.4306766

Problems, pages 401–402
1. a. $-\dfrac{3.8 \log 0.2}{\log 2}$ **b.** 8.82 d
3. a. $\dfrac{\log 4}{12 \log 1.01}$ **b.** 11.6 y
5. a. $\dfrac{20 \log 3}{\log 2}$ **b.** 31.7 y
7. a. 4 antilog $\left(\dfrac{\log 4 - \log 3}{20}\right) - 4$ **b.** 6%

9. a. antilog $(4 \log 1.03) - 1$ **b.** 12.55%

Chapter Review, pages 403–405   **1.** c   **2.** a
3. d   **4.** b   **5.** a   **6.** b   **7.** b   **8.** d   **9.** a
10. b   **11.** b   **12.** c   **13.** c   **14.** a   **15.** c
16. b

CHAPTER 11   SEQUENCES AND SERIES

Written Exercises, pages 410–411
1. 9, 11, 13   **3.** 39, 48, 57   **5.** 1, 4, 7
7. -30, -39, -48 **9.** 10, 11.1, 12.2
11. $8x$, $10x$, $12x$ **13.** 35   **15.** 97   **17.** 775
19. 69   **21.** 62   **23.** $t_n = 2n$
25. $t_n = 10n - 3$ **27.** $t_n = 10n - 5$
29. $t_n = 5n - 4$ **31.** 14   **33.** 20   **35. a.** 36
b. 30, 42   **c.** 27, 36, 45   **37.** $3x - y$,
$4x + 2y$ **39.** 128   **41.** 3

Problems, pages 411   **1.** $17,400   **3.** Job B
5. a. 19 bricks   **b.** 15 rows

Written Exercises, pages 414–415
1. 40, 80, 160; $t_n = 5 \cdot 2^{n-1}$ **3.** -8, 4, -2;
$t_n = 64\left(-\dfrac{1}{2}\right)^{n-1}$ **5.** 1, $\dfrac{3}{2}$, $\dfrac{9}{4}$; $t_n = \dfrac{8}{27}\left(\dfrac{3}{2}\right)^{n-1}$
7. -0.0001, 0.00001, -0.000001;
$t_n = 0.1(-0.1)^{n-1}$ **9.** $a^{11}b^{-6}$, $a^{13}b^{-9}$, $a^{15}b^{-12}$;
$t_n = a^5b^3\left(\dfrac{a^2}{b^3}\right)^{n-1}$ **11.** $8 \log m$, $16 \log m$,
$32 \log m$; $t_n = \log m \cdot 2^{n-1}$ **13. a.** 6.5   **b.** 6
15. a. $25\dfrac{1}{4}$ **b.** 5   **17. a.** $\dfrac{241}{180}$ **b.** $\dfrac{2}{3}$
19. 384   **21.** -2430 **23.** $k^{11}b^{30}$
25. a. $16 = 8(r)^2$; $2 = r^2$; $r = \pm\sqrt{2}$
b. $\sqrt[3]{2}$ **27.** 9, 18, 36, 72   **29.** 96, 48, 24, 12,
6, 3   **31.** $4x^{-1}y^5$, $12x^2y^4$, $36x^5y^3$, $108x^8y^2$

Problems, pages 415–416   **1.** $P_2 = P_1 \cdot 1.08$
3. $P_2 = P_1 \cdot 1.5$ **5.** $P_2 = P_1 \cdot 0.98$
7. $P_2 = 1.1 P_1$; $P_3 = 1.1 P_2 = 1.1(1.1 P_1) = $
$1.21 P_1 = P_1 + 0.21 P_1$. $\therefore$ the new price is
21% more than the original price.
9. $86,400   **11.** Job B; Job B
13. $t_{13} = t_1 r^{12}$; $440 = 220r^{12}$; $r^{12} = 2$; $r = 2^{\frac{1}{12}}$

Written Exercises, pages 419–420
1. 10,600   **3.** 155   **5.** 320   **7.** $675x$ **9.** 60
11. 2601   **13.** -5010 **15.** -275
17. $\displaystyle\sum_{n=1}^{5} 2n$ **19.** $\displaystyle\sum_{n=1}^{32} 3n + 2$
21. $\displaystyle\sum_{n=1}^{21} -3n + 13$ **23.** 477   **25.** 1665
27. 247,500

29. a. $\sum_{i=1}^{n} i = \dfrac{n}{2}(1+n) = \dfrac{n+n^2}{2} = \dfrac{n^2+n}{2}$

b. 20 **31.** $t_1 = 5$, $t_2 = 9$ **33.** 17

35. $\sum_{k=1}^{3} k \log 3 = \log 3 + 2\log 3 + 3\log 3 =$
$6\log 3 = \log 3^6$ **37.** 2

Problems, pages 420–421 **1.** 78 times
3. 1749 bricks **5.** 22 matches **7.** 12 mo
9. 625 **11.** 9 d **13.** 34 credits

Written Exercises, pages 423–424 **1.** 242

3. 31.5 **5.** 13 **7.** $\dfrac{1023}{1024}$ **9.** 19,682

13. a. 39 **b.** approximately 57.275

15. a. $\sum_{k=1}^{n} 2^{k-1} = \dfrac{1-2^n}{1-2} = \dfrac{1-2^n}{-1} = 2^n - 1$.

b. 20 terms **19.** 0, 24, 40; neither
arithmetic nor geometric.
21. (guesses will vary) **a.** 0.00000095
b. 0.000026 **c.** 0.00001429

Problems, pages 424–425
1. 2046 ancestors **3.** \$29304.48
5. 336.16 cm **7.** \$13,971.64 **9.** 6 rounds
11. a. \$4.05 **b.** \$3,250,000

Written Exercises, pages 427–428 **1.** 8
3. 10.8 **5.** no sum **7.** 1.8 **9.** no sum
11. $4\sqrt{2} + 4$ **13.** $S_1 = 8$, $S_2 = 10$,
$S_3 = 10\dfrac{1}{2}$, $S_4 = 10\dfrac{5}{8}$, $S_5 = 10\dfrac{21}{32}$, $S = 10\dfrac{2}{3}$

15. $S_1 = \dfrac{3}{4}$, $S_2 = \dfrac{3}{8}$, $S_3 = \dfrac{9}{16}$, $S_4 = \dfrac{15}{32}$,

$S_5 = \dfrac{33}{64}$, $S = \dfrac{1}{2}$ **17.** 2, $\dfrac{4}{3}$, $\dfrac{8}{9}$

19. 25, -20, 16 **21.** $\dfrac{4}{9}$ **23.** $\dfrac{4}{11}$ **25.** $\dfrac{7}{22}$

27. $\dfrac{aab}{999}$, or $\dfrac{110a+b}{999}$

Problems, pages 428–429 **1.** 22.5 m
3. $96 + 48\sqrt{2}$ cm **5.** 288 cm^2 **7.** 93.3 cm
9. a. $S = \dfrac{250,000}{1-0.95} = \dfrac{250,000}{0.05} = 5,000,000.$
Since $S = 5,000,000$, the well will never
produce more than 5,000,000 barrels.
b. 10 months

Application, page 430 **b.** \$18,392.80

Written Exercises, page 433 **1.** ninth row:
1, 8, 28, 56, 70, 56, 28, 8, 1; tenth row: 1, 9,
36, 84, 126, 126, 84, 36, 9, 1

3. a. $a^6 + 6a^5b + 15a^4b^2 + 20a^3b^3 + 15a^2b^4 +$
$6ab^5 + b^6$ **b.** $a^6 - 6a^5b + 15a^4b^2 - 20a^3b^3 +$
$15a^2b^4 - 6ab^5 + b^6$ **5. a.** $p^8 + 8p^7 + 28p^6 +$
$56p^5 + 70p^4 + 56p^3 + 28p^2 + 8p + 1$
b. $p^8 - 8p^7 + 28p^6 - 56p^5 + 70p^4 - 56p^3 +$
$28p^2 - 8p + 1$
7. $x^{10} + 5x^8 + 10x^6 + 10x^4 + 5x^2 + 1$
9. $64h^6 + 576h^5 + 2160h^4 + 4320h^3 + 4860h^2$
$+ 2916h + 729$

11. $27c^3 - 9c^2d + cd^2 - \dfrac{d^3}{27}$

13. $625m^4 - 500m^{\frac{7}{2}} + 150m^3 - 20m^{\frac{5}{2}} + m^2$
15. p^{50}, $-100p^{49}$, $4900p^{48}$
17. 1, $100a^2$, $4950a^4$ **19.** $240d^2$
21. $135x^2y^8$ **23.** $-16,807x^{15}$ **25.** $231p^2q^{20}$,
$-22pq^{21}$, q^{22} **27.** $-792x^5y^7$ **29.** a^n,

$na^{n-1}b^1$, $\dfrac{n(n-1)}{2}a^{n-2}b^2$,

$\dfrac{n(n-1)(n-2)}{6}a^{n-3}b^3$

Written Exercises, page 435 **1.** 12
3. 120 **5.** $n+1$ **7.** $(n+1)n$ **9.** a^{20},
$20a^{19}b$, $190a^{18}b^2$, $1140a^{17}b^3$ **11.** x^{18},
$-18x^{17}y$, $153x^{16}y^2$, $-816x^{15}y^3$ **13.** $56a^5x^3$
15. $-792u^{14}v^5$ **17.** $-2016a^4b^5$ **19.** $20x^6y^6$
21. 3432 **25.** $p^{\frac{1}{2}}$, $\dfrac{1}{2}p^{-\frac{1}{2}}q$, $-\dfrac{1}{8}p^{-\frac{3}{2}}q^2$

27. a, $-\dfrac{1}{2}a^{-1}$, $-\dfrac{1}{8}a^{-3}$

Chapter Review, page 437 **1.** d **2.** b
3. a **4.** d **5.** a **6.** c **7.** b **8.** a **9.** d
10. a

Cumulative Review, pages 438–439
1. $\left\{\left(\dfrac{41}{10}, \dfrac{13}{10}\right)\right\}$ **3.** $\{(0, -3), (2, 5)\}$

5.

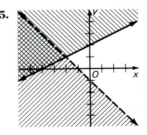

7. It is a factor. **9. a.** $\sqrt{73}$ **b.** $(-2, 2.5)$
11. $3x - y = -5$ **13.** $x^2 = 8y - 24$
15. $\dfrac{x^2}{9} - \dfrac{y^2}{36} = 1$ **17.** $\dfrac{1}{27}$ **19.** 6 **21.** 3

23. $\dfrac{1}{8}$ **25.** 21.6 **27.** $-\dfrac{2}{3}$

29. $1023\sqrt{2} - 2046$ **31.** $28p^6q^2$

Written Exercises, pages 444–445
1. a.

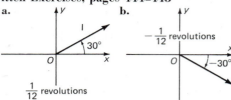

first-quadrant   fourth-quadrant
angle   angle

3. a.   **b.**

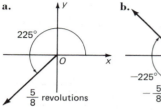

third-quadrant   second-quadrant
angle   angle

5.   **7.**

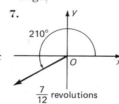

first-quadrant   third-quadrant
angle   angle

9.   **11.**

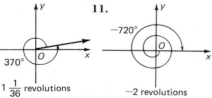

first-quadrant   quadrantal angle
angle

13. $35°45'$ **15.** $14°6'$ **17.** $6°30'18''$
19. $18°18'0''$ **21.** $128.7°$ **23.** $7.59°$

25.   **27.**

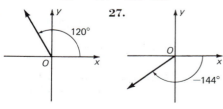

29.

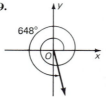

31–37. Answers may vary. 31. $435°$,
$-285°$ **33.** $180°$, $-540°$ **35.** $155°$, $-205°$
37. $1°$, $-359°$ **39. a.** $n = -1$: $-312°$;
$n = 0$: $48°$; $n = 1$: $408°$; $n = 2$: $768°$
b. $48°$ **41. a.** $x^2 + y^2 = 32$
b. $\angle POX = 135°$ **43. a.** $x^2 + y^2 = 2$
b. $\angle POX = 225°$ **45. a.** $x^2 + y^2 = 1$
b. $\angle POX = 45°$ **47. a.** $P(\sqrt{2}, \sqrt{2})$,
$Q(-\sqrt{2}, -\sqrt{2})$ **b.** $\angle POX = 45°$,
$\angle QOX = 225°$

Written Exercises, pages 448–449   1. $\dfrac{\pi}{2}^{R}$

3. $\dfrac{2\pi}{3}^{R}$ **5.** $\dfrac{\pi}{4}^{R}$ **7.** $\dfrac{5\pi}{4}^{R}$ **9.** $\dfrac{\pi}{3}^{R}$ **11.** π^{R}
13. $180°$ **15.** $300°$ **17.** $240°$ **19.** $150°$
21. $90°$ **23.** $120°$ **25.** $\dfrac{2\pi}{5}^{R}$ **27.** $\dfrac{11\pi}{18}^{R}$

29. $\dfrac{19\pi}{9}^{R}$ **31.** $-\dfrac{5\pi}{12}^{R}$ **33.** $72°$ **35.** $220°$

37. $408°$ **39.** $-50°$ **41.** 0.6632^{R}
43. 0.0087^{R} **45.** $64.74°$ **47.** $85.94°$ **49.** $90°$,
1.5708^{R} **51.** $30°$, 0.5236^{R} **53.** $135°$, 2.3562^{R}

Problems, page 449   1. 5969 m
3. 212.21 revolutions   **5.** $1{,}737{,}000$ m

Written Exercises, pages 453–454
1. $\sin 90° = 1$, $\cos 90° = 0$
3. $\sin(-180°) = 0$, $\cos(-180°) = -1$
5. $\sin \pi^{R} = 0$, $\cos \pi^{R} = -1$ **7.** $\sin \dfrac{3\pi}{2}^{R} = -1$,
$\cos \dfrac{3\pi}{2}^{R} = 0$ **9.** $\sin\theta = \dfrac{3}{5}$, $\cos\theta = \dfrac{4}{5}$
11. $\sin\theta = \dfrac{3}{5}$, $\cos\theta = -\dfrac{4}{5}$ **13.** $\sin\theta = 1$,
$\cos\theta = 0$ **15.** $\sin\theta = -\dfrac{1}{2}$, $\cos\theta = \dfrac{\sqrt{3}}{2}$
17. $\sin\theta = -\dfrac{15}{17}$, $\cos\theta = \dfrac{8}{17}$
19. $\sin\theta = -\dfrac{\sqrt{3}}{2}$, $\cos\theta = -\dfrac{1}{2}$ **21.** $\dfrac{4}{5}$
23. $-\dfrac{7}{25}$ **25.** $-\dfrac{3}{\sqrt{10}}$ **27.** $\dfrac{\sqrt{2}}{2}$ **29.** $>$
31. $=$ **33.** $=$ **35.** $<$ **37.** $<$ **39.** $0°$
41. $180°$ **43.** $90°$, $270°$ **45.** $45°$, $135°$

Written Exercises, page 457   1. 0.8813
3. 0.4914 **5.** 0.6435 **7.** 0.5255 **9.** 0.8709
11. 0.1413 **13.** 50.0° **15.** 12.0° **17.** 48.0°
19. 30°16′ **21.** 14°46′ **23.** 61°38′
25. 0.622^R **27.** 0.308^R **29.** 0.167^R
31. 53°10′ **33.** 62°00′ **35.** 70°30′
37. 16°40′ **39.** 71°34′

Calculator Key-In, page 457   1. 1.0000
3. 1.0000

Written Exercises, page 461

1. a. 36°
b.

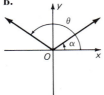

c. −0.8090

3. a. 35.6°
b.

c. −0.5821

5. a. 57°50′
b.

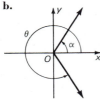

c. −0.8465

7. a. 20°
b.

c. 0.3420

9. a. 79°45′
b.

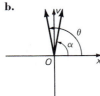

c. −0.1779

11. a. 0.14^R
b.

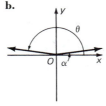

c. −0.9902

13. a. 1.071^R
b.

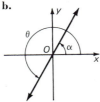

c. −0.8777

15. a. 0.72^R
b.

c. 0.6594

17. −0.7431 **19.** 0.9336 **21.** −0.1045
23. −0.8192 **25.** −0.9359 **27.** 0.7956
29. 197° **31.** 251.3° **33.** 160.5°
35. 121.3° **37.** 233°10′ **39.** 118°
41. 131°50′ **43.** 327°40′

Written Exercises, pages 467–468
1.

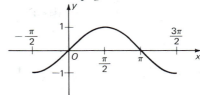

3. a. maximum: 3; minimum: −3 **b.** 2π
c.

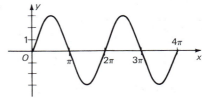

5. a. maximum: 1; minimum: −1 **b.** π
c.

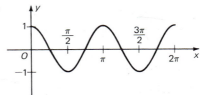

7. a. maximum: 5; minimum: −5 **b.** π
c.

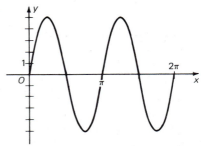

9. $y = \dfrac{1}{2}\sin 2x$ **11.** $y = 4\sin 2x$
13. a. maximum: 1; minimum: −1 **b.** 4π
c.

15. a. maximum: 4; minimum: -4 **b.** 4π

c.

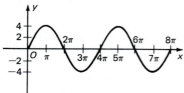

17. a. maximum: 1; minimum: -1 **b.** 365

c.

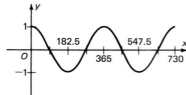

19. a. maximum: 4; minimum: 2 **b.** 2π

c.

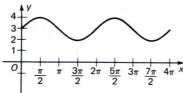

21. a. maximum: $2\frac{1}{2}$; minimum: $1\frac{1}{2}$ **b.** $\frac{2\pi}{3}$

c.

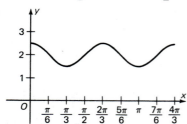

23. $3\cos\frac{\pi}{4}x$ **25.** $y = 4 + 2\cos\frac{\pi}{5}x$

27. $y = 32\cos\frac{\pi}{26}x$ **29.** $y = 2 + 5\sin 20\pi x$

31. a.

$y = \frac{1}{2}\sin\frac{1}{2}x \qquad y = -\frac{1}{2}\sin\frac{1}{2}x$

b. The graphs are reflections of one another about the x-axis.

Written Exercises, pages 473–474 **1.** $\cos\theta$
3. $\cot\theta$ **5.** $\cos\theta$ **7.** $\cot A$ **9.** $\cot B$
11. 1 **13.** $\cot^2\theta$ **15.** $\cot\theta$ **17.** 0.364
19. -0.091 **21.** 1.452 **23.** -1.010
25. -1.402 **27.** 0.0145 **29.** -1 **31.** -1

33. -1 **35.** $\dfrac{\sqrt{3}}{3}$

37. a. See figure. **b.** $\cos\theta = \dfrac{4}{5}$, $\tan\theta = \dfrac{3}{4}$,
$\cot\theta = \dfrac{4}{3}$, $\sec\theta = \dfrac{5}{4}$, $\csc\theta = \dfrac{5}{3}$ **39. a.** See
figure. **b.** $\sin\theta = \dfrac{4}{5}$, $\cos\theta = \dfrac{3}{5}$, $\cot\theta = \dfrac{3}{4}$,
$\sec\theta = \dfrac{5}{3}$, $\csc\theta = \dfrac{5}{4}$ **41. a.** See figure.
b. $\sin\theta = \dfrac{\sqrt{5}}{3}$, $\cos\theta = -\dfrac{2}{3}$, $\tan\theta = -\dfrac{\sqrt{5}}{2}$,
$\csc\theta = \dfrac{3\sqrt{5}}{5}$, $\cot\theta = -\dfrac{2\sqrt{5}}{5}$ **43. a.** See
figure. **b.** $\sin\theta = -\dfrac{\sqrt{3}}{2}$, $\cos\theta = \dfrac{1}{2}$,
$\cot\theta = -\dfrac{\sqrt{3}}{3}$, $\csc\theta = \dfrac{-2\sqrt{3}}{3}$, $\sec\theta = 2$
45. a. See figure. **b.** $\sin\theta = \dfrac{-\sqrt{5}}{5}$,
$\cos\theta = \dfrac{-2\sqrt{5}}{5}$, $\tan\theta = \dfrac{1}{2}$, $\cot\theta = 2$,
$\csc\theta = -\sqrt{5}$

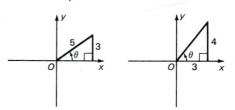

Ex. 37   Ex. 39

Ex. 41   Ex. 43

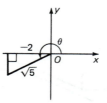

Ex. 45

47. $\{62.96°, 297.04°\}$ or $\{62°58', 297°2'\}$
49. $\{233.13°, 306.87°\}$ or $\{233°8', 306°52'\}$
51. $\{125.55°, 234.45°\}$ or $\{125°33', 234°27'\}$
53. $\{0, \pi, 2\pi, \ldots\}$ **55.** $\left\{\dfrac{\pi}{2}, \dfrac{3\pi}{2}, \dfrac{5\pi}{2}, \ldots\right\}$
59. $\{30°, 150°\}$ **61.** $\{30°, 210°\}$
63.

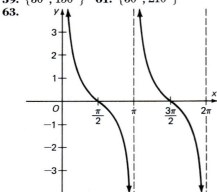

65.

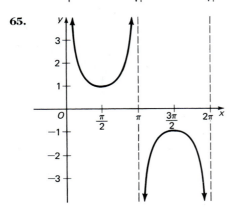

Written Exercises, pages 478–479 **1.** 1
3. $\sec^2 x$ **5.** $\cos y$ **7.** 1 **9.** $\sin^2 x$
11. $\sin x$ **13.** 1 **15.** $\csc^2 \beta$ **17.** $\csc x$
19. $\sin^2 A$ **21.** 1 **23.** $-\cos^2 \theta$
25. $\dfrac{\pm\sqrt{1-\sin^2\theta}}{\sin\theta}$ **27.** $\dfrac{\pm\sqrt{1-\cos^2\theta}}{\cos^2 x}$
39. $\cot\beta$ **41.** $\sin\theta$ **43.** $\sec x$ **45.** $-\cot\alpha$
47. $2\csc\beta$ **49.** $\sin\alpha$ **51.** $\sin^2\theta$
53. $2\sec^2 A$

Extra Exercises, page 482
1.

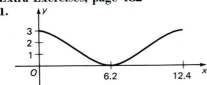

3.

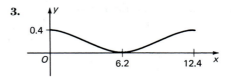

5. 7.25 m **7. a.** between Sept. 1 and
Sept. 22 **b.** Sept. and March

Chapter Review, pages 483–484 **1.** c **2.** a
3. d **4.** a **5.** d **6.** b **7.** c **8.** c **9.** c
10. b **11.** c **12.** a **13.** c **14.** c **15.** d
16. a **17.** a

CHAPTER 13   TRIANGLE TRIGONOMETRY; VECTORS

Written Exercises, pages 490–491
1.

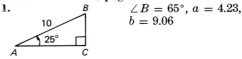

$\angle B = 65°$, $a = 4.23$, $b = 9.06$

3.

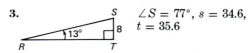

$\angle S = 77°$, $s = 34.6$, $t = 35.6$

5.

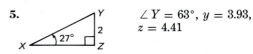

$\angle Y = 63°$, $y = 3.93$, $z = 4.41$

7.

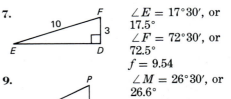

$\angle E = 17°30'$, or
17.5°
$\angle F = 72°30'$, or
72.5°
$f = 9.54$

9.

$\angle M = 26°30'$, or
26.6°
$\angle P = 63°30'$, or
63.4°
$n = 15.7$

11. $\angle C = 70°$, $\angle A = 40°$, $C = 10$,
$a = 6.84$ **13.** $b = 10$; $\angle A = 23°$;
$\angle B = 78°30'$, or 78.5°; $\angle C = 78°30'$, or
78.5° **15.** $\angle B = 70°$, $\angle C = 70°$, **b.** 29.2,
$c = 29.2$ **17.** 73°40', or 73.8° **19.** 51°20', or
51.3° **21.** 12.9

Problems, pages 491–492 **1.** 83.9 m
3. 59°0', or 59.0° **5.** 22°40', or 22.6°
7. 16.3 m **9.** 1070 m **11.** 6120 km
13. 59.4 m **15.** $CD = 66.4$ m; height $= 85$ m

Written Exercises, pages 494–495
1. 1.5 **3.** 16.5 **5. a.** 8.66 **b.** 8.66 **7.** 41.3
9. 20 **11.** 30° or 150° **13.** 277 **15.** 1130
17. $\angle A = 53°10'$, or 53.1°; area $= 12$
19. $\dfrac{nr^2}{2} \sin\left(\dfrac{360}{n}\right)$

Written Exercises, pages 497–498 **1.** 20°10′,
or 20.1° **3.** 19°30′, or 19.5° **5.** 90°
7. 12.2 **9.** 15 **11.** $p = 5.71$; area $= 13.7$
13. 30 **15.** 3

Problems, page 498 **1.** 130 m **3.** 64 cm
5. $\overline{BD} = 6.25$, $\overline{DE} = 5.5$, $\overline{EC} = 6.25$

Written Exercises, page 501 **1.** 8.72
3. 4.95 **5.** 9.64 **7.** 4.47 **9.** 78°30′, or 78.5°
11. 101° **13. a.** 90° **15.** $DB = 6.22$,
$AC = 7.16$ **17. a.** $-\dfrac{13}{85}$ **b.** $\dfrac{84}{85}$ **c.** 84
19. a. $\dfrac{4}{5}$ **b.** $\cos C = \dfrac{3}{5}$ or $\cos C = -\dfrac{3}{5}$
c. If $\cos C = \dfrac{3}{5}$, $c = 5$. If $\cos C = -\dfrac{3}{5}$,
$c = 9.85$

Problems, pages 501–502 **1.** 2482 km
3. 818 m **5.** 60°40′, or 60.6°

Written Exercises, page 506
1. $\angle A = 43°50'$, or 43.8°; $\angle B = 56°10'$, or
56.2°; $c = 7.11$ **3.** $\angle Z = 94°$, $z = 24.5$,
$y = 21.7$ **5.** $\angle L = 90°$, $j = 2.57$, $k = 3.06$
7. $\angle K = 44°20'$, or 44.4°; $\angle S = 35°40'$, or
35.6°; $i = 8.45$ **9.** 4.36 **11.** 15.7
13. $QS = 18.8$, $PR = 6.84$ **15.** $HF = 10$,
$GE = 9.73$

Problems, pages 506–507 **1.** 10.8 km
3. 49.3 km **5.** 13.2 m **7.** 1960 m **9.** 87.8 m

Written Exercises, pages 510–511
1.   **3.** The sum is   **5.**
the zero vector.

7.   **9.**

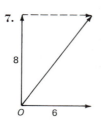

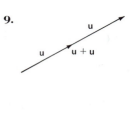

11.   **13.**

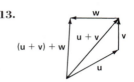

15. 8.72 N; 143°30′, or 143.4° **17.** 703 km/h;
125°50′ or 125.8°

Problems, page 511 **1.** 4.12 km/h
3. 15.8 km/h at a bearing of 341°30′, or
341.6° **5.** 84.5 N **7.** at a bearing of
189°0′ or 189.0°

Written Exercises, pages 513–514
1. $x = 6.16$, $y = 7.88$ **3.** $x = -4.33$,
$y = 2.5$ **5.** $x = -2.29$, $y = 3.28$
7. magnitude: 10; direction: 53°10′, or
53.1° **9.** magnitude: 6.33; direction: 108°30′,
or 108.4° **11.** magnitude 7.07; direction:
135° **13.** $(-7, 2)$ **15.** $(7, -2)$ **17.** $(1, -4)$
19. a. $(3, 4)$ **b.** magnitude: 5;
direction: 53°10′, or 53.1° **21. a.** $(1, 4)$
b. magnitude: 4.12; direction: 76°

Problems, pages 514–515 **1.** 181 N
3. 122 N **5.** yes **7.** The Clothing Shop
sign **9.** 3120 N

Chapter Review, pages 516–517 **1.** c **2.** a
3. d **4.** c **5.** b **6.** a **7.** a **8.** c **9.** a
10. c **11.** b **12.** a **13.** d **14.** b

CHAPTER 14 IDENTITIES, INVERSES, AND EQUATIONS

Written Exercises, pages 522–523
1. $\dfrac{\sqrt{6} + \sqrt{2}}{4}$ **3.** $\dfrac{\sqrt{6} - \sqrt{2}}{4}$
5. $\sin 90° = 1$ **7.** $\cos 60° = \dfrac{1}{2}$ **9.** $\cos 280°$
11. $\cos(-2.2^R) = \cos 2.2^R$
13. $\sin(3\alpha - 2\beta)$ **27.** $\cos \alpha$
31. $\sin \alpha = -\dfrac{2\sqrt{6}}{5}$, $\sin \beta = -\dfrac{4}{5}$,

$\sin(\alpha+\beta)=\dfrac{-6\sqrt{6}-4}{25}$ **33. a.** $\alpha=30°,$

$\beta=60°$ **b.** $\tan(\alpha+\beta)=\dfrac{\tan\alpha+\tan\beta}{1-\tan\alpha\tan\beta}$

Written Exercises, pages 525–526
1. $\tan 60°=\sqrt{3}$ **3.** $\tan 180°=0$
5. $\tan 135°=-1$ **7.** $\tan 1$ **9.** $\tan 3\alpha$
11. $2+\sqrt{3}$ **13.** $-2-\sqrt{3}$
15. $\tan\left(\dfrac{\pi}{4}+x\right)=3,\ \tan\left(\dfrac{\pi}{4}-x\right)=\dfrac{1}{3}$
17. $\tan\left(\dfrac{3\pi}{4}+z\right)=-\dfrac{1}{2},$

$\tan\left(\dfrac{3\pi}{4}-z\right)=-2$

23. a. $\cot(\alpha-\beta)=\dfrac{\cot\alpha\cot\beta+1}{\cot\beta-\cot\alpha}$
b. $2+\sqrt{3}$

Calculator Key-In, page 526
1. a. 0.98480775
b. $\sin 80°=\sin(90°-10°),$
$\cos 80°=\cos(90°-10°)$

Written Exercises, pages 528–529
1. $\cos 20°$ **3.** $\tan 160°$ **5.** 1 **7.** $\sin 6x$
9. $\cos 10\alpha$ **11.** $\cos\dfrac{\beta}{2}$ **13.** $\cos 30°=\dfrac{\sqrt{3}}{2}$
15. $\cos 210°=-\dfrac{\sqrt{3}}{2}$ **17.** $\tan\dfrac{3\pi}{4}=-1$
19. $\dfrac{1}{2}\sin 150°=\dfrac{1}{4}$ **21.** $3\sin 330°=-1.5$
23. a. $-\dfrac{3}{5}$ **b.** $-\dfrac{24}{25}$ **c.** $-\dfrac{7}{25}$ **d.** $\dfrac{336}{625}$
e. $\left(-\dfrac{24}{25}\right)^2+\left(-\dfrac{7}{25}\right)^2=\dfrac{576}{625}+\dfrac{49}{625}=1$
25. a. $-\dfrac{7}{9}$ **b.** $\dfrac{17}{81}$ **c.** $\dfrac{3\sqrt{2}}{4}$ **d.** $-\dfrac{9\sqrt{2}}{8}$
27. a.

b. period: π; amplitude: $\dfrac{1}{2}$

37. $\sin 3\theta=\sin\theta(4\cos^2\theta-1)$
39. $\cot 2\alpha=\dfrac{\cot^2\alpha-1}{2\cot\alpha}$

Written Exercises, pages 532–533
1. $\dfrac{\sqrt{2-\sqrt{3}}}{2},\ \dfrac{\sqrt{2+\sqrt{3}}}{2},\ 2-\sqrt{3}$

3. $-\dfrac{\sqrt{2+\sqrt{2}}}{2},\ \dfrac{\sqrt{2-\sqrt{2}}}{2},$

$-\sqrt{2}-1$ **5.** $\dfrac{\sqrt{6}}{4},\ \dfrac{\sqrt{10}}{4},\ \dfrac{\sqrt{15}}{5}$
7. $\dfrac{\sqrt{30}}{6},\ \dfrac{\sqrt{6}}{6},\ \sqrt{5}$ **9.** $\dfrac{\sqrt{10}}{10},\ \dfrac{3\sqrt{10}}{10},\ \dfrac{1}{3}$
11. $\dfrac{\sqrt{30}}{10},\ -\dfrac{\sqrt{70}}{10},\ -\dfrac{\sqrt{21}}{7}$ **13.** $\dfrac{4}{5},\ \dfrac{3\sqrt{10}}{10}$
15. $-2,\ \dfrac{1+\sqrt{5}}{2}$ **17.** $-\dfrac{4}{5},\ -\dfrac{336}{625}$

Written Exercises, page 536
1.

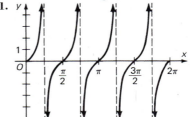

3.

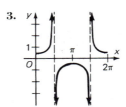

5.

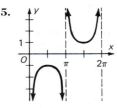

7.

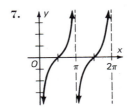

9.

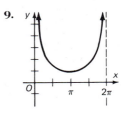

11.

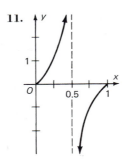

13.

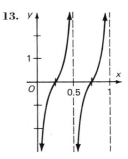

15.

17.

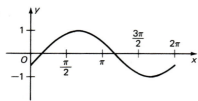

19.

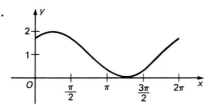

21.

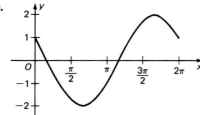

Written Exercises, page 539   1. $-\dfrac{\pi}{2}$ 3. π

5. $\dfrac{\pi}{4}$ 7. $\dfrac{2\pi}{3}$ 9. $\dfrac{4}{5}$ 11. $\dfrac{5}{13}$ 13. $\dfrac{\sqrt{3}}{2}$

15. 0

17. **a.** $y = x$
b.

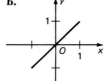

19. **a.** $y = \sqrt{1 - x^2}$
b.

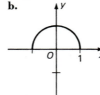

Written Exercises, page 542   1. $\dfrac{7}{4}$ 3. $\dfrac{17}{8}$

5. $-\dfrac{5}{6}$ 7. $\dfrac{\sqrt{5}}{2}$ 9. $\dfrac{\sqrt{5}}{5}$ 11. $-\dfrac{24}{25}$ 3. $\dfrac{\sqrt{2}}{2}$

15. -1 17. $\dfrac{2x\sqrt{1 - 4x^2}}{1 - 4x^2}$ 19. $\dfrac{1 - x^2}{1 + x^2}$

21. $y\sqrt{1 - x^2} + x\sqrt{1 - y^2}$

Computer Key-In, page 543

```
1. 10    PRINT "TO SOLVE TRIANGLE ABC WITH"
   20    PRINT "SIDES A1, B1, AND C1,
         GIVEN:"
   30    PRINT " SIDE A1, SIDE B1, ANGLE C
         (IN DEGREES)"
   40    LET R=3.14159/180
   50    PRINT "INPUT A1,B1, AND C.";
   60    INPUT A1,B1,C
   70    LET C1=SQR (A1↑2+B1↑2-2*A1*B1*
         COS (R*C))
   80    LET P=(B1↑2+C1↑2-A1↑2)/(2*B1*C1)
   90    LET S=(A1*SIN(R*C))/C1
   100   LET A=ATN(S/P)
   110   PRINT "ANGLE A=";A/R;" DEGREES"
   120   PRINT "ANGLE B=";180-C-A/R;
         " DEGREES"
   130   PRINT "SIDE C1=";C1
   140   END
```

Written Exercises, page 547

1. $\{48.6°, 131.4°\}$ 3. $\{78.7°, 258.7°\}$
5. $\{45°, 135°, 225°, 315°\}$
7. $\{30°, 150°, 210°, 330°\}$ 9. $\{0°, 180°\}$
11. $\{30°, 210°\}$ 13. $\{0.38, 2.76\}$
15. $\{0.64, 3.78\}$ 17. $\emptyset$
19. $\{0.56, 2.58, 3.70, 5.72\}$ 21. $\{0.25, 3.39\}$
23. $\left\{\dfrac{\pi}{4}, \dfrac{5\pi}{4}\right\}$ 25. $\{0°, 11.3°, 180°, 191.3°\}$
27. $\{90°, 199.5°, 340.5°\}$
29. $\{45°, 63.4°, 225°, 243.4°\}$
31. $\{26.6°, 45°, 206.6°, 225°\}$
33. $\{60°, 120°, 240°, 300°\}$
35. $\{0°, 120°, 240°\}$ 37. $\{60°, 180°, 300°\}$
39. $\{270°\}$ 41. $\{30°, 150°, 270°\}$
43. $\{0°, 60°, 180°, 300°\}$ 45. $\{90°, 153.4°,$
$270°, 333.4°\}$ 47. $\{75°, 315°\}$ 49. $\{27.4°,$
$62.6°, 117.4°, 152.6°, 207.4°, 242.6°, 297.4°,$
$332.6°\}$ 51. $\{152.0°\}$ 53. $\{20°, 40°, 80°,$
$100°, 140°, 160°, 200°, 220°, 260°, 280°, 320°,$
$340°\}$ 55. $\{0°, 60°, 120°, 180°, 240°, 300°\}$
57. $\{67.5°, 157.5°, 247.5°, 337.5°\}$
59. $\{30.4°, 73.7°, 210.4°, 253.7°\}$

Written Exercises, page 550

1.

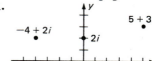

3.

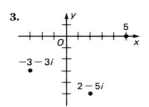

5.

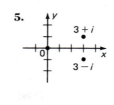

7. $2\sqrt{3} + 2i$ **9.** $-3 + 3i$ **11.** 5

13. $\dfrac{\sqrt{3}}{2} - \dfrac{3}{2}i$ **15.** $-2.3511 + 3.2361i$

17. $9.9122 - 1.3226i$

19. $2\sqrt{2}(\cos 45° + i \sin 45°)$

21. $4(\cos 330° + i \sin 330°)$

23. $5(\cos 306.9° + i \sin 306.9°)$

25. $\sqrt{5}(\cos 26.6° + i \sin 26.6°)$

27. $3(\cos 0° + i \sin 0°)$

29. $3(\cos 90° + i \sin 90°)$

31. a. $3\sqrt{3} - 3 + (3\sqrt{3} + 3)i$

b. $|z_1| = 3\sqrt{2}$, $|z_2| = 2$, $|z_1 z_2| = 6\sqrt{2}$;

$|z_1 z_2| = |z_1| \cdot |z_2|$

c.

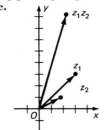

Extra Exercises, pages 552–553

1. $6(\cos 50° + i \sin 50°)$

3. $8(\cos 70° + i \sin 70°)$

5. $8(\cos 30° + i \sin 30°)$

7. $16(\cos 120° + i \sin 120°)$ **9. a.** $-1 + i$

b. $z_1 = 1(\cos 90° + i \sin 90°)$,

$z_2 = \sqrt{2}(\cos 45° + i \sin 45°)$

c. $z_1 z_2 = \sqrt{2}(\cos 135° + i \sin 135°) =$

$\sqrt{2}\left(-\dfrac{\sqrt{2}}{2} + i\dfrac{\sqrt{2}}{2}\right) = -1 + i$ **d.** See

figure.   **11. a.** $-5 + 12i$

b. $z_1 = \sqrt{13}(\cos 56.3° + i \sin 56.3°)$,

$z_2 = \sqrt{13}(\cos 56.3° + i \sin 56.3°)$

c. $z_1 z_2 = 13(\cos 112.6° + i \sin 112.6°) =$

$13(-0.3843 + 0.9232i) \approx -5 + 12i$ **d.** See

figure.   **13. a.** $-6 - 2i$

b. $z_1 = \sqrt{10}(\cos 18.4° + i \sin 18.4°)$,

$z_2 = 2(\cos 180° + i \sin 180°)$

c. $z_1 z_2 = 2\sqrt{10}(\cos 198.4° + i \sin 198.4°) =$

$2\sqrt{10}(-0.9489 - 0.3156i) \approx -6 - 2i$

d. See figure.   **15. a.** $2(\cos 30° + i \sin 30°)$

b. See figure.

17. $z^2 = 4(\cos 120° + i \sin 120°)$,

$z^3 = 8(\cos 180° + i \sin 180°)$,

$z^4 = 16(\cos 240° + i \sin 240°)$; see figure for

diagram.   **19. a.** $z = (\cos 120° + i \sin 120°)$,

$z^3 = (\cos 360° + i \sin 360°)$,

$z^4 = (\cos 480° + i \sin 480°)$ **25.** 1,

$-\dfrac{1}{2} + \dfrac{\sqrt{3}}{2}i$, $-\dfrac{1}{2} - \dfrac{\sqrt{3}}{2}i$

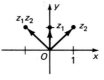

Ex. 9

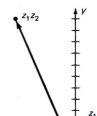

Ex. 11

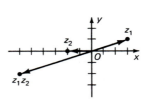

Ex. 13

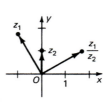

Ex. 15

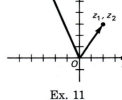

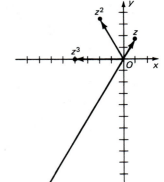

Ex. 17

Chapter Review, pages 554–556   **1.** c   **2.** a

3. d   **4.** b   **5.** d   **6.** d   **7.** a   **8.** c   **9.** b

10. c   **11.** b   **12.** c   **13.** a   **14.** d   **15.** d

16. c   **17.** a   **18.** b

Cumulative Review, page 557 **1.** $-432°$

3. $112.5°$ **5.** $y = 3 \sin \frac{\pi}{3} x$

7. period $= 2\pi$

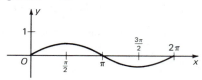

9. period $= \frac{\pi}{2}$

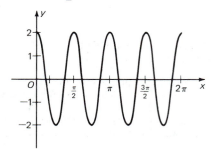

11. $-\sqrt{2}$ **13.** 1 **15.** $\cos x$
19. $\angle X = 38°0'$, or $38.0°$; $\angle Z = 52°0'$, or
$52.0°$; $z = 10.2$ **21.** magnitude: 11.2;
direction angle: $10.3°$ **23. a.** $\frac{3}{5}$ **b.** $-\frac{24}{25}$

c. $-\frac{7}{25}$ **d.** $\frac{24}{7}$ **e.** $-\frac{44}{125}$ **25.** $48.2°$, $120°$,
$240°$, $311.8°$

CHAPTER 15 MATRICES AND DETERMINANTS

Written Exercises, pages 560–561

1. $\begin{bmatrix} 0 \\ 0 \end{bmatrix}$ **3.** $[0 \ \ 0 \ \ 0]$

5. $x = 0, y = 0, z = 0$ **7.** $x = 1, y = -4$,
$z = 7$ **9.** $x = 5, y = -3$ **11.** $x = -2$,
$y = 3, z = -5$ **13.** $x = 3, y = -4, z = -4$
15. $x = \dfrac{1-b}{a}$, $y = -\dfrac{d}{c}$ **17.** $x = \dfrac{d-b}{ad-bc}$,
$y = \dfrac{a-c}{ad-bc}$

Written Exercises, pages 564–565

1. $\begin{bmatrix} 7 & 3 \\ 1 & 1 \end{bmatrix}$ **3.** $\begin{bmatrix} 5 & 3 \\ 1 & 4 \end{bmatrix}$

5. $\begin{bmatrix} 4 & 11 \\ 9 & 0 \\ 3 & -2 \end{bmatrix}$ **7.** $\begin{bmatrix} 14 & 3 & 3 \\ 8 & 3 & -11 \end{bmatrix}$

9. $\begin{bmatrix} 13 & 6 \\ -4 & 9 \\ 6 & 19 \end{bmatrix}$ **11.** $\begin{bmatrix} -1 & -1 & 2 \\ 7 & 11 & -8 \end{bmatrix}$

13. $\begin{bmatrix} 6 & 2 & 5 \\ -2 & 7 & 0 \end{bmatrix}$ **15.** $\begin{bmatrix} 18 \\ 41 \\ 34 \end{bmatrix}$

17. $\begin{bmatrix} 4 & -4 \\ -5 & -4 \end{bmatrix}$ **19.** $\begin{bmatrix} 11 & 8 \\ 0 & 0 \end{bmatrix}$

Written Exercises, page 570

1. [38] **3.** $\begin{bmatrix} 15 & 0 & 5 & 25 \\ -3 & 0 & -1 & -5 \end{bmatrix}$

5. $\begin{bmatrix} 3 & 11 \\ 4 & 12 \end{bmatrix}$ **7.** $\begin{bmatrix} -3 & 1 & 2 \\ 0 & -5 & -4 \\ -4 & -2 & -4 \end{bmatrix}$

9. $\begin{bmatrix} 2 & 0 & -2 & 2 \\ 0 & -1 & -3 & 1 \\ 1 & 2 & 5 & -1 \end{bmatrix}$

11. $\begin{bmatrix} r + 3x & s + 3y & t + 3z \\ 2r - u & 2s - v & 2t - w \\ -3u + 2x & -3v + 2y & -3w + 2z \end{bmatrix}$

13. $AB = \begin{bmatrix} 1 & 0 \\ 0 & -1 \end{bmatrix}$, $BA = \begin{bmatrix} -1 & 4 \\ 0 & 1 \end{bmatrix}$

15. $(AB)C = \begin{bmatrix} 0 & -2 \\ -1 & 0 \end{bmatrix}$,
$A(BC) = \begin{bmatrix} 0 & -2 \\ -1 & 0 \end{bmatrix}$

17. $(A + B)(A - B) = \begin{bmatrix} -8 & 4 \\ -4 & 4 \end{bmatrix}$,
$A^2 - B^2 = \begin{bmatrix} -6 & 0 \\ -4 & 2 \end{bmatrix}$

19. $O_{2\times2} \cdot A = \begin{bmatrix} 0 & 0 \\ 0 & 0 \end{bmatrix}$, $A \times O_{2\times2} = \begin{bmatrix} 0 & 0 \\ 0 & 0 \end{bmatrix}$

21. $\begin{bmatrix} 1 & 0 \\ 0 & 1 \end{bmatrix}$ **23. a.** $\begin{bmatrix} 3 & -2 & 2 \\ 1 & 0 & -1 \\ 1 & 1 & 1 \end{bmatrix}$

b. $\begin{bmatrix} 5 & 0 & 4 \\ 0 & 1 & 2 \\ 2 & -2 & 3 \end{bmatrix}$ **c.** $\begin{bmatrix} 3 & -2 & 2 \\ 1 & 0 & -1 \\ 1 & 1 & 1 \end{bmatrix}$

Written Exercises, pages 574–576

1.

3. $\begin{bmatrix} 1 & 0 & 1 & 1 & 0 \\ 0 & 3 & 0 & 0 & 2 \\ 1 & 0 & 1 & 1 & 0 \\ 1 & 0 & 1 & 1 & 0 \\ 0 & 0 & 0 & 0 & 0 \end{bmatrix}$

5. $\begin{bmatrix} 460 & 250 \end{bmatrix}$

7. $\begin{bmatrix} 0 & 1 & 1 & 1 \\ 1 & 0 & 0 & 0 \\ 1 & 1 & 0 & 1 \\ 1 & 0 & 0 & 0 \end{bmatrix}$; $\begin{bmatrix} 3 & 1 & 0 & 1 \\ 0 & 1 & 1 & 1 \\ 2 & 1 & 1 & 1 \\ 0 & 1 & 1 & 1 \end{bmatrix}$

9. $\begin{bmatrix} 2 & 3 & 3 & 3 \\ 3 & 1 & 0 & 1 \\ 3 & 3 & 2 & 3 \\ 3 & 1 & 0 & 1 \end{bmatrix}$

11. 1: 2 ways; 2: 2 ways; 3: 2 ways; 4: 2 ways; 5: 2 ways **13.** points 3 and 5

Written Exercises, page 579 1. 5 **3.** 19 **5.** 137 **7.** 135

Written Exercises, page 582

1. $\begin{bmatrix} \dfrac{3}{5} & -\dfrac{2}{5} \\ \dfrac{1}{5} & \dfrac{1}{5} \end{bmatrix}$ **3.** $\begin{bmatrix} \dfrac{1}{5} & \dfrac{1}{10} \\ -\dfrac{2}{5} & \dfrac{3}{10} \end{bmatrix}$

5. $\begin{bmatrix} 2 & -\dfrac{3}{2} \\ 1 & -\dfrac{1}{2} \end{bmatrix}$ **7.** $\begin{bmatrix} -\dfrac{5}{8} & \dfrac{3}{8} \\ -\dfrac{1}{8} & \dfrac{1}{8} \end{bmatrix}$

9. $(2, 7)$ **11.** $(2, -3)$ **13.** $(-2, 3)$ **15.** no solution

17. $A = \begin{bmatrix} 34 & -2 \\ -10 & 1 \end{bmatrix}$ **19.** $A = \begin{bmatrix} 1 & \dfrac{1}{2} \\ -1 & \dfrac{1}{2} \end{bmatrix}$

Written Exercises, pages 587–588 1. -26 **3.** -60 **5.** -39 **7.** -30 **9.** 22 **11.** 49 **13.** 5 **15.** $\{-2, 2\}$ **17.** -210

Written Exercises, page 591 1. 0 **3.** 125 **5.** 0 **7.** 23 **9.** 20 **11.** 16

Written Exercises, pages 595–596

1. $(2, 3, 4)$ **3.** $(2, -2, 1)$ **5.** $\left(\dfrac{3}{2}, 4, -3\right)$

7. $\left(\dfrac{3}{2}, -1, -\dfrac{1}{2}\right)$ **9.** more than one solution **11.** one solution **13.** $(2, 2, -2, -1)$

Chapter Review, page 597 1. c **2.** a **3.** b **4.** c **5.** c **6.** a **7.** b **8.** c **9.** a **10.** c

CHAPTER 16 PROBABILITY AND STATISTICS

Written Exercises, pages 603–604 1. 288 **3.** 3^{10}, or 59,049 **5.** 336 **7.** 37,856 license plates **9.** 11,125 code words **11.** 129 positive even integers **13.** 216 positive odd integers **15.** 7 multiples of three **17.** 4^{10} or 1,048,576

Written Exercises, page 607 1. 5040 **3.** 120 **5.** 10 **7.** 30 **9.** 12 **11.** 30 **13.** 24 **15.** 720 **17.** 240 positive integers **25.** $n = 18$

Written Exercises, page 609 1. 180 **3.** 60 **5.** 2520 **7.** 30 **9.** 1260 **11.** 60 **13.** 10

Written Exercises, page 612–613
1. a. $\{2, 6, 8\}, \{2, 6\}, \{2, 8\}, \{6, 8\}, \{2\}, \{6\},$ $\{8\}, \emptyset$ **b.** $\{2, 6\}, \{2\}, \{6\}, \{8\}$ **3.** 56 **5.** 21 **7.** 364 **9.** 66 **11. a.** 5 **b.** 10 **c.** 10 **13.** 38,760 **15.** 21 **17.** 20 **19.** 126 **21.** 740,999,259 **23.** 717,759,900 **25.** 64

Written Exercises, page 615
1. a. $\{A, B, C, D, E, F, G, H, I, J\}$ **b.** $\{A, E, I\}$ **3.** 36 **5.** $\{(6, 5), (5, 6)\}$ **7.** $\{(5, 3), (3, 5), (6, 3), (3, 6), (4, 4), (6, 2), (2, 6),$ $(5, 4), (4, 5), (5, 5), (6, 4), (4, 6), (5, 6), (6, 5), (6, 6)\}$ **9.** $\{(H, 1), (H, 2), (H, 3), (H, 4), (H, 5), (H, 6),$ $(T, 1), (T, 2), (T, 3), (T, 4), (T, 5), (T, 6)\};$ $\{(H, 1), (H, 2), (H, 3), (T, 1), (T, 2), (T, 3)\}$ **11.** $\{(1, 4), (4, 1), (2, 3), (3, 2)\}$ **13.** $\{(1, 1),$ $(1, 2), (1, 3), (1, 4), (1, 5), (1, 6), (2, 2), (2, 4),$ $(2, 6), (3, 3), (3, 6), (4, 4), (5, 5), (6, 6)\}$ **15.** $\{(1, 5), (1, 6), (2, 5), (2, 6), (3, 5), (3, 6),$ $(4, 5), (4, 6), (5, 5), (5, 6), (6, 5), (6, 6)\}$ **17.** $\{(2, 1), (2, 2), (2, 3), (2, 4), (2, 5), (2, 6),$ $(4, 1), (4, 2), (4, 3), (4, 4), (4, 5), (4, 6), (6, 1),$ $(6, 2), (6, 3), (6, 4), (6, 5), (6, 6), (1, 1), (3, 1),$ $(5, 1), (1, 3), (3, 3), (5, 3), (1, 5), (3, 5), (5, 5)\}$

Written Exercises, page 617–618 1. a. $\dfrac{1}{13}$

b. $\dfrac{1}{4}$ **c.** $\dfrac{1}{52}$ **d.** $\dfrac{1}{26}$ **e.** $\dfrac{2}{13}$ **f.** 0 **3. a.** $\dfrac{1}{2}$

b. 0 **c.** $\dfrac{11}{14}$ **d.** $\dfrac{1}{2}$ **5. a.** $\dfrac{1}{8}$ **b.** $\dfrac{1}{8}$ **c.** $\dfrac{3}{8}$

d. $\dfrac{7}{8}$ **7. a.** 1 **b.** $\dfrac{1}{125}$ **c.** $\dfrac{124}{125}$ **9. a.** $\dfrac{1}{66}$

b. $\dfrac{1}{11}$ **c.** $\dfrac{5}{22}$ **d.** $\dfrac{5}{22}$ **e.** $\dfrac{4}{33}$

11. a. $\dfrac{{}_4C_4 \cdot {}_{48}C_9}{{}_{52}C_{13}}$, or approximately 0.00264

b. $\dfrac{{}_4C_0 \cdot {}_{48}C_{13}}{{}_{52}C_{13}}$, or approximately 0.304

Written Exercises, pages 623–625 1. $\dfrac{1}{36}$

3. a. $\{(1,H),(2,H),(3,H),(4,H),(5,H),$
$(6,H),(1,T),(2,T),(3,T),(4,T),(5,T),$
$(6,T)\}$
b. $A = \{(2,H),(4,H),(6,H),(2,T),(4,T),$
$(6,T)\};$
$B = \{(1,T),(2,T),(3,T),(4,T),(5,T),$
$(6,T)\}; A \cup B = \{(2,H),(4,H),(6,H),$
$(2,T),(4,T),(6,T),(1,T),(3,T),(5,T)\};$
$A \cap B = \{(2,T),(4,T),(6,T)\}$
c. $P(A) = \dfrac{1}{2}; P(B) = \dfrac{1}{2}; P(A \cup B) = \dfrac{3}{4};$

$P(A \cap B) = \dfrac{1}{4}$ **d.** No; yes **5. a.** $\dfrac{1}{18}$ **b.** $\dfrac{1}{12}$

7. a. $\dfrac{1}{2}$ **b.** $\dfrac{7}{8}$; the events are not

independent. **9.** $\dfrac{2}{8!}$, or $\dfrac{1}{20,160}$

11. a. independent **b.** independent **c.** not
independent **13. a.** $\dfrac{1}{6}$ **b.** $\dfrac{2}{9}$ **c.** $\dfrac{1}{2}$ **d.** $\dfrac{8}{9}$

15. a. $\dfrac{{}_{26}C_2}{{}_{52}C_2}$, or $\dfrac{25}{102}$ **b.** $\dfrac{{}_4C_2}{{}_{52}C_2}$, or $\dfrac{1}{221}$

c. $\dfrac{{}_{26}C_2 + {}_4C_2 - {}_2C_2}{{}_{52}C_2}$, or $\dfrac{55}{221}$

Written Exercises, page 629 1. mean = 56;
var. = 239; st. dev. = 15; range = 39
3. mean = 50; var. = 21; st. dev. = 5;
range = 14 **5.** mean = 13.893;

st. dev. = 9.565 **7.** 90 **9.** The mean would
increase by 8 points; the range would not
change; the st. dev. would not change.
11. a. 3750 **b.** 3200 **c.** 77.22

Written Exercises, pages 633–634 1. 1024
square units **3.** 0.2257 **5.** 0.0013
7. a. 50% **b.** 15.87% **c.** 2.28%
9. var. = 1 **13. a.** 0.399 **b.** 0.242 **c.** 0.054

Chapter Review, page 636 1. c **2.** c **3.** d
4. a **5.** c **6.** c **7.** b **8.** a **9.** c **10.** b
11. b

Written Exercises, page 676
1. hyperbola; left 1 unit, down 3 units
3. ellipse; right 6 units, up 1 unit
5.

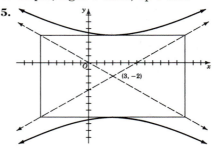

(3, −2)

7.

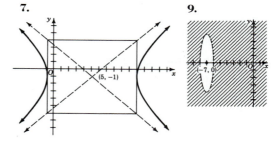

(5, −1)

9.

(−7, 0)

Written Exercises, page 678
1. 1, −2 **3.** 1, −3 **5.** 3, −2

ACKNOWLEDGMENTS

Illustrations by ANCO/Boston and Dan Collins

Photographs provided by the following sources: opposite p. 1, The Picture Cube/Read D. Brugger; p. 19, Harvard University Archives; p. 32, The Picture Group/Andrew Popper; p. 36 (top), The Bettmann Archive, (bottom), Bell Laboratories; p. 44 U.S. Geological Survey, MIT, and NASA Ames Research Center; p. 53, Culver Pictures Inc.; p. 67, The Picture Cube/Frank Siteman; p. 82, Photo Researchers/Alvin E. Staffan; p. 86, Bryn Mawr College Library; p. 95, Wes Williams; p. 130, De Wys Inc.; p. 136, United Nations; p. 162, Photo Researchers/Russell D. Lamb; p. 167, Wes Williams; p. 176, Society of Mining Engineers of AIME; p. 208, United States Steel; p. 213, Wes Williams; p. 248, Photo Researchers (Rapho)/Carl Scholfield; p. 282, Photo Researchers (Rapho)/Brett Westen; p. 317, Johnson Publishing Co.; p. 324, Alex McLean; p. 335, The American Mining Congress; p. 349, Culver Pictures Inc.; p. 357, Tyrone Hall; p. 372, Editorial Photocolor Archives/Scala; p. 406, Steinway and Sons; p. 440, Photo Researchers/Allen Green; p. 486, Stock, Boston/George Bellerose; p. 518, Stock, Boston/Peter Menzel; p. 536, Burndy Library; p. 558, Bell Laboratories; p. 600, Photo Researchers/Charlie Ott

EFGHIJ-RM-898765